# Everyday Mathematics®

The University of Chicago School Mathematics Project

Meeting All Expectations

Everyday **Mathematics** *Meeting*

# all expectations

## An inspired mission

*Everyday Mathematics* was developed through the University of Chicago School Mathematics Project (UCSMP) in order to enable children in elementary grades to learn more mathematical content and become life-long mathematical thinkers.

- ✦ The National Science Foundation, Amoco, GTE and other leading corporations supported the project through substantial, long-term funding.
- ✦ A strong partnership was developed among researchers, mathematics educators, classroom teachers, students and administrators.
- ✦ A core author team at the University of Chicago collaborates on all grade levels to provide a cohesive and well-articulated K–6 curriculum.

## Research that matters

*Everyday Mathematics* begins with the premise that students can, and must, learn more mathematics than has been expected from them in the past. This premise is based on the research the UCSMP author team undertook prior to writing the curriculum. Here are some of the major findings of this research:

- ✦ The typical U.S. mathematics curriculum is arithmetic-driven, slow-paced with isolated instruction, and broad without depth of content.
- ✦ International studies show that U.S. students learn much less mathematics than students in other countries.
- ✦ Children are capable of learning more mathematics in a richer curriculum.
- ✦ All children can be successful mathematical thinkers.
- ✦ Mathematics is meaningful to children when it is varied, rich, and rooted in real world problems and applications.

# Instruction with impact

The *Everyday Mathematics* instructional design was carefully crafted to capitalize on student interest and maximize student learning.

- High expectations for all students
- Concepts and skills developed over time and in a wide variety of contexts
- Balance among mathematical strands
- Dynamic applications
- Multiple methods and strategies for problem solving
- Concrete modeling as a pathway to abstract understanding
- Collaborative learning in partner and small group activities
- Cross-curricular applications

# Field test validation

*Everyday Mathematics* was originally field-tested for one full year per grade level in hundreds of classrooms across the U.S. Prior to second edition development, additional classroom observation and research was conducted. One research component included evaluation of all first edition lessons by numerous teachers using the curriculum. Second edition content was then developed and field-tested in a variety of educational settings.

Based on teacher and student feedback, and classroom observation by authors, revisions were made prior to publication.

# Everyday Mathematics *Doing* more with mathematics

*Everyday Mathematics* is organized into six mathematical content strands that cover a number of skills and concepts. This provides a rich yet balanced curriculum—attention to numeration and computation without neglecting geometry, data, and algebraic thinking.

Every strand is addressed throughout all grade levels of the program. Each grade level builds on and extends concept understanding so that children approach each new challenge from a firmly established foundation.

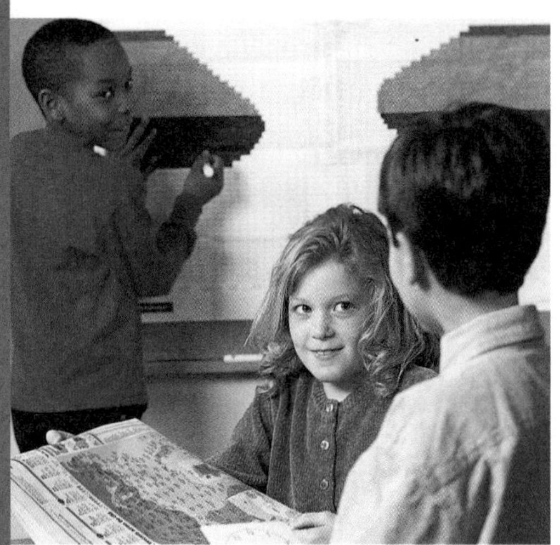

Within the content of *Everyday Mathematics*, emphasis is placed on

- ✦ Establishing links from past experience
- ✦ Discussing and sharing ideas
- ✦ Using and comparing equivalent expressions
- ✦ Expressing numbers in context by including units
- ✦ Learning about the reversibility of most things

**By becoming a part of everyday work and play, these ideas gradually shape students' ways of thinking about mathematics and foster the development of mathematical intuition and understanding.**

skills & concepts K–6

# content strands

| OPERATIONS & COMPUTATION | NUMERATION | PATTERNS, FUNCTIONS & ALGEBRA | DATA & CHANCE | MEASUREMENT & REFERENCE FRAMES | GEOMETRY |
|---|---|---|---|---|---|
| Facts | Counting | Number and Visual Patterns | Mean | Linear Measures | Two Dimensional |
| Mental Math | Order | Properties | Median | Weight | Three Dimensional |
| Algorithms | Relations | Sequences | Range | Capacity | Symmetry |
| Estimation | Estimation | Functions | Mode | Money | Congruence |
| Number Stories | Odd/Even | Number Sentences | Tally Charts | Time | Angles |
| Money | Fractions | Equations and Inequalities | Line Plots | Temperature | |
| Powers of Ten | Decimals | Variables | Graphs | Perimeter | |
| Exponents | Percents | Formulas | Probability | Area | |
| | | | | Volume | |
| | | | | Diameter and Circumference | |
| | | | | Angle | |
| | | | | Coordinate Grid | |

# Everyday Mathematics *Providing* classroom support

*Everyday Mathematics* was written in collaboration with teachers, for teachers as well as for students. *Everyday Mathematics* provides all the tools needed for instruction.

components

## student materials

**Student Reference Book (Grades 3–6)**
Students use this hardbound reference book to access mathematical information and procedures that support the program. Game rules, ongoing routines, reference tables, a glossary of terms and calculator usage information are all included.

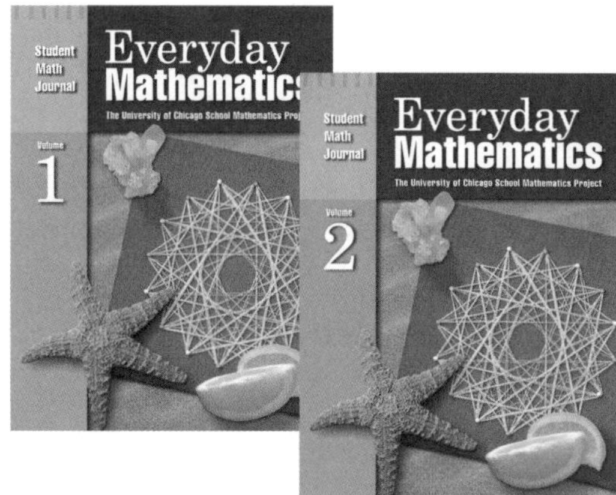


**Student Math Journal, Volumes 1 & 2 (Grades 1–6)**
These consumable books provide lesson support material for students to solve and complete. They provide a long-term record of each student's mathematical development.

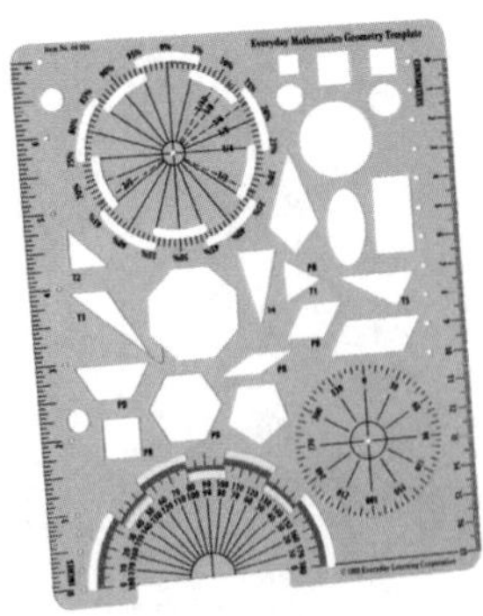


**Geometry Template (Grades 4–6)**
This unique drawing/measuring device is a useful companion for lesson activities.

## teacher materials

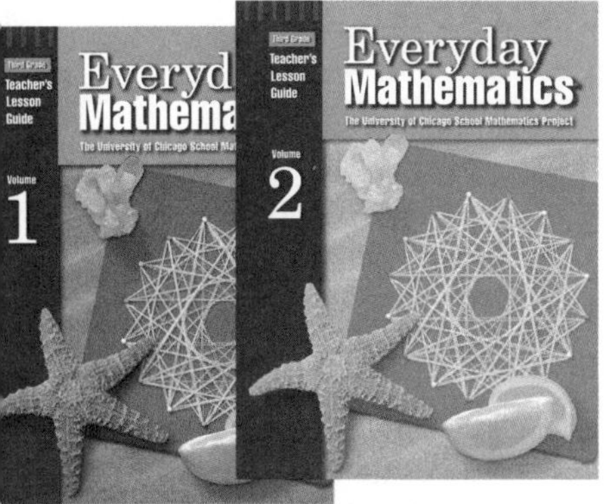


**Teacher's Lesson Guide, Volumes 1 & 2 (Grades 1–6)**
Easy-to-follow three-part daily lesson plans. A unit organizer provides learning goals, planning tips, content highlights, and suggestions on problem-solving, cross-curricular links, and support for special student populations.

**Minute Math+ (Grades 1–3)**
Brief activities for transition time and for spare moments throughout the day.

**Math Masters (Grades 1–6)**
Blackline masters that support daily lesson activities. Includes Home/Study Link and Assessment Masters.

## teacher resources

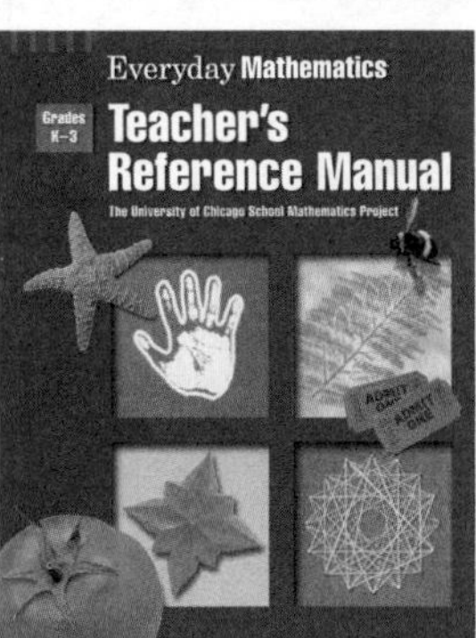

**Teacher's Reference Manual**
Contains comprehensive background information about mathematical content and program management for Grades K–3 and 4–6.

**Assessment Handbook**
Grade level specific handbook that provides ideas for portfolio, ongoing, and product assessment.

**Teacher's Assessment Assistant (Grades 1–6)**
The grade-specific *Teacher's Assessment Assistant* makes assessment more manageable and productive and offers teachers the ability to customize written assessment materials.

**Home Connection Handbook**
Provides suggestions for enhancing home-school communication and involvement in the program for Grades K–6.

## early childhood

*Everyday Mathematics* is also available for Kindergarten and Pre-Kindergarten.

# Everyday Mathematics Unit Organizer

Each Unit begins with comprehensive support information to assist in successful implementation and instruction. In addition to the sections detailed on the following pages, the Unit Organizer also includes:

- ✦ Unit Overview
- ✦ Table of Contents
- ✦ Problem-Solving Opportunities
- ✦ Cross-Curricular Links
- ✦ Materials Chart
- ✦ Detailed Content Highlights

**Program Content Links**
**Connections to prior and future content both within and across grade levels.**

**Unit 9**
**Multiplication & Division**

**learning goals in perspective**

| learning goals | links to the past | links to the future |
|---|---|---|
| 9a **Beginning Goal** Solve number stories involving positive and negative numbers. **(Lesson 9.13)** | In second grade, children experienced negative numbers by working with temperatures, number lines, and number grids. *(Related Grade 3 lessons: 4.1–4.4, 7.4, 7.5, 7.9, 8.7)* | In fourth grade, children will use positive and negative numbers in "credits and debits" number stories. *(Related Grade 3 lesson: 11.9)* |
| 9b **Beginning/Developing Goal** Multiply multidigit numbers by 1- or 2-digit numbers. **(Lessons 9.4, 9.5, 9.9, 9.11, and 9.12)** | In second grade, children developed their own strategies for solving multidigit multiplication problems. In Grade 3 Unit 2, children worked with addition and subtraction algorithms. *(Related Grade 3 lessons: 2.7, 2.8, 4.8, 7.1–7.3, 7.6, 7.8)* | In fourth grade, children will review the basic principles of multiplication with multidigit numbers, and practice using the partial-products algorithm. The partial-products algorithm is used in later grades, in algebra, to find the products of binomials, such as $(x + 2)(x + 5)$. *(Related Grade 3 lessons: 10.2, 10.6)* |
| 9c **Beginning/Developing Goal** Find factors of a number. **(Lesson 9.6)** | Skip counting by 2s, 5s, and 10s in previous grades prepared children to learn multiplication by these factors. Children were also introduced to multiplication/division fact families in second grade. *(Related Grade 3 lessons: 1.8, 4.2, 4.4–4.8, 7.1–7.3, 7.6, 7.8)* | In later grades, children will further explore factors and products in a branch of mathematics called number theory. Children will develop factoring skills by using arrays to identify all the possible factor pairs for a given number. |
| 9d **Beginning/Developing Goal** Interpret remainders in division problems. **(Lesson 9.8)** | Second graders used counters to solve real-life division problems, and were introduced to the idea of remainders. *(Related Grade 3 lessons: 3.1, 4.3, 4.4, 4.6, 7.6)* | Children will continue to interpret remainders in division problems throughout the grades. |
| **Developing Goal** Solve | In second grade, children worked with | Children will continue to work with fact ...ons in *Fourth Grade Everyday ...atics.* |
| | | ...hout the grades, children will continue ...e and solve division number stories. |

**Unit Learning Goals**
**Indicates developmental level expected and lesson reference.**

**assessment**
**ongoing • product • periodic**

**Informal Assessment**

**Math Boxes** These *Math Journal* pages provide opportunities for cumulative review or assessment of concepts and skills.

**Ongoing Assessment: Kid Watching** Use the Ongoing Assessment suggestions in the following lessons to make quick, on-the-spot observations about children's understanding of:
- Operations and Computation **(Lessons 9.4–9.13)**
- Measurement and Reference Frames **(Lessons 9.7 and 9.13 )**

**Portfolio Ideas** Samples of children's work may be obtained from the following assignments:
- Solving an Allowance Problem **(Lesson 9.2)**
- Using Count-By Patterns **(Lesson 9.4)**
- Sharing Money **(Lesson 9.7)**
- Multiplying and Dividing Multiples of 10 in the Context of Time **(Lesson 9.9)**
- Finding Number Patterns by Filing Equilateral Triangles **(Lesson 9.10)**

**Unit 9 Review and Assessment**

**Math Message** Use the question in Lesson 9.14 to assess children's progress toward the following learning goal: Goal 9b

**Slate Assessments** Use oral or slate assessments during Lesson 9.14 to assess children's progress toward the following learning goals: Goals 9e and 9f

**Written Assessment** Use a written review during Lesson 9.14 to assess children's progress toward the following learning goals: Goals 9a, 9b, 9c, 9d, 9e, and 9f

**Performance/Group Assessment** Use a small-group activity in Lesson 9.14 to assess children's progress toward the following learning goals: Goals 9c, 9e, and 9f

**assessment handbook**

For more information on how to use different types of assessment in Unit 9, see the Assessment Overview on pages 69–71 in the *Assessment Handbook.* The following Assessment Masters can be found in the *Math Masters* book:
- Unit 9 Checking Progress, pp. 386 and 387
- Unit 9 Class Checklist, p. 420
- Unit 9 Individual Profile of Progress, p. 421
- Class Progress Indicator, p. 441
- Math Logs, pp. 446–448
- Self-Assessment Forms, pp. 449 and 450

**Assessment Support**
**Suggestions for informal assessments and use of the *Assessment Handbook* are also included.**

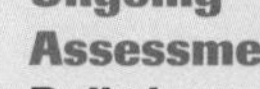

**Ongoing Assessment**
**Built-in evaluation techniques and opportunities teachers may use to assess student attainment of unit learning goals.**

Examples from Third Grade, Unit 9

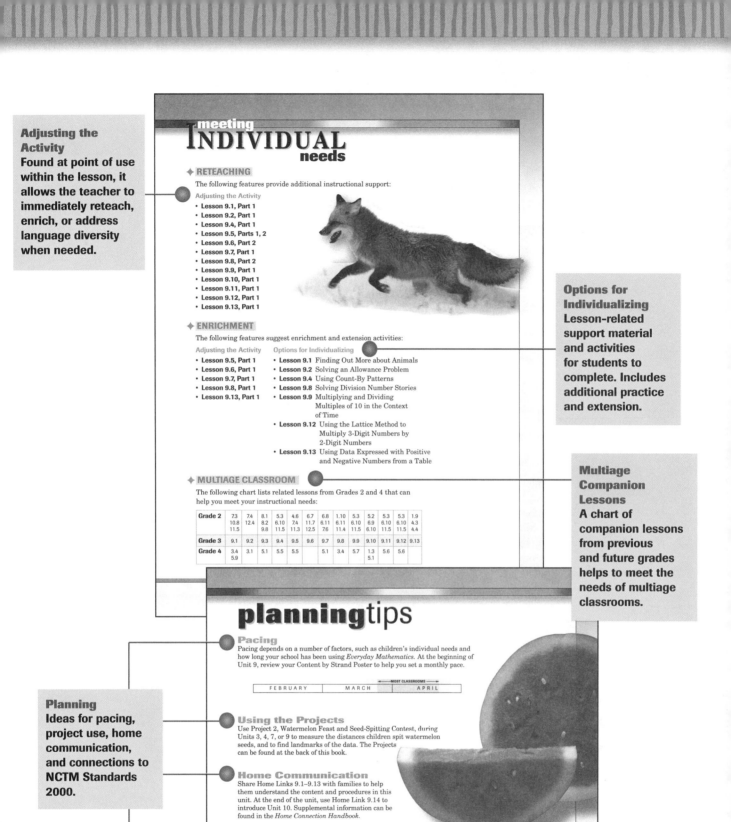

**Adjusting the Activity**
Found at point of use within the lesson, it allows the teacher to immediately reteach, enrich, or address language diversity when needed.

# meeting INDIVIDUAL needs

## ✦ RETEACHING

The following features provide additional instructional support:

Adjusting the Activity

- **Lesson 9.1, Part 1**
- **Lesson 9.2, Part 1**
- **Lesson 9.4, Part 1**
- **Lesson 9.5, Parts 1, 2**
- **Lesson 9.6, Part 2**
- **Lesson 9.7, Part 1**
- **Lesson 9.8, Part 2**
- **Lesson 9.9, Part 1**
- **Lesson 9.10, Part 1**
- **Lesson 9.11, Part 1**
- **Lesson 9.12, Part 1**
- **Lesson 9.13, Part 1**

## ✦ ENRICHMENT

The following features suggest enrichment and extension activities:

Adjusting the Activity

- **Lesson 9.5, Part 1**
- **Lesson 9.6, Part 1**
- **Lesson 9.7, Part 1**
- **Lesson 9.8, Part 1**
- **Lesson 9.13, Part 1**

Options for Individualizing

- **Lesson 9.1** Finding Out More about Animals
- **Lesson 9.2** Solving an Allowance Problem
- **Lesson 9.4** Using Count-By Patterns
- **Lesson 9.8** Solving Division Number Stories
- **Lesson 9.9** Multiplying and Dividing Multiples of 10 in the Context of Time
- **Lesson 9.12** Using the Lattice Method to Multiply 3-Digit Numbers by 2-Digit Numbers
- **Lesson 9.13** Using Data Expressed with Positive and Negative Numbers from a Table

**Options for Individualizing**
Lesson-related support material and activities for students to complete. Includes additional practice and extension.

## ✦ MULTIAGE CLASSROOM

The following chart lists related lessons from Grades 2 and 4 that can help you meet your instructional needs:

| **Grade 2** | 7.3 10.8 11.5 | 7.4 12.4 | 8.1 8.2 9.8 | 5.3 6.10 11.5 | 4.6 7.4 11.3 | 6.7 11.7 12.5 | 6.8 6.11 7.6 | 1.10 6.11 11.4 | 5.3 6.10 11.5 | 5.2 6.9 6.10 | 5.3 6.10 11.5 | 5.3 6.10 11.5 | 1.9 4.3 4.4 |
|---|---|---|---|---|---|---|---|---|---|---|---|---|---|
| **Grade 3** | 9.1 | 9.2 | 9.3 | 9.4 | 9.5 | 9.6 | 9.7 | 9.8 | 9.9 | 9.10 | 9.11 | 9.12 | 9.13 |
| **Grade 4** | 3.4 5.9 | 3.1 | 5.1 | 5.5 | 5.5 | | 5.1 | 3.4 | 5.7 | 1.3 5.1 | 5.6 | 5.6 | |

**Multiage Companion Lessons**
A chart of companion lessons from previous and future grades helps to meet the needs of multiage classrooms.

# planningtips

**Planning**
Ideas for pacing, project use, home communication, and connections to NCTM Standards 2000.

## Pacing

Pacing depends on a number of factors, such as children's individual needs and how long your school has been using *Everyday Mathematics.* At the beginning of Unit 9, review your Content by Strand Poster to help you set a monthly pace.

| FEBRUARY | MARCH | APRIL |
|---|---|---|

← MOST CLASSROOMS →

## Using the Projects

Use Project 2, Watermelon Feast and Seed-Spitting Contest, during Units 3, 4, 7, or 9 to measure the distances children spit watermelon seeds, and to find landmarks of the data. The Projects can be found at the back of this book.

## Home Communication

Share Home Links 9.1–9.13 with families to help them understand the content and procedures in this unit. At the end of the unit, use Home Link 9.14 to introduce Unit 10. Supplemental information can be found in the *Home Connection Handbook.*

## NCTM Standards

| Standard | 1 | 2 | 3 | 4 | 5 | 6 | 7 | 8 | 9 | 10 |
|---|---|---|---|---|---|---|---|---|---|---|
| Unit 9 Lessons | 1–13 | 1–13 | 3, 4, 10–12 | 3, 5, 7, 10, 12 | 2 | 1–13 | 1–13 | 1–13 | 1–13 | 1–13 |

Content Standards
- **1** Number and Operations
- **2** Algebra
- **3** Geometry
- **4** Measurement
- **5** Data Analysis and Probability

Process Standards
- **6** Problem Solving
- **7** Reasoning and Proof
- **8** Communication
- **9** Connections
- **10** Representation

## PRACTICE *through* Games

*Everyday Mathematics* uses games to help children develop good fact power and other math skills.

- Compare fractions with *Fraction Top-It* **(Lesson 9.3)**
- Identify the factors of whole numbers in *Factor Bingo* **(Lessons 9.6, 9.7, 9.10, and 9.14)**
- Practice multiplication facts pictured on dot arrays in *Array Bingo* **(Lesson 9.6)**
- … with *Angle Race* **(Lesson 9.11)**

# Everyday Mathematics Lesson Highlights

Each lesson has been designed to follow an easy-to-use three-part plan. This assists teachers in focusing on lesson objectives, provides ongoing practice for all students, and addresses individual student needs for a variety of populations.

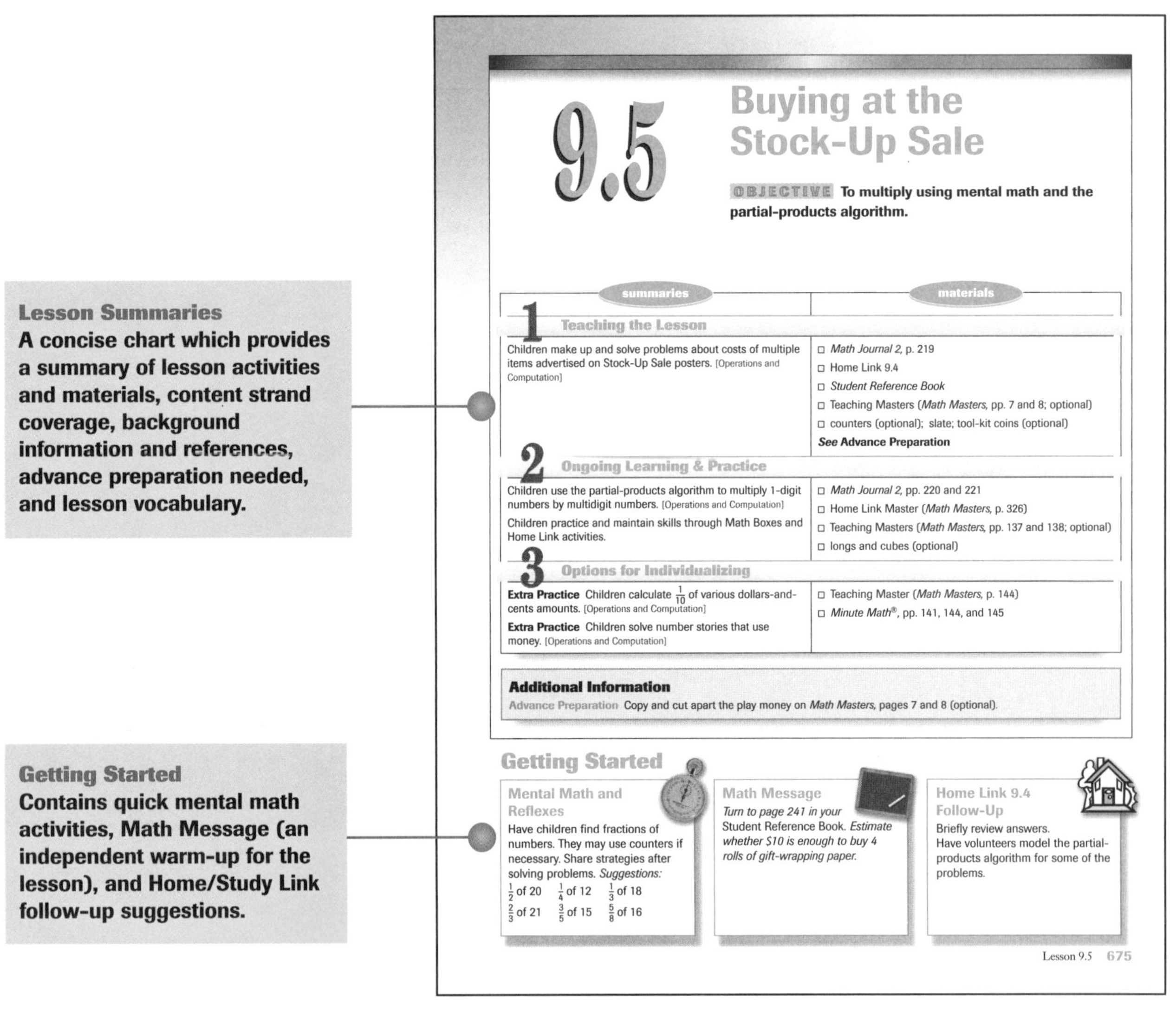

**Lesson Summaries**
**A concise chart which provides a summary of lesson activities and materials, content strand coverage, background information and references, advance preparation needed, and lesson vocabulary.**

**Getting Started**
**Contains quick mental math activities, Math Message (an independent warm-up for the lesson), and Home/Study Link follow-up suggestions.**

## 9.5 Buying at the Stock-Up Sale

**OBJECTIVE** **To multiply using mental math and the partial-products algorithm.**

| summaries | materials |
|---|---|
| **1 Teaching the Lesson** | |
| Children make up and solve problems about costs of multiple items advertised on Stock-Up Sale posters. [Operations and Computation] | □ *Math Journal 2,* p. 219<br>□ Home Link 9.4<br>□ *Student Reference Book*<br>□ Teaching Masters (*Math Masters,* pp. 7 and 8; optional)<br>□ counters (optional); slate; tool-kit coins (optional)<br>***See* Advance Preparation** |
| **2 Ongoing Learning & Practice** | |
| Children use the partial-products algorithm to multiply 1-digit numbers by multidigit numbers. [Operations and Computation]<br>Children practice and maintain skills through Math Boxes and Home Link activities. | □ *Math Journal 2,* pp. 220 and 221<br>□ Home Link Master (*Math Masters,* p. 326)<br>□ Teaching Masters (*Math Masters,* pp. 137 and 138; optional)<br>□ longs and cubes (optional) |
| **3 Options for Individualizing** | |
| **Extra Practice** Children calculate $\frac{1}{10}$ of various dollars-and-cents amounts. [Operations and Computation]<br>**Extra Practice** Children solve number stories that use money. [Operations and Computation] | □ Teaching Master (*Math Masters,* p. 144)<br>□ *Minute Math*®, pp. 141, 144, and 145 |

**Additional Information**
Advance Preparation Copy and cut apart the play money on *Math Masters,* pages 7 and 8 (optional).

### Getting Started

**Mental Math and Reflexes**
Have children find fractions of numbers. They may use counters if necessary. Share strategies after solving problems. *Suggestions:*
$\frac{1}{2}$ of 20 $\frac{1}{4}$ of 12 $\frac{1}{3}$ of 18
$\frac{2}{3}$ of 21 $\frac{3}{5}$ of 15 $\frac{5}{8}$ of 16

**Math Message**
*Turn to page 241 in your* Student Reference Book. *Estimate whether $10 is enough to buy 4 rolls of gift-wrapping paper.*

**Home Link 9.4 Follow-Up**
Briefly review answers.
Have volunteers model the partial-products algorithm for some of the problems.

Lesson 9.5 675

Examples from Third Grade, Unit 9, Lesson 5

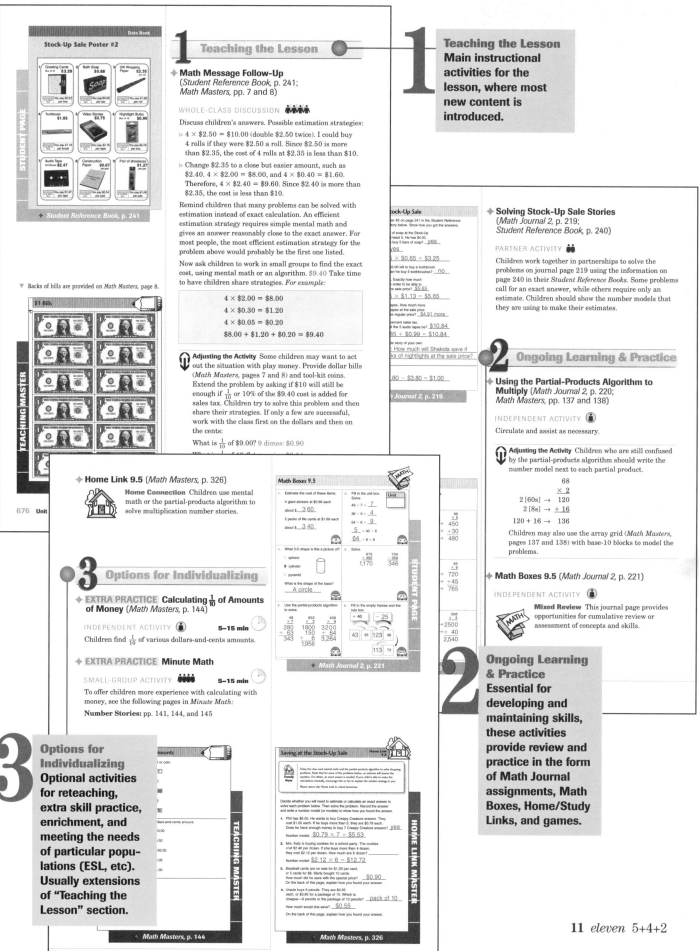

Data Bank

Stock-Up Sale Poster #2

STUDENT PAGE

Student Reference Book, p. 241

# 1 Teaching the Lesson

### Math Message Follow-Up
(*Student Reference Book,* p. 241; *Math Masters,* pp. 7 and 8)

WHOLE-CLASS DISCUSSION

Discuss children's answers. Possible estimation strategies:

- $4 \times \$2.50 = \$10.00$ (double \$2.50 twice). I could buy 4 rolls if they were \$2.50 a roll. Since \$2.50 is more than \$2.35, the cost of 4 rolls at \$2.35 is less than \$10.
- Change \$2.35 to a close but easier amount, such as \$2.40. $4 \times \$2.00 = \$8.00$, and $4 \times \$0.40 = \$1.60$. Therefore, $4 \times \$2.40 = \$9.60$. Since \$2.40 is more than \$2.35, the cost is less than \$10.

Remind children that many problems can be solved with estimation instead of exact calculation. An efficient estimation strategy requires simple mental math and gives an answer reasonably close to the exact answer. For most people, the most efficient estimation strategy for the problem above would probably be the first one listed.

Now ask children to work in small groups to find the exact cost, using mental math or an algorithm. \$9.40 Take time to have children share strategies. *For example:*

$$4 \times \$2.00 = \$8.00$$
$$4 \times \$0.30 = \$1.20$$
$$4 \times \$0.05 = \$0.20$$
$$\$8.00 + \$1.20 + \$0.20 = \$9.40$$

**Adjusting the Activity** Some children may want to act out the situation with play money. Provide dollar bills (*Math Masters,* pages 7 and 8) and tool-kit coins. Extend the problem by asking if \$10 will still be enough if $\frac{1}{10}$ or 10% of the \$9.40 cost is added for sales tax. Children try to solve this problem and then share their strategies. If only a few are successful, work with the class first on the dollars and then on the cents:

What is $\frac{1}{10}$ of \$9.00? 9 dimes: \$0.90

▼ Backs of bills are provided on *Math Masters,* page 8.

$1 Bills

TEACHING MASTER

## 1 Teaching the Lesson
**Main instructional activities for the lesson, where most new content is introduced.**

### Solving Stock-Up Sale Stories
(*Math Journal 2,* p. 219; *Student Reference Book,* p. 240)

PARTNER ACTIVITY

Children work together in partnerships to solve the problems on journal page 219 using the information on page 240 in their *Student Reference Books.* Some problems call for an exact answer, while others require only an estimate. Children should show the number models that they are using to make their estimates.

Journal 2, p. 219

# 2 Ongoing Learning & Practice

### Using the Partial-Products Algorithm to Multiply (*Math Journal 2,* p. 220; *Math Masters,* pp. 137 and 138)

INDEPENDENT ACTIVITY

Circulate and assist as necessary.

**Adjusting the Activity** Children who are still confused by the partial-products algorithm should write the number model next to each partial product.

$$\begin{array}{lr} & 68 \\ & \times\ 2 \\ 2\,[60s] \rightarrow & 120 \\ 2\,[8s] \rightarrow & +\ 16 \\ 120 + 16 \rightarrow & 136 \end{array}$$

Children may also use the array grid (*Math Masters,* pages 137 and 138) with base-10 blocks to model the problems.

### Math Boxes 9.5 (*Math Journal 2,* p. 221)

INDEPENDENT ACTIVITY

**Mixed Review** This journal page provides opportunities for cumulative review or assessment of concepts and skills.

## 2 Ongoing Learning & Practice
**Essential for developing and maintaining skills, these activities provide review and practice in the form of Math Journal assignments, Math Boxes, Home/Study Links, and games.**

### Home Link 9.5 (*Math Masters,* p. 326)

**Home Connection** Children use mental math or the partial-products algorithm to solve multiplication number stories.

Math Boxes 9.5

STUDENT PAGE

Math Journal 2, p. 221

# 3 Options for Individualizing

### EXTRA PRACTICE Calculating $\frac{1}{10}$ of Amounts of Money (*Math Masters,* p. 144)

INDEPENDENT ACTIVITY 5–15 min

Children find $\frac{1}{10}$ of various dollars-and-cents amounts.

### EXTRA PRACTICE Minute Math

SMALL-GROUP ACTIVITY 5–15 min

To offer children more experience with calculating with money, see the following pages in *Minute Math:*

**Number Stories:** pp. 141, 144, and 145

## 3 Options for Individualizing
**Optional activities for reteaching, extra skill practice, enrichment, and meeting the needs of particular populations (ESL, etc). Usually extensions of "Teaching the Lesson" section.**

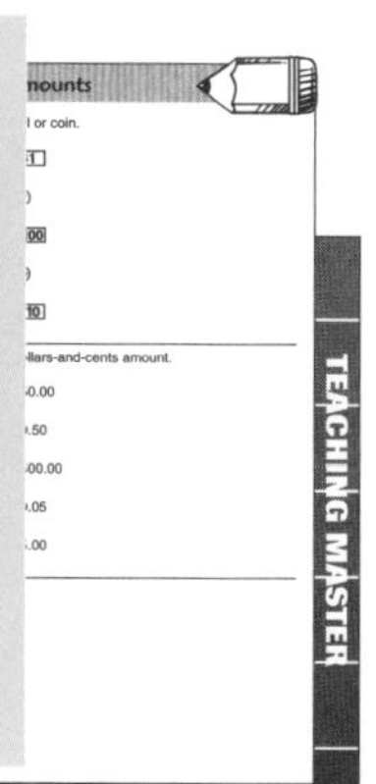
TEACHING MASTER

Math Masters, p. 144

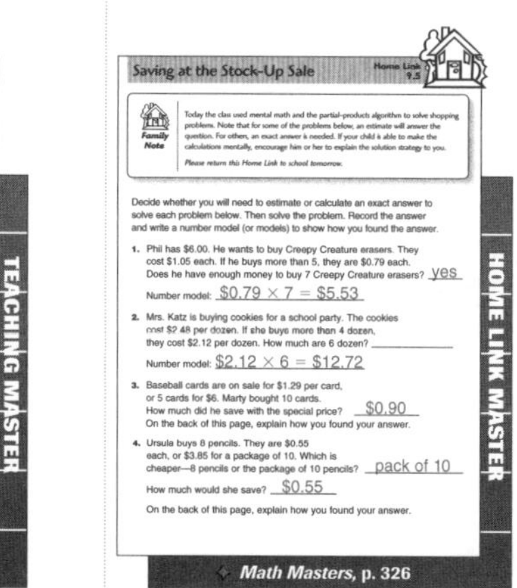
Saving at the Stock-Up Sale

HOME LINK MASTER

Math Masters, p. 326

# Everyday Mathematics Student Reference Book

Grades 3–6

The grade-specific *Student Reference Book* contains

- **Mathematical Essays** Sections organized around mathematical topics which provide explanations and examples. Students may use these pages during lesson instruction and when they need information to complete independent work.
- **Game Section** Provides directions for games introduced at each grade level. They are helpful for clarification of rules, adaptations for various abilities, and home use.
- **Data Section** Contains charts, tables, and other information provided for use with student lesson activities and projects.

In addition, a comprehensive glossary, an answer key for every **Check Your Understanding,** and an index are found at the back of the book.

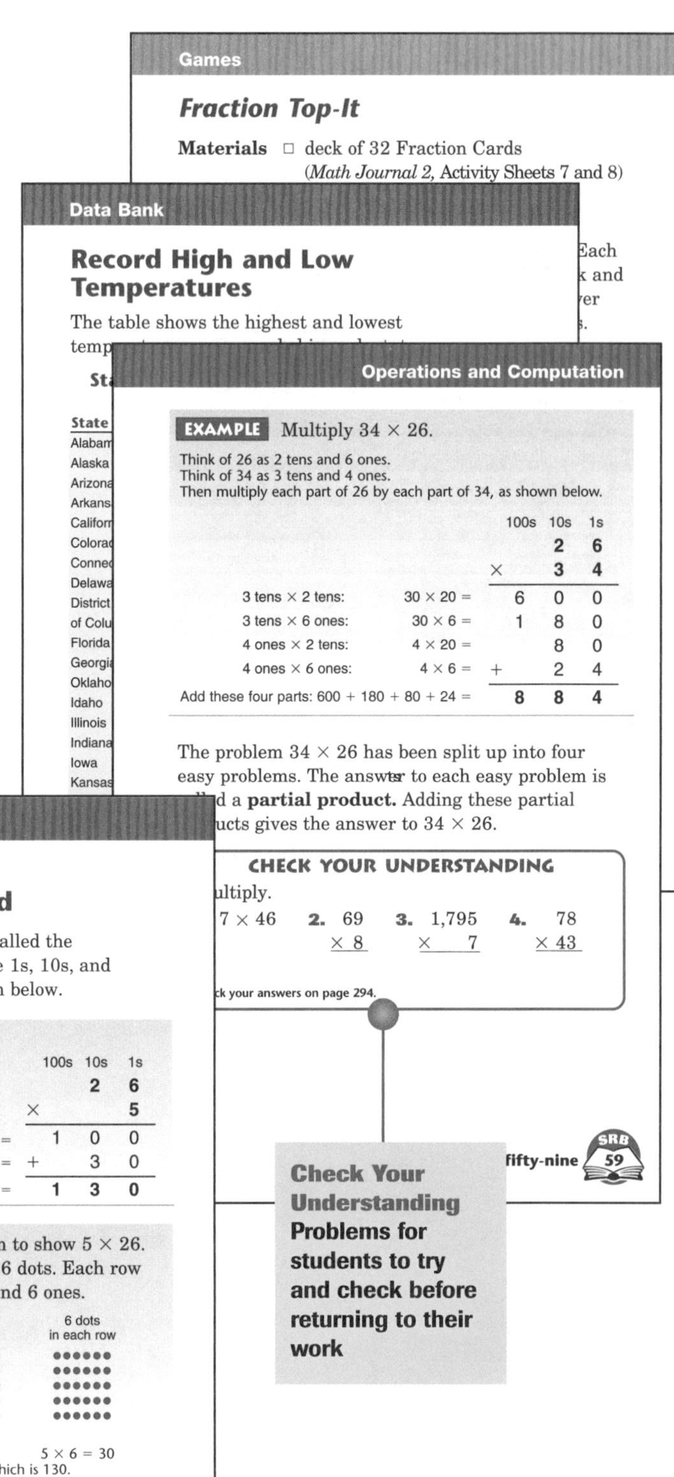

Games

*Fraction Top-It*

**Materials** □ deck of 32 Fraction Cards (*Math Journal 2,* Activity Sheets 7 and 8)

Data Bank

**Record High and Low Temperatures**

The table shows the highest and lowest temp…

Operations and Computation

**EXAMPLE** Multiply 34 × 26.

Think of 26 as 2 tens and 6 ones.
Think of 34 as 3 tens and 4 ones.
Then multiply each part of 26 by each part of 34, as shown below.

| | | 100s | 10s | 1s |
|---|---|---|---|---|
| | | | 2 | 6 |
| | | × | 3 | 4 |
| 3 tens × 2 tens: | 30 × 20 = | 6 | 0 | 0 |
| 3 tens × 6 ones: | 30 × 6 = | 1 | 8 | 0 |
| 4 ones × 2 tens: | 4 × 20 = | | 8 | 0 |
| 4 ones × 6 ones: | 4 × 6 = | + | 2 | 4 |
| Add these four parts: 600 + 180 + 80 + 24 = | | 8 | 8 | 4 |

The problem 34 × 26 has been split up into four easy problems. The answer to each easy problem is called a **partial product.** Adding these partial products gives the answer to 34 × 26.

**CHECK YOUR UNDERSTANDING**

Multiply.

1. 7 × 46 2. 69 × 8 3. 1,795 × 7 4. 78 × 43

Check your answers on page 294.

fifty-nine 59

**Title Bar** Highlights page contents

**Vocabulary** Notes words that may also be found in the glossary

**Examples** Provides examples of mathematical processes

**Check Your Understanding** Problems for students to try and check before returning to their work

Operations and Computation

**Partial-Products Multiplication Method**

One way to multiply numbers is called the **partial-products method.** Write 1s, 10s, and 100s above the columns, as shown below.

**EXAMPLE** Multiply 5 × 26.

Think of 26 as 2 tens and 6 ones.
Then multiply each part of 26 by 5.

| | | 100s | 10s | 1s |
|---|---|---|---|---|
| | | | 2 | 6 |
| | | × | | 5 |
| 5 ones × 2 tens: | 5 × 20 = | 1 | 0 | 0 |
| 5 ones × 6 ones: | 5 × 6 = | + | 3 | 0 |
| Add these two parts: | 100 + 30 = | 1 | 3 | 0 |

**EXAMPLE** Use an array diagram to show 5 × 26.
There are 5 rows. Each row has 26 dots. Each row has been divided to show 2 tens and 6 ones.



Multiply each part: 5 × 20 = 100 5 × 6 = 30
Add these two parts: 5 × 26 = 100 + 30, which is 130.

58 fifty-eight

Examples from Third Grade *Student Reference Book*

# Assessment

## Assessment Handbook

The grade-specific *Assessment Handbook* provides ideas to make assessment and instruction more manageable, productive, and exciting, as well as offer a more complete picture of each student's progress and instructional needs. It guides teachers as they develop a plan that balances techniques and tools from four different assessment areas.

- ✦ **Ongoing Assessment** Informal student observation and anecdotal record keeping during teacher-guided instruction, strategy sharing, game play, and slate routines.
- ✦ **Product Assessment** Samples of student work from Math Boxes, Math Journals, Portfolios, and Projects.
- ✦ **Periodic Assessment** Unit, mid-year, and end-of-year assessments and Math Boxes.
- ✦ **Outside Tests** School, district, or state assessments and standardized achievement tests.

**Ongoing Assessment** **Suggestions from lesson activities throughout the unit. Refers teachers back to unit learning goals and development levels.**

### Unit 9 Assessment Overview

At this stage in *Everyday Mathematics,* children are expected to be at a Beginning/Developing level for multiplying multidigit numbers by 1- or 2-digit numbers. Because this is such a critical skill, five ongoing assessment opportunities are provided in Unit 9 (see Goal 9b in the chart below).

By this time, perhaps you have tried several different types of assessment strategies. Remember, as you use a balance of assessment approaches, the overall effectiveness of your assessment plan should improve. If there is still a major type of assessment, such as Ongoing, Product, or Periodic, that you haven't used, this unit might be a good time to try it.

**Ongoing Assessment Opportunities**

Ongoing assessment opportunities are opportunities to observe children during regular interactions, as they work independently and in groups. You can conduct ongoing assessment during teacher-guided instruction, Math Boxes sessions, mathematical mini-interviews, games, Mental Math and Reflexes sessions, strategy sharing, and slate work. The chart below provides a summary of ongoing assessment opportunities in Unit 9, as they relate to specific Unit 9 learning goals.

| Goal | Lessons |
|---|---|
| 9a **Beginning Goal** Solve number stories involving positive and negative integers. (Lesson 9.13) | Lesson 9.13, p. 722 |
| 9b **Beginning/Developing Goal** Multiply multidigit numbers by 1- or 2-digit numbers. (Lessons 9.2, 9.4, 9.5, 9.9, 9.11, and 9.12) | Lesson 9.2, p. 660<br>Lesson 9.4, p. 672<br>Lesson 9.9, p. 699<br>Lesson 9.11, p. 710<br>Lesson 9.12, p. 715 |
| 9c **Beginning/Developing Goal** Find factors of a number. (Lessons 9.6 and 9.10) | Lesson 9.6, p. 681<br>Lesson 9.10, p. 705 |
| 9d **Beginning/Developing Goal** Interpret remainders in division problems. (Lesson 9.8) | Lesson 9.8, p. 693 |

Assessment Overviews 69

**Product Assessment Opportunities**

*Math Journals,* Math Boxes, activity sheets, masters, Math Logs, and the results of Explorations and Projects all provide product assessment opportunities. Here is an example of how you might use a rubric to assess children's abilities to solve equal-sharing problems.

Lesson 9.7, p. 689

**EXTRA PRACTICE Sharing Money**

Circulate around the room as children work in pairs to complete *Math Masters,* page 148. Children record the problem, a number model, and the answer. This activity can help you assess children's ability to solve equal-sharing problems with remainders. The sample rubric below will help you evaluate children's work.

Portfolio Ideas

**Sample Rubric**

**Beginning (B)**
The pair of children is able to set up the problem by rolling the die and drawing two cards. However, the number model may be written incorrectly or children may need teacher assistance. Problems b–f are difficult for partners to solve without teacher assistance. Children may get through only one of the equal-sharing problems.

**Developing (D)**
The pair of children sets up the problem without teacher assistance using the die and number cards. The number model is written correctly in both problems and the numbers of $10 bills and $1 bills are correct. It may be difficult for children to calculate how many cents each friend would receive if the leftover money were shared equally (Problem e). Therefore, their final answer may be incorrect.

**Secure (S)**
The pair of children sets up and solves the problems without teacher assistance. The number sentences are written correctly, and the numbers of $10 bills and $1 bills are correct. Children are able to calculate how the leftover money can be shared equally; thus they have a correct total for the amount that each friend would receive. Children may also be able to solve more than two problems.

**Periodic Assessment Opportunities**

Here is a summary of the periodic assessment opportunities that are provided in Unit 9. Refer to Lesson 9.14 for details.

***Oral and Slate Assessment***

In Lesson 9.14, you will find oral and slate assessment problems on pages 725–727.

***Written Assessment***

In Lesson 9.14, you will find written assessment problems on pages 727–728 (*Math Masters,* pages 386 and 387).

See the chart on the next page to find slate and written assessment problems that address specific learning goals.

70 Assessment Handbook

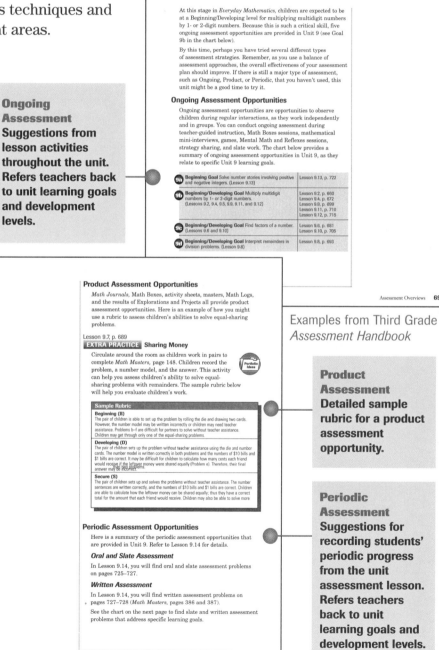

Examples from Third Grade *Assessment Handbook*

**Product Assessment** **Detailed sample rubric for a product assessment opportunity.**

**Periodic Assessment** **Suggestions for recording students' periodic progress from the unit assessment lesson. Refers teachers back to unit learning goals and development levels.**

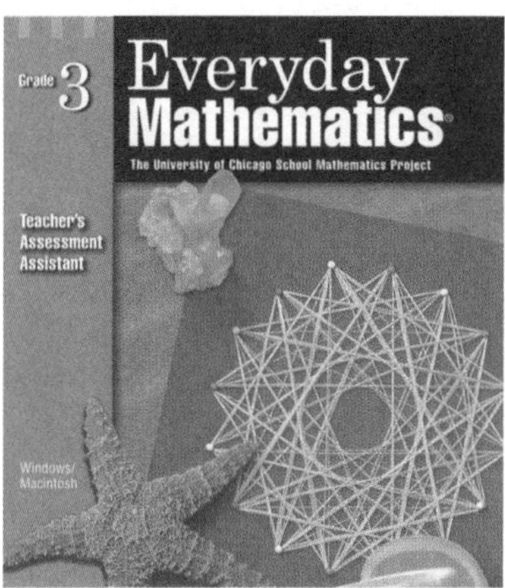


## Teacher's Assessment Assistant

The grade-specific *Teacher's Assessment Assistant* on CD-ROM offers the ability to create and customize assessment materials.

# Everyday Mathematics *Making* a mark in education

*Everyday Mathematics* is used in a variety of settings throughout the United States as shown here on the map.

**Nearly 2.5 million students in 125,000 classrooms** are engaged in this exciting curriculum.

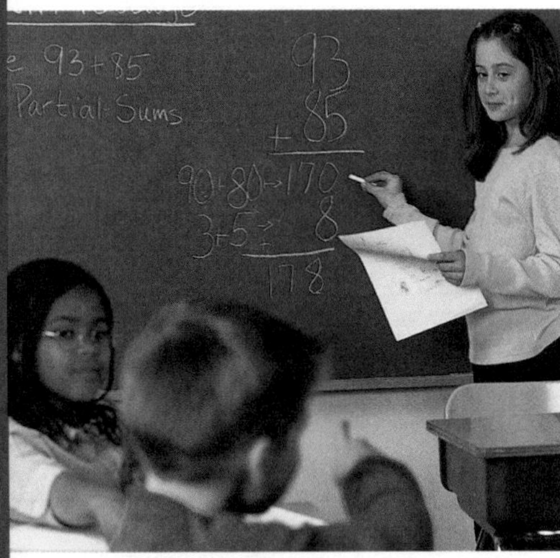


**Look for users in your area.**

**WASHINGTON**
Franklin Pierce SD 402
Longview SD 122
Northshore SD 417
Silverdale Elementary
South Kitsap SD 402

**OREGON**
Beavertown SD 48J
Portland Jewish Academy

**CALIFORNIA**
Center for Early Education
Glendale Unified SD
Hillsborough City SD
Poway Unified SD
Woodside Elementary SD

**NEVADA**
Alexander Dawson Sch
Washoe County SD (Reno)

**IDAHO**
Coeur D'Alene SD 271
Lewiston ISD 1
Nampa SD 131

**UTAH**
Park City SD
Rolling Meadows Elementary

**ARIZONA**
Amphitheater SD 1
Cave Creek Unfd SD 93
Kyrene Elem SD 28

**MONTANA**
Bigfork SD 38
Butte SD
Livingston SD 1 & 4

**WYOMING**
Sheridan County SD 2

**COLORADO**
Cherry Creek SD 5
Colorado Springs SD 11
Douglas County SD R-1
Eagleton Elementary
Julesburg SD R-1
Lewis-Palmer SD 38

**NEW MEXICO**
Bernalillo Public SD
Bloomfield SD
Pojoaque Valley SD
Rio Rancho Public SD
Taos Day School-Bureau of Indian Affairs

**NORTH DAKOTA**
Fargo SD
Grand Forks SD 1

**SOUTH DAKOTA**
Beresford SD 61-2
Pierre Indian School

**ALASKA**
Anchorage SD
Matanuska-Susitna Boro SD

**HAWAII**
Ewa Beach Elementary
Nanakuli Elementary
Waipahu Elementary

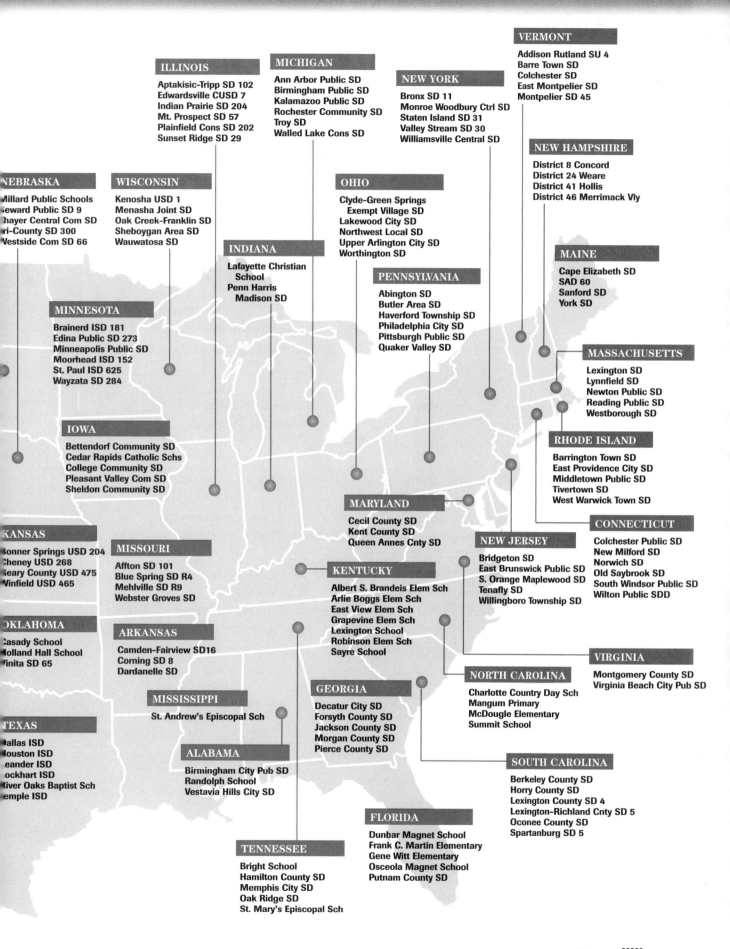

### VERMONT
Addison Rutland SU 4
Barre Town SD
Colchester SD
East Montpelier SD
Montpelier SD 45

### ILLINOIS
Aptakisic-Tripp SD 102
Edwardsville CUSD 7
Indian Prairie SD 204
Mt. Prospect SD 57
Plainfield Cons SD 202
Sunset Ridge SD 29

### MICHIGAN
Ann Arbor Public SD
Birmingham Public SD
Kalamazoo Public SD
Rochester Community SD
Troy SD
Walled Lake Cons SD

### NEW YORK
Bronx SD 11
Monroe Woodbury Ctrl SD
Staten Island SD 31
Valley Stream SD 30
Williamsville Central SD

### NEW HAMPSHIRE
District 8 Concord
District 24 Weare
District 41 Hollis
District 46 Merrimack Vly

### EBRASKA
illard Public Schools
eward Public SD 9
hayer Central Com SD
i-County SD 300
estside Com SD 66

### WISCONSIN
Kenosha USD 1
Menasha Joint SD
Oak Creek-Franklin SD
Sheboygan Area SD
Wauwatosa SD

### OHIO
Clyde-Green Springs
Exempt Village SD
Lakewood City SD
Northwest Local SD
Upper Arlington City SD
Worthington SD

### INDIANA
Lafayette Christian
School
Penn Harris
Madison SD

### MAINE
Cape Elizabeth SD
SAD 60
Sanford SD
York SD

### PENNSYLVANIA
Abington SD
Butler Area SD
Haverford Township SD
Philadelphia City SD
Pittsburgh Public SD
Quaker Valley SD

### MINNESOTA
Brainerd ISD 181
Edina Public SD 273
Minneapolis Public SD
Moorhead ISD 152
St. Paul ISD 625
Wayzata SD 284

### MASSACHUSETTS
Lexington SD
Lynnfield SD
Newton Public SD
Reading Public SD
Westborough SD

### IOWA
Bettendorf Community SD
Cedar Rapids Catholic Schs
College Community SD
Pleasant Valley Com SD
Sheldon Community SD

### RHODE ISLAND
Barrington Town SD
East Providence City SD
Middletown Public SD
Tiverton SD
West Warwick Town SD

### MARYLAND
Cecil County SD
Kent County SD
Queen Annes Cnty SD

### KANSAS
onner Springs USD 204
heney USD 268
eary County USD 475
infield USD 465

### MISSOURI
Affton SD 101
Blue Spring SD R4
Mehlville SD R9
Webster Groves SD

### CONNECTICUT
Colchester Public SD
New Milford SD
Norwich SD
Old Saybrook SD
South Windsor Public SD
Wilton Public SDD

### NEW JERSEY
Bridgeton SD
East Brunswick Public SD
S. Orange Maplewood SD
Tenafly SD
Willingboro Township SD

### KENTUCKY
Albert S. Brandeis Elem Sch
Arlie Boggs Elem Sch
East View Elem Sch
Grapevine Elem Sch
Lexington School
Robinson Elem Sch
Sayre School

### KLAHOMA
asady School
olland Hall School
inita SD 65

### ARKANSAS
Camden-Fairview SD16
Corning SD 8
Dardanelle SD

### VIRGINIA
Montgomery County SD
Virginia Beach City Pub SD

### NORTH CAROLINA
Charlotte Country Day Sch
Mangum Primary
McDougle Elementary
Summit School

### GEORGIA
Decatur City SD
Forsyth County SD
Jackson County SD
Morgan County SD
Pierce County SD

### MISSISSIPPI
St. Andrew's Episcopal Sch

### TEXAS
allas ISD
ouston ISD
eander ISD
ockhart ISD
iver Oaks Baptist Sch
emple ISD

### ALABAMA
Birmingham City Pub SD
Randolph School
Vestavia Hills City SD

### SOUTH CAROLINA
Berkeley County SD
Horry County SD
Lexington County SD 4
Lexington-Richland Cnty SD 5
Oconee County SD
Spartanburg SD 5

### FLORIDA
Dunbar Magnet School
Frank C. Martin Elementary
Gene Witt Elementary
Osceola Magnet School
Putnam County SD

### TENNESSEE
Bright School
Hamilton County SD
Memphis City SD
Oak Ridge SD
St. Mary's Episcopal Sch

# Acknowledgments

The first edition of the K–6 *Everyday Mathematics* program was made possible by sustained support over several years from the GTE Corporation and the National Science Foundation. Additional help came from the Amoco Foundation through its support of the University of Chicago School Mathematics Project (UCSMP).

Earlier projects supported by the National Science Foundation, the National Institute of Education, and the Benton Foundation provided us with insights into the often surprising capabilities of young children.

Research and development of the second edition of the K–6 *Everyday Mathematics* program was funded by Everyday Learning Corporation and by the authors.

For both editions, feedback and advice from teachers willing to take risks in trying development versions have been essential and enormously helpful. There are too many such teachers to list, but their contributions are gratefully acknowledged.

For both editions, many University of Chicago and UCSMP colleagues have been helpful. Finally, we acknowledge dedicated and resourceful help on production and technical tasks by many people on our various development staffs and also at Wright Group/McGraw-Hill.

James McBride
*Director, Second Edition*

Max Bell
*Director, First Edition*

Fifth Grade

# Everyday Mathematics®

## Teacher's Lesson Guide

### Volume 1

The University of Chicago
School Mathematics Project

The McGraw·Hill Companies

**UCSMP Elementary Materials Component**

Max Bell, Director

**Authors**

Max Bell
John Bretzlauf
Amy Dillard
Robert Hartfield
Andy Isaacs
James McBride, Director
Kathleen Pitvorec
Peter Saecker
Robert Balfanz*
William Carroll*

**Technical Art**

Diana Barrie

*First Edition only

**Photo Credits**

Phil Martin/ Photography

**Contributors**

Tammy Belgrade, Diana Carry, Debra Dawson, Kevin Dorken, James Flanders, Laurel Hallman, Ann Hemwall, Elizabeth Homewood, Linda Klaric, Lee Kornhauser, Judy Korshak-Samuels, Deborah Arron Leslie, Joseph C. Liptak, Sharon McHugh, Janet M. Meyers, Susan Mieli, Donna Nowatzki, Sheila Sconiers, Kevin J. Smith, Theresa Sparlin, Laura Sunseri, Kim Van Haitsma, John Wilson, Mary Wilson, Carl Zmola, Theresa Zmola

This material is based upon work supported by the National Science Foundation under Grant No. ESI-9252984. Any opinions, findings, and conclusions or recommendations expressed in this material are those of the authors and do not necessarily reflect the views of the National Science Foundation.

Printed in the United States of America.

Send all inquiries to:
Wright Group/McGraw-Hill
P.O. Box 812960
Chicago, IL 60681

ISBN 0-07-600038-9

8 9 10 11 QPD 09 08 07 06

The McGraw·Hill Companies

# Contents

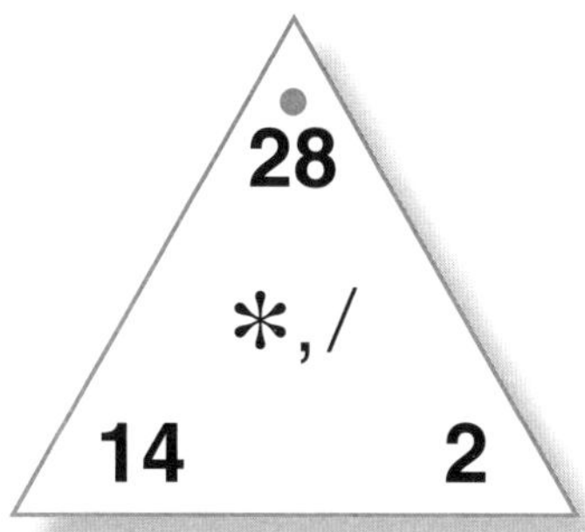


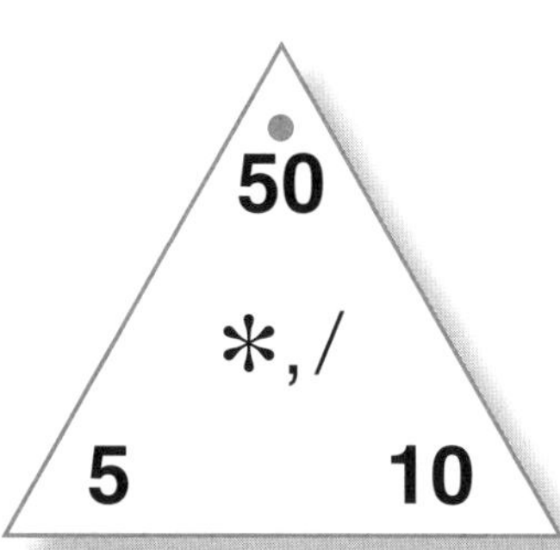


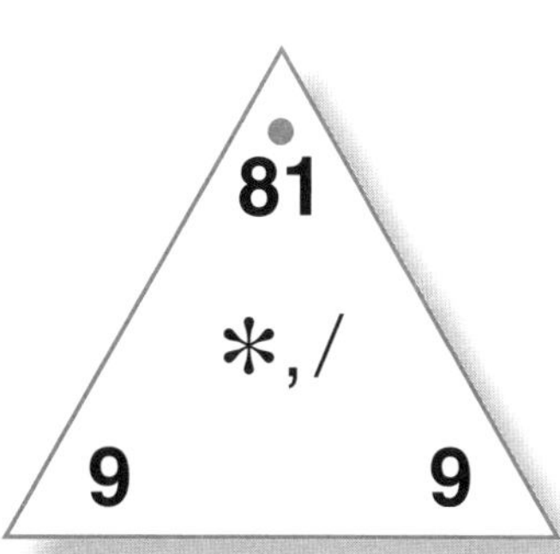


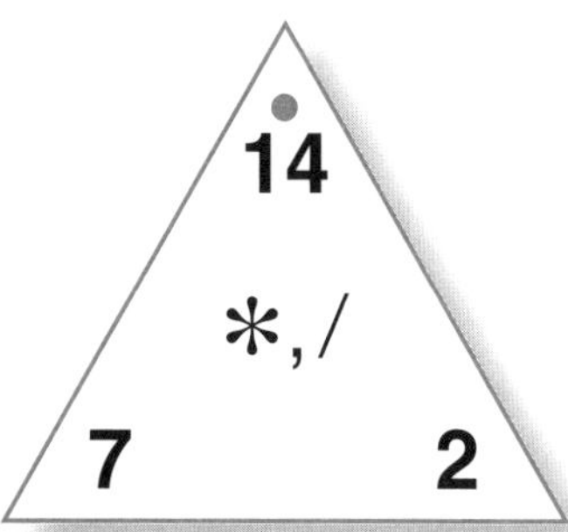


## Volume 1

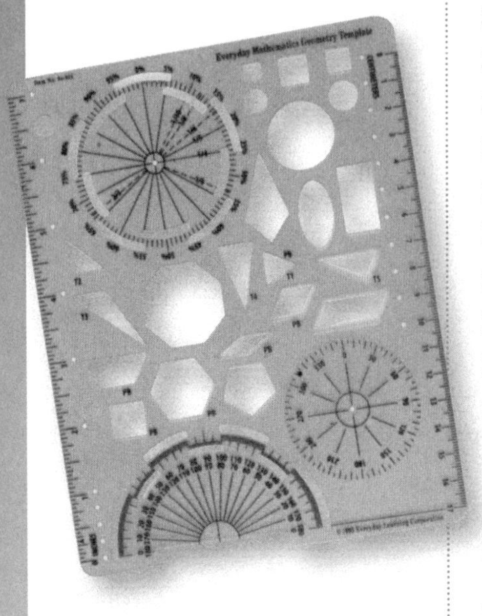

## Unit 6 Using Data; Addition and Subtraction of Fractions 338



## Appendices 409



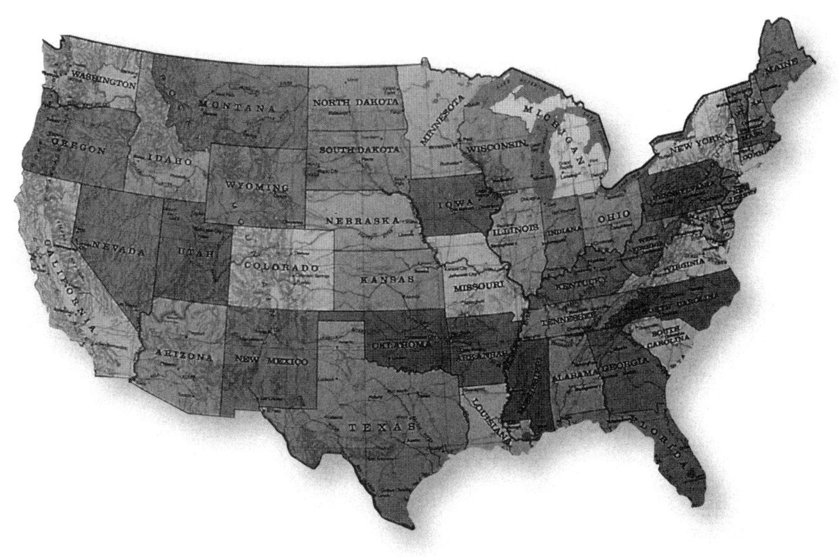

## Volume 2

Welcome to *Everyday Mathematics,* the elementary school mathematics curriculum developed by the University of Chicago School Mathematics Project (UCSMP).

*Fifth Grade Everyday Mathematics* emphasizes the following content strands:

- **Numeration** Reading, writing, and comparing negative numbers, fractions, whole numbers through billions, and decimals through thousandths; reading, writing, and interpreting whole-number powers of 10; translating between exponential and standard notation; understanding and identifying prime numbers, composite numbers, and square numbers.
- **Operations and Computation** Using paper-and-pencil algorithms to add, subtract, multiply, and divide multidigit whole numbers and decimals; using mental arithmetic to compute exact answers and to estimate; rounding from billions to hundredths; translating among fractions, decimals, and percents; prime factoring; converting between fractions and mixed numbers; adding and subtracting fractions and mixed numbers with unlike denominators; finding least common multiples and greatest common factors; multiplying and dividing fractions.
- **Data and Chance** Comparing probabilities for different outcomes; comparing theoretical and experimental probabilities; expressing probabilities as fractions, decimals, and percents; drawing justifiable conclusions from data; displaying data in more than one way; formulating a question, carrying out a survey or experiment, recording data, and communicating results; drawing and interpreting circle graphs and stem-and-leaf plots; understanding measures of central tendency (mean, median, mode).
- **Geometry** Constructing a circle with a given radius or diameter; defining and creating tessellations; measuring and drawing angles, including reflex and straight angles; identifying and defining right, isosceles, and equilateral triangles; plotting points in four quadrants; using translations, reflections, and rotations; solving perimeter, area, and volume problems; understanding the relationship between the volumes of cones/pyramids and cylinders/prisms; finding the surface area of a cube and the area of a circle; identifying angle relationships in triangles and in quadrilaterals.
- **Measurement and Reference Frames** Measuring and estimating length, area, volume, weight, and capacity; converting and computing with common units of measure; creating scale drawings.
- **Patterns, Functions, and Algebra** Evaluating simple algebraic expressions; finding rules for patterns; finding the $n$th term in a sequence; solving simple open number sentences and simple rate problems; working with equations by doing the same thing to both sides; understanding simple direct proportion; using variables and equations to represent situations; graphing ordered pairs; translating among verbal, numerical, and graphical representations.

Within these content strands, *Everyday Mathematics* emphasizes:

- A problem-solving approach based on everyday situations that develops critical thinking.

- Mathematical communication, including understanding and evaluating the mathematical thinking and strategies of others.
- Frequent practice of basic skills through ongoing program routines and mathematical games.
- An instructional approach that revisits topics regularly to ensure full concept development.
- Activities that explore a wide variety of mathematical content and offer opportunities for students to apply their knowledge.

*Everyday Mathematics* offers you and your students a broad and rich experience in mathematics. *Everyday Mathematics* will help you and your students incorporate mathematics in your everyday work and play, gradually shaping students' ways of thinking about mathematics and fostering the development of mathematical intuition and understanding.

Have an exciting year!

# Professional Preparation

| ***Go to...*** | ***When you need...*** |
|---|---|
| *Teacher's Lesson Guide* | Daily lessons; unit support information; key vocabulary; scope and sequence for Grades 4–6 |
| *Math Masters* | Blackline masters for Teaching Masters, Study Links, projects, and assessments |
| *Assessment Handbook* | Suggestions for portfolio, ongoing, and product assessment |
| *Teacher's Reference Manual* | Background on mathematical content; ideas for curriculum and classroom management for Grades 4–6 |
| *Home Connection Handbook* | Suggestions for home-school communication for Grades K–6 |
| Content by Strand Poster | Skills organized by content strand and paced by month (side one); learning goals organized by unit for the year (side two) |
| *Student Math Journal* | Lesson support material for students to solve and complete; a yearlong record of each student's mathematical development |
| *Student Reference Book* | Concise explanations of fundamental mathematics; worked examples, often showing multiple solution methods; game directions; information for the American Tour; a reference for students, parents, and others new to the program |

## Suggested Reading & Lesson Preparation

To prepare for effective classroom and curriculum management, the authors suggest that the following activities take place before you teach *Everyday Mathematics* for the first time.

### Reading and Planning

- ❑ Review each of the components in your Teacher's Resource Package (TRP). Locate information and materials so that you can find them as needed throughout the school year. See the chart on page XXV.
- ❑ Browse through the *Teacher's Reference Manual,* the *Assessment Handbook,* the *Home Connection Handbook,* and the *Student Reference Book.*
- ❑ Read the Unit Organizer for Unit 1 and the first three to four lessons in your *Teacher's Lesson Guide.*
- ❑ Prepare a daily math schedule. *Everyday Mathematics* lessons have several parts, which can be done at different times throughout the day. Your schedule should include time for Getting Started activities (Math Message, Mental Math and Reflexes, and Study Link follow-up); Teaching the Lesson; Ongoing Learning & Practice activities, including Math Boxes and games; and possibly Options for Individualizing.

### Materials Preparation

Prepare materials as indicated for the first four lessons. Special items for consideration include:

- ❑ Gather dice, centimeter cubes, counters, calculators, an overhead calculator (optional), pennies, Fact Triangles, and dictionaries. See *Teacher's Reference Manual* and *Teacher's Lesson Guide* Unit 1 Organizer, page 8.
- ❑ Prepare a lost-and-found box for misplaced items.
- ❑ Assign an ID number to each student to simplify matching students and manipulatives. See *Teacher's Lesson Guide,* Unit 1, Lesson 1, page 14.
- ❑ Review the following games. Try the games with a colleague or small group of students. Consider any adaptations you may need to make for various abilities.

  *Baseball Multiplication* (*Student Reference Book,* page 259)
  *Multiplication Top-It* (*Student Reference Book,* page 294)
  *Beat the Calculator* (*Student Reference Book,* page 261)
  *Factor Captor* (*Student Reference Book,* page 271)
- ❑ Create an Arrays Museum. See *Teacher's Lesson Guide,* Unit 1, Lesson 2, page 18.
- ❑ Gather Everything Math Decks or modify decks of playing cards. See *Teacher's Lesson Guide,* Unit 1, Lesson 3, page 22.
- ❑ Create Tool Kits. See *Teacher's Reference Manual* and *Teacher's Lesson Guide,* Unit 1, Lesson 1, page 14.
- ❑ Obtain the following book (optional):
  *Arithmetic* by Carl Sandburg (Harcourt Brace Jovanovich, 1993)
- ❑ Prepare a supply of paper:
  Blank $8\frac{1}{2}$ x 11 (full-, half-, and quarter-sheets)
  Graph paper $\frac{1}{2}$ inch

# Organizing Your Classroom

## Items for Display

Before the school year begins, the authors suggest that you prepare the following items for classroom display. By taking time to prepare these items your first year and laminating them if possible, you will be able to re-use them year after year. Refer to the Management Guide in your *Teacher's Reference Manual* for more information.

- ❑ Number Line (-35 to 180)
- ❑ Probability Meter Poster

Also prepare a Class Data Pad (for example, chart paper on an easel)

## Classroom Set-Up

The following items should be considered as you set up your *Everyday Mathematics* classroom. Try several configurations until you find one that is comfortable and effective for both you and your students. Visit other classrooms in your building to observe and discuss what works for your colleagues.

- ❑ Prepare and label a location in the classroom where students may deposit written work, such as Math Messages and Study Links.
- ❑ Arrange classroom desks/tables to allow for easy access to manipulatives and to facilitate efficient transitions for individual, partner, and small-group activities.
- ❑ Organize class and individual manipulatives for easy access and efficient use of storage space.
- ❑ Allow (table) space for math center(s). Particular games and activities may then be left in this space for ongoing practice or free exploration.
- ❑ Identify a place where the daily Math Message will be posted. See the *Teacher's Reference Manual* for information about the Math Message.

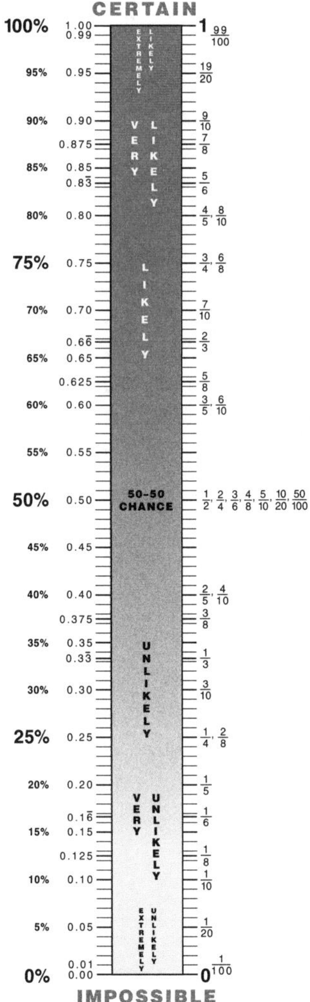


Probability Meter

## Manipulatives for *Fifth Grade Everyday Mathematics* Activities

The following list has been organized to highlight the items that are used on a regular basis throughout *Fifth Grade Everyday Mathematics*. Some lessons call for minor additional materials, which you or your students may bring in at the appropriate time.

**Additional Valuable Classroom Resources**

*Overhead Projector Materials*

*Class Data Pad*

*World and U.S. Maps*

| Quantity | Item |
|---|---|
| 1 per student | Calculator* (TI-15 recommended) |
| 1 per student | Compass (Helix recommended) |
| 1 pkg. (2,000) | Connectors (twist-ties) |
| 1 set | Cup Set, standard |
| 1 per student | Die, dot |
| 3 pkg. (18 total) | Dice, polyhedral |
| 15 decks | Everything Math Deck |
| 1 per student | Geometry Template (in student materials set) |
| 15 | Transparent Mirror |
| 1 | Liter Pitcher |
| 1 | Liter Volume Cube |
| 10 | Meter-stick, dual scale |
| 1 | Number Line (-35 to 180) |
| 1 set | Pattern Blocks |
| 1 | Rocker Balance |
| 1 per student | Slate (chalk or marker board) |
| 1 pkg. (500) | Straws |
| 15 | Tape Measures, retractable |
| 1 | Tape Measure, 30m/100ft |
| 1 per student | Tool-Kit Bag* |

All of the above items are available from Everyday Learning Corporation. They may be purchased either as a comprehensive classroom manipulatives kit or as individual components. The Everyday Learning classroom kit provides appropriate quantities for a class of 25 and comes packaged in durable plastic tubs with labels.

**Calculators and tool-kit bags available from Everyday Learning Corporation for individual purchase only.*

# Instruction

The following sections introduce instructional methods and suggestions for successful *Everyday Mathematics* implementation. Teachers are encouraged to read these pages and refer to them as needed throughout the school year.

## Program Routines

*Everyday Mathematics* uses a number of routines throughout all grade levels. These routines provide a consistent and familiar format for ongoing practice and applications.

Below is a list of routines you will encounter in *Fifth Grade Everyday Mathematics.* The unit and lesson in which each routine is first used have been noted. Refer to the Management Guide in the *Teacher's Reference Manual* for more information.

| ***Routine*** | ***First Used*** |
|---|---|
| Math Message | Unit 1, Lesson 1 |
| Mental Math and Reflexes | Unit 2, Lesson 1 |
| Study Links | Unit 1, Lesson 1 |
| Games | Unit 1, Lesson 3 |
| Name-Collection Boxes | Unit 1, Lesson 9 |
| Math Boxes | Unit 1, Lesson 1 |
| Fact Triangles | Unit 1, Lesson 3 |
| "What's My Rule?"/ Function Machines | Unit 3, Lesson 2 |

Students who used *Fourth Grade Everyday Mathematics* will be familiar with the above routines so most can be re-introduced with a minimum of explanation.

## Projects

*Everyday Mathematics* includes special optional projects that integrate mathematics with science, social studies, art, and language arts. These projects are built around themes that interest students. Projects are suggested in Unit Organizers in the *Teacher's Lesson Guide* at appropriate times throughout the year. They typically take one to two days to complete, depending upon how many of the suggested activities you incorporate. Projects allow the teacher to assess the students' abilities to apply mathematics in other areas of the curriculum. Projects are also memorable events for students.

Refer to the Management Guide of the *Teacher's Reference Manua*l and the Unit Organizers in the *Teacher's Lesson Guide* for more information. Detailed explanations for the projects are found at the back of the *Teachers Lesson Guides.*

## The American Tour

In *Fifth Grade Everyday Mathematics,* students also go on a yearlong American Tour, collecting, analyzing, and representing information about our nation. The tour is easily linked to American history and other social studies and language arts topics. The *Fifth Grade Everyday Mathematics Student Reference Book* has a special American Tour section, which is a source of information for the yearlong project. This section contains maps, data about the states, and essays of interest. The American Tour is introduced in Lesson 3.1.

## Problem Solving

In *Everyday Mathematics,* problem solving can be described as the process of modeling everyday situations using tools from mathematics. Each unit organizer contains a list of strategies that students might use in that unit. Also included is a summary of activities in the unit that teach *through* problem solving, not just *about* problem solving. More information on problem solving can be found in the *Teacher's Reference Manual.*

## Assessment

*Everyday Mathematics* encourages a balanced approach to student assessment, one that reveals the development of a child's mathematical understanding while giving the teacher useful feedback about instructional needs. Assessments also provide information and documentation to help assign grades. *Everyday Mathematics* aims to provide information that can be used for diagnosing learning problems, planning instruction, and recognizing achievement.

Assessment information is drawn from multiple sources, including ongoing observations and product and periodic assessment. Refer to the *Assessment Handbook* and the Unit Organizers in the *Teacher's Lesson Guide* for detailed information regarding ongoing, product, and periodic assessment.

If this is your first year with the program, focus in the beginning of the year on teaching Parts 1 and 2 of the three-part lesson plan. Later, as possible, experiment with some of the informal techniques suggested in the Unit Organizers and begin to incorporate activities from Part 3 of the lesson plan. As you continue to teach *Everyday Mathematics,* you will gain greater insight into your students' mathematical thinking and will become more able to use the alternative assessment techniques described in the *Assessment Handbook.*

## Providing for Home-School Communications

Comprehensive and consistent home-school communication regarding program content, routines, and student assessment is essential for successful implementation. *Everyday Mathematics* provides a number of support materials to facilitate this communication. The *Home Connection Handbook* is a tool that can help you introduce parents and primary caregivers to the *Everyday Mathematics* curriculum. Grade-specific Family Letters and Study Links, found in the *Math Masters* book, serve as a basis for ongoing communication as well as a vehicle to engage parents as partners in the learning process. Individual assessment checklists from the *Assessment Handbook* enable teachers to describe in detail each student's progress and can be a valuable communication tool during conferences.

Refer to the *Home Connection Handbook* for more information.

# 4–6 Games Correlation Chart

| Game | Grade 4 Lesson | Grade 5 Lesson | Grade 6 Lesson | Basic Facts | Operations | Calculator | Numeration | Geometry | Data | Algebra | Reference Frames | Mental Math | Strategy |
|---|---|---|---|---|---|---|---|---|---|---|---|---|---|
| | | | | **Skill and Concept Areas** | | | | | | | | | |
| *Addition Top-It* | 2.5 | 2.3 | | | | | | | | | | | |
| *Algebra Election* | | 4.6 | 6.7 | | | | | | | | | | |
| *Angle Tangle* | | 3.6 | 5.1 | | | | | | | | | | |
| *Baseball Multiplication (1 to 6 facts)* | 3.2 | 1.3 | * | | | | | | | | | | |
| *Baseball Multiplication (Advanced Version)* | * | * | * | | | | | | | | | | |
| *Beat the Calculator* | 3.3 | 1.3 | | | | | | | | | | | |
| *Broken Calculator* | 3.10 | 7.10 | 6.8 | | | | | | | | | | |
| *Build-It* | | 8.1 | | | | | | | | | | | |
| *Buzz* | * | | 4.2 | | | | | | | | | | |
| *Calculator 10,000* | * | | | | | | | | | | | | |
| *Credits/Debits Game* | 10.6 | | * | | | | | | | | | | |
| *Credits/Debits Game (Advanced Version)* | 11.6 | 7.8 | 6.3 | | | | | | | | | | |
| *Dart Game* | 10.2 | | | | | | | | | | | | |
| *Division Arrays* | 3.4 | | | | | | | | | | | | |
| *Division Dash* | 6.2 | 4.1 | 2.10 | | | | | | | | | | |
| *Division Top-It* | * | * | * | | | | | | | | | | |
| *Doggone Decimal* | | | 2.4 | | | | | | | | | | |
| *Estimation Squeeze* | | 5.5 | * | | | | | | | | | | |
| *Exponent Ball* | | 7.1 | 2.7 | | | | | | | | | | |
| *Fact Triangle Sort* | 3.1 | 3.1 | | | | | | | | | | | |
| *Factor Bingo* | 3.1 | 1.9 | | | | | | | | | | | |
| *Factor Captor* | | 1.4 | * | | | | | | | | | | |
| *Factor Top-It* | | 1.7 | | | | | | | | | | | |
| *First to 100* | | 4.6 | * | | | | | | | | | | |
| *500* | | 7.7 | | | | | | | | | | | |
| *Frac-Tac-Toe* | | 5.7 | 4.8 | | | | | | | | | | |
| *Fraction Action, Fraction Friction* | | 8.4 | 4.3 | | | | | | | | | | |
| *Fraction Capture* | | 6.9 | | | | | | | | | | | |
| *Fraction Multiplication Top-It* | | 8.6 | | | | | | | | | | | |
| *Fraction/Percent Concentration* | 9.3 | 5.8 | | | | | | | | | | | |
| *Fraction Spin* | | 8.5 | | | | | | | | | | | |
| *Fraction Top-It* | 7.10 | * | 4.2 | | | | | | | | | | |
| *Fraction/Whole Number Multiplication Top-It* | | 8.7 | | | | | | | | | | | |
| *Geometry 5 Questions* | 1.4 | | | | | | | | | | | | |
| *Getting to One* | 9.3 | 2.1 | 9.10 | | | | | | | | | | |
| *Greedy* | | | 7.3 | | | | | | | | | | |
| *Grid Search* | 6.5 | | | | | | | | | | | | |
| *Hidden Treasure* | | 9.1 | 3.10 | | | | | | | | | | |
| *Hidden Treasure (Advanced Version)* | | 9.3 | 5.4 | | | | | | | | | | |
| *High-Number Toss* | 2.4 | 2.4 | | | | | | | | | | | |
| *High-Number Toss (Decimal Version)* | | 7.8 | 2.6 | | | | | | | | | | |
| *Landmark Shark* | | | 1.4 | | | | | | | | | | |
| *Mixed Number Spin* | | 8.3 | | | | | | | | | | | |
| *Multiplication Bull's-Eye* | | 2.7 | | | | | | | | | | | |
| *Multiplication Top-It* | 3.3 | 1.3 | | | | | | | | | | | |
| *Multiplication Wrestling* | 5.2 | 2.8 | 9.1 | | | | | | | | | | |
| *Musical Name-Collection Boxes* | 7.7 | | | | | | | | | | | | |
| *Name That Number* | 2.2 | 1.9 | 1.3 | | | | | | | | | | |
| *Name That Polygon* | 1.5 | | | | | | | | | | | | |
| *Number Top-It (7-digit numbers)* | 2.4 | 2.10 | | | | | | | | | | | |

## Skill and Concept Areas

| Game | Grade 4 Lesson | Grade 5 Lesson | Grade 6 Lesson | Basic Facts | Operations | Calculator | Numeration | Geometry | Data | Algebra | Reference Frames | Mental Math | Strategy |
|---|---|---|---|---|---|---|---|---|---|---|---|---|---|
| *Number Top-It (2-place decimals)* | 4.2 | | | | | | ■ | | | | | | |
| *Number Top-It (3-place decimals)* | 4.6 | * | | | | | ■ | | | | | | |
| *Pocket-Billiards Game* | 10.2 | | | | | | | ■ | | | | | |
| *Polygon Capture* | | 3.7 | 5.9 | | | | | ■ | | | | | |
| *Robot* | 6.6 | 3.4 | | | | | | ■ | | | ■ | | |
| *Scientific Notation Toss* | | 7.4 | 2.8 | | | | ■ | | | | | | |
| *Solution Search* | | | 6.12 | | | | | | | ■ | | | |
| *Spoon Scramble* | | 12.6 | 4.12 | | | | ■ | | | | | ■ | |
| *Spreadsheet Scramble* | | | 3.7 | | ■ | | | | | ■ | | ■ | |
| *Subtraction Target Practice* | 2.9 | 2.3 | | ■ | ■ | | | | | | | | |
| *Subtraction Top-It* | 2.6 | | | ■ | ■ | | ■ | | | | | ■ | |
| *3-D Shape Sort* | | 11.2 | 9.12 | | | | | ■ | | | | | |
| *Top-It Games with Positive and Negative Numbers* | | 7.7 | 6.4 | ■ | ■ | | ■ | | | ■ | | ■ | |
| *Touch-and-Match Quadrangles* | 1.3 | | | | | | | ■ | | | | | |
| *What's My Weight?* | 11.1 | | | | | | | | | | ■ | | |

Number indicates first exposure at grade level. *Available in the Games section of the *Student Reference Book.*

# Unit 1 Number Theory

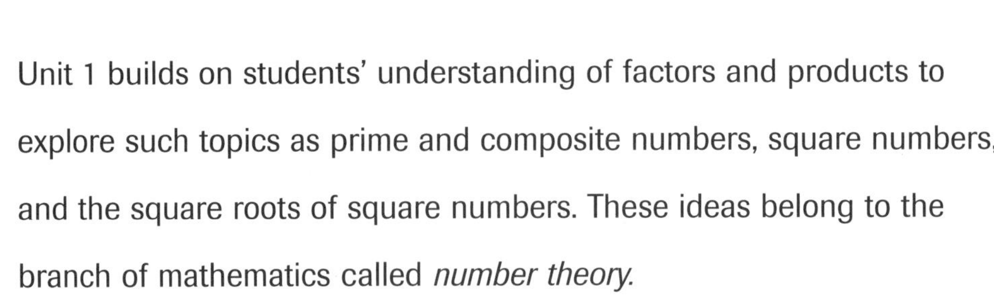


Unit 1 builds on students' understanding of factors and products to explore such topics as prime and composite numbers, square numbers, and the square roots of square numbers. These ideas belong to the branch of mathematics called *number theory.*

The new material in this unit builds on students' prior informal work with multiplication and division of whole numbers. The activities are designed to start everyone on an equal footing. This will allow a relatively relaxed beginning of the new school year while you get acquainted with students and institute yearlong routines.

Powerful tools and consequences come from simple but precise principles, definitions, and calculations. Number theory makes the point that mathematics is more than computation. Since number theory features a technical vocabulary where precise meanings of words really matter, it is strongly linked to language arts.

UNIT 1

# contents

# learning goals in perspective

| learning goals | links to the past | links to the future |
|---|---|---|
| 1a **Beginning Goal** Find the prime factorizations of numbers. **(Lesson 1.9)** | Grades 1–4: Use a Name-Collection Box routine to express numbers in many ways.<br>Grades 2–4: Use arrays to find factors of numbers. | Grade 5: Use factor trees to find prime factorizations, greatest common factors, and least common multiples (Unit 12).<br>Grades 5–6: Continue and extend the Name-Collection Box routine. |
| 1b **Beginning/Developing Goal** Rename numbers written in exponential notation. **(Lessons 1.7 - 1.9)** | Grades 2–3: Model square numbers with arrays.<br>Grade 4: Introduce exponential notation for powers of 10. | Grade 5: Review exponential notation and introduce negative exponents; introduce scientific notation for large numbers (Unit 7).<br>Grade 6: Read and write both large and small numbers in scientific notation. |
| 1c **Developing/Secure Goal** Use a divisibility test to determine if a number is divisible by another number. **(Lesson 1.5)** | Grades 2–3: Explore division with arrays.<br>Grade 4: Define *dividend, divisor, quotient,* and *remainder;* use Fact Triangles to reinforce the relationship between division and multiplication. | Grade 5: Solve division problems mentally by partitioning dividends into "friendly" numbers (Unit 4); use common denominators to add and subtract fractions (Unit 6), and to divide fractions (Unit 8). |
| 1d **Developing/Secure Goal** Identify prime and composite numbers. **(Lessons 1.6 and 1.9)** | Grades 1–3: Use arrays to identify odd, even, and square numbers; find number patterns in a multiplication facts table. | Grade 5: Represent numbers as products of factors, and of prime factors (Units 1, 12).<br>Grade 6: Applications and maintenance. |
| 1e **Developing/Secure Goal** Understand how square numbers and their square roots are related. **(Lesson 1.8)** | Grades 2–3: Model square numbers with arrays.<br>Grade 4: Find the square of a number, and write it in exponential notation. | Grade 5: Review exponential notation; introduce negative exponents; introduce scientific notation (Unit 7).<br>Grade 6: Use squares and square roots of numbers in applications of the Pythagorean Theorem. |
| 1f **Secure Goal** Draw arrays to model multiplication. **(Lessons 1.2 and 1.7)** | Grades 1–3: Model multiplication problems as arrays on geoboards, with pattern blocks, and with other counters; represent a given number with all possible arrays. | Grades 5-6: Applications and maintenance. |
| 1g **Secure Goal** Know multiplication facts. **(Lessons 1.2 - 1.9)** | Grades 2–4: Introduce and practice multiplication facts with Fact Triangles, skip counting, and through games. | Grades 5-6: Applications and maintenance. |
| 1h **Secure Goal** Identify even and odd numbers. **(Lessons 1.4 and 1.5)** | Grades 1–3: Model odd and even numbers with counters; identify the even-odd pattern in a multiplication facts table. | Grades 5-6: Applications and maintenance. |
| 1i **Secure Goal** Find the factors of numbers. **(Lessons 1.3, 1.4, 1.6, and 1.9)** | Grades 2–4: Define *factor* and *product;* introduce and practice the multiplication facts; use arrays to model multiplication; practice extended multiplication facts. | Grade 5: Represent a number as a product of factors, and of prime factors (Units 1, 12).<br>Grade 6: Applications and maintenance. |

# assessment

**ongoing • product • periodic**

## Informal Assessment

**Math Boxes** These *Math Journal* pages provide opportunities for cumulative review or assessment of concepts and skills.

**Ongoing Assessment: Kid Watching** Use the Ongoing Assessment suggestions in the following lessons to make quick, on-the-spot observations about students' understanding of:

- Multiple Strands **(Lesson 1.1, Part 1)**
- Numeration **(Lesson 1.4, Part 1; Lesson 1.8, Part 1)**
- Operations and Computation **(Lesson 1.5, Part 1)**

**Portfolio Ideas** Samples of students' work may be obtained from the following assignments:

- Exploring a Divisibility Test by 4 **(Lesson 1.5)**
- Investigating Goldbach's Conjecture **(Lesson 1.6)**
- Making Square-Number Collections **(Lesson 1.8)**

## Unit 1 Review and Assessment

**Math Message** Use Time to Reflect Problem 2 in Lesson 1.10 to assess students' progress toward the following learning goal: **Goal 1f**

**Oral and Slate Assessments** Use oral or slate assessments during Lesson 1.10 to assess students' progress toward the following learning goals: **Goals 1c, 1d, 1e, and 1h**

**Written Assessment** Use a written review during Lesson 1.10 to assess students' progress toward the following learning goals: **Goals 1a–1i**

**Alternative Assessment Options** Use partner or small-group alternative assessments in Lesson 1.10 to assess students' progress toward the following learning goals: **Goals 1d, 1g, and 1i**

# assessmenthandbook

For more information on how to use different types of assessment in Unit 1, see the Assessment Overview on pages 36–38 in the *Assessment Handbook.* The following Assessment Masters can be found in the *Math Masters* book:

- Unit 1 Checking Progress, pp. 379 and 380
- Unit 1 Individual Profile of Progress, p. 429
- Unit 1 Class Checklist, p. 428
- Class Progress Indicator, p. 471
- Math Logs, pp. 474–476
- Self-Assessment Forms, pp. 477 and 478
- Interest Inventories, pp. 472 and 473

# problemsolving

## *A process of modeling everyday situations using tools from mathematics*

Encourage students to use a variety of strategies when attacking a given problem—and to explain those strategies. *Strategies students might use in this unit:*

- Use a reference book
- Draw a diagram (arrays and factor rainbows)
- Write a number model
- Make an organized list
- Use computation
- Use logical reasoning
- Try and check

Four Problem-Solving **REPRESENTATIONS**

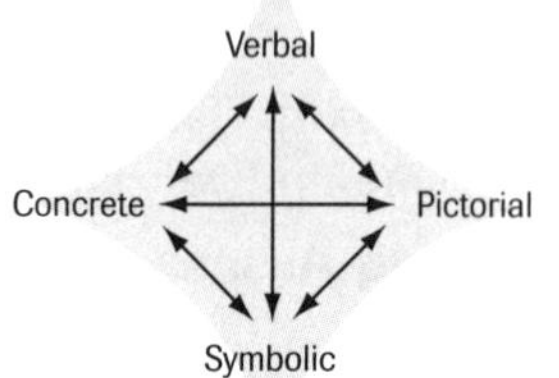


### Lessons that teach *through* problem solving, not just *about* problem solving

| Lesson | Activity | Lesson | Activity |
|---|---|---|---|
| **1.1** | Look for information in a reference book to solve problems | **1.5** | Use divisibility tests to check whether given numbers are divisible by 2, 3, 5, 6, 9, or 10 |
| **1.2, 1.3, 1.7** | Find all possible rectangular arrays that represent a number; identify the square numbers | **1.6** | Develop a winning strategy for the game *Factor Captor* |
| **1.4, 1.6, 1.9** | Find as many factors as possible for given whole numbers | **1.8** | Find the square root of numbers |

For more information about problem solving in *Everyday Mathematics,* see the *Teacher's Reference Manual.*

# cross-curricularlinks

### language arts

- Students practice reference skills by using the Table of Contents, Glossary, and Index in the *Student Reference Book.* **(Lesson 1.1)**
- Discuss the meanings and uses of the prefix *un-*. **(Lesson 1.8)**

### literature

- Read aloud the poem "Arithmetic" by Carl Sandburg. Discuss uses of mathematics in students' daily lives. **(Lesson 1.1)**

### social studies

- Students investigate Goldbach's Conjecture–an unproved eighteenth century theory relating even numbers and prime numbers. **(Lesson 1.6)**

# meeting INDIVIDUAL needs

## ✦ RETEACHING

The following features provide additional instructional support.

**Adjusting the Activity**

- **Lesson 1.3, Part 1**
- **Lesson 1.8, Part 1**

**Options for Individualizing**

- **Lesson 1.2** Making Cube Arrays
- **Lesson 1.7** Making Square Arrays
- **Lesson 1.9** Playing *Name That Number*

## ✦ ENRICHMENT

The following features suggest enrichment and extension activities.

**Adjusting the Activity**

- **Lesson 1.2, Part 1**
- **Lesson 1.4, Part 1**
- **Lesson 1.6, Part 1**
- **Lesson 1.9, Part 1**

**Options for Individualizing**

- **Lesson 1.1** Appreciating Arithmetic in Poetry
- **Lesson 1.2** Finding Rectangular Arrays in a Perpetual Calendar
- **Lesson 1.4** Playing the Advanced Version of *Factor Captor*
- **Lesson 1.5** Exploring a Divisibility Test by 4
- **Lesson 1.6** Investigating Goldbach's Conjecture
- **Lesson 1.7** Completing Patterns

## ✦ LANGUAGE DIVERSITY

The following features suggest ways to support students who are acquiring proficiency in English.

**Adjusting the Activity**

- **Lesson 1.1, Part 1**

**Options for Individualizing**

- **Lesson 1.4** Building Background for Mathematics Words
- **Lesson 1.5** Building Background for Mathematics Words

## ✦ MULTIAGE CLASSROOM

The following chart lists related lessons from Grades 4 and 6 that can help you meet your instructional needs:

| **Grade 4** | 1.1 | | 3.1–3.3 | 3.1–3.3 | | | 5.9 | | | |
|---|---|---|---|---|---|---|---|---|---|---|
| **Grade 5** | 1.1 | 1.2 | 1.3 | 1.4 | 1.5 | 1.6 | 1.7 | 1.8 | 1.9 | 1.10 |
| **Grade 6** | | | | | 6.4 | 6.5 | 2.8<br>2.9<br>6.5 | 6.5 | | |

# materials

| lesson | math masters pages | manipulative kit items | other items |
|---|---|---|---|
| 1.1 | Study Link Masters, pp. 211–214 | | *Arithmetic* by Carl Sandburg<br>***See* Advance Preparation, p. 14** |
| 1.2 | Study Link Master, p. 215<br>Teaching Master, p. 2<br>transparency of Teaching Master, p. 1 (optional) | dice | centimeter cubes (40 per partnership)<br>12 counters<br>Arrays Museum<br>***See* Advance Preparation, p. 18** |
| 1.3 | Study Link Master, p. 216<br>Teaching Masters, pp. 1, 3, and 4<br>transparency of Teaching Master, p. 1 (optional)<br>***See* Advance Preparation, p. 22** | 2 regular dice<br>4 each of number cards 1–10 | 18 counters<br>Multiplication/Division Facts Table (optional)<br>calculator<br>4 pennies<br>envelopes (optional) |
| 1.4 | Study Link Master, p. 217<br>Teaching Masters, pp. 3, 5, and 6<br>transparencies of Teaching Masters, pp. 5 and 6 (optional)<br>Assessment Master, p. 479 | Per partnership:<br>2 regular dice<br>number cards 0–10 | Fact Triangles<br>Per partnership:<br>Multiplication/Division Facts Table (optional)<br>calculator<br>4 pennies<br>70 counters |
| 1.5 | Study Link Master, p. 218<br>Teaching Masters, pp. 3 and 5–7<br>Assessment Master, p. 479 | | calculator<br>overhead calculator (optional)<br>counters<br>dictionary |
| 1.6 | Study Link Master, p. 219<br>Teaching Masters, pp. 1, 3, 4, 6, and 8<br>***See* Advance Preparation, p. 37** | Per partnership:<br>2 regular dice<br>number cards 1–10 | Class Data Pad (optional)<br>Fact Triangles<br>Per partnership:<br>Multiplication/Division Facts Table (optional)<br>calculator<br>4 pennies<br>70 counters |
| 1.7 | Study Link Master, p. 220<br>Teaching Masters, p. 1 (optional); and pp. 2, 3, and 9 | Per partnership:<br>number cards 0–9 | counters<br>calculator<br>***See* Advance Preparation, p. 42** |
| 1.8 | Study Link Master, p. 221<br>Teaching Master, p. 3<br>Assessment Master, p. 479 | | calculator<br>posterboard and markers (optional)<br>***See* Advance Preparation, p. 46** |
| 1.9 | Study Link Master, p. 222<br>Teaching Masters, pp. 3 and 10 | deck of number cards<br>***See* Advance Preparation, p. 50** | calculator<br>12 pennies or counters |
| 1.10 | Study Link Masters, pp. 223–226<br>Teaching Masters, pp. 5, 6, and 11<br>Assessment Masters, pp. 379, 380, and 479 | number cards 1–10 | slate or marker board<br>chalk or dry-erase marker<br>calculator<br>48 counters |

# planningtips

## Pacing

Pacing depends on a number of factors, such as students' individual needs and how long your school has been using *Everyday Mathematics.* At the beginning of Unit 1, review your Content by Strand Poster to help you set a monthly pace.

| AUGUST | SEPTEMBER | OCTOBER |
|---|---|---|
| ← MOST CLASSROOMS → | | |

## Using the Projects

Use Project 1, The Sieve of Eratosthenes, during or after Unit 1 to identify the prime numbers from 1 to 100 and to look for patterns in the prime numbers. Use Project 2, Deficient, Abundant, and Perfect Numbers, during or after Unit 1 to classify the whole numbers through 50 according to the sums of their proper factors. The Projects can be found at the back of this book.

## Home Communication

Share Study Links 1.1–1.9 with families to help them understand the content and procedures in this unit. At the end of the unit, use Study Link 1.10 to introduce Unit 2. Supplemental information can be found in the *Home Connection Handbook.*

## NCTM Standards

| Standard | 1 | 2 | 3 | 4 | 5 | 6 | 7 | 8 | 9 | 10 |
|---|---|---|---|---|---|---|---|---|---|---|
| Unit 1 Lessons | 1.1–1.9 | 1.1–1.3, 1.7 | 1.1 | 1.1 | 1.1 | 1.1–1.10 | 1.1–1.10 | 1.1–1.10 | 1.1–1.10 | 1.1–1.10 |

**Content Standards**
**1** Number and Operations
**2** Algebra
**3** Geometry
**4** Measurement
**5** Data Analysis and Probability

**Process Standards**
**6** Problem Solving
**7** Reasoning and Proof
**8** Communication
**9** Connections
**10** Representation

## PRACTICE *through* Games

*Everyday Mathematics* uses games to help students develop good fact power and other math skills.

- *Baseball Multiplication* to practice multiplication facts **(Lessons 1.3, 1.4, and 1.6)**
- *Beat the Calculator* to practice multiplication facts **(Lessons 1.3, 1.4, 1.6, and 1.10)**
- *Multiplication Top-It* to practice multiplication facts **(Lessons 1.3, 1.4, and 1.6)**
- *Factor Captor* to practice finding factors of a number **(Lessons 1.4–1.6 and 1.10)**
- *Factor Top-It* to practice calculating sums of factors **(Lesson 1.7)**
- *Factor Bingo* to practice finding factors of a number **(Lesson 1.9)**
- *Name That Number* to practice using the four operations to name numbers **(Lesson 1.9)**

# unit 1 content highlights

*The discussion below highlights the major content ideas presented in Unit 1 and may help you establish instructional priorities.*

## Number Theory (Lessons 1.1–1.10)

Number theory is the branch of theoretical mathematics that focuses on whole numbers and their properties. Because number theory methods and results often can be stated simply, this area of mathematics attracts nonprofessionals interested in mathematics, including children. Paradoxically, some of the simplest propositions turn out to be difficult to verify, and number theory is a fruitful source of unsolved problems.

Number theory is one of a number of topics studied in *Everyday Mathematics* that reinforce the idea that there is more to mathematics than computation.

NOTE: The *Everyday Mathematics* authors believe that people should learn and practice the special skills involved in obtaining information from mathematics books, almanacs, encyclopedias, and other resources. Regular use of the *Student Reference Book* can be an important aspect of your language arts program.

## The *Student Reference Book* (Lesson 1.1)

The *Student Reference Book* is a resource book containing summaries of the principal concepts and skills students encounter in their study of mathematics. It provides review and reinforcement of critical mathematics topics and calculator usage, as well as rules of mathematical games, reference tables, a glossary of mathematical terms, information for the American Tour project, and other helpful information. Presented in a concise, reference-oriented format, these materials invite students to look up needed information on their own, thereby encouraging them to take responsibility for their own learning. The book also serves as a resource for students making up work missed while absent and for parents or others helping at home.

From time to time, an icon [SRB] appears in the journal to indicate pages in the *Student Reference Book* where there is information on the topic at hand.

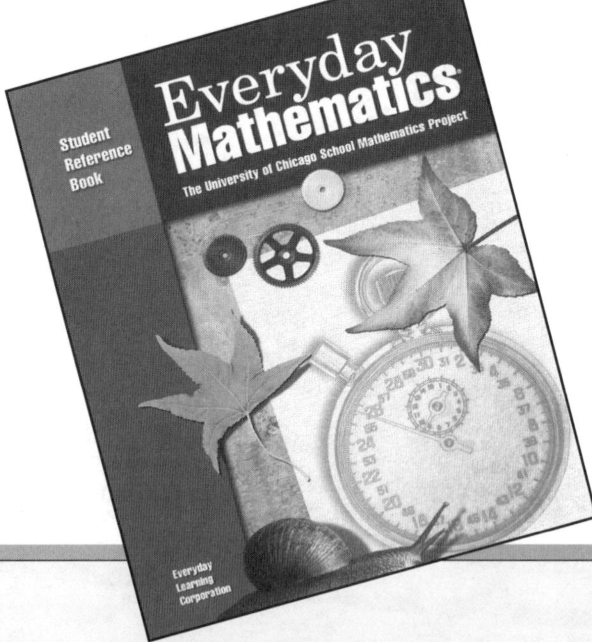

## Arrays as Representations of Products and Quotients (Lesson 1.2)

In more traditional school mathematics textbooks, arrays (if shown at all) are said to represent products of whole numbers. Students of *Everyday Mathematics,* however, know that multiplication and division are inextricably linked, so that arrays represent division as well as multiplication. For multiplication, the number of rows and the number of columns in an array are factors, and the total number of elements in the array is the product. For division, the total number of elements in the array is the dividend; the number of rows (or the number of columns) is the divisor; and the number of columns (or the number of rows) is the quotient. If a given dividend (total) cannot be displayed as a rectangular array in which the number of rows or columns is equal to the divisor (because there are too few leftover elements to make another row or column), the array corresponds to a division problem with a remainder.

3-by-5 array
3 * 5 = 15
15/3 = 5
15/5 = 3

26 / 6 → 4 R2
26 / 4 → 6 R2

Arrays have been featured as "pictures" of products and quotients since *First Grade Everyday Mathematics*. If this is your first year teaching *Everyday Mathematics,* arrays may be unfamiliar to you; in any case, the students, as always, will need review.

What may be new to students is the frequent request to show a given number not merely with one array, but with as many rectangular arrays as possible. What may also be new is the linking of arrays to various subsets of whole numbers: to *even numbers*, whose arrays have two rows or columns; to *prime numbers*, whose arrays have only a single row or column; and to *square numbers*, whose arrays have the same number of rows as columns.

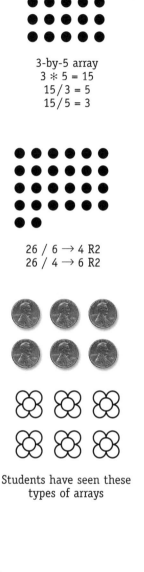

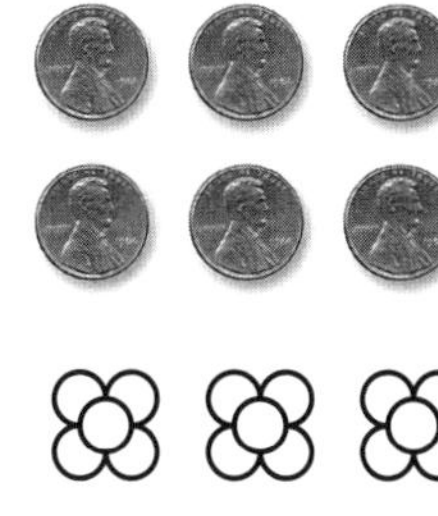

Students have seen these types of arrays

## Automatic Basic Facts "Reflexes" for Multiplication and Division (Lessons 1.3, 1.4, and 1.6)

Unit 1 sets up procedures for review and practice of the multiplication facts. Many students may already have achieved mastery of these facts, or, with a little practice, they may soon recall facts that they may have forgotten over the summer. However, there may be a few students who are unlikely ever to achieve quick, automatic recall. These students should be encouraged to compensate in various ways. While mastery of multiplication facts is an important matter to be assessed, and then attended to as needed, it is only a small component of the lessons in this unit.

Fact Triangles help students realize that multiplication is linked to division.

NOTE: These triangles are also available from Everyday Learning Corporation on more permanent stock.

In *Everyday Mathematics,* students have learned that division facts are linked to multiplication facts—once you know a multiplication fact, you know at least one, and usually two, division facts. Students are not expected to achieve instant, reflexive recall of division facts. However, they should be encouraged to apply the link between multiplication and division in dealing with the division facts.

## Factors and Factorization (Lessons 1.3–1.6 and 1.9)

Factors are numbers that are multiplied together. Usually they are whole numbers, positive or negative integers, fractions, or decimals; in number theory, however, *factor* always means a whole number. Factors have many applications, and the terms *prime numbers, composite numbers, prime factorization, square numbers,* and *square roots of numbers* are all defined in terms of factors.

My factor rainbow for the number 70

## Tests for Divisibility (Lesson 1.5)

Students in *Everyday Mathematics* learned to recognize even numbers as early as first grade. They found that an even number must end in 0, 2, 4, 6, or 8. This means that an even number must have 2 as a factor, or, stated another way, an even number must be divisible by 2. Similarly, from many counting-on exercises, most students know that numbers that end in 0 have 10 as a factor (are divisible by 10), and numbers that end in either 0 or 5 have 5 as a factor (are divisible by 5). The new divisibility tests of this lesson involve surprising facts: Numbers, however large, whose digits add up to a multiple of 9 must have 9 as a factor and, hence, are divisible by 9. A similar rule applies to divisibility by 3. By combining rules for divisibility by 2, 3, 5, 9, and 10, other rules can be formulated. For example, if a number is divisible by both 2 and 3, it is divisible by 6; even numbers divisible by 9 are divisible by 18; and so on.

NOTE: If your students are using calculators that can display an answer to a division problem as a quotient along with a whole-number remainder, you might want to demonstrate the procedure. With the TI-15 calculator, this is done by pressing the (Int÷) key instead of the (÷) key. For example, if you press 27 (Int÷) 5 (Enter), the display will show a quotient of 5 with a remainder of 2.

If possible, try to use an overhead calculator to demonstrate how to perform more demanding exercises.

## Squaring and Unsquaring, or Square Numbers and Square Roots (Lessons 1.7 and 1.8)

Except for informal exposures in Grades K–4, these lessons are the first time *Everyday Mathematics* focuses on square numbers and square roots.

NOTE: Starting in *Fourth Grade Everyday Mathematics,* the asterisk (*) is used in place of the traditional "×" symbol and the slash ( / ) in place of the traditional "÷" symbol. Both the asterisk and the slash are used in computer applications, such as spreadsheets. Use both the traditional operation symbols and the asterisk and slash when writing them in number sentences.

## Review and Assessment (Lesson 1.10)

Like every unit in *Fifth Grade Everyday Mathematics,* Unit 1 ends with a review and assessment lesson. This lesson provides a list of unit goals, as well as suggested questions for oral and slate evaluation. Assessment Masters provide review items for students to complete in writing; each item is keyed to a unit goal.

**For additional information on the following topics, see the *Teacher's Reference Manual:***

- calculators for *Everyday Mathematics*
- daily routines
- games
- prime and composite numbers, divisibility
- Math Boxes
- Math Messages
- Mental Math and Reflexes
- name-collection boxes
- number lines
- *Student Reference Book*
- Study Links
- the Everything Math Deck

# 1.1 Introduction to the *Student Reference Book*

**OBJECTIVE** **To acquaint students with the content and organization of the *Math Journal* and *Student Reference Book*.**

| summaries | materials |
| --- | --- |
| **1 Teaching the Lesson** | |
| Students examine their journals and discuss the introduction and overview. They become familiar with the *Student Reference Book* by using it to solve problems and find information. [multiple strands] | ☐ *Math Journal 1,* pp. 1–4<br>☐ *Student Reference Book*<br>***See*** **Advance Preparation** |
| **2 Ongoing Learning & Practice** | |
| Students practice and maintain skills by completing Math Boxes.<br>Students take home a Family Letter introducing *Everyday Mathematics* and Unit 1. | ☐ *Math Journal 1,* p. 5<br>☐ Study Link Masters (*Math Masters,* pp. 211–214) |
| **3 Options for Individualizing** | |
| **Enrichment** Students read a poem about mathematics. [Operations and Computation] | ☐ *Arithmetic*<br>***See*** **Advance Preparation** |

## Additional Information

**Background Information** For additional information on the following topics, see the *Teacher's Reference Manual:* Math Messages, Groups and Partnerships, Reading Strategies, Study Links, and Family Letters.

**Advance Preparation** Before beginning the lesson, designate the place where the daily Math Message will be posted. Assign and record an ID number for each student. Each student will need a resealable plastic bag. Number the bags with the ID numbers. Pass them out, and tell students that the numbers on the bags will be their ID numbers for materials they borrow during the school year. The numbers will help identify the owners of misplaced items. Put a Lost-and-Found Box in a prominent place and remind students of its purpose.

Plan to spend 2 days on this lesson.

For the optional Enrichment activity in Part 3, obtain the book *Arithmetic* by Carl Sandburg (Harcourt Brace Jovanovich, 1993.)

## Getting Started

### Math Message

*Browse through your journal. Then read "Welcome to* Fifth Grade Everyday Mathematics,*" on page 1 in your journal.*

# 1 Teaching the Lesson

## ◆ Math Message Follow-Up (*Math Journal 1*, p. 1)

WHOLE-CLASS DISCUSSION

Ask students to share features of the journal that they found while browsing. Be sure to discuss the following journal features:

- The last pages in this *Math Journal* are perforated Activity Sheets. These sheets will be torn out at appropriate times.
- There is a page in the last lesson of each unit on which students are invited to record their thoughts about the unit that they have just completed.
- Discuss journal page 1 with the class. Ask students to name other mathematical topics that they would be interested in exploring during the year.

## ◆ Examining the *Student Reference Book*

WHOLE-CLASS DISCUSSION

Ask students to browse through the *Student Reference Book*. After a few minutes, bring the class together to discuss the organization and use of the book. Use your usual group reading procedure to read the page titled "About the *Student Reference Book*" (page xi).

Choose a reference page in the *Student Reference Book*, preferably one on a topic most students will be comfortable with, such as "Comparing Numbers and Amounts" on page 9. Work through the page to model how a student would use it. Have students try the Check Your Understanding problems and then check their own answers.

From time to time, an icon, which is shown below, appears on Math Boxes pages in the journal and on Study Links. The icon indicates pages in the *Student Reference Book* where there is information on the current topic.

SRB

STUDENT PAGE

### Welcome to *Fifth Grade Everyday Mathematics*

Much of what you learned in the first few years of *Everyday Mathematics* was basic training in mathematics and its uses. This year, you will practice and extend the skills and ideas you have learned. But you will also study more new ideas in mathematics—some of which your parents and older siblings may not have learned until high school! The authors of *Everyday Mathematics* believe that fifth graders in the 2000s can learn more and do more than people thought was possible 10 or 20 years ago.

Here are some of the things you will be asked to do in *Fifth Grade Everyday Mathematics:*

- Practice and extend your number sense, measure sense, and estimation skills.
- Review and extend your arithmetic, calculator, and thinking skills. You will work with fractions, decimals, percents, large whole numbers, and negative numbers.
- Continue your work with algebra, using variables in place of numbers.
- Refine your understanding of geometry. You will define and classify geometric figures more carefully than before. You will construct and transform figures. You will find the areas of 2-dimensional figures and volumes of 3-dimensional figures.
- Embark on the American Tour. You will study data about the history, people, and environment of the United States. You will learn to use and interpret many kinds of maps, graphs, and tables.
- Do many probability and statistics explorations with numerical data. You will use data that comes from questionnaires and experiments.

This year's activities will help you appreciate the beauty and usefulness of mathematics. We hope you will enjoy *Fifth Grade Everyday Mathematics*. We want you to become better at using mathematics, so that you may better understand the world you live in.

◆ *Math Journal 1*, p. 1

STUDENT PAGE

### *Student Reference Book* Scavenger Hunt

Solve the problems on this page and on the next two pages. Use your *Student Reference Book* to help you.

Also, record where to find information in the *Student Reference Book* for each problem. You may not need to look for help in the *Student Reference Book*, but you will earn additional points for telling where you would look if you needed to.

When the class goes over the answers, keep score as follows:

- Give yourself **3 points** for each correct answer to a problem.
- Give yourself **5 points** for each correct page number in the *Student Reference Book*.

| | Problem Points | Page Points |
|---|---|---|
| 1. Circle the prime numbers in the following list:<br>1 (2) 6 9 (13) 20 (31) 63 72<br>SRB *Student Reference Book*, page ______ | ____ | ____ |
| 2. Circle the composite numbers in the following list:<br>1 2 (6) (9) 13 (20) 31 (63) (72)<br>SRB *Student Reference Book*, page ______ | ____ | ____ |
| 3. 5 meters = 500 centimeters<br>SRB *Student Reference Book*, page ______ | ____ | ____ |
| 4. 300 mm = 30 cm<br>SRB *Student Reference Book*, page ______ | ____ | ____ |
| 5. What is the perimeter of this figure? (4 ft, 7 ft)<br>22 ft<br>SRB *Student Reference Book*, page ______ | ____ | ____ |

◆ *Math Journal 1*, p. 2

## Student Reference Book Scavenger Hunt (cont.)

| | Problem Points | Page Points |
|---|---|---|
| 6. 3 tablespoons = 9 teaspoons<br>Student Reference Book, page ____ | | |
| 7. Is angle RST acute or obtuse? acute<br>How can you tell? It measures less than 90°.<br>Student Reference Book, page ____ | | |
| 8. Rosie had the following scores on her spelling tests last month: 95, 87, 100, 92, and 78.<br>What is the mean (or average) of these scores? 90.4<br>Student Reference Book, page ____ | | |
| 9. 23 * 37 = 851<br>Student Reference Book, page ____ | | |
| 10. 369 + 1,347 = 1,716<br>Student Reference Book, page ____ | | |
| 11. a. Is 73,491 divisible by 3? yes<br>b. How can you tell without actually dividing? Add the digits. If the sum of the digits is divisible by 3, then the number is divisible by 3. 24 ÷ 3 = 8, so 73,491 is divisible by 3.<br>Student Reference Book, page ____ | | |

STUDENT PAGE

◆ Math Journal 1, p. 3

### ONGOING ASSESSMENT

To informally assess class strengths and weaknesses, have students put check marks next to the problems that they were able to answer without assistance from the *Student Reference Book.*

## Student Reference Book Scavenger Hunt (cont.)

| | Problem Points | Page Points |
|---|---|---|
| 12. Name two fractions equivalent to $\frac{4}{6}$. Sample answers: $\frac{2}{3}$ and $\frac{8}{12}$<br>Student Reference Book, page ____ | | |
| 13. What materials do you need to play *Estimation Squeeze?*<br>Calculator, paper, pencil<br>Student Reference Book, page ____ | | |
| 14. What is the definition of a scalene triangle?<br>A triangle with sides of 3 different lengths and angles of 3 different measures.<br>Student Reference Book, page ____ | | |
| 15. Use your calculator to find the square root of 9. 3<br>Record the key sequence you used.<br>[√] [9] [)] [Enter]<br>Student Reference Book, page ____ | | |

Total Problem Points ____

Total Page Points ____

Total Points ____

STUDENT PAGE

◆ Math Journal 1, p. 4

## ◆ Solving Problems Using the *Student Reference Book* (*Math Journal 1,* pp. 2–4; *Student Reference Book*)

PARTNER ACTIVITY 

**Language Arts Link** As students solve these problems on topics covered in previous grades of *Everyday Mathematics,* many will need to refer to the *Student Reference Book* for help. Using the Table of Contents, Glossary, and Index in the book will help students to gain and practice reference skills.

The focus of this activity should be on locating pages in the *Student Reference Book* that provide assistance with difficult problems, rather than obtaining correct answers. Scoring 3 points for a correct answer but 5 points for citing a page emphasizes this.

Circulate and assist as needed. When most students have completed the assignment, review the answers as well as the pages in the *Student Reference Book* where students located the information. Helpful information can often be found in several places in the *Student Reference Book.* Encourage students to cite multiple sources.

Have students calculate two separate scores—one for total correct answers, and one for total correct pages.

**Adjusting the Activity** Work with students having difficulty to identify key words in each question. Students should use a highlighter or coloring pencil to mark the words in their journals. They may try to locate these words in the Index or Table of Contents.

# 2 Ongoing Learning & Practice

## ◆ Math Boxes 1.1 (*Math Journal 1,* p. 5)

INDEPENDENT ACTIVITY 

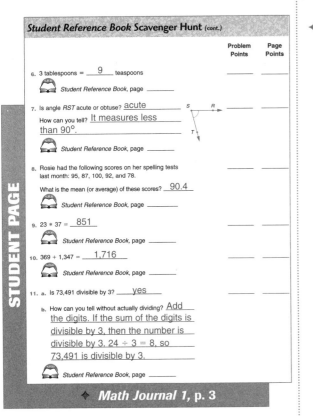

**Mixed Review** Math Boxes are an important routine for reviewing and maintaining skills. Students can complete them either independently or with partners. Circulate and assist where needed. This is an opportunity to observe students' progress. If many students are having trouble with a particular problem, plan to discuss it with the class at a convenient time.

Call students' attention to the "no-calculator" icon. Whenever they see one next to a problem or a set of problems, it means that they are not to use a calculator to solve the problem(s). (See, for example, Math Boxes on journal page 5.)

The Math Boxes problems in Unit 1 address skills that students practiced in *Fourth Grade Everyday Mathematics.* Math Boxes in this lesson are paired with Math Boxes in Lesson 1.3. The skill in Problem 1 is a prerequisite for Unit 2.

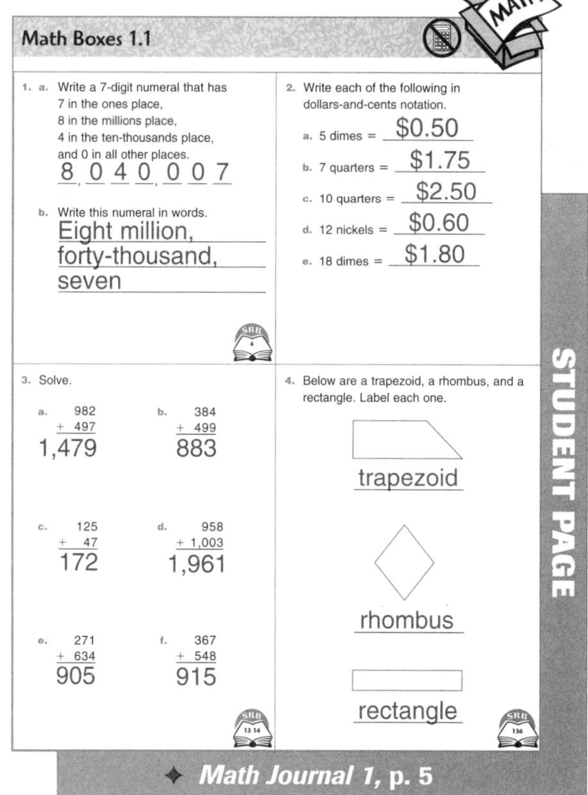

STUDENT PAGE

Math Boxes 1.1

MATH

1. a. Write a 7-digit numeral that has 7 in the ones place, 8 in the millions place, 4 in the ten-thousands place, and 0 in all other places.

8,040,007

b. Write this numeral in words.

Eight million, forty-thousand, seven

SRB 4

2. Write each of the following in dollars-and-cents notation.

a. 5 dimes = $0.50

b. 7 quarters = $1.75

c. 10 quarters = $2.50

d. 12 nickels = $0.60

e. 18 dimes = $1.80

3. Solve.

a. 982 + 497 = 1,479

b. 384 + 499 = 883

c. 125 + 47 = 172

d. 958 + 1,003 = 1,961

e. 271 + 634 = 905

f. 367 + 548 = 915

SRB 13 14

4. Below are a trapezoid, a rhombus, and a rectangle. Label each one.

trapezoid

rhombus

rectangle

SRB 136

◆ *Math Journal 1*, p. 5

## ◆ Study Link 1.1 (*Math Masters,* pp. 211–214)

**Home Connection** The Family Letter provides an introduction to the content of *Fifth Grade Everyday Mathematics* and to the topics covered in Unit 1.

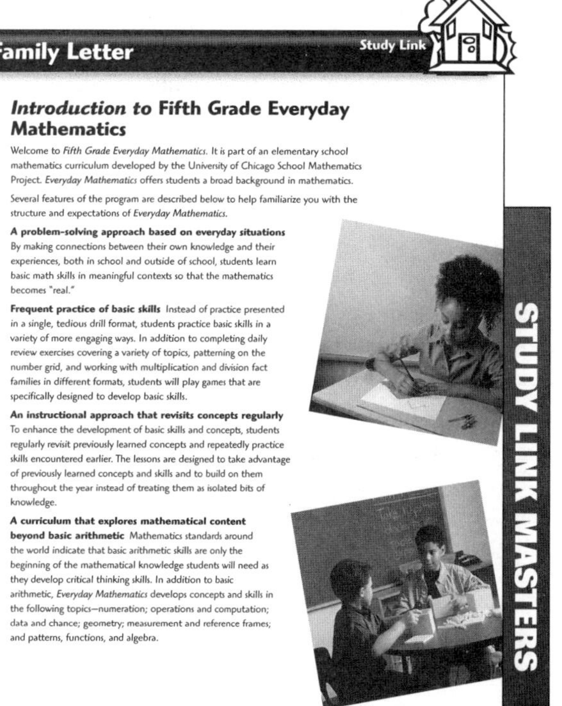

STUDY LINK MASTERS

Family Letter

Study Link

***Introduction** to* **Fifth Grade Everyday Mathematics**

Welcome to *Fifth Grade Everyday Mathematics.* It is part of an elementary school mathematics curriculum developed by the University of Chicago School Mathematics Project. *Everyday Mathematics* offers students a broad background in mathematics.

Several features of the program are described below to help familiarize you with the structure and expectations of *Everyday Mathematics.*

**A problem-solving approach based on everyday situations** By making connections between their own knowledge and their experiences, both in school and outside of school, students learn basic math skills in meaningful contexts so that the mathematics becomes "real."

**Frequent practice of basic skills** Instead of practice presented in a single, tedious drill format, students practice basic skills in a variety of more engaging ways. In addition to completing daily review exercises covering a variety of topics, patterning on the number grid, and working with multiplication and division fact families in different formats, students will play games that are specifically designed to develop basic skills.

**An instructional approach that revisits concepts regularly** To enhance the development of basic skills and concepts, students regularly revisit previously learned concepts and repeatedly practice skills encountered earlier. The lessons are designed to take advantage of previously learned concepts and skills and to build on them throughout the year instead of treating them as isolated bits of knowledge.

**A curriculum that explores mathematical content beyond basic arithmetic** Mathematics standards around the world indicate that basic arithmetic skills are only the beginning of the mathematical knowledge students will need as they develop critical thinking skills. In addition to basic arithmetic, *Everyday Mathematics* develops concepts and skills in the following topics—numeration; operations and computation; data and chance; geometry; measurement and reference frames; and patterns, functions, and algebra.

**Please keep this Family Letter for reference as your child works through Unit 1.**

◆ *Math Masters,* pp. 211–214

# 3 Options for Individualizing

## ◆ ENRICHMENT Appreciating Arithmetic in Poetry

WHOLE-CLASS ACTIVITY **15–30 min**

**Literature Link** It is intended that the activities in *Fifth Grade Everyday Mathematics* will help students appreciate the beauty and widespread usefulness of mathematics, as well as to improve their mathematical skills so that they may better understand the world they live in.

The poem "Arithmetic," found in the book of the same name by Carl Sandburg, focuses on one aspect of mathematics—arithmetic or computation. After reading the poem aloud to students, challenge them to think of as many other uses of and topics in mathematics as they can.

# 1.2 Rectangular Arrays

**OBJECTIVES** **To review rectangular arrays; and to use multiplication number models to represent such arrays.**

| summaries | materials |
| --- | --- |
| **1 Teaching the Lesson** | |
| Students discuss examples of rectangular arrays displayed in the Arrays Museum. They use counters to make rectangular arrays, and write multiplication number models for arrays. [Operations and Computation; Patterns, Functions, and Algebra] | ☐ *Math Journal 1,* p. 6<br>☐ *Student Reference Book,* p. 10<br>☐ Transparency (*Math Masters,* p. 1; optional)<br>☐ 12 counters ☐ Arrays Museum<br>***See*** **Advance Preparation** |
| **2 Ongoing Learning & Practice** | |
| Students practice and maintain skills through Math Boxes and Study Link activities. | ☐ *Math Journal 1,* p. 7<br>☐ Study Link Master (*Math Masters,* p. 215) |
| **3 Options for Individualizing** | |
| **Enrichment** A perpetual calendar is used to identify years in which the calendar for February is a rectangular array. [Operations and Computation; Patterns, Functions, and Algebra]<br>**Reteaching** Students use centimeter cubes to build arrays. [Operations and Computation] | ☐ Teaching Master (*Math Masters,* p. 2)<br>☐ *Student Reference Book,* pp. 197 and 198<br>☐ dice<br>☐ centimeter cubes (40 cubes per partnership) |

**Additional Information**

**Background Information** Post the "Working with a Partner" principles. For additional information on this topic, see the *Teacher's Reference Manual.*

**Advance Preparation** In Part 1, create an Arrays Museum by collecting arrays, such as tables of numbers and pictures of objects arranged in an array. (Start with one or two examples, then add more arrays over the coming days.) Prepare a place for the Arrays Museum on a bulletin board, poster, or other place in your classroom.

**Vocabulary • rectangular array • number model • turn-around rule (for multiplication) • perpetual calendar**

**Vocabulary (teacher) • commutative property for multiplication**

## Getting Started

### Math Message

*Read page 10 in your* Student Reference Book. *Then draw a rectangular array made up of 12 dots. You may use counters to help you.*

# 1 Teaching the Lesson

## ◆ Math Message Follow-Up

WHOLE-CLASS DISCUSSION

Students share their solutions as you draw the arrays on the board. Sample answers: 1-by-12, 12-by-1, 2-by-6, 6-by-2, 3-by-4, and 4-by-3 arrays.

## ◆ Reviewing Arrays (*Math Masters*, p. 1)

WHOLE-CLASS ACTIVITY

Display examples of **rectangular arrays** from the Arrays Museum. Stress these key elements:

▷ Each row has the same number of parts.

▷ Each column also has the same number of parts.

▷ Each array has a rectangular shape.

Ask students to name the number of rows and columns in each example.

In the next week, students should collect other examples of rectangular arrays to add to the Arrays Museum.

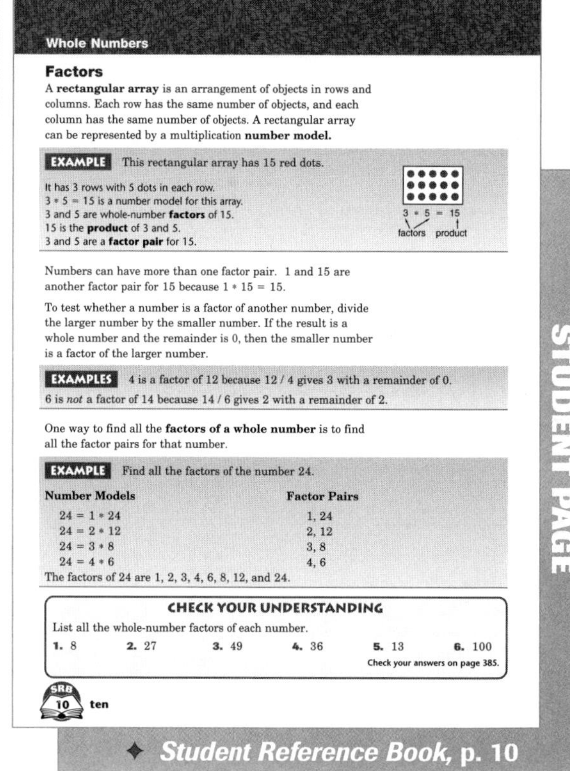

STUDENT PAGE

Whole Numbers

**Factors**

A **rectangular array** is an arrangement of objects in rows and columns. Each row has the same number of objects, and each column has the same number of objects. A rectangular array can be represented by a multiplication **number model.**

EXAMPLE This rectangular array has 15 red dots.

It has 3 rows with 5 dots in each row.
3 ∗ 5 = 15 is a number model for this array.
3 and 5 are whole-number **factors** of 15.
15 is the **product** of 3 and 5.
3 and 5 are a **factor pair** for 15.



Numbers can have more than one factor pair. 1 and 15 are another factor pair for 15 because 1 ∗ 15 = 15.

To test whether a number is a factor of another number, divide the larger number by the smaller number. If the result is a whole number and the remainder is 0, then the smaller number is a factor of the larger number.

EXAMPLES 4 is a factor of 12 because 12 / 4 gives 3 with a remainder of 0.
6 is *not* a factor of 14 because 14 / 6 gives 2 with a remainder of 2.

One way to find all the **factors of a whole number** is to find all the factor pairs for that number.

EXAMPLE Find all the factors of the number 24.

| Number Models | Factor Pairs |
|---|---|
| 24 = 1 ∗ 24 | 1, 24 |
| 24 = 2 ∗ 12 | 2, 12 |
| 24 = 3 ∗ 8 | 3, 8 |
| 24 = 4 ∗ 6 | 4, 6 |

The factors of 24 are 1, 2, 3, 4, 6, 8, 12, and 24.

**CHECK YOUR UNDERSTANDING**

List all the whole-number factors of each number.

**1.** 8 **2.** 27 **3.** 49 **4.** 36 **5.** 13 **6.** 100

Check your answers on page 385.

SRB 10 ten

◆ *Student Reference Book,* p. 10

**Adjusting the Activity** Consider reserving a section of the display for arrangements that are "almost arrays" but do not satisfy all of the conditions for rectangular arrays. Examples are some calculator keypads; certain playing cards, such as the nine of diamonds; a double-3 domino; and a calendar for a month, such as the month of August. *(See the margin.)*

| August | | | | | | |
|---|---|---|---|---|---|---|
| S | M | T | W | T | F | S |
| 1 | 2 | 3 | 4 | 5 | 6 | 7 |
| 8 | 9 | 10 | 11 | 12 | 13 | 14 |
| 15 | 16 | 17 | 18 | 19 | 20 | 21 |
| 22 | 23 | 24 | 25 | 26 | 27 | 28 |
| 29 | 30 | 31 | | | | |

This is not an array; the fifth row has only 3 days.

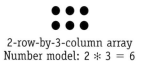

Arrays were first introduced in *Second Grade Everyday Mathematics*. The following discussion can serve as a quick review of arrays before students work independently to solve array problems.

1. Ask students to take out 6 counters and arrange them into a rectangular array.
2. Draw a 2-row-by-3-column array of dots on the board or on the overhead transparency of *Math Masters,* page 1. Label the array and write a **number model** to represent the array. *(See the margin.)*

2-row-by-3-column array
Number model: 2 ∗ 3 = 6

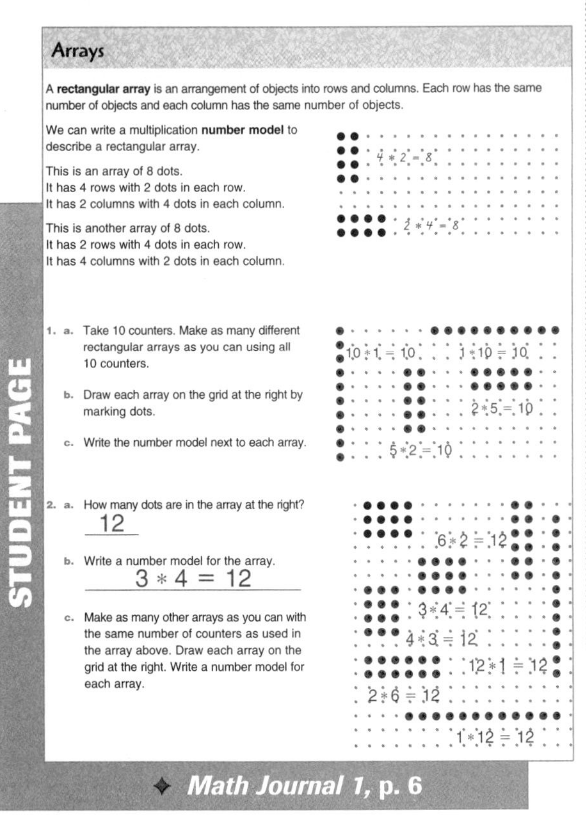
STUDENT PAGE

**Arrays**

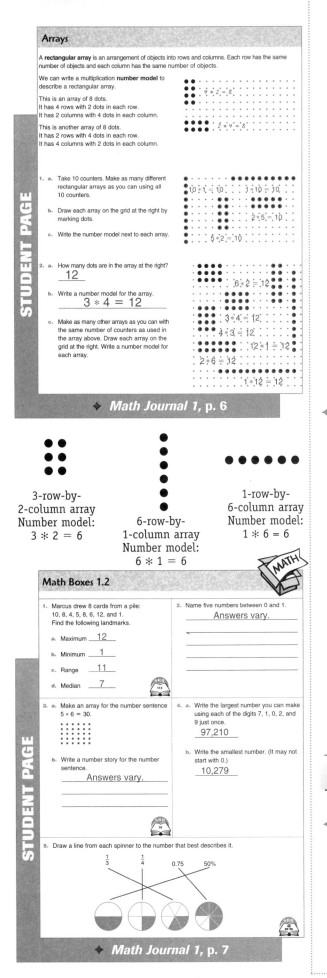

A **rectangular array** is an arrangement of objects into rows and columns. Each row has the same number of objects and each column has the same number of objects.

We can write a multiplication **number model** to describe a rectangular array.

This is an array of 8 dots.
It has 4 rows with 2 dots in each row.
It has 2 columns with 4 dots in each column.

This is another array of 8 dots.
It has 2 rows with 4 dots in each row.
It has 4 columns with 2 dots in each column.

1. a. Take 10 counters. Make as many different rectangular arrays as you can using all 10 counters.
   b. Draw each array on the grid at the right by marking dots.
   c. Write the number model next to each array.

2. a. How many dots are in the array at the right? 12
   b. Write a number model for the array. 3 * 4 = 12
   c. Make as many other arrays as you can with the same number of counters as used in the array above. Draw each array on the grid at the right. Write a number model for each array.



◆ *Math Journal 1*, p. 6

3-row-by-2-column array
Number model:
$3 * 2 = 6$

6-row-by-1-column array
Number model:
$6 * 1 = 6$

1-row-by-6-column array
Number model:
$1 * 6 = 6$

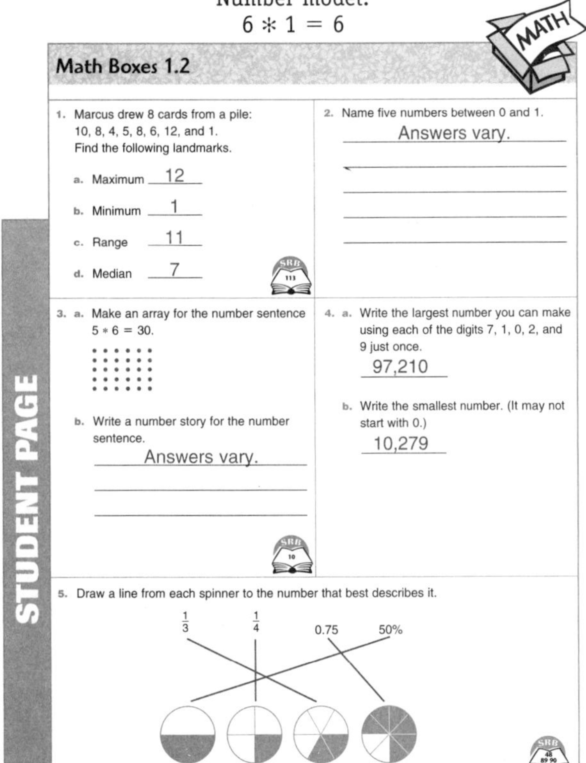
STUDENT PAGE

**Math Boxes 1.2**

1. Marcus drew 8 cards from a pile: 10, 8, 4, 5, 8, 6, 12, and 1. Find the following landmarks.
   a. Maximum 12
   b. Minimum 1
   c. Range 11
   d. Median 7

2. Name five numbers between 0 and 1.
   Answers vary.

3. a. Make an array for the number sentence 5 * 6 = 30.
   b. Write a number story for the number sentence.
   Answers vary.

4. a. Write the largest number you can make using each of the digits 7, 1, 0, 2, and 9 just once.
   97,210
   b. Write the smallest number. (It may not start with 0.)
   10,279

5. Draw a line from each spinner to the number that best describes it.



◆ *Math Journal 1*, p. 7

3. Review the use of multiplication number models as a way of representing rectangular arrays.
4. Ask students to arrange the 6 counters into other rectangular arrays. Show students' responses on the board or on the overhead transparency until all four possibilities have been displayed and discussed.

Point out that both the 3-row-by-2-column and the 2-row-by-3-column arrays have the same number of dots, but not the same number of rows and columns. To avoid confusion when naming an $x$-by-$y$ array, let $x$ represent the number of rows and $y$ the number of objects in each row (the number of columns). *(See the margin.)*

Tell students that the order in which two numbers are multiplied makes no difference; for example, $2 * 3 = 6$ and $3 * 2 = 6$. This property of multiplication is called the **turn-around rule** for multiplication. It is also called the **commutative property for multiplication,** but do not insist that students use this term.

### ◆ Finding All Possible Rectangular Arrays for a Number (*Math Journal 1*, p. 6)

PARTNER ACTIVITY

Review the "Working with a Partner" principles you have posted. Ask students for additional suggestions to help make the classroom more pleasant when students are working with partners or in small groups.

Ask partners to make all possible rectangular arrays out of 8 counters. A 4-by-2 array, an 8-by-1 array, and their reverses Partners then work on journal page 6. Circulate and assist students who are having difficulty. Some students may benefit from using counters; others may be able to solve the problems without counters.

## 2 Ongoing Learning & Practice

### ◆ Math Boxes 1.2 (*Math Journal 1*, p. 7)

INDEPENDENT ACTIVITY 

**Mixed Review** Math Boxes in this lesson are paired with Math Boxes in Lesson 1.4. The skill in Problem 1 is a prerequisite for Unit 2.

## ✦ Study Link 1.2 (*Math Masters,* p. 215)

**Home Connection** Students represent numbers by forming as many arrays as possible with counters or pennies. Students also represent multiplication number models as dot arrays.

# 3 Options for Individualizing

### ✦ ENRICHMENT Finding Rectangular Arrays in a Perpetual Calendar
(*Student Reference Book,* pp. 197 and 198)

INDEPENDENT ACTIVITY  **15–30 min**

Ask students to read about **perpetual calendars** on pages 197 and 198 in their *Student Reference Book.* Fourteen different calendars are shown. Ask students these questions:

- Which calendar has a month in which the squares for the days form a rectangular array? The month of February for Calendar 5
- Why is February the only month for which the calendar can be arranged in a rectangular array? February has 28 days, except in leap years. If February 1 is a Sunday, the days on the calendar form a 4-by-7 array. The other months have either 30 or 31 days. These cannot be shown with a rectangular array made up of 7 columns.

Ask students to list the next three years after 2000 whose calendars will include a rectangular array. 2009, 2015, 2026

### ✦ RETEACHING Making Cube Arrays
(*Math Masters,* p. 2)

PARTNER ACTIVITY   **15–30 min**

Partners take turns rolling dice. One die determines the number of rows; the other determines the number of cubes in each row. Students use centimeter cubes to build a rectangle that corresponds to the numbers on the dice.

Students record the rectangular arrays on *Math Masters,* page 2 by shading in the correct number and arrangement of centimeter grid squares. For each array, students write the number of rows, the number of cubes in each row, and how many cubes in all.

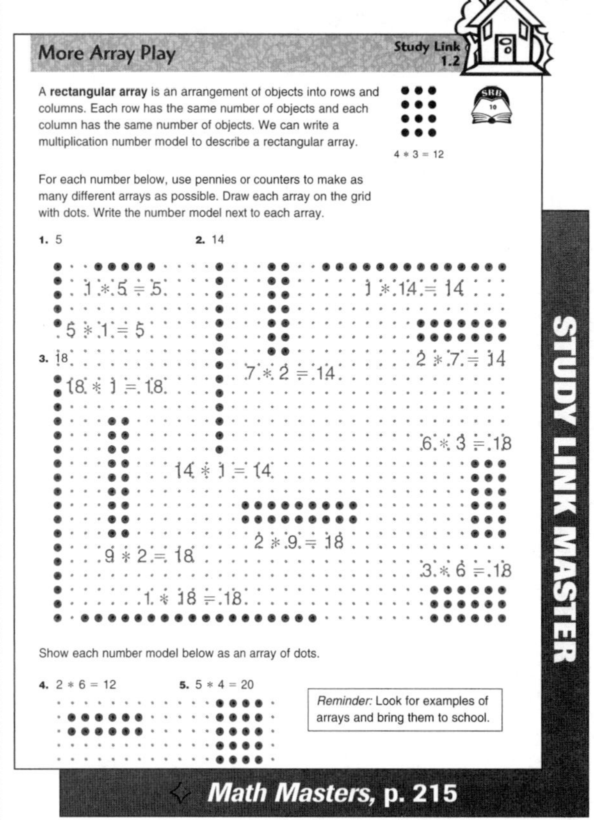

More Array Play — Study Link 1.2

A **rectangular array** is an arrangement of objects into rows and columns. Each row has the same number of objects and each column has the same number of objects. We can write a multiplication number model to describe a rectangular array.

4 * 3 = 12

For each number below, use pennies or counters to make as many different arrays as possible. Draw each array on the grid with dots. Write the number model next to each array.

1. 5 — 1 * 5 = 5; 5 * 1 = 5
2. 14 — 1 * 14 = 14; 2 * 7 = 14; 7 * 2 = 14; 14 * 1 = 14
3. 18 — 18 * 1 = 18; 9 * 2 = 18; 1 * 18 = 18; 2 * 9 = 18; 6 * 3 = 18; 3 * 6 = 18

Show each number model below as an array of dots.

4. 2 * 6 = 12
5. 5 * 4 = 20

*Reminder:* Look for examples of arrays and bring them to school.

STUDY LINK MASTER

Math Masters, p. 215

**PLANNING AHEAD**

Remind students to collect examples of arrays for the Arrays Museum. The Arrays Museum will be used in Lesson 1.3 and following.

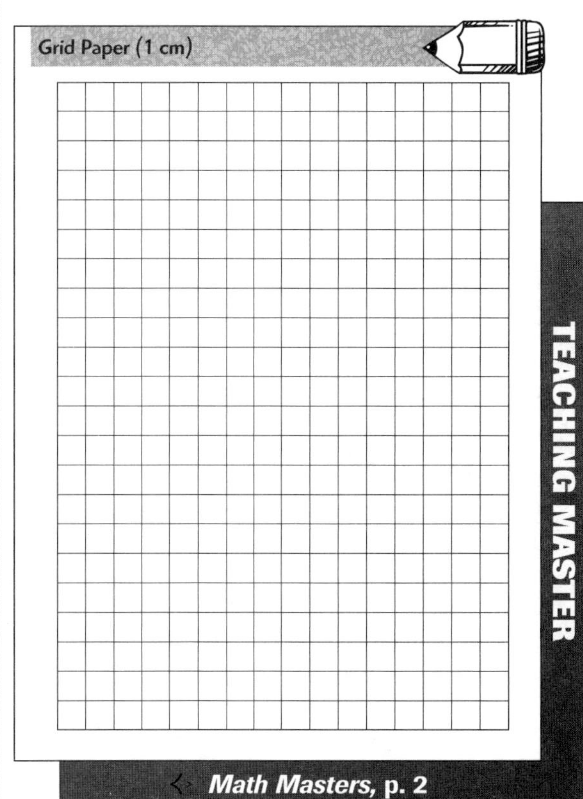


Math Masters, p. 2

# 1.3 Factors

**OBJECTIVES** **To review the meanings of *factor* and *product;* to find all factor pairs for a number; and to assess and develop instant recall of the multiplication facts.**

| summaries | materials |
| --- | --- |
| **1 Teaching the Lesson** | |
| Students begin a routine to assess and practice instant recall of the multiplication facts. They form arrays; write number models for the arrays; and list factor pairs for given whole numbers. [Operations and Computation; Patterns, Functions, and Algebra] | □ *Math Journal 1,* pp. 8 and 9<br>□ Study Link 1.2<br>□ Teaching Master (*Math Masters,* p. 1), 1 per partnership<br>□ Teaching Master (*Math Masters,* p. 3), for teacher only<br>□ Transparency *(Math Masters,* p. 1; optional)<br>□ 18 counters<br>□ Multiplication/Division Facts Table (optional) |
| **2 Ongoing Learning & Practice** | |
| Students use Fact Triangles to practice the multiplication facts. [Operations and Computation]<br>Students practice and maintain skills through Math Boxes and Study Link activities. | □ *Math Journal 1,* p. 10 and Activity Sheets 1 and 2<br>□ Study Link Master (*Math Masters,* p. 216)<br>□ scissors; envelopes (optional) |
| **3 Options for Individualizing** | |
| **Extra Practice** Students practice multiplication facts by playing *Baseball Multiplication, Multiplication Top-It,* and *Beat the Calculator.* [Operations and Computation] | □ *Student Reference Book,* pp. 259–261 and 295<br>□ Teaching Master (*Math Masters,* p. 4)<br>□ 4 each of the number cards 1–10 (from the Everything Math Deck, if available)<br>□ calculator; 2 regular dice; 4 pennies<br>***See* Advance Preparation** |

## Additional Information

**Advance Preparation** For the optional games in Part 3, students will need a calculator to play *Beat the Calculator.* Use a permanent marker to write students' ID numbers on the calculators. If you are using ordinary decks of playing cards, use a permanent marker to change the cards as follows: (1) Mark Aces with the number 1. (2) Mark the Queens with the number 0. (3) Number the remaining face cards (Kings and Jacks) 11–18. (4) Number the Jokers 19 and 20. The resulting deck will have the same frequency of each number card as an Everything Math Deck.

**Vocabulary** • **factor** • **product** • **factor pair**

# Getting Started

**Math Message**

*Take a sheet of dot paper. Use counters to make all possible arrays of 15 objects. Record the arrays on the dot paper. Write a number model for each array.*

**Study Link 1.2 Follow-Up**

Students share examples of arrays they brought to school. Encourage them to look for additional examples.

## 1 Teaching the Lesson

### ✦ Math Message Follow-Up

WHOLE-CLASS DISCUSSION

Students share their arrays and number models. Record students' solutions on an overhead transparency of *Math Masters*, page 1 or on the board. 1-by-15 and 3-by-5 arrays and their reverses

### ✦ Introducing the Multiplication Facts Routine
(*Math Journal 1,* p. 8; *Math Masters,* p. 3)

WHOLE-CLASS ACTIVITY

The authors of *Everyday Mathematics* believe that students should learn the basic facts of addition and multiplication to the level of instant recall. Mastery of the basic facts will give students surprising power in making quick estimates and in operating with large numbers.

The authors expect that most, if not all, of your fifth grade students have mastered the addition facts and that most already have rapid recall of the multiplication facts. *Everyday Mathematics* has developed a routine designed to help students increase their speed and accuracy with the multiplication facts, and to provide an ongoing evaluation of students' progress. You can use the following:

1. Select 10 problems from the A List on *Math Masters,* page 3; 5 problems from the B List; and 1 Bonus Problem. Number the problems from 1 to 16 in a column next to the problems. (The Bonus Problem should be Problem 16.)
2. Each student numbers a sheet of paper from 1 to 16.
3. Give the 16 problems orally, repeating each problem once. Students write their answers on their papers. Proceed fairly rapidly.

**Multiplication Facts**

| A List |
|---|
| 3 * 6 = 18 |
| 6 * 3 = 18 |
| 3 * 7 = 21 |
| 7 * 3 = 21 |
| 3 * 8 = 24 |
| 8 * 3 = 24 |
| 3 * 9 = 27 |
| 9 * 3 = 27 |
| 4 * 6 = 24 |
| 6 * 4 = 24 |
| 4 * 7 = 28 |
| 7 * 4 = 28 |
| 4 * 8 = 32 |
| 8 * 4 = 32 |
| 4 * 9 = 36 |
| 9 * 4 = 36 |
| 5 * 7 = 35 |
| 7 * 5 = 35 |
| 5 * 9 = 45 |
| 9 * 5 = 45 |
| 6 * 6 = 36 |
| 6 * 7 = 42 |
| 7 * 6 = 42 |
| 6 * 8 = 48 |
| 8 * 6 = 48 |
| 6 * 9 = 54 |
| 9 * 6 = 54 |
| 7 * 7 = 49 |
| 7 * 8 = 56 |
| 8 * 7 = 56 |
| 7 * 9 = 63 |
| 9 * 7 = 63 |
| 8 * 8 = 64 |
| 8 * 9 = 72 |
| 9 * 8 = 72 |
| 9 * 9 = 81 |

| B List |
|---|
| 3 * 3 = 9 |
| 3 * 4 = 12 |
| 4 * 3 = 12 |
| 3 * 5 = 15 |
| 5 * 3 = 15 |
| 4 * 4 = 16 |
| 4 * 5 = 20 |
| 5 * 4 = 20 |
| 5 * 5 = 25 |
| 5 * 6 = 30 |
| 6 * 5 = 30 |
| 5 * 8 = 40 |
| 8 * 5 = 40 |
| 6 * 10 = 60 |
| 10 * 6 = 60 |
| 7 * 10 = 70 |
| 10 * 7 = 70 |
| 8 * 10 = 80 |
| 10 * 8 = 80 |
| 9 * 10 = 90 |
| 10 * 9 = 90 |
| 10 * 10 = 100 |

| Bonus Problems |
|---|
| 11 * 11 = 121 |
| 11 * 12 = 132 |
| 5 * 12 = 60 |
| 12 * 6 = 72 |
| 7 * 12 = 84 |
| 12 * 8 = 96 |
| 9 * 12 = 108 |
| 10 * 12 = 120 |
| 5 * 13 = 65 |
| 15 * 7 = 105 |
| 12 * 12 = 144 |
| 6 * 14 = 84 |

TEACHING MASTER

Math Masters, p. 3

**Multiplication Facts Master List**

Make a check mark next to each fact you missed and need to study.
Once you have learned a fact, write "OK" next to the check mark. Answers vary.

| 3s | 5s | 7s | 9s |
|---|---|---|---|
| 3 * 3 | 5 * 3 | 7 * 3 | 9 * 3 |
| 3 * 4 | 5 * 4 | 7 * 4 | 9 * 4 |
| 3 * 5 | 5 * 5 | 7 * 5 | 9 * 5 |
| 3 * 6 | 5 * 6 | 7 * 6 | 9 * 6 |
| 3 * 7 | 5 * 7 | 7 * 7 | 9 * 7 |
| 3 * 8 | 5 * 8 | 7 * 8 | 9 * 8 |
| 3 * 9 | 5 * 9 | 7 * 9 | 9 * 9 |
| | | 7 * 10 | 9 * 10 |

| 4s | 6s | 8s | 10s |
|---|---|---|---|
| 4 * 3 | 6 * 3 | 8 * 3 | 10 * 3 |
| 4 * 4 | 6 * 4 | 8 * 4 | 10 * 4 |
| 4 * 5 | 6 * 5 | 8 * 5 | 10 * 5 |
| 4 * 6 | 6 * 6 | 8 * 6 | 10 * 6 |
| 4 * 7 | 6 * 7 | 8 * 7 | 10 * 7 |
| 4 * 8 | 6 * 8 | 8 * 8 | 10 * 8 |
| 4 * 9 | 6 * 9 | 8 * 9 | 10 * 9 |
| | 6 * 10 | 8 * 10 | 10 * 10 |

STUDENT PAGE

✦ Math Journal 1, p. 8

4. Students exchange papers or correct their own, as you go over problems and answers. Students make check marks on the Master List on journal page 8, next to the problems they missed and need to study.
5. Circle the problems that are missed most frequently on *Math Masters,* page 3 so that you may repeat them for continued practice.

Plan to give such a quiz most days for about two weeks. Thereafter, give the quiz once or twice a week, as needed. Tell the class that a student will be excused from taking the quiz as soon as he or she has gotten at least 15 correct answers on each of three quizzes.

**Adjusting the Activity** Some students do not perform well when problems are given orally. Prepare a written quiz as an alternative.

NOTE: Although a factor may be a whole number, decimal, or fraction, Unit 1 deals with whole-number factors only.

NOTE: The work with factors in this unit involves many basic multiplication and division facts. Students probably already know many, if not most, of the facts. If a problem calls for a multiplication or division fact students don't know, they should look it up in the Multiplication/Division Facts Table on the inside front cover of their journals.

## Reviewing the Meanings of *Factor, Product,* and *Factor Pair*

WHOLE-CLASS ACTIVITY

Remind students that in a number model such as $3 * 5 = 15$ or $5 * 3 = 15$, the 3 and the 5 are called **factors;** and 15, the result of multiplying, is called the **product** of 3 and 5. The factors 3 and 5 are a **factor pair** for the number 15. The factors 1 and 15 are another factor pair for 15. In fact, 1 and $n$ are always factors of $n$.

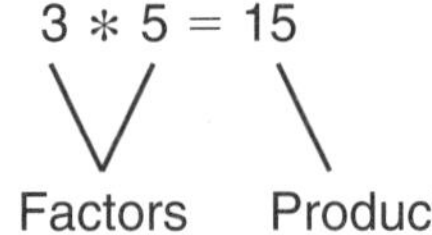


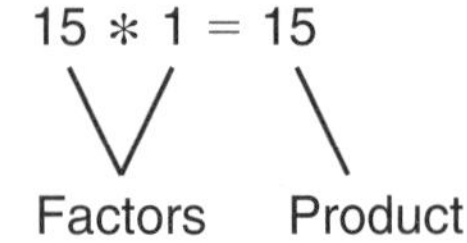


- Are there other whole-number factor pairs for 15? no

With the class, list all the whole-number factor pairs for 18. 1 and 18, 2 and 9, 3 and 6 If students have trouble finding factor pairs, ask them to use counters to make all possible arrays of 18 objects. Then write a number model for each array. $1 * 18 = 18$, $18 * 1 = 18$, $2 * 9 = 18$, $9 * 2 = 18$, $3 * 6 = 18$, $6 * 3 = 18$

## Finding Factor Pairs (*Math Journal 1,* p. 9)

INDEPENDENT ACTIVITY 

Students can work independently or with partners to complete the problems on the journal page. Encourage students to solve the problems without the help of counters. Circulate and assist as needed.

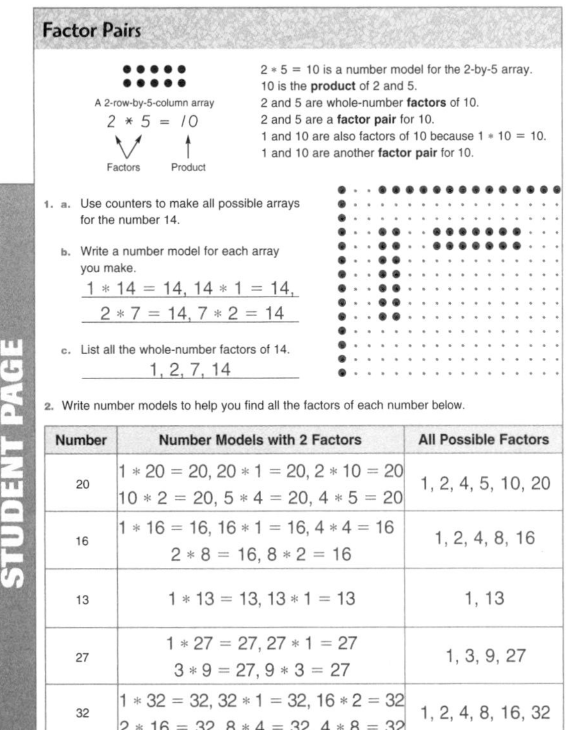

STUDENT PAGE

**Factor Pairs**

A 2-row-by-5-column array

2 * 5 = 10

Factors Product

2 * 5 = 10 is a number model for the 2-by-5 array.
10 is the **product** of 2 and 5.
2 and 5 are whole-number **factors** of 10.
2 and 5 are a **factor pair** for 10.
1 and 10 are also factors of 10 because 1 * 10 = 10.
1 and 10 are another **factor pair** for 10.

1. a. Use counters to make all possible arrays for the number 14.

   b. Write a number model for each array you make.
   1 * 14 = 14, 14 * 1 = 14,
   2 * 7 = 14, 7 * 2 = 14

   c. List all the whole-number factors of 14.
   1, 2, 7, 14

2. Write number models to help you find all the factors of each number below.

| Number | Number Models with 2 Factors | All Possible Factors |
|---|---|---|
| 20 | 1 * 20 = 20, 20 * 1 = 20, 2 * 10 = 20<br>10 * 2 = 20, 5 * 4 = 20, 4 * 5 = 20 | 1, 2, 4, 5, 10, 20 |
| 16 | 1 * 16 = 16, 16 * 1 = 16, 4 * 4 = 16<br>2 * 8 = 16, 8 * 2 = 16 | 1, 2, 4, 8, 16 |
| 13 | 1 * 13 = 13, 13 * 1 = 13 | 1, 13 |
| 27 | 1 * 27 = 27, 27 * 1 = 27<br>3 * 9 = 27, 9 * 3 = 27 | 1, 3, 9, 27 |
| 32 | 1 * 32 = 32, 32 * 1 = 32, 16 * 2 = 32<br>2 * 16 = 32, 8 * 4 = 32, 4 * 8 = 32 | 1, 2, 4, 8, 16, 32 |

*Math Journal 1,* p. 9

**Adjusting the Activity** Students who are having difficulty finding factor pairs should form arrays and write number models for the arrays.

# 2 Ongoing Learning & Practice

## ✦ Using Fact Triangles to Practice Multiplication Facts

(*Math Journal 1,* Activity Sheets 1 and 2)

PARTNER ACTIVITY

Students can use Fact Triangles to help them memorize the facts they don't know. You may want to have students store the Fact Triangles in envelopes after they have been cut out.

## ✦ Math Boxes 1.3 (*Math Journal 1,* p. 10)

INDEPENDENT ACTIVITY 

**Mixed Review** Math Boxes in this lesson are paired with Math Boxes in Lesson 1.1. The skill in Problem 1 is a prerequisite for Unit 2.

## ✦ Study Link 1.3 (*Math Masters,* p. 216)

**Home Connection** Students explore arrays consisting of two rows. Encourage students to bring examples of arrays to school.

# 3 Options for Individualizing

## ✦ EXTRA PRACTICE Playing Fact-Skills Games to Practice Multiplication Facts

(*Student Reference Book,* pp. 259–261 and 295; *Math Masters,* p. 4)

PARTNER ACTIVITY **5–15 min**

To develop reflex multiplication skills, students can play games that were introduced in previous grades, such as *Multiplication Top-It, Beat the Calculator,* and *Baseball Multiplication.* The rules for these games are found in the *Student Reference Book*. The *Baseball Multiplication* Playing Mat is found on *Math Masters,* p. 4.

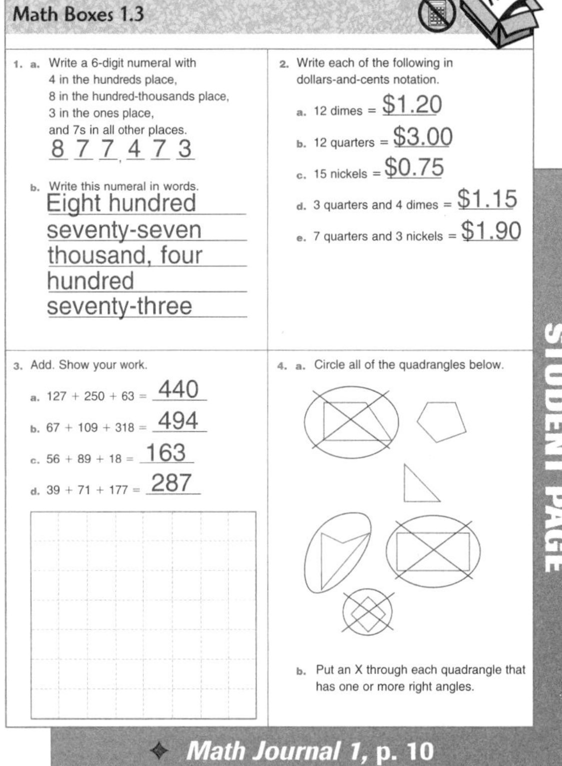
Math Boxes 1.3

1. a. Write a 6-digit numeral with 4 in the hundreds place, 8 in the hundred-thousands place, 3 in the ones place, and 7s in all other places. 877,473
b. Write this numeral in words. Eight hundred seventy-seven thousand, four hundred seventy-three

2. Write each of the following in dollars-and-cents notation.
a. 12 dimes = $1.20
b. 12 quarters = $3.00
c. 15 nickels = $0.75
d. 3 quarters and 4 dimes = $1.15
e. 7 quarters and 3 nickels = $1.90

3. Add. Show your work.
a. 127 + 250 + 63 = 440
b. 67 + 109 + 318 = 494
c. 56 + 89 + 18 = 163
d. 39 + 71 + 177 = 287

4. a. Circle all of the quadrangles below.
b. Put an X through each quadrangle that has one or more right angles.

STUDENT PAGE

✦ *Math Journal 1,* p. 10

NOTE: Students should continue to practice the multiplication facts throughout the school year until they have memorized them all. Encourage them to use both the Fact Triangles and the multiplication games.

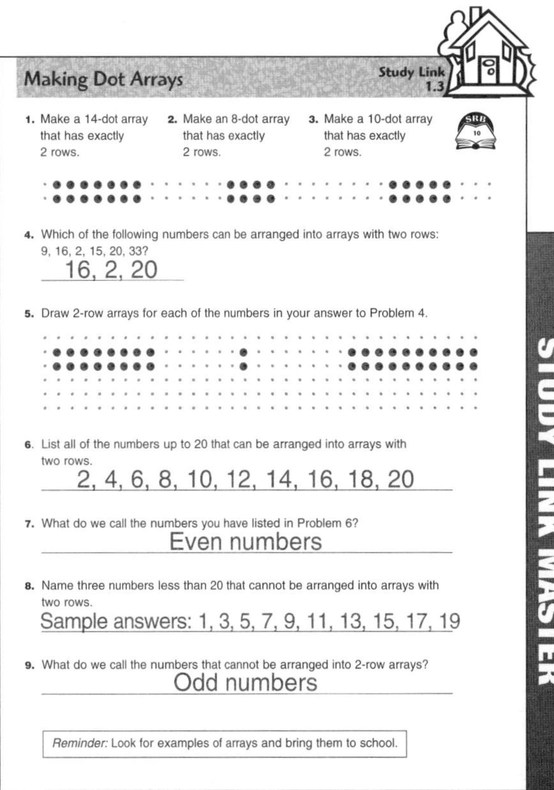
Making Dot Arrays — Study Link 1.3

1. Make a 14-dot array that has exactly 2 rows.
2. Make an 8-dot array that has exactly 2 rows.
3. Make a 10-dot array that has exactly 2 rows.

4. Which of the following numbers can be arranged into arrays with two rows: 9, 16, 2, 15, 20, 33? 16, 2, 20

5. Draw 2-row arrays for each of the numbers in your answer to Problem 4.

6. List all of the numbers up to 20 that can be arranged into arrays with two rows. 2, 4, 6, 8, 10, 12, 14, 16, 18, 20

7. What do we call the numbers you have listed in Problem 6? Even numbers

8. Name three numbers less than 20 that cannot be arranged into arrays with two rows. Sample answers: 1, 3, 5, 7, 9, 11, 13, 15, 17, 19

9. What do we call the numbers that cannot be arranged into 2-row arrays? Odd numbers

*Reminder:* Look for examples of arrays and bring them to school.

STUDY LINK MASTER

✦ *Math Masters,* p. 216

# 1.4 The *Factor Captor* Game

**OBJECTIVES** **To find all factors of a given number; to review divisibility; to relate factors and divisibility; and to continue the multiplication facts routine.**

| summaries | materials |
|---|---|
| **1 Teaching the Lesson** | |
| Students review what it means for a number to be divisible by another number. They practice finding factors of numbers by playing *Factor Captor.* [Numeration; Operations and Computation] | ☐ *Student Reference Book,* p. 271 ☐ Study Link 1.3<br>☐ Teaching Master (*Math Masters,* p. 5), 1 per partnership<br>☐ Transparency (*Math Masters,* p. 5; optional)<br>☐ Assessment Master (*Math Masters,* p. 479)<br>☐ counters (50 per partnership)<br>***See* Advance Preparation** |
| **2 Ongoing Learning & Practice** | |
| Students continue the multiplication facts routine to practice recall of the facts; develop reflex multiplication skills by using Fact Triangles; and play *Baseball Multiplication, Multiplication Top-It,* and *Beat the Calculator,* which review facts. [Operations and Computation]<br>Students practice and maintain skills through Math Boxes and Study Link activities. | ☐ *Math Journal 1,* pp. 8 and 11<br>☐ *Student Reference Book,* pp. 259–261 and 295<br>☐ Teaching Master (*Math Masters,* p. 3), for teacher only<br>☐ Study Link Master (*Math Masters,* p. 217)<br>☐ *Baseball Multiplication* Game Mat (*Math Masters,* p. 4)<br>☐ Fact Triangles (cut from *Math Journal 1,* Activity Sheets 1 and 2)<br>☐ Teaching Master (*Math Masters,* p. 5)<br>Per partnership:<br>☐ 4 each of the number cards 0–10 (from the Everything Math Deck, if available)<br>☐ a Multiplication/Division Facts Table (optional)<br>☐ calculator; 2 regular dice; 4 pennies |
| **3 Options for Individualizing** | |
| **Enrichment** Students find factors of larger numbers by playing the advanced version of *Factor Captor.* [Numeration; Operations and Computation]<br>**Language Diversity** Students create a Number Theory Dictionary, which includes definitions and illustrations. [Numeration] | ☐ *Student Reference Book,* p. 271<br>☐ Teaching Master (*Math Masters,* p. 6), 1 per partnership<br>☐ Transparency (*Math Masters,* p. 6; optional)<br>☐ counters (70 per partnership) |

## Additional Information

**Advance Preparation** In Part 1 of the lesson, students work in partnerships to play *Factor Captor* and will need 1 copy of *Math Masters,* page 5, per partnership. But each student will need 1 copy to take home with Study Link 1.4.

**Vocabulary** • **even number** • **factor (of a number)** • **odd number** • **remainder** • **divisible by**

# Getting Started

## Math Message

*Which of the following numbers are factors of 36?*

*1, 2, 3, 4, 5, 6, 7, 8, 9, 10*

## Study Link 1.3 Follow-Up

Discuss the problems. Guide students to the following conclusions:

- If a number can be represented by a rectangular array consisting of two rows (or two columns), then the number is an **even number.** Therefore, 2 is a **factor** of every even number.
- If a number cannot be represented by an array consisting of two rows (or two columns), then the number is an **odd number.** Therefore, 2 cannot be a factor of an odd number.

Students share examples of arrays they brought to school. Encourage them to look for additional examples.

# 1 Teaching the Lesson

## ✦ Math Message Follow-Up

WHOLE-CLASS DISCUSSION 

The factors of 36 up through 10 are 1, 2, 3, 4, 6, and 9. Prompt students to "prove" their answers. *For example:*

- Why is 4 a factor of 36? Because $4 * 9 = 36$; therefore, both 4 and 9 are factors of 36.
- Why is 5 *not* a factor of 36? Because there is no whole number that gives an answer of 36 when you multiply it by 5.

Someone may mention that 4 is a factor of 36, because 36 divided by 4 "comes out even"—that is, the answer is 9, with a **remainder** of zero. Similarly, 5 is not a factor of 36, because 36 divided by 5 "doesn't come out even"—that is, the answer has a remainder that is not zero.

**Adjusting the Activity** Challenge students to name the factors of 36 that are greater than 10. 12, 18, and 36

STUDENT PAGE

Games

### Factor Captor

**Materials** ☐ calculators for each player
☐ paper and pencil
☐ a *Factor Captor* grid—either Grid 1 or Grid 2 (*Math Masters,* pp. 5 and 6)
☐ coin-size counters (48 for Grid 1, 70 for Grid 2)

**Players** 2

**Directions**

1. To start the first round, Player 1 (James) chooses a 2-digit number on the number grid. James covers it with a counter, and records the number on scratch paper. This is James's score for the round.
2. Player 2 (Emma) covers all of the factors of James's number. Emma finds the sum of the factors, and records it on scratch paper. This is Emma's score for the round.

**A factor may only be covered once during a round.**

3. If Emma missed any factors, James can cover them with counters and add them to his score.
4. In the next round, players switch roles. Player 2 (Emma) chooses a number that is not covered by a counter. Player 1 (James) covers all factors of that number.
5. Any number that is covered by a counter is no longer available and may not be used again.
6. The first player in a round may not cover a number less than 10, unless no other numbers are available.
7. Play continues with players trading roles in each round, until all numbers on the grid have been covered. Players then use their calculators to find their total scores. The player with the higher total score wins the game.

| 1 | 2 | 2 | 2 | 2 | 2 |
|---|---|---|---|---|---|
| 2 | 3 | 3 | 3 | 3 | 3 |
| 3 | 4 | 4 | 4 | 4 | 5 |
| 5 | 5 | 5 | 6 | 6 | 7 |
| 7 | 8 | 8 | 9 | 9 | 10 |
| 10 | 11 | 12 | 13 | 14 | 15 |
| 16 | 18 | 20 | 21 | 22 | 24 |
| 25 | 26 | 27 | 28 | 30 | 32 |

| 1 | 2 | 2 | 2 | 2 | 2 | 3 |
|---|---|---|---|---|---|---|
| 3 | 3 | 3 | 3 | 4 | 4 | 4 |
| 4 | 5 | 5 | 5 | 5 | 6 | 6 |
| 6 | 7 | 7 | 8 | 8 | 9 | 9 |
| 10 | 10 | 11 | 12 | 13 | 14 | 15 |
| 16 | 17 | 18 | 19 | 20 | 21 | 22 |
| 23 | 24 | 25 | 26 | 27 | 28 | 30 |
| 32 | 33 | 34 | 35 | 36 | 38 | 39 |
| 40 | 42 | 44 | 45 | 46 | 48 | 49 |
| 50 | 51 | 52 | 54 | 55 | 56 | 60 |

**EXAMPLE**

**Round 1:** James covers 27 and scores 27 points. Emma covers 1, 3, and 9, and scores 1 + 3 + 9 = 13 points.

**Round 2:** Emma covers 18 and scores 18 points. James covers 2, 3, and 6, and scores 2 + 3 + 6 = 11 points. Emma covers 9 with a counter, because 9 is also a factor of 18. Emma adds 9 points to her score.

two hundred seventy-one

*Student Reference Book,* p. 271

TEACHING MASTER

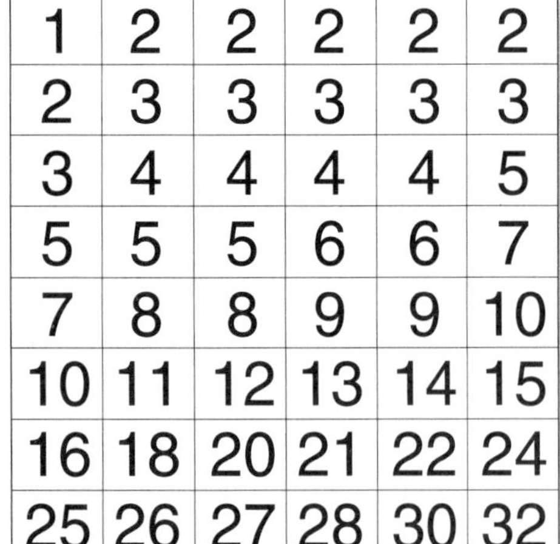

*Factor Captor* Grid 1 (Beginning Level)

| 1 | 2 | 2 | 2 | 2 | 2 |
|---|---|---|---|---|---|
| 2 | 3 | 3 | 3 | 3 | 3 |
| 3 | 4 | 4 | 4 | 4 | 5 |
| 5 | 5 | 5 | 6 | 6 | 7 |
| 7 | 8 | 8 | 9 | 9 | 10 |
| 10 | 11 | 12 | 13 | 14 | 15 |
| 16 | 18 | 20 | 21 | 22 | 24 |
| 25 | 26 | 27 | 28 | 30 | 32 |

*Math Masters,* p. 5

## ✦ Reviewing the Meaning of Divisibility

WHOLE-CLASS ACTIVITY

*Everyday Mathematics* has always emphasized the relationship between multiplication and division. For example, to find the quotient of 42 divided by 7, students are encouraged to think: *7 times what number is 42?* The ideas of factors and divisibility are just another way of expressing this relationship. For example, you can say that 7 is a factor of 42, because 42 is **divisible by** 7.

Ask students to share what they know about division. Then, remind the class that a number is divisible by another number if the result of the division is a whole number, with a remainder of zero. For example, 28 is divisible by 7, because 28 divided by 7 is 4, with a remainder of zero. Since 28 is divisible by 7, 7 is a factor of 28.

To illustrate the relationship between factors and divisibility, pose a few problems, such as the following:

- Is 54 divisible by 9? Yes, because 54 divided by 9 is 6, with remainder 0.
- Is 25 divisible by 6? No, because 25 divided by 6 is 4, with remainder 1.
- Is 8 a factor of 48? Yes, because 48 is divisible by 8.
- Is 4 a factor of 30? No, because 30 is not divisible by 4.

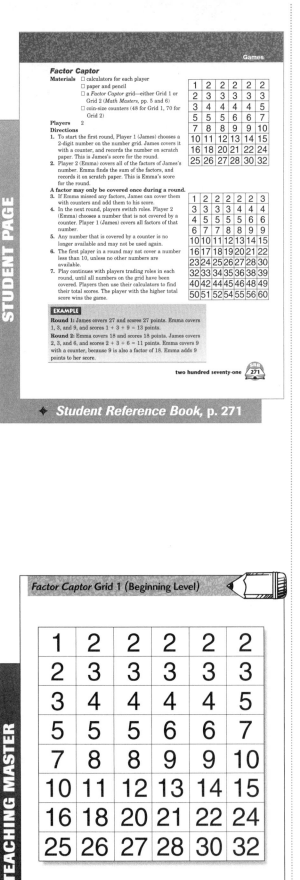

## ✦ Playing *Factor Captor*
(*Student Reference Book,* p. 271; *Math Masters,* pp. 5 and 479)

PARTNER ACTIVITY

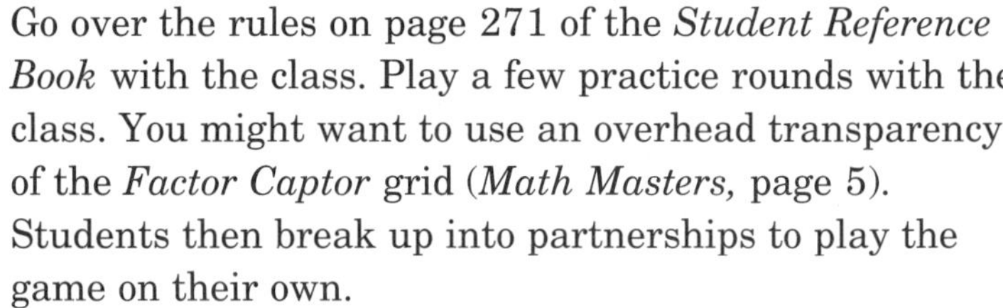

Go over the rules on page 271 of the *Student Reference Book* with the class. Play a few practice rounds with the class. You might want to use an overhead transparency of the *Factor Captor* grid (*Math Masters,* page 5). Students then break up into partnerships to play the game on their own.

Students enjoy this game, and they should be encouraged to play it often. It is a valuable way of solidifying their grasp of the multiplication and division facts.

## ONGOING ASSESSMENT

**After playing several rounds, have students complete an Exit Slip describing strategies that maximize scoring. Expect this description to include some of the following points:**

- ▷ **It is best to cover numbers that have only the number and 1 as its factors.**
- ▷ **25 is a good number to cover because then the other player can only cover 1 and 5.**
- ▷ **It is better to cover an odd number than an even number. If you cover an even number, then the other player can cover a number that is half as much of the number plus any other factors.**

**Multiplication Facts Master List**

Make a check mark next to each fact you missed and need to study.
Once you have learned a fact, write "OK" next to the check mark. Answers vary.

| 3s | 5s | 7s | 9s |
|---|---|---|---|
| 3 * 3 | 5 * 3 | 7 * 3 | 9 * 3 |
| 3 * 4 | 5 * 4 | 7 * 4 | 9 * 4 |
| 3 * 5 | 5 * 5 | 7 * 5 | 9 * 5 |
| 3 * 6 | 5 * 6 | 7 * 6 | 9 * 6 |
| 3 * 7 | 5 * 7 | 7 * 7 | 9 * 7 |
| 3 * 8 | 5 * 8 | 7 * 8 | 9 * 8 |
| 3 * 9 | 5 * 9 | 7 * 9 | 9 * 9 |
| | | 7 * 10 | 9 * 10 |

| 4s | 6s | 8s | 10s |
|---|---|---|---|
| 4 * 3 | 6 * 3 | 8 * 3 | 10 * 3 |
| 4 * 4 | 6 * 4 | 8 * 4 | 10 * 4 |
| 4 * 5 | 6 * 5 | 8 * 5 | 10 * 5 |
| 4 * 6 | 6 * 6 | 8 * 6 | 10 * 6 |
| 4 * 7 | 6 * 7 | 8 * 7 | 10 * 7 |
| 4 * 8 | 6 * 8 | 8 * 8 | 10 * 8 |
| 4 * 9 | 6 * 9 | 8 * 9 | 10 * 9 |
| | 6 * 10 | 8 * 10 | 10 * 10 |

STUDENT PAGE

✦ *Math Journal 1,* p. 8

# 2 Ongoing Learning & Practice

Choose one or more of the following activities for assessing and practicing the multiplication facts.

NOTE: The TI-15 calculator can also be used for practicing multiplication facts. The calculator can generate basic or extended facts for students to answer. See *Math Masters,* pages 480 and 481.

### ✦ Practicing the Multiplication Facts Routine
(*Math Journal 1,* p. 8; *Math Masters,* p. 3)

WHOLE-CLASS ACTIVITY

Select another 16 problems from *Math Masters,* page 3 for a multiplication facts quiz. Repeat problems that you circled on *Math Masters,* page 3 because they were missed most frequently. See Lesson 1.3 for additional directions.

### ✦ Using Fact Triangles to Practice Multiplication Facts
(*Math Journal 1,* Activity Sheets 1 and 2)

PARTNER ACTIVITY

If students have not previously cut out the Fact Triangles, you may wish to have them do so at this time. Students use the Fact Triangles to help them memorize the facts they don't know.

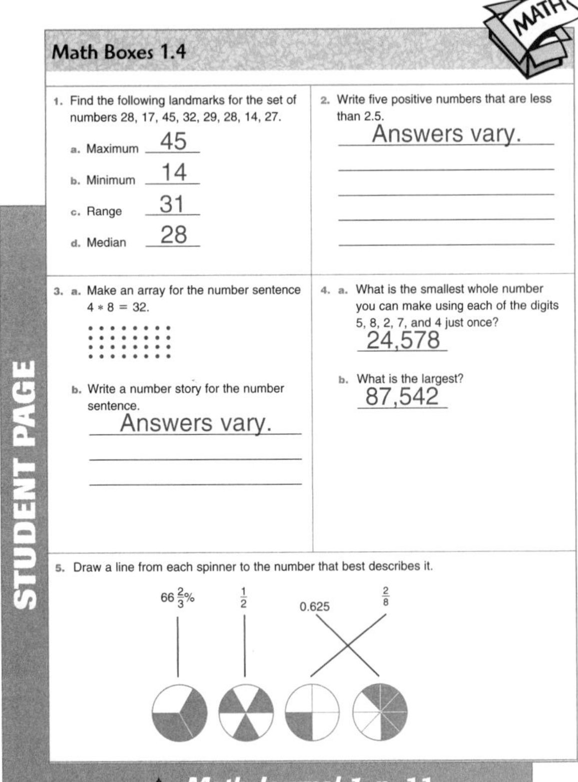

STUDENT PAGE

**Math Boxes 1.4**

1. Find the following landmarks for the set of numbers 28, 17, 45, 32, 29, 28, 14, 27.
   a. Maximum 45
   b. Minimum 14
   c. Range 31
   d. Median 28

2. Write five positive numbers that are less than 2.5.
   Answers vary.

3. a. Make an array for the number sentence $4 * 8 = 32$.
   b. Write a number story for the number sentence.
   Answers vary.

4. a. What is the smallest whole number you can make using each of the digits 5, 8, 2, 7, and 4 just once?
   24,578
   b. What is the largest?
   87,542

5. Draw a line from each spinner to the number that best describes it.
   $66\frac{2}{3}\%$  $\frac{1}{2}$  0.625  $\frac{2}{8}$

✦ *Math Journal 1,* p. 11

## ✦ Practicing Multiplication Facts through Games
(*Student Reference Book,* pp. 259–261 and 295; *Math Masters,* p. 4)

PARTNER ACTIVITY 

To develop reflex multiplication skills, students can play *Multiplication Top-It, Beat the Calculator,* and *Baseball Multiplication.* The rules for these games are found in the *Student Reference Book.*

## ✦ Math Boxes 1.4 (*Math Journal 1,* p. 11)

INDEPENDENT ACTIVITY 

**Mixed Review** Math Boxes in this lesson are paired with Math Boxes in Lesson 1.2. The skill in Problem 1 is a prerequisite for Unit 2.

## ✦ Study Link 1.4 (*Math Masters,* pp. 5 and 217)

**Home Connection** Students find as many factors as they can for whole numbers. They can write number sentences to help them identify factor pairs. Give each student a copy of *Math Masters,* page 5, so that they can play *Factor Captor* with someone at home.

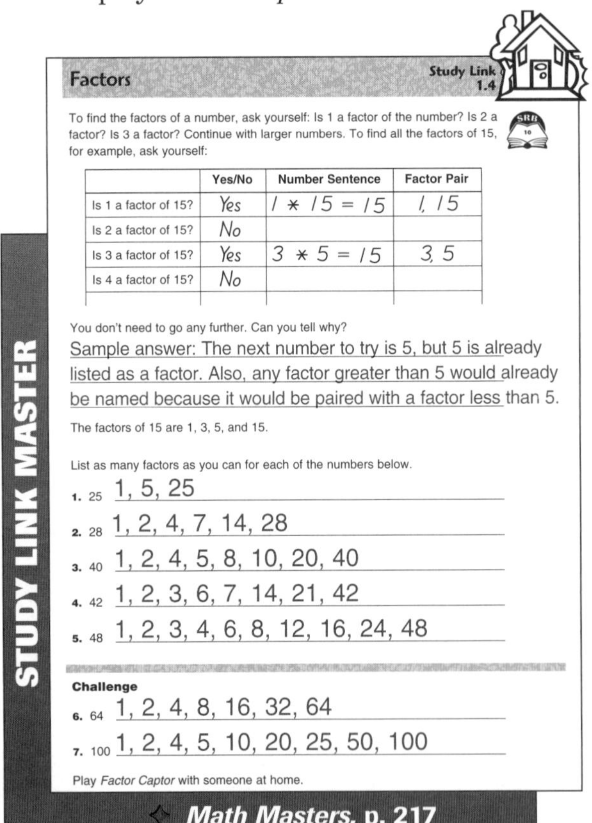

STUDY LINK MASTER

**Factors** Study Link 1.4

To find the factors of a number, ask yourself: Is 1 a factor of the number? Is 2 a factor? Is 3 a factor? Continue with larger numbers. To find all the factors of 15, for example, ask yourself:

| | Yes/No | Number Sentence | Factor Pair |
|---|---|---|---|
| Is 1 a factor of 15? | Yes | $1 * 15 = 15$ | 1, 15 |
| Is 2 a factor of 15? | No | | |
| Is 3 a factor of 15? | Yes | $3 * 5 = 15$ | 3, 5 |
| Is 4 a factor of 15? | No | | |

You don't need to go any further. Can you tell why?
Sample answer: The next number to try is 5, but 5 is already listed as a factor. Also, any factor greater than 5 would already be named because it would be paired with a factor less than 5.

The factors of 15 are 1, 3, 5, and 15.

List as many factors as you can for each of the numbers below.

1. 25 1, 5, 25
2. 28 1, 2, 4, 7, 14, 28
3. 40 1, 2, 4, 5, 8, 10, 20, 40
4. 42 1, 2, 3, 6, 7, 14, 21, 42
5. 48 1, 2, 3, 4, 6, 8, 12, 16, 24, 48

**Challenge**

6. 64 1, 2, 4, 8, 16, 32, 64
7. 100 1, 2, 4, 5, 10, 20, 25, 50, 100

Play *Factor Captor* with someone at home.

✦ *Math Masters,* p. 217

# Options for Individualizing

## ✦ ENRICHMENT Playing the Advanced Version of *Factor Captor*

(*Student Reference Book,* p. 271; *Math Masters,* p. 6)

PARTNER ACTIVITY **15–30 min**

After students have played a few games of *Factor Captor* on the beginning level, encourage them to use the more advanced grid on *Math Masters,* page 6. Some students may also want to experiment with their own number grids, using even larger numbers. Caution them that the game works best if the smaller factors are repeated several times.

You may choose to use an overhead transparency of the advanced grid to discuss strategies.

*Factor Captor* Grid 2 (Advanced Level)

| | | | | | | |
|---|---|---|---|---|---|---|
| 1 | 2 | 2 | 2 | 2 | 2 | 3 |
| 3 | 3 | 3 | 3 | 4 | 4 | 4 |
| 4 | 5 | 5 | 5 | 5 | 6 | 6 |
| 6 | 7 | 7 | 8 | 8 | 9 | 9 |
| 10 | 10 | 11 | 12 | 13 | 14 | 15 |
| 16 | 17 | 18 | 19 | 20 | 21 | 22 |
| 23 | 24 | 25 | 26 | 27 | 28 | 30 |
| 32 | 33 | 34 | 35 | 36 | 38 | 39 |
| 40 | 42 | 44 | 45 | 46 | 48 | 49 |
| 50 | 51 | 52 | 54 | 55 | 56 | 60 |

TEACHING MASTER

✦ *Math Masters,* p. 6

## ✦ LANGUAGE DIVERSITY Building Background for Mathematics Words

PARTNER ACTIVITY **15–30 min**

Unit 1 is rich in vocabulary associated with number theory. Consider pairing a student who is just learning English with a proficient English speaker to create a Number Theory Dictionary. For each word, students include a definition and an illustration or example. If students are familiar with the concept and know the equivalent word in their own language, they should add it to the dictionary entry.

# 1.5 Divisibility

**OBJECTIVES** **To test for divisibility by using a calculator; and to introduce divisibility tests for division by 2, 3, 5, 6, 9, and 10.**

| summaries | materials |
| --- | --- |
| **1 Teaching the Lesson** | |
| Students make a factor rainbow to organize and display all the factors of a number; use a calculator to test for divisibility by a whole number; and learn and practice divisibility tests that do not require a calculator. [Operations and Computation] | □ *Math Journal 1,* pp. 12 and 13<br>□ Study Link 1.4<br>□ Assessment Master (*Math Masters,* p. 479) optional<br>□ calculator □ overhead calculator (optional) |
| **2 Ongoing Learning & Practice** | |
| Students continue the multiplication facts routine to practice instant recall of the facts. They find factors of numbers by playing the *Factor Captor* game. [Operations and Computation]<br>Students practice and maintain skills through Math Boxes and Study Link activities. | □ *Math Journal 1,* pp. 8 and 14<br>□ *Student Reference Book,* p. 271<br>□ Teaching Master (*Math Masters,* p. 3), for teacher only<br>□ Study Link Master (*Math Masters,* p. 218)<br>□ *Factor Captor* Grids 1 and 2 (*Math Masters,* pp. 5 and 6)<br>□ counters |
| **3 Options for Individualizing** | |
| **Enrichment** Students investigate a test for divisibility by 4. [Operations and Computation]<br>**Language Diversity** Students define the word *rainbow* in their own words, and discuss why *factor rainbow* is a good name for listing factor pairs of a number. [Numeration] | □ Teaching Master (*Math Masters,* p. 7)<br>□ calculator<br>□ dictionary |

## Additional Information

**Background Information** The emphasis in Lessons 1.2–1.5 is on developing students' factoring skills. In the remainder of the unit, students will use these skills to investigate the properties of prime, composite, and square numbers. For additional information on these topics, see the *Teacher's Reference Manual.*

**Vocabulary** • **factor rainbow** • **divisible** • **quotient** • **divisibility test**

# Getting Started

### Math Message

*Solve Problems 1 and 2 at the top of journal page 12.*

## Study Link 1.4 Follow-Up

Go over the answers. A good way to check for errors is to make a **factor rainbow.** For example, to make a factor rainbow for the number 48, list all the factors of 48 in ascending order. Then connect factor pairs (see art at the right). Every factor should be paired with another factor. If there is an odd number of factors, the middle factor is paired with itself. The product of each pair of factors should be 48.

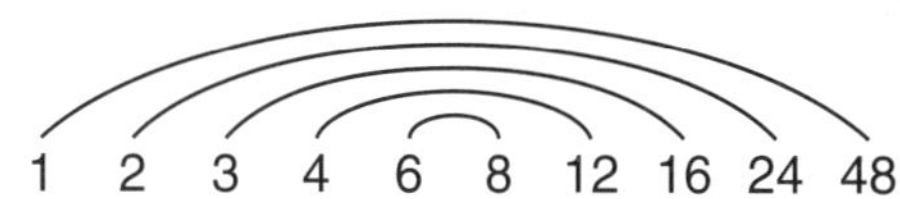


# 1 Teaching the Lesson

## Math Message Follow-Up

WHOLE-CLASS DISCUSSION

Students share solution strategies. Most will realize that the numbers divisible by 2 are even numbers—numbers that end in 0, 2, 4, 6, or 8.

## Using a Calculator to Test for Divisibility by a Whole Number (*Math Journal 1,* p. 12)

INDEPENDENT ACTIVITY 

Remind students that a whole number is **divisible** by a whole number if the remainder in the division is zero. The result (the **quotient** of the numbers) must be a whole number. If the remainder is not zero, then the first number is *not* divisible by the second number.

When testing for divisibility with a calculator that does not display remainders, the first number is not divisible by the second number if the quotient has a decimal part. For example, 27 is not divisible by 5, because the result is 5.4—not a whole number.

Students complete Problems 3–10 on the journal page. This should not take more than 5 or 10 minutes.

## Introducing Divisibility Tests (*Math Journal 1,* p. 13)

WHOLE-CLASS ACTIVITY

Most students probably know that a number is divisible by 2 if it ends in 0, 2, 4, 6, or 8, and that it is divisible by 10 if it ends in 0. There are also tests to determine whether a whole number is divisible by 3, 5, 6, or 9.

NOTE: If your students are using calculators that can display an answer to a division problem as a quotient along with a whole-number remainder, you might want to demonstrate the procedure. With the TI-15 calculator, this is done by pressing the [Int÷] key instead of the [÷] key. For example, if you press 27 [Int÷] 5 [=], the display will show a quotient of 5 with a remainder of 2.

If possible, try to use an overhead calculator to demonstrate how to perform more demanding exercises.

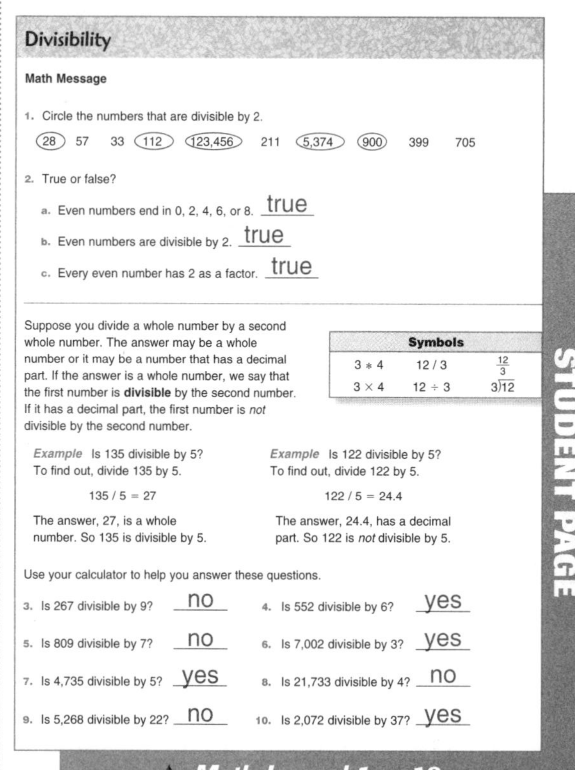

**Divisibility**

**Math Message**

1. Circle the numbers that are divisible by 2.

(28) 57 33 (112) (123,456) 211 (5,374) (900) 399 705

2. True or false?

a. Even numbers end in 0, 2, 4, 6, or 8. true

b. Even numbers are divisible by 2. true

c. Every even number has 2 as a factor. true

Suppose you divide a whole number by a second whole number. The answer may be a whole number or it may be a number that has a decimal part. If the answer is a whole number, we say that the first number is **divisible** by the second number. If it has a decimal part, the first number is *not* divisible by the second number.

| Symbols | | |
|---|---|---|
| 3 ∗ 4 | 12 / 3 | $\frac{12}{3}$ |
| 3 × 4 | 12 ÷ 3 | $3\overline{)12}$ |

*Example* Is 135 divisible by 5?
To find out, divide 135 by 5.

135 / 5 = 27

The answer, 27, is a whole number. So 135 is divisible by 5.

*Example* Is 122 divisible by 5?
To find out, divide 122 by 5.

122 / 5 = 24.4

The answer, 24.4, has a decimal part. So 122 is *not* divisible by 5.

Use your calculator to help you answer these questions.

3. Is 267 divisible by 9? no
4. Is 552 divisible by 6? yes
5. Is 809 divisible by 7? no
6. Is 7,002 divisible by 3? yes
7. Is 4,735 divisible by 5? yes
8. Is 21,733 divisible by 4? no
9. Is 5,268 divisible by 22? no
10. Is 2,072 divisible by 37? yes

STUDENT PAGE

Math Journal 1, p. 12

STUDENT PAGE

## Divisibility Tests

For many numbers, even large ones, it is possible to test for divisibility without actually dividing.

Here are the most useful divisibility tests:

- All numbers are **divisible by 1.**
- All even numbers (ending in 0, 2, 4, 6, or 8) are **divisible by 2.**
- A number is **divisible by 3** if the sum of its digits is divisible by 3.
  *Example* 246 is divisible by 3 because 2 + 4 + 6 = 12, and 12 is divisible by 3.
- A number is **divisible by 6** if it is divisible by both 2 and 3.
  *Example* 246 is divisible by 6 because it is divisible by 2 and by 3.
- A number is **divisible by 9** if the sum of its digits is divisible by 9.
  *Example* 51,372 is divisible by 9 because 5 + 1 + 3 + 7 + 2 = 18, and 18 is divisible by 9.
- A number is **divisible by 5** if it ends in 0 or 5.
- A number is **divisible by 10** if it ends in 0.

1. Test each number below for divisibility. Then check on your calculator.

| | Divisible... | | | | | |
|---|---|---|---|---|---|---|
| **Number** | by 2? | by 3? | by 6? | by 9? | by 5? | by 10? |
| 75 | | ✓ | | | ✓ | |
| 7,960 | ✓ | | | | ✓ | ✓ |
| 384 | ✓ | ✓ | ✓ | | | |
| 3,725 | | | | | ✓ | |
| 90 | ✓ | ✓ | ✓ | ✓ | ✓ | ✓ |
| 36,297 | | ✓ | | ✓ | | |

2. Find a 3-digit number that is divisible by both 3 and 5.
Sample answers: 735; 540

3. Find a 4-digit number that is divisible by both 6 and 9.
Sample answers: 1,800; 5,454

✦ *Math Journal 1,* **p. 13**

**ONGOING ASSESSMENT**

**Have students complete an Exit Slip explaining how they found the answer to Problem 3 on p.13. Any explanation must show that the answer is divisible by 2, 3, and 9.**

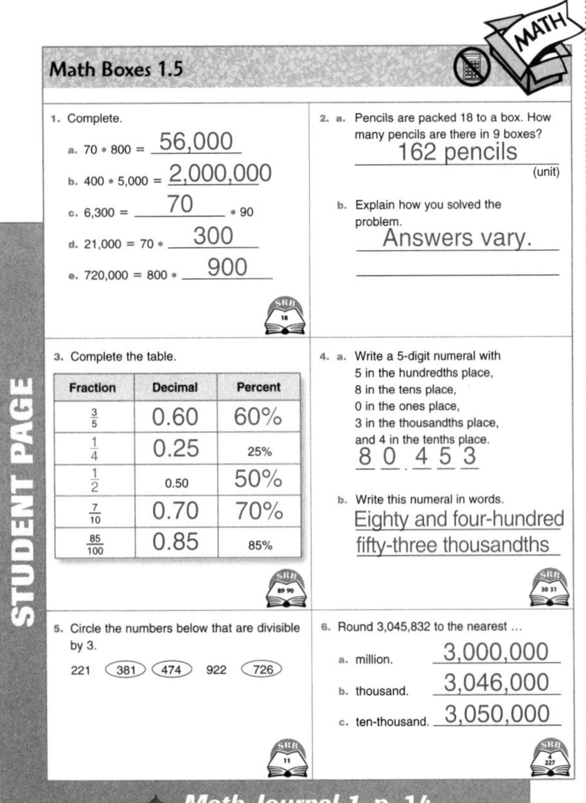

STUDENT PAGE

## Math Boxes 1.5

1. Complete.
   a. 70 ∗ 800 = 56,000
   b. 400 ∗ 5,000 = 2,000,000
   c. 6,300 = 70 ∗ 90
   d. 21,000 = 70 ∗ 300
   e. 720,000 = 800 ∗ 900

2. a. Pencils are packed 18 to a box. How many pencils are there in 9 boxes?
   162 pencils (unit)
   b. Explain how you solved the problem.
   Answers vary.

3. Complete the table.

| Fraction | Decimal | Percent |
|---|---|---|
| $\frac{3}{5}$ | 0.60 | 60% |
| $\frac{1}{4}$ | 0.25 | 25% |
| $\frac{1}{2}$ | 0.50 | 50% |
| $\frac{7}{10}$ | 0.70 | 70% |
| $\frac{85}{100}$ | 0.85 | 85% |

4. a. Write a 5-digit numeral with 5 in the hundredths place, 8 in the tens place, 0 in the ones place, 3 in the thousandths place, and 4 in the tenths place.
   8 0 . 4 5 3
   b. Write this numeral in words.
   Eighty and four-hundred fifty-three thousandths

5. Circle the numbers below that are divisible by 3.
   221 (381) (474) 922 (726)

6. Round 3,045,832 to the nearest ...
   a. million. 3,000,000
   b. thousand. 3,046,000
   c. ten-thousand. 3,050,000

✦ *Math Journal 1,* **p. 14**

You might use the following routine to introduce the **divisibility test** for division by 3:

1. Go over the description of the divisibility-by-3 test on journal page 13: A number is divisible by 3 if the sum of its digits is divisible by 3.
2. Illustrate with several examples.
   - Is 237 divisible by 3? Yes, because 2 + 3 + 7 = 12, and 12 is divisible by 3.
   - Is 415 divisible by 3? No, because 4 + 1 + 5 = 10, and 10 is not divisible by 3.
3. Ask students to provide examples of a number that is divisible by 3 and a number that is not. Encourage them to apply the divisibility-by-3 test and check that it works by carrying out the division on their calculators.

Introduce each of the other divisibility tests in the same way.

### ✦ Practicing with Divisibility Tests
(*Math Journal 1,* p. 13; *Math Masters,* p. 479)

PARTNER ACTIVITY

Students complete Problems 1–3 independently. Then they check each other's work.

## 2 Ongoing Learning & Practice

### ✦ Practicing the Multiplication Facts Routine
(*Math Journal 1,* p. 8; *Math Masters,* p. 3)

WHOLE-CLASS ACTIVITY

Select another 16 problems from *Math Masters,* page 3 for a multiplication facts quiz. Repeat problems that you circled on the previous quiz because they were missed most frequently. See Lesson 1.3.

### ✦ Playing *Factor Captor* (*Student Reference Book,* p. 271; *Math Masters,* pp. 5 and 6)

PARTNER ACTIVITY

Students can use the number grid on *Math Masters,* page 5 or the grid on *Math Masters,* page 6 if they are ready to move on to a more advanced level of the game. If students play the advanced level, they could limit the gameboard by leaving out the last two rows. Later on, students can use all but the last row, and, finally, the entire number grid. As more numbers are used, the scoring rules increasingly reward a player for planning ahead and anticipating an opponent's moves.

## ◆ Math Boxes 1.5 (*Math Journal 1,* p. 14)

INDEPENDENT ACTIVITY 

**Mixed Review** Math Boxes in this lesson are paired with Math Boxes in Lessons 1.7 and 1.9. The skill in Problem 1 is a prerequisite for Unit 2.

## ◆ Study Link 1.5 (*Math Masters,* p. 218)

**Home Connection** Students use divisibility tests to check whether numbers are divisible by 2, 3, 5, 6, 9, or 10. They learn the divisibility rule for 4 and check whether these numbers are also divisible by 4.

**Divisibility Tests** — Study Link 1.5

- All even numbers are **divisible by 2.**
- A number is **divisible by 3** if the sum of its digits is divisible by 3.
- A number is **divisible by 6** if it is divisible by both 2 and 3.
- A number is **divisible by 9** if the sum of its digits is divisible by 9.
- A number is **divisible by 10** if it ends in 0.
- A number is **divisible by 5** if it ends in 0 or 5.

1. Use divisibility tests to check whether the following numbers are divisible by 2, 3, 5, 6, 9, or 10.

| Number | Divisible ... | | | | | |
|---|---|---|---|---|---|---|
| | by 2? | by 3? | by 6? | by 9? | by 5? | by 10? |
| *998,876 | ✓ | | | | | |
| 5,890 | ✓ | | | | ✓ | ✓ |
| *72,344 | ✓ | | | | | |
| *36,540 | ✓ | ✓ | ✓ | ✓ | ✓ | ✓ |
| 861 | | ✓ | | | | |
| 33,015 | | ✓ | | | ✓ | |
| 1,098 | ✓ | ✓ | ✓ | ✓ | | |
| 45,369 | | ✓ | | ✓ | | |
| 4,009,721 | | | | | | |

A number is divisible by 4 if the tens and ones digits form a number that is divisible by 4.

***Example*** 47,8**36** is divisible by 4, because 36 is divisible by 4.

It isn't always easy to tell whether the last two digits form a number that is divisible by 4. A quick way to check is to divide the number by 2, and then divide the result by 2. This is the same as dividing by 4, but it is often easier to do mentally.

***Example*** 5,3**84** is divisible by 4, because 84 / 2 = 42 and 42 / 2 = 21.

***Example*** **922** is not divisible by 4, because 22 / 2 = 11, but 11 / 2 = $5\frac{1}{2}$.

**Challenge**

2. Put a star next to any number in the table that is divisible by 4.

STUDY LINK MASTER

**Math Masters, p. 218**

# 3 Options for Individualizing

## ◆ ENRICHMENT Exploring a Divisibility Test by 4 (*Math Masters,* p. 7)

PARTNER ACTIVITY  **15–30 min**

Students use their knowledge of place value to discover why only the last 2 digits in a number determine whether the number is divisible by 4. They identify a test for divisibility by 4.

**Divisibility by 4**

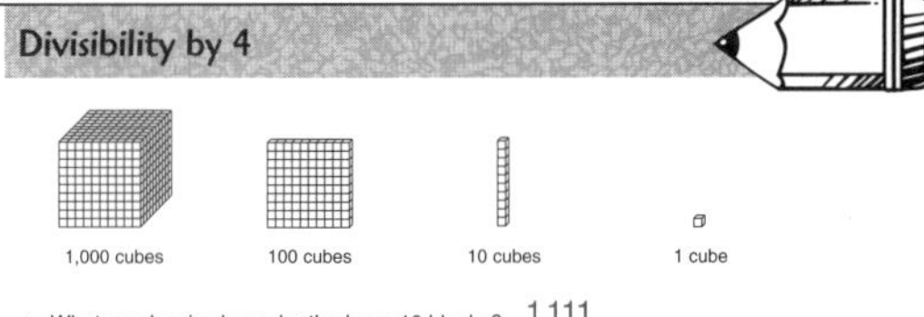


1. What number is shown by the base-10 blocks? 1,111
2. Which of the base-10 blocks could be divided evenly into 4 piles of cubes? The groups of 1,000 cubes and 100 cubes
3. Is the number shown by the base-10 blocks divisible by 4? no
4. Circle the numbers that you think are divisible by 4.
   (324) 5,821 7,430 (35,782,916)
   Use a calculator to check your answers.

**Challenge**

5. Use what you know about base-10 blocks to explain why you only need to look at the last two digits of a number to decide if it is divisible by 4.
   Sample answer: The numbers that the thousands place and the hundreds place represent are always divisible by 4. So you only have to look at the number formed by the tens and ones digits.
6. Complete the following statement:
   A number is divisible by 4 if the tens and ones digits form a number divisible by 4.

TEACHING MASTER

**Math Masters, p. 7**

## ◆ LANGUAGE DIVERSITY Building Background for Mathematics Words

PARTNER ACTIVITY  **15–30 min**

Pair a student just learning English with a proficient English speaker. Have them look up the term *rainbow* in the dictionary and summarize the definition in their own words. Then ask them to draw a rainbow.

*Example:* An arc of color that is seen in the sky opposite the sun, especially after it rains. It is caused by the sun's rays shining through tiny drops of water.

When listing all of the factor pairs of a number, students are encouraged to make a *factor rainbow.* Have students discuss why *factor rainbow* is a good name for this strategy.

# 1.6 Prime and Composite Numbers

**OBJECTIVES To discuss prime and composite numbers; and to classify whole numbers as prime or composite numbers.**

| summaries | materials |
| --- | --- |
| **1 Teaching the Lesson** | |
| Students use arrays and factor rainbows to develop definitions for prime and composite numbers; classify the numbers 2 through 39 as prime or composite by listing the factors for each number; and use their understanding of prime numbers to develop strategies for playing *Factor Captor.* [Numeration; Operations and Computation] | □ *Math Journal 1,* pp. 15 and 16<br>□ *Student Reference Book,* p. 271<br>□ Study Link 1.5<br>□ Teaching Master (*Math Masters,* p. 1)<br>□ Class Data Pad (optional)<br>***See* Advance Preparation** |
| **2 Ongoing Learning & Practice** | |
| Students continue the multiplication facts routine to practice instant recall of the facts. They also practice multiplication facts by playing *Baseball Multiplication, Multiplication Top-It,* and *Beat the Calculator.* [Operations and Computation]<br>Students practice and maintain skills through Math Boxes and Study Link activities. | □ *Math Journal 1,* pp. 8 and 17<br>□ *Student Reference Book,* pp. 259–261 and 295<br>□ Teaching Master (*Math Masters,* p. 3), for teacher only<br>□ Study Link Master (*Math Masters,* p. 219)<br>□ *Baseball Multiplication* Playing Mat (*Math Masters,* p. 4)<br>□ Fact Triangles (cut from *Math Journal 1,* Activity Sheets 1 and 2)<br>Per partnership:<br>□ 4 each of the number cards 1–10 (from the Everything Math Deck, if available)<br>□ a Multiplication/Division Facts Table (optional)<br>□ calculator; 2 regular dice; 4 pennies |
| **3 Options for Individualizing** | |
| **Enrichment** Students investigate Goldbach's Conjecture by expressing whole numbers as the sum of two prime numbers. [Numeration]<br>**Extra Practice** Students apply their understanding of prime numbers to play the advanced version of *Factor Captor.* [Numeration; Operations and Computation] | □ *Student Reference Book,* p. 271<br>□ Teaching Master (*Math Masters,* p. 8)<br>Per partnership:<br>□ *Factor Captor* Grid 2 (*Math Masters,* p. 6)<br>□ 70 counters |

## Additional Information

**Background Information** The emphasis in Lessons 1.2–1.5 has been on developing students' factoring skills. In the remainder of the unit, students will use these skills to explore the properties of prime, composite, and square numbers. For additional information on these topics, see the *Teacher's Reference Manual.*

**Advance Preparation** For Part 1, make a copy of *Math Masters,* page 1 for each pair of students. Cut the copies in half and place them near the Math Message.

**Vocabulary** • **composite number** • **prime number**

# Getting Started

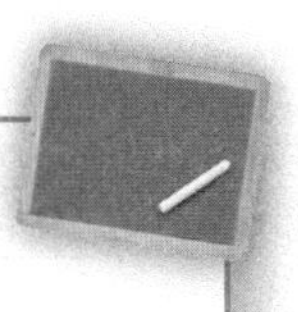

### Math Message

*Take a sheet of dot paper.*
*Do the following:*

1. *Draw all the arrays you can to show these numbers: 4, 10, 16.*
2. *Draw all the arrays you can to show these numbers: 2, 5, 11.*

### Study Link 1.5 Follow-Up

Partners compare answers. Then, using a calculator, they check the answers on which they disagree.

# 1 Teaching the Lesson

## ◆ Math Message Follow-Up

WHOLE-CLASS DISCUSSION 

Draw a vertical line on the board. Use the left side for the numbers 4, 10, and 16 and the right side for the numbers 2, 5, and 11. With the help of the class, record all possible arrays and the factor rainbow for each number. *(See the margin.)*

## ◆ Defining Prime and Composite Numbers

WHOLE-CLASS ACTIVITY

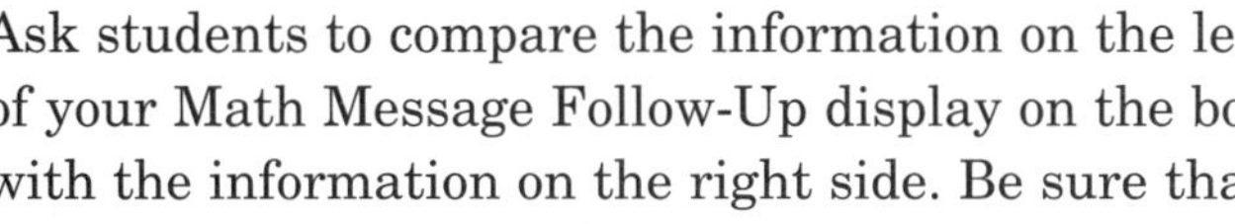

Ask students to compare the information on the left side of your Math Message Follow-Up display on the board with the information on the right side. Be sure that the following observations are included in the discussion:

▷ Each number on the right side is represented by exactly two arrays. Each array has either one row or one column. Each number on the left side is represented by more than two arrays. At least one array has more than one row *and* more than one column.

**4-dot arrays**
1 by 4
2 by 2
4 by 1

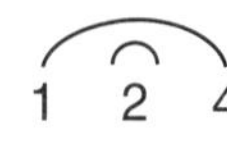

1 2 4

**10-dot arrays**
1 by 10
2 by 5
5 by 2
10 by 1

1 2 5 10

**16-dot arrays**
1 by 16
2 by 8
4 by 4
8 by 2
16 by 1

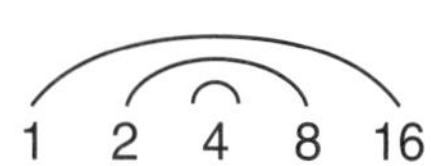

1 2 4 8 16

**2-dot arrays**
1 by 2
2 by 1

1 2

**5-dot arrays**
1 by 5
5 by 1

1 5

**11-dot arrays**
1 by 11
11 by 1

1 11

STUDENT PAGE

## Prime and Composite Numbers

A **prime number** has exactly two factors—1 and the number itself.
A **composite number** has more than two factors.

1. List all the factors of each number in the table. Write P if it is a prime number or C if it is a composite number.

| Number | Factors | P or C | Number | Factors | P or C |
|---|---|---|---|---|---|
| 2 | 1, 2 | P | 21 | 1, 3, 7, 21 | C |
| 3 | 1, 3 | P | 22 | 1, 2, 11, 22 | C |
| 4 | 1, 2, 4 | C | 23 | 1, 23 | P |
| 5 | 1, 5 | P | 24 | 1, 2, 3, 4, 6, 8, 12, 24 | C |
| 6 | 1, 2, 3, 6 | C | 25 | 1, 5, 25 | C |
| 7 | 1, 7 | P | 26 | 1, 2, 13, 26 | C |
| 8 | 1, 2, 4, 8 | C | 27 | 1, 3, 9, 27 | C |
| 9 | 1, 3, 9 | C | 28 | 1, 2, 4, 7, 14, 28 | C |
| 10 | 1, 2, 5, 10 | C | 29 | 1, 29 | P |
| 11 | 1, 11 | P | 30 | 1, 2, 3, 5, 6, 10, 15, 30 | C |
| 12 | 1, 2, 3, 4, 6, 12 | C | 31 | 1, 31 | P |
| 13 | 1, 13 | P | 32 | 1, 2, 4, 8, 16, 32 | C |
| 14 | 1, 2, 7, 14 | C | 33 | 1, 3, 11, 33 | C |
| 15 | 1, 3, 5, 15 | C | 34 | 1, 2, 17, 34 | C |
| 16 | 1, 2, 4, 8, 16 | C | 35 | 1, 5, 7, 35 | C |
| 17 | 1, 17 | P | 36 | 1, 2, 3, 4, 6, 9, 12, 18, 36 | C |
| 18 | 1, 2, 3, 6, 9, 18 | C | 37 | 1, 37 | P |
| 19 | 1, 19 | P | 38 | 1, 2, 19, 38 | C |
| 20 | 1, 2, 4, 5, 10, 20 | C | 39 | 1, 3, 13, 39 | C |

2. How many factors does each prime number have? two

3. Can a composite number have exactly 2 factors? no

If yes, give an example of such a composite number. ______

✦ *Math Journal 1*, p. 15

STUDENT PAGE

## *Factor Captor* Strategies

Work alone to answer the questions below. Then compare your answers with your partner's. If your answers don't agree with your partner's answers, try to convince your partner that your answers are correct.

| 1 | 2 | 3 | 4 | 5 | 6 | 7 | 8 | 9 | 10 |
|---|---|---|---|---|---|---|---|---|---|
| 11 | 12 | 13 | 14 | 15 | 16 | 17 | 18 | 19 | 20 |
| 21 | 22 | 23 | 24 | 25 | 26 | 27 | 28 | 29 | 30 |

1. Suppose you played *Factor Captor* using the above number grid. No numbers have been covered yet. Which is the best number choice you could make? Why?
Sample answer: I could cover 29 and score 29 points. My opponent could then cover only 1 and would score 1 point.

2. Suppose that the 29 and 1 squares have already been covered. Which is the best number choice you could make? Why?
Sample answer: I could cover 23 and score 23 points. My opponent could not cover any number and would score 0 points.

3. Suppose that the 29, 23, and 1 squares have already been covered. Which is the best number choice you could make? Why?
Sample answer: I could cover 25 and score 25 points. My opponent could then cover only 5 and would score 5 points.

✦ *Math Journal 1*, p. 16

▷ Each number on the right side has exactly two factors. Each number on the left side has more than two factors.

Tell students that the numbers on the left side are called **composite numbers** and the numbers on the right side are called **prime numbers.** Summarize as follows:

- A **prime number** has exactly two factors—1 and the number itself.
- A **composite number** has more than two factors.

The number 1 is neither prime nor composite. This is a mathematical convention—something upon which all mathematicians and other people agree.

## ✦ Classifying Prime and Composite Numbers
(*Math Journal 1,* p. 15)

PARTNER ACTIVITY 

Assign journal page 15. Students first find all of the factors for each number; then they classify the number as prime (if there are exactly 2 factors) or composite (if there are more than 2 factors).

Bring the class together to go over the answers. List the prime numbers through 39 on the board or Class Data Pad. 2, 3, 5, 7, 11, 13, 17, 19, 23, 29, 31, 37

**Adjusting the Activity** As an ongoing project for the rest of the unit, ask students to look for other prime numbers to be added to the list. Keep this class list of prime numbers on display. Whenever a new prime-number candidate is proposed, the class should check that it is a prime number by looking for factors of the number other than 1 and the number itself. The next five prime numbers to add to the list are 41, 43, 47, 53, and 59.

## ✦ Developing a Strategy for *Factor Captor*
(*Math Journal 1,* p. 16; *Student Reference Book,* p. 271)

PARTNER ACTIVITY 

Students determine the best first three moves for a game of *Factor Captor* played on a number grid consisting of the whole numbers up to 30. (See Lesson 1.4 for detailed instructions.) Encourage students to find these moves on their own and then to discuss their solutions with their partners. Students should conclude that it is usually (though not always) to their advantage to cover the highest available prime number, since a prime number has only the factor 1 besides itself.

*Example:* The best choice for a first move is 29, since it results in a score of 29 against a score of 1 for the other player, for a *net score* of 28. Some students may have chosen 30, but this would result in a score of 42 for the other player, since the available factors of 30 are 1, 2, 3, 5, 6, 10, and 15.

The best choice for a second move is 23—which results in a net score of 23, because the number 1 has already been covered.

The best choice for a third move is 25, since it results in a net score of 20—because the other player can cover only the 5. Some students may have chosen 19, with a net score of 19, having concluded that the best move is always to choose the highest available prime number—not in this case!

**Adjusting the Activity** To extend the *Factor Captor* activity, discuss situations that result in negative net scores. For example, if player 1 scores 30 and player 2 scores 42, then player 1's net score is −12.

## 2 Ongoing Learning & Practice

Choose one or more of the following activities for assessing and practicing the multiplication facts.

### ✦ Practicing the Multiplication Facts Routine (*Math Journal 1,* p. 8; *Math Masters,* p. 3)

WHOLE-CLASS ACTIVITY

Select another 16 problems from *Math Masters,* page 3 for a multiplication facts quiz. Repeat problems that you circled on *Math Masters,* page 3 because they were missed most frequently. See Lesson 1.3 for additional directions.

NOTE: The TI-15 calculator can also be used for practicing basic facts. See *Math Masters,* pages 480 and 481.

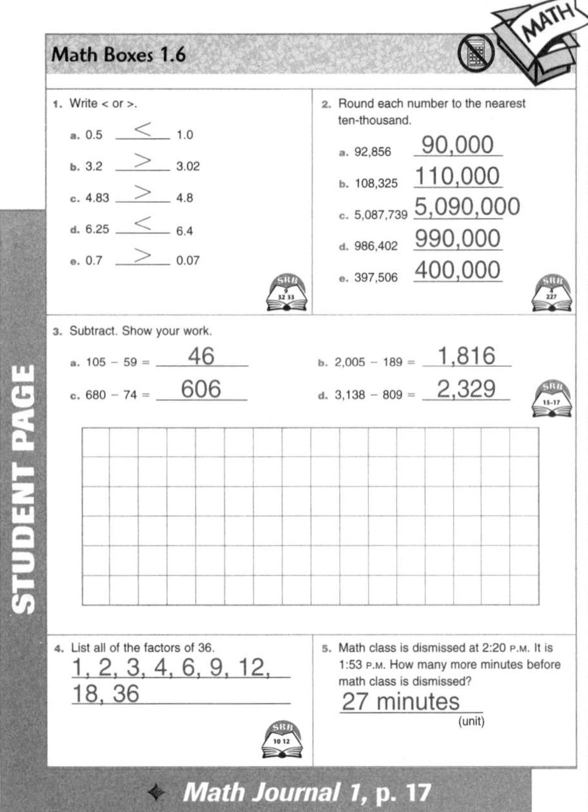

Math Boxes 1.6

1. Write < or >.
   a. 0.5 < 1.0
   b. 3.2 > 3.02
   c. 4.83 > 4.8
   d. 6.25 < 6.4
   e. 0.7 > 0.07

2. Round each number to the nearest ten-thousand.
   a. 92,856 90,000
   b. 108,325 110,000
   c. 5,087,739 5,090,000
   d. 986,402 990,000
   e. 397,506 400,000

3. Subtract. Show your work.
   a. 105 − 59 = 46
   b. 2,005 − 189 = 1,816
   c. 680 − 74 = 606
   d. 3,138 − 809 = 2,329

4. List all of the factors of 36.
   1, 2, 3, 4, 6, 9, 12, 18, 36

5. Math class is dismissed at 2:20 P.M. It is 1:53 P.M. How many more minutes before math class is dismissed?
   27 minutes (unit)

STUDENT PAGE

Math Journal 1, p. 17

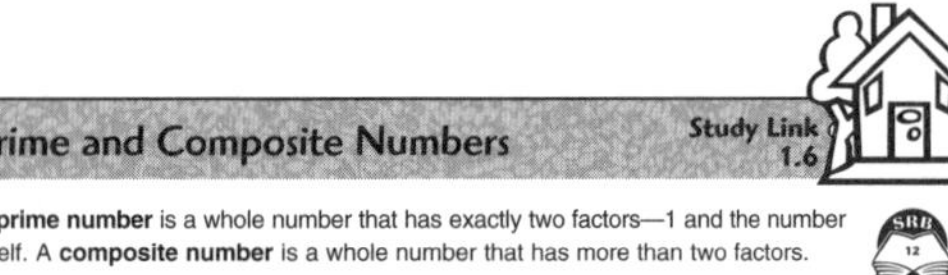

Prime and Composite Numbers — Study Link 1.6

A **prime number** is a whole number that has exactly two factors—1 and the number itself. A **composite number** is a whole number that has more than two factors.

1. Tell whether the following numbers are **prime** or **composite**.
   a. The number of quarts in a gallon composite
   b. The number of months in a year composite
   c. The number of days in a week prime
   d. The number of sides in a hexagon composite
   e. The number of sides in a pentagon prime

2. For each number:
   - list all of its factors
   - tell whether the number is prime or composite
   - circle any of the factors that are prime numbers

| Number | Factors | Prime or Composite? |
|---|---|---|
| 11 | 1, (11) | P |
| 18 | 1, (2) (3) 6, 9, 18 | C |
| 24 | 1, (2) (3) 4, 6, 8, 12, 24 | C |
| 28 | 1, (2) 4, (7) 14, 28 | C |
| 36 | 1, (2) (3) 4, 6, 9, 12, 18, 36 | C |
| 49 | 1, (7) 49 | C |
| 50 | 1, (2) (5) 10, 25, 50 | C |
| 70 | 1, (2) (5) (7) 10, 14, 35, 70 | C |
| 100 | 1, (2) 4, (5) 10, 20, 25, 50, 100 | C |

STUDY LINK MASTER

Math Masters, p. 219

## Using Fact Triangles to Practice Multiplication Facts
(*Math Journal 1,* Activity Sheets 1 and 2)

PARTNER ACTIVITY 

Students use Fact Triangles to help them memorize the facts they don't know.

## Practicing Multiplication Facts through Games
(*Student Reference Book,* pp. 259–261 and 295)

PARTNER ACTIVITY 

Students play *Multiplication Top-It, Beat the Calculator,* and *Baseball Multiplication* to practice the multiplication facts. The rules for these games are in the *Student Reference Book.*

## Math Boxes 1.6 (*Math Journal 1,* p. 17)

INDEPENDENT ACTIVITY 

**Mixed Review** Math Boxes in this lesson are paired with Math Boxes in Lesson 1.8. The skill in Problem 1 is a prerequisite for Unit 2.

## Study Link 1.6 (*Math Masters,* p. 219)

**Home Connection** Students identify numbers related to measurement and geometry as prime or composite. Then students find the factors of whole numbers and identify the numbers as prime or composite numbers.

# 3 Options for Individualizing

## ENRICHMENT Investigating Goldbach's Conjecture (*Math Masters,* p. 8)

PARTNER ACTIVITY  15–30 min 

**Social Studies Link** Christian Goldbach, who lived in the eighteenth century, had a theory—Goldbach's Conjecture—that every even number greater than 2 can be written as the sum of two prime numbers. This conjecture may be true, but no one has ever proved it. Students investigate Goldbach's Conjecture by writing whole numbers as the sum of two prime numbers.

Portfolio Ideas

## EXTRA PRACTICE Playing the Advanced Version of *Factor Captor*

*Student Reference Book,* p. 271; *Math Masters,* p. 6)

PARTNER ACTIVITY  15–30 min 

Students play *Factor Captor* on the advanced grid. Encourage them to consider strategies for making "best" moves. For detailed instructions, see Lesson 1.4.

**Goldbach's Conjecture** 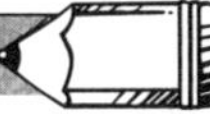

1. Write each of the following numbers as the sum of two prime numbers. Sample answers:

*Examples* 56 = 43 + 13 26 = 13 + 13

a. 6 = 3 + 3 b. 12 = 7 + 5

c. 18 = 13 + 5 d. 22 = 11 + 11

e. 24 = 17 + 7 f. 34 = 17 + 17

The answers to these problems are examples of **Goldbach's Conjecture.** Christian Goldbach lived in the eighteenth century. He had a theory that every even number greater than 2 can be written as the sum of two prime numbers.

A **conjecture** is something you believe is true even though you can't be certain that it is true. Goldbach's Conjecture may be true, but no one has ever proved it. Anyone who can either prove or disprove Goldbach's Conjecture will become famous.

2. Can any of the numbers above be written as the sum of two prime numbers in more than one way? If so, give an example. Show all possible ways.
18: 7 + 11; 24: 19 + 5, 11 + 13
22: 19 + 3, 5 + 17; 34: 29 + 5, 11 + 23, 3 + 31

**Challenge**

3. Write 70 as the sum of two primes in as many ways as you can.
3 + 67, 11 + 59, 17 + 53, 23 + 47, 29 + 41

TEACHING MASTER

Math Masters 1, p. 8

# 1.7 Square Numbers

**OBJECTIVES** **To represent square numbers as square arrays and as numbers written with exponents; and to introduce the exponent key on a calculator.**

| summaries | materials |
|---|---|
| **1 Teaching the Lesson** | |
| Students form arrays to identify square numbers and investigate properties of square numbers; use exponential notation to represent square numbers; and use the exponent key on a calculator. [Numeration; Operations and Computation] | □ *Math Journal 1,* pp. 18 and 19<br>□ Study Link 1.6<br>□ Teaching Master (*Math Masters,* p. 1; optional)<br>□ counters (25 per student) □ calculator<br>***See* Advance Preparation** |
| **2 Ongoing Learning & Practice** | |
| Students continue the multiplication facts routine to practice instant recall of the facts. [Operations and Computation]<br>Students practice finding the factors of whole numbers by playing *Factor Top-It.* [Operations and Computation; Numeration]<br>Students practice and maintain skills through Math Boxes and Study Link activities. | □ *Math Journal 1,* pp. 8 and 20<br>□ *Student Reference Book,* p. 272<br>□ Teaching Master (*Math Masters,* p. 3), for teacher only<br>□ Study Link Master (*Math Masters,* p. 220)<br>□ 4 each of the number cards 0–9 (from the Everything Math Deck, if available) per partnership |
| **3 Options for Individualizing** | |
| **Reteaching** Students use centimeter grid paper to make arrays. [Numeration; Operations and Computation]<br>**Enrichment** Students complete visual and number patterns. [Patterns, Functions, and Algebra] | □ Teaching Masters (*Math Masters,* pp. 2 and 9) |

**Additional Information**

**Advance Preparation** For Part 1, check to see whether the calculators your students are using have a [^] key.

**Vocabulary** • **square array** • **square number** • **exponential notation** • **exponent key** [^] • **exponent**

## Getting Started

### Math Message

*Use your counters. Try to make a rectangular array that has an equal number of rows and columns for each of the following numbers:*

*14 16 18*

*For which numbers were you able to make this kind of array?*

### Study Link 1.6 Follow-Up

Briefly go over the answers.

# 1 Teaching the Lesson

## ✦ Math Message Follow-Up

WHOLE-CLASS DISCUSSION

Of the three numbers, 16 is the only one that can be represented by an array that has the same number of rows and columns. A 4-by-4 array Ask someone to draw this array on the board and to draw a square around it. Because this array is shaped like a square, it is called a **square array,** and the number it represents is called a **square number.** The number 16 is a square number.

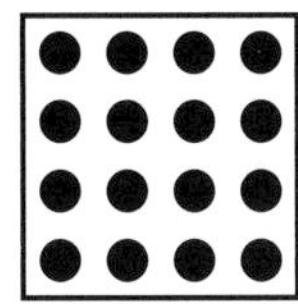

## ✦ Finding Other Square Numbers

WHOLE-CLASS ACTIVITY

Draw arrays for the numbers 1 and 4 on the board *(see the margin)*. Draw a square around each array.

Students may argue that the single dot for 1 is not an array. However, it should be thought of as a square array having one row and one column, each containing one dot. The second square array has two rows and two columns, each containing two dots. These arrays represent the first two square numbers, 1 and 4.

Ask someone to draw the next square array *(see the margin)*. How many rows and how many columns does the array have? 3 What square number does this array represent? 9

Repeat for the next square number. 4-by-4 array for 16

## ✦ Investigating the Properties of Square Numbers
(*Math Journal 1,* pp. 18 and 19; *Math Masters,* p. 1)

PARTNER ACTIVITY

On journal page 18, students list all square numbers through 100. Students should complete this page on their own, and then compare their answers with their partners'.

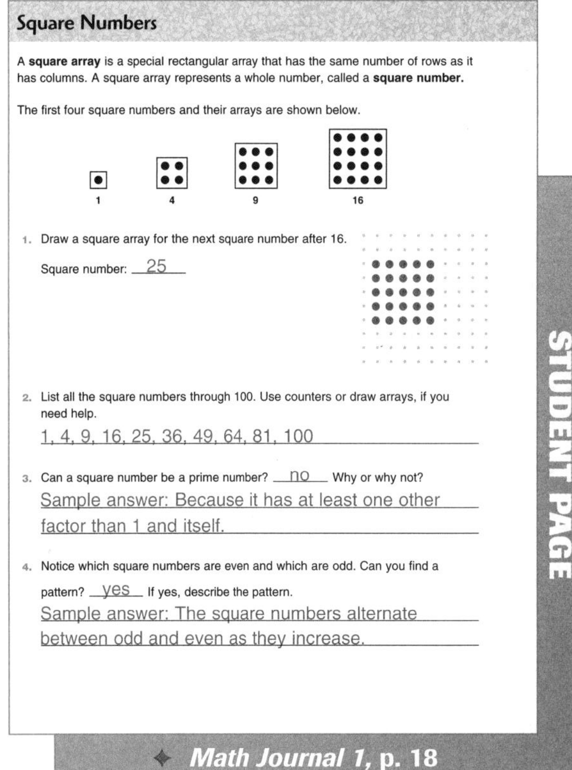

**Square Numbers**

A **square array** is a special rectangular array that has the same number of rows as it has columns. A square array represents a whole number, called a **square number.**

The first four square numbers and their arrays are shown below.

1 4 9 16

1. Draw a square array for the next square number after 16.
   Square number: 25
2. List all the square numbers through 100. Use counters or draw arrays, if you need help.
   1, 4, 9, 16, 25, 36, 49, 64, 81, 100
3. Can a square number be a prime number? no Why or why not?
   Sample answer: Because it has at least one other factor than 1 and itself.
4. Notice which square numbers are even and which are odd. Can you find a pattern? yes If yes, describe the pattern.
   Sample answer: The square numbers alternate between odd and even as they increase.

STUDENT PAGE

✦ *Math Journal 1,* p. 18

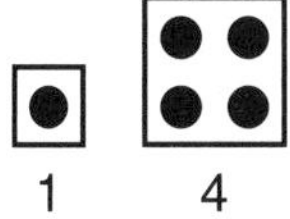

Square arrays for the square numbers 1 and 4

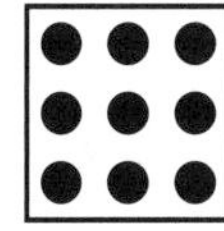

Square array for the square number 9

NOTE: The numbers along the diagonal from the upper left-hand corner of a Multiplication/Division Facts Table to the lower right-hand corner are square numbers. Students can find a Multiplication/Division Facts Table on the inside front cover of their journals.

## Square Numbers (cont.)

Any square number can be written as the product of a number multiplied by itself.

*Example* The third square number, 9, can be written as 3 * 3.

There is a shorthand way of writing square numbers: $9 = 3 * 3 = 3^2$.

You can read $3^2$ as "3 times 3," "3 squared," or "3 to the second power." The raised 2 is called an **exponent.** It tells that 3 is used as a factor 2 times. Numbers written with an exponent are said to be in **exponential notation.**

Be careful! The number $3^2$ is not the same as the product of 3 * 2. $3^2$ equals 3 * 3, which is 9, and 3 * 2 = 6.

5. Fill in the blanks.

| Product | Exponential Notation | Square Number |
|---|---|---|
| 4 * 4 | $4^2$ | 16 |
| 7 * 7 | $7^2$ | 49 |
| 10 * 10 | $10^2$ | 100 |
| 11 * 11 | $11^2$ | 121 |

Some calculators have a key with the symbol [^] on it. It is called the **exponent key** and can be used to find the square of a number.

6. Press 3 [^] 2 [Enter]. What does the display show? 9

If your calculator has an exponent key, use it to solve the following problems. If not, you can use the multiplication key.

7. $8^2$ = 64
8. $12^2$ = 144
9. $14^2$ = 196
10. $20^2$ = 400
11. $43^2$ = 1,849
12. $67^2$ = 4,489
13. Start with 4. Square it. Now square the result. What do you get? 256

STUDENT PAGE

✦ *Math Journal 1,* p. 19

For Problem 2, even if students pool their resources, they will not have enough counters to make arrays for the large square numbers. Students who need the help of arrays could draw arrays on dot paper (*Math Masters,* page 1).

The first part of journal page 19 introduces **exponential notation** for square numbers. The second part introduces the **exponent key** ([^]), which is found on some calculators. If students' calculators have this key, they should use it to solve Problems 6 through 13. If their calculators do not have this key, they can find the answers by using the multiplication key.

After students have completed both pages, go over the answers. Make sure that students understand the answers to Problems 3 and 4. Briefly discuss the new vocabulary (**exponent** and **exponential notation**).

Also, discuss the difference between *doubling* a number and *squaring* a number. Illustrate this by asking:

- What do you get when you double 10? 20 When you square 10? 100

## Math Boxes 1.7

MATH

1. Complete.
   a. 900 * 800 = 720,000
   b. 5,000 * 60 = 300,000
   c. 5,400 = 90 * 60
   d. 42,000 = 60 * 700
   e. 1,500 = 500 * 3

2. a. How many crayons are there in 10 boxes, if each box contains 48 crayons? 480 crayons (unit)
   b. How many crayons are there in 1,000 boxes? 48,000 crayons (unit)

3. Complete the table.

| Fraction | Decimal | Percent |
|---|---|---|
| $\frac{1}{2}$ | 0.50 | 50% |
| $\frac{1}{8}$ | 0.125 | $12\frac{1}{2}$% |
| $\frac{4}{5}$ | 0.80 | 80% |
| $\frac{3}{4}$ | 0.75 | 75% |
| $\frac{32}{100}$ | 0.32 | 32% |

4. a. Write a 6-digit numeral with 4 in the hundredths place, 3 in the hundreds place, 6 in the thousands place, 5 in the tens place, and 2s in all other places. 6, 3 5 2 . 2 4
   b. Write this numeral in words. Six thousand, three hundred, fifty-two and twenty-four hundredths

5. Circle the numbers that are divisible by 6.
   (438) 629 (702) 320 843

6. Round 15,783,406 to the nearest ...
   a. million. 16,000,000
   b. thousand. 15,783,000
   c. hundred-thousand. 15,800,000

STUDENT PAGE

✦ *Math Journal 1,* p. 20

# 2 Ongoing Learning & Practice

### ✦ Practicing the Multiplication Facts Routine
(*Math Journal 1,* p. 8; *Math Masters,* p. 3)

WHOLE-CLASS ACTIVITY

Select another 16 problems from *Math Masters,* page 3 for a multiplication facts quiz. Repeat problems that you circled on the previous quiz because they were missed most frequently. See Lesson 1.3 for additional directions.

### ✦ Playing *Factor Top-It*
(*Student Reference Book,* p. 272)

PARTNER ACTIVITY

In this game, students draw two cards and form a 2-digit number. The sum of the factors is the player's score for each round. Partners play five rounds and add the sum of the five rounds to determine their total score. The player with the highest score is the winner.

## ◆ Math Boxes 1.7 (*Math Journal 1,* p. 20)

INDEPENDENT ACTIVITY 

**Mixed Review** Math Boxes in this lesson are paired with Math Boxes in Lessons 1.5 and 1.9. The skill in Problem 1 is a prerequisite for Unit 2.

## ◆ Study Link 1.7 (*Math Masters,* p. 220)

**Home Connection** Students solve problems involving square numbers, explain why an array represents a square number, and find the sums of two numbers expressed in exponential notation.

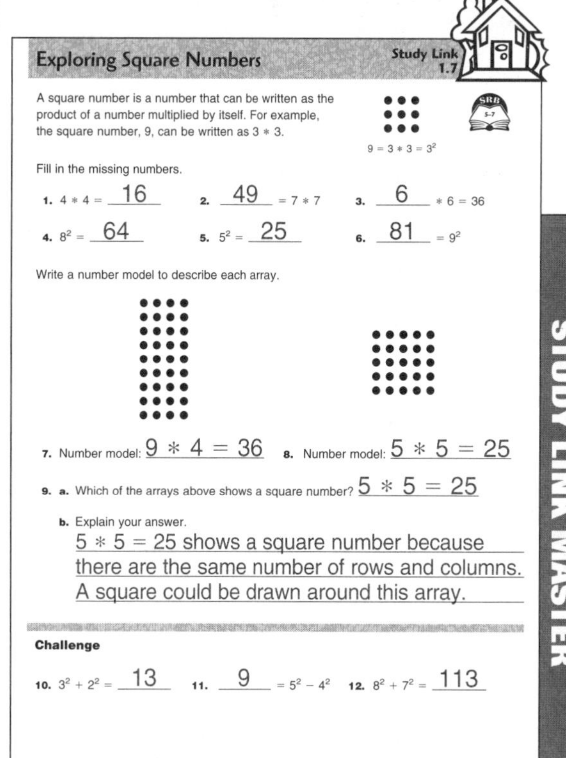

Exploring Square Numbers — Study Link 1.7

A square number is a number that can be written as the product of a number multiplied by itself. For example, the square number, 9, can be written as 3 ∗ 3.

$9 = 3 * 3 = 3^2$

Fill in the missing numbers.

1. 4 ∗ 4 = 16
2. 49 = 7 ∗ 7
3. 6 ∗ 6 = 36
4. $8^2$ = 64
5. $5^2$ = 25
6. 81 = $9^2$

Write a number model to describe each array.

7. Number model: 9 ∗ 4 = 36
8. Number model: 5 ∗ 5 = 25
9. a. Which of the arrays above shows a square number? 5 ∗ 5 = 25
   b. Explain your answer.
   5 ∗ 5 = 25 shows a square number because there are the same number of rows and columns. A square could be drawn around this array.

Challenge

10. $3^2 + 2^2$ = 13
11. 9 = $5^2 - 4^2$
12. $8^2 + 7^2$ = 113

STUDY LINK MASTER

◆ *Math Masters,* p. 220

# 3 Options for Individualizing

## ◆ RETEACHING Making Square Arrays (*Math Masters,* p. 2)

PARTNER ACTIVITY  **15–30 min**

Some students may benefit from additional hands-on work with the making of square arrays. Have students cut out square arrays for as many numbers as possible from centimeter grid paper (*Math Masters,* page 2). Students should label each array diagram with the correct number model. Then they make a table of the factors and the products, and describe any number patterns they see.

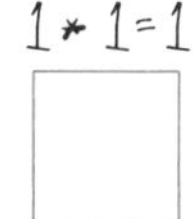


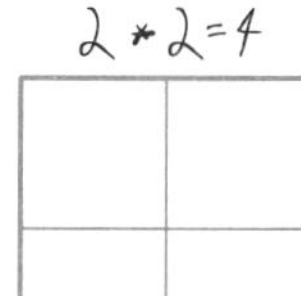


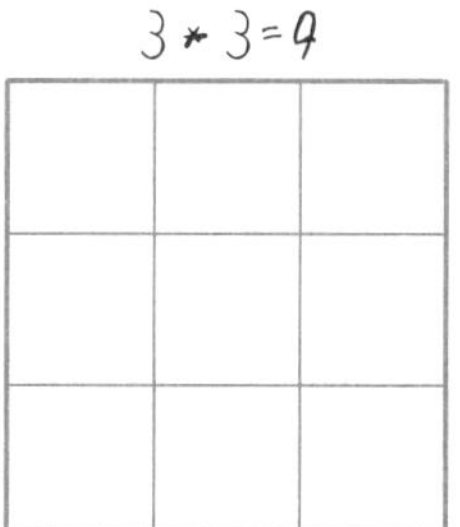


## ◆ ENRICHMENT Completing Patterns (*Math Masters,* p. 9)

INDEPENDENT ACTIVITY  **5–15 min**

Students complete dot-figure and number patterns.

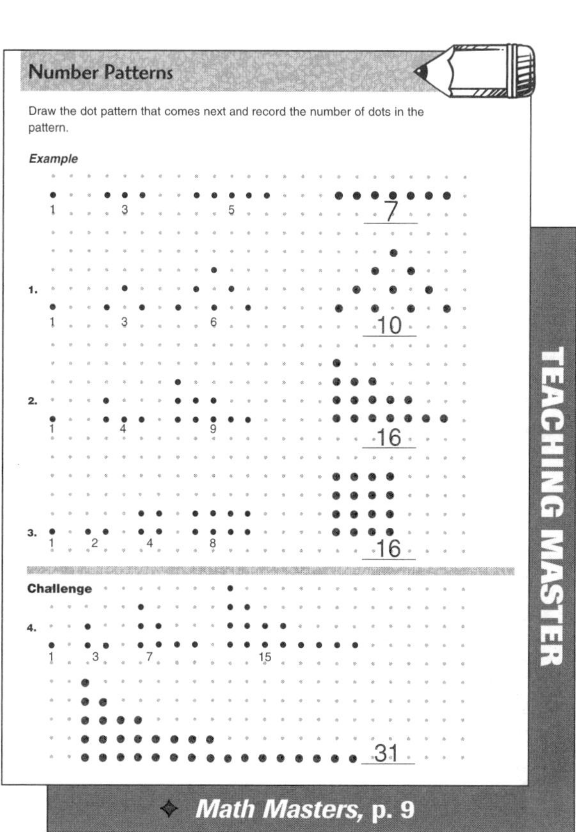

Number Patterns

Draw the dot pattern that comes next and record the number of dots in the pattern.

*Example*: 1, 3, 5, 7

1. 1, 3, 6, 10
2. 1, 4, 9, 16
3. 1, 2, 4, 8, 16

Challenge

4. 1, 3, 7, 15, 31

TEACHING MASTER

◆ *Math Masters,* p. 9

# 1.8 Unsquaring Numbers

**OBJECTIVES** **To find the square root of a square number; and to use the square-root key on a calculator to find the square root of any positive number.**

| summaries | materials |
|---|---|
| **1 Teaching the Lesson** | |
| Students investigate ways of "unsquaring" numbers without using the square-root key on a calculator and then use the square-root key to check answers. They observe that numbers that have decimal square roots are not square numbers. [Numeration; Operations and Computation] | ☐ *Math Journal 1,* p. 21<br>☐ Study Link 1.7<br>☐ Assessment Master (*Math Masters,* p. 479) optional<br>☐ calculator<br>***See*** **Advance Preparation** |
| **2 Ongoing Learning & Practice** | |
| Students compare numbers with their squares; they observe that the squared number may be greater than, less than, or equal to the original number. [Numeration; Operations and Computations]<br>Students continue the multiplication facts routine to practice instant recall of the facts. [Operations and Computation]<br>Students practice and maintain skills through Math Boxes and Study Link activities. | ☐ *Math Journal 1,* pp. 8, 21, and 22<br>☐ Teaching Master (*Math Masters,* p. 3), for teacher only<br>☐ Study Link Master (*Math Masters,* p. 221)<br>☐ calculator |
| **3 Options for Individualizing** | |
| **Extra Practice** Students collect representations of square numbers. [Numeration; Operations and Computation] | ☐ posterboard and markers (optional) |

**Additional Information**

Advance Preparation Experiment with the square-root key on the calculator your students are using. The square-root key does not work the same way on all types of calculators.

Vocabulary • **"unsquaring" a number** • **square root** • **square-root key (√)**

## Getting Started

### Math Message

*Find the numbers* n *and* m *that make these statements true:*

$n * n = 4$ $\quad m^2 = 81$

### Study Link 1.7 Follow-Up

Briefly go over the answers.

# Teaching the Lesson

## Math Message Follow-Up

WHOLE-CLASS DISCUSSION

If students had trouble finding the answer to the second problem, remind them that $m^2$ can be read as "$m$ times $m$." Then rephrase the problem as follows: *What number, multiplied by itself, is equal to 81?* 9

## "Unsquaring" Numbers

WHOLE-CLASS ACTIVITY

Tell the class that solving a problem such as the Math Message problems involves **"unsquaring" a number.** That is the same as undoing the result of squaring a number.

Pose the following problem: *What number, multiplied by itself, is equal to 289?* Give students a few minutes to find the number. They may use their calculators, if they wish.

After a few minutes, bring the class together to share solution strategies. *For example:*

▷ **The random method:** Some students may have tried various numbers without much of a system.

▷ **The "squeeze" method:** Other students may have tried various numbers, each time narrowing the interval between the numbers. For example, to "unsquare" 289, you might:

- Try 10: $10^2 = 100$; much less than 289
- Try 20: $20^2 = 400$; more than 289

Then try numbers between 10 and 20, probably closer to 20 than to 10.

- Try 18: $18^2 = 324$; still too large, but closer
- Try 17: $17^2 = 289$; the answer is 17.

▷ **Endings and products:** Once an interval, such as the interval from 10 to 20, has been established, someone may have reasoned as follows: *17 ends in 7, and $7 * 7 = 49$. Since 289 also ends in 9, I will try $17 * 17$.*

If a student mentions the square-root key, tell the class that this is an easy way of "unsquaring" a number, but for the time being, students should pretend that the square-root key does not work.

| | |
|---|---|
| $4 * 4 = p$ | Square the number 4 to find $p$. |
| $n * n = 16$ | Unsquare the number 16 to find $n$. |

The difference between squaring and unsquaring a number.

### Language Arts Link

The prefix *un-* was added to the term *squaring* to create the term *unsquaring*—the opposite of squaring. The prefix *un-* can mean not, the opposite of, or contrary to. Have students think of other words which contain the prefix *un-* and use them in a sentence. *For example:*

▷ Maria *untied* her muddy shoes and took them off before she came into the house.

▷ Jackson was *unhappy* because his soccer game was rained out.

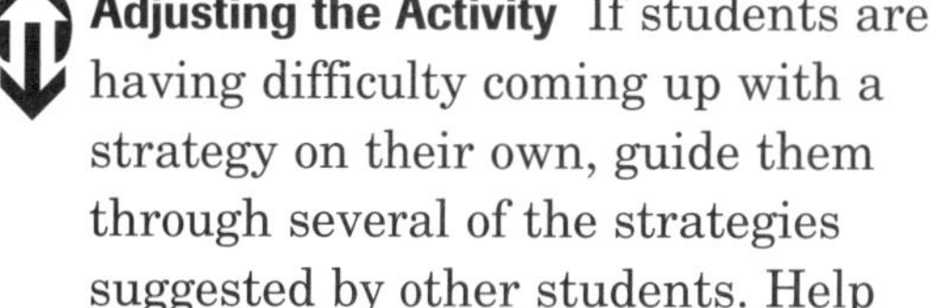

**Adjusting the Activity** If students are having difficulty coming up with a strategy on their own, guide them through several of the strategies suggested by other students. Help students decide upon the strategy that works best for them.

| | | | |
|---|---|---|---|
| 196 14 | 441 21 | 676 26 | 900 30 |
| 1,024 32 | 1,849 43 | 3,136 56 | 5,041 71 |
| 7,225 85 | 10,000 100 | | |

Suggested square numbers for students to "unsquare"

NOTE: Students using the TI-15 calculator often forget to press the closing parenthesis key ( ) ) when finding a square root.

√ 81 Enter will display an error message.

Press Clear ) Enter to display 9, the correct answer.

**ONGOING ASSESSMENT**

Have students complete an Exit Slip explaining in their own words what a square number is.

STUDENT PAGE

**Unsquaring Numbers**

You know that $6^2 = 6 * 6 = 36$. The number 36 is called the **square** of 6. If you **unsquare** 36, the result is 6. The number 6 is called the **square root** of 36.

1. "Unsquare" each number. The result is its square root. Do not use the √ key on the calculator.

*Example* 12 $^2$ = 144 The square root of 144 is 12.

a. 15 $^2$ = 225 The square root of 225 is 15.

b. 27 $^2$ = 729 The square root of 729 is 27.

c. 40 $^2$ = 1,600 The square root of 1,600 is 40.

d. 19 $^2$ = 361 The square root of 361 is 19.

2. Which of the following are square numbers? Circle them.

(576) 794 1,044 (4,356) (6,400) 5,770

**Comparing Numbers with Their Squares**

3. a. Unsquare the number 1. 1 $^2$ = 1

b. Unsquare the number 0. 0 $^2$ = 0

4. a. Is 5 greater than or less than 1? Greater than

b. $5^2$ = 25 c. Is $5^2$ greater than or less than 5? Greater than

5. a. Is 0.50 greater than or less than 1? Less than

b. Use your calculator. $0.50^2$ = 0.25

c. Is $0.50^2$ greater than or less than 0.50? Less than

6. a. When you square a number, is the result always greater than the number you started with? no

b. Can it be less? yes

c. Can it be the same? yes

Math Journal 1, p. 21

Give students a few more square numbers to "unsquare." Challenge them to "unsquare" the numbers using as few guesses as possible. *(See suggestions in the margin.)*

Finally, tell students that "unsquaring" a number is the same as finding the **square root** of the number. For example, since $8 * 8 = 64$, the square root of 64 is 8.

## Finding the Square Root of Numbers (*Math Journal 1,* p. 21)

PARTNER ACTIVITY

Partners complete Problems 1 and 2. (Problems 3–6 will be completed in Part 2, Ongoing Learning & Practice.) After a few minutes, ask for suggestions for checking the answers in Problem 1. *Some possibilities:*

- Multiply the square root of a number by itself.
- Use the **square-root key** ( √ ) to find the square root of a number. For example, to find the square root of 81 on the TI-15 calculator, press √ 81 ) Enter. The display will show 9.

Use the square-root key to check the answers in Problem 2.

- If the display shows a whole number, then the number is a square number. For example, 576 is a square number, because √ 576 ) Enter displays 24.
- If the display shows a decimal, then the number is not a square number. For example, 794 is not a square number, because √ 794 ) Enter displays a decimal.

# 2 Ongoing Learning & Practice

## Comparing Numbers with Their Squares (*Math Journal 1,* p. 21)

PARTNER ACTIVITY

Students complete Problems 3–6 on journal page 21. Help them to recognize that squaring a number does not necessarily result in a number that is greater than the original number. For example, both 0 and 1 are equal to their squares (see Problem 3). Also, the square of a number that is greater than 0, but less than 1, is always less than the original number (see Problem 5).

## Practicing the Multiplication Facts Routine
(*Math Journal 1,* p. 8; *Math Masters,* p. 3)

WHOLE-CLASS ACTIVITY

Select another 16 problems from *Math Masters,* page 3 for a multiplication facts quiz. Repeat problems that you circled on the previous quiz because they were missed most frequently. See Lesson 1.3 for additional directions.

## Math Boxes 1.8 (*Math Journal 1,* p. 22)

INDEPENDENT ACTIVITY 

**Mixed Review** Math Boxes in this lesson are paired with Math Boxes in Lesson 1.6. The skill in Problem 1 is a prerequisite for Unit 2.

## Study Link 1.8 (*Math Masters,* p. 221)

**Home Connection** Students list all the factors of the first 10 square numbers. They write each number in exponential notation, and identify the square root.

**Math Boxes 1.8**

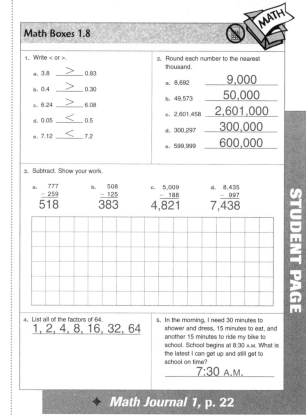

1. Write < or >.
   a. 3.8 > 0.83
   b. 0.4 > 0.30
   c. 6.24 > 6.08
   d. 0.05 < 0.5
   e. 7.12 < 7.2

2. Round each number to the nearest thousand.
   a. 8,692 9,000
   b. 49,573 50,000
   c. 2,601,458 2,601,000
   d. 300,297 300,000
   e. 599,999 600,000

3. Subtract. Show your work.
   a. 777 − 259 = 518
   b. 508 − 125 = 383
   c. 5,009 − 188 = 4,821
   d. 8,435 − 997 = 7,438

4. List all of the factors of 64.
   1, 2, 4, 8, 16, 32, 64

5. In the morning, I need 30 minutes to shower and dress, 15 minutes to eat, and another 15 minutes to ride my bike to school. School begins at 8:30 A.M. What is the latest I can get up and still get to school on time?
   7:30 A.M.

STUDENT PAGE

*Math Journal 1,* p. 22

# 3 Options for Individualizing

## EXTRA PRACTICE Making Square-Number Collections

PARTNER ACTIVITY  **15–30 min**

Assign a square number to a student or partnership. Students collect representations of the square number, such as arrays, multiplication expressions, and expressions containing exponents or square-root symbols. For example, representations for the number 100 might include:

Portfolio Ideas

| | |
|---|---|
| A 10-by-10 array | A 5-by-20 array |
| $5 * 5 * 4$ | $10^2$ |
| $20^2 - 10^2 - 10^2 - 10^2$ | $5^2 * 2^2$ |
| $30^2 / 9$ | $\sqrt{10{,}000}$ |

Students may want to make a colorful poster display of the representations they have collected.

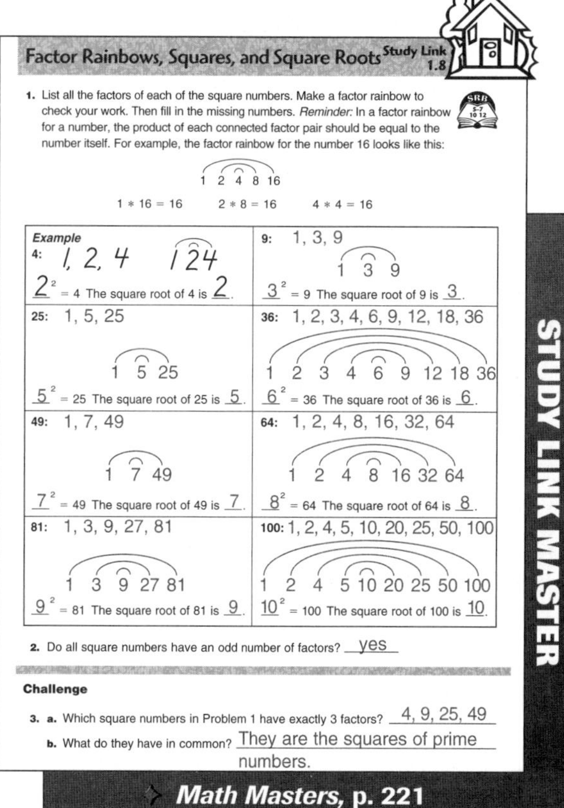

**Factor Rainbows, Squares, and Square Roots** Study Link 1.8

1. List all the factors of each of the square numbers. Make a factor rainbow to check your work. Then fill in the missing numbers. *Reminder:* In a factor rainbow for a number, the product of each connected factor pair should be equal to the number itself. For example, the factor rainbow for the number 16 looks like this:

   1 2 4 8 16

   1 ∗ 16 = 16 2 ∗ 8 = 16 4 ∗ 4 = 16

| | |
|---|---|
| Example 4: 1, 2, 4 — 1 2 4 — $2^2$ = 4 The square root of 4 is 2. | 9: 1, 3, 9 — 1 3 9 — $3^2$ = 9 The square root of 9 is 3. |
| 25: 1, 5, 25 — 1 5 25 — $5^2$ = 25 The square root of 25 is 5. | 36: 1, 2, 3, 4, 6, 9, 12, 18, 36 — 1 2 3 4 6 9 12 18 36 — $6^2$ = 36 The square root of 36 is 6. |
| 49: 1, 7, 49 — 1 7 49 — $7^2$ = 49 The square root of 49 is 7. | 64: 1, 2, 4, 8, 16, 32, 64 — 1 2 4 8 16 32 64 — $8^2$ = 64 The square root of 64 is 8. |
| 81: 1, 3, 9, 27, 81 — 1 3 9 27 81 — $9^2$ = 81 The square root of 81 is 9. | 100: 1, 2, 4, 5, 10, 20, 25, 50, 100 — 1 2 4 5 10 20 25 50 100 — $10^2$ = 100 The square root of 100 is 10. |

2. Do all square numbers have an odd number of factors? yes

**Challenge**

3. a. Which square numbers in Problem 1 have exactly 3 factors? 4, 9, 25, 49
   b. What do they have in common? They are the squares of prime numbers.

STUDY LINK MASTER

*Math Masters,* p. 221

# 1.9 Factor Strings and Prime Factorizations

**OBJECTIVES To review name-collection boxes; and to represent numbers as products of factors (factor strings) and as products of prime factors (prime factorizations).**

| summaries | materials |
|---|---|
| **1 Teaching the Lesson** | |
| Students use name-collection boxes to review the idea that numbers can be represented in many different ways. [Numeration]<br>Students represent composite numbers as factor strings; identify the prime factorization of a number as the longest factor string, which consists of only prime numbers; and practice finding the prime factorization of numbers. [Numeration; Operations and Computation] | □ *Math Journal 1,* pp. 23 and 24<br>□ Study Link 1.8<br>□ calculator |
| **2 Ongoing Learning & Practice** | |
| Students continue the multiplication facts routine to practice instant recall of the facts. [Operations and Computation]<br>Students solve a set of problems to review some of the important ideas presented in this unit. [Numeration; Operations and Computation]<br>Students practice and maintain skills through Math Boxes and Study Link activities. | □ *Math Journal 1,* pp. 8, 25, and 26<br>□ Teaching Master (*Math Masters,* p. 3), for teacher only<br>□ Study Link Master (*Math Masters,* p. 222)<br>□ calculator |
| **3 Options for Individualizing** | |
| **Reteaching** Students play *Name That Number* to review the concept that numbers can be named in many different ways. [Numeration; Operations and Computations]<br>**Extra Practice** Students play *Factor Bingo* to practice identifying the factors of 2-digit whole numbers. [Operations and Computation] | □ *Student Reference Book,* pp. 270 and 286<br>□ Teaching Master (*Math Masters,* p. 10)<br>□ deck of number cards (use the Everything Math Deck, if available)<br>***See* Advanced Preparation** |

## Additional Information

**Advance Preparation** For Part 3, use Everything Math Decks or change ordinary card decks as described in the Advance Preparation section in Lesson 1.3.

**Vocabulary** • **name-collection box** • **factor string** • **length of factor string** • **prime factorization** • **exponent**

# Getting Started

**Math Message**

*8 + 8 and 4 * 4 are two names for the number 16. Write at least five other names for 16.*

**Study Link 1.8 Follow-Up**

Go over the answers. Help the class draw the following conclusion: Numbers whose square root is a prime number have exactly three factors.

# 1 Teaching the Lesson

## ✦ Math Message Follow-Up

WHOLE-CLASS DISCUSSION 

The idea that a number can be represented in many equivalent ways is so important that it has been taught and practiced throughout the *Everyday Mathematics* program. Since first grade, students have been filling **name-collection boxes** with names for given numbers. *(See the example in the margin.)*

Draw a name-collection box for 16. Students share the names they made up for 16 as you record them on the board in the name-collection box.

**Adjusting the Activity** Repeat this activity with a couple of other numbers. Challenge students to come up with especially unusual names.

| 16 |
|---|
| $4^2$ |
| $\sqrt{256}$ |
| (4 + 6) * 6 − 4 * 11 |
| XVI |

A typical name-collection box for 16—there are infinitely many possibilities

## ✦ Introducing Factor Strings

WHOLE-CLASS ACTIVITY

A **factor string** is a name for a number written as a product of at least two factors that are greater than 1. In a factor string, the number 1 may not be used as a factor.

*Example:* A factor string for the number 24 is 2 * 3 * 4. This factor string has three factors, so the **length of the factor string** is 3. Note that the factors may be written in any order—2 * 3 * 4 and 3 * 4 * 2 are considered the same factor string.

1. Ask for other factor strings for 24. Record all possible factor strings on the board (see below).

| Number | Factor String | Length |
|---|---|---|
| 24 | 2 * 3 * 4 | 3 |
| | 4 * 6 | 2 |
| | 2 * 12 | 2 |
| | 3 * 8 | 2 |
| | 2 * 2 * 6 | 3 |
| | 2 * 2 * 2 * 3 | 4 |

Remember to exclude 1 as a factor. One result is that there are no factor strings for prime numbers.

2. Have students find all possible factor strings for other numbers—for example, for 30, 50, 54, and 72. Record them in tables on the board.

3. Share students' strategies for finding the longest factor strings. For example, for the number 36, you might start with 4 * 9, and then rename 4 as 2 * 2 and 9 as 3 * 3. Another strategy is to try the prime numbers in order:
Is 2 a factor of 36? yes So 36 = 2 * 18.
Is 2 a factor of 18? yes So 36 = 2 * 2 * 9.
Is 2 a factor of 9? no Is 3 a factor of 9? yes
So 36 = 2 * 2 * 3 * 3.

What kind of numbers make up the longest possible factor string for a number? Prime numbers

Tell the class that the longest factor string for a number is called the **prime factorization** of the number. For example, the prime factorization of 24 is 2 * 2 * 2 * 3.

## ✦ Finding Factor Strings and Prime Factorization

(*Math Journal 1,* pp. 23 and 24)

PARTNER ACTIVITY

Students complete both journal pages. Circulate and assist as needed. Problems 3 and 4 offer additional practice in writing and decoding exponential notation.

STUDENT PAGE

### Factor Strings

A **factor string** is a name for a number written as a product of two or more factors. In a factor string, 1 may not be used as a factor.

The **length of a factor string** is equal to the number of factors in the string. The longest factor string for a number is made up of prime numbers. The longest factor string for a number is called the **prime factorization** of that number.

*Example*

| Number | Factor Strings | Length |
|---|---|---|
| 20 | 2 * 10 | 2 |
| | 4 * 5 | 2 |
| | 2 * 2 * 5 | 3 |
| | | |

The order of the factors is not important. For example, 2 * 10 and 10 * 2 are the same factor string.

The longest factor string for 20 is 2 * 2 * 5. So the prime factorization of 20 is 2 * 2 * 5.

1. Find all the factor strings for each number below.

a.

| Number | Factor Strings | Length |
|---|---|---|
| 12 | 3 * 4 | 2 |
| | 2 * 6 | 2 |
| | 3 * 2 * 2 | 3 |
| | | |

b.

| Number | Factor Strings | Length |
|---|---|---|
| 16 | 4 * 4 | 2 |
| | 4 * 2 * 2 | 3 |
| | 8 * 2 | 2 |
| | 2*2*2*2 | 4 |

c.

| Number | Factor Strings | Length |
|---|---|---|
| 18 | 9 * 2 | 2 |
| | 6 * 3 | 2 |
| | 3 * 3 * 2 | 3 |
| | | |

d.

| Number | Factor Strings | Length |
|---|---|---|
| 28 | 7 * 4 | 2 |
| | 14 * 2 | 2 |
| | 7 * 2 * 2 | 3 |
| | | |

✦ *Math Journal 1*, p. 23

# Ongoing Learning & Practice

## ✦ Practicing the Multiplication Facts Routine (*Math Journal 1,* p. 8; *Math Masters,* p. 3)

WHOLE-CLASS ACTIVITY

Select another 16 problems from *Math Masters,* page 3 for a multiplication facts quiz. Repeat problems that you circled on the previous quiz because they were missed most frequently. See Lesson 1.3 for additional directions.

## ✦ Reviewing Key Ideas in Unit 1 (*Math Journal 1,* p. 25)

INDEPENDENT ACTIVITY 

Students review the following topics from this unit: square numbers, factor rainbow, divisibility, prime and composite numbers, prime factorization, and expressing numbers using exponential notation.

**Factor Strings** (cont.)

2. Write the prime factorization (the longest factor string) for each number.

a. 27 = $3 * 3 * 3$ b. 40 = $2 * 2 * 2 * 5$

c. 36 = $2 * 2 * 3 * 3$ d. 42 = $2 * 3 * 7$

e. 48 = $2 * 2 * 2 * 2 * 3$ f. 60 = $2 * 2 * 3 * 5$

g. 100 = $2 * 2 * 5 * 5$

An **exponent** is a raised number that shows how many times the number to its left is used as a factor.

*Examples* $5^2$ ← exponent: $5^2$ means $5 * 5$, which is 25. $5^2$ is read as "5 squared" or as "5 to the second power."

$10^3$ ← exponent: $10^3$ means $10 * 10 * 10$, which is 1,000. $10^3$ is read as "10 cubed" or as "10 to the third power."

$2^4$ ← exponent: $2^4$ means $2 * 2 * 2 * 2$, which is 16. $2^4$ is read as "2 to the fourth power."

3. Write each number as a product of factors. Then find the answer.

*Examples* $2^3$ = $2 * 2 * 2$ = 8

$2^2 * 9$ = $2 * 2 * 9$ = 36

a. $10^4$ = $10 * 10 * 10 * 10$ = 10,000

b. $3^2 * 5$ = $3 * 3 * 5$ = 45

c. $2^4 * 10^2$ = $2 * 2 * 2 * 2 * 10 * 10$ = 1,600

4. Rewrite each product using exponents.

*Examples* $5 * 5 * 5$ = $5^3$ $5 * 5 * 3 * 3$ = $5^2 * 3^2$

a. $3 * 3 * 3 * 3$ = $3^4$ b. $4 * 7 * 7$ = $4 * 7^2$

c. $2 * 5 * 5 * 7$ = $2 * 5^2 * 7$ d. $2 * 2 * 2 * 5 * 5$ = $2^3 * 5^2$

STUDENT PAGE

✦ *Math Journal 1,* p. 24

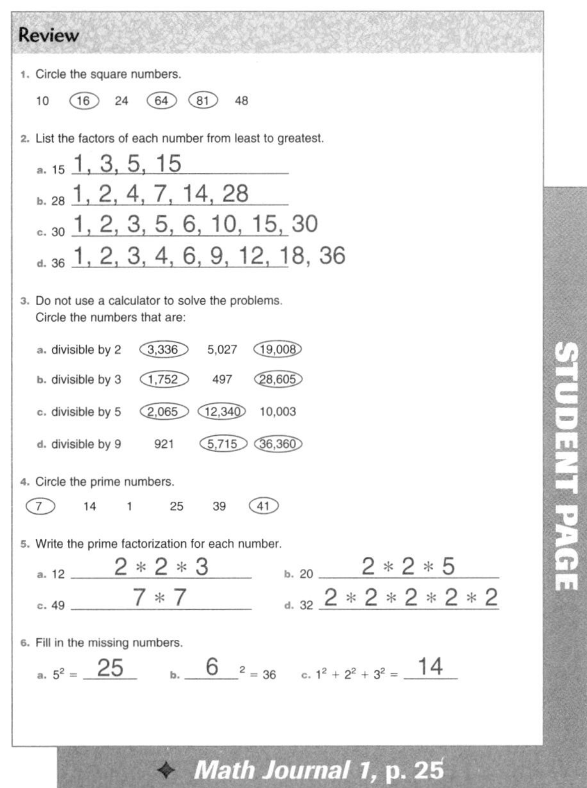

**Review**

1. Circle the square numbers.

10 (16) 24 (64) (81) 48

2. List the factors of each number from least to greatest.

a. 15 1, 3, 5, 15

b. 28 1, 2, 4, 7, 14, 28

c. 30 1, 2, 3, 5, 6, 10, 15, 30

d. 36 1, 2, 3, 4, 6, 9, 12, 18, 36

3. Do not use a calculator to solve the problems. Circle the numbers that are:

a. divisible by 2 (3,336) 5,027 (19,008)

b. divisible by 3 (1,752) 497 (28,605)

c. divisible by 5 (2,065) (12,340) 10,003

d. divisible by 9 921 (5,715) (36,360)

4. Circle the prime numbers.

(7) 14 1 25 39 (41)

5. Write the prime factorization for each number.

a. 12 $2 * 2 * 3$ b. 20 $2 * 2 * 5$

c. 49 $7 * 7$ d. 32 $2 * 2 * 2 * 2 * 2$

6. Fill in the missing numbers.

a. $5^2$ = 25 b. $6^2 = 36$ c. $1^2 + 2^2 + 3^2$ = 14

STUDENT PAGE

✦ *Math Journal 1,* p. 25

**Math Boxes 1.9**

1. Complete.
   a. 300 * 40 = 12,000
   b. 16,000 = 80 * 200
   c. 540,000 = 900 * 600
   d. 6,400 = 80 * 80
   e. 36,000 = 600 * 60

2. a. How many marbles are there in 7 bags, if each bag contains 8 marbles? 56 marbles (unit)
   b. How many marbles are there in 700 bags? 5,600 marbles (unit)

3. Complete the table.

| Fraction | Decimal | Percent |
|---|---|---|
| $\frac{3}{8}$ | 0.375 | $37\frac{1}{2}\%$ |
| $\frac{6}{10}$ | 0.6 | 60% |
| $\frac{2}{5}$ | 0.4 | 40% |
| $\frac{55}{100}$ | 0.55 | 55% |
| $\frac{8}{100}$ | 0.08 | 8% |

4. a. Write a 6-digit numeral with 7 in the thousands place, 5 in the hundredths place, 4 in the tenths place, 3 in the tens place, and 9s in all other places. 7,939.45
   b. Write this numeral in words. Seven thousand, nine hundred, thirty-nine and forty-five hundredths

5. Circle the numbers that are divisible by 9.
   (360) (252) (819) 426 651

6. Round 385.27 to the nearest …
   a. hundred. 400
   b. whole number. 385
   c. tenth. 385.3

STUDENT PAGE

Math Journal 1, p. 26

## Math Boxes 1.9 (*Math Journal 1*, p. 26)

INDEPENDENT ACTIVITY 

**Mixed Review** Math Boxes in this lesson are paired with Math Boxes in Lessons 1.5 and 1.7. The skill in Problem 1 is a prerequisite for Unit 2.

## Study Link 1.9 (*Math Masters*, p. 222)

**Home Connection** Students write numbers with **exponents** as factor strings and vice versa. Then they find the prime factorization of numbers and express the prime factorization using exponents.

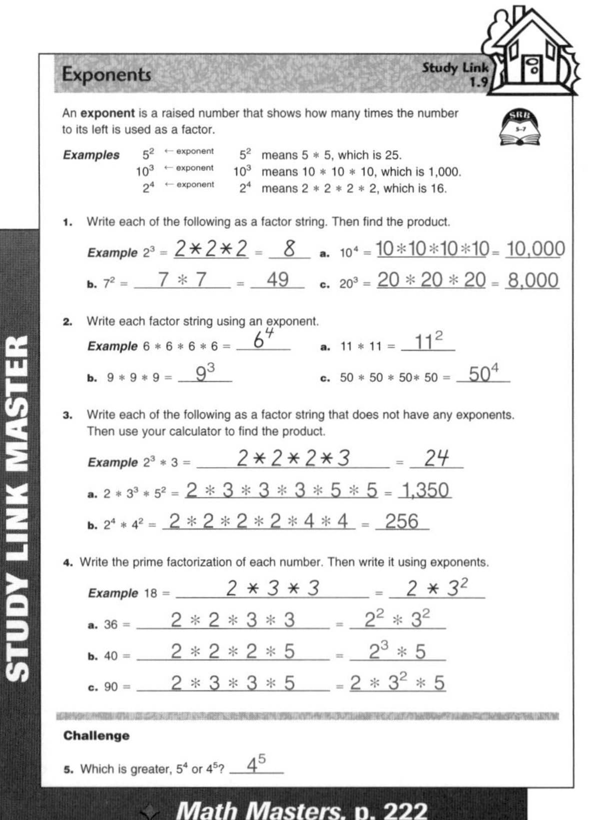
**Exponents** Study Link 1.9

An **exponent** is a raised number that shows how many times the number to its left is used as a factor.

*Examples* $5^2$ ← exponent, $10^3$ ← exponent, $2^4$ ← exponent

$5^2$ means 5 * 5, which is 25.
$10^3$ means 10 * 10 * 10, which is 1,000.
$2^4$ means 2 * 2 * 2 * 2, which is 16.

1. Write each of the following as a factor string. Then find the product.
   *Example* $2^3$ = 2*2*2 = 8
   a. $10^4$ = 10*10*10*10 = 10,000
   b. $7^2$ = 7 * 7 = 49
   c. $20^3$ = 20 * 20 * 20 = 8,000

2. Write each factor string using an exponent.
   *Example* 6 * 6 * 6 * 6 = $6^4$
   a. 11 * 11 = $11^2$
   b. 9 * 9 * 9 = $9^3$
   c. 50 * 50 * 50 * 50 = $50^4$

3. Write each of the following as a factor string that does not have any exponents. Then use your calculator to find the product.
   *Example* $2^3 * 3$ = 2*2*2*3 = 24
   a. $2 * 3^3 * 5^2$ = 2 * 3 * 3 * 3 * 5 * 5 = 1,350
   b. $2^4 * 4^2$ = 2 * 2 * 2 * 2 * 4 * 4 = 256

4. Write the prime factorization of each number. Then write it using exponents.
   *Example* 18 = 2 * 3 * 3 = $2 * 3^2$
   a. 36 = 2 * 2 * 3 * 3 = $2^2 * 3^2$
   b. 40 = 2 * 2 * 2 * 5 = $2^3 * 5$
   c. 90 = 2 * 3 * 3 * 5 = $2 * 3^2 * 5$

**Challenge**

5. Which is greater, $5^4$ or $4^5$? $4^5$

STUDY LINK MASTER

Math Masters, p. 222

# Options for Individualizing

## ✦ RETEACHING Playing *Name That Number* (*Student Reference Book*, p. 286)

PARTNER ACTIVITY **15–30 min**

*Name That Number* is a popular game that students played previously in *Everyday Mathematics*. It reviews the concept that any number can be named in many different ways. See page 286 in the *Student Reference Book* for directions.

## ✦ EXTRA PRACTICE Playing *Factor Bingo* (*Student Reference Book*, p. 270; *Math Masters*, p. 10)

PARTNER ACTIVITY **15–30 min**

This game provides practice with identifying factors of 2-digit whole numbers. See page 270 in the *Student Reference Book* for directions. When appropriate, extend the game by having students complete their grids with 3-digit numbers.

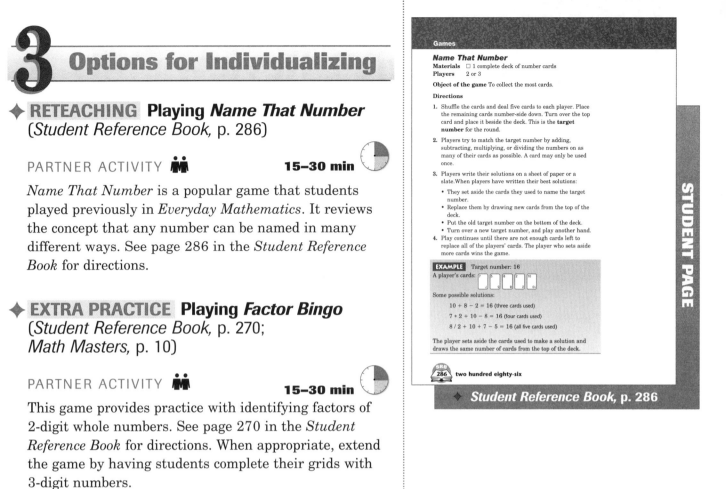

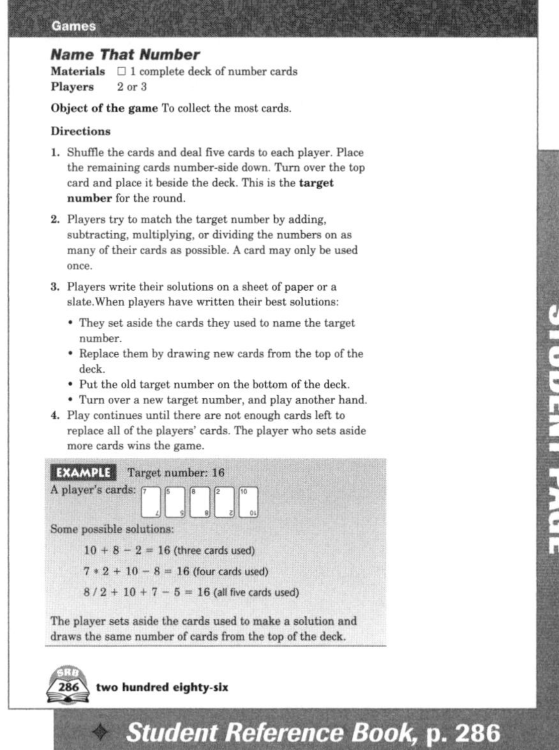

Games

***Name That Number***

**Materials** ☐ 1 complete deck of number cards

**Players** 2 or 3

**Object of the game** To collect the most cards.

**Directions**

1. Shuffle the cards and deal five cards to each player. Place the remaining cards number-side down. Turn over the top card and place it beside the deck. This is the **target number** for the round.
2. Players try to match the target number by adding, subtracting, multiplying, or dividing the numbers on as many of their cards as possible. A card may only be used once.
3. Players write their solutions on a sheet of paper or a slate.When players have written their best solutions:
   - They set aside the cards they used to name the target number.
   - Replace them by drawing new cards from the top of the deck.
   - Put the old target number on the bottom of the deck.
   - Turn over a new target number, and play another hand.
4. Play continues until there are not enough cards left to replace all of the players' cards. The player who sets aside more cards wins the game.

**EXAMPLE** Target number: 16

A player's cards: 7 5 8 2 10

Some possible solutions:

$10 + 8 - 2 = 16$ (three cards used)

$7 * 2 + 10 - 8 = 16$ (four cards used)

$8 / 2 + 10 + 7 - 5 = 16$ (all five cards used)

The player sets aside the cards used to make a solution and draws the same number of cards from the top of the deck.

SRB 286 two hundred eighty-six

STUDENT PAGE

✦ Student Reference Book, p. 286

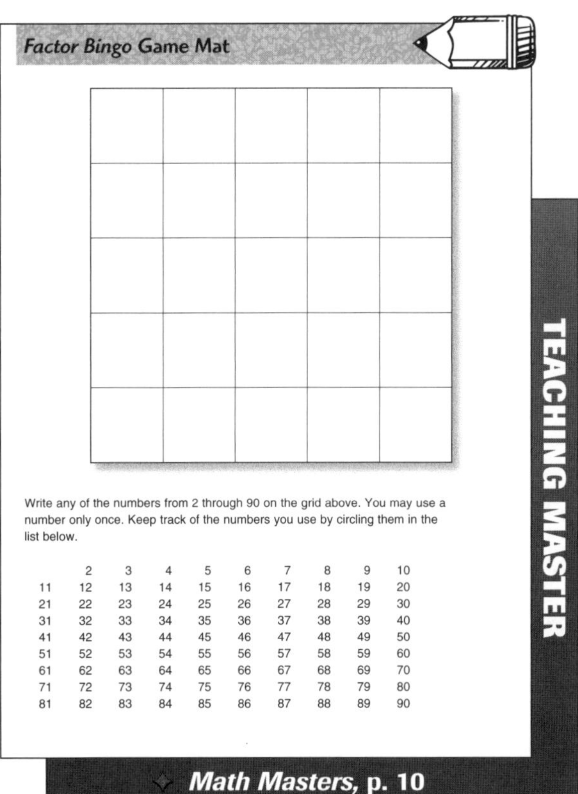

Factor Bingo Game Mat

Write any of the numbers from 2 through 90 on the grid above. You may use a number only once. Keep track of the numbers you use by circling them in the list below.

| | | | | | | | | |
|---|---|---|---|---|---|---|---|---|
| | 2 | 3 | 4 | 5 | 6 | 7 | 8 | 9 | 10 |
| 11 | 12 | 13 | 14 | 15 | 16 | 17 | 18 | 19 | 20 |
| 21 | 22 | 23 | 24 | 25 | 26 | 27 | 28 | 29 | 30 |
| 31 | 32 | 33 | 34 | 35 | 36 | 37 | 38 | 39 | 40 |
| 41 | 42 | 43 | 44 | 45 | 46 | 47 | 48 | 49 | 50 |
| 51 | 52 | 53 | 54 | 55 | 56 | 57 | 58 | 59 | 60 |
| 61 | 62 | 63 | 64 | 65 | 66 | 67 | 68 | 69 | 70 |
| 71 | 72 | 73 | 74 | 75 | 76 | 77 | 78 | 79 | 80 |
| 81 | 82 | 83 | 84 | 85 | 86 | 87 | 88 | 89 | 90 |

TEACHING MASTER

✦ Math Masters, p. 10

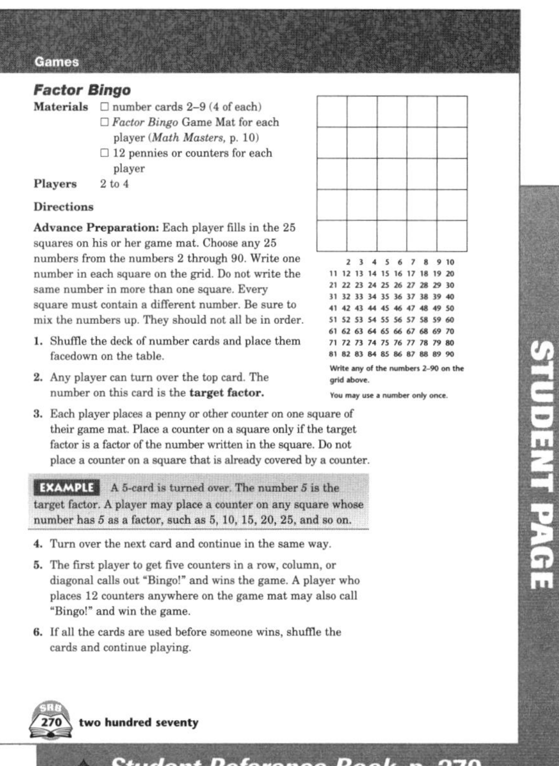

Games

***Factor Bingo***

**Materials** ☐ number cards 2–9 (4 of each)
☐ *Factor Bingo* Game Mat for each player (*Math Masters*, p. 10)
☐ 12 pennies or counters for each player

**Players** 2 to 4

**Directions**

**Advance Preparation:** Each player fills in the 25 squares on his or her game mat. Choose any 25 numbers from the numbers 2 through 90. Write one number in each square on the grid. Do not write the same number in more than one square. Every square must contain a different number. Be sure to mix the numbers up. They should not all be in order.

| | | | | | | | | | |
|---|---|---|---|---|---|---|---|---|---|
| | 2 | 3 | 4 | 5 | 6 | 7 | 8 | 9 | 10 |
| 11 | 12 | 13 | 14 | 15 | 16 | 17 | 18 | 19 | 20 |
| 21 | 22 | 23 | 24 | 25 | 26 | 27 | 28 | 29 | 30 |
| 31 | 32 | 33 | 34 | 35 | 36 | 37 | 38 | 39 | 40 |
| 41 | 42 | 43 | 44 | 45 | 46 | 47 | 48 | 49 | 50 |
| 51 | 52 | 53 | 54 | 55 | 56 | 57 | 58 | 59 | 60 |
| 61 | 62 | 63 | 64 | 65 | 66 | 67 | 68 | 69 | 70 |
| 71 | 72 | 73 | 74 | 75 | 76 | 77 | 78 | 79 | 80 |
| 81 | 82 | 83 | 84 | 85 | 86 | 87 | 88 | 89 | 90 |

Write any of the numbers 2–90 on the grid above.

You may use a number only once.

1. Shuffle the deck of number cards and place them facedown on the table.
2. Any player can turn over the top card. The number on this card is the **target factor.**
3. Each player places a penny or other counter on one square of their game mat. Place a counter on a square only if the target factor is a factor of the number written in the square. Do not place a counter on a square that is already covered by a counter.

**EXAMPLE** A 5-card is turned over. The number *5* is the target factor. A player may place a counter on any square whose number has *5* as a factor, such as 5, 10, 15, 20, 25, and so on.

4. Turn over the next card and continue in the same way.
5. The first player to get five counters in a row, column, or diagonal calls out "Bingo!" and wins the game. A player who places 12 counters anywhere on the game mat may also call "Bingo!" and win the game.
6. If all the cards are used before someone wins, shuffle the cards and continue playing.

SRB 270 two hundred seventy

STUDENT PAGE

✦ Student Reference Book, p. 270

# 1.10 Unit 1 Review and Assessment

**OBJECTIVE To review and assess students' progress on the material covered in Unit 1.**

## 1 Assess Progress

| learning goals | activities |
|---|---|
| 1a **Beginning Goal** Find the prime factorizations of numbers. **(Lesson 1.9)** | ❑ Written Assessment, Problems 6 and 7 |
| 1b **Beginning/Developing Goal** Rename numbers written in exponential notation. **(Lessons 1.7–1.9)** | ❑ Written Assessment, Problems 7 and 8 |
| 1c **Developing/Secure Goal** Use a divisibility test to determine if a number is divisible by another number. **(Lesson 1.5)** | ❑ Slate Assessment, Problem 4<br>❑ Written Assessment, Problems 11, 12, and 14 |
| 1d **Developing/Secure Goal** Identify prime and composite numbers. **(Lessons 1.6 and 1.9)** | ❑ Slate Assessment, Problem 3<br>❑ Written Assessment, Problems 4, 5, 13, and 14 |
| 1e **Developing/Secure Goal** Understand how square numbers and their square roots are related. **(Lesson 1.8)** | ❑ Slate Assessment, Problem 1<br>❑ Written Assessment, Problem 8 |
| 1f **Secure Goal** Draw arrays to model multiplication. **(Lessons 1.2 and 1.7)** | ❑ Written Assessment, Problem 1 |
| 1g **Secure Goal** Know multiplication facts. **(Lessons 1.2–1.9)** | ❑ Written Assessment, Problems 1, 4, and 8 |
| 1h **Secure Goal** Identify even and odd numbers. **(Lessons 1.4 and 1.5)** | ❑ Slate Assessment, Problem 3<br>❑ Written Assessment, Problems 2 and 13 |
| 1i **Secure Goal** Find the factors of numbers. **(Lessons 1.3 1.4, 1.6, and 1.9)** | ❑ Written Assessment, Problems 3, 9, and 10 |

**materials**

- □ *Math Journal 1,* p. 27 □ Study Link 1.9
- □ *Student Reference Book,* pp. 261 and 271
- □ Assessment Masters (*Math Masters,* pp. 379, 380, and 479)
- □ Teaching Masters (*Math Masters,* pp. 5, 6, and 11)
- □ number cards 1–10 (Everything Math Deck, if available)
- □ slate or marker board; calculator; chalk or dry-erase marker; 48 counters

## 2 Build Background for Unit 2

| summaries | materials |
|---|---|
| Students practice and maintain skills through Math Boxes and Study Link activities. | □ *Math Journal 1,* p. 28<br>□ Study Link Masters (*Math Masters,* pp. 223–226) |

Each **learning goal** listed above indicates a level of performance that might be expected at this point in the *Everyday Mathematics* K–6 curriculum. For a variety of reasons, the levels indicated may not accurately portray your class's performance.

### Additional Information

**Advance Preparation** For additional information on assessment for Unit 1, see the *Assessment Handbook,* pages 36–38. For assessment checklists, see *Math Masters,* pages 428, 429, and 469–471.

# Getting Started

### Math Message

*Complete the* Time to Reflect *questions on journal page 27.*

### Study Link 1.9 Follow-Up

Briefly go over the answers. Have a volunteer explain how to solve the Challenge problem.

# 1 Assess Progress

## Math Message Follow-Up

WHOLE-CLASS DISCUSSION 

Discuss students' responses to questions about the unit.

## Slate Assessments

WHOLE-CLASS ACTIVITY

Instead of doing the oral and slate activities with the whole class, you might want to work with small groups of students, one at a time, over several days. While you do this, the rest of the class can work on the written review page. It is not necessary to record every student's performance on every problem. Instead, you need only keep a record of students who are struggling. You can go back later and enter positive comments as these students progress.

If the following suggested problems are not appropriate for your class's level of performance, adjust the numbers or the problems themselves to better assess your students' abilities.

**Time to Reflect**

1. Describe what you liked or did not like about playing the game *Factor Captor.*
   Answers vary for Problems 1–4.
2. Explain how making an array might help someone find factors of a number.

Look back through journal pages 2–24.

3. What activity or lesson did you enjoy most in this unit and what did you learn from it?
4. What was your least favorite lesson or activity in this unit and why?

STUDENT PAGE

✦ ***Math Journal 1*, p. 27**

NOTE: Some of these assessment suggestions relate to learning goals that have been addressed in previous grades. (For example, suggestion 2 relates to extended multiplication facts.) Now is a good time to evaluate students' progress toward those goals.

*Slate Assessment Suggestions*

1. How much is 7 squared? 49 5 squared? 25 8 squared? 64 The square root of 36? 6 The square root of 81? 9 What number squared equals 16? 4 100? 10 **Goal 1e**

2. Solve extended multiplication problems. *Suggestions:*

   7 [60s] = ? 420 5 [80s] = ? 400
   70 [60s] = ? 4,200 50 [80s] = ? 4,000
   700 [60s] = ? 42,000 500 [80s] = ? 40,000

   9 [40s] = ? 360
   90 [40s] = ? 3,600
   900 [40s] = ? 36,000

3. Write the following:
   - An even number between 100 and 120 102, 104, 106, 108, 110, 112, 114, 116, 118
   - A number between 55 and 60 that is divisible by 3 57
   - A prime number between 20 and 25 23
   - A composite number that is less than 100 Answers vary.
   - An odd number between 40 and 50; 41, 43, 45, 47, 49 keep your slate up if it is a prime number. 41, 43, or 47 **Goals 1d and 1h**

4. Write 345 on the board.
   - Is 345 divisible by 2? no By 3? yes By 4? no By 5? yes By 6? no By 9? no By 10? no
   - Is 282 divisible by 2? yes By 3? yes By 4? no By 5? no By 6? yes By 9? no By 10? no **Goal 1c**

## ✦ Written Assessment
(*Math Masters,* pp. 379 and 380)

INDEPENDENT ACTIVITY 

Depending on the needs of students, you may want to work through an example together, reading a problem aloud, discussing it, and providing additional examples as necessary before students work the problem independently.

For your convenience, each of the problems is described below and paired with one or more of this unit's learning goals.

- Draw arrays to model multiplication. (Problem 1) **Goals 1f and 1g**

- Determine if a number is even or odd. (Problem 2) **Goal 1h**
- List the factors of a number. (Problem 3) **Goal 1i**
- Identify a number as prime or composite. (Problem 4) **Goals 1d and 1g**
- Identify prime numbers. (Problem 5) **Goal 1d**
- Find the prime factorization of a number. (Problems 6 and 7) **Goals 1a and 1b**
- Rename numbers written in exponential notation. (Problem 8) **Goals 1b, 1e, and 1g**
- Identify the factors of a number. (Problems 9 and 10) **Goal 1i**
- Use divisibility tests to determine if one number is divisible by another number. (Problems 11 and 12) **Goal 1c**
- Identify numbers as even or odd; identify numbers as prime or composite; identify numbers as square numbers. (Problem 13) **Goals 1d and 1h**
- Identify a number as prime or composite. (Problem 14) **Goals 1c and 1d**

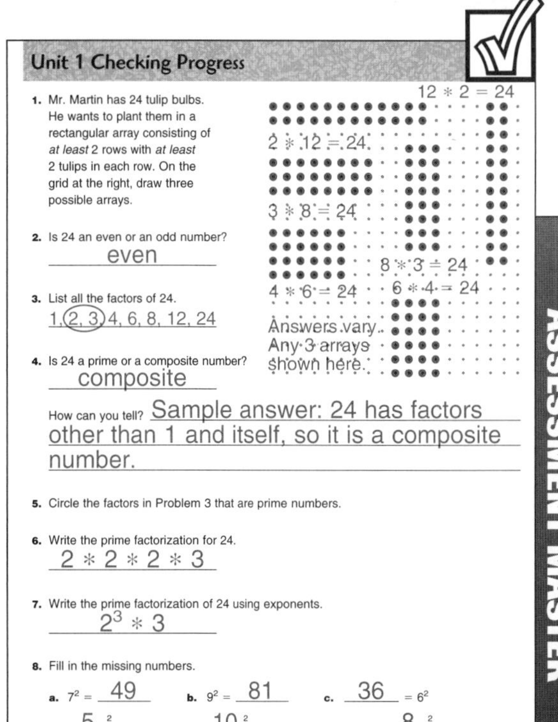

**Unit 1 Checking Progress**

1. Mr. Martin has 24 tulip bulbs. He wants to plant them in a rectangular array consisting of *at least* 2 rows with *at least* 2 tulips in each row. On the grid at the right, draw three possible arrays.

   12 * 2 = 24
   2 * 12 = 24
   3 * 8 = 24
   8 * 3 = 24
   4 * 6 = 24
   6 * 4 = 24
   Answers vary. Any 3 arrays shown here.

2. Is 24 an even or an odd number? even
3. List all the factors of 24. 1, (2, 3), 4, 6, 8, 12, 24
4. Is 24 a prime or a composite number? composite

   How can you tell? Sample answer: 24 has factors other than 1 and itself, so it is a composite number.

5. Circle the factors in Problem 3 that are prime numbers.
6. Write the prime factorization for 24. 2 * 2 * 2 * 3
7. Write the prime factorization of 24 using exponents. $2^3 * 3$
8. Fill in the missing numbers.

   a. $7^2 = 49$ b. $9^2 = 81$ c. $36 = 6^2$
   d. $5^2 = 25$ e. $10^2 = 100$ f. $8 * 8 = 8^2$

ASSESSMENT MASTER

Math Masters, p. 379

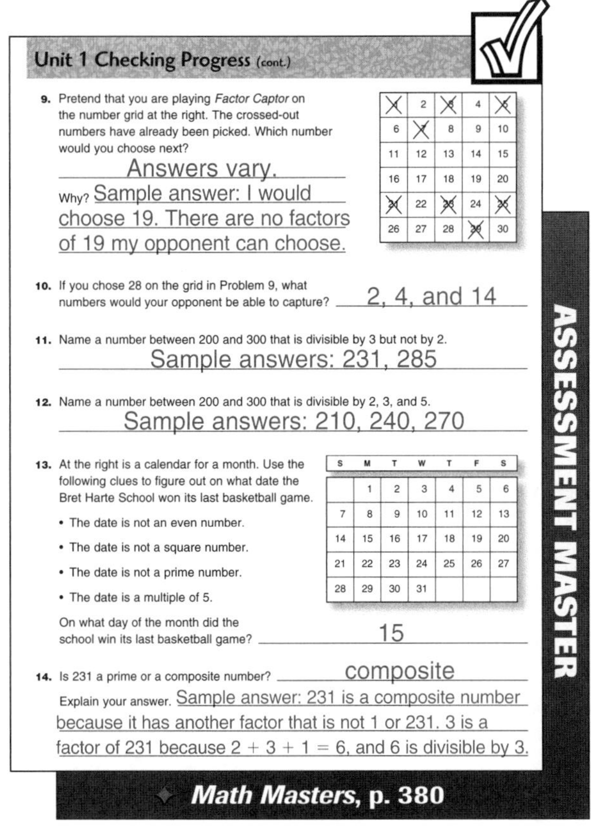

**Unit 1 Checking Progress (cont.)**

9. Pretend that you are playing *Factor Captor* on the number grid at the right. The crossed-out numbers have already been picked. Which number would you choose next?

   Answers vary.

   Why? Sample answer: I would choose 19. There are no factors of 19 my opponent can choose.

| X | 2 | X | 4 | X |
|---|---|---|---|---|
| 6 | X | 8 | 9 | 10 |
| 11 | 12 | 13 | 14 | 15 |
| 16 | 17 | 18 | 19 | 20 |
| X | 22 | X | 24 | X |
| 26 | 27 | 28 | X | 30 |

10. If you chose 28 on the grid in Problem 9, what numbers would your opponent be able to capture? 2, 4, and 14
11. Name a number between 200 and 300 that is divisible by 3 but not by 2. Sample answers: 231, 285
12. Name a number between 200 and 300 that is divisible by 2, 3, and 5. Sample answers: 210, 240, 270
13. At the right is a calendar for a month. Use the following clues to figure out on what date the Bret Harte School won its last basketball game.
    - The date is not an even number.
    - The date is not a square number.
    - The date is not a prime number.
    - The date is a multiple of 5.

| S | M | T | W | T | F | S |
|---|---|---|---|---|---|---|
|  | 1 | 2 | 3 | 4 | 5 | 6 |
| 7 | 8 | 9 | 10 | 11 | 12 | 13 |
| 14 | 15 | 16 | 17 | 18 | 19 | 20 |
| 21 | 22 | 23 | 24 | 25 | 26 | 27 |
| 28 | 29 | 30 | 31 |  |  |  |

    On what day of the month did the school win its last basketball game? 15

14. Is 231 a prime or a composite number? composite

    Explain your answer. Sample answer: 231 is a composite number because it has another factor that is not 1 or 231. 3 is a factor of 231 because 2 + 3 + 1 = 6, and 6 is divisible by 3.

ASSESSMENT MASTER

Math Masters, p. 380

## ✦ ALTERNATIVE ASSESSMENT OPTION

### Play *Beat the Calculator*

(*Student Reference Book,* p. 261; *Math Masters,* p. 11)

SMALL-GROUP ACTIVITY 

Have students play this game to assess the facts for which they need more practice. For detailed instructions, see Lesson 1.3.

Each student needs a copy of *Math Masters,* page 11 on which to cross out facts for which he or she beats the calculator. Collect this record or have students make a note of which facts they still need to practice.

## ✦ ALTERNATIVE ASSESSMENT OPTION

### Play *Factor Captor*

(*Student Reference Book,* p. 271; *Math Masters,* pp. 5, 6, and 479)

PARTNER ACTIVITY 

Have students play this game from Lesson 1.4 to assess their ability to identify factors of a number as well as to distinguish between prime and composite numbers.

Collect an Exit Slip from each student describing what he or she thinks is a winning strategy for the game.

TEACHING MASTER

**Multiplication Facts Master List**

Make a check mark next to each fact for which you beat the calculator.

| 1s | 3s | 5s | 7s | 9s |
|---|---|---|---|---|
| 1 * 1 | 3 * 1 | 5 * 1 | 7 * 1 | 9 * 1 |
| 1 * 2 | 3 * 2 | 5 * 2 | 7 * 2 | 9 * 2 |
| 1 * 3 | 3 * 3 | 5 * 3 | 7 * 3 | 9 * 3 |
| 1 * 4 | 3 * 4 | 5 * 4 | 7 * 4 | 9 * 4 |
| 1 * 5 | 3 * 5 | 5 * 5 | 7 * 5 | 9 * 5 |
| 1 * 6 | 3 * 6 | 5 * 6 | 7 * 6 | 9 * 6 |
| 1 * 7 | 3 * 7 | 5 * 7 | 7 * 7 | 9 * 7 |
| 1 * 8 | 3 * 8 | 5 * 8 | 7 * 8 | 9 * 8 |
| 1 * 9 | 3 * 9 | 5 * 9 | 7 * 9 | 9 * 9 |
| 1 * 10 | 3 * 10 | 5 * 10 | 7 * 10 | 9 * 10 |

| 2s | 4s | 6s | 8s | 10s |
|---|---|---|---|---|
| 2 * 1 | 4 * 1 | 6 * 1 | 8 * 1 | 10 * 1 |
| 2 * 2 | 4 * 2 | 6 * 2 | 8 * 2 | 10 * 2 |
| 2 * 3 | 4 * 3 | 6 * 3 | 8 * 3 | 10 * 3 |
| 2 * 4 | 4 * 4 | 6 * 4 | 8 * 4 | 10 * 4 |
| 2 * 5 | 4 * 5 | 6 * 5 | 8 * 5 | 10 * 5 |
| 2 * 6 | 4 * 6 | 6 * 6 | 8 * 6 | 10 * 6 |
| 2 * 7 | 4 * 7 | 6 * 7 | 8 * 7 | 10 * 7 |
| 2 * 8 | 4 * 8 | 6 * 8 | 8 * 8 | 10 * 8 |
| 2 * 9 | 4 * 9 | 6 * 9 | 8 * 9 | 10 * 9 |
| 2 * 10 | 4 * 10 | 6 * 10 | 8 * 10 | 10 * 10 |

✧ *Math Masters,* p. 11

# Build Background for Unit 2

## ✦ Math Boxes 1.10 (*Math Journal 1,* p. 28)

INDEPENDENT ACTIVITY 

**Mixed Review** The skills in Problems 1–5 are prerequisites for Unit 2.

### Math Boxes 1.10

1. a. Write a 7-digit numeral with 3 in the tens place, 5 in the hundredths place, 7 in the hundreds place, 2 in the ten-thousands place, and 4s in all other places.
   2 4, 7 3 4 . 4 5
   b. Write this numeral in words.
   Twenty-four thousand, seven hundred thirty-four and forty-five hundredths

2. Phoebe received these math test scores: 93, 96, 85, 100, 98, 100, 99, 95.
   a. Maximum 100
   b. Minimum 85
   c. Range 15
   d. Median 97

3. Complete.
   a. 27,000 = 300 ∗ 90
   b. 480,000 = 800 ∗ 600
   c. 5,600,000 = 700 ∗ 8,000
   d. 30,000 = 50 ∗ 600
   e. 350 = 7 ∗ 50

4. Write < or >.
   a. 0.90 > 0.89
   b. 3.52 < 3.8
   c. 6.91 > 6.3
   d. 4.05 < 4.2
   e. 0.38 < 0.5

5. Solve.
   a. 207 − 158 = 49
   b. 325 + 116 = 441
   c. 829 + 580 = 1,409
   d. 628 − 444 = 184
   e. 385 − 179 = 206
   f. 523 + 478 = 1,001

STUDENT PAGE

✦ *Math Journal 1,* p. 28

## ✦ Study Link 1.10: Unit 2 Family Letter (*Math Masters,* pp. 223–226)

**Home Connection** This Study Link is a four-page newsletter that introduces parents and guardians to Unit 2's topics and terms. The letter also offers ideas for mathematics activities that are supportive of classroom work and can be done at home.

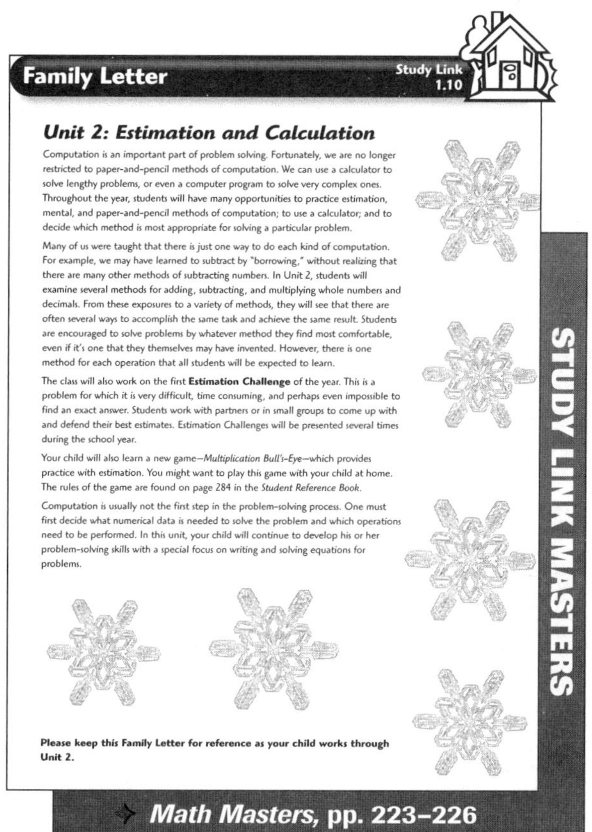

**Family Letter** Study Link 1.10

***Unit 2: Estimation and Calculation***

Computation is an important part of problem solving. Fortunately, we are no longer restricted to paper-and-pencil methods of computation. We can use a calculator to solve lengthy problems, or even a computer program to solve very complex ones. Throughout the year, students will have many opportunities to practice estimation, mental, and paper-and-pencil methods of computation; to use a calculator; and to decide which method is most appropriate for solving a particular problem.

Many of us were taught that there is just one way to do each kind of computation. For example, we may have learned to subtract by "borrowing," without realizing that there are many other methods of subtracting numbers. In Unit 2, students will examine several methods for adding, subtracting, and multiplying whole numbers and decimals. From these exposures to a variety of methods, they will see that there are often several ways to accomplish the same task and achieve the same result. Students are encouraged to solve problems by whatever method they find most comfortable, even if it's one that they themselves may have invented. However, there is one method for each operation that all students will be expected to learn.

The class will also work on the first **Estimation Challenge** of the year. This is a problem for which it is very difficult, time consuming, and perhaps even impossible to find an exact answer. Students work with partners or in small groups to come up with and defend their best estimates. Estimation Challenges will be presented several times during the school year.

Your child will also learn a new game—*Multiplication Bull's-Eye*—which provides practice with estimation. You might want to play this game with your child at home. The rules of the game are found on page 284 in the *Student Reference Book*.

Computation is usually not the first step in the problem-solving process. One must first decide what numerical data is needed to solve the problem and which operations need to be performed. In this unit, your child will continue to develop his or her problem-solving skills with a special focus on writing and solving equations for problems.

**Please keep this Family Letter for reference as your child works through Unit 2.**

STUDY LINK MASTERS

✦ *Math Masters,* pp. 223–226

# Unit 2
# Estimation and Computation

## overview

Unit 2 focuses on three topics: estimation, computational procedures, and data analysis.

Algorithms for addition, subtraction, and multiplication are reviewed and extended to decimals. The importance of making estimates is emphasized, since estimates are used both as acceptable answers in certain situations and as a means of checking that an answer to a computational problem is reasonable.

*Everyday Mathematics* continues to emphasize data analysis and probabilities linked to data gathering. Students perform experiments, gather and analyze data, make predictions, and draw conclusions.

Students also extend their understanding of numbers through an exploration that addresses the enormous differences between millions, billions, and trillions—words often heard on TV and seen in the newspaper, but often not clearly understood.

# contents

# learning goals in perspective

| learning goals | links to the past | links to the future |
|---|---|---|
| 2a **Beginning Goal** Write and solve open sentences for number stories. **(Lesson 2.4)** | Grades 1-3: Introduce and use the relation symbols (=, >, <); use situation diagrams to organize information and solve number stories.<br>Grades 3-4: Introduce problem-solving steps for solving number stories.<br>Grade 4: Use situation diagrams to write open sentences for number stories. | Grade 5: Use number sentences to represent multiplication and division number stories; use a variable to represent a range of values; substitute for variables in open sentences (Unit 4).<br>Grade 6: Solve inequalities; define equivalent equations; use a systematic method to simplify and solve equations. |
| 2b **Developing Goal** Round numbers to designated places. **(Lesson 2.7)** | Grades 1-4: Round numbers to solve number stories; round numbers to make magnitude estimates for addition, subtraction, multiplication, and division problems. | Grade 5: Round numbers to estimate answers to decimal multiplication and division problems (Unit 4); round decimals up, down, and to the nearest place (Unit 5). |
| 2c **Developing/Secure Goal** Make magnitude estimates. **(Lesson 2.7)** | See Goal 2b. | See Goal 2b. |
| 2d **Developing/Secure Goal** Find the product of multidigit whole numbers and decimals. **(Lessons 2.8 and 2.9)** | Grade 3: Introduce the partial-products and lattice methods for multiplying whole numbers. Model the partial-products method with base-10 blocks and arrays.<br>Grade 4: Extend the partial-products and lattice multiplication methods to products of whole numbers and decimals. | Grades 4-6: Applications and maintenance to develop proficiency with the partial-products and lattice algorithms for whole number and decimal multiplication.<br>Grade 6: Discuss the traditional shortcut for placing the decimal point correctly in decimal products. |
| 2e **Developing/Secure Goal** Know place value to billions. **(Lesson 2.10)** | Grades 1-4: Develop place-value concepts using base-10 blocks, place-value books, slate routines, and games.<br>Grade 4: Extend place value to 100 millions; write place value as powers of 10. | Grade 5: Discuss the reliability of big numbers in context (Unit 3); review exponential notation, introduce negative exponents and scientific notation (Unit 7).<br>Grade 6: Extend place value to trillions and to thousandths; read and write both large and small numbers in scientific notation. |
| 2f **Secure Goal** Find the sum and difference of multidigit whole numbers and decimals. **(Lessons 2.2 and 2.3)** | Grades 1-3: Invent, share, and discuss paper-and-pencil methods for adding and subtracting multidigit whole numbers.<br>Grade 4: Extend whole-number addition and subtraction methods to 1- and 2-place decimals. | Grades 4-6: Applications and maintenance to develop proficiency with the focus algorithms for whole number and decimal addition (the partial-sums method) and subtraction (the trade-first method). |
| 2g **Secure Goal** Identify the maximum, minimum, median, mode, and mean for a data set. **(Lesson 2.5)** | Grades 1-2: Define and calculate minimum, maximum, middle value (median), and mode by tallying or listing data.<br>Grades 3-4: Define and calculate mean (average) and range. Use tally charts, lists, line plots, and bar graphs to determine landmarks. | Grade 5: Use stem-and-leaf plots to organize data, calculate landmarks, and match mystery plots to data sets (Unit 6).<br>Grade 6: Applications and maintenance, using larger data sets and more complicated contexts. |

# assessment

## ongoing • product • periodic

### Informal Assessment

**Math Boxes** These *Math Journal* pages provide opportunities for cumulative review or assessment of concepts and skills.

**Ongoing Assessment: Kid Watching** Use the Ongoing Assessment suggestions in the following lessons to make quick, on-the-spot observations about students' understanding of:

- Operation and Computation **(Lesson 2.3, Part 1; Lesson 2.8, Part 1; Lesson 2.9, Part 1; Lesson 2.10, Part 1)**
- Data and Chance **(Lesson 2.5, Part 1; Lesson 2.6, Part 1)**
- Numeration **(Lesson 2.10, Part 1)**

**Portfolio Ideas** Samples of students' work may be obtained from the following assignments:

- Reading a Book about Estimation **(Lesson 2.1)**
- Finding the Statistical Landmarks for a Set of Data **(Lesson 2.5)**
- Conducting Spinner Experiments **(Lesson 2.6)**
- Exploring an Ancient Multiplication Method **(Lesson 2.9)**
- Solving a Large Number Problem **(Lesson 2.10)**
- Write Place-Value Puzzles **(Lesson 2.11)**

### Unit 2 Review and Assessment

**Math Message** Use Time to Reflect Problem 2 in Lesson 2.11 to assess students' progress toward the following learning goal: **Goal 2d**

**Oral and Slate Assessments** Use oral or slate assessments during Lesson 2.11 to assess students' progress toward the following learning goals: **Goals 2b, 2d, and 2e**

**Written Assessment** Use a written review during Lesson 2.11 to assess students' progress toward the following learning goals: **Goals 2a–2g**

**Alternative Assessment Options** Use independent alternative assessments in Lesson 2.11 to assess students' progress toward the following learning goals: **Goals 2e and 2f**

## assessmenthandbook

For more information on how to use different types of assessment in Unit 2, see the Assessment Overview on pages 39–41 in the *Assessment Handbook.* The following Assessment Masters can be found in the *Math Masters* book:

- Unit 2 Checking Progress, pp. 381–383
- Unit 2 Individual Profile of Progress, p. 431
- Unit 2 Class Checklist, p. 430
- Class Progress Indicator, p. 471
- Math Logs, pp. 474 and 475
- Self-Assessment Forms, pp. 477 and 478
- Interest Inventories, pp. 472 and 473

# problemsolving

## *A process of modeling everyday situations using tools from mathematics.*

Encourage students to use a variety of strategies when attacking a given problem—and to explain those strategies. *Strategies students might use in this unit:*

- Use estimation
- Use logical reasoning
- Use open number sentences
- Use computation
- Act out the problem
- Use data in a table
- Use a number line (probability meter)

Four Problem-Solving **REPRESENTATIONS**

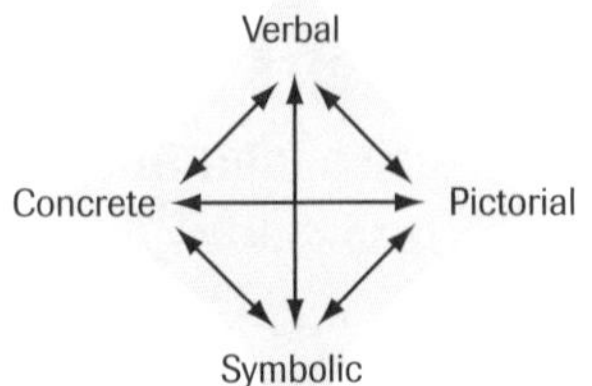


### Lessons that teach *through* problem solving, not just *about* problem solving

| Lesson | Activity | Lesson | Activity |
|---|---|---|---|
| **2.1** | About how many footsteps will you have to take to get to a destination? | **2.5** | Answer questions about winning speeds for the Indianapolis 500 race |
| **2.2** | Solve number-hunt puzzles. | **2.6** | What is the chance that a thumbtack will land point down? |
| **2.4, 2.7** | Write and solve number stories involving addition and subtraction. | **2.10** | How long would it take you to tap your desk 1 million times, without any interruptions? |
| **2.5** | Which of your hands has a quicker reaction time? | | |

For more information about problem solving in *Everyday Mathematics,* see the *Teacher's Reference Manual.*

# cross-curricularlinks

**literature**

- Read and discuss *Counting on Frank* by Rod Clement, a story about a boy who spends his days collecting facts and estimating quantities. **(Lesson 2.1)**
- Read and discuss a million, a billion, and a trillion in *How Much Is a Million?* by David M. Schwartz. **(Lesson 2.10)**

**science**

- Students experiment with reaction times to stimuli. **(Lesson 2.5)**

**social studies**

- Students estimate distances and times based on an imaginary trip. **(Lesson 2.1)**

**language arts**

- Discuss the origins of the word *algorithm.* **(Lesson 2.2)**

# meeting INDIVIDUAL needs

UNIVERSAL ACCESS

## ✦ RETEACHING

The following features provide some additional instructional support:

**Adjusting the Activity**

- **Lesson 2.2, Part 1**
- **Lesson 2.3, Part 1**
- **Lesson 2.4, Part 1**
- **Lesson 2.9, Part 1**

**Options for Individualizing**

- **Lesson 2.1** Discussing Estimation and Calculation Strategies
- **Lesson 2.7** Playing *Beat the Calculator* with Extended Facts
- **Lesson 2.8** Modeling the Partial-Products Method with Base-10 Blocks
- **Lesson 2.10** Playing *Number Top-It*

## ✦ ENRICHMENT

The following features suggest enrichment and extension activities:

**Adjusting the Activity**

- **Lesson 2.1, Part 1**
- **Lesson 2.6, Part 1**

**Options for Individualizing**

- **Lesson 2.1** Reading a Book about Estimation
- **Lesson 2.2** Solving Place-Value Puzzles
- **Lesson 2.4** Solving Challenging Number Stories
- **Lesson 2.5** Displaying Reaction Time in Line Plots
- **Lesson 2.6** Making Predictions Based on Outcomes of a Probability Experiment
- **Lesson 2.9** Exploring an Ancient Multiplication Method
- **Lesson 2.10** Solving a Large Number Problem
- **Lesson 2.10** Reading about Large Numbers

## ✦ LANGUAGE DIVERSITY

The following features suggest ways to support students who are acquiring proficiency in English:

**Adjusting the Activity**

- **Lesson 2.6, Part 1**

**Options for Individualizing**

- **Lesson 2.1** Listing and Using Estimation Vocabulary
- **Lesson 2.4** Writing Addition and Subtraction Number Stories
- **Lesson 2.5** Building Background for Mathematics Words

## ✦ MULTIAGE CLASSROOM

The following chart lists related lessons from Grades 4 and 6 that can help you meet your instructional needs:

| **Grade 4** | | 2.3<br>2.4<br>2.7<br>4.4 | 2.3<br>2.4<br>2.7<br>2.9 | 2.2<br>3.7<br>3.10<br>6.3 | | | 5.4 | 3.1–<br>3.3<br>5.1 | 3.1–<br>3.3<br>5.7 | 5.8 | |
|---|---|---|---|---|---|---|---|---|---|---|---|
| **Grade 5** | 2.1 | 2.2 | 2.3 | 2.4 | 2.5 | 2.6 | 2.7 | 2.8 | 2.9 | 2.10 | 2.11 |
| **Grade 6** | | 2.1 | 2.1 | 6.3 | | 7.1–<br>7.3 | | 2.2<br>2.3 | | 2.5 | |

# materials

| lesson | math masters pages | manipulative kit items | other items |
|---|---|---|---|
| **2.1** | Study Link Master, p. 227<br>Teaching Master, p. 4 | 2 regular dice<br>4 each of the number cards 1–10<br>slate | yardstick, meterstick, or tape measure;<br>copy of road map per partnership or small group (optional)<br>clock or watch; calculator; 4 pennies<br>a Multiplication/Division Facts Table (optional)<br>*Counting on Frank* by Rod Clement<br>***See* Advance Preparation, p. 74** |
| **2.2** | Study Link Master, p. 228<br>Teaching Masters, p. 12 (optional); and p. 13<br>***See* Advance Preparation, p. 79** | | slate |
| **2.3** | Study Link Master, p. 229<br>Teaching Master, p. 12 (optional)<br>***See* Advance Preparation, p. 85** | 4 each of the number cards 0–10, per partnership | slate |
| **2.4** | Study Link Master, p. 230<br>Teaching Masters, pp. 12 and 14 | 4 each of the number cards 0–9, per partnership | |
| **2.5** | Study Link Master, p. 231<br>Teaching Master, p. 15 | | calculator; scissors<br>dictionary (optional)<br>a timer such as a stopwatch, a digital watch, or a clock<br>stick-on notes (optional)<br>***See* Advance Preparation, p. 98** |
| **2.6** | Study Link Master, p. 232<br>Teaching Master, p. 16<br>Assessment Master, p. 479 (optional) | | Per partnership: 10 thumbtacks or other counters; small cup; large paper clip; red, blue, and green crayons or coloring pencils; straightedge<br>Per group: paper bag; 8 blocks (in 3 colors); slate (optional)<br>Probability Meter Poster; stick-on notes; calculator<br>***See* Advance Preparation, p. 104** |
| **2.7** | Study Link Master, p. 233<br>***See* Advance Preparation, p. 110** | Per partnership: 1 six-sided die; 4 each of the number cards 0–10 | Per partnership: slate; calculator |
| **2.8** | Study Link Master, p. 234<br>transparencies of Teaching Masters, pp. 17 and 18<br>***See* Advance Preparation, p. 114** | | overhead marker<br>base-10 blocks |
| **2.9** | Study Link Master, p. 235<br>Teaching Masters, p. 19 (optional); and pp. 20 and 21<br>Assessment Master, p. 479 (optional)<br>***See* Advance Preparation, p. 120** | | |
| **2.10** | Study Link Master, p. 236<br>Teaching Masters, pp. 22 and 23<br>Assessment Master, p. 479 (optional) | 4 each of the number cards 0–9, per partnership | half-sheets of paper; calculator;<br>watch or timer with second hand<br>*How Much Is a Million?* by David M. Schwartz<br>***See* Advance Preparation, p. 125** |
| **2.11** | Study Link Masters, pp. 237–240<br>Teaching Masters, pp. 12, 13, 22, and 23<br>Assessment Masters, pp. 381–383 | 4 each of the number cards 0–9, per partnership | slate |

# planningtips

## Pacing

Pacing depends on a number of factors, such as students' individual needs and how long your school has been using *Everyday Mathematics*. At the beginning of Unit 2, review your Content by Strand Poster to help you set a monthly pace.

| ← MOST CLASSROOMS → | | |
|---|---|---|
| SEPTEMBER | OCTOBER | NOVEMBER |

## Using the Projects

Use Project 3, An Ancient Multiplication Algorithm, during or after Unit 2 to examine a multiplication algorithm that was invented in Egypt more than 4,000 years ago. In this project, students examine several examples of this algorithm and try to figure out how the algorithm works. Then they use it to solve multiplication problems. Students also explore a variation of the ancient Egyption method. Use Project 4, Magic Computation Tricks, during or after Unit 2 to figure out, perform, and explain computation tricks. The Projects can be found at the back of this book.

## Home Communication

Share Study Links 2.1–2.10 with families to help them understand the content and procedures in this unit. At the end of the unit, use Study Link 2.11 to introduce Unit 3. Supplemental information can be found in the *Home Connection Handbook.*

## NCTM Standards

| Standard | 1 | 2 | 3 | 4 | 5 | 6 | 7 | 8 | 9 | 10 |
|---|---|---|---|---|---|---|---|---|---|---|
| Unit 2 Lessons | 2.2, 2.3, 2.5, 2.7, 2.10 | 2.4 | | 2.1 | 2.5, 2.6 | 2.1–2.11 | 2.1–2.11 | 2.1–2.11 | 2.1–2.11 | 2.1–2.11 |

**Content Standards**
- **1** Number and Operations
- **2** Algebra
- **3** Geometry
- **4** Measurement
- **5** Data Analysis and Probability

**Process Standards**
- **6** Problem Solving
- **7** Reasoning and Proof
- **8** Communication
- **9** Connections
- **10** Representation

## PRACTICE through Games

*Everyday Mathematics* uses games to help students develop good fact power and other math skills.

- *Beat the Calculator* to practice multiplication facts and extended facts **(Lessons 2.1 and 2.7)**
- *Baseball Multiplication* to practice multiplication facts **(Lesson 2.1)**
- *Getting to One* to practice estimation and using trial-and-error to find mystery numbers **(Lesson 2.1)**
- *Addition Top-It* to practice addition facts **(Lesson 2.3)**
- *Subtraction Target Practice* to practice subtraction facts **(Lessons 2.3 and 2.11)**
- *High-Number Toss* to practice comparing decimals **(Lesson 2.4)**
- *Multiplication Bull's-Eye* to practice estimating products **(Lesson 2.7)**
- *Multiplication Wrestling* to practice using the partial-products algorithm **(Lesson 2.8)**
- *Number Top-It* to practice comparing numbers **(Lesson 2.10)**

# unit 2 content highlights

*The discussion below highlights the major content ideas presented in Unit 2. These discussions may help you establish instructional priorities.*

## Estimation Challenge (Lesson 2.1)

The Estimation Challenge is a new routine in *Everyday Mathematics*. Several times during the year, students will be presented with a problem for which finding an exact answer is difficult, time-consuming, or even impossible. They will be challenged to come up with best estimation strategies and will be asked to defend their choices.

Typically, the problem will be introduced in class and discussed briefly. Then students will be given one or more days to think about the problem and prepare their estimates. The spirit of the challenge is one of open inquiry. Students should be given as little direction as possible. The challenges promote both estimation skills and problem formulation.

About how many base-10 cubes are in the basket?

NOTE: Students should not use their calculators while exploring and practicing the algorithms for adding and subtracting multidigit numbers. The journal pages, Study Links, and Assessment Masters with these lessons are marked with the "no-calculator" icon to remind students of this. However, calculator usage is encouraged in other parts of the program. For example, students might use a calculator in solving an Estimation Challenge or in working on some of the problems in Lesson 2.10.

## Addition and Subtraction Algorithms (Lessons 2.2 and 2.3)

Lessons 2.2 and 2.3 focus on algorithms for addition and subtraction. Students first review methods for adding and subtracting multidigit whole numbers. These methods are then extended to decimals. This process is easy; the only new task is keeping track of decimal place values along with whole-number place values.

Computational algorithms are systematic procedures, and they are important in mathematics. In programming computers, for example, systematic procedures are developed for working out complex calculations. But in a calculator and computer age, the authors believe that the usual school attention to drilling and enforcing particular algorithms for doing complex paper-and-pencil calculations is not worthwhile. The plain truth is that if a person has many calculations to do, the sensible choice is to reach for a calculator, to program the calculations into a computer, or to use a computer spreadsheet or other software to make the calculations. This is not to say that students should not learn to perform paper-and-pencil calculations; but it is not the goal of *Everyday Mathematics* to enable students to do all the things that a $5.00 calculator can do for them.

The authors also believe that it is harmful to suggest to students that there is only one proper way to do each operation. Hence, *Everyday Mathematics* exposes students to several methods for adding, subtracting, multiplying, and dividing whole numbers and decimals. For each of these operations, all students are expected to know a particular algorithm. (For addition, it is the partial-sums algorithm; for subtraction, the trade-first algorithm.) But they are encouraged to use whatever algorithm they like to solve problems, or even invent one of their own.

NOTE: For students who have already learned reliable addition and subtraction algorithms, these lessons remind them that there is more than one way to solve a problem. Students who are still struggling have an opportunity to learn reliable methods that will work for them.

## Magnitude Estimates (Lesson 2.7)

It is often useful to know a rough ballpark answer to a problem: Is the number less than 1? Is it in the hundreds? In the thousands? In the millions? In the billions? In science and in other applications, "orders of magnitude" are powers of 10, and **magnitude estimates** are powers-of-10 estimates.

The magnitude-estimate routine invites students to estimate the magnitude of answers to problems in advance and to mark their estimates on a magnitude bar. Eventually this routine will become part of "inner speech"—the conversation a student should have with himself or herself (silently or aloud) while solving problems: "Is the answer I'm looking for in the tens? Hundreds? Thousands?" With well-developed intuition, students can make many decisions, and know when they have gotten a silly result on a calculator or when information doesn't make sense.

## Multiplication Algorithms (Lessons 2.8 and 2.9)

In *Third* and *Fourth Grade Everyday Mathematics*, students were introduced to two multiplication algorithms: the **partial-products** algorithm and the **lattice** algorithm.

The partial-products algorithm is a low-stress algorithm. One may carry out the algorithm from left to right (although this is not required), so that, as with estimation, the largest products are obtained first. Every part of one factor is multiplied by every part of the other factor. Each *partial product* is written on a separate line. Adding partial products is usually fairly simple and has the additional benefit of providing practice with column addition. The partial-products algorithm also reinforces place-value skills. It encourages students to say to themselves which numbers, rather than which digits, are being multiplied. For example, in the problem in the margin, the first partial product is not 3 times 7, but 30 seventies, or 30 * 70.

**The Partial-Products Algorithm**

```
   75
*  32
 2100  (30 * 70)
  150  (30 * 5)
  140  (2 * 70)
   10  (2 * 5)
 2400
```

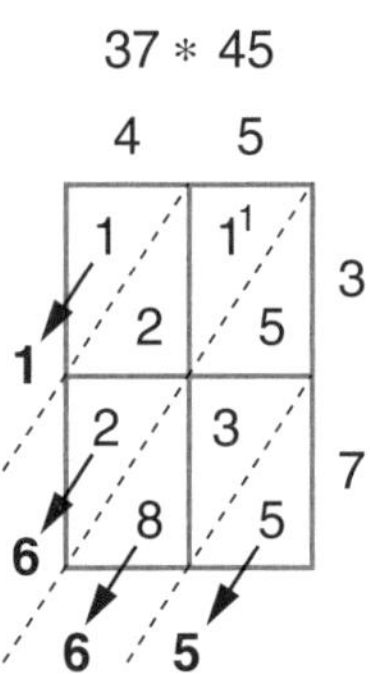


Lattice algorithm

$$\begin{array}{r} 75 \\ *\ \ 32 \\ \hline 150 \\ 2250 \\ \hline 2400 \end{array}$$

Right-to-left multiplication algorithm

The **lattice algorithm,** an ancient method invented in India, is popular with students because it requires only simple computations. However, while this algorithm makes it fairly easy to get a correct answer, it does not promote an understanding of the multiplication process. For this reason, all students are expected to learn the partial-products algorithm. However, remember that students may use any algorithm they wish when solving a problem.

As with the addition and subtraction algorithms presented in this program, both multiplication algorithms are easily extended to decimals.

Although the traditional **right-to-left multiplication algorithm** is not formally taught, the authors are not opposed to its use. If you decide to teach it, fill out each partial product with zeros rather than with blanks, and discuss the meaning of each of the steps. The authors recommend that it be taught as one of several multiplication algorithms.

## Using Open Sentences in Problem Solving (Lesson 2.4)

In Grades 1–3, students used **situation diagrams** to help them solve number stories involving addition and subtraction. They wrote number sentences after they solved a problem in order to summarize what they did. In Grade 4, students learned to use diagrams to help them write addition and subtraction open sentences (sentences containing a variable) for number stories. Then they solved the open sentences to find the answers to the stories. Diagrams were used as an intermediate step to writing open sentences. In Lesson 2.4, students are encouraged to write open sentences for number stories without first using a situation diagram. (See the *Teacher's Reference Manual* for a discussion of situation diagrams.) Work with number sentences will be extended throughout fifth and sixth grades in *Everyday Mathematics,* thus providing a solid foundation for the content of future middle- and high-school mathematics courses.

NOTE: The Grab-it Gauge used in Lesson 2.5 to measure reaction time has been calibrated to show the distance that an object will drop during the first $\frac{1}{4}$ second of free fall. (Because a falling object accelerates and will drop 4 feet during the first $\frac{1}{2}$ second, the gauge would have to be 4 feet long to measure reaction times up to $\frac{1}{2}$ second.)

## Collecting, Organizing, and Describing Data (Lessons 2.5 and 2.6)

Working with data provides both context and motivation for developing number skills and for practicing computation strategies. Many sources of data will be used during the school year. Students will gather their data in various ways. The lessons in this unit rely on counting and measuring in the classroom. In future lessons, students will collect data by observing and measuring at home, by taking surveys, and by recording information from reference books.

Lesson 2.5 reviews "landmarks" in the data: the *maximum, minimum, median, mean,* and *mode*. Students use landmarks as reference points when they discuss features of the data, just as cartographers use landmarks when they discuss maps.

The Probability Meter, a device used to record the data results that describe chances or probabilities of events, is introduced in Lesson 2.6. Consider attaching stick-on notes to the Probability Meter to indicate chance results. The meter is big enough to accommodate large displays—for a single day, or for much longer.

The Probability Meter can also be used for number-line work throughout the year. The meter is a number line from 0 to 1 that is marked to show fraction, decimal, and percent divisions. It can be used to find equivalent fractions, to convert fractions to decimals or to percents, to compare fractions or decimals, and so on.

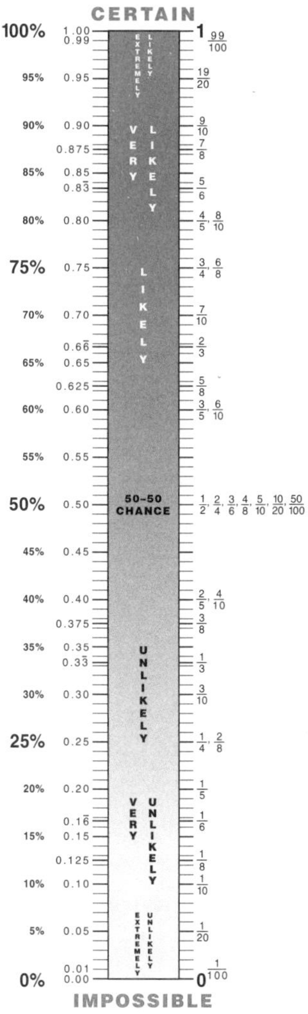

Probability Meter

## Comparing Millions, Billions, and Trillions (Lesson 2.10)

This lesson is designed to provide exposure to large numbers. Most people have a poor concept of the magnitude of large numbers. For example, it is not uncommon for children and even adults to view a billion as roughly twice as much as a million. Few people comprehend what "1,000 times as much" really means! To help students grasp the concept of 1,000 times, you might provide examples like the following:

- What can you buy with \$2 versus \$2,000? \$20 versus \$20,000?
- What type of transportation might you use to travel 24 miles? 24,000 miles?
- How long might it take you to read 2 pages of a book? 2,000 pages?

## Review and Assessment (Lesson 2.11)

Like every unit in *Fifth Grade Everyday Mathematics,* Unit 2 ends with a review and assessment lesson. This lesson provides a list of unit goals, as well as suggested questions for oral and slate evaluation. Assessment Masters provide review items for students to complete in writing; each item is keyed to a unit goal.

**For additional information on the following topics, see the *Teacher's Reference Manual:***

- algorithms
- estimation
- data collection, organization, and analysis
- extreme numbers
- teaching problem solving
- Probability Meter
- situation diagrams
- solving open sentences
- Why study probability?

# 2.1 Estimation Challenge

**OBJECTIVE** **To devise an estimation strategy to solve a problem for which finding an exact answer is impossible.**

| summaries | materials |
| --- | --- |
| **1 Teaching the Lesson** | |
| Students estimate the time and the number of steps it would take to get from school to a designated location. [Measurement and Reference Frames] | ☐ *Math Journal 1,* pp. 29 and 30<br>☐ copy of road map per partnership/small group (optional)<br>☐ yardstick, meterstick, or tape measure<br>☐ clock or watch ☐ calculator<br>***See* Advance Preparation** |
| **2 Ongoing Learning & Practice** | |
| Students practice multiplication facts by playing *Beat the Calculator* and *Baseball Multiplication.* [Operations and Computation]<br>Students practice and maintain skills through Math Boxes and Study Link activities. | ☐ *Math Journal 1,* p. 31<br>☐ *Student Reference Book,* pp. 259–261, 280<br>☐ Study Link Master (*Math Masters,* p. 227)<br>☐ Baseball Multiplication Playing Mat (*Math Masters,* p. 4)<br>☐ 4 each of the number cards 1–10 (from the Everything Math Deck, if available)<br>☐ a Multiplication/Division Facts Table (optional)<br>☐ calculator; 2 regular dice; 4 pennies |
| **3 Options for Individualizing** | |
| **Extra Practice** Students play *Getting to One* to practice the trial-and-error method in simple problem situations. [Patterns, Functions, and Algebra]<br>**Reteaching** Students discuss different situations to determine whether an estimate or an exact answer is more appropriate. [Measurement and Reference Frames]<br>**Enrichment** Students read a story about estimating quantities and create estimation problems. [Numeration; Measurement and Reference Frames]<br>**Language Diversity** Students make a list of estimation words and phrases. [Measurement and Reference Frames] | ☐ *Counting on Frank*<br>***See* Advance Preparation** |

## Additional Information

**Advance Preparation** For Part 1, select an interesting or noteworthy location that is 40 to 200 miles away from your school. Give students the approximate distance between the school and the selected destination. You may want to make copies of a road map that show the location of the school and the selected destination (1 copy for each partnership or group of 3 to 5 students). Students can use the map to choose a route and determine the distance between the two locations.

For the optional Enrichment activity in Part 3, obtain a copy of *Counting on Frank* by Rod Clement (Gareth Stevens, 1991).

# Getting Started

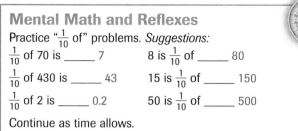

### Mental Math and Reflexes

Practice "$\frac{1}{10}$ of" problems. *Suggestions:*

$\frac{1}{10}$ of 70 is ____ 7 | 8 is $\frac{1}{10}$ of ____ 80

$\frac{1}{10}$ of 430 is ____ 43 | 15 is $\frac{1}{10}$ of ____ 150

$\frac{1}{10}$ of 2 is ____ 0.2 | 50 is $\frac{1}{10}$ of ____ 500

Continue as time allows.

### Math Message

*Pretend you have $5.00 to spend on school supplies. You want to buy a notebook for $2.49, a pen for $2.29, and a ruler for 79 cents. Do you have enough money?*

# 1 Teaching the Lesson

## Math Message Follow-Up

WHOLE-CLASS DISCUSSION

Students share solution strategies. Some may have found the exact total cost of the supplies: $2.49 + $2.29 + $0.79 = $5.57. Others may have used estimation: Round $2.49 to $2.50 and $2.29 to $2.30. Since $2.50 + $2.30 = $4.80, an additional 79 cents will bring the cost to more than 5 dollars.

Point out that in this situation, it is not necessary to find the exact total cost. An estimate will allow students to answer the question. In other situations, it is impossible or impractical to find the exact answer. The best way to address these situations is by making a good estimate.

## Introducing the Estimation Challenge Problem (*Math Journal 1,* pp. 29 and 30)

SMALL-GROUP ACTIVITY

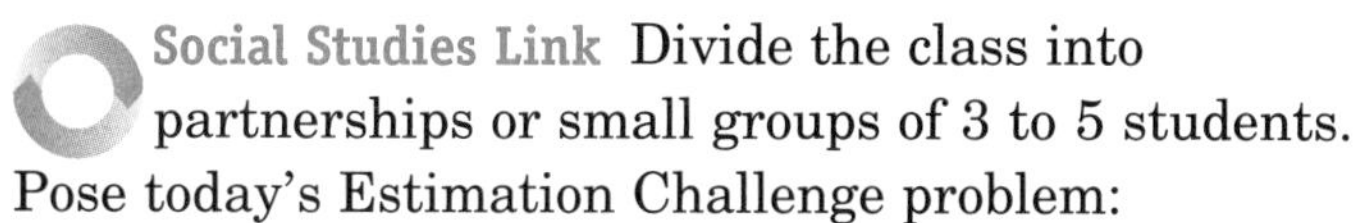

**Social Studies Link** Divide the class into partnerships or small groups of 3 to 5 students. Pose today's Estimation Challenge problem:

- About how many footsteps would it take to travel from school to *(name of destination you have chosen)*?
- About how long would it take to cover the distance with no stops to rest, eat, or sleep?
- About how long would it take, when taking the necessary stops into account?

If you made copies of a road map, pass out one copy to each group. If maps are not available, give students the approximate distance to the location and have them record this information in their journals.

**Estimation Challenge**

Sometimes you will be asked to solve a problem for which it is difficult, or even impossible, to find an **exact** answer. Your job will be to make your best estimate and then defend it. We call this kind of problem an **Estimation Challenge.**

Estimation Challenges can be difficult and they take time to solve. Usually, you will work with a partner or as part of a small group.

**Estimation Challenge Problem**

Imagine that you are living in a time when there are no cars, trains, or planes. You do not own a horse, a boat, or any other means of transportation.

You plan to travel to ____________ (location given by your teacher). You will have to walk there.

**Information needed to solve the problem.**

Definition of a "step." 1 mile = 5,280 feet

Length of a step

1. About how many miles is it from your school to your destination?
   About Answers vary. miles
2. a. About how many footsteps will you have to take to get from your school to your destination?
   About Answers vary. footsteps
   b. What did you do to estimate the number of footsteps you would take?
   Answers vary.

STUDENT PAGE

*Math Journal 1,* p. 29

**Adjusting the Activity** Use the following approach to challenge groups to answer their own questions, with little outside help.

Each member of the group is given a Question Token—a chip or an index card. If the group wants to ask the teacher a question, it hands in a token, but only after all members of the group agree on the question. When the group has used all its tokens, it may ask no more questions. Students will soon consider the questions very carefully before they ask them.

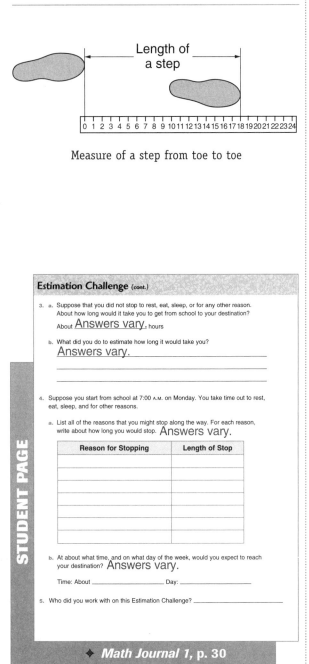

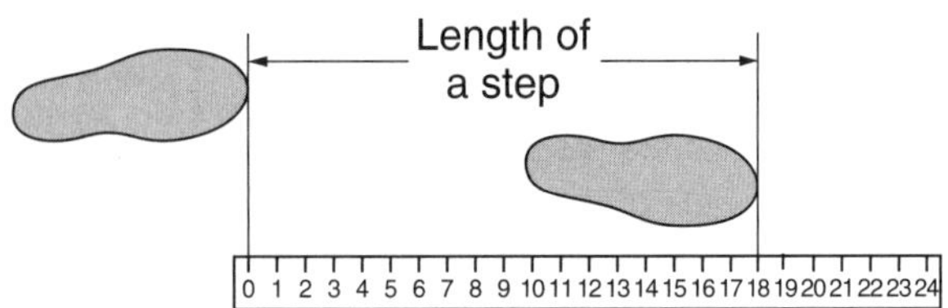


Measure of a step from toe to toe

**Estimation Challenge** (cont.)

3. a. Suppose that you did not stop to rest, eat, sleep, or for any other reason. About how long would it take you to get from school to your destination?
About Answers vary. hours

b. What did you do to estimate how long it would take you?
Answers vary.

4. Suppose you start from school at 7:00 A.M. on Monday. You take time out to rest, eat, sleep, and for other reasons.

a. List all of the reasons that you might stop along the way. For each reason, write about how long you would stop. Answers vary.

| Reason for Stopping | Length of Stop |
|---|---|
| | |
| | |
| | |
| | |
| | |
| | |
| | |

b. At about what time, and on what day of the week, would you expect to reach your destination? Answers vary.
Time: About ______ Day: ______

5. Who did you work with on this Estimation Challenge? ______

STUDENT PAGE

✦ *Math Journal 1*, p. 30

Discuss why it is not possible to find exact answers to Problems 2–4. Sample answers: Step length will vary. Walking speed will vary. Stopping along the way and the lengths of these stops cannot be predicted exactly.

Students should be encouraged to devise their own solution strategies. If necessary, help them plan how to proceed. One possible approach:

1. Use the scale or miles information on a road map to find the distance between school and the destination.
2. Measure the length of a typical step. Use this information to calculate the approximate number of steps in 1 mile. (1 mile = 5,280 feet)

   *Example:* Students in a group measure the length of their steps and find the median step length for their group. Students then divide 5,280 by the median step length. Suppose the median step length is $1\frac{1}{2}$ feet; then it will take about 3,520 steps to walk a mile. *(See the margin.)*
3. Estimate the number of steps between the two locations.

   *Example:* If the distance between locations is 200 miles, it will take about 200 ∗ 3,520 steps; or 704,000 steps to walk 200 miles.
4. Estimate an average distance you can walk in 1 minute. Use this information to estimate the amount of time it would take to walk the given distance.

   *Example:* Each student in a group walks for 1 minute and counts his or her steps. Students then find the median number of steps for their group. Suppose the median number of steps for 1 minute is 120 steps. Since each step is about $1\frac{1}{2}$ feet, a student will walk about 180 feet in 1 minute. To find the amount of time it will take to walk 1 mile, divide 5,280 by 180. It will take about 30 minutes or $\frac{1}{2}$ hour to walk 1 mile. To find out how long it would take to walk 200 miles, multiply 200 by $\frac{1}{2}$ hour. It will take about 100 hours to walk 200 miles without stops.

## ✦ Sharing Results (*Math Journal 1,* pp. 29 and 30)

WHOLE-CLASS DISCUSSION

When all groups have completed the Estimation Challenge problem, bring the class together to share their estimates and their strategies. This is an important part of the activity, so plan to provide an opportunity for all groups to make a contribution to the discussion.

Discussion questions might include:

- What information needed to solve the problem was not given to you?
- If you used a map, how did you determine the distance between the two locations?
- How did you determine the number of steps it would take to get to your destination?
- What were some of the factors that would affect your travel time?
- How did you determine how long it would take to walk this distance?
- How did you determine when you would reach your destination?

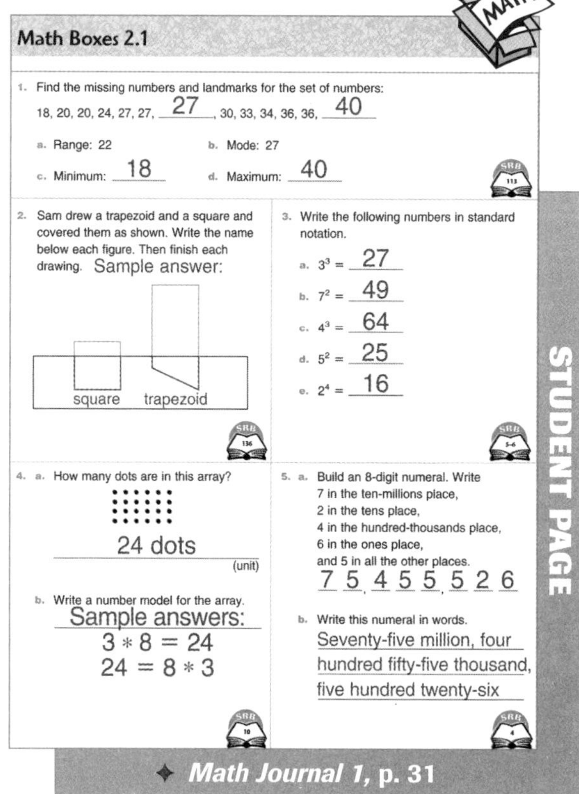
**Math Boxes 2.1**

1. Find the missing numbers and landmarks for the set of numbers:
18, 20, 20, 24, 27, 27, 27, 30, 33, 34, 36, 36, 40
a. Range: 22 b. Mode: 27
c. Minimum: 18 d. Maximum: 40

2. Sam drew a trapezoid and a square and covered them as shown. Write the name below each figure. Then finish each drawing. Sample answer:
square trapezoid

3. Write the following numbers in standard notation.
a. $3^3$ = 27
b. $7^2$ = 49
c. $4^3$ = 64
d. $5^2$ = 25
e. $2^4$ = 16

4. a. How many dots are in this array?
24 dots (unit)
b. Write a number model for the array.
Sample answers:
$3 * 8 = 24$
$24 = 8 * 3$

5. a. Build an 8-digit numeral. Write 7 in the ten-millions place, 2 in the tens place, 4 in the hundred-thousands place, 6 in the ones place, and 5 in all the other places.
7 5, 4 5 5, 5 2 6
b. Write this numeral in words.
Seventy-five million, four hundred fifty-five thousand, five hundred twenty-six

STUDENT PAGE

Math Journal 1, p. 31

## Ongoing Learning & Practice

NOTE: Students who have TI-15 calculators can also use the Arithmetic Training mode to practice multiplication facts. See *Math Masters,* pp 480–482.

### Playing Games Using Multiplication Facts (*Student Reference Book,* pp. 259–261; *Math Masters,* p. 4)

PARTNER ACTIVITY 

To help develop automaticity with multiplication facts, students play *Beat the Calculator* and *Baseball Multiplication.* The rules for these games are found in the *Student Reference Book.*

### Math Boxes 2.1 (*Math Journal 1,* p. 31)

INDEPENDENT ACTIVITY 

**Mixed Review** Math Boxes in this lesson are paired with Math Boxes in Lesson 2.3. The skill in Problem 1 is a prerequisite for Unit 3.

### Study Link 2.1 (*Math Masters,* p. 227)

**Home Connection** Students determine whether a measurement given in a context is too small, reasonable, or too large.

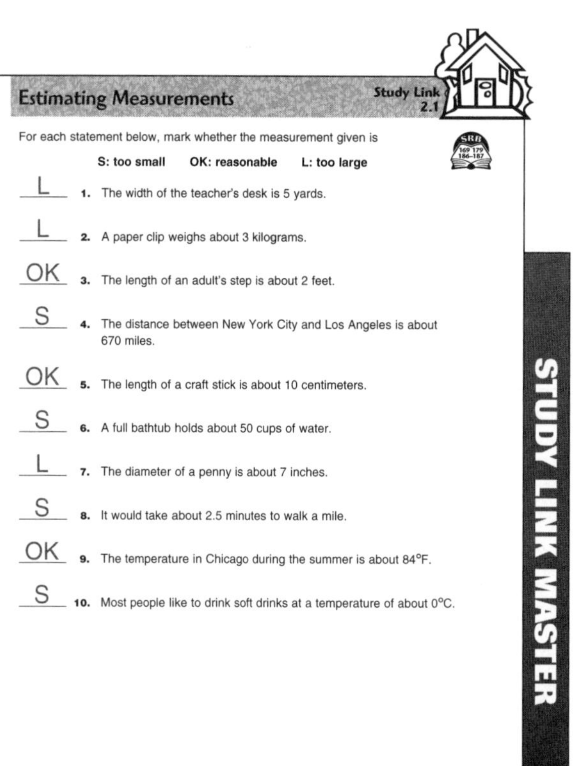
**Estimating Measurements** Study Link 2.1

For each statement below, mark whether the measurement given is
S: too small OK: reasonable L: too large

L 1. The width of the teacher's desk is 5 yards.
L 2. A paper clip weighs about 3 kilograms.
OK 3. The length of an adult's step is about 2 feet.
S 4. The distance between New York City and Los Angeles is about 670 miles.
OK 5. The length of a craft stick is about 10 centimeters.
S 6. A full bathtub holds about 50 cups of water.
L 7. The diameter of a penny is about 7 inches.
S 8. It would take about 2.5 minutes to walk a mile.
OK 9. The temperature in Chicago during the summer is about 84°F.
S 10. Most people like to drink soft drinks at a temperature of about 0°C.

STUDY LINK MASTER

Math Masters, p. 227

# 3 Options for Individualizing

## ✦ EXTRA PRACTICE Playing *Getting to One* (*Student Reference Book,* p. 280)

PARTNER ACTIVITY  **5–15 min**

Students play this game, introduced in *Fourth Grade Everyday Mathematics,* to practice using trial-and-error for guessing mystery numbers. This game also helps strengthen proportional reasoning skills.

Games

***Getting to One***

**Materials** ☐ calculator

**Players** 2

**Object of the game** To guess a mystery number in as few tries as possible.

**Directions**

1. Player A chooses a mystery number that is less than 100. Suppose the mystery number is 65.
2. Player B guesses the mystery number.
3. Player A uses a calculator to divide the guessed number by the mystery number. Player A then reads the answer that appears in the calculator display. If the answer has more than two decimal places, only the first two decimal places are read.
4. Player B continues to guess until the result is 1. Player B keeps track of the number of guesses.
5. When Player B has guessed the mystery number, players trade roles and follow Steps 1–4. The player who guesses the mystery number in the fewest number of guesses wins the round. The first player to win three rounds wins the game.

**EXAMPLE** Player A chooses the mystery number 65.

Player B guesses: 55. Player A keys in: 55 ÷ 65 Enter. Answer: 0.8461538462 Too small.

Player B guesses: 70. Player A keys in: 70 ÷ 65 Enter. Answer: 1.076923077 Too big.

Player B guesses: 65. Player A keys in: 65 ÷ 65 Enter. Answer: 1 Just right!

***Advanced Version*** Allow mystery numbers up to 1,000.

two hundred eighty

✦ *Student Reference Book,* p. 280

## ✦ RETEACHING Discussing Estimation and Calculation Strategies

SMALL-GROUP ACTIVITY  **5–15 min**

Some students may benefit from a discussion concerning situations in which an estimate is sufficient versus when it is more appropriate to be exact. Write students' suggestions on the board. *(See example in the margin.)*

| Estimation | Calculation |
|---|---|
| • length of time it takes to drive from Atlanta, Georgia, to Dallas, Texas | • amount of money that is in a savings account at the bank |
| • amount of water that is in a swimming pool | • amount of air that is in a scuba diver's tank and how long the air will last |

Examples of situations in which estimation is sufficient or calculations must be exact

## ✦ ENRICHMENT Reading a Book about Estimation

WHOLE-CLASS ACTIVITY  **15–30 min** 

**Literature Link** Students read the following book.

***Counting on Frank***

*Summary:* A boy spends his days collecting facts and estimating quantities.

Students can try to figure out the estimation strategies that Frank might have used. You may want to have students invent their own estimation problems by using situations inspired by those presented in this book.

Portfolio Ideas

## ✦ LANGUAGE DIVERSITY Listing and Using Estimation Vocabulary

SMALL-GROUP ACTIVITY  **5–15 min** 

Group students learning English with a few proficient English speakers and have them make a list of as many estimation words and phrases as they can. Encourage students to use each word in a sentence. A few examples are: *about, close, a little more than, a little less than, approximately, nearly, almost,* and so on.

# 2.2 Procedures for Addition of Whole Numbers and Decimals

**OBJECTIVES** **To review place-value concepts for whole numbers and decimals; and to add using the partial-sums and column-addition methods.**

| summaries | materials |
|---|---|
| **1 Teaching the Lesson** | |
| Students use place-value charts to review place-value concepts. [Numeration]<br>Students discuss examples of the partial-sums and column-addition methods. They use these methods as well as any other methods they know to solve problems. [Operations and Computation] | □ *Math Journal 1,* p. 32<br>□ *Student Reference Book,* pp. 13, 14, 27, 29, 30 and 35<br>□ Study Link 2.1<br>□ Teaching Master (*Math Masters,* p. 12; optional)<br>□ slate<br>***See*** **Advance Preparation** |
| **2 Ongoing Learning & Practice** | |
| Students practice and maintain skills through Math Boxes and Study Link activities. | □ Study Link Master (*Math Masters,* p. 228)<br>□ *Math Journal 1,* p. 33 |
| **3 Options for Individualizing** | |
| **Enrichment** Students solve place-value puzzles to identify numbers. [Numeration; Operations and Computation]<br>**Extra Practice** Students read and write decimals. [Numeration] | □ *Student Reference Book*, p. 27<br>□ Teaching Master (*Math Masters,* p. 13) |

### Additional Information

**Advance Preparation** For Part 1, you may want to review the partial-sums and column-addition methods before working with your students. You may want to distribute copies of the computation grid on *Math Masters,* page 12, for students to use as they do addition problems.

**Vocabulary • value • digit • place • place value • algorithm • partial-sums method • column-addition method**

## Getting Started

### Math Message

*Study the examples on page 27 of your* Student Reference Book. *Then write the following numbers in words on a half-sheet of paper:*

*6,028  112,303  0.27  4.925*

### Study Link 2.1 Follow-Up

Briefly go over the answers. Ask students to describe how they chose their answers.

## Mental Math and Reflexes

In the next few lessons, the Mental Math and Reflexes problems will focus on extended multiplication facts—that is, on products of multiples of powers of 10. These problems will prepare students for the work on multiplication algorithms that begins in Lesson 2.7.

Do not pose the problems orally; write each set of three problems on the board so that students can recognize a pattern. Have students write their answers on their slates.

| *Suggestions:* | **Set A** | **Set B** | **Set C** |
|---|---|---|---|
| | 7 * 10 70 | 4 * 10 40 | 10 [8s] 80 |
| | 7 * 30 210 | 4 * 60 240 | 90 [8s] 720 |
| | 70 * 30 2,100 | 40 * 60 2,400 | 90 [80s] 7,200 |

Discuss at least one set of problems. For example, for Set A, since 7 * 10 = 70, 7 * 30 is three times as much as 7 * 10, and 70 * 30 is ten times as much as 7 * 30.

NOTE: In *Everyday Mathematics,* brackets are used in phrases that name "so many of a certain amount." For example, 90 [80s] represents the phrase "90 eighties."

# 1 Teaching the Lesson

## ✦ Math Message Follow-Up (*Student Reference Book,* pp. 27, 29 and 30)

WHOLE-CLASS ACTIVITY

For each number, ask questions such as the following:

- How do you say this number? 6 thousand, 28; 112 thousand, 303; 27 hundredths or 0 point 27; 4 and 925 thousandths or 4 point 925
- What is the **value** of the **digit** 2 in this number? 20 in 6,028; 2,000 in 112,303; 2 tenths in 0.27; 2 hundredths in 4.925
- What **digit** is in the hundreds (tens, tenths, and so on) **place?** What is the **value** of that digit? 0 and 0 for 6,028; 3 and 3 hundred for 112,303

Your students' responses will help you assess their understanding of **place-value** concepts.

If you find that additional review is necessary, discuss the whole-number and decimal place-value examples on the *Student Reference Book* pages. Review the relationship between adjacent places:

▷ Each place has a value that is one-tenth the value of the place to its left. For example, 100 is $\frac{1}{10}$ of 1,000; 10 is $\frac{1}{10}$ of 100; 1 is $\frac{1}{10}$ of 10; 0.1 is $\frac{1}{10}$ of 1; 0.01 is $\frac{1}{10}$ of 0.1.

▷ Each place has a value that is 10 times the value of the place to its right. For example, 1,000 is 10 times as much as 100; 100 is 10 times as much as 10; 10 is 10 times as much as 1; 1 is 10 times as much as 0.1; 0.1 is 10 times as much as 0.01.

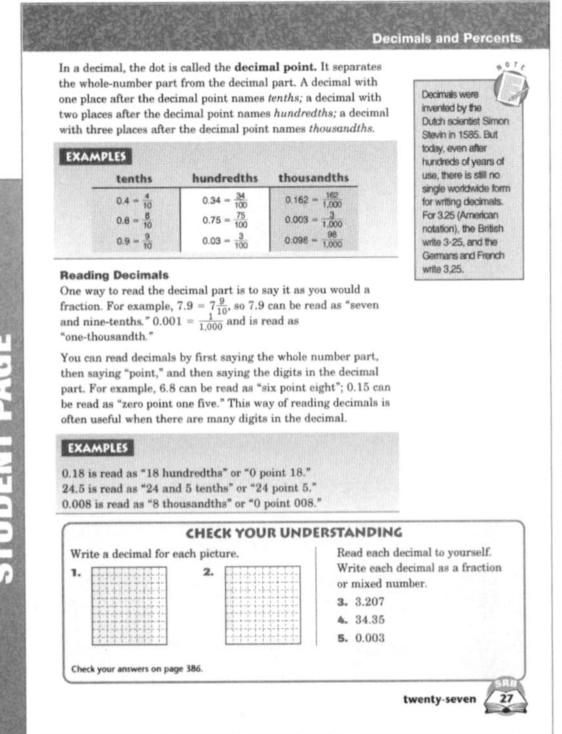

STUDENT PAGE

Decimals and Percents

In a decimal, the dot is called the **decimal point.** It separates the whole-number part from the decimal part. A decimal with one place after the decimal point names *tenths;* a decimal with two places after the decimal point names *hundredths;* a decimal with three places after the decimal point names *thousandths.*

NOTE: Decimals were invented by the Dutch scientist Simon Stevin in 1585. But today, even after hundreds of years of use, there is still no single worldwide form for writing decimals. For 3.25 (American notation), the British write 3·25, and the Germans and French write 3,25.

**EXAMPLES**

| tenths | hundredths | thousandths |
|---|---|---|
| $0.4 = \frac{4}{10}$ | $0.34 = \frac{34}{100}$ | $0.162 = \frac{162}{1{,}000}$ |
| $0.8 = \frac{8}{10}$ | $0.75 = \frac{75}{100}$ | $0.003 = \frac{3}{1{,}000}$ |
| $0.9 = \frac{9}{10}$ | $0.03 = \frac{3}{100}$ | $0.098 = \frac{98}{1{,}000}$ |

**Reading Decimals**

One way to read the decimal part is to say it as you would a fraction. For example, $7.9 = 7\frac{9}{10}$, so 7.9 can be read as "seven and nine-tenths." $0.001 = \frac{1}{1{,}000}$ and is read as "one-thousandth."

You can read decimals by first saying the whole number part, then saying "point," and then saying the digits in the decimal part. For example, 6.8 can be read as "six point eight"; 0.15 can be read as "zero point one five." This way of reading decimals is often useful when there are many digits in the decimal.

**EXAMPLES**

0.18 is read as "18 hundredths" or "0 point 18."
24.5 is read as "24 and 5 tenths" or "24 point 5."
0.008 is read as "8 thousandths" or "0 point 008."

**CHECK YOUR UNDERSTANDING**

Write a decimal for each picture.

1.

2.

Read each decimal to yourself. Write each decimal as a fraction or mixed number.

3. 3.207
4. 34.35
5. 0.003

Check your answers on page 386.

twenty-seven SRB 27

✦ *Student Reference Book,* p. 27

## ✦ Reviewing Addition Algorithms
(*Math Journal 1,* p. 32; *Student Reference Book,* pp. 13 and 35; *Math Masters,* p. 12)

WHOLE-CLASS DISCUSSION

Pose a few problems similar to the ones shown below. Have volunteers describe how they got their answers.

$39 + 23 = 62$

$1.56 + 8.72 = 10.28$

$$\begin{array}{r} 607 \\ 46 \\ +\ 239 \\ \hline 892 \end{array}$$

Most students probably have mastered an algorithm of their choice for addition. If they are comfortable with their algorithm, there is no reason for them to change to another one. However, it is strongly suggested that all students be able to use the partial-sums method since it helps students develop a good understanding of place value and addition.

NOTE: Since students have used the algorithms discussed below in *Fourth Grade Everyday Mathematics,* they may be able to proceed to the problems on journal page 32 with little preliminary whole-class practice.

### *The Partial-Sums Method*

All students are expected to know the **partial-sums method** for addition, even if they favor other addition methods.

In this method, addition is performed from left to right, column by column; the sum for each column is recorded on a separate line. The partial sums are added, either at each step or at the end. We suggest working from left to right because this is consistent with the process of making estimates.

Use examples like those on pages 13 and 35 of the *Student Reference Book* to demonstrate this method.

| *Example:* 348 + 177 = ? | | | 100s | 10s | 1s |
|---|---|---|---|---|---|
| | | | 3 | 4 | 8 |
| | | | + 1 | 7 | 7 |
| *Add the 100s:* | *300 + 100* | ⟶ | 4 | 0 | 0 |
| *Add the 10s:* | *40 + 70* | ⟶ | 1 | 1 | 0 |
| *Add the 1s:* | *8 + 7* | ⟶ | + | 1 | 5 |
| *Find the total:* | | | | | |
| | *400 + 110 + 15* | ⟶ | 5 | 2 | 5 |

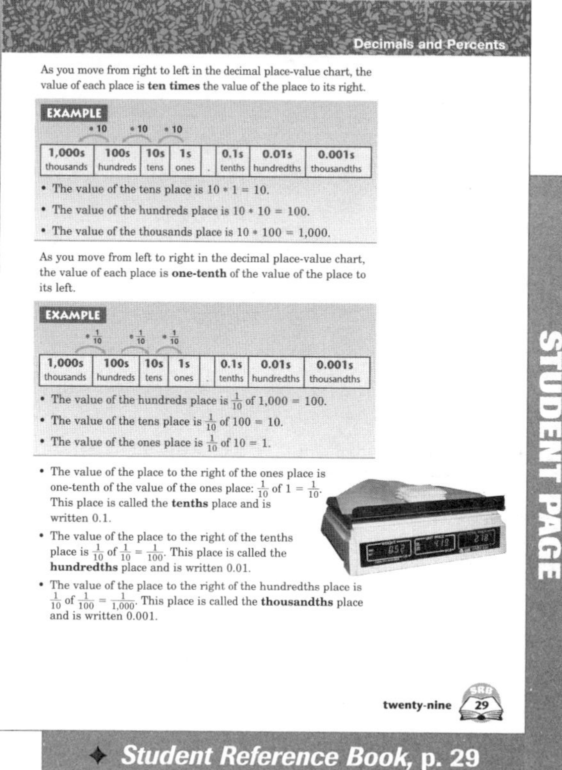
Decimals and Percents

As you move from right to left in the decimal place-value chart, the value of each place is **ten times** the value of the place to its right.

EXAMPLE

∗ 10 ∗ 10 ∗ 10

| 1,000s thousands | 100s hundreds | 10s tens | 1s ones | . | 0.1s tenths | 0.01s hundredths | 0.001s thousandths |
|---|---|---|---|---|---|---|---|

- The value of the tens place is 10 ∗ 1 = 10.
- The value of the hundreds place is 10 ∗ 10 = 100.
- The value of the thousands place is 10 ∗ 100 = 1,000.

As you move from left to right in the decimal place-value chart, the value of each place is **one-tenth** of the value of the place to its left.

EXAMPLE

∗ $\frac{1}{10}$ ∗ $\frac{1}{10}$ ∗ $\frac{1}{10}$

| 1,000s thousands | 100s hundreds | 10s tens | 1s ones | . | 0.1s tenths | 0.01s hundredths | 0.001s thousandths |
|---|---|---|---|---|---|---|---|

- The value of the hundreds place is $\frac{1}{10}$ of 1,000 = 100.
- The value of the tens place is $\frac{1}{10}$ of 100 = 10.
- The value of the ones place is $\frac{1}{10}$ of 10 = 1.

- The value of the place to the right of the ones place is one-tenth of the value of the ones place: $\frac{1}{10}$ of $1 = \frac{1}{10}$. This place is called the **tenths** place and is written 0.1.
- The value of the place to the right of the tenths place is $\frac{1}{10}$ of $\frac{1}{10} = \frac{1}{100}$. This place is called the **hundredths** place and is written 0.01.
- The value of the place to the right of the hundredths place is $\frac{1}{10}$ of $\frac{1}{100} = \frac{1}{1{,}000}$. This place is called the **thousandths** place and is written 0.001.

twenty-nine SRB 29

STUDENT PAGE

✦ *Student Reference Book,* p. 29

**Language Arts Link** The word ***algorithm*** is used to name a step-by-step procedure for solving a mathematical problem. The word is derived from the name of a ninth-century Muslim mathematician, Al-Khowarizimi. You may want to use it with your class—many students (and adults) delight in using esoteric words; you may find that some of your students have a budding interest in etymology (word origins).

NOTE: Neither you nor the students should record the part of the algorithm shown in italics. However, students should always keep in mind (and probably say aloud or to themselves) what numbers they are adding; for example, 500 + 200, not 5 + 2; 70 + 60, not 7 + 6.

STUDENT PAGE

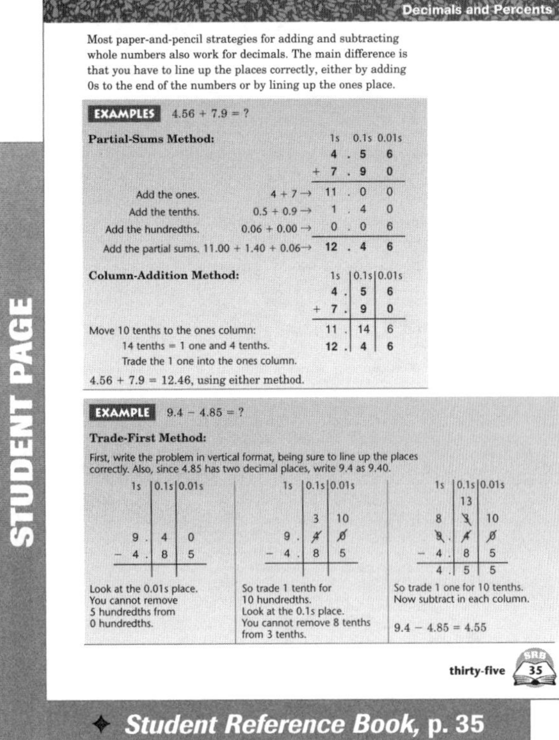

Decimals and Percents

Most paper-and-pencil strategies for adding and subtracting whole numbers also work for decimals. The main difference is that you have to line up the places correctly, either by adding 0s to the end of the numbers or by lining up the ones place.

**EXAMPLES** 4.56 + 7.9 = ?

**Partial-Sums Method:**

| | | 1s | 0.1s | 0.01s |
|---|---|---|---|---|
| | | 4 . | 5 | 6 |
| | | + 7 . | 9 | 0 |
| Add the ones. | 4 + 7 → | 11 . | 0 | 0 |
| Add the tenths. | 0.5 + 0.9 → | 1 . | 4 | 0 |
| Add the hundredths. | 0.06 + 0.00 → | 0 . | 0 | 6 |
| Add the partial sums. | 11.00 + 1.40 + 0.06 → | 12 . | 4 | 6 |

**Column-Addition Method:**

| | 1s | 0.1s | 0.01s |
|---|---|---|---|
| | 4 . | 5 | 6 |
| | + 7 . | 9 | 0 |
| Move 10 tenths to the ones column: | 11 . | 14 | 6 |
| 14 tenths = 1 one and 4 tenths. Trade the 1 one into the ones column. | 12 . | 4 | 6 |

4.56 + 7.9 = 12.46, using either method.

**EXAMPLE** 9.4 − 4.85 = ?

**Trade-First Method:**

First, write the problem in vertical format, being sure to line up the places correctly. Also, since 4.85 has two decimal places, write 9.4 as 9.40.

| 1s | 0.1s | 0.01s |
|---|---|---|
| 9 . | 4 | 0 |
| − 4 . | 8 | 5 |

Look at the 0.01s place. You cannot remove 5 hundredths from 0 hundredths.

| 1s | 0.1s | 0.01s |
|---|---|---|
| | 3 | 10 |
| 9 . | ~~4~~ | ~~0~~ |
| − 4 . | 8 | 5 |

So trade 1 tenth for 10 hundredths. Look at the 0.1s place. You cannot remove 8 tenths from 3 tenths.

| 1s | 0.1s | 0.01s |
|---|---|---|
| | 13 | |
| 8 | ~~3~~ | 10 |
| ~~9~~ . | ~~4~~ | ~~0~~ |
| − 4 . | 8 | 5 |
| 4 . | 5 | 5 |

So trade 1 one for 10 tenths. Now subtract in each column.

9.4 − 4.85 = 4.55

thirty-five 35

✦ *Student Reference Book*, p. 35

**Adjusting the Activity** Suggest to students who struggle with the decimal example to think in terms of dollars and cents.

STUDENT PAGE

Whole Numbers

**Addition Algorithms**

**Partial-Sums Method**

The **partial-sums method** is used to find sums mentally or with paper and pencil.

To use the partial-sums method, add from left to right, one column at a time. Then add the partial sums.

**EXAMPLE** 348 + 177 = ?

| | | 100s | 10s | 1s |
|---|---|---|---|---|
| | | 3 | 4 | 8 |
| | | + 1 | 7 | 7 |
| Add the 100s. | 300 + 100 → | 4 | 0 | 0 |
| Add the 10s. | 40 + 70 → | 1 | 1 | 0 |
| Add the 1s. | 8 + 7 → | | 1 | 5 |
| Add the partial sums. | 400 + 110 + 15 → | 5 | 2 | 5 |

348 + 177 = 525

**Column-Addition Method**

The **column-addition method** can be used to find sums with paper and pencil, but it is not a good method for finding sums mentally.

To add numbers using the column-addition method:

- Draw lines to separate the 1s, 10s, 100s, or any other places.
- Add the numbers in each column. Write each sum in its column.
- If the sum of any column is a 2-digit number, adjust that column sum. Trade part of the sum into the column to the left.

**EXAMPLE** 359 + 298 = ?

| | 100s | 10s | 1s |
|---|---|---|---|
| | 3 | 5 | 9 |
| | + 2 | 9 | 8 |
| Add the numbers in each column. | 5 | 14 | 17 |
| Adjust the 1s and 10s: 17 ones = 1 ten and 7 ones. Trade the 1 ten into the tens column. | 5 | 15 | 7 |
| Adjust the 10s and 100s: 15 tens = 1 hundred and 5 tens. Trade the 1 hundred into the hundreds column. | 6 | 5 | 7 |

359 + 298 = 657

thirteen 13

✦ *Student Reference Book*, p. 13

Remind students that each digit in a numeral has a value that depends on its place in the numeral.

| *Example:* 4.65 + 3.25 = ? | | 1s | 0.1s | 0.01s |
|---|---|---|---|---|
| | | 4. | 6 | 5 |
| | | + 3. | 2 | 5 |
| *Add the ones:* | *4 + 3* → | 7. | 0 | 0 |
| *Add the tenths:* | *0.6 + 0.2* → | 0. | 8 | 0 |
| *Add the hundredths:* | *0.05 + 0.05* → | + 0. | 1 | 0 |
| *Find the total:* | *7.00 + 0.80 + 0.10* → | 7. | 9 | 0 |

Stress that by this method, addition problems involving decimals are done in the same way as problems involving only whole numbers.

### *The Column-Addition Method*

The **column-addition method** has the advantage that it is similar to the traditional addition algorithm that most adults know. It can become a reliable method for students who are still struggling with addition.

Demonstrate the method using examples like those on pages 13 and 35 of the *Student Reference Book*. In this method, each column of numbers is added separately, and in any order.

▷ If adding results in a single digit in each column, the sum has been found.

▷ If the sum in any column is a 2-digit number, it is renamed and part of it is added to the sum in the column on its left.

This adjustment serves the same purpose as "carrying" in the traditional algorithm.

| *Example:* 359 + 298 = ? | 100s | 10s | 1s |
|---|---|---|---|
| | 3 | 5 | 9 |
| | + 2 | 9 | 8 |
| *Add the numbers in each column.* | 5 | 14 | 17 |
| *Adjust the ones and tens: 17 ones = 1 ten and 7 ones. Trade the 1 ten into the tens column.* | 5 | 15 | 7 |
| *Adjust the tens and hundreds: 15 tens = 1 hundred and 5 tens. Trade the 1 hundred into the hundreds column.* | 6 | 5 | 7 |

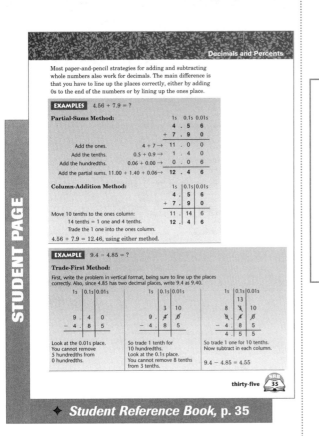

Stress that by this method, addition problems involving decimals are done in the same way as problems involving only whole numbers.

## ✦ Practicing Addition of Whole Numbers and Decimals (*Math Journal 1,* p. 32; *Student Reference Book,* pp. 13, 14, and 35)

PARTNER ACTIVITY

Students solve the problems on their own and then check each other's answers. Circulate and assist as needed.

Examples of addition of whole numbers are shown on pages 13 and 14 of the *Student Reference Book;* and examples of addition of decimals are shown on page 35.

## ✦ Sharing Results (*Math Journal 1,* p. 32)

WHOLE-CLASS DISCUSSION

Bring the class together to share solutions. Some possible discussion questions include:

- Which method of addition do you prefer? Why?
- What are some of the advantages of each method?
- What are some of the disadvantages?
- When might a particular method be useful? When might it not be useful?

# 2 Ongoing Learning & Practice

## ✦ Math Boxes 2.2 (*Math Journal 1,* p. 33)

INDEPENDENT ACTIVITY 

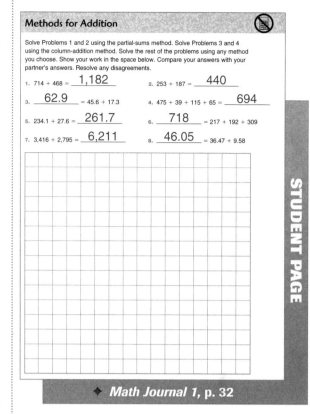

**Mixed Review** Math Boxes in this lesson are paired with Math Boxes in Lesson 2.4. The skill in Problem 1 is a prerequisite for Unit 3.

**Methods for Addition** 

Solve Problems 1 and 2 using the partial-sums method. Solve Problems 3 and 4 using the column-addition method. Solve the rest of the problems using any method you choose. Show your work in the space below. Compare your answers with your partner's answers. Resolve any disagreements.

1. 714 + 468 = 1,182
2. 253 + 187 = 440
3. 62.9 = 45.6 + 17.3
4. 475 + 39 + 115 + 65 = 694
5. 234.1 + 27.6 = 261.7
6. 718 = 217 + 192 + 309
7. 3,416 + 2,795 = 6,211
8. 46.05 = 36.47 + 9.58

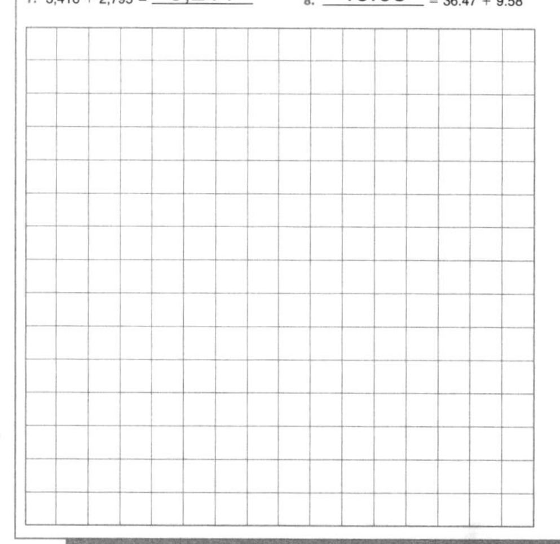

✦ Math Journal 1, p. 32

STUDENT PAGE

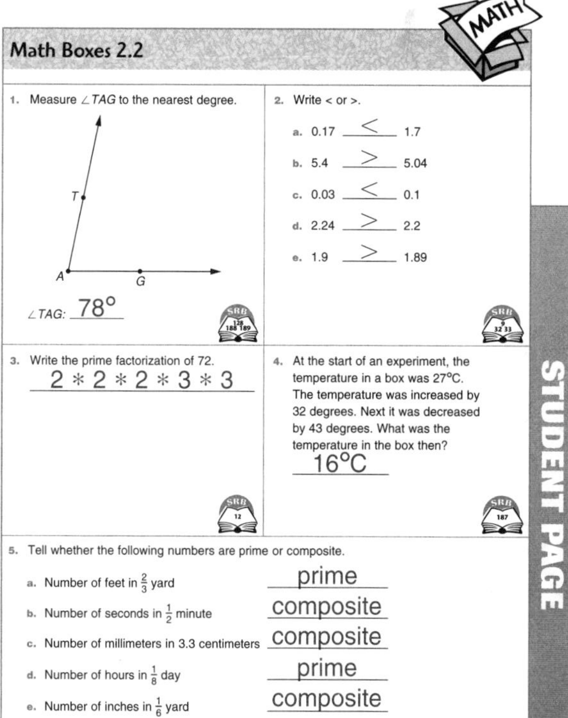
**Math Boxes 2.2**

1. Measure ∠*TAG* to the nearest degree.

∠*TAG*: 78°

2. Write < or >.
   a. 0.17 < 1.7
   b. 5.4 > 5.04
   c. 0.03 < 0.1
   d. 2.24 > 2.2
   e. 1.9 > 1.89

3. Write the prime factorization of 72.
   2 ∗ 2 ∗ 2 ∗ 3 ∗ 3

4. At the start of an experiment, the temperature in a box was 27°C. The temperature was increased by 32 degrees. Next it was decreased by 43 degrees. What was the temperature in the box then?
   16°C

5. Tell whether the following numbers are prime or composite.
   a. Number of feet in $\frac{2}{3}$ yard — prime
   b. Number of seconds in $\frac{1}{2}$ minute — composite
   c. Number of millimeters in 3.3 centimeters — composite
   d. Number of hours in $\frac{1}{8}$ day — prime
   e. Number of inches in $\frac{1}{6}$ yard — composite

✦ Math Journal 1, p. 33

STUDENT PAGE

**Number Hunt** Study Link 2.2

*Reminder:* A (no calculator symbol) means *"Do not use a calculator."*

Use the numbers in the following table to answer the questions below. You may not use a number more than once.

Sample answers:

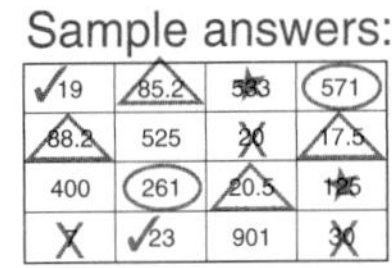

| ✓19 | △85.2 | ★533 | (571) |
|---|---|---|---|
| △88.2 | 525 | X20 | △17.5 |
| 400 | (261) | △20.5 | ★125 |
| X7 | ✓23 | 901 | X30 |

1. Circle two numbers whose sum is 832.
2. Make an X in the boxes containing three numbers whose sum is 57.
3. Make a check mark in the boxes containing two prime numbers whose sum is 42.
4. Make a star in the boxes containing two numbers whose sum is 658.
5. Make a triangle in the boxes containing two numbers whose sum is 105.7. Explain how you found the answer.
Sample answer: Since the sum has ".7" in the tenths place, look for numbers with tenths that add to 0.7. 85.2 + 20.5 = 105.7; and 88.2 + 17.5 = 105.7.

Solve Problems 6–9 using any method you want. Show your work in the space below.

6. 3,804 + 768 = 4,572
7. 2.83 + 1.57 = 4.4
8. 33 + 148 + 65 = 246
9. 1.055 + 0.863 = 1.918

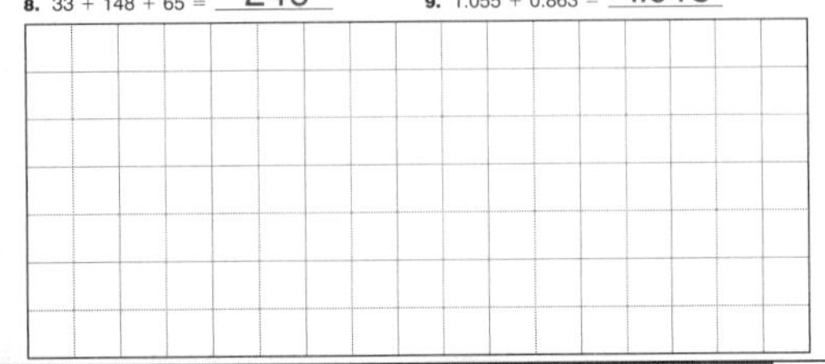

STUDY LINK MASTER

Math Masters, p. 228

## Study Link 2.2 (*Math Masters,* p. 228)

**Home Connection** Students practice estimating and finding sums. Students can solve problems using any method they choose.

# 3 Options for Individualizing

## ENRICHMENT Solving Place-Value Puzzles (*Math Masters,* p. 13)

INDEPENDENT ACTIVITY  **15–30 min** 

These number puzzles provide additional place-value review.

**Place-Value Puzzles**

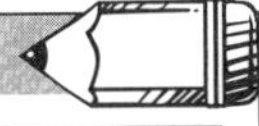

| Millions | | | Thousands | | | Ones | | |
|---|---|---|---|---|---|---|---|---|
| Hundred-millions | Ten-millions | Millions | Hundred-thousands | Ten-thousands | Thousands | Hundreds | Tens | Ones |
| | | | | | | | | |

Use the clues to solve the puzzles.

**Puzzle 1**

- The value of the digit in the **thousandths** place is equal to the sum of the measures of the angles in a triangle (180°) divided by 30.
- If you multiply the digit in the **tens** place by 1,000; the answer will be 9,000.
- Double 35. Divide the result by 10. Write the answer in the **tenths** place.
- The value of the digit in the **hundreds** place is $\frac{1}{2}$ the value of the digit in the thousandths place.
- When you multiply the digit in the **ones** place by itself, the answer is 0.
- Write a digit in the **hundredths** place so that the sum of all six digits in this number is 30.

**What is the number?** 3 9 0 . 7 5 6

**Puzzle 2**

- Double 12. Divide the result by 8. Write the answer in the **millions** place.
- If you multiply the digit in the **tens** place by 10, the answer will be 40.
- The digit in the **ten-thousands** place is a prime number. If you multiply it by itself, the answer will be 49.
- Multiply 7 and 3. Subtract 12. Write the answer in the **ones** place.
- Multiply the digit in the tens place by the digit in the millions place. Subtract 7 from the result. Write the answer in the **hundreds** place.
- The digit in the **thousands** place is an odd digit that has not been used yet.
- The value of the digit in the **hundred-thousands** place is the same as the number of sides of a quadrilateral.

**What is the number?** 3 , 4 7 1 , 5 4 9

***Check:*** The sum of the answers to both puzzles is 3,471,939.756.

TEACHING MASTER

Math Masters, p. 13

## EXTRA PRACTICE Reading and Writing Decimals (*Student Reference Book,* p. 27)

INDEPENDENT ACTIVITY  **15–30 min** 

For students who need additional review of place-value concepts, assign the Check Your Understanding problems on page 27 of the *Student Reference Book.*

# 2.3 Procedures for Subtraction of Whole Numbers and Decimals

**OBJECTIVE** **To subtract multidigit whole numbers and decimals by using the trade-first and partial-differences methods.**

| summaries | materials |
|---|---|
| **1 Teaching the Lesson** | |
| Students discuss examples of the trade-first and partial-differences methods; students use these methods, as well as any other methods they know to solve problems. [Operations and Computation] | □ *Math Journal 1,* p. 34<br>□ *Student Reference Book,* pp. 15–17, 35, and 36<br>□ Study Link 2.2<br>□ Teaching Master (*Math Masters,* p. 12; optional)<br>□ slate<br>***See*** **Advance Preparation** |
| **2 Ongoing Learning & Practice** | |
| Students play *Addition Top-It* to practice finding sums of whole numbers. [Operations and Computation]<br>Students practice and maintain skills through Math Boxes and Study Link activities. | □ *Math Journal 1,* p. 35<br>□ *Student Reference Book,* p. 294<br>□ Study Link Master (*Math Masters,* p. 229)<br>□ 4 each of the number cards 1–10 per partnership (from the Everything Math Deck, if available) |
| **3 Options for Individualizing** | |
| **Extra Practice** Students subtract multidigit whole numbers and decimals by playing *Subtraction Target Practice.* [Operations and Computation] | □ *Student Reference Book,* p. 292<br>□ Teaching Master (*Math Masters,* p. 12; optional)<br>□ 4 each of the number cards 0–9 per partnership (from the Everything Math Deck, if available)<br>***See*** **Advance Preparation** |

## Additional Information

**Advance Preparation** The Math Message provides an opportunity to evaluate students' mastery of paper-and-pencil subtraction. If most students do not demonstrate mastery, plan to spend a couple of days on this lesson. If only a few lack mastery, move on after one day. Students can practice subtraction by playing *Subtraction Target Practice* and by solving the problems on pages 15 and 16 of the *Student Reference Book.*

For Part 1, you may want to review the trade-first and partial-differences methods before working with your students.

For the optional activity in Part 3, review the directions for playing *Subtraction Target Practice.* Play it yourself before introducing the game to your class. You may want to distribute copies of the computation grid on *Math Masters,* page 12 for students to use as they do subtraction problems.

**Vocabulary • trade-first method • partial-differences method**

**Vocabulary (teacher) • minuend**

# Getting Started

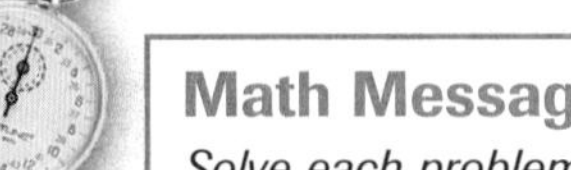

### Mental Math and Reflexes

Write each set of problems on the board.
Have students write answers on their slates.

| Set A | Set B | Set C |
|---|---|---|
| 8 * 4 32 | 60 * 2 120 | 30 [10s] 300 |
| 8 * 40 320 | 60 * 20 1,200 | 300 [10s] 3,000 |
| 80 * 400 32,000 | 60 * 200 12,000 | 300 [100s] 30,000 |

### Math Message

*Solve each problem.*

81 − 47　　608 − 73　　35.26 − 19.62

### Study Link 2.2 Follow-Up

Briefly review the answers and ask students to share the strategies they used to solve the problems. One good approach is to estimate, using the process of elimination. For example, to find two numbers with a sum of 832, students could eliminate 901 since it is greater than 832. They could also eliminate all combinations of pairs of numbers in the 500s, since each of their sums is greater than 1,000. Similarly, any combination of two 2-digit numbers can be eliminated. A quick way to focus in on a solution is to look at 3-digit numbers whose ones digits add to a sum ending in 2.

# 1 Teaching the Lesson

## ✦ Math Message Follow-Up

WHOLE-CLASS DISCUSSION

Students share solution strategies.

Students often experience more difficulties with subtraction problems than with addition problems, especially if they have learned the traditional "borrowing" algorithm (not taught in *Everyday Mathematics*). If so, they may find one of the algorithms in this lesson easier to use.

## ✦ Reviewing Subtraction Algorithms (*Student Reference Book,* pp. 15–17, 35, and 36; *Math Masters,* p. 12)

WHOLE-CLASS DISCUSSION

### *The Trade-First Method*

Students in previous grades of *Everyday Mathematics* used the **trade-first method** to find differences. It is an algorithm that all students are expected to know, even if they favor other subtraction methods. It is important that students master an efficient subtraction algorithm in order to perform long division.

NOTE: Students are not expected to use the word *minuend.*

Use examples like those on pages 15 and 35 of the *Student Reference Book* to demonstrate this method. Problems are written in vertical form. If each digit of the **minuend** (the larger number) is greater than or equal to the digit directly below it, the problem is very easy to solve. Subtraction is performed separately in each column.

*Example:* Each digit of the minuend is greater than or equal to the digit directly below it. Subtract separately in each column.

$$\begin{array}{r} 93 \\ -\ 21 \\ \hline 72 \end{array} \qquad \begin{array}{r} 6.48 \\ -\ 3.45 \\ \hline 3.03 \end{array} \qquad \begin{array}{r} 54{,}729 \\ -\ 34{,}026 \\ \hline 20{,}703 \end{array}$$

If any digit of the minuend is less than the digit directly below it, then the minuend is adjusted *before* any subtracting is done. The minuend is adjusted by "trading." For example, we might need to trade 1 of the tens for 10 ones and 1 of the hundreds for 10 tens.

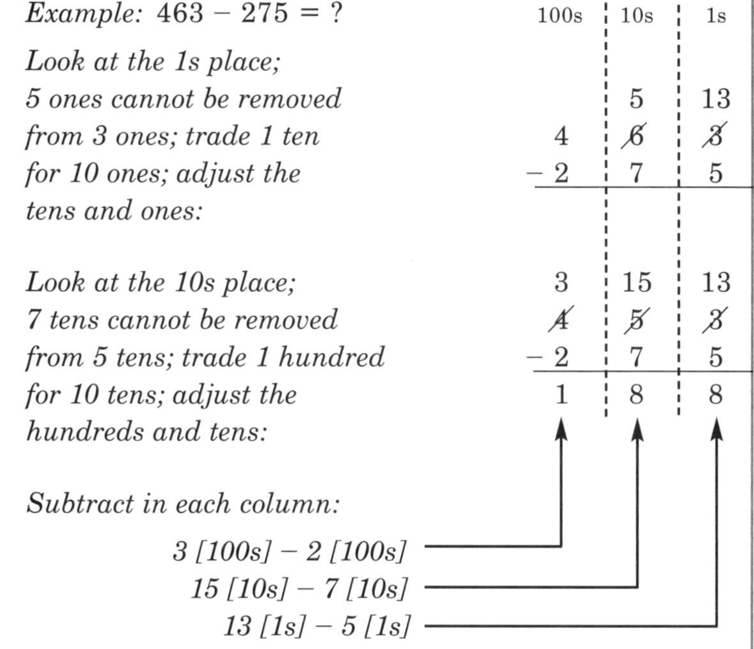

*Example:* 463 – 275 = ?

*Look at the 1s place; 5 ones cannot be removed from 3 ones; trade 1 ten for 10 ones; adjust the tens and ones:*

| 100s | 10s | 1s |
|---|---|---|
| | 5 | 13 |
| 4 | ~~6~~ | ~~3~~ |
| – 2 | 7 | 5 |

*Look at the 10s place; 7 tens cannot be removed from 5 tens; trade 1 hundred for 10 tens; adjust the hundreds and tens:*

| 100s | 10s | 1s |
|---|---|---|
| 3 | 15 | 13 |
| ~~4~~ | ~~5~~ | ~~3~~ |
| – 2 | 7 | 5 |
| 1 | 8 | 8 |

*Subtract in each column:*

*3 [100s] – 2 [100s]*
*15 [10s] – 7 [10s]*
*13 [1s] – 5 [1s]*

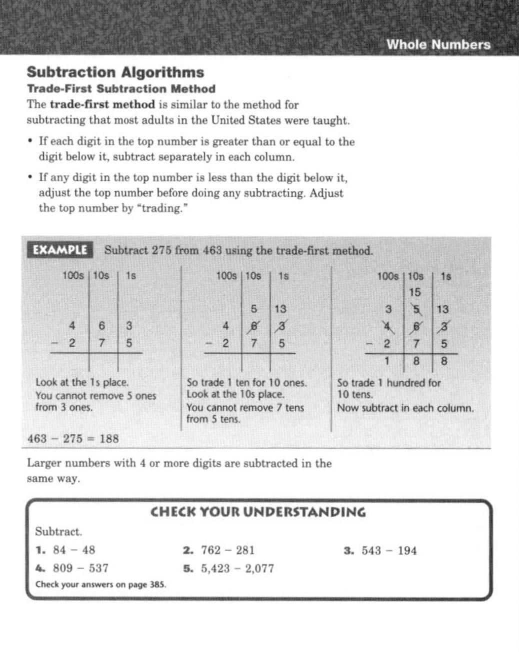

Whole Numbers

**Subtraction Algorithms**

**Trade-First Subtraction Method**

The **trade-first method** is similar to the method for subtracting that most adults in the United States were taught.

- If each digit in the top number is greater than or equal to the digit below it, subtract separately in each column.
- If any digit in the top number is less than the digit below it, adjust the top number before doing any subtracting. Adjust the top number by "trading."

**EXAMPLE** Subtract 275 from 463 using the trade-first method.

| 100s | 10s | 1s |
|---|---|---|
| | | |
| 4 | 6 | 3 |
| – 2 | 7 | 5 |

Look at the 1s place. You cannot remove 5 ones from 3 ones.

| 100s | 10s | 1s |
|---|---|---|
| | 5 | 13 |
| 4 | ~~6~~ | ~~3~~ |
| – 2 | 7 | 5 |

So trade 1 ten for 10 ones. Look at the 10s place. You cannot remove 7 tens from 5 tens.

| 100s | 10s | 1s |
|---|---|---|
| | 15 | |
| 3 | ~~5~~ | 13 |
| ~~4~~ | ~~6~~ | ~~3~~ |
| – 2 | 7 | 5 |
| 1 | 8 | 8 |

So trade 1 hundred for 10 tens. Now subtract in each column.

463 – 275 = 188

Larger numbers with 4 or more digits are subtracted in the same way.

**CHECK YOUR UNDERSTANDING**

Subtract.

**1.** 84 – 48 **2.** 762 – 281 **3.** 543 – 194
**4.** 809 – 537 **5.** 5,423 – 2,077

Check your answers on page 385.

fifteen SRB 15

STUDENT PAGE

✦ *Student Reference Book, p. 15*

NOTE: Adjusting by "trading" serves the same purpose as "borrowing and renaming" in the traditional subtraction algorithm. Because all trades are done first—*before* any subtractions—there is much less chance for computation error than with the traditional subtraction algorithm.

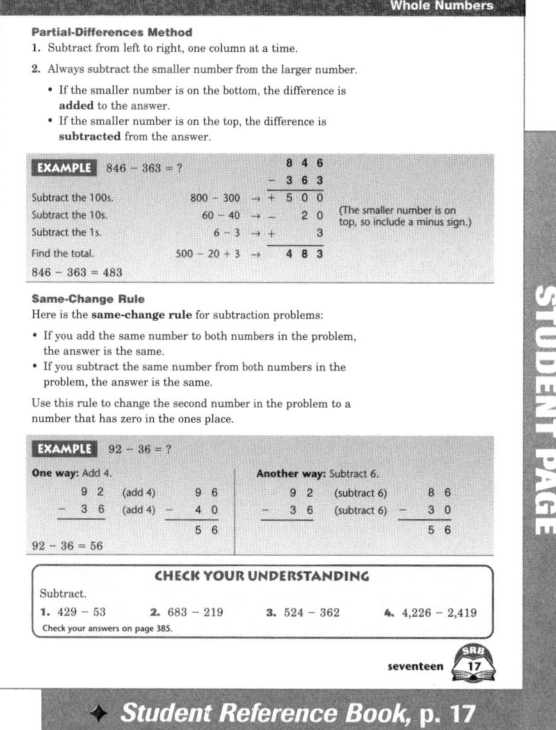

Whole Numbers

**Partial-Differences Method**

1. Subtract from left to right, one column at a time.
2. Always subtract the smaller number from the larger number.
   - If the smaller number is on the bottom, the difference is **added** to the answer.
   - If the smaller number is on the top, the difference is **subtracted** from the answer.

**EXAMPLE** 846 – 363 = ?

| | | | |
|---|---|---|---|
| | | | 8 4 6 |
| | | | – 3 6 3 |
| Subtract the 100s. | 800 – 300 | → | + 5 0 0 |
| Subtract the 10s. | 60 – 40 | → | – 2 0 (The smaller number is on top, so include a minus sign.) |
| Subtract the 1s. | 6 – 3 | → | + 3 |
| Find the total. | 500 – 20 + 3 | → | 4 8 3 |

846 – 363 = 483

**Same-Change Rule**

Here is the **same-change rule** for subtraction problems:

- If you add the same number to both numbers in the problem, the answer is the same.
- If you subtract the same number from both numbers in the problem, the answer is the same.

Use this rule to change the second number in the problem to a number that has zero in the ones place.

**EXAMPLE** 92 – 36 = ?

**One way:** Add 4.

| | | |
|---|---|---|
| 9 2 | (add 4) | 9 6 |
| – 3 6 | (add 4) | – 4 0 |
| | | 5 6 |

**Another way:** Subtract 6.

| | | |
|---|---|---|
| 9 2 | (subtract 6) | 8 6 |
| – 3 6 | (subtract 6) | – 3 0 |
| | | 5 6 |

92 – 36 = 56

**CHECK YOUR UNDERSTANDING**

Subtract.

**1.** 429 – 53 **2.** 683 – 219 **3.** 524 – 362 **4.** 4,226 – 2,419

Check your answers on page 385.

seventeen SRB 17

STUDENT PAGE

✦ *Student Reference Book, p. 17*

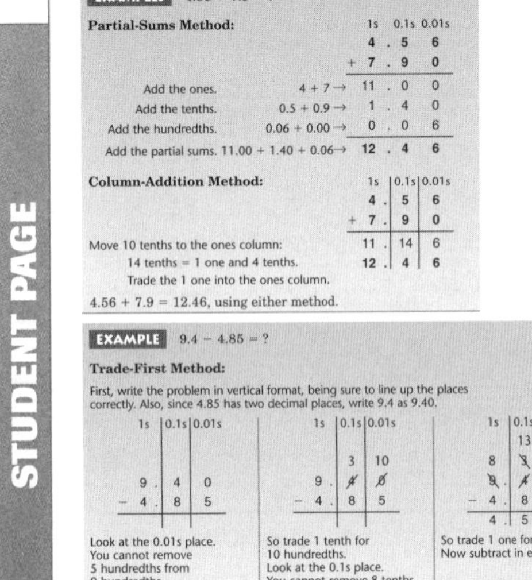

Decimals and Percents

Most paper-and-pencil strategies for adding and subtracting whole numbers also work for decimals. The main difference is that you have to line up the places correctly, either by adding 0s to the end of the numbers or by lining up the ones place.

**EXAMPLES** 4.56 + 7.9 = ?

**Partial-Sums Method:**

| | | 1s | 0.1s | 0.01s |
|---|---|---|---|---|
| | | 4 . | 5 | 6 |
| | | + 7 . | 9 | 0 |
| Add the ones. | 4 + 7 → | 11 . | 0 | 0 |
| Add the tenths. | 0.5 + 0.9 → | 1 . | 4 | 0 |
| Add the hundredths. | 0.06 + 0.00 → | 0 . | 0 | 6 |
| Add the partial sums. | 11.00 + 1.40 + 0.06 → | 12 . | 4 | 6 |

**Column-Addition Method:**

| 1s | 0.1s | 0.01s |
|---|---|---|
| 4 . | 5 | 6 |
| + 7 . | 9 | 0 |
| 11 . | 14 | 6 |
| 12 . | 4 | 6 |

Move 10 tenths to the ones column:
14 tenths = 1 one and 4 tenths.
Trade the 1 one into the ones column.

4.56 + 7.9 = 12.46, using either method.

**EXAMPLE** 9.4 − 4.85 = ?

**Trade-First Method:**

First, write the problem in vertical format, being sure to line up the places correctly. Also, since 4.85 has two decimal places, write 9.4 as 9.40.

| 1s | 0.1s | 0.01s |
|---|---|---|
| 9 . | 4 | 0 |
| − 4 . | 8 | 5 |

Look at the 0.01s place. You cannot remove 5 hundredths from 0 hundredths.

| 1s | 0.1s | 0.01s |
|---|---|---|
| | 3 | 10 |
| 9 . | ~~4~~ | ~~0~~ |
| − 4 . | 8 | 5 |

So trade 1 tenth for 10 hundredths. Look at the 0.1s place. You cannot remove 8 tenths from 3 tenths.

| 1s | 0.1s | 0.01s |
|---|---|---|
| | 13 | |
| 8 | ~~3~~ | 10 |
| ~~9~~ . | ~~4~~ | ~~0~~ |
| − 4 . | 8 | 5 |
| 4 . | 5 | 5 |

So trade 1 one for 10 tenths. Now subtract in each column.

9.4 − 4.85 = 4.55

thirty-five SRB 35

◆ Student Reference Book, p. 35

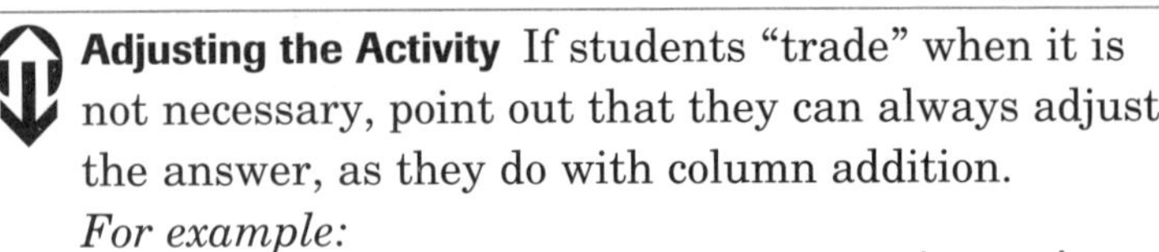

**Adjusting the Activity** If students "trade" when it is not necessary, point out that they can always adjust the answer, as they do with column addition.

*For example:*

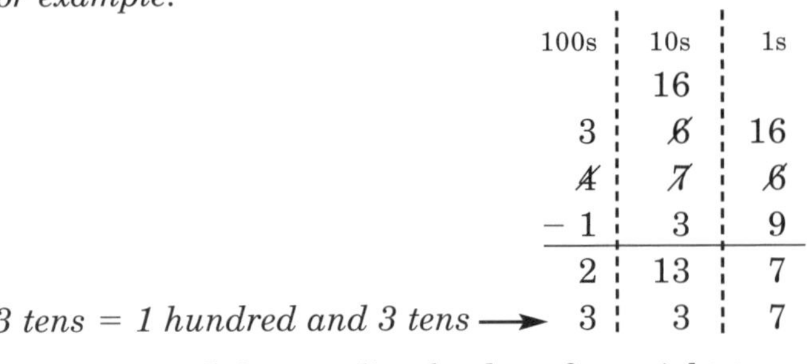

| | 100s | 10s | 1s |
|---|---|---|---|
| | | 16 | |
| | 3 | ~~6~~ | 16 |
| | ~~4~~ | ~~7~~ | ~~6~~ |
| | − 1 | 3 | 9 |
| | 2 | 13 | 7 |
| *13 tens = 1 hundred and 3 tens* → | 3 | 3 | 7 |

We recommend that trading be done from right to left. But it is fine if a student prefers to do the trading from left to right. What's important is that a student trades correctly, and that the final adjusted number has each digit greater than or equal to the digit directly below it.

Stress that subtraction problems involving decimals are done in the same way as problems involving only whole numbers.

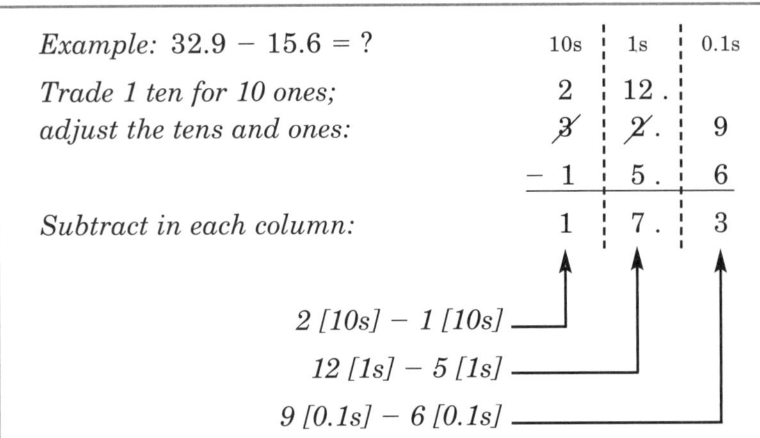

*Example:* 32.9 − 15.6 = ?

*Trade 1 ten for 10 ones; adjust the tens and ones:*

*Subtract in each column:*

| 10s | 1s | 0.1s |
|---|---|---|
| 2 | 12 . | |
| ~~3~~ | ~~2~~ . | 9 |
| − 1 | 5 . | 6 |
| 1 | 7 . | 3 |



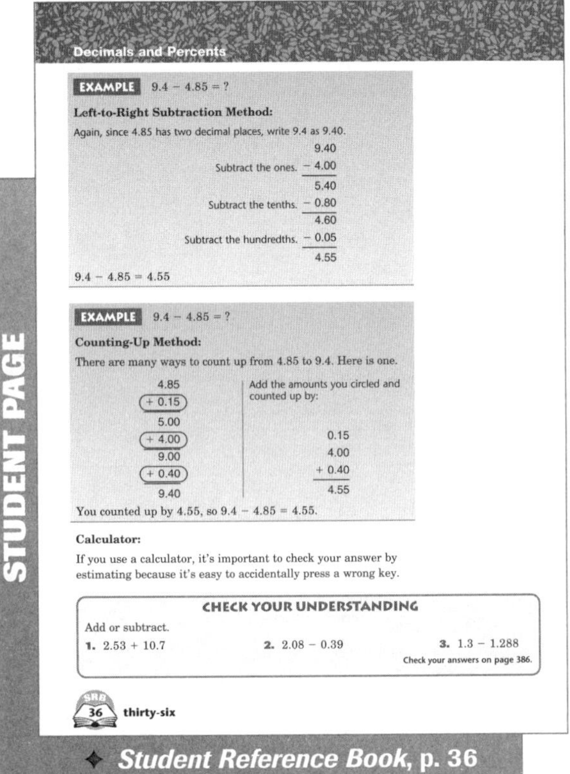

Decimals and Percents

**EXAMPLE** 9.4 − 4.85 = ?

**Left-to-Right Subtraction Method:**

Again, since 4.85 has two decimal places, write 9.4 as 9.40.

| | |
|---|---|
| | 9.40 |
| Subtract the ones. | − 4.00 |
| | 5.40 |
| Subtract the tenths. | − 0.80 |
| | 4.60 |
| Subtract the hundredths. | − 0.05 |
| | 4.55 |

9.4 − 4.85 = 4.55

**EXAMPLE** 9.4 − 4.85 = ?

**Counting-Up Method:**

There are many ways to count up from 4.85 to 9.4. Here is one.

4.85
(+ 0.15)
5.00
(+ 4.00)
9.00
(+ 0.40)
9.40

Add the amounts you circled and counted up by:

0.15
4.00
+ 0.40
4.55

You counted up by 4.55, so 9.4 − 4.85 = 4.55.

**Calculator:**

If you use a calculator, it's important to check your answer by estimating because it's easy to accidentally press a wrong key.

**CHECK YOUR UNDERSTANDING**

Add or subtract.

1. 2.53 + 10.7
2. 2.08 − 0.39
3. 1.3 − 1.288

Check your answers on page 386.

SRB 36 thirty-six

◆ Student Reference Book, p. 36

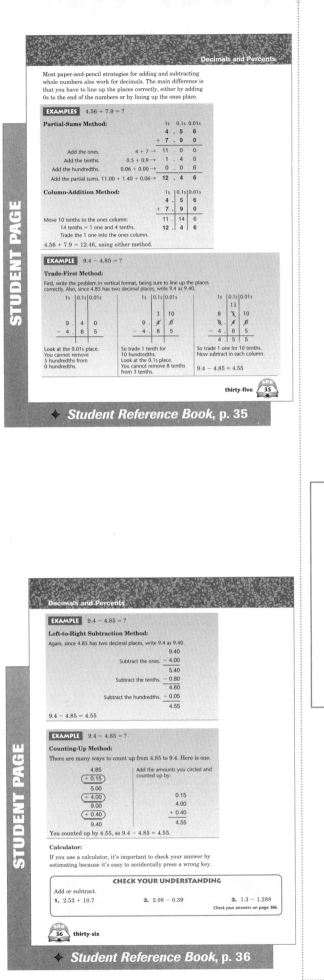

When students use the trade-first method, make sure that they align the numbers properly in columns. It will help at first if they separate the columns with vertical lines. Struggling students may also write place-value reminders such as 100s, 10s, and 1s above the columns. Once they become proficient using this method, they can omit the use of vertical lines and place-value reminders.

### *The Partial-Differences Method*

Use an example like that on page 17 of the *Student Reference Book* to demonstrate the **partial-differences method.**

| *Example:* 4,261 − 2,637 = ? | | 4261 |
|---|---|---|
| | | − 2637 |
| *Subtract the thousands:* | *4,000 − 2,000* ⟶ | + 2000 |
| *Subtract the hundreds:* | *600 − 200* ⟶ | − 400 |
| (Smaller number is on top; so include minus sign.) | | |
| *Subtract the tens:* | *60 − 30* ⟶ | + 30 |
| *Subtract the ones:* | *7 − 1* ⟶ | − 6 |
| (Smaller number is on top; so include minus sign.) | | |
| *Find the total:* | *2,000 − 400 + 30 − 6* ⟶ | 1624 |

Point out that:

- ▷ The subtraction is performed from left to right, column by column.
- ▷ The smaller number in each column is always subtracted from the larger number.
  - If the bottom number is less than the top number, then the result will be added to obtain the final answer.
  - If the bottom number is greater than the top number, then the result will be subtracted to obtain the final answer.
- ▷ To find the final answer, the partial differences are added or subtracted.

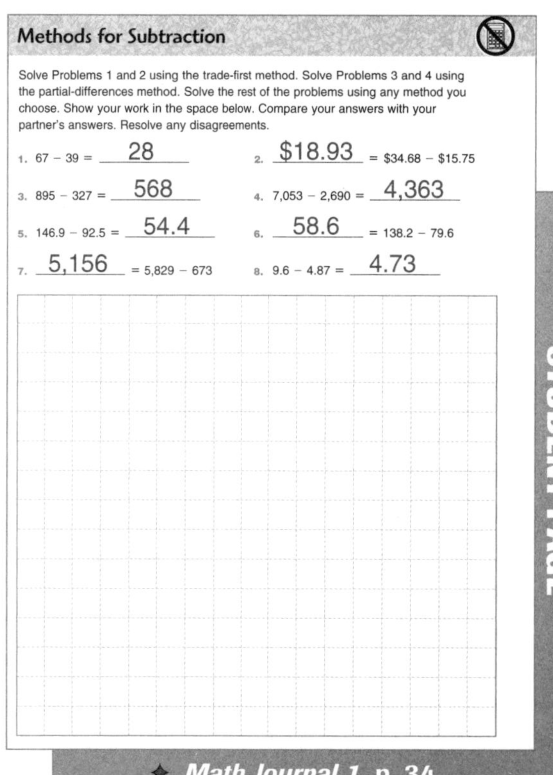
**Methods for Subtraction**

Solve Problems 1 and 2 using the trade-first method. Solve Problems 3 and 4 using the partial-differences method. Solve the rest of the problems using any method you choose. Show your work in the space below. Compare your answers with your partner's answers. Resolve any disagreements.

1. 67 − 39 = 28
2. $18.93 = $34.68 − $15.75
3. 895 − 327 = 568
4. 7,053 − 2,690 = 4,363
5. 146.9 − 92.5 = 54.4
6. 58.6 = 138.2 − 79.6
7. 5,156 = 5,829 − 673
8. 9.6 − 4.87 = 4.73

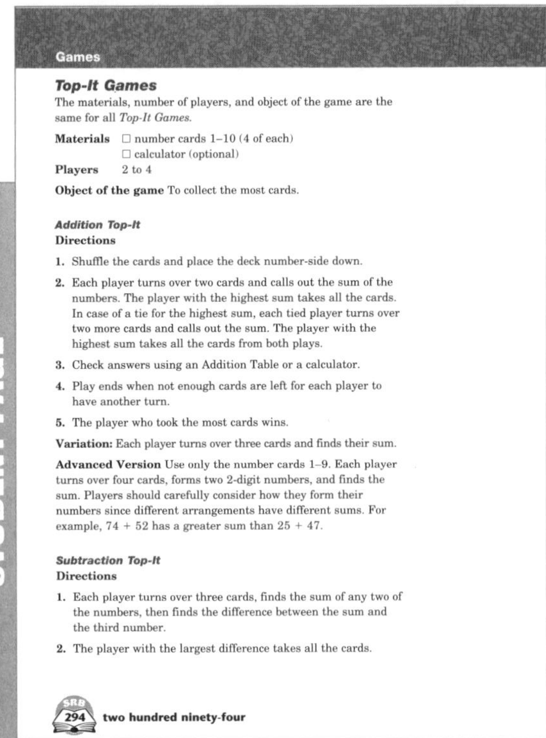

Games

**Top-It Games**

The materials, number of players, and object of the game are the same for all *Top-It Games.*

**Materials** ☐ number cards 1–10 (4 of each)
☐ calculator (optional)

**Players** 2 to 4

**Object of the game** To collect the most cards.

**Addition Top-It**

**Directions**

1. Shuffle the cards and place the deck number-side down.
2. Each player turns over two cards and calls out the sum of the numbers. The player with the highest sum takes all the cards. In case of a tie for the highest sum, each tied player turns over two more cards and calls out the sum. The player with the highest sum takes all the cards from both plays.
3. Check answers using an Addition Table or a calculator.
4. Play ends when not enough cards are left for each player to have another turn.
5. The player who took the most cards wins.

**Variation:** Each player turns over three cards and finds their sum.

**Advanced Version** Use only the number cards 1–9. Each player turns over four cards, forms two 2-digit numbers, and finds the sum. Players should carefully consider how they form their numbers since different arrangements have different sums. For example, 74 + 52 has a greater sum than 25 + 47.

**Subtraction Top-It**

**Directions**

1. Each player turns over three cards, finds the sum of any two of the numbers, then finds the difference between the sum and the third number.
2. The player with the largest difference takes all the cards.

SRB 294 two hundred ninety-four

✦ *Student Reference Book,* p. 294

STUDENT PAGE

**Math Boxes 2.3**

1. Find the missing numbers and landmarks for the set of numbers:
48, 50, 51, 51, 57, 59, 60, 63, 69, 76, 76, 76
 a. Range: 28
 b. Mode: 76
 c. Minimum: 48
 d. Maximum: 76

2. I am a polygon. I have five sides and two right angles.
 a. Draw me in the space below.
 Sample drawing:
 b. I am called a pentagon.

3. Write the following numbers in standard notation.
 a. $6^2$ = 36
 b. $10^5$ = 100,000
 c. $14^2$ = 196
 d. $8^3$ = 512
 e. $3^4$ = 81

4. a. How many dots are in this array?
 42 dots (unit)
 b. Write a number model for the array.
 Sample answers:
 $6 * 7 = 42$
 $42 = 7 * 6$

5. a. Build a 9-digit numeral. Write 2 in the hundreds place, 5 in the ten-thousands place, 7 in the millions place, 6 in the hundred-millions place, and 3 in all other places.
 637,353,233
 b. Write this numeral in words.
 Six hundred thirty-seven million, three hundred fifty-three thousand, two-hundred thirty-three

✦ *Math Journal 1,* p. 35

Stress that subtraction problems involving decimals are done in the same way as problems involving only whole numbers.

| *Example:* 76.38 − 39.81 = ? | | 76.38 |
|---|---|---|
| | | − 39.81 |
| *Subtract the tens:* | *70 − 30* → | + 40.00 |
| *Subtract the ones:* | *9 − 6* → | − 3.00 |
| *Subtract the tenths:* | *0.8 − 0.3* → | − 0.50 |
| *Subtract the hundredths:* | *0.08 − 0.01* → | + 0.07 |
| *Find the total: 40.00 − 3.00 − 0.50 + 0.07* | = | 36.57 |

## ✦ Practicing Subtraction of Whole Numbers and Decimals

(*Math Journal 1,* p. 34; *Student Reference Book,* pp. 15–17, 35, and 36)

PARTNER ACTIVITY

Students solve the problems on their own, and then check each other's answers. Circulate and assist.

## ✦ Sharing Results (*Math Journal 1,* p. 34)

WHOLE-CLASS DISCUSSION

Bring the class together to share solutions. Some possible discussion questions include:

▷ Which method of subtraction do you prefer? Why?

▷ What are some of the advantages of each method?

▷ What are some of the disadvantages?

▷ When might a particular method be useful? When might it not be useful?

▷ How is the partial-sums method similar to the partial-differences method? How are the methods different?

**ONGOING ASSESSMENT**

Ask students to write the answers to the first three questions above.

# 2 Ongoing Learning & Practice

## ✦ Playing *Addition Top-It* (*Student Reference Book*, p. 294)

PARTNER ACTIVITY

This game provides students with practice adding whole numbers. Students have played this game in earlier grades, so they should be familiar with the rules.

## ✦ Math Boxes 2.3 (*Math Journal 1*, p. 35)

INDEPENDENT ACTIVITY 

**Mixed Review** Math Boxes in this lesson are paired with Math Boxes in Lesson 2.1. The skill in Problem 1 is a prerequisite for Unit 3.

## ✦ Study Link 2.3 (*Math Masters*, p. 229)

**Home Connection** Students practice estimating and finding differences. Students can solve problems using any method they choose.

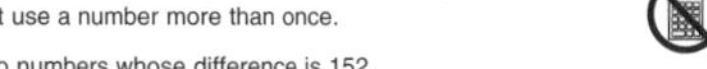

**Another Number Hunt** — Study Link 2.3

Use the numbers in the following table to answer the questions below. You may not use a number more than once.

1. Circle two numbers whose difference is 152.
2. Make an X in the boxes of two numbers whose difference is 25.6.
3. Make a check mark in the boxes of two numbers whose difference is greater than 1,000.

Sample answer given.

4. Make a star in the boxes of two numbers whose difference is less than 10.
5. Make a triangle in the boxes of two numbers whose difference is equal to the sum of 538 and 259.
6. Make a smiley face in the boxes of two numbers whose difference is equal to $4^2$.

| 17 | 16 | 9 | 75.03 |
|---|---|---|---|
| 100.9 | 803 | 25 | 451 |
| 1,500 | 5,000 | 1 | 3,096 |
| 299 | 703 | 75.3 | 40.03 |

Subtract. Show your work in the space below.

7. 247 − 186 = 61
8. 137 = 405 − 268
9. 24.5 − 18.7 = 5.8
10. 18.85 = 62.7 − 43.85

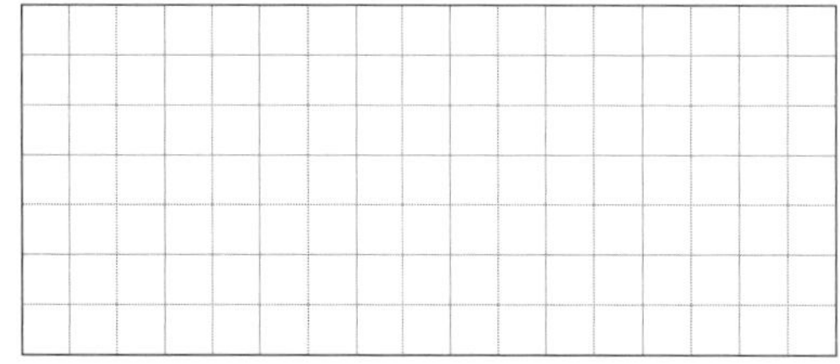

STUDY LINK MASTER

✦ *Math Masters*, p. 229

# 3 Options for Individualizing

## ✦ EXTRA PRACTICE Playing *Subtraction Target Practice* (*Student Reference Book*, p. 292; *Math Masters*, p. 12)

PARTNER ACTIVITY  **15–30 min**

You may want to have students play this game if they need additional practice with subtraction. Since this game was introduced in *Fourth Grade Everyday Mathematics*, many students should be familiar with the rules.

To practice subtraction of decimals, have players use counters to represent decimal points. A player draws two cards and makes a decimal number with one digit in the tenths place. The player subtracts the number from 20. The game continues as in *Subtraction Target Practice* until one player reaches 0 without going below 0.

Revisit the game from time to time over the next few weeks.

**Games**

***Subtraction Target Practice***

**Materials** ☐ number cards 0–9 (4 of each)
☐ calculator for each player

**Players** 1 or more

**Object of the game** To get as close to 0 as possible, without going below 0.

**Directions**

1. Shuffle the cards and place the deck facedown on the playing surface. Each player starts at 250.
2. Players take turns doing the following:
   - Turn over the top two cards and make a 2-digit number. (You can place the cards in either order.) Subtract this number from 250 on scratch paper. Check the answer on a calculator.
   - Turn over the next two cards and make another 2-digit number. Subtract this number from the result obtained in the previous subtraction. Check the answer on a calculator.
   - Do this three more times: take two cards; make a 2-digit number; subtract it from the last result; check the answer on a calculator.
3. The player whose final result is closest to 0, without going below 0, is the winner. If the final results for all players are below 0, no one wins.

If there is only one player, the object of the game is to get as close to 0 as possible, without going below 0.

**EXAMPLE**

| | |
|---|---|
| *Turn 1:* Draw 4 and 5. Subtract 45 or 54. | 250 − 45 = 205 |
| *Turn 2:* Draw 0 and 6. Subtract 6 or 60. | 205 − 60 = 145 |
| *Turn 3:* Draw 4 and 1. Subtract 41 or 14. | 145 − 41 = 104 |
| *Turn 4:* Draw 3 and 2. Subtract 32 or 23. | 104 − 23 = 81 |
| *Turn 5:* Draw 6 and 9. Subtract 69 or 96. | 81 − 69 = 12 |

**Variation:** Each player starts at 100 instead of 250.

STUDENT PAGE

✦ *Student Reference Book*, p. 292

# 2.4 Addition and Subtraction Number Stories

**OBJECTIVES** **To review a guide for solving number stories and concepts about number sentences; and to use open sentences as aids in solving number stories.**

| summaries | materials |
|---|---|
| **1 Teaching the Lesson** | |
| Students review solving number stories and the meanings of the terms *number sentence* and *variable;* they write open number sentences to model addition and subtraction stories; and they solve the number sentences to find the answers to the stories. [Operations and Computation; Patterns, Functions, and Algebra] | ☐ *Math Journal 1,* pp. 36 and 37<br>☐ *Student Reference Book,* pp. 220 and 221<br>☐ Study Link 2.3<br>☐ Teaching Master (*Math Masters,* p. 12) |
| **2 Ongoing Learning & Practice** | |
| Students play the decimal version of *High-Number Toss.* [Numeration; Operations and Computation]<br>Students practice and maintain skills through Math Boxes and Study Link activities. | ☐ *Math Journal 1,* p. 38<br>☐ *Student Reference Book,* p. 283<br>☐ Study Link Master (*Math Masters,* p. 230)<br>☐ 4 each of the number cards 0–9 per partnership (from the Everything Math Deck, if available) |
| **3 Options for Individualizing** | |
| **Enrichment** Students write and solve number sentences to solve challenging number stories. [Operations and Computation; Patterns, Functions, and Algebra]<br>**Language Diversity** Students write addition and subtraction number stories. [Numeration; Operations and Computation] | ☐ Teaching Master (*Math Masters,* p. 14) |

## Additional Information

**Background Information** In Grades 1–3, students used **situation diagrams** to help them solve number stories involving addition and subtraction. Then they wrote number sentences to summarize what they did to solve the stories. In Grade 4, students learned to use diagrams to help them write addition and subtraction open sentences for number stories. Then they solved the open sentences to find the answers to the stories. An intermediate step was using diagrams to write open sentences. In this lesson, students are encouraged to write open sentences for number stories without first using a situation diagram. For additional information about situation diagrams, see the *Teacher's Reference Manual.*

**Vocabulary** • **number sentence** • **true number sentence** • **false number sentence** • **relation symbol** • **operation symbol** • **variable** • **open sentence** • **solution**

**Vocabulary (teacher)** • **situation diagram** • **equation** • **inequality** • **change-to-more story** • **change-to-less story** • **parts-and-total story** • **comparison story**

## Getting Started

### Mental Math and Reflexes

Students estimate the answers to the following problems:

- Michael has \$8.00. Does he have enough money to buy 3 fancy pencils for \$1.98 each and an eraser for \$1.73? yes
- Lucy takes about 48 minutes to walk from her house to the store. If she must get back in an hour and a half, does she have enough time to walk to the store and back? no
- Jeremy can drive his car about 32 miles per gallon of gas. He has about 5 gallons in his tank. He is driving to his sister's house, which is 84 miles away. Does he have enough gas to get there and back? no

### Math Message

*What is the value of* x *in* $34 - x = 18$?

### Study Link 2.3 Follow-Up

Ask students to share their solution strategies to Problems 1–6.

## 1 Teaching the Lesson

### ✦ Math Message Follow-Up

WHOLE-CLASS DISCUSSION 

Ask volunteers to tell what they know about **number sentences.** Make sure that the following points are mentioned:

▷ Number sentences are similar to English sentences, except that they use math symbols instead of words.

▷ Some number sentences are true and some are false. For example, $10 - 2 = 8$ is a **true number sentence.** The number sentence $8 / 2 > 4 * 100$ is a **false number sentence.**

▷ A number sentence must have a **relation symbol.** Students should be familiar with the relation symbols *shown in the margin.* For example, the number sentence $10 - 2 = 8$ contains the relation symbol "=." The number sentence $8 / 2 < 4 * 100$ contains the relation symbol "<."

▷ Number sentences also contain numbers and **operation symbols.** *(See the margin.)* For example, the number sentence $10 - 2 = 8$ contains three numbers (10, 2, and 8) and the operation symbol "–." The number sentence $8 / 2 < 4 * 100$ contains four numbers (8, 2, 4, and 100) and the operation symbols "/" and "*."

NOTE: The TI-15 calculator can be used to decide whether number sentences that are entered are true or not. See *Math Masters,* page 482.

| Relation Symbols |
|---|
| < means *is less than* |
| > means *is greater than* |
| = means *is equal to* |

| Operation Symbols |
|---|
| + means *plus* |
| – means *minus* |
| × or * means *times* |
| ÷ or / means *divided by* |

| $x$ | $34 - x = 18$ | |
|---|---|---|
| 0 | $34 - 0 = 18$ | False |
| 10 | $34 - 10 = 18$ | False |
| 22 | $34 - 22 = 18$ | False |
| 18 | $34 - 18 = 18$ | False |
| 16 | $34 - 16 = 18$ | True |

NOTE: At this point, restrict the problems to equations, number sentences that contain the relation symbol "=." Inequalities, or number sentences that contain the relation symbol "<" or ">" will be covered in Unit 7.

NOTE: You can expect that many students will be able to solve simple addition and subtraction number stories without first having to write an open sentence. The main purpose of this lesson is to introduce the use of open sentences so that students may use them to solve more complex problems.

NOTE: It is important for students to understand that problem solving is a creative activity that cannot be performed according to a prescription. Emphasize that there is more than one way to do most things. People think in different ways; what works for one person may not work for another.

Discuss the Math Message problem. The number sentence $34 - x = 18$ is an example of a number sentence in which one of the numbers is missing. We write the letter $x$ in place of the missing number. The letter $x$ is called a **variable.** Number sentences that contain a variable are called **open sentences.** Open sentences are neither true nor false. Only when we replace the variable with a number do we get a number sentence that is either true or false.

With students' help, create a table on the board in which you replace $x$ with various numbers. For each number sentence, determine whether it is true or false. *(See the margin.)*

A number used in place of $x$ that makes the number sentence true is called a **solution** of the sentence. The solution of $34 - x = 18$ is 16, because $34 - \mathbf{16} = 18$ is a true number sentence.

Remind students that they have been using variables since Kindergarten, without calling them variables. They may have seen number sentences written with question marks, blank rules, or empty boxes. For example, in the number sentence $34 - \square = 18$, the empty box is used to stand for the missing number. The $\square$ is the variable, and the number 16 is the solution.

Pose a few more problems involving number sentences with variables. To find the solution, make a table in which you replace the variable with various numbers. Determine whether each number sentence is true or false. *Suggestions:*

$26 - n = 12$ $\quad d * 3 = 27$

$8 = 32 / n$ $\quad 146 + 34 = t$

## Reviewing the Guide for Solving Number Stories and Using Open Sentences
(*Student Reference Book,* pp. 220 and 221)

WHOLE-CLASS ACTIVITY

Briefly discuss problem solving and the guide for solving number stories on pages 220 and 221 in the *Student Reference Book.* Then use one of the Check Your Understanding problems to illustrate the steps outlined in the guide. Try to maintain a brisk pace.

Use the following examples to review situation diagrams that were used in earlier grades. The diagrams were used to model four different kinds of number stories: **change-to-more, change-to-less, parts-and-total,** and **comparison.** Have students focus on writing an open sentence that models the story; and then solve the open sentence to find the answer to the story. Pose several of each kind of number story to the class.

*Example 1:* At breakfast, the temperature outside was 47 °F. By lunchtime, the temperature had gone up to 63 °F. How many degrees warmer was it by lunchtime?

This is a change-to-more story, where we want to find by how much the starting number is increased. To solve the story, follow these steps:

**Step 1.** We know that the temperature at breakfast was 47 °F and that by lunchtime, it had gone up to 63 °F. Decide on a letter variable to use for the missing number (the number of degrees the temperature has increased). Any letter may be used, but it often helps if the letter can serve as a reminder of what is to be found. For example, $t$ (for **t**emperature) or $d$ (for **d**egrees) are sensible choices for this story.

**Step 2.** Ask students to write an open sentence showing how the variable and other numbers in the story are related. Depending on how students view this problem, both $47 + t = 63$ and $63 - 47 = t$ are possible open sentences.

**Step 3.** Finally, ask students to solve their open sentences. What number should replace the variable $t$ to make the sentence true? 16

**Adjusting the Activity** Students who have difficulty writing an open sentence for the story should first draw a change-to-more diagram.

*Example 2:* Mary had $32.50 in her savings account. After she withdrew some money, she had $17.25 left in her account. How much money did she withdraw from her account?

This is a change-to-less story, where we want to find by what amount the starting number is decreased.

1. Open sentence: $32.50 - b = 17.25$ (or $32.50 - 17.25 = b$), where $b$ is the money she withdrew from her account.
2. Solution: 15.25
3. Answer: Mary withdrew $15.25 from her account.

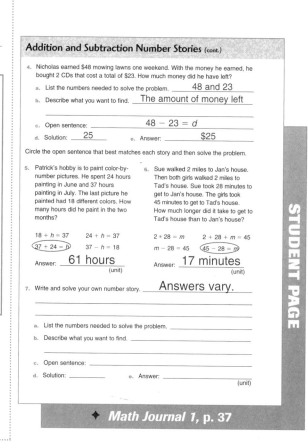

STUDENT PAGE

## Addition and Subtraction Number Stories

For each problem on pages 36 and 37, fill in the blanks and solve the problem.

*Example* Maria had 2 decks of cards. One of the decks had only 36 cards instead of 52. The rest were missing from the deck. How many cards were missing?

- List the numbers needed to solve the problem. 36 and 52
- Describe what you want to find. The number of missing cards
- Write an open sentence: $36 + c = 52$
- Find the missing number in the open sentence. Solution: 16
- Write the answer to the number story. Answer: 16 cards (unit)

1. Anthony got a new bike. He rode 18 miles the first week, 27 miles the second week, and 34 miles the third week. How many miles did he ride altogether?
   a. List the numbers needed to solve the problem. 18, 27, and 34
   b. Describe what you want to find. The total number of miles
   c. Open sentence: $18 + 27 + 34 = m$
   d. Solution: 79  e. Answer: 79 miles (unit)

2. Regina has $23.08. Her sister has $16.47. Her brother has only $5.00. How much more money does Regina have than her sister?
   a. List the numbers needed to solve the problem. 23.08 and 16.47
   b. Describe what you want to find. How much more money Regina has than her sister
   c. Open sentence: $23.08 - 16.47 = r$
   d. Solution: 6.61  e. Answer: $6.61

3. Lucas was having 12 friends over for breakfast. He started with 19 eggs. He bought 1 dozen more eggs. How many eggs did he have to cook for breakfast?
   a. List the numbers needed to solve the problem. 19 and 12
   b. Describe what you want to find. The total number of eggs
   c. Open sentence: $19 + 12 = e$
   d. Solution: 31  e. Answer: 31 eggs (unit)

✦ **Math Journal 1, p. 36**

Journal pages 36 and 37 accompany the *Solving Addition and Subtraction Number Stories* activity on the next page.

STUDENT PAGE

## Addition and Subtraction Number Stories (cont.)

4. Nicholas earned $48 mowing lawns one weekend. With the money he earned, he bought 2 CDs that cost a total of $23. How much money did he have left?
   a. List the numbers needed to solve the problem. 48 and 23
   b. Describe what you want to find. The amount of money left
   c. Open sentence: $48 - 23 = d$
   d. Solution: 25  e. Answer: $25

Circle the open sentence that best matches each story and then solve the problem.

5. Patrick's hobby is to paint color-by-number pictures. He spent 24 hours painting in June and 37 hours painting in July. The last picture he painted had 18 different colors. How many hours did he paint in the two months?

   $18 + h = 37$  $24 + h = 37$
   ($37 + 24 = h$) (circled)  $37 - h = 18$

   Answer: 61 hours (unit)

6. Sue walked 2 miles to Jan's house. Then both girls walked 2 miles to Tad's house. Sue took 28 minutes to get to Jan's house. The girls took 45 minutes to get to Tad's house. How much longer did it take to get to Tad's house than to Jan's house?

   $2 * 28 = m$  $2 + 28 + m = 45$
   $m - 28 = 45$  ($45 - 28 = m$) (circled)

   Answer: 17 minutes (unit)

7. Write and solve your own number story. Answers vary.
   a. List the numbers needed to solve the problem. ______
   b. Describe what you want to find. ______
   c. Open sentence: ______
   d. Solution: ______  e. Answer: ______ (unit)

✦ **Math Journal 1, p. 37**

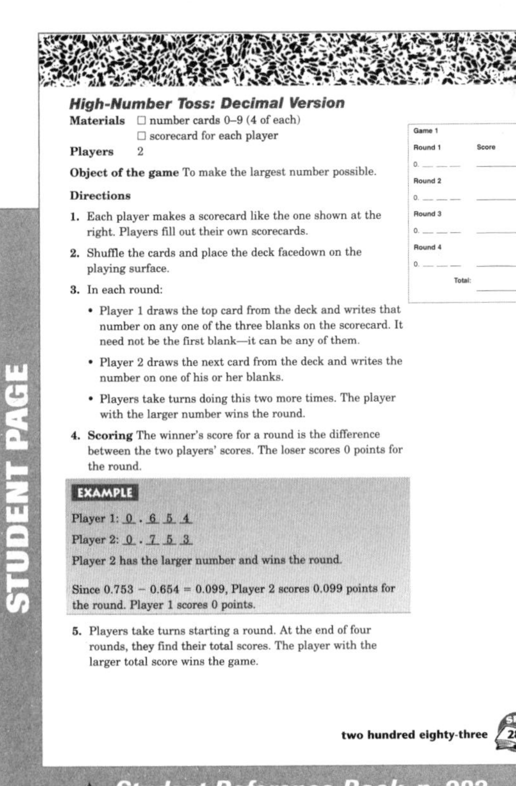

STUDENT PAGE

**High-Number Toss: Decimal Version**

**Materials** □ number cards 0–9 (4 of each)
□ scorecard for each player

**Players** 2

**Object of the game** To make the largest number possible.

**Directions**

1. Each player makes a scorecard like the one shown at the right. Players fill out their own scorecards.
2. Shuffle the cards and place the deck facedown on the playing surface.
3. In each round:
   - Player 1 draws the top card from the deck and writes that number on any one of the three blanks on the scorecard. It need not be the first blank—it can be any of them.
   - Player 2 draws the next card from the deck and writes the number on one of his or her blanks.
   - Players take turns doing this two more times. The player with the larger number wins the round.
4. **Scoring** The winner's score for a round is the difference between the two players' scores. The loser scores 0 points for the round.

| Game 1 | Score |
|---|---|
| Round 1 | |
| 0. _ _ _ | ____ |
| Round 2 | |
| 0. _ _ _ | ____ |
| Round 3 | |
| 0. _ _ _ | ____ |
| Round 4 | |
| 0. _ _ _ | ____ |
| Total: | ____ |

**EXAMPLE**

Player 1: 0 . 6 5 4

Player 2: 0 . 7 5 3

Player 2 has the larger number and wins the round.

Since 0.753 – 0.654 = 0.099, Player 2 scores 0.099 points for the round. Player 1 scores 0 points.

5. Players take turns starting a round. At the end of four rounds, they find their total scores. The player with the larger total score wins the game.

two hundred eighty-three SRB 283

✦ *Student Reference Book*, p. 283

The TI-15 calculator has a (?) key, which can be used to enter equations with unknowns. See *Math Masters*, page 482.

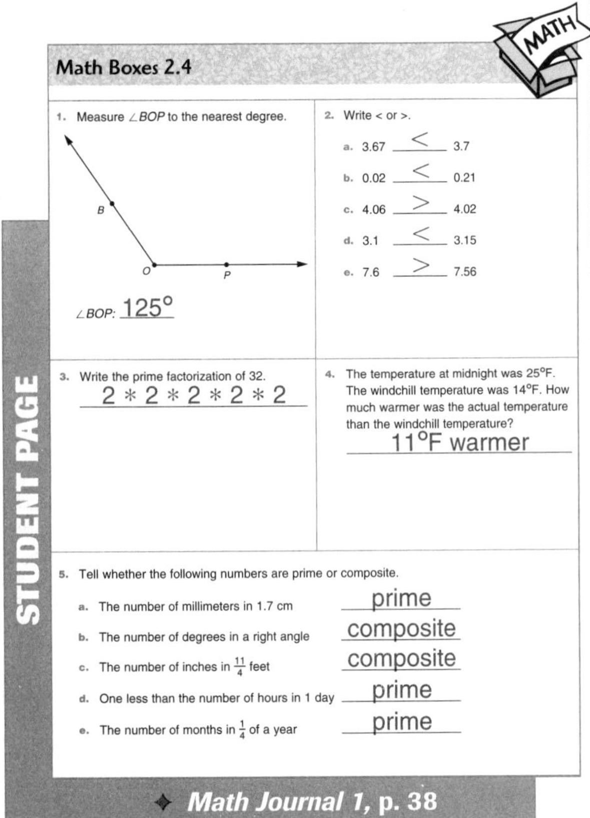

STUDENT PAGE

**Math Boxes 2.4**

1. Measure ∠*BOP* to the nearest degree.

∠*BOP*: 125°

2. Write < or >.

a. 3.67 < 3.7
b. 0.02 < 0.21
c. 4.06 > 4.02
d. 3.1 < 3.15
e. 7.6 > 7.56

3. Write the prime factorization of 32.

2 ∗ 2 ∗ 2 ∗ 2 ∗ 2

4. The temperature at midnight was 25°F. The windchill temperature was 14°F. How much warmer was the actual temperature than the windchill temperature?

11°F warmer

5. Tell whether the following numbers are prime or composite.

a. The number of millimeters in 1.7 cm prime
b. The number of degrees in a right angle composite
c. The number of inches in $\frac{11}{4}$ feet composite
d. One less than the number of hours in 1 day prime
e. The number of months in $\frac{1}{4}$ of a year prime

✦ *Math Journal 1*, p. 38

*Example 3:* The school library has 486 fiction books and 321 nonfiction books. How many books does the library have in all?

This is a parts-and-total story, where two or more separate parts are known and we want to find the total.

1. Open sentence: $486 + 321 = t$, where $t$ is the total number of books in the library.
2. Solution: 807
3. Answer: The library has 807 books in all.

*Example 4:* Mrs. Snow is 49 years old. Her son, Kevin, is celebrating his 24th birthday today. Mr. Snow is 6 years older than Mrs. Snow. How old was Mrs. Snow when Kevin was born?

This is a comparison story involving the difference between two quantities.

1. Open sentence: $49 - 24 = d$ (or $24 + d = 49$), where $d$ is the difference in their ages.
2. Solution: 25
3. Answer: Mrs. Snow was 25 years old when Kevin was born.

Note that the fact that Mr. Snow is 6 years older than Mrs. Snow is not relevant to the solution of the story.

### ✦ Solving Addition and Subtraction Number Stories
(*Math Journal 1*, pp. 36 and 37; *Math Masters*, p. 12)

PARTNER ACTIVITY

Distribute a computation grid to each student. Do the first problem as a class. Remind students to write the appropriate unit as part of the answer. Partners then complete the rest of the problems on the journal pages.

Reserve sufficient time to discuss students' answers.

### ✦ Playing *High-Number Toss*
(*Student Reference Book*, p. 283)

PARTNER ACTIVITY

Students play the decimal version of *High-Number Toss*.

## Math Boxes 2.4 (*Math Journal 1*, p. 38)

INDEPENDENT ACTIVITY  **5–15 min**

**Mixed Review** Math Boxes in this lesson are paired with Math Boxes in Lesson 2.2. The skill in Problem 1 is a prerequisite for Unit 3.

## Study Link 2.4 (*Math Masters*, p. 230)

**Home Connection** Students solve addition and subtraction number stories. Point out to students that they may not need to use all of the numbers given in each problem.

**Open Sentences and Number Stories** — Study Link 2.4

For each problem on this page, fill in the blanks and solve the problem.

SRB 209–211

1. Althea and her brother collect baseball cards. Althea has 148 cards. Her brother has 127 cards. How many cards do they have altogether?
   a. List the numbers needed to solve the problem. 148 and 127
   b. Describe what you want to find. The total number of baseball cards
   c. Open sentence: $148 + 127 = b$
   d. Solution: 275 e. Answer: 275 baseball cards (unit)

2. Julie was driving from Chicago, Illinois, to Topeka, Kansas. Before she started, she filled her tank with 10 gallons of gas. She paid $14.08. After driving about 305 miles, she stopped for gas in Iowa. Again, she got 10 gallons of gas and paid $11.85. How much more did she pay for gas in Chicago than in Iowa?
   a. List the numbers needed to solve the problem. 14.08 and 11.85
   b. Describe what you want to find. How much more Julie paid for gas in Chicago than in Iowa
   c. Open sentence: $14.08 - 11.85 = g$
   d. Solution: 2.23 e. Answer: $2.23

3. Mark paid for his burger and fries with a $20 bill. His burger cost $3.89; his fries cost $1.49. How much change did he receive?
   a. List the numbers needed to solve the problem. 20.00; 3.89; 1.49
   b. Describe what you want to find. The amount of change
   c. Open sentence: $20.00 - 3.89 - 1.49 = c$
   d. Solution: 14.62 e. Answer: $14.62

Circle the open sentence that best matches the story. Then solve the problem.

4. Ralph and Adeline saved their money for 6 weeks. Ralph saved $27.23. Adeline saved $34.98. How much more did Adeline save than Ralph?

   $\$27.23 + \$34.98 = s$ $6 * s = \$34.98$

   (circled) $\$27.23 + s = \$34.98$ $6 + s = \$34.98 - \$27.23$ Answer: $7.75

STUDY LINK MASTER

Math Masters, p. 230

# 3 Options for Individualizing

## ENRICHMENT Solving Challenging Number Stories (*Math Masters*, p. 14)

INDEPENDENT ACTIVITY  **5–15 min**

Students who are ready for a challenge can solve this set of number-story problems.

**Number Story Challenge**

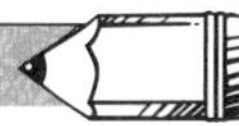

Solve each problem.

1. Lucas was comparing prices on a pair of mini-speakers. At one store, the pair of speakers cost $19.95. At a second store, the same speakers cost $24.70. At a third store, they cost $18.50. If he buys the speakers at the lowest price, how much will he save over the highest price?
   a. List the numbers needed to solve the problem. 18.50 and 24.70
   b. Describe what you want to find. The difference between the prices of the most and least expensive speakers
   c. Open sentence: $24.70 - 18.50 = d$
   d. Solution: 6.20 e. Answer: $6.20

2. Lucas earned $45.50 babysitting. Could he buy both the lowest-priced speakers and a CD costing $12.99? yes

   Describe what you did to solve the problem. Answers vary.

3. Lucas decided to buy only the lowest-priced speakers. His brother Max wanted to pay half of the cost so that he could share the speakers. Lucas agreed. How much money did Lucas have left after paying for half of a set of speakers?
   a. List the numbers needed to solve the problem. 45.50, $\frac{1}{2}$, and 18.50
   b. Describe what you want to find. How much money Lucas had left after paying for half of the least expensive speakers
   c. Open sentence: $45.50 - \frac{1}{2} * 18.50$
   d. Solution: 36.25 e. Answer: $36.25

4. On the back of this page, write a number story of your own using the information on this page. Then solve the problem.

TEACHING MASTER

Math Masters, p. 14

## LANGUAGE DIVERSITY Writing Addition and Subtraction Number Stories

PARTNER ACTIVITY  **5–15 min**

Pair a student proficient in the English language with a student who is learning to speak and write in English. Students work together to write, illustrate, and solve addition and subtraction number stories.

# 2.5 Estimate Your Reaction Time

**OBJECTIVES** **To review statistical landmarks for sets of data; to estimate reaction times; and to use statistical landmarks to describe experimental data.**

| summaries | materials |
|---|---|
| **1 Teaching the Lesson** | |
| Students review how to find the mean of a set of data. They conduct an experiment to estimate the mean time it takes a student to react to having his or her hand squeezed. Students collect individual reaction time data by using a calibrated Grab-It Gauge, find statistical landmarks for the data, and estimate individual reaction times. [Data and Chance; Operations and Computation] | □ *Math Journal 1,* pp. 39 and 40 and Activity Sheet 3<br>□ *Student Reference Book*, pp. 113 and 115<br>□ Study Link 2.4<br>□ calculator □ dictionary (optional)<br>□ a timer such as a stopwatch, a digital watch, or a clock<br>□ stick-on notes (optional) □ scissors<br>***See* Advance Preparation** |
| **2 Ongoing Learning & Practice** | |
| Students interpret data displayed in a table. [Data and Chance; Operations and Computation]<br>Students practice and maintain skills through Math Boxes and Study Link activities. | □ *Math Journal 1,* pp. 41 and 42<br>□ Study Link Master (*Math Masters,* p. 231) |
| **3 Options for Individualizing** | |
| **Enrichment** Students make line plots for the reaction times data they have collected. [Data and Chance]<br>**Language Diversity** Students discuss other meanings for the term *median.* [Data and Chance]<br>**Extra Practice** Students choose a set of data in their *Student Reference Books* and find the statistical landmarks for the data. [Data and Chance; Operations and Computation] | □ *Student Reference Book*<br>□ Teaching Master (*Math Masters,* p. 15) |

## Additional Information

**Advance Preparation** For the hand-squeezing experiment in Part 1, you will need a timing device capable of measuring time to the nearest second. Use a stopwatch, a digital watch, or a clock with a sweeping second hand. Construct your own Grab-It Gauge from *Math Journal 1,* Activity Sheet 3 to use as a model for the students.

**Vocabulary • mean (also called average) • stimulus • reaction time • minimum • maximum • range • mode • median**

**Vocabulary (teacher) • statistical landmark**

# Getting Started

## Mental Math and Reflexes

Students write numbers from dictation and identify digits in given places. *Suggestions:*

- 243,564 Circle the digit in the ten-thousands place; underline the digit in the hundreds place.
- 1,407,829 Circle the thousands digit; underline the millions digit.
- 24.67 Circle the tenths digit; underline the ones digit.
- 518.03 Circle the hundredths digit; underline the hundreds digit.

## Math Message

*Read page 115 in your* Student Reference Book. *Then find the mean of the data shown at the bottom of that page.*

## Study Link 2.4 Follow-Up

Briefly go over the answers. Ask someone to explain how he or she chose the correct open sentence in Problem 4.

# 1 Teaching the Lesson

## ✦ Math Message Follow-Up (*Student Reference Book,* p. 115)

WHOLE-CLASS DISCUSSION 

Briefly discuss the example of the **mean** (or average) of a set of data on page 115 in the *Student Reference Book*. Go over the answer to the problem at the bottom of that page.

## ✦ Estimating a Mean Reaction Time for the Class

WHOLE-CLASS ACTIVITY

**Science Link** Ask the class if anyone can give an example of a **stimulus,** or have someone look up the word in a dictionary. A stimulus is something that causes a response. For example, your eyes may tear when you chop onions: The onion's fumes are a stimulus.

Tell students that they are going to conduct an experiment to estimate how fast their hands react to stimuli. By doing this experiment, they will be able to estimate the average time it takes a student to react to having his or her right hand squeezed. This is called the **reaction time.**

Assign one student to be the Timer. You and the remaining students, all holding hands, form a large circle around the room.

1. You, as the Leader, give the Timer the signal to start the timing device. Gently squeeze the hand of the person on your left.

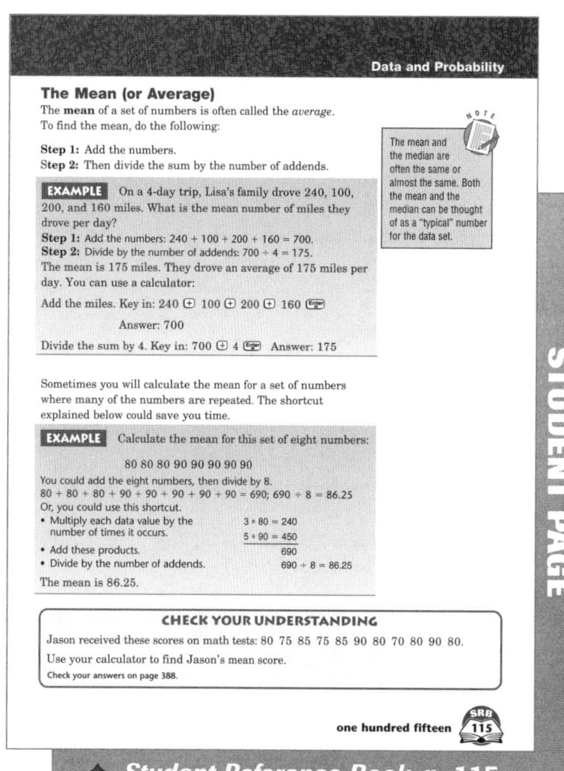

Data and Probability

**The Mean (or Average)**

The **mean** of a set of numbers is often called the *average*. To find the mean, do the following:

**Step 1:** Add the numbers.
**Step 2:** Then divide the sum by the number of addends.

**EXAMPLE** On a 4-day trip, Lisa's family drove 240, 100, 200, and 160 miles. What is the mean number of miles they drove per day?

**Step 1:** Add the numbers: 240 + 100 + 200 + 160 = 700.
**Step 2:** Divide by the number of addends: 700 ÷ 4 = 175.

The mean is 175 miles. They drove an average of 175 miles per day. You can use a calculator:

Add the miles. Key in: 240 [+] 100 [+] 200 [+] 160 [Enter] Answer: 700

Divide the sum by 4. Key in: 700 [÷] 4 [Enter] Answer: 175

NOTE: The mean and the median are often the same or almost the same. Both the mean and the median can be thought of as a "typical" number for the data set.

Sometimes you will calculate the mean for a set of numbers where many of the numbers are repeated. The shortcut explained below could save you time.

**EXAMPLE** Calculate the mean for this set of eight numbers:

80 80 80 90 90 90 90 90

You could add the eight numbers, then divide by 8.
80 + 80 + 80 + 90 + 90 + 90 + 90 + 90 = 690; 690 ÷ 8 = 86.25
Or, you could use this shortcut.

- Multiply each data value by the number of times it occurs. 3 * 80 = 240; 5 * 90 = 450
- Add these products. 690
- Divide by the number of addends. 690 ÷ 8 = 86.25

The mean is 86.25.

**CHECK YOUR UNDERSTANDING**

Jason received these scores on math tests: 80 75 85 75 85 90 80 70 80 90 80.

Use your calculator to find Jason's mean score.

Check your answers on page 388.

one hundred fifteen SRB 115

STUDENT PAGE

✦ *Student Reference Book,* p. 115

**Rounding to the nearest tenth:**

Use the hundredths digit to round to the nearest tenth:

| | | |
|---|---|---|
| If the hundredths digit is 4 or less, round down. | 0.542 | → 0.5 |
| | 0.431538 | → 0.4 |
| | 0.4194949 | → 0.4 |
| If the hundredths digit is 5 or more, round up. | 0.45 | → 0.5 |
| | 0.551674 | → 0.6 |
| | 0.491 | → 0.5 |

Tester
(holding Grab-It Gauge)

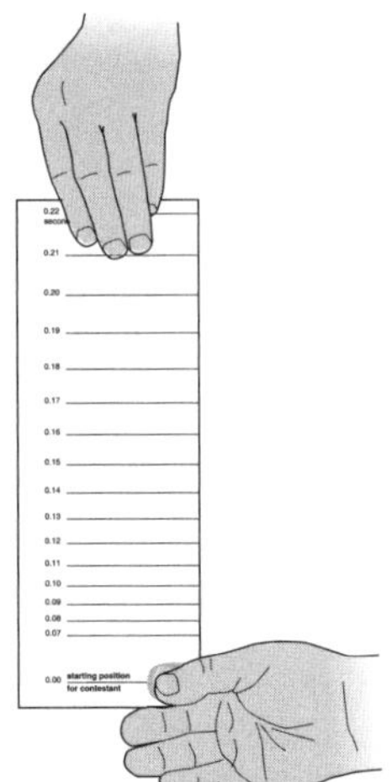


Contestant
(not quite touching
Grab-It Gauge)

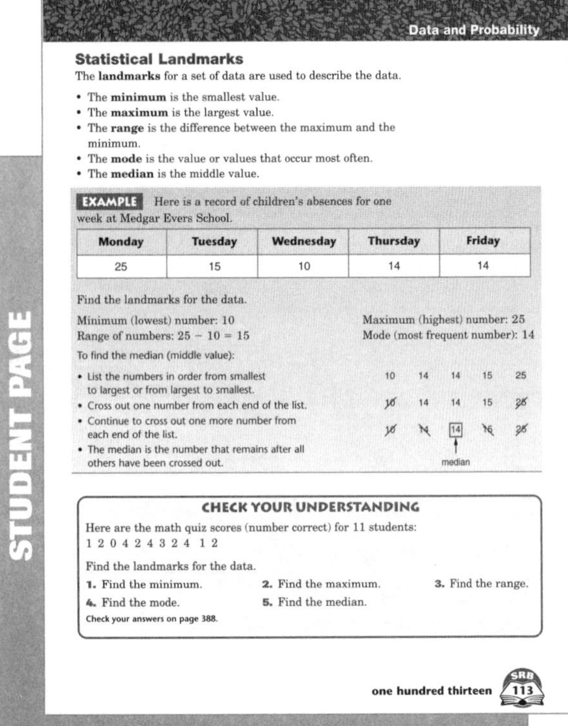

Data and Probability

**Statistical Landmarks**

The **landmarks** for a set of data are used to describe the data.

- The **minimum** is the smallest value.
- The **maximum** is the largest value.
- The **range** is the difference between the maximum and the minimum.
- The **mode** is the value or values that occur most often.
- The **median** is the middle value.

**EXAMPLE** Here is a record of children's absences for one week at Medgar Evers School.

| Monday | Tuesday | Wednesday | Thursday | Friday |
|---|---|---|---|---|
| 25 | 15 | 10 | 14 | 14 |

Find the landmarks for the data.

Minimum (lowest) number: 10
Range of numbers: 25 − 10 = 15

Maximum (highest) number: 25
Mode (most frequent number): 14

To find the median (middle value):

- List the numbers in order from smallest to largest or from largest to smallest. 10 14 14 15 25
- Cross out one number from each end of the list. ~~10~~ 14 14 15 ~~25~~
- Continue to cross out one more number from each end of the list. ~~10~~ ~~14~~ 14 ~~15~~ ~~25~~
- The median is the number that remains after all others have been crossed out. (14 — median)

**CHECK YOUR UNDERSTANDING**

Here are the math quiz scores (number correct) for 11 students:
1 2 0 4 2 4 3 2 4 1 2

Find the landmarks for the data.

1. Find the minimum.
2. Find the maximum.
3. Find the range.
4. Find the mode.
5. Find the median.

Check your answers on page 388.

one hundred thirteen SRB 113

STUDENT PAGE

✦ *Student Reference Book*, p. 113

2. The person on your left squeezes the hand of the person on his or her left.
3. The squeeze continues around the circle until it reaches the Leader, who calls out "Stop!"
4. The Timer records the elapsed time.

Practice once or twice; then perform the experiment and record the answer. (Note that you may want to have students close their eyes so they can't anticipate the squeeze by watching it travel from person to person.)

Ask the class to calculate the mean reaction time per student to the nearest tenth of a second. Divide the total reaction time for the class by the total number of people in the circle.

Discuss with the class how to interpret the calculator display after dividing. It would not be practical to use the entire display. Students should round the results to the nearest tenth of a second. (*See the margin.*)

## ✦ Reviewing the Meaning of Some Statistical Landmarks (*Student Reference Book,* p. 113)

WHOLE-CLASS DISCUSSION

Read page 113 as a class. To check that students know how to find the **statistical landmarks** discussed on this page, have them find the **minimum, maximum, range, mode,** and **median** of the set of data at the bottom of the page.

## ✦ Estimating Individual Reaction Times (*Math Journal 1,* pp. 39 and 40 and Activity Sheet 3)

PARTNER ACTIVITY

Ask students if they think their left or right hand is quicker. Some students may reason that if they are right-handed, their right hand would react more quickly than their left hand, and conversely if they are left-handed. Tell them that they will perform an experiment to check which hand reacts more quickly.

Have each student cut out the Grab-It Gauge on Activity Sheet 3. Go over the directions for the experiment on the journal page. Discuss the markings on the Grab-It Gauge: The times increase by 0.01 second as you go from the bottom of the gauge to the top.

Have two students demonstrate how to use the Grab-It Gauge. Partners then proceed with the experiment. Independently, they record the results of the experiment, find the landmarks for the data, and record their conclusions. Circulate and assist.

## ✦ Sharing Results
(*Math Journal 1,* pp. 39 and 40)

WHOLE-CLASS DISCUSSION 

Bring the class together to discuss the results of the experiment. Ask students which landmarks they chose as the best estimates of their reaction times, and why. The mode, median, and mean can all be justified as reasonable estimates of their typical reaction time. The minimum is an estimate of their fastest reaction time, but is not a good estimate of their *typical* reaction time. The maximum is an estimate of their *slowest* reaction time, but is not a good estimate of their *typical* reaction time.

Other possible discussion questions:

- From your results, as well as the results of your classmates, are you able to state a rule about reaction times and left-handed or right-handed people? Do you have enough data? Studies have shown that a right-handed person can react with the right hand about 3% faster than with the left hand, and conversely for a left-handed person. Students would probably need to collect much more data to detect such slight differences.
- Would a difference of one or two hundredths in the medians make a meaningful difference? Not necessarily, considering that the tool and method of measuring are not very precise.
- Why do you think it might be important to know a reaction time? In what sports or professions would this information be useful? Sample answer: It might be important to know a reaction time in sports such as baseball or hockey, or in professions such as pilots or astronauts.

# 2 Ongoing Learning & Practice

## ✦ Interpreting a Table of Data
(*Math Journal 1,* p. 41)

PARTNER ACTIVITY

Students answer questions based on data about winning speeds for the Indianapolis 500 race. These questions involve reading the table, subtracting decimals, and finding the range and median of the data.

### Estimating Your Reaction Time

Tear out Activity Sheet 3 from the back of your journal. Cut out the Grab-It Gauge.

It takes two people to perform this experiment. The *tester* holds the Grab-It Gauge at the top. The *contestant* gets ready to catch the gauge by placing his or her thumb and index finger at the bottom of the gauge, *without quite touching it.* (See the picture.)

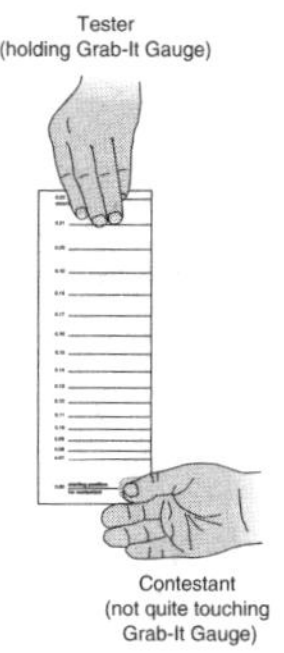


When the contestant is ready, the tester lets go of the gauge. The contestant tries to grab it with his or her thumb and index finger as quickly as possible.

The number grasped by the contestant shows that person's reaction time, to the nearest hundredth of a second. The contestant then records that reaction time in the data table shown below.

Partners take turns being tester and contestant. Each person should perform the experiment 10 times with each hand.

| Reaction Time (in seconds) | | | |
|---|---|---|---|
| Left Hand | | Right Hand | |
| 1. | 6. | 1. | 6. |
| 2. | 7. | 2. | 7. |
| 3. | 8. | 3. | 8. |
| 4. | 9. | 4. | 9. |
| 5. | 10. | 5. | 10. |

STUDENT PAGE

✦ *Math Journal 1,* p. 39

**ONGOING ASSESSMENT**
Ask students to write a definition of the median (or some other landmark) in their own words.

### Estimating Your Reaction Time (cont.)

Use the results of your Grab-It experiment to answer the following questions.

Answers vary for Problems 1–8.

1. What was the **maximum** reaction time for your left hand? _______ right hand? _______
2. What was the **minimum** reaction time for your left hand? _______ right hand? _______
3. What was the **range** of reaction times for your left hand? _______ right hand? _______
4. What reaction time was the **mode** for your left hand? _______ right hand? _______
5. What was the **median** reaction time for your left hand? _______ right hand? _______
6. What was the **mean** reaction time for your left hand? _______ right hand? _______
7. If you could use just one number to estimate your reaction time, which number would you choose as the best estimate? Circle one.
   minimum maximum mode median mean
   Explain. _______
8. Which of your hands reacted more quickly in the Grab-It experiment? _______

STUDENT PAGE

✦ *Math Journal 1,* p. 40

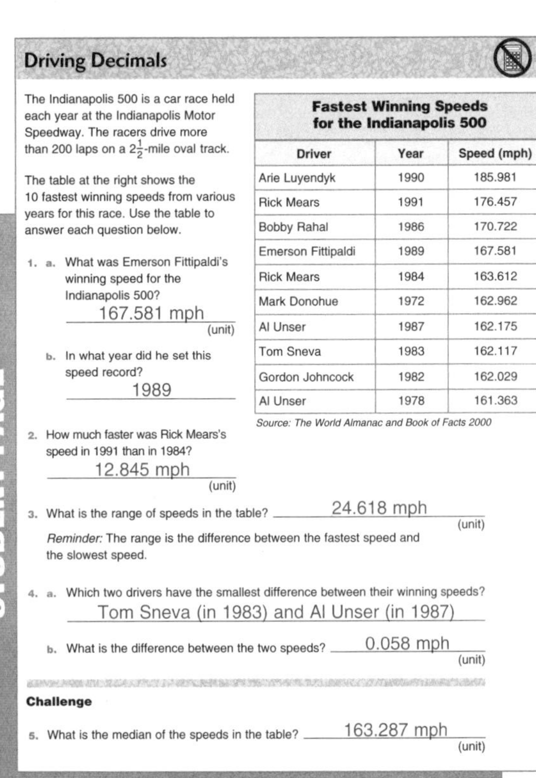

**Driving Decimals**

The Indianapolis 500 is a car race held each year at the Indianapolis Motor Speedway. The racers drive more than 200 laps on a $2\frac{1}{2}$-mile oval track.

The table at the right shows the 10 fastest winning speeds from various years for this race. Use the table to answer each question below.

**Fastest Winning Speeds for the Indianapolis 500**

| Driver | Year | Speed (mph) |
|---|---|---|
| Arie Luyendyk | 1990 | 185.981 |
| Rick Mears | 1991 | 176.457 |
| Bobby Rahal | 1986 | 170.722 |
| Emerson Fittipaldi | 1989 | 167.581 |
| Rick Mears | 1984 | 163.612 |
| Mark Donohue | 1972 | 162.962 |
| Al Unser | 1987 | 162.175 |
| Tom Sneva | 1983 | 162.117 |
| Gordon Johncock | 1982 | 162.029 |
| Al Unser | 1978 | 161.363 |

*Source: The World Almanac and Book of Facts 2000*

1. a. What was Emerson Fittipaldi's winning speed for the Indianapolis 500? 167.581 mph (unit)
   b. In what year did he set this speed record? 1989
2. How much faster was Rick Mears's speed in 1991 than in 1984? 12.845 mph (unit)
3. What is the range of speeds in the table? 24.618 mph (unit)
   *Reminder:* The range is the difference between the fastest speed and the slowest speed.
4. a. Which two drivers have the smallest difference between their winning speeds? Tom Sneva (in 1983) and Al Unser (in 1987)
   b. What is the difference between the two speeds? 0.058 mph (unit)

**Challenge**

5. What is the median of the speeds in the table? 163.287 mph (unit)

STUDENT PAGE

✦ *Math Journal 1,* p. 41

NOTE: The TI-15 calculator can round numbers to any place from thousandths to thousands. See *Student Reference Book,* page 243.

**Math Boxes 2.5**

1. I have four sides. All opposite sides are parallel. I have no right angles.
   a. Draw me in the space below.
   Sample drawing:
   b. I am called a parallellogram or rhombus

SRB 136

2. Write < or >.
   a. 0.45 < $\frac{3}{4}$
   b. 0.89 > $\frac{8}{10}$
   c. $\frac{4}{5}$ > 0.54
   d. $\frac{1}{3}$ < 0.35
   e. $\frac{7}{8}$ < 0.9

SRB 83 89

3. Complete each pattern.
   a. 25, 43, 61, 79
   b. 87, 65, 43, 21
   c. 21, 35, 49, 63
   d. 64, 56, 48, 40, 32
   e. 61, 66, 71, 76, 81

4. Solve. (Solution)
   a. $23 + x = 60$ $x =$ 37
   b. $36 = p * 4$ $p =$ 9
   c. $200 = 50 * m$ $m =$ 4
   d. $55 + t = 70$ $t =$ 15
   e. $28 - b = 13$ $b =$ 15

SRB 209

5. Add.
   a. 632 + 859 = 1,491
   b. 2.24 + 3.85 = 6.09
   c. 1,902 + 478 = 2,380
   d. 3,341 + 799 = 4,140
   e. 1,654 + 2,020 = 3,674

SRB 13-14

STUDENT PAGE

✦ *Math Journal 1,* p. 42

For the Challenge problem—finding the median of the winning speeds—you need to find the number halfway between the fifth- and sixth-highest entries in the table. One way is to add the two numbers and divide the result by 2. 163.612 + 162.962 = 326.574; 326.574 / 2 = 163.287 Another way is to find the difference between the fifth- and sixth-highest speeds, divide the difference by 2, and then add the result to the lower speed. 163.612 − 162.962 = 0.650; 0.650 / 2 = 0.325; 162.962 + 0.325 = 163.287

## ✦ Math Boxes 2.5 (*Math Journal 1,* p. 42)

INDEPENDENT ACTIVITY 

**Mixed Review** Math Boxes in this lesson are paired with Math Boxes in Lesson 2.8. The skill in Problem 1 is a prerequisite for Unit 3.

## ✦ Study Link 2.5 (*Math Masters,* p. 231)

**Home Connection** Students use their Grab-It Gauge to collect data from two people at home. They compare the results with the class data for the experiment.

Remind students that they will need to take their Grab-It Gauges home.

# 3 Options for Individualizing

## ✦ ENRICHMENT Displaying Reaction Time in Line Plots

INDEPENDENT ACTIVITY  **15–30 min** 

You can extend the *Estimating Individual Reaction Times* activity by having students make line plots for their data. Have each student write the median time for the right hand on one stick-on note, and the median time for the left hand on another stick-on note. Students then come to the board and make two line plots, one for each hand, by putting their stick-on notes in the appropriate places. Display one line plot over the other for ease of comparison. Students can then compare the shapes of the two line plots. Are the stick-on notes evenly spread? Do some occur in clusters? Are there gaps?

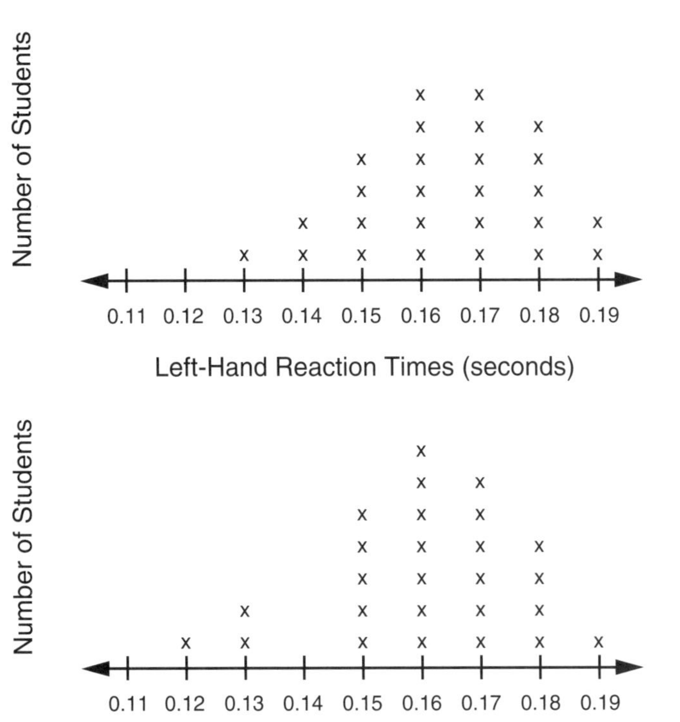


### Comparing Reaction Times

Study Link 2.5

Use your Grab-It Gauge. Collect reaction-time data from two people at home. One person should be at least 25 years old.

Answers vary for Problems 1–5.

1.

| Person 1 | |
|---|---|
| Left | Right |
| | |
| | |
| | |
| | |
| | |
| | |
| | |
| | |
| | |
| | |

2.

| Person 2 | |
|---|---|
| Left | Right |
| | |
| | |
| | |
| | |
| | |
| | |
| | |
| | |
| | |
| | |

3. Median times:
Left hand _______
Right hand _______

4. Median times:
Left hand _______
Right hand _______

5. How do the results for the two people compare to your class data?

STUDY LINK MASTER

Math Masters, p. 231

## LANGUAGE DIVERSITY Building Background for Mathematics Words

SMALL-GROUP ACTIVITY  5–15 min 

Group students just learning English with a few proficient English speakers and ask them if they have heard the term *median* used in other ways. Prompt students with questions such as the following:

- What is the median, or median strip, or median area of a highway? The median divides the road in the middle—half the roadway is on one side, half on the other. The median may be a grassy strip, concrete barrier, or a painted line down the middle of the road.
- Who is the mediator of an argument or discussion? A person who takes the middle position or neutral ground between opposing sides. A mediator is said to *mediate* an argument or discussion.

## EXTRA PRACTICE Finding the Statistical Landmarks for a Set of Data

(*Student Reference Book; Math Masters,* p. 15)

INDEPENDENT ACTIVITY  15–30 min

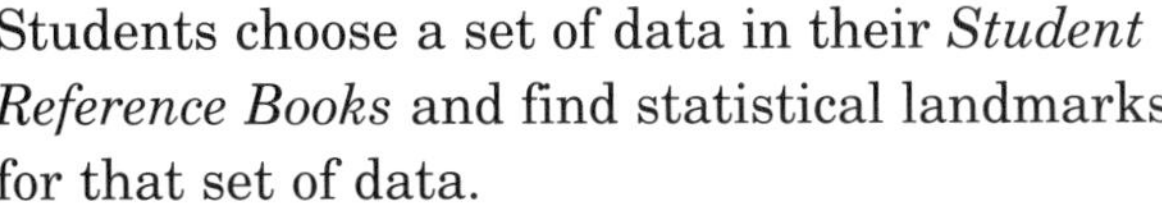

Students choose a set of data in their *Student Reference Books* and find statistical landmarks for that set of data.

### Statistical Landmarks

1. Choose a set of data in your *Student Reference Book* for which you can find statistical landmarks. Answers vary for Problems 1–4.
2. Describe the set of data you chose. (Give the page number in your *Student Reference Book.*)
3. Find the following landmarks for the data you chose.
Maximum _______ Minimum _______
Range _______ Mode _______
Mean _______ Median _______
4. Describe at least one observation you made about the data.

TEACHING MASTER

Math Masters, p. 15

# 2.6 Chance Events

**OBJECTIVE** **To review and apply vocabulary associated with chance events; to introduce the Probability Meter Poster; and to estimate the probability of an event.**

| summaries | materials |
|---|---|
| **1 Teaching the Lesson** | |
| Students use words, phrases, fractions, percents, and decimals to describe various chance events and use stick-on notes to record these probabilities on the Probability Meter Poster. Students perform an experiment to estimate the probability that a thumbtack will land point down when tossed, and record their estimates on the Probability Meter Poster. [Data and Chance; Operations and Computation] | □ *Math Journal 1,* pp. 43 and 44 □ Study Link 2.5<br>□ *Student Reference Book,* p. 360<br>□ Assessment Master (*Math Masters,* p. 479; optional)<br>□ Probability Meter Poster □ stick-on notes □ calculator<br>Per partnership:<br>□ 10 thumbtacks (or two-color counters or pennies); small cup<br>***See* Advance Preparation** |
| **2 Ongoing Learning & Practice** | |
| Students practice identifying statistical landmarks for given data sets. [Data and Chance; Operations and Computation]<br>Students practice and maintain skills through Math Boxes and Study Link activities. | □ *Math Journal 1,* pp. 45 and 46<br>□ Study Link Master (*Math Masters,* p. 232) |
| **3 Options for Individualizing** | |
| **Enrichment** Students perform a probability experiment and then make predictions based on the outcomes. [Data and Chance]<br>**Extra Practice** Students predict the results of a spinner experiment and then perform the experiment. [Data and Chance; Operations and Computation] | □ Teaching Master (*Math Masters,* p. 16)<br>Per group:<br>□ paper bag; 8 blocks (2 of one color, 2 of a second color, 4 of a third color); slate (optional)<br>Per partnership:<br>□ large paper clip; straightedge; red, blue, and green crayons or coloring pencils |

## Additional Information

**Advance Preparation** Cut the Probability Meter Poster into two pieces and tape the pieces together at the 50% mark. You may want to laminate the poster for durability. The Probability Meter Poster will be used throughout the school year, so you should post it in an accessible and visible area. The meter will be used both as a device for recording probabilities and as a handy reference for equivalent names for fractions.

For Part 1, each partnership will need 10 solid-head steel thumbtacks and a small cup. If you are uncomfortable with the use of thumbtacks for the experiment in this lesson, you may substitute 10 pennies, or two-color counters. If you do, students will need to change the directions on journal page 44. Pushpins should not be used.

**Vocabulary** • **impossible** • **certain** • **Probability Meter Poster** • **(very, extremely) likely** • **50–50 chance** • **(very, extremely) unlikely**

# Getting Started

### Mental Math and Reflexes

*Round to the nearest whole number.*

| 17.7 | 205.32 | 83.54 |
|---|---|---|
| 18 | 205 | 84 |

*Round to the nearest tenth.*

| 45.52 | 60.18 | 123.45 |
|---|---|---|
| 45.5 | 60.2 | 123.5 |

### Math Message

*Complete page 43 in your journal.*

### Study Link 2.5 Follow-Up

Students share the results of the experiments they did at home. How did the results of the home experiments compare to the results of the class experiments? Were the results from people over the age of 25 different from the class results?

# 1 Teaching the Lesson

## ✦ Math Message Follow-Up
(*Math Journal 1,* p. 43)

WHOLE-CLASS DISCUSSION

Students of *Everyday Mathematics* have conducted spinner experiments in previous grades. While they are most likely to use fractions to describe the chances of landing on the colored part of a spinner, they should be encouraged to use decimal and percent names as well. *For example:*

▷ If you spin a lot, you should land on black half the time. That's a 50% chance that black will come up. It is **impossible** to land on neither black nor white, and it is **certain** that you will land on black or white.

▷ It's hard to predict, but if you spin a lot, black will come up about 1 out of 4 spins, or $\frac{1}{4}$ of the time. You can say it in other ways, too: The spinner will land on black about 25% of the time, or 0.25 ($\frac{25}{100}$) of the time.

Expect students to disagree on some of the answers in Part 2. That's OK—for some events they must make educated guesses and therefore, their answers will vary. Ask students to explain their choices. (Information on some items is given in the activity that follows.)

## ✦ Introducing the Probability Meter Poster
(*Math Journal 1,* p. 43; *Student Reference Book,* p. 360)

WHOLE-CLASS DISCUSSION

Focus the class's attention on the **Probability Meter Poster.** The Probability Meter Poster appears on page 360 of the *Student Reference Book.*

**Adjusting the Activity** Challenge students to use a variety of words and phrases to describe chance events. Some examples are: likely, unlikely, 1 out of 4, one-fourth of the time, 25% of the time, the chances are, one may expect.

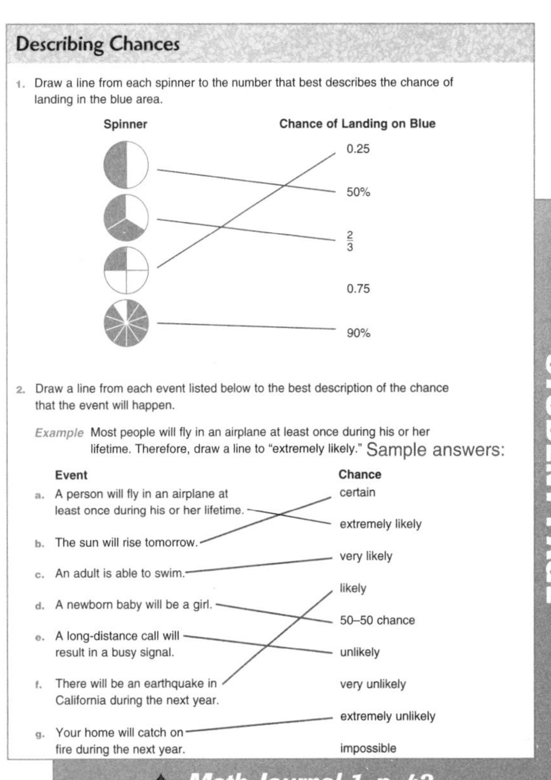

**Describing Chances**

1. Draw a line from each spinner to the number that best describes the chance of landing in the blue area.

| Spinner | Chance of Landing on Blue |
|---|---|
| | 0.25 |
| | 50% |
| | $\frac{2}{3}$ |
| | 0.75 |
| | 90% |

2. Draw a line from each event listed below to the best description of the chance that the event will happen.

*Example* Most people will fly in an airplane at least once during his or her lifetime. Therefore, draw a line to "extremely likely." Sample answers:

| Event | Chance |
|---|---|
| a. A person will fly in an airplane at least once during his or her lifetime. | certain |
| b. The sun will rise tomorrow. | extremely likely |
| c. An adult is able to swim. | very likely |
| d. A newborn baby will be a girl. | likely |
| e. A long-distance call will result in a busy signal. | 50–50 chance |
| f. There will be an earthquake in California during the next year. | unlikely |
| g. Your home will catch on fire during the next year. | very unlikely |
| | extremely unlikely |
| | impossible |

STUDENT PAGE

✦ *Math Journal 1,* p. 43

Tell the class that they will use the Probability Meter Poster throughout the year to display the chances of various events happening. Ask students to describe what they see on the Probability Meter Poster. The following should be mentioned in the course of the discussion:

- ▷ The Probability Meter Poster is part of a number line from 0 to 1 that is divided into 100 equal parts by little black marks.
- ▷ Each black mark sections off $\frac{1}{100}$ or 0.01 or 1% of the Probability Meter Poster. (There are also some red marks to show simple fractions of the meter that fall between black marks.)
- ▷ Fractions, decimals, and percents all appear on the meter. For some numbers, such as $\frac{3}{4}$ and $\frac{1}{10}$, all three names for the number appear.

You can use the events in Problem 2 on page 43 to demonstrate how to display probabilities on the meter. For example, a large sample of birth records shows that more boys (51%) are born than girls (49%). Attach stick-on notes in the appropriate places on the meter to display these probabilities *(see the margin)*.

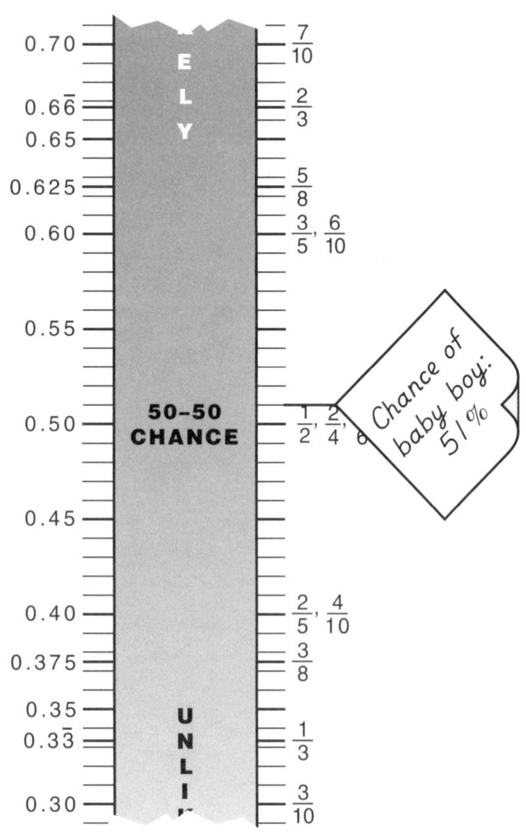


Here are some other probabilities, based on surveys of many people, telephone records, fire reports, and so on:

- ▷ There is about a 1% chance of one's home catching on fire during the next year.
- ▷ There is about a 10% chance of getting a busy signal when calling long distance.
- ▷ There is about a 90% chance that there will be an earthquake in California during the next year.
- ▷ There is about a $\frac{2}{3}$ chance that an adult knows how to swim.

You may want to discuss how data are collected in real life. Ask students how the probabilities shown for these events might have been obtained.

- How do we know that about 2 out of 3 adults can swim? By asking a large number of adults whether they can swim
- How do we know that there is 1 chance in 100 that a home will catch on fire during the next year? By using fire reports to estimate the number of house fires per year

Discuss phrases, such as **very (extremely) likely (unlikely), 50–50 chance,** and **extremely (very) unlikely (likely),** shown on the Probability Meter Poster. Each phrase is useful in identifying an approximate location on the meter. Encourage students to use these phrases—they are a meaningful way of describing the chances that an event will occur.

## ✦ Estimating the Chance that a Thumbtack Will Land Point Down

(*Math Journal 1*, p. 44; *Math Masters*, p. 479)

PARTNER ACTIVITY

1. **Introduce the problem.**

   Tell the class that if you drop a thumbtack, it will land either with the point up or with the point down. Demonstrate these two positions by placing a thumbtack on a table with the point up and another thumbtack with the point down. (Do not toss the thumbtacks.)

   Ask students to guess whether a thumbtack is more likely to land with the point up or with the point down and to record their guesses at the top of the journal page. Take a vote and record the class results on the board.

2. **Perform an experiment to check students' guesses.**

   Have students read the instructions in Problem 1 on the journal page while you pass out 1 cup, 10 tacks, and a stick-on note to each partnership. Demonstrate how you want students to shake and toss a set of 10 thumbtacks.

   Each partnership makes a total of 10 tosses of 10 thumbtacks (or 100 total thumbtack tosses) and records the results of each toss in their journals.

   Partners write the fraction of the thumbtacks that landed point down on a stick-on note. This should be a fraction with a denominator of 100. Partners also write the equivalent decimal and percent names. For example, if students observed 35 point-down outcomes out of 100, they would write $\frac{35}{100}$, 0.35, and 35%.

   Next, they post their stick-on notes on the *right* side of the Probability Meter Poster, with a corner of the stick-on note pointing to the appropriate mark on the meter.

3. **Interpret the results of the experiment.**

   The results of the experiment will likely vary from partnership to partnership. By combining results from all partnerships, students can make a reasonable estimate of the chance that a thumbtack will land point down.

   **a.** First, make a rough estimate. Students use the distribution of stick-on notes to estimate the fraction of thumbtacks landing point down for the whole class.

   **b.** Next, find the fraction of thumbtacks landing point down for the whole class:

STUDENT PAGE

**A Thumbtack Experiment**

**Make a guess:** If you drop a thumbtack, is it more likely to land with the point up or with the point down? Answers vary.

The experiment described below will enable you to make a careful estimate of the chance that a thumbtack will land point down. Answers vary for Problems 1–4.

1. Work with a partner. You should have 10 thumbtacks and 1 small cup. Do the experiment at your desk or table so that you are working over a smooth, hard surface.

   Place the 10 thumbtacks inside the cup. Shake the cup a few times, and then drop the tacks on the desk surface. Record the number of thumbtacks that land point up and the number that land point down.

   Toss the 10 thumbtacks 9 more times and record the results each time.

| Toss | Number Landing Point Up | Number Landing Point Down |
|---|---|---|
| 1 | | |
| 2 | | |
| 3 | | |
| 4 | | |
| 5 | | |
| 6 | | |
| 7 | | |
| 8 | | |
| 9 | | |
| 10 | | |
| | **Total Up =** | **Total Down =** |

2. In making your 10 tosses, you dropped a total of 100 thumbtacks. What fraction of the thumbtacks landed point down? ______
3. Write this fraction on a small stick-on note. Also, write it as a decimal and as a percent.
4. *Do this later:* For the whole class, the chance a tack lands point down is ______ .

✦ *Math Journal 1*, p. 44

STUDENT PAGE

## Describing a Set of Data

1. Justin, Vincent, Gregory, Bernard, Melinda, Frieda, and Marina estimated the number of jellybeans in a jar. They made the following estimates:

| | |
|---|---|
| Justin | 247 |
| Vincent | 375 |
| Gregory | 199 |
| Bernard | 252 |
| Melinda | 305 |
| Frieda | 200 |
| Marina | 299 |

a. What was the minimum estimate? 199

b. What was the maximum estimate? 375

c. What was the mode of the estimates? No mode since each number occurred only once.

d. What was the range of the estimates? 176

e. What was the median estimate? 252

f. There were 270 jellybeans in the jar. Whose estimate was closest? Bernard's

2. Eight friends were comparing their science test scores. There were 50 questions on the test. Their scores were as follows:

80, 96, 88, 100, 88, 94, 90, 88

a. What was the minimum score? 80

b. What was the maximum score? 100

c. What was the mode of the scores? 88

d. What was the range of the scores? 20

e. What was the median score? 89

f. Explain how you would find the mean for the eight scores. Sample answer: Add all 8 scores and then divide the total by 8.

✦ *Math Journal 1,* p. 45

**ONGOING ASSESSMENT**

Have students complete an Exit Slip for the following: Why do you think that the combined results for the whole class may be more reliable than the results for a single student?

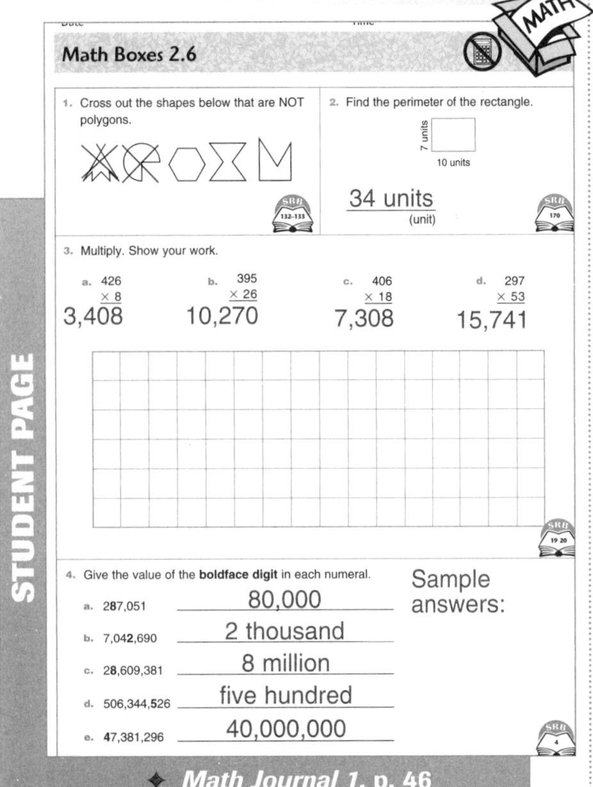

STUDENT PAGE

Math Boxes 2.6

1. Cross out the shapes below that are NOT polygons.

2. Find the perimeter of the rectangle. 7 units, 10 units

34 units (unit)

3. Multiply. Show your work.

a. 426 × 8 = 3,408
b. 395 × 26 = 10,270
c. 406 × 18 = 7,308
d. 297 × 53 = 15,741

4. Give the value of the **boldface digit** in each numeral. Sample answers:

a. 287,051 — 80,000
b. 7,042,690 — 2 thousand
c. 28,609,381 — 8 million
d. 506,344,526 — five hundred
e. 47,381,296 — 40,000,000

✦ *Math Journal 1,* p. 46

**(1)** Find the total number of thumbtacks that landed point down by adding the results on all the stick-on notes.

**(2)** Students use their calculators to divide the total number of thumbtacks that landed point down by the total number of throws, which is 100 times the number of stick-on notes.

For example, if 12 partnerships tossed 1,200 thumbtacks and 491 of these landed point down, students would divide 491 by 1,200 using their calculators. The result is 0.41, rounded to the nearest hundredth. This can also be written as $\frac{41}{100}$, or 41%. Students record this class estimate in Problem 4. Record the class estimate on a stick-on note and post it on the *left* side of the Probability Meter Poster, with a corner pointing to the correct mark on the meter (see the example below). Remove the stick-on notes on the *right* side of the meter.

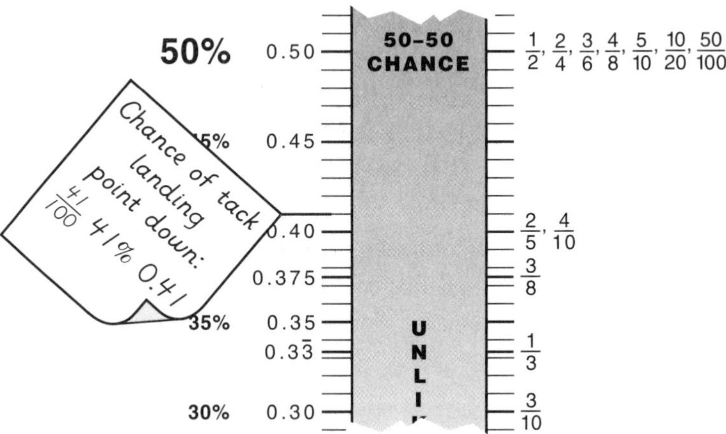


You should use the *left* side of the Probability Meter to keep a record of chances for various events throughout the school year. Use the *right* side of the meter for temporary displays, such as the individual results of the thumbtack experiment.

# 2 Ongoing Learning & Practice

## ✦ Identifying Statistical Landmarks

(*Math Journal 1,* p. 45)

INDEPENDENT ACTIVITY 

Students find the minimum, maximum, range, mode, and median for given data sets. They describe how to find the mean for a set of data. If students are having difficulty identifying or calculating one or more of the landmarks, refer them to pages 113 and 114 in the *Student Reference Book.*

## ✦ Math Boxes 2.6 (*Math Journal 1*, p. 46)

INDEPENDENT ACTIVITY 

**Mixed Review** Math Boxes in this lesson are paired with Math Boxes in Lesson 2.9. The skill in Problem 1 is a prerequisite for Unit 3.

## ✦ Study Link 2.6 (*Math Masters*, p. 232)

**Home Connection** Students use the Probability Meter Poster to translate between probabilities expressed in words and those expressed with percents.

# 3 Options for Individualizing

## ✦ ENRICHMENT Making Predictions Based on Outcomes of a Probability Experiment

SMALL-GROUP ACTIVITY  **15–30 min** 

Secretly place 8 blocks in a paper bag—2 of one color, 2 of a second color, and 4 of a third color. Each block should be the same size and shape. Tell students how many blocks are in the bag, but do not reveal their colors.

Students take turns taking a block out of the bag, showing it to their group, and replacing it. One student should be assigned the task of recording the color on a slate or a piece of paper. After a number of draws, a pattern should develop. Students try to determine the color of the blocks and the number of blocks of each color. Encourage students to explain their reasoning.

## ✦ EXTRA PRACTICE Conducting Spinner Experiments (*Math Masters*, p. 16)

PARTNER ACTIVITY  **15–30 min** 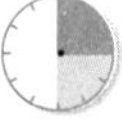

Students make a spinner, predict the results of spinning the spinner different numbers of times, perform the experiment, and compare the results of the experiment to their predictions.

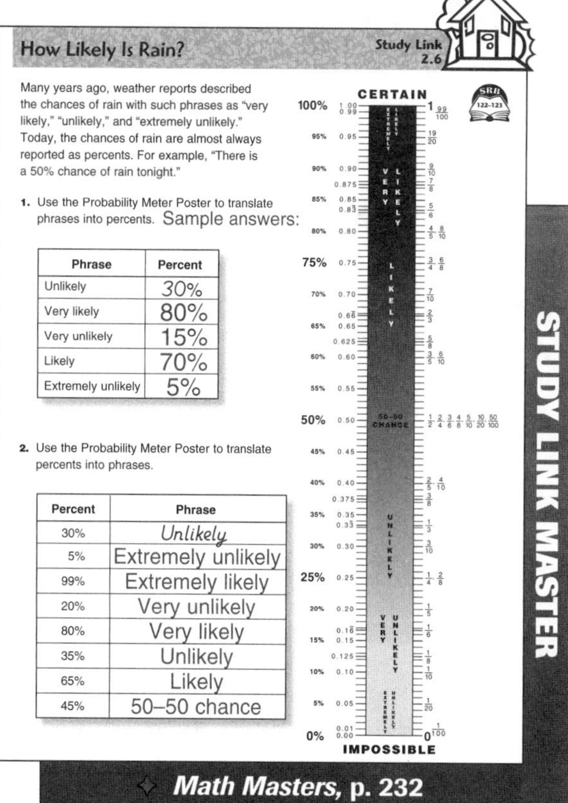

**How Likely Is Rain?** Study Link 2.6

Many years ago, weather reports described the chances of rain with such phrases as "very likely," "unlikely," and "extremely unlikely." Today, the chances of rain are almost always reported as percents. For example, "There is a 50% chance of rain tonight."

1. Use the Probability Meter Poster to translate phrases into percents. Sample answers:

| Phrase | Percent |
|---|---|
| Unlikely | 30% |
| Very likely | 80% |
| Very unlikely | 15% |
| Likely | 70% |
| Extremely unlikely | 5% |

2. Use the Probability Meter Poster to translate percents into phrases.

| Percent | Phrase |
|---|---|
| 30% | Unlikely |
| 5% | Extremely unlikely |
| 99% | Extremely likely |
| 20% | Very unlikely |
| 80% | Very likely |
| 35% | Unlikely |
| 65% | Likely |
| 45% | 50–50 chance |



STUDY LINK MASTER

✧ Math Masters, p. 232

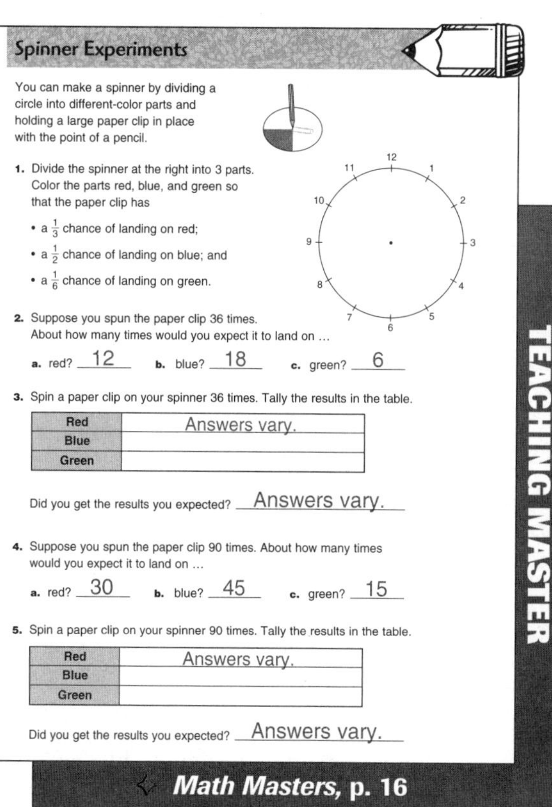

**Spinner Experiments**

You can make a spinner by dividing a circle into different-color parts and holding a large paper clip in place with the point of a pencil.

1. Divide the spinner at the right into 3 parts. Color the parts red, blue, and green so that the paper clip has
   - a $\frac{1}{3}$ chance of landing on red;
   - a $\frac{1}{2}$ chance of landing on blue; and
   - a $\frac{1}{6}$ chance of landing on green.



2. Suppose you spun the paper clip 36 times. About how many times would you expect it to land on …
   a. red? 12 b. blue? 18 c. green? 6
3. Spin a paper clip on your spinner 36 times. Tally the results in the table.

| Red | Answers vary. |
|---|---|
| Blue | |
| Green | |

Did you get the results you expected? Answers vary.

4. Suppose you spun the paper clip 90 times. About how many times would you expect it to land on …
   a. red? 30 b. blue? 45 c. green? 15
5. Spin a paper clip on your spinner 90 times. Tally the results in the table.

| Red | Answers vary. |
|---|---|
| Blue | |
| Green | |

Did you get the results you expected? Answers vary.

TEACHING MASTER

✧ Math Masters, p. 16

# 2.7 Estimating Products

**OBJECTIVE** **To make magnitude estimates for products of multidigit numbers, including decimals.**

| summaries | materials |
|---|---|
| **1 Teaching the Lesson** | |
| Students estimate whether products are in the tenths, ones, tens, hundreds, or thousands, and mark their estimates on a magnitude bar. They practice estimating products by playing *Multiplication Bull's-Eye.* [Numeration; Operations and Computation] | □ *Math Journal 1,* p. 47 □ Study Link 2.6<br>□ *Student Reference Book,* p. 284<br>Per partnership:<br>□ 4 each of the number cards 0–9 (from the Everything Math Deck, if available); 1 six-sided die<br>***See* Advance Preparation** |
| **2 Ongoing Learning & Practice** | |
| Students practice solving addition and subtraction number stories. They write open sentences as part of their solutions. [Operations and Computation; Patterns, Functions, and Algebra]<br>Students practice and maintain skills through Math Boxes and Study Link activities. | □ *Math Journal 1,* pp. 48 and 49<br>□ Study Link Master (*Math Masters,* p. 233) |
| **3 Options for Individualizing** | |
| **Reteaching** To practice solving extended facts, students play a variation of *Beat the Calculator.* [Operations and Computation] | □ *Student Reference Book,* p. 261<br>Per partnership:<br>□ 4 each of the number cards 1–10 (from the Everything Math Deck, if available); calculator; slate |

**Additional Information**

**Advance Preparation** For Part 1, play a round of *Multiplication Bull's-Eye* yourself before introducing the game to students.

**Vocabulary** • **magnitude estimate**

## Getting Started

### Mental Math and Reflexes

What number am I thinking of?

- How many minutes are in 1 hour? Multiply that number by 5. Subtract 200. 100
- How many days are in 2 weeks? Multiply that number by 10. Subtract 50. 90
- How many inches are in 1 foot? Multiply that number by 20. Subtract 80. 160
- How many centimeters are in 1 meter? Multiply that number by 7. Subtract 150. 550
- How many months are in 3 years? Multiply that number by 100. Subtract 1. 3,599

**Math Message**

*What is the largest number you can make using each of the digits 9, 0, 3, 7, 2, and 1 just once? What is the smallest number you can make?*

**Study Link 2.6 Follow-Up**

Briefly review the answers.

# 1 Teaching the Lesson

## ✦ Math Message Follow-Up

WHOLE-CLASS DISCUSSION

The largest number you can make is 973,210. The smallest *whole number* you can make is 102,379. The *decimal* 0.12379 is even smaller. Or, omitting the zero to the left of the decimal point, the decimal .012379 is the smallest number. What is the largest possible number less than 1? 0.97321

NOTE: Magnitude estimates for products and quotients are made in the same way. Students will practice making magnitude estimates for quotients in Unit 3.

## ✦ Estimating Products (*Math Journal 1,* p. 47)

WHOLE-CLASS DISCUSSION

Whenever students solve a multiplication or division problem, whether with a calculator or using paper and a pencil, they should get into the habit of making a **magnitude estimate.** This is a very rough estimate that answers questions such as, *Is the solution in the tens? Hundreds? Thousands?* A magnitude estimate indicates whether the solution to a problem is "in the right ballpark."

Pose the following problem: *Is the result of 14 * 17 in the tens? Hundreds? Thousands?* Ask students to justify their answers. Sample answer: The product 14 * 17 must be greater than 10 * 10 = 100; it must be less than 20 * 20 = 400. So the product is in the hundreds.

Discuss the rounding approach to estimating a product of two numbers:

1. Round both factors to the nearest multiple of a power of 10.
2. Then find the product of the rounded numbers.

For example, to estimate 14 * 17, round 14 to 10 and 17 to 20. Since 10 * 20 = 200, 14 * 17 is in the hundreds.

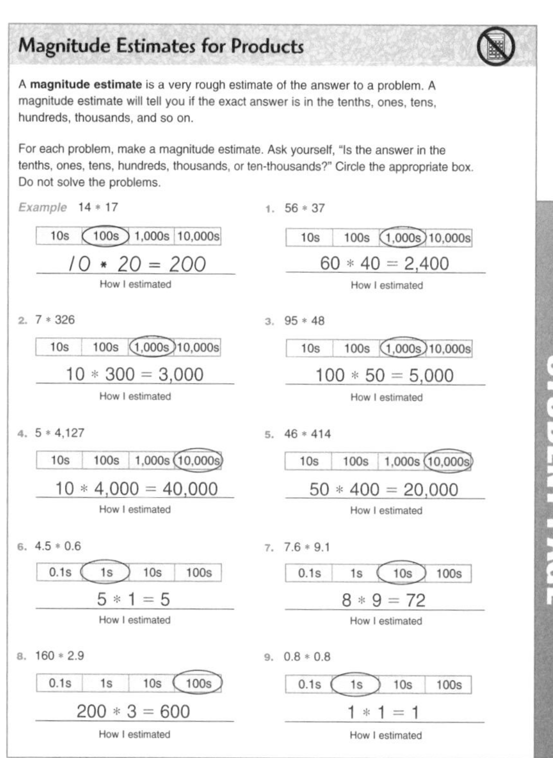

**Magnitude Estimates for Products**

A **magnitude estimate** is a very rough estimate of the answer to a problem. A magnitude estimate will tell you if the exact answer is in the tenths, ones, tens, hundreds, thousands, and so on.

For each problem, make a magnitude estimate. Ask yourself, "Is the answer in the tenths, ones, tens, hundreds, thousands, or ten-thousands?" Circle the appropriate box. Do not solve the problems.

*Example* 14 * 17
10s | (100s) | 1,000s | 10,000s
10 * 20 = 200
How I estimated

1. 56 * 37
10s | 100s | (1,000s) | 10,000s
60 * 40 = 2,400
How I estimated

2. 7 * 326
10s | 100s | (1,000s) | 10,000s
10 * 300 = 3,000
How I estimated

3. 95 * 48
10s | 100s | (1,000s) | 10,000s
100 * 50 = 5,000
How I estimated

4. 5 * 4,127
10s | 100s | 1,000s | (10,000s)
10 * 4,000 = 40,000
How I estimated

5. 46 * 414
10s | 100s | 1,000s | (10,000s)
50 * 400 = 20,000
How I estimated

6. 4.5 * 0.6
0.1s | (1s) | 10s | 100s
5 * 1 = 5
How I estimated

7. 7.6 * 9.1
0.1s | 1s | (10s) | 100s
8 * 9 = 72
How I estimated

8. 160 * 2.9
0.1s | 1s | 10s | (100s)
200 * 3 = 600
How I estimated

9. 0.8 * 0.8
0.1s | (1s) | 10s | 100s
1 * 1 = 1
How I estimated

STUDENT PAGE

✦ *Math Journal 1,* p. 47

STUDENT PAGE

Games

### *Multiplication Bull's-eye*

**Materials** ☐ number cards 0–9 (4 of each)
☐ 1 six-sided die
☐ calculator

**Players** 2

**Directions**

1. Shuffle the cards and place them facedown on the playing surface.
2. Players take turns. When it is your turn:
   - Roll the die. Look up the target range of the product in the table.
   - Take four cards from the top of the deck.
   - Use the cards to try to form two numbers whose product falls within the target range. **Do not use a calculator.**
   - Multiply the two numbers on your calculator to determine whether the product falls within the target range. If it does, you have hit the bull's-eye and score 1 point. If it doesn't, you score 0 points.
   - Sometimes it is impossible to form two numbers whose product falls within the target range. If this happens, you score 0 points for that turn.
3. The game ends when each player has had five turns.
4. The player scoring more points wins the game.

| Number on Die | Target Range of Product |
|---|---|
| 1 | 500 or less |
| 2 | 501–1,000 |
| 3 | 1,001–3,000 |
| 4 | 3,001–5,000 |
| 5 | 5,001–7,000 |
| 6 | more than 7,000 |

**EXAMPLE**

Tom rolls a 3, so the target range of the product is from 1,001 to 3,000.
He turns over a 5, a 7, a 2, and a 9.
Tom uses estimation to try to form two numbers whose product falls within the target range—for example, 97 and 25.
He finds the product on the calculator: 97 * 25 = 2,425.
Since the product is between 1,001 and 3,000, Tom has hit the bull's-eye and scores 1 point.

Some other possible winning products from the 5, 7, 2, and 9 cards are: 25 * 79, 27 * 59, 9 * 257, and 2 * 579.

two hundred eighty-four

✦ *Student Reference Book,* p. 284

STUDENT PAGE

**Solving Number Stories**

For each problem, fill in the blanks and solve the problem.

1. Linell and Ben pooled their money to buy a video game. Linell had \$12.40 and Ben had \$15.88. How much money did they have in all?
   a. List the numbers needed to solve the problem. 12.40 and 15.88
   b. Describe what you want to find. The total amount of money
   c. Open sentence: 12.40 + 15.88 = *m*
   d. Solution: 28.28  e. Answer: \$28.28
2. If the video game cost \$22.65, how much money did they have left?
   a. List the numbers needed to solve the problem. 22.65 and 28.28
   b. Describe what you want to find. The amount of money left
   c. Open sentence: 28.28 − 22.65 = *m*
   d. Solution: 5.63  e. Answer: \$5.63
3. Linell and Ben borrowed money so they could also buy a CD for \$13.79. How much did they have to borrow so that they would have enough money to buy the CD?
   a. List the numbers needed to solve the problem. 13.79 and 5.63
   b. Describe what you want to find. The amount of money borrowed
   c. Open sentence: 5.63 + *m* = 13.79
   d. Solution: 8.16  e. Answer: \$8.16
4. How much more did the video game cost than the CD?
   a. List the numbers needed to solve the problem. 22.65 and 13.79
   b. Describe what you want to find out. How much more the video game costs
   c. Open sentence: 22.65 − 13.79 = *m*
   d. Solution: 8.86  e. Answer: \$8.86

✦ *Math Journal 1,* p. 48

Stress the use of "friendly numbers" that are close to the numbers being multiplied and easy to work with. Emphasize that students should make estimates without attempting to find the exact answers to the problems.

Use rounding to do Problem 1 ($56 * 37$) on the journal page with the class:

1. Round 56 to 60. Round 37 to 40.
2. $60 * 40 = 2{,}400$, so $56 * 37$ is in the thousands.

Students record their estimates on a magnitude bar, and show how they estimated in the spaces beneath.

| 10s | 100s | (1,000s) | 10,000s |
|---|---|---|---|

60 * 40 = 2,400

How I estimated

Stress that the same strategy can be used to make magnitude estimates for products of decimals. Do Problem 6 ($4.5 * 0.6$) with the class.

1. Round 4.5 to 5. Round 0.6 to 1.
2. $5 * 1 = 5$, so $4.5 * 0.6$ is in the ones.

As before, students record their estimates on a magnitude bar, and show how they estimated in the spaces beneath.

Students do the rest of the problems on their own. When most students have completed the page, write some of the problems on the board and have students describe how they estimated. Discuss various estimation strategies. Ask: *Did anyone use a different strategy?*

## ✦ Playing *Multiplication Bull's-Eye* (*Student Reference Book,* p. 284)

PARTNER ACTIVITY

The purpose of this game is to provide practice in estimating products. While the rules of the game call for two players, the game can also be played by one player. If a student plays alone, the game ends after 10 turns and the goal of the game is to top previous scores.

Go over the rules of the game on page 284 in the *Student Reference Book.* Play a few rounds with the class.

# 2 Ongoing Learning & Practice

## ✦ Solving Number Stories (*Math Journal 1,* p. 48)

INDEPENDENT ACTIVITY 

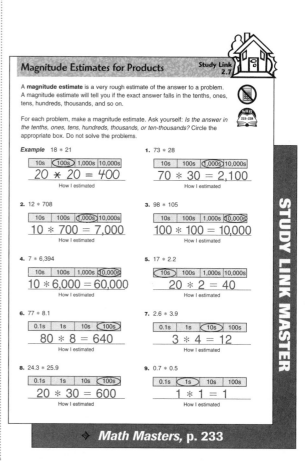

Students solve addition and subtraction number stories. They write an open sentence for each problem and solve the open sentence to find the answer to the problem.

## ✦ Math Boxes 2.7 (*Math Journal 1,* p. 49)

INDEPENDENT ACTIVITY 

**Mixed Review** Math Boxes in this lesson are paired with Math Boxes in Lesson 2.10. The skill in Problem 1 is a prerequisite for Unit 3.

## ✦ Study Link 2.7 (*Math Masters,* p. 233)

**Home Connection** Students practice making magnitude estimates. Remind them to round each number and then multiply the products. Stress that students should not find exact answers.

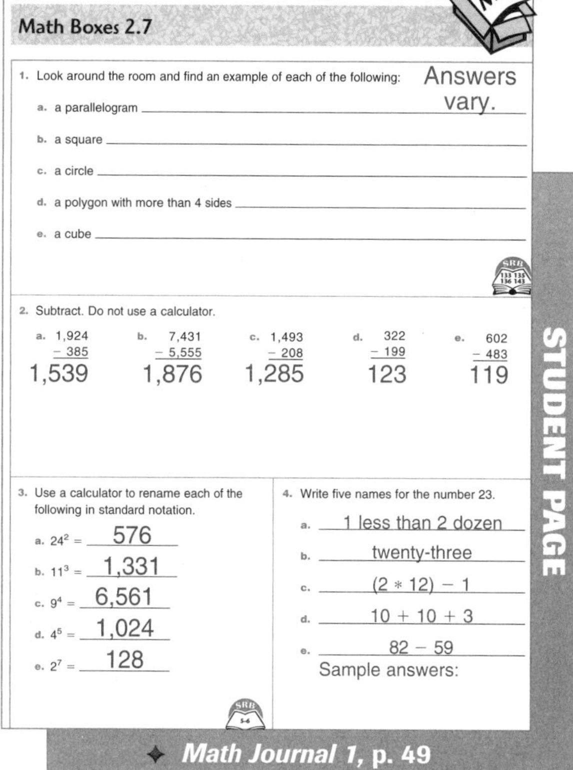

**Math Boxes 2.7**

1. Look around the room and find an example of each of the following: *Answers vary.*
   a. a parallelogram
   b. a square
   c. a circle
   d. a polygon with more than 4 sides
   e. a cube

2. Subtract. Do not use a calculator.
   a. 1,924 − 385 = *1,539*
   b. 7,431 − 5,555 = *1,876*
   c. 1,493 − 208 = *1,285*
   d. 322 − 199 = *123*
   e. 602 − 483 = *119*

3. Use a calculator to rename each of the following in standard notation.
   a. $24^2$ = *576*
   b. $11^3$ = *1,331*
   c. $9^4$ = *6,561*
   d. $4^5$ = *1,024*
   e. $2^7$ = *128*

4. Write five names for the number 23.
   a. *1 less than 2 dozen*
   b. *twenty-three*
   c. *(2 ∗ 12) − 1*
   d. *10 + 10 + 3*
   e. *82 − 59*

   *Sample answers:*

STUDENT PAGE

✦ *Math Journal 1,* p. 49

# 3 Options for Individualizing

## ✦ RETEACHING Playing *Beat the Calculator* with Extended Facts
(*Student Reference Book,* p. 261)

PARTNER ACTIVITY **15–30 min** 

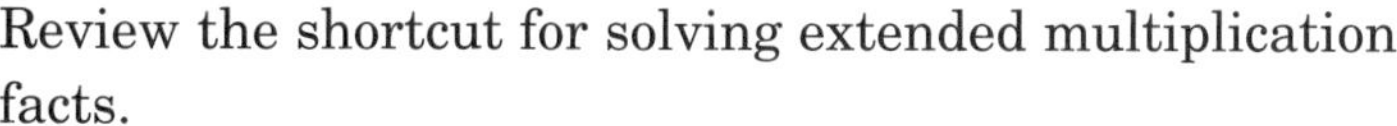

Review the shortcut for solving extended multiplication facts.

Shortcut: Solve the basic fact and attach as many zeros to the product as there are in the factors. *For example:*

▷ To solve **50** ∗ **90**, solve the basic fact 5 ∗ 9 = 45, and then attach two zeros to get 4,5**00**.

To practice solving extended facts, students play a variation of *Beat the Calculator.* The Caller draws two cards and poses the problem as an extended fact by attaching one or more zeros to either one or both factors.

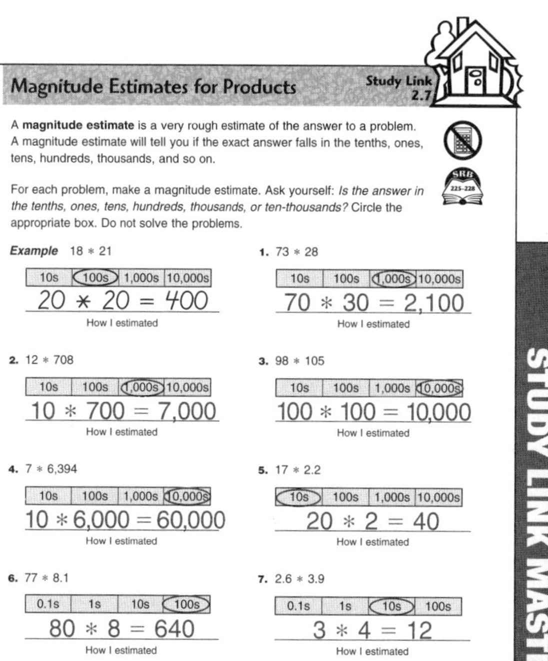

**Magnitude Estimates for Products** — Study Link 2.7

A **magnitude estimate** is a very rough estimate of the answer to a problem. A magnitude estimate will tell you if the exact answer falls in the tenths, ones, tens, hundreds, thousands, and so on.

For each problem, make a magnitude estimate. Ask yourself: *Is the answer in the tenths, ones, tens, hundreds, thousands, or ten-thousands?* Circle the appropriate box. Do not solve the problems.

*Example* 18 ∗ 21 — 10s | 100s (circled) | 1,000s | 10,000s — How I estimated: *20 ∗ 20 = 400*

1. 73 ∗ 28 — 10s | 100s | 1,000s (circled) | 10,000s — How I estimated: *70 ∗ 30 = 2,100*
2. 12 ∗ 708 — 10s | 100s | 1,000s (circled) | 10,000s — How I estimated: *10 ∗ 700 = 7,000*
3. 98 ∗ 105 — 10s | 100s | 1,000s | 10,000s (circled) — How I estimated: *100 ∗ 100 = 10,000*
4. 7 ∗ 6,394 — 10s | 100s | 1,000s | 10,000s (circled) — How I estimated: *10 ∗ 6,000 = 60,000*
5. 17 ∗ 2.2 — 10s (circled) | 100s | 1,000s | 10,000s — How I estimated: *20 ∗ 2 = 40*
6. 77 ∗ 8.1 — 0.1s | 1s | 10s | 100s (circled) — How I estimated: *80 ∗ 8 = 640*
7. 2.6 ∗ 3.9 — 0.1s | 1s | 10s (circled) | 100s — How I estimated: *3 ∗ 4 = 12*
8. 24.3 ∗ 25.9 — 0.1s | 1s | 10s | 100s (circled) — How I estimated: *20 ∗ 30 = 600*
9. 0.7 ∗ 0.5 — 0.1s | 1s (circled) | 10s | 100s — How I estimated: *1 ∗ 1 = 1*

STUDY LINK MASTER

✦ *Math Masters,* p. 233

# 2.8 Multiplication of Whole Numbers and Decimals

**OBJECTIVES** **To use the partial-products method to multiply multidigit whole numbers; and to introduce products of decimals.**

| summaries | materials |
|---|---|
| **1 Teaching the Lesson** | |
| Students review examples of the partial-products method for multiplication; and they use magnitude estimates to solve multiplication problems, in which both factors are whole numbers or one or both factors are decimals. [Operations and Computation] | □ *Math Journal 1,* pp. 50 and 51<br>□ *Student Reference Book,* pp. 19, 38, and 39<br>□ Study Link 2.7<br>***See*** **Advance Preparation** |
| **2 Ongoing Learning & Practice** | |
| Students practice and maintain skills through Math Boxes and Study Link activities. | □ *Math Journal 1,* p. 52<br>□ Study Link Master (*Math Masters,* p. 234) |
| **3 Options for Individualizing** | |
| **Reteaching** Students use base-10 blocks to model the partial-products method. [Operations and Computation]<br>**Extra Practice** Students practice the partial-products method by playing *Multiplication Wrestling.* [Operations and Computation] | □ *Student Reference Book,* p. 285<br>□ Transparencies (*Math Masters,* pp. 17 and 18)<br>□ base-10 blocks □ overhead marker<br>***See*** **Advance Preparation** |

### Additional Information

**Advance Preparation** For Part 1, review the partial-products method yourself, before working with your students.

For the optional Extra Practice activity in Part 3, learn how to play *Multiplication Wrestling.* For the optional Reteaching activity, make transparencies of *Math Masters,* pages 17 and 18. Cut out the grids and tape them together.

**Vocabulary • partial-products method**

## Getting Started

### Mental Math and Reflexes

Pose problems such as the following:

| | | |
|---|---|---|
| 3 * 8 24 | 6 * 5 30 | 7 * 9 63 |
| 3 * 80 240 | 60 * 5 300 | 70 * 9 630 |
| 30 * 80 2,400 | 60 * 50 3,000 | 70 * 90 6,300 |
| 300 * 80 24,000 | 600 * 50 30,000 | 700 * 90 63,000 |

### Math Message

*Multiply. Show your work.*

253 * 8 37 * 62

### Study Link 2.7 Follow-Up

Briefly review the answers.

# 1 Teaching the Lesson

## ✦ Math Message Follow-Up

WHOLE-CLASS DISCUSSION

Ask volunteers to show how they solved the problems. 253 * 8 = 2,024 and 37 * 62 = 2,294.

## ✦ Reviewing the Partial-Products Method for Whole Numbers

(*Student Reference Book*, p. 19)

WHOLE-CLASS ACTIVITY

The **partial-products method** for multiplying has been stressed since *Third Grade Everyday Mathematics*. It is an algorithm that all students are expected to know, even if they favor other multiplication methods, because it helps students develop a good understanding of place value and multiplication.

Use examples like those on page 19 of the *Student Reference Book* to demonstrate this method. Each part of one factor is multiplied by each part of the other factor. Each partial product is written on a separate line. These partial products are then added. This process is usually fairly simple, and has the additional benefit of providing practice with column addition.

| *Example:* 43 * 26 = ? | | 100s | 10s | 1s |
|---|---|---|---|---|
| *Think of 26 as 20 + 6:* | | | 2 | 6 |
| *Think of 43 as 40 + 3:* | | * | 4 | 3 |
| *Multiply each part of 26 by each part of 43:* | *40 * 20* ⟶ | 8 | 0 | 0 |
| | *40 * 6* ⟶ | 2 | 4 | 0 |
| | *3 * 20* ⟶ | | 6 | 0 |
| | *3 * 6* ⟶ | | 1 | 8 |
| *Add four partial products:* | | 11 | 1 | 8 |

Have students solve a few more multiplication problems using this method.

NOTE: Make sure that the digits students write are properly aligned in columns. It will also help if they write place-value reminders (such as 100s, 10s, and 1s) above the columns.

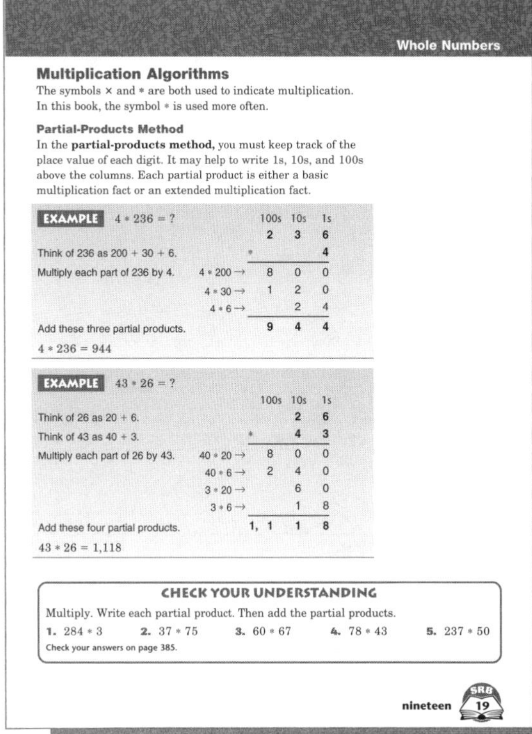
Whole Numbers

**Multiplication Algorithms**

The symbols × and * are both used to indicate multiplication. In this book, the symbol * is used more often.

**Partial-Products Method**

In the **partial-products method,** you must keep track of the place value of each digit. It may help to write 1s, 10s, and 100s above the columns. Each partial product is either a basic multiplication fact or an extended multiplication fact.

EXAMPLE 4 * 236 = ?

| | | 100s | 10s | 1s |
|---|---|---|---|---|
| | | 2 | 3 | 6 |
| Think of 236 as 200 + 30 + 6. | * | | | 4 |
| Multiply each part of 236 by 4. | 4 * 200 → | 8 | 0 | 0 |
| | 4 * 30 → | 1 | 2 | 0 |
| | 4 * 6 → | | 2 | 4 |
| Add these three partial products. | | 9 | 4 | 4 |

4 * 236 = 944

EXAMPLE 43 * 26 = ?

| | | 100s | 10s | 1s |
|---|---|---|---|---|
| Think of 26 as 20 + 6. | | | 2 | 6 |
| Think of 43 as 40 + 3. | * | | 4 | 3 |
| Multiply each part of 26 by 43. | 40 * 20 → | 8 | 0 | 0 |
| | 40 * 6 → | 2 | 4 | 0 |
| | 3 * 20 → | | 6 | 0 |
| | 3 * 6 → | | 1 | 8 |
| Add these four partial products. | | 1, 1 | 1 | 8 |

43 * 26 = 1,118

CHECK YOUR UNDERSTANDING

Multiply. Write each partial product. Then add the partial products.

1. 284 * 3 2. 37 * 75 3. 60 * 67 4. 78 * 43 5. 237 * 50

Check your answers on page 385.

nineteen 19

STUDENT PAGE

✦ Student Reference Book, p. 19

NOTE: Working from left to right is consistent with the process of estimating products.

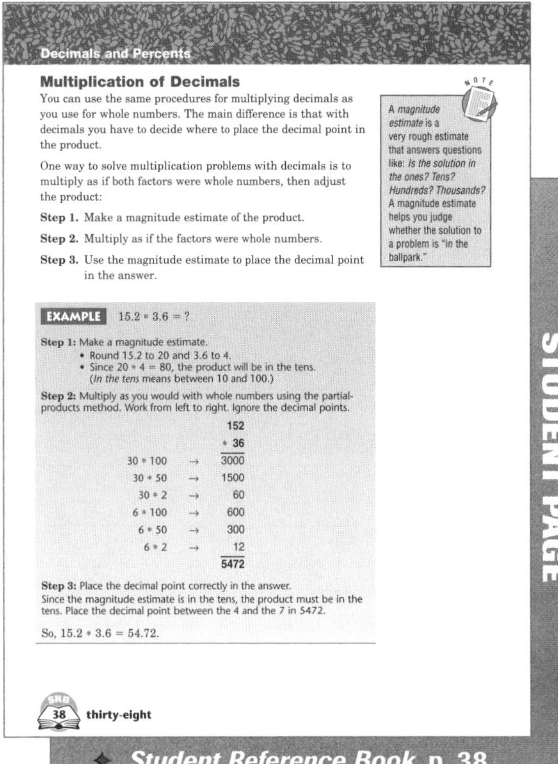
Decimals and Percents

**Multiplication of Decimals**

You can use the same procedures for multiplying decimals as you use for whole numbers. The main difference is that with decimals you have to decide where to place the decimal point in the product.

One way to solve multiplication problems with decimals is to multiply as if both factors were whole numbers, then adjust the product:

**Step 1.** Make a magnitude estimate of the product.

**Step 2.** Multiply as if the factors were whole numbers.

**Step 3.** Use the magnitude estimate to place the decimal point in the answer.

NOTE: A *magnitude estimate* is a very rough estimate that answers questions like: *Is the solution in the ones? Tens? Hundreds? Thousands?* A magnitude estimate helps you judge whether the solution to a problem is "in the ballpark."

EXAMPLE 15.2 * 3.6 = ?

**Step 1:** Make a magnitude estimate.
- Round 15.2 to 20 and 3.6 to 4.
- Since 20 * 4 = 80, the product will be in the tens. (*In the tens* means between 10 and 100.)

**Step 2:** Multiply as you would with whole numbers using the partial-products method. Work from left to right. Ignore the decimal points.

| | | |
|---|---|---|
| | | 152 |
| | | * 36 |
| 30 * 100 | → | 3000 |
| 30 * 50 | → | 1500 |
| 30 * 2 | → | 60 |
| 6 * 100 | → | 600 |
| 6 * 50 | → | 300 |
| 6 * 2 | → | 12 |
| | | 5472 |

**Step 3:** Place the decimal point correctly in the answer. Since the magnitude estimate is in the tens, the product must be in the tens. Place the decimal point between the 4 and the 7 in 5472.

So, 15.2 * 3.6 = 54.72.

38 thirty-eight

STUDENT PAGE

✦ Student Reference Book, p. 38

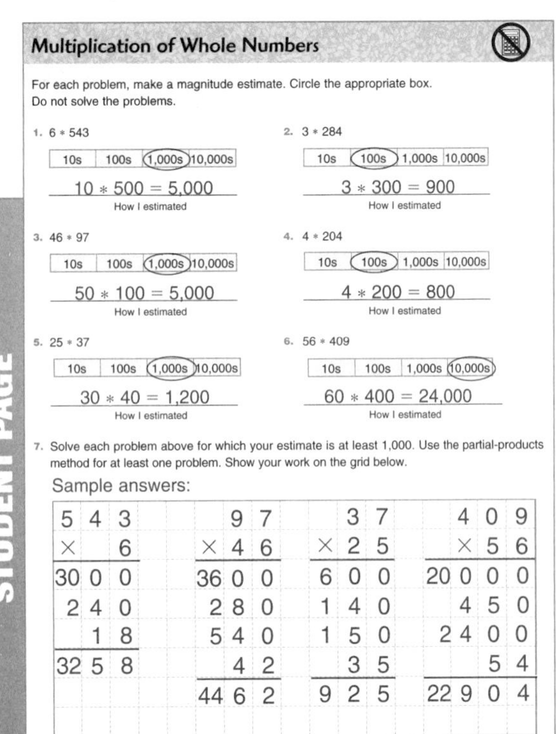

**Multiplication of Whole Numbers**

For each problem, make a magnitude estimate. Circle the appropriate box. Do not solve the problems.

1. 6 * 543 — 10s | 100s | **(1,000s)** | 10,000s — 10 * 500 = 5,000 (How I estimated)
2. 3 * 284 — 10s | **(100s)** | 1,000s | 10,000s — 3 * 300 = 900 (How I estimated)
3. 46 * 97 — 10s | 100s | **(1,000s)** | 10,000s — 50 * 100 = 5,000 (How I estimated)
4. 4 * 204 — 10s | **(100s)** | 1,000s | 10,000s — 4 * 200 = 800 (How I estimated)
5. 25 * 37 — 10s | 100s | **(1,000s)** | 10,000s — 30 * 40 = 1,200 (How I estimated)
6. 56 * 409 — 10s | 100s | 1,000s | **(10,000s)** — 60 * 400 = 24,000 (How I estimated)
7. Solve each problem above for which your estimate is at least 1,000. Use the partial-products method for at least one problem. Show your work on the grid below.

Sample answers:

| 543 × 6 | 97 × 46 | 37 × 25 | 409 × 56 |
|---|---|---|---|
| 3000 | 3600 | 600 | 20000 |
| 240 | 280 | 140 | 450 |
| 18 | 540 | 150 | 2400 |
| 3258 | 42 | 35 | 54 |
| | 4462 | 925 | 22904 |

STUDENT PAGE

✦ *Math Journal 1*, p. 50

NOTE: At this time, do not teach the shortcut of counting decimal places in the factors as a way of locating the decimal in the product. It is very important that students become proficient at estimating decimal answers.

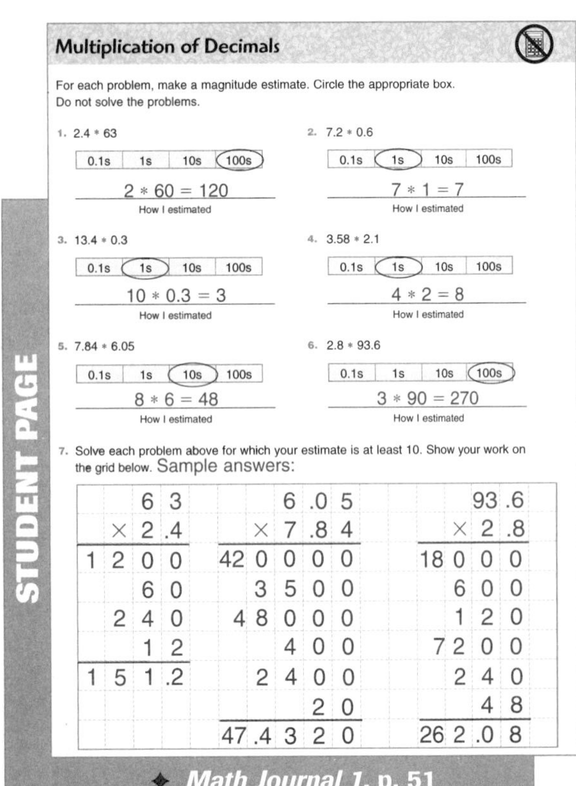

**Multiplication of Decimals**

For each problem, make a magnitude estimate. Circle the appropriate box. Do not solve the problems.

1. 2.4 * 63 — 0.1s | 1s | 10s | **(100s)** — 2 * 60 = 120 (How I estimated)
2. 7.2 * 0.6 — 0.1s | **(1s)** | 10s | 100s — 7 * 1 = 7 (How I estimated)
3. 13.4 * 0.3 — 0.1s | **(1s)** | 10s | 100s — 10 * 0.3 = 3 (How I estimated)
4. 3.58 * 2.1 — 0.1s | **(1s)** | 10s | 100s — 4 * 2 = 8 (How I estimated)
5. 7.84 * 6.05 — 0.1s | 1s | **(10s)** | 100s — 8 * 6 = 48 (How I estimated)
6. 2.8 * 93.6 — 0.1s | 1s | 10s | **(100s)** — 3 * 90 = 270 (How I estimated)
7. Solve each problem above for which your estimate is at least 10. Show your work on the grid below. Sample answers:

| 63 × 2.4 | 6.05 × 7.84 | 93.6 × 2.8 |
|---|---|---|
| 1200 | 42000 | 18000 |
| 60 | 3500 | 600 |
| 240 | 48000 | 120 |
| 12 | 400 | 7200 |
| 151.2 | 2400 | 240 |
| | 20 | 48 |
| | 47.4320 | 262.08 |

STUDENT PAGE

✦ *Math Journal 1*, p. 51

## ✦ Introducing Multiplication of Decimals
(*Student Reference Book,* pp. 38 and 39)

WHOLE-CLASS ACTIVITY

Ask students to solve the following problem: 1.3 * 5. After a couple of minutes, have them share their solution strategies. Expect that they may have difficulty because one of the factors is a decimal.

One way to solve multiplication problems containing decimal factors is to multiply as if both factors were whole numbers and then adjust the product. *Specifically:*

1. First make a magnitude estimate of the product.
2. Multiply the numbers as though they were whole numbers.
3. Then use the magnitude estimate as a guide to reinsert the decimal point at the correct location in the answer.

*Example:* 1.3 * 5 = ?

1. Round 1.3 to 1; since 1 * 5 = 5, the product will be in the ones.
2. Ignore the decimal point and multiply 13 * 5 as though both factors were whole numbers: 13 * 5 = 65.
3. Since the magnitude estimate is in the ones, the product must be in the ones. The answer must be 6.5. So, 1.3 * 5 = 6.5.

Working as a class, solve several multiplication problems in which one of the factors is a decimal. Suggestions are 25 * 0.6 15; 400 * 1.7 680.

Next, use examples like those on pages 38 and 39 of the *Student Reference Book* to demonstrate how to find the product of two decimals.

*Example:* 3.4 * 4.6 = ?

1. Round 3.4 to 3 and 4.6 to 5; since 3 * 5 = 15, the product will be in the tens.
2. Ignore the decimal points and multiply 34 * 46 as though both factors were whole numbers: 34 * 46 = 1,564.
3. Since the magnitude estimate is in the tens, the product must be in the tens. The answer must be 15.64. Thus, 3.4 * 4.6 = 15.64.

Working as a class, solve several multiplication problems in which both factors are decimals. Suggestions are 6.3 * 1.8 11.34; 0.71 * 3.2 2.272.

## Practicing Multiplication of Whole Numbers and Decimals

(*Math Journal 1,* pp. 50 and 51)

PARTNER ACTIVITY 

Make sure that students understand that they do not have to solve all of the problems on the journal pages. They should first make a magnitude estimate for each problem to determine if they should continue and solve the problem.

Ask partners to check each other's answers. Circulate and assist. Bring the class together to share solutions.

**ONGOING ASSESSMENT**

**If the majority of students are having difficulty with paper-and-pencil multiplication, spend more time working with them. However, mastery is not expected at this time. There will be opportunities for additional multiplication practice in Unit 3 (in combination with division work). After Unit 3, near-mastery of multiplication should be expected. There will be other opportunities for multiplication practice during the year, including systematic practice in Math Boxes, but this other practice will not be concentrated.**

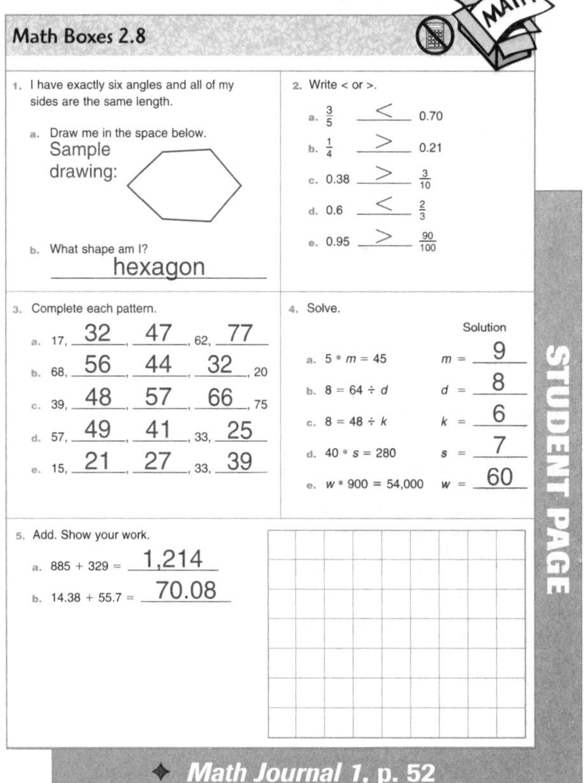

Math Boxes 2.8

1. I have exactly six angles and all of my sides are the same length.
   a. Draw me in the space below. Sample drawing:
   b. What shape am I? hexagon

2. Write < or >.
   a. $\frac{3}{5}$ < 0.70
   b. $\frac{1}{4}$ > 0.21
   c. 0.38 > $\frac{3}{10}$
   d. 0.6 < $\frac{2}{3}$
   e. 0.95 > $\frac{90}{100}$

3. Complete each pattern.
   a. 17, 32, 47, 62, 77
   b. 68, 56, 44, 32, 20
   c. 39, 48, 57, 66, 75
   d. 57, 49, 41, 33, 25
   e. 15, 21, 27, 33, 39

4. Solve. (Solution)
   a. 5 * m = 45   m = 9
   b. 8 = 64 ÷ d   d = 8
   c. 8 = 48 ÷ k   k = 6
   d. 40 * s = 280   s = 7
   e. w * 900 = 54,000   w = 60

5. Add. Show your work.
   a. 885 + 329 = 1,214
   b. 14.38 + 55.7 = 70.08

STUDENT PAGE

*Math Journal 1,* p. 52

# 2 Ongoing Learning & Practice

## Math Boxes 2.8 (*Math Journal 1,* p. 52)

INDEPENDENT ACTIVITY 

**Mixed Review** Math Boxes in this lesson are paired with Math Boxes in Lesson 2.5. The skill in Problem 1 is a prerequisite for Unit 3.

## Study Link 2.8 (*Math Masters,* p. 234)

**Home Connection** Students make magnitude estimates for and then solve multiplication problems in which the factors are whole numbers and/or decimals.

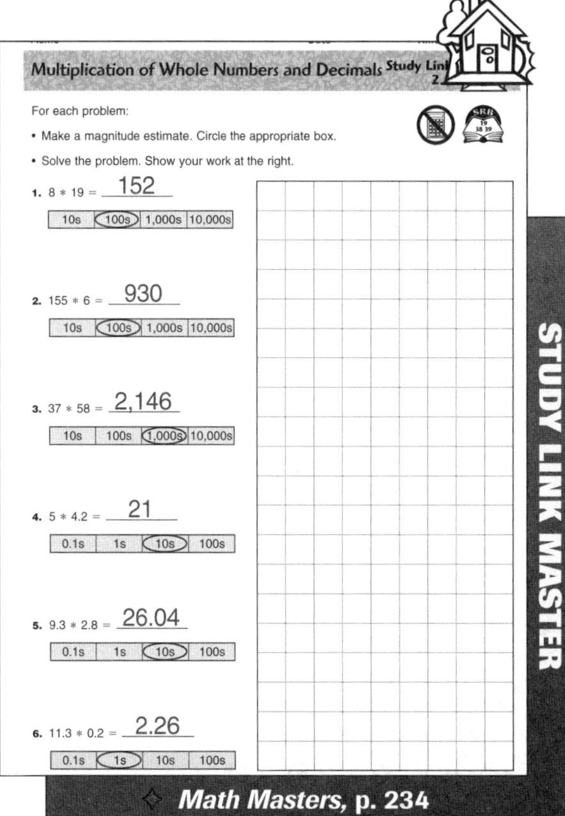

Multiplication of Whole Numbers and Decimals — Study Link 2.8

For each problem:
- Make a magnitude estimate. Circle the appropriate box.
- Solve the problem. Show your work at the right.

1. 8 * 19 = 152   [10s | (100s) | 1,000s | 10,000s]
2. 155 * 6 = 930   [10s | (100s) | 1,000s | 10,000s]
3. 37 * 58 = 2,146   [10s | 100s | (1,000s) | 10,000s]
4. 5 * 4.2 = 21   [0.1s | 1s | (10s) | 100s]
5. 9.3 * 2.8 = 26.04   [0.1s | 1s | (10s) | 100s]
6. 11.3 * 0.2 = 2.26   [0.1s | (1s) | 10s | 100s]

STUDY LINK MASTER

*Math Masters,* p. 234

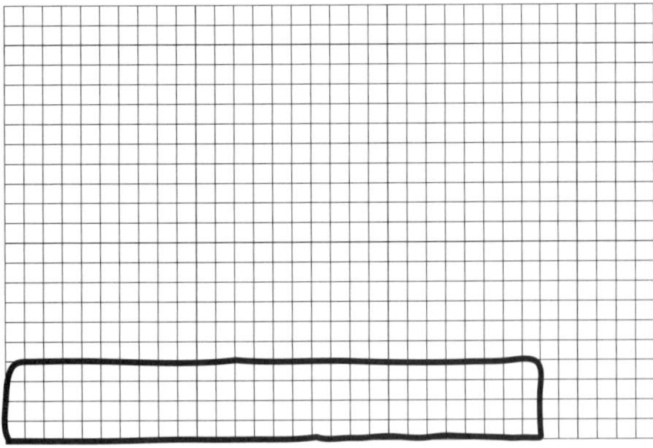

Array model of 4 * 28

# 3 Options for Individualizing

## ✦ RETEACHING Modeling the Partial-Products Method with Base-10 Blocks

(*Math Masters,* pp. 17 and 18)

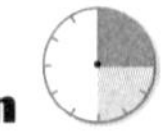

SMALL-GROUP ACTIVITY **15–30 min**

Some students may benefit from seeing 1-digit * 2-digit and 2-digit * 2-digit multiplication problems modeled with base-10 blocks. Make transparencies of *Math Masters,* pages 17 and 18. Cut out the grids and tape them together. Place the assembled grids on a table. (Do not use an overhead projector.) Gather a small group of students around the table. Use an overhead marker to show a 4-by-28 array. *(See the margin.)*

Ask students to cover the array using as few base-10 blocks as possible.

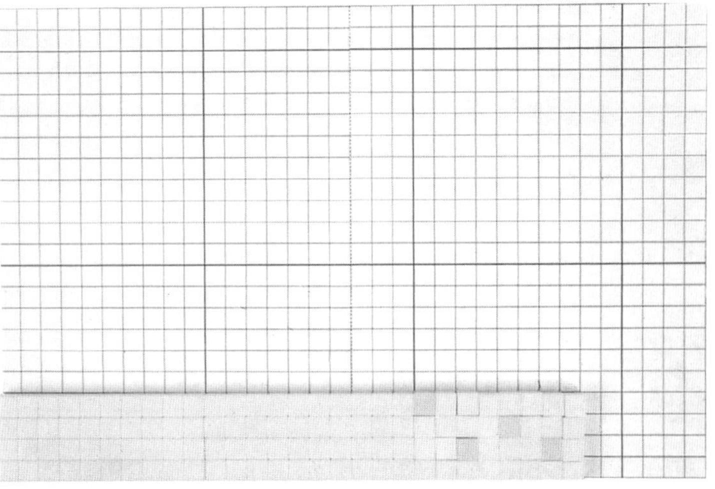

Base-10 block model of 4 * 28

With students, use the partial-products method to solve 4 * 28. Now match each part of the 4-by-28 array with a partial product.

1. There are 2 longs in each of 4 rows, so there are 80 cubes in all.
2. There are 8 cubes in each of 4 rows, so there are 32 cubes in all.
3. There are 80 + 32, or 112 cubes in all.

Clear the masters. Now use an overhead marker to mark off a 17-by-32 array. *(See the margin.)*

Ask students to cover the array using as few base-10 blocks (flats, longs, and cubes) as possible.

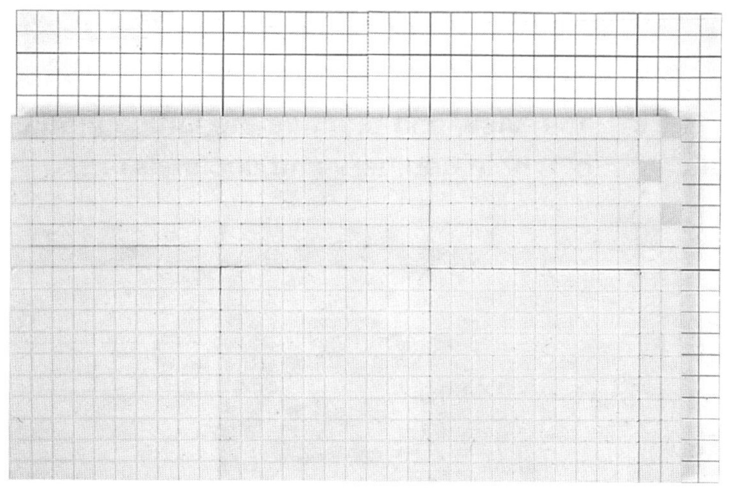

Base-10 block model of 17 * 32

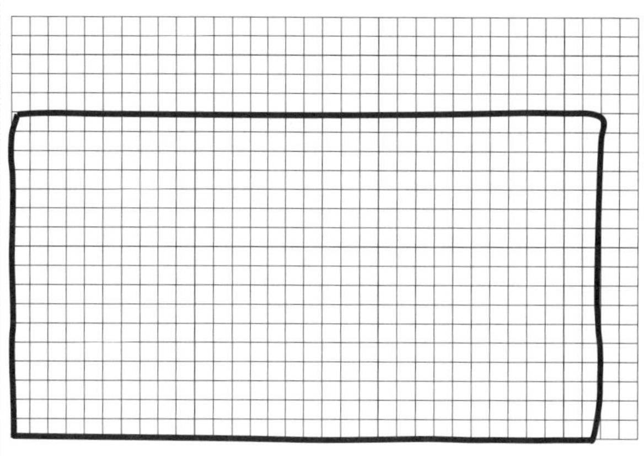

Array model of 17 * 32

With students, use the partial-products method to solve 17 * 32. Now match each part of the 17-by-32 array with a partial product.

1. There are 10 rows with 30 cubes in each row (3 flats).
2. There are 7 rows with 30 cubes in each row (21 longs).
3. There are 10 rows with 2 cubes in each row (2 longs).
4. There are 7 rows with 2 cubes in each row (14 cubes).
5. There are 300 + 210 + 20 + 14, or 544 cubes in all.

Use base-10 blocks to solve additional 1-digit * 2-digit and 2-digit * 2-digit problems.

## ✦ EXTRA PRACTICE Playing *Multiplication Wrestling* (*Student Reference Book*, p. 285)

PARTNER ACTIVITY **15–30 min**

Students play *Multiplication Wrestling* to practice the partial-products method. This game was introduced in *Fourth Grade Everyday Mathematics.*

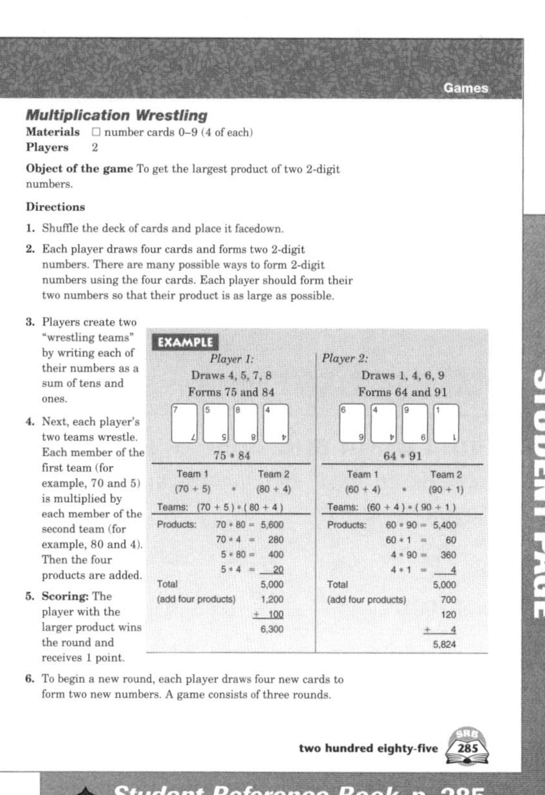

Games

***Multiplication Wrestling***

**Materials** □ number cards 0–9 (4 of each)

**Players** 2

**Object of the game** To get the largest product of two 2-digit numbers.

**Directions**

1. Shuffle the deck of cards and place it facedown.
2. Each player draws four cards and forms two 2-digit numbers. There are many possible ways to form 2-digit numbers using the four cards. Each player should form their two numbers so that their product is as large as possible.
3. Players create two "wrestling teams" by writing each of their numbers as a sum of tens and ones.
4. Next, each player's two teams wrestle. Each member of the first team (for example, 70 and 5) is multiplied by each member of the second team (for example, 80 and 4). Then the four products are added.
5. **Scoring:** The player with the larger product wins the round and receives 1 point.
6. To begin a new round, each player draws four new cards to form two new numbers. A game consists of three rounds.

EXAMPLE

| *Player 1:* | *Player 2:* |
|---|---|
| Draws 4, 5, 7, 8 | Draws 1, 4, 6, 9 |
| Forms 75 and 84 | Forms 64 and 91 |
| 7 5 8 4 | 6 4 9 1 |
| 75 * 84 | 64 * 91 |
| Team 1 (70 + 5) * Team 2 (80 + 4) | Team 1 (60 + 4) * Team 2 (90 + 1) |
| Teams: (70 + 5) * (80 + 4) | Teams: (60 + 4) * (90 + 1) |
| Products: 70 * 80 = 5,600 | Products: 60 * 90 = 5,400 |
| 70 * 4 = 280 | 60 * 1 = 60 |
| 5 * 80 = 400 | 4 * 90 = 360 |
| 5 * 4 = 20 | 4 * 1 = 4 |
| Total (add four products) 5,000 | Total (add four products) 5,000 |
| 1,200 | 700 |
| + 100 | 120 |
| 6,300 | + 4 |
| | 5,824 |

two hundred eighty-five SRB 285

STUDENT PAGE

✦ *Student Reference Book*, p. 285

# 2.9 The Lattice Method of Multiplication

**OBJECTIVE** **To review and practice the lattice method for multiplication of whole numbers and decimals.**

| summaries | materials |
|---|---|
| **1 Teaching the Lesson** | |
| Students review and practice the lattice method for multiplying multidigit whole numbers; students learn and practice using the lattice method for multiplying decimals. [Operations and Computation] | □ *Math Journal 1,* p. 53 □ Study Link 2.8<br>□ *Student Reference Book,* pp. 20 and 40<br>□ Teaching Masters (*Math Masters,* p. 19, optional; and p. 21)<br>□ Assessment Master (*Math Masters,* p. 479; optional)<br>***See* Advance Preparation** |
| **2 Ongoing Learning & Practice** | |
| Students practice and maintain skills through Math Boxes and Study Link activities. | □ *Math Journal 1,* p. 54<br>□ Study Link Master (*Math Masters,* p. 235) |
| **3 Options for Individualizing** | |
| **Enrichment** Students analyze an ancient multiplication method and use that method to solve a multiplication problem. [Numeration; Operations and Computation] | □ Teaching Master (*Math Masters,* p. 20) |

**Additional Information**

**Advance Preparation** For Part 1, try out the lattice method yourself before working with your students.

**Vocabulary** • **lattice method** • **lattice**

## Getting Started

### Mental Math and Reflexes

Have students find $\frac{1}{10}$ of a number and 10 times a number. *Suggestions:*

- $\frac{1}{10}$ of 800 80 — 10 ∗ 6 60
- $\frac{1}{10}$ of 100 10 — 10 ∗ 0.6 6
- $\frac{1}{10}$ of 105 10.5 — 10 ∗ 0.65 6.5
- $\frac{1}{10}$ of 10 1 — 10 ∗ 37 370
- $\frac{1}{10}$ of 15 1.5 — 10 ∗ 3.7 37

Continue as time allows.

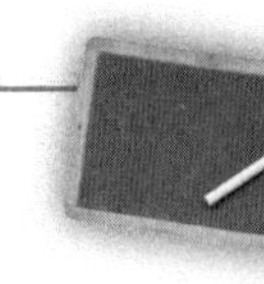

### Math Message

*Multiply. Show your work.*

32 ∗ 146 4.5 ∗ 0.82

### Study Link 2.8 Follow-Up

Students show how they solved the problems.

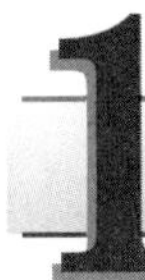

# Teaching the Lesson

## ✦ Math Message Follow-Up

WHOLE-CLASS DISCUSSION

Ask volunteers to show how they solved the problems. 32 ∗ 146 = 4,672 and 4.5 ∗ 0.82 = 3.69.

## ✦ Reviewing the Lattice Method of Multiplication

(*Student Reference Book*, pp. 20 and 40; *Math Masters*, pp. 19 and 21)

WHOLE-CLASS ACTIVITY

The **lattice method** for multiplying has been used since *Third Grade Everyday Mathematics*. This method is very easy to use because it relies almost entirely on recall of the basic multiplication facts. Students who have difficulty with other multiplication methods are often very successful with the lattice method.

Use examples like those on pages 20 and 40 of the *Student Reference Book* to demonstrate this method.

***The Lattice Method for Multiplying Whole Numbers***

*Example:* 42 ∗ 37 = ?

1. The box with squares and diagonals is called a **lattice.** Write 37 above the lattice. Write 42 on the right side.

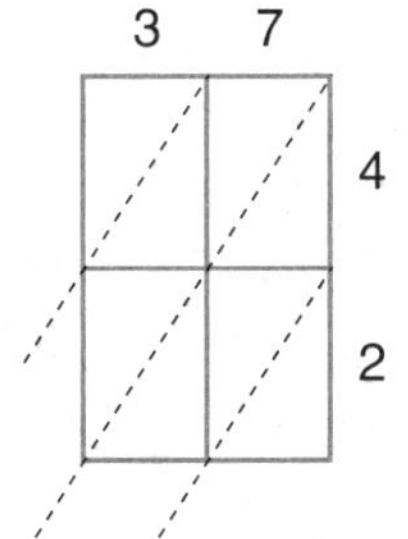


2. Multiply 4 ∗ 7. Then multiply 4 ∗ 3. Multiply 2 ∗ 7. Then multiply 2 ∗ 3. Write the answers as shown.

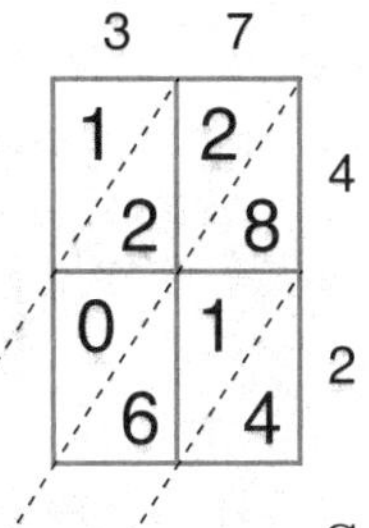


Continued on page 122.

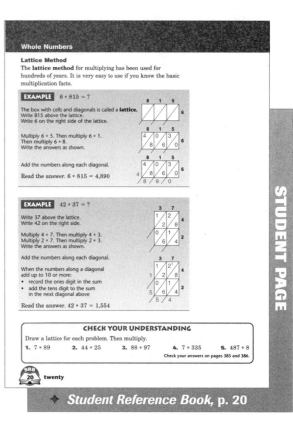

Whole Numbers

**Lattice Method**

The **lattice method** for multiplying has been used for hundreds of years. It is very easy to use if you know the basic multiplication facts.

**EXAMPLE** 6 ∗ 815 = ?

The box with cells and diagonals is called a **lattice.** Write 815 above the lattice. Write 6 on the right side of the lattice.

Multiply 6 ∗ 5. Then multiply 6 ∗ 1. Then multiply 6 ∗ 8. Write the answers as shown.

Add the numbers along each diagonal.

Read the answer. 6 ∗ 815 = 4,890

**EXAMPLE** 42 ∗ 37 = ?

Write 37 above the lattice. Write 42 on the right side.

Multiply 4 ∗ 7. Then multiply 4 ∗ 3. Multiply 2 ∗ 7. Then multiply 2 ∗ 3. Write the answers as shown.

Add the numbers along each diagonal.

When the numbers along a diagonal add up to 10 or more:

- record the ones digit in the sum
- add the tens digit to the sum in the next diagonal above

Read the answer. 42 ∗ 37 = 1,554

**CHECK YOUR UNDERSTANDING**

Draw a lattice for each problem. Then multiply.

**1.** 7 ∗ 89 **2.** 44 ∗ 25 **3.** 88 ∗ 97 **4.** 7 ∗ 335 **5.** 487 ∗ 8

Check your answers on pages 385 and 386.

SRB 20 twenty

STUDENT PAGE

✦ *Student Reference Book*, p. 20

NOTE: The lattice method is a very efficient algorithm, no matter how many digits make up the factors. For simpler problems with 1- and 2-digit multipliers, the lattice method takes about the same amount of time as the partial-products method or the traditional multiplication algorithm. For problems that have three or more digits in the factors, the lattice method is much faster, once it is set up in the grid, and much more likely to yield a correct answer.

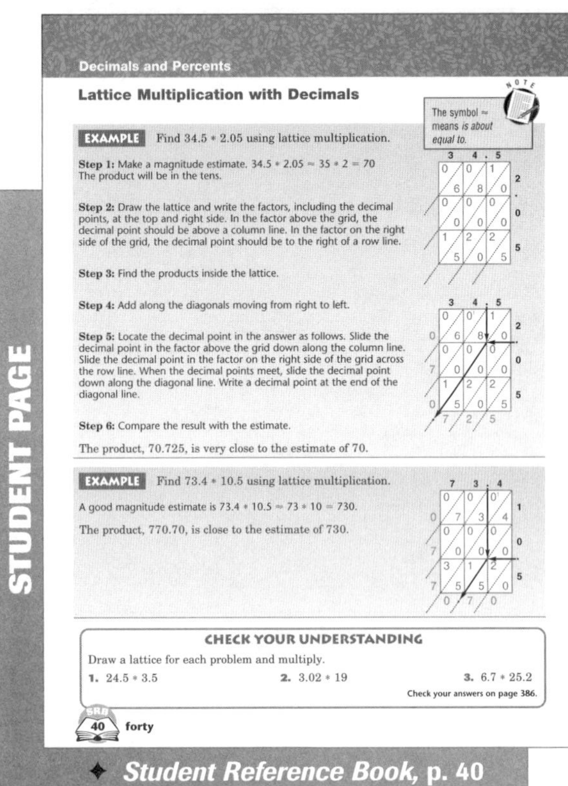

STUDENT PAGE

Decimals and Percents

## Lattice Multiplication with Decimals

NOTE: The symbol ≈ means *is about equal to.*

**EXAMPLE** Find 34.5 ∗ 2.05 using lattice multiplication.

**Step 1:** Make a magnitude estimate. 34.5 ∗ 2.05 ≈ 35 ∗ 2 = 70
The product will be in the tens.

**Step 2:** Draw the lattice and write the factors, including the decimal points, at the top and right side. In the factor above the grid, the decimal point should be above a column line. In the factor on the right side of the grid, the decimal point should be to the right of a row line.

**Step 3:** Find the products inside the lattice.

**Step 4:** Add along the diagonals moving from right to left.

**Step 5:** Locate the decimal point in the answer as follows. Slide the decimal point in the factor above the grid down along the column line. Slide the decimal point in the factor on the right side of the grid across the row line. When the decimal points meet, slide the decimal point down along the diagonal line. Write a decimal point at the end of the diagonal line.

**Step 6:** Compare the result with the estimate.

The product, 70.725, is very close to the estimate of 70.

**EXAMPLE** Find 73.4 ∗ 10.5 using lattice multiplication.

A good magnitude estimate is 73.4 ∗ 10.5 ≈ 73 ∗ 10 = 730.

The product, 770.70, is close to the estimate of 730.

**CHECK YOUR UNDERSTANDING**

Draw a lattice for each problem and multiply.

1. 24.5 ∗ 3.5
2. 3.02 ∗ 19
3. 6.7 ∗ 25.2

Check your answers on page 386.

SRB 40 forty

◆ *Student Reference Book,* p. 40

3. Add the numbers along each diagonal. Begin with the diagonal in the bottom right-hand corner.

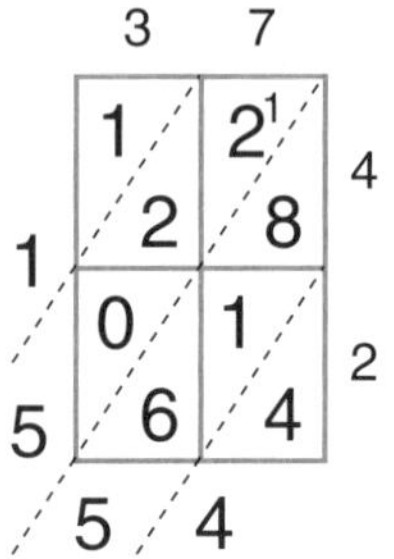


If the sum on a diagonal is 10 or more, write the ones digit in the answer space and the tens digit at the top of the next diagonal. Then add the numbers in that diagonal. For example, the sum of the numbers in the second diagonal is 15, so write 1 above the 2 in the third diagonal. The sum of the numbers in that diagonal is 1 + 2 + 2 = 5.

4. The answer is shown, starting on the left side of the lattice and continuing below the lattice.
42 ∗ 37 = 1,554

Pass out a lattice-computation grid (*Math Masters,* page 21) to each student. Working as a class, students use the lattice method to solve several multiplication problems in which both factors are whole numbers.

◆ *Math Masters,* p. 21

### *The Lattice Method for Multiplying Decimals*

One advantage of the lattice method is that products of decimals are as easy to calculate as products of whole numbers.

The lattice method does not require students to make magnitude estimates in order to locate the position of the decimal point in the answer. For this reason, students who have difficulty making magnitude estimates will find the lattice method ideal because it can automatically locate the position of the decimal in the final answer. Students who are able to make magnitude estimates should, of course, always do so. Even if they use the lattice method to find a product, the magnitude estimate can be used to check their answers.

▷ When writing the factors above and on the right side of the lattice, include the decimal points. In the factor above the grid, the decimal point should be above a column line. In the factor on the right side of the grid, the decimal point should be to the right of a row line.

▷ Locate the decimal point in the answer as follows: Slide the decimal point in the factor above the grid down. Slide the decimal point in the factor on the right side of the grid across. The decimal points will intersect on a diagonal line. Slide that decimal point down along the diagonal line. Write a decimal point at the end of the diagonal line.

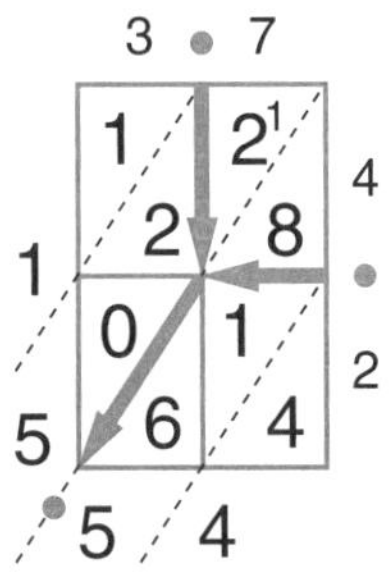


4.2 ∗ 3.7 = 15.54

Working as a class, students use the lattice method to solve several multiplication problems in which at least one factor is a decimal.

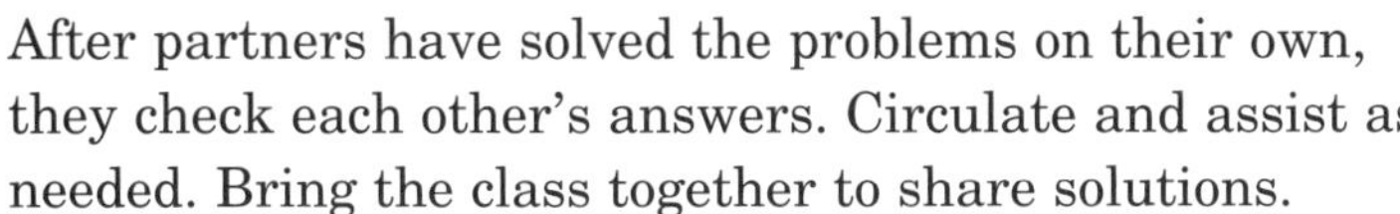

## ✦ Multiplying Whole Numbers and Decimals by the Lattice Method (*Math Journal 1,* p. 53)

PARTNER ACTIVITY

After partners have solved the problems on their own, they check each other's answers. Circulate and assist as needed. Bring the class together to share solutions.

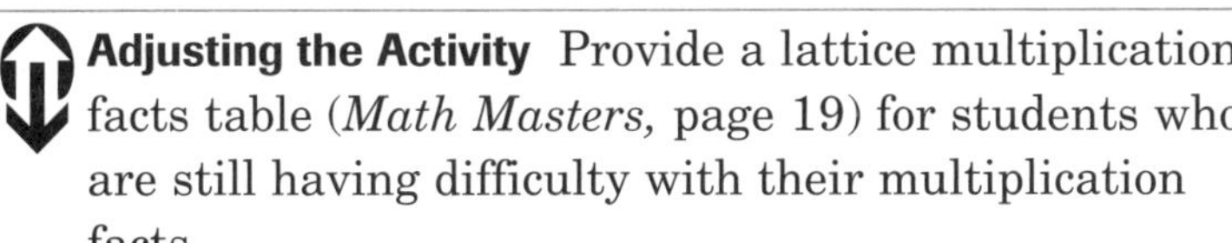

**Adjusting the Activity** Provide a lattice multiplication facts table (*Math Masters,* page 19) for students who are still having difficulty with their multiplication facts.

# 2 Ongoing Learning & Practice

## ✦ Math Boxes 2.9 (*Math Journal 1,* p. 54)

INDEPENDENT ACTIVITY 

**Mixed Review** Math Boxes in this lesson are paired with Math Boxes in Lesson 2.6. The skill in Problem 1 is a prerequisite for Unit 3.

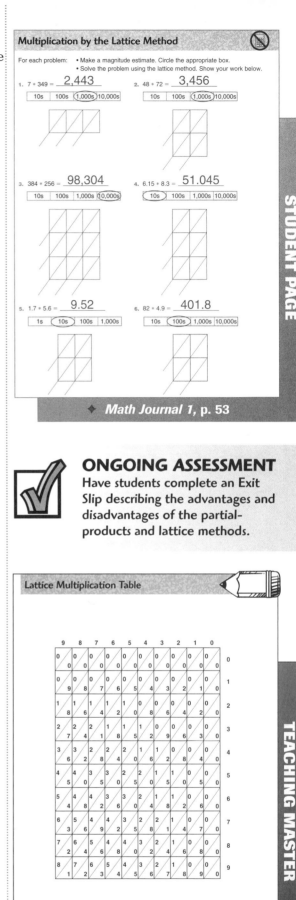

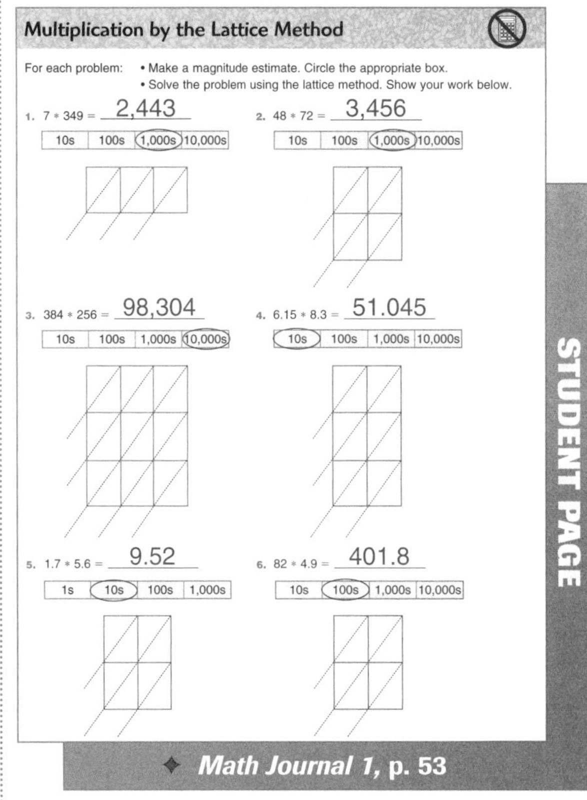

**Multiplication by the Lattice Method**

For each problem:
- Make a magnitude estimate. Circle the appropriate box.
- Solve the problem using the lattice method. Show your work below.

1. 7 ∗ 349 = 2,443
   10s | 100s | (1,000s) | 10,000s
2. 48 ∗ 72 = 3,456
   10s | 100s | (1,000s) | 10,000s
3. 384 ∗ 256 = 98,304
   10s | 100s | 1,000s | (10,000s)
4. 6.15 ∗ 8.3 = 51.045
   (10s) | 100s | 1,000s | 10,000s
5. 1.7 ∗ 5.6 = 9.52
   1s | (10s) | 100s | 1,000s
6. 82 ∗ 4.9 = 401.8
   10s | (100s) | 1,000s | 10,000s

STUDENT PAGE

✦ *Math Journal 1,* p. 53

**ONGOING ASSESSMENT**

Have students complete an Exit Slip describing the advantages and disadvantages of the partial-products and lattice methods.

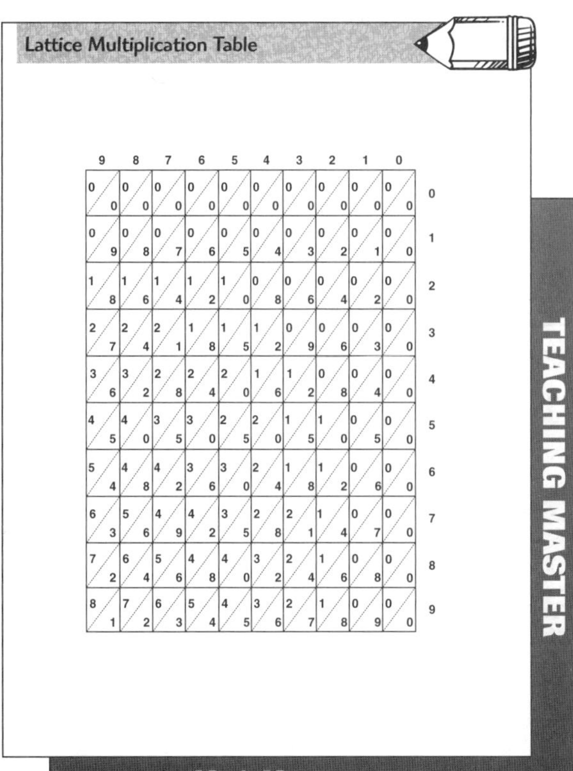

**Lattice Multiplication Table**

| | 9 | 8 | 7 | 6 | 5 | 4 | 3 | 2 | 1 | 0 | |
|---|---|---|---|---|---|---|---|---|---|---|---|
| | 0 / 0 | 0 / 0 | 0 / 0 | 0 / 0 | 0 / 0 | 0 / 0 | 0 / 0 | 0 / 0 | 0 / 0 | 0 / 0 | 0 |
| | 0 / 9 | 0 / 8 | 0 / 7 | 0 / 6 | 0 / 5 | 0 / 4 | 0 / 3 | 0 / 2 | 0 / 1 | 0 / 0 | 1 |
| | 1 / 8 | 1 / 6 | 1 / 4 | 1 / 2 | 1 / 0 | 0 / 8 | 0 / 6 | 0 / 4 | 0 / 2 | 0 / 0 | 2 |
| | 2 / 7 | 2 / 4 | 2 / 1 | 1 / 8 | 1 / 5 | 1 / 2 | 0 / 9 | 0 / 6 | 0 / 3 | 0 / 0 | 3 |
| | 3 / 6 | 3 / 2 | 2 / 8 | 2 / 4 | 2 / 0 | 1 / 6 | 1 / 2 | 0 / 8 | 0 / 4 | 0 / 0 | 4 |
| | 4 / 5 | 4 / 0 | 3 / 5 | 3 / 0 | 2 / 5 | 2 / 0 | 1 / 5 | 1 / 0 | 0 / 5 | 0 / 0 | 5 |
| | 5 / 4 | 4 / 8 | 4 / 2 | 3 / 6 | 3 / 0 | 2 / 4 | 1 / 8 | 1 / 2 | 0 / 6 | 0 / 0 | 6 |
| | 6 / 3 | 5 / 6 | 4 / 9 | 4 / 2 | 3 / 5 | 2 / 8 | 2 / 1 | 1 / 4 | 0 / 7 | 0 / 0 | 7 |
| | 7 / 2 | 6 / 4 | 5 / 6 | 4 / 8 | 4 / 0 | 3 / 2 | 2 / 4 | 1 / 6 | 0 / 8 | 0 / 0 | 8 |
| | 8 / 1 | 7 / 2 | 6 / 3 | 5 / 4 | 4 / 5 | 3 / 6 | 2 / 7 | 1 / 8 | 0 / 9 | 0 / 0 | 9 |

TEACHING MASTER

✧ *Math Masters,* p. 19

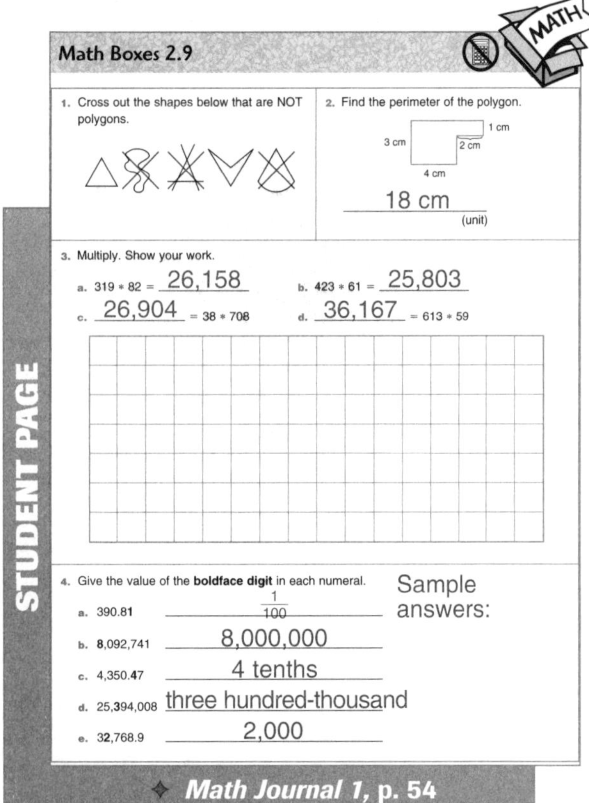

Math Boxes 2.9
1. Cross out the shapes below that are NOT polygons.
2. Find the perimeter of the polygon.
3 cm
1 cm
2 cm
4 cm
18 cm
(unit)
3. Multiply. Show your work.
a. 319 * 82 = 26,158
b. 423 * 61 = 25,803
c. 26,904 = 38 * 708
d. 36,167 = 613 * 59
4. Give the value of the boldface digit in each numeral.
Sample answers:
a. 390.81 1/100
b. 8,092,741 8,000,000
c. 4,350.47 4 tenths
d. 25,394,008 three hundred-thousand
e. 32,768.9 2,000
STUDENT PAGE
Math Journal 1, p. 54

## Study Link 2.9 (*Math Masters,* p. 235)

**Home Connection** Students make magnitude estimates and then solve multiplication problems by the lattice method. Remind students to round each factor and then multiply the rounded factors in order to make their estimates.

# 3 Options for Individualizing

## ENRICHMENT Exploring an Ancient Multiplication Method (*Math Masters,* p. 20)

PARTNER ACTIVITY **5–15 min**

Students are shown how three multiplication problems are solved using a method developed by the ancient Egyptians. Students try to figure out how to use the method and solve a problem by this method.

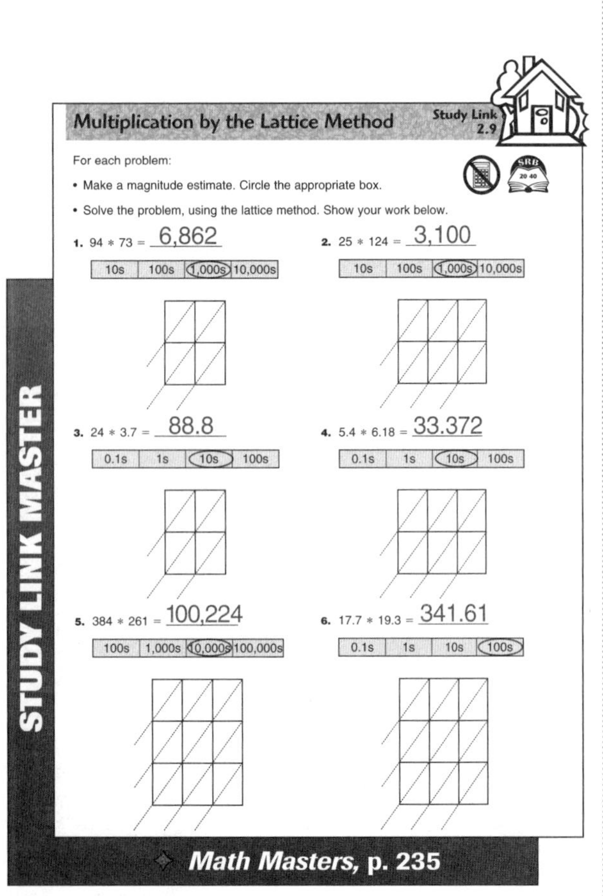


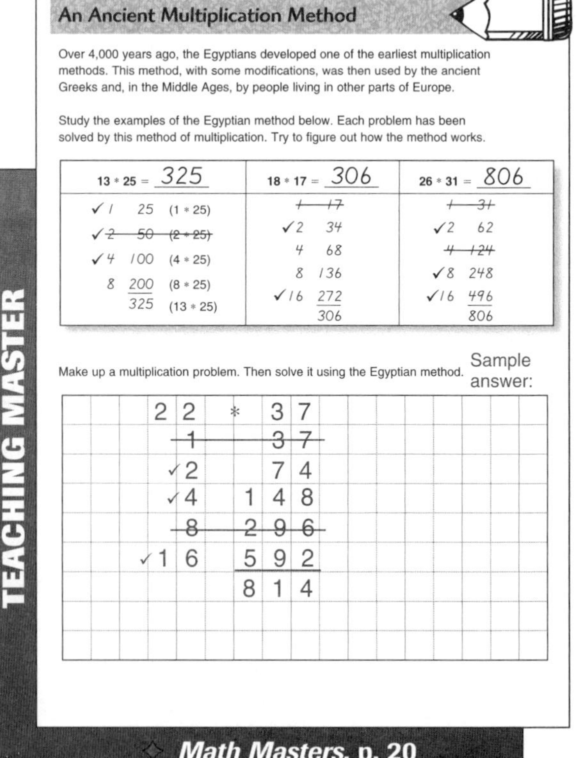

An Ancient Multiplication Method
Over 4,000 years ago, the Egyptians developed one of the earliest multiplication methods. This method, with some modifications, was then used by the ancient Greeks and, in the Middle Ages, by people living in other parts of Europe.
Study the examples of the Egyptian method below. Each problem has been solved by this method of multiplication. Try to figure out how the method works.
13 * 25 = 325
18 * 17 = 306
26 * 31 = 806
Make up a multiplication problem. Then solve it using the Egyptian method.
Sample answer:
22 * 37
814
TEACHING MASTER
Math Masters, p. 20

# 2.10 Comparing Millions, Billions, and Trillions

**OBJECTIVES** **To understand the relative sizes of 1 million, 1 billion, and 1 trillion; and to make an informed estimate from a sample of experimental data.**

| summaries | materials |
| --- | --- |
| **1 Teaching the Lesson** | |
| Students review the conversion factors for units of time. They count about how many times they can tap their desks in 10 seconds and use this result to estimate how long it would take to tap 1 million times. Students then use the estimate for 1 million times to estimate how long it would take to tap 1 billion and 1 trillion times. [Operations and Computation; Numeration] | ☐ *Math Journal 1,* p. 55<br>☐ *Student Reference Book,* p. 4<br>☐ Study Link 2.9<br>☐ Assessment Master (*Math Masters,* p. 479; optional)<br>☐ calculator ☐ watch or timer with second hand<br>☐ half-sheets of paper<br>***See* Advance Preparation** |
| **2 Ongoing Learning & Practice** | |
| Students practice multiplication with whole numbers and decimals. [Operations amd Computation]<br>Students practice and maintain skills through Math Boxes and Study Link activities. | ☐ *Math Journal 1,* pp. 56 and 57<br>☐ Study Link Master (*Math Masters,* p. 236) |
| **3 Options for Individualizing** | |
| **Reteaching** Students practice comparing large numbers by playing *Number Top-It.* [Numeration]<br>**Enrichment** Students solve a computation problem that involves large numbers. [Operations and Computation]<br>**Enrichment** Students read a book in which the magnitudes of a million, a billion, and a trillion are compared. [Numeration] | ☐ *Student Reference Book,* p. 287<br>☐ Teaching Masters (*Math Masters,* pp. 22 and 23)<br>☐ 4 each of the number cards 0–9 per partnership (from the Everything Math Deck, if available)<br>☐ *How Much Is a Million?*<br>***See* Advance Preparation** |

## Additional Information

**Advance Preparation** Experienced teachers have suggested that students make tally marks on paper rather than tap their desks. This eliminates the noise and helps students who tap quickly but lose count. Students can also count on their calculators using any number key. (The TI-15 calculator, however, cannot be used for this tapping experiment because the response rate of its keypad is too slow.)

For the optional Reteaching activity in Part 3, each partnership will need one copy of *Math Masters,* pages 22 and 23. These masters must be taped together to create the playing board.

For the second optional Enrichment activity in Part 3, obtain a copy of the book *How Much Is a Million?* by David M. Schwartz (Lothrop, Lee & Shepard Books, 1985).

**Vocabulary** • **sample**

# Getting Started

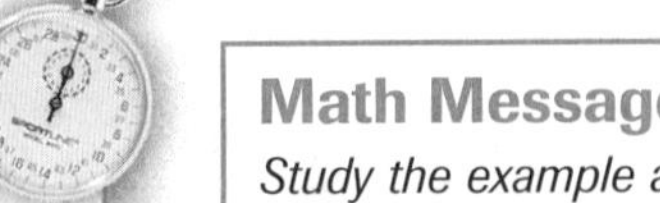

## Mental Math and Reflexes

The time equivalencies in the following problems will be used in making the estimates in Part 1.

- How many seconds are in ...
  1 minute? 60  3 minutes? 180  100 minutes? 6,000
- How many minutes are in ...
  1 hour? 60  5 hours? 300  50 hours? 3,000
- How many hours are in ...
  1 day? 24  2 days? 48  200 days? 4,800
- How many days are in ...
  1 year? 365, except 366 in leap years
  10 years? about 3,650
  100 years? about 36,500

## Math Message

*Study the example at the bottom of page 4 of your* Student Reference Book. *Complete Problems 1–4. Write the answers in words on a half-sheet of paper.*

## Study Link 2.9 Follow-Up

Volunteers show how they solved the problems.

NOTE: Some students may find it difficult to make an initial guess. Remind students that first guesses are usually wrong, even among scientists. Sometimes it doesn't matter if first guesses are even close—they are simply a starting point for an investigation.

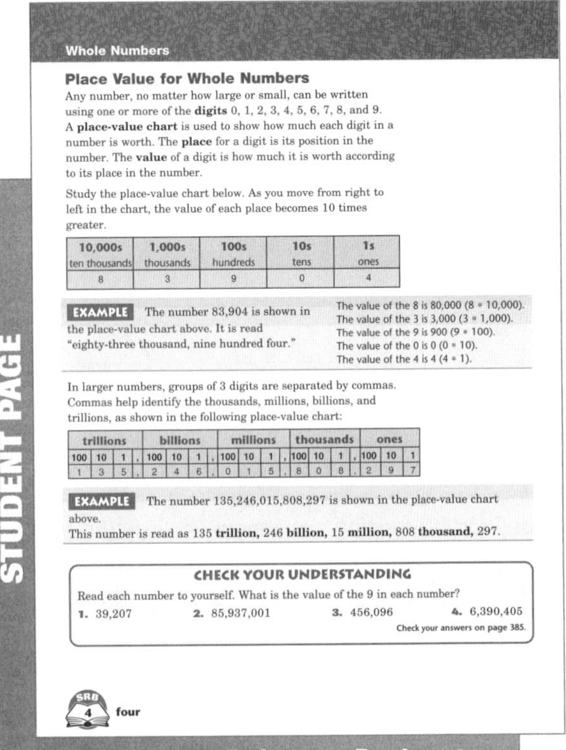

STUDENT PAGE

Whole Numbers

**Place Value for Whole Numbers**

Any number, no matter how large or small, can be written using one or more of the **digits** 0, 1, 2, 3, 4, 5, 6, 7, 8, and 9. A **place-value chart** is used to show how much each digit in a number is worth. The **place** for a digit is its position in the number. The **value** of a digit is how much it is worth according to its place in the number.

Study the place-value chart below. As you move from right to left in the chart, the value of each place becomes 10 times greater.

| 10,000s ten thousands | 1,000s thousands | 100s hundreds | 10s tens | 1s ones |
|---|---|---|---|---|
| 8 | 3 | 9 | 0 | 4 |

**EXAMPLE** The number 83,904 is shown in the place-value chart above. It is read "eighty-three thousand, nine hundred four."

The value of the 8 is 80,000 (8 * 10,000).
The value of the 3 is 3,000 (3 * 1,000).
The value of the 9 is 900 (9 * 100).
The value of the 0 is 0 (0 * 10).
The value of the 4 is 4 (4 * 1).

In larger numbers, groups of 3 digits are separated by commas. Commas help identify the thousands, millions, billions, and trillions, as shown in the following place-value chart:

| trillions | | | | billions | | | | millions | | | | thousands | | | | ones | | |
|---|---|---|---|---|---|---|---|---|---|---|---|---|---|---|---|---|---|---|
| 100 | 10 | 1 | , | 100 | 10 | 1 | , | 100 | 10 | 1 | , | 100 | 10 | 1 | , | 100 | 10 | 1 |
| 1 | 3 | 5 | , | 2 | 4 | 6 | , | 0 | 1 | 5 | , | 8 | 0 | 8 | , | 2 | 9 | 7 |

**EXAMPLE** The number 135,246,015,808,297 is shown in the place-value chart above.
This number is read as 135 **trillion,** 246 **billion,** 15 **million,** 808 **thousand,** 297.

**CHECK YOUR UNDERSTANDING**

Read each number to yourself. What is the value of the 9 in each number?

1. 39,207  2. 85,937,001  3. 456,096  4. 6,390,405

Check your answers on page 385.

SRB 4 four

Student Reference Book, p. 4

# 1 Teaching the Lesson

## Math Message Follow-Up
(*Student Reference Book,* p. 4)

WHOLE-CLASS DISCUSSION

Have students read the numbers aloud. Use the place-value chart at the bottom of the *Student Reference Book* page to resolve any disagreements.

## Solving a Tapping Problem with Sampling Strategies (*Math Journal 1,* p. 55)

WHOLE-CLASS DISCUSSION

Ask the class to guess how long it would take to tap their desks 1 million times, assuming no interruptions. Students record their guesses on the journal page and share them with the class.

Discuss the difference between a *guess* and an *estimate.* A guess is an opinion that you might state without having much background information. An estimate is based on some knowledge about the subject, and is often called an "educated guess" or "informed estimate." Students can only guess the amount of time it would take to tap 1 million times until they collect additional information.

Ask students to describe strategies they might use to enable them to make more informed estimates. Expect or elicit suggestions such as the following:

▷ Count how many times you can tap your desk in a set amount of time—say, 10 seconds.

▷ Time how long it takes you to tap a certain number of times—say, 100 times.

▷ Pick a reasonable rate of tapping and make an estimate based on that rate—for example, 3 taps per second.

Today the class studies how to use the first of these strategies. Each student will take a 10-second **sample** count of their own finger tapping. Practice taking sample counts by timing the students as they tap and count for 10 seconds.

## ✦ Using Sampling to Make an Estimate (*Math Journal 1*, p. 55)

PARTNER ACTIVITY 

Have partners implement the estimating strategy outlined below. Then have them record their results on the journal page. Circulate and assist.

**Take a sample count.**

One partner taps and counts for 10 seconds. The second partner times the activity, telling when to start and stop. Partners then reverse roles.

**Use the sample count to estimate how long it would take to tap 1 million times.**

Students then use their 10-second sample counts to estimate the number of taps they could make in 1 minute, in 1 hour, and in 1 day. Encourage them to use rounded numbers and their calculators.

Next, students use their estimates of the number of taps in 1 day to calculate the approximate number of days it would take to tap 1 million times. One approach is to divide 1 million by the number of taps per day.

## ✦ Making Time Estimates for 1 Billion and 1 Trillion Taps (*Math Journal 1*, p. 55)

PARTNER ACTIVITY 

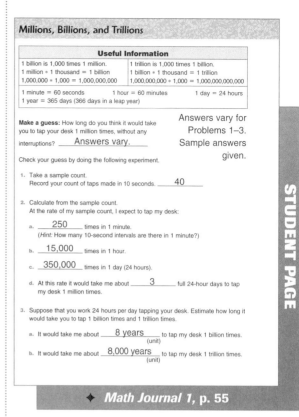

Students use their time estimates for 1 million taps to estimate the time it would take to tap 1 billion and 1 trillion times. One way is to multiply the time for 1 million taps by 1,000 to get the time for 1 billion taps, and to multiply the time for 1 billion taps by 1,000 to get

**Millions, Billions, and Trillions**

| Useful Information | |
|---|---|
| 1 billion is 1,000 times 1 million.<br>1 million * 1 thousand = 1 billion<br>1,000,000 * 1,000 = 1,000,000,000 | 1 trillion is 1,000 times 1 billion.<br>1 billion * 1 thousand = 1 trillion<br>1,000,000,000 * 1,000 = 1,000,000,000,000 |
| 1 minute = 60 seconds   1 hour = 60 minutes   1 day = 24 hours<br>1 year = 365 days (366 days in a leap year) | |

**Make a guess:** How long do you think it would take you to tap your desk 1 million times, without any interruptions? Answers vary.

Answers vary for Problems 1–3. Sample answers given.

Check your guess by doing the following experiment.

1. Take a sample count.
   Record your count of taps made in 10 seconds. 40

2. Calculate from the sample count.
   At the rate of my sample count, I expect to tap my desk:
   a. 250 times in 1 minute.
   (*Hint:* How many 10-second intervals are there in 1 minute?)
   b. 15,000 times in 1 hour.
   c. 350,000 times in 1 day (24 hours).
   d. At this rate it would take me about 3 full 24-hour days to tap my desk 1 million times.

3. Suppose that you work 24 hours per day tapping your desk. Estimate how long it would take you to tap 1 billion times and 1 trillion times.
   a. It would take me about 8 years (unit) to tap my desk 1 billion times.
   b. It would take me about 8,000 years (unit) to tap my desk 1 trillion times.

STUDENT PAGE

✦ *Math Journal 1*, p. 55

NOTE: A **sample** of anything is a small piece or part that is intended to give information about the whole thing. Consumers use product samples to decide if products suit their needs and if they will purchase them in the future. Pollsters use population samples to estimate information for the whole population. The finger-tapping samples here are time samples: The count of taps in a 10-second sample is used to determine a tapping rate, and the rate is then used to estimate how long it would take to make large numbers of taps.

NOTE: Expect that the tapping rate for most students will fall in the range of 25 to 75 taps per 20 seconds. A student who taps 40 times in 10 seconds might tap about 250 times in 1 minute (6 * 40, rounded up); 15,000 times in 1 hour (60 * 250); and 350,000 times in 1 day (24 * 15,000; rounded down). At this rate it would take about 3 days, without interruptions, to tap 1 million times; about 3,000 days or more than 8 years to tap 1 billion times; and more than 8,000 years to tap 1 trillion times.

**Multiplication Practice**

Solve the problems using your favorite multiplication method. Show your work.

1. 24 * 73 = 1,752
2. 46 * 82 = 3,772
3. 7.9 * 35 = 276.5
4. 147 * 8 = 1,176
5. 67.4 * 9.3 = 626.82
6. 0.5 * 432 = 216

STUDENT PAGE

✦ *Math Journal 1,* p. 56

the time for 1 trillion taps. Help students decide whether to report their estimates for 1 billion and 1 trillion taps as days or years.

## ✦ Sharing and Discussing the Results (*Math Journal 1,* p. 55; *Math Masters,* p. 479)

WHOLE-CLASS DISCUSSION

Compare and discuss students' estimates:

- How does your estimate of the time for 1 million taps compare with your initial guess?
- How did you use your estimate for the number of taps in 1 day to estimate how long it would take to tap 1 million times?
- How did you use the time for 1 million taps to estimate the time for 1 billion and 1 trillion taps?
- Are you surprised by how long it would take to tap your desk 1 million, 1 billion, and 1 trillion times? Could you tap to a trillion in your lifetime, even if you did so around the clock?

**ONGOING ASSESSMENT**

**Have students record their answers to the third question on an Exit Slip. Ask them to justify their answers.**

**Math Boxes 2.10**

1. Look around the room and find an example of each of the following: Answers vary.
   a. parallel lines
   b. a rectangle
   c. a cylinder
   d. a sphere
   e. a trapezoid

2. Subtract. Show your work.
   a. 1,543 − 285 = 1,258
   b. $4.48 − $3.82 = $0.66

3. Use a calculator to rename each of the following in standard notation.
   a. $28^2$ = 784
   b. $17^3$ = 4,913
   c. $8^3$ = 512
   d. $6^4$ = 1,296
   e. $5^4$ = 625

4. Write five names for the number 15.
   a. XV
   b. $\frac{30}{2}$
   c. (10 ÷ 2) ∗ 3
   d. 5 + 5 + 5
   e. $\frac{1}{4}$ of an hour

   Sample answers:

STUDENT PAGE

✦ *Math Journal 1,* p. 57

# 2 Ongoing Learning & Practice

## ✦ Practicing Multiplication of Whole Numbers and Decimals (*Math Journal 1,* p. 56)

INDEPENDENT ACTIVITY

Students solve multiplication problems using any method they choose.

## ✦ Math Boxes 2.10 (*Math Journal 1,* p. 57)

INDEPENDENT ACTIVITY

**Mixed Review** Math Boxes in this lesson are paired with Math Boxes in Lesson 2.7. The skill in Problem 1 is a prerequisite for Unit 3.

## ✦ Study Link 2.10 (*Math Masters,* p. 236)

**Home Connection** Students use estimation and paper-and-pencil algorithms to solve number stories.

# 3 Options for Individualizing

## ✦ RETEACHING Playing *Number Top-It* (*Student Reference Book,* p. 287; *Math Masters,* pp. 22 and 23)

PARTNER ACTIVITY **15–30 min**

Students play *Number Top-It* to practice comparing 7-digit whole numbers.

## ✦ ENRICHMENT Solving a Large Number Problem

INDEPENDENT ACTIVITY  **15–30 min** 

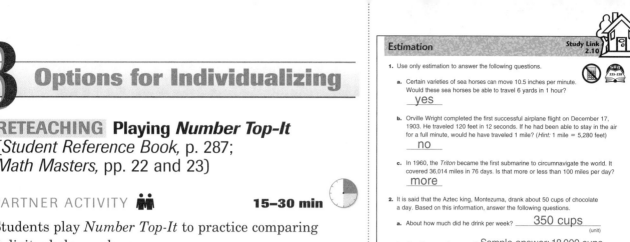

This is a very challenging problem, which some of your advanced students may want to tackle:

Portfolio Ideas

> An extremely fast personal computer processes information at the rate of 11.6 gigabytes per second. (1 gigabyte = 1 billion bytes)
>
> Suppose that you were a *slow* computer that is able to process information at the rate of 1 byte per second. About how long would it take you to process as much information as the fastest computer can process in 1 second?

Of course, students may use a calculator to solve the problem. Ask students who solve the problem to share their answers and solution strategies with the class.

## ✦ ENRICHMENT Reading about Large Numbers

SMALL-GROUP ACTIVITY  **5–15 min**

Literature Link Read the following book with students.

*How Much Is a Million?*

*Summary:* The magnitudes of a million, a billion, and a trillion are compared. Four fantasy examples illustrate the size of a million: finding how high a column of 1 million children standing on each other's shoulders would reach, finding how long it would take to count to 1 million, finding a bowl large enough to hold 1 million goldfish, and finding how many pages in the book would be needed to hold 1 million tiny stars. These examples are modified and extended to show 1 billion and 1 trillion.

**Estimation** Study Link 2.10

1. Use only estimation to answer the following questions.
   a. Certain varieties of sea horses can move 10.5 inches per minute. Would these sea horses be able to travel 6 yards in 1 hour? yes
   b. Orville Wright completed the first successful airplane flight on December 17, 1903. He traveled 120 feet in 12 seconds. If he had been able to stay in the air for a full minute, would he have traveled 1 mile? (*Hint:* 1 mile = 5,280 feet) no
   c. In 1960, the *Triton* became the first submarine to circumnavigate the world. It covered 36,014 miles in 76 days. Is that more or less than 100 miles per day? more
2. It is said that the Aztec king, Montezuma, drank about 50 cups of chocolate a day. Based on this information, answer the following questions.
   a. About how much did he drink per week? 350 cups (unit)
   b. About how much per year? Sample answer: 18,000 cups (unit)

Source: The Kids' World Almanac of Records and Facts

**Challenge**

3. Use paper and pencil to solve the following problem.

The second edition of the *Oxford English Dictionary* was published, in 20 volumes, in 1989. The dictionary contains about 2,436,600 quotations. There are more quotations from the works of Shakespeare than from any other author—about 33,300. There are about 487,200 from the twentieth century, about 755,300 from the nineteenth century, and about 268,000 from the eighteenth century. About how many quotations are there from before the eighteenth century?

About 926,100 quotations (unit)

STUDY LINK MASTER

✦ *Math Masters,* p. 236

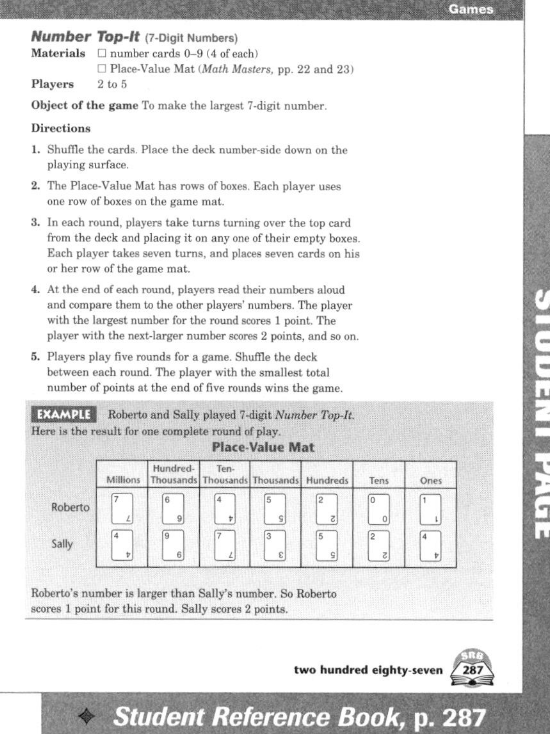

Games

***Number Top-It*** (7-Digit Numbers)

**Materials** ☐ number cards 0–9 (4 of each)
☐ Place-Value Mat (*Math Masters,* pp. 22 and 23)

**Players** 2 to 5

**Object of the game** To make the largest 7-digit number.

**Directions**

1. Shuffle the cards. Place the deck number-side down on the playing surface.
2. The Place-Value Mat has rows of boxes. Each player uses one row of boxes on the game mat.
3. In each round, players take turns turning over the top card from the deck and placing it on any one of their empty boxes. Each player takes seven turns, and places seven cards on his or her row of the game mat.
4. At the end of each round, players read their numbers aloud and compare them to the other players' numbers. The player with the largest number for the round scores 1 point. The player with the next-larger number scores 2 points, and so on.
5. Players play five rounds for a game. Shuffle the deck between each round. The player with the smallest total number of points at the end of five rounds wins the game.

EXAMPLE Roberto and Sally played 7-digit *Number Top-It.* Here is the result for one complete round of play.

**Place-Value Mat**

| | Millions | Hundred-Thousands | Ten-Thousands | Thousands | Hundreds | Tens | Ones |
|---|---|---|---|---|---|---|---|
| Roberto | 7 | 6 | 4 | 5 | 2 | 0 | 1 |
| Sally | 4 | 9 | 7 | 3 | 5 | 2 | 4 |

Roberto's number is larger than Sally's number. So Roberto scores 1 point for this round. Sally scores 2 points.

two hundred eighty-seven 287

STUDENT PAGE

✦ *Student Reference Book,* p. 287

# 2.11 Unit 2 Review and Assessment

**OBJECTIVE** **To review and assess students' progress on the material covered in Unit 2.**

## 1 Assess Progress

| learning goals | activities |
|---|---|
| 2a **Beginning Goal** Write and solve open sentences for number stories. **(Lesson 2.4)** | ❑ Written Assessment, Problem 19 |
| 2b **Developing Goal** Round numbers to designated places. **(Lesson 2.7)** | ❑ Slate Assessment, Problem 1<br>❑ Written Assessment, Problems 7–10 |
| 2c **Developing/Secure Goal** Make magnitude estimates. **(Lesson 2.7)** | ❑ Written Assessment, Problems 13–17 |
| 2d **Developing/Secure Goal** Find the product of multidigit whole numbers and decimals. **(Lessons 2.8 and 2.9)** | ❑ Slate Assessment, Problem 2<br>❑ Written Assessment, Problems 12–17 |
| 2e **Developing/Secure Goal** Know place value to billions. **(Lesson 2.10)** | ❑ Slate Assessment, Problem 3<br>❑ Written Assessment, Problem 11 |
| 2f **Secure Goal** Find the sum and difference of multidigit whole numbers and decimals. **(Lessons 2.2 and 2.3)** | ❑ Written Assessment, Problems 1–6 |
| 2g **Secure Goal** Identify the maximum, minimum, median, mode, and mean for a data set. **(Lesson 2.5)** | ❑ Written Assessment, Problem 18 |

**materials**

- ☐ *Math Journal 1,* p. 58
- ☐ *Student Reference Book,* pp. 287 and 292
- ☐ Study Link 2.10
- ☐ Teaching Masters (*Math Masters,* pp. 13, 22, and 23)
- ☐ Assessment Masters (*Math Masters,* pp. 381–383)
- ☐ 4 each of the number cards 0–9 per partnership (from the Everything Math Deck, if available)
- ☐ slate
- ☐ computation grid (*Math Masters,* p. 12)

## 2 Build Background for Unit 3

| summaries | materials |
|---|---|
| Students practice and maintain skills through Math Boxes and Study Link activities. | ☐ *Math Journal 1,* p. 59<br>☐ Study Link Masters (*Math Masters,* pp. 237–240) |

Each **learning goal** listed above indicates a level of performance that might be expected at this point in the *Everyday Mathematics* K–6 curriculum. For a variety of reasons, the levels indicated may not accurately portray your class's performance.

### Additional Information

**Advance Preparation** For additional information on assessment for Unit 2, see the *Assessment Handbook,* pages 39–41. For assessment checklists, see *Math Masters,* pages 430, 431, and 469–471.

# Getting Started

**Math Message**
*Answer the Time to Reflect questions on journal page 58.*

**Study Link 2.10 Follow-Up**
Students share their estimation strategies for Problems 1 and 2. Have a volunteer demonstrate how to solve the Challenge problem.

# 1 Assess Progress

## Math Message Follow-Up

WHOLE-CLASS DISCUSSION 

Students share their responses to questions about the unit.

## Slate Assessment

WHOLE-CLASS ACTIVITY 

If the suggested problems below are not appropriate for your class's level of performance, adjust the numbers or the problems themselves to better assess your students' abilities.

1. Round.
   - 574 to the nearest hundred. 600
   - 1,234 to the nearest ten. 1,230
   - 812 to the nearest hundred. 800
   - 16.89 to the nearest one. 17
   - 24.06 to the nearest tenth. 24.1 **Goal 2b**
2. Solve.

| | | |
|---|---|---|
| 6 [50s] 300 | 70 [7s] 490 | 9 [60s] 540 |
| 60 [50s] 3,000 | 70 [70s] 4,900 | 90 [60s] 5,400 |
| 600 [50s] 30,000 | 700 [70s] 49,000 | 900 [60s] 54,000 |

   **Goal 2d**
3. Dictate numbers and have students identify digits in given places.
   - 543,607: Circle the ten-thousands digit. 4 Underline the hundred-thousands digit. 5
   - 4,723,095: Circle the thousands digit. 3 Underline the hundred-thousands digit. 7
   - 204.39: Circle the tenths digit. 3 Underline the tens digit. 0
   - 519.64: Circle the hundredths digit. 4 Underline the tenths digit. 6 **Goal 2e**

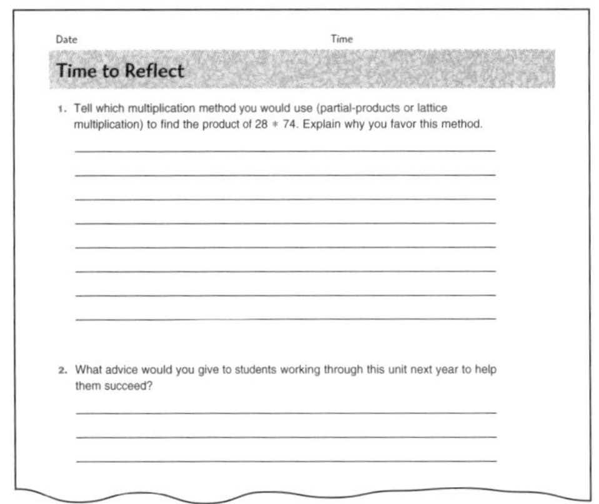

Date Time

**Time to Reflect**

1. Tell which multiplication method you would use (partial-products or lattice multiplication) to find the product of 28 ∗ 74. Explain why you favor this method.
2. What advice would you give to students working through this unit next year to help them succeed?

*Math Journal 1*, p. 58

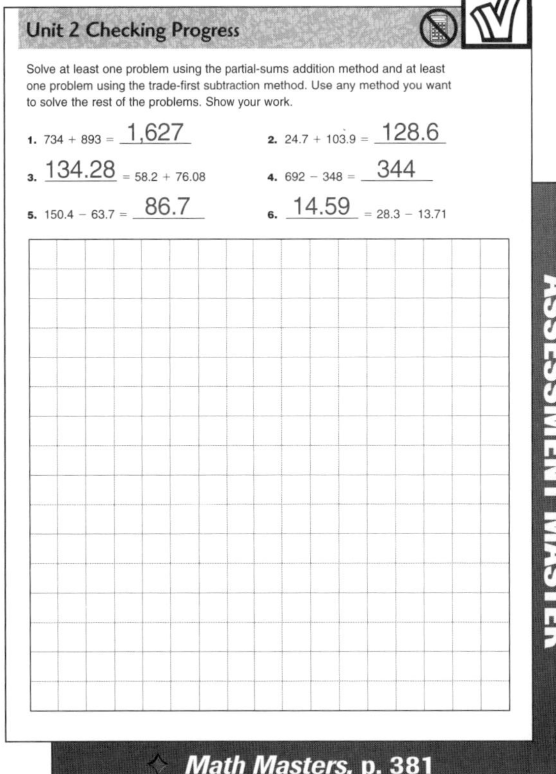

**Unit 2 Checking Progress**

Solve at least one problem using the partial-sums addition method and at least one problem using the trade-first subtraction method. Use any method you want to solve the rest of the problems. Show your work.

1. 734 + 893 = 1,627
2. 24.7 + 103.9 = 128.6
3. 134.28 = 58.2 + 76.08
4. 692 − 348 = 344
5. 150.4 − 63.7 = 86.7
6. 14.59 = 28.3 − 13.71

ASSESSMENT MASTER

*Math Masters*, p. 381

**ASSESSMENT MASTER**

### Unit 2 Checking Progress (cont.)

Round to the nearest ...

**7.** hundred.
- **a.** 84 100
- **b.** 1,659 1,700
- **c.** 46,310 46,300

**8.** one.
- **a.** 243.6 244
- **b.** 170.3 170
- **c.** 1,419.78 1,420

**9.** tenth.
- **a.** 604.37 604.4
- **b.** 291.06 291.1
- **c.** 12.74 12.7

**10.** ten.
- **a.** 493 490
- **b.** 1,508 1,510
- **c.** 124.63 120

**11.** Write the number that has
6 in the ones place,
4 in the thousands place,
7 in the ten-thousands place,
2 in the tenths place,
and 5 in all of the remaining places. 74,556.255

**12.** Identify the errors in the following problems and correct them.

**a.**
```
   28
 × 46
   80  – Should be 800
  120
  320
 + 48
  488  – Should be 1,288
```

**b.**

Should be 1
Should be 3
Should be 9
Should be 0
Should be 0
Should be 0

**13.** Choose one of the problems above and explain why making a quick estimate of the answer before solving the problem would be helpful.
Sample answer: By making an estimate, you would know that your answer was wrong because the estimate and the answer would be very different.

◇ *Math Masters,* p. 382

**ASSESSMENT MASTER**

### Unit 2 Checking Progress (cont.)

For each problem, make a magnitude estimate. Circle the appropriate box. Then solve the problem. Show your work.

**14.** 64 ∗ 83 = 5,312

| 10s | 100s | (1,000s) | 10,000s |
|---|---|---|---|

**15.** 5 ∗ 209 = 1,045

| 10s | 100s | (1,000s) | 10,000s |
|---|---|---|---|

**16.** 12.2 ∗ 1.56 = 19.032

| (10s) | 100s | 1,000s | 10,000s |
|---|---|---|---|

**17.** 25 ∗ 15.3 = 382.5

| 10s | (100s) | 1,000s | 10,000s |
|---|---|---|---|

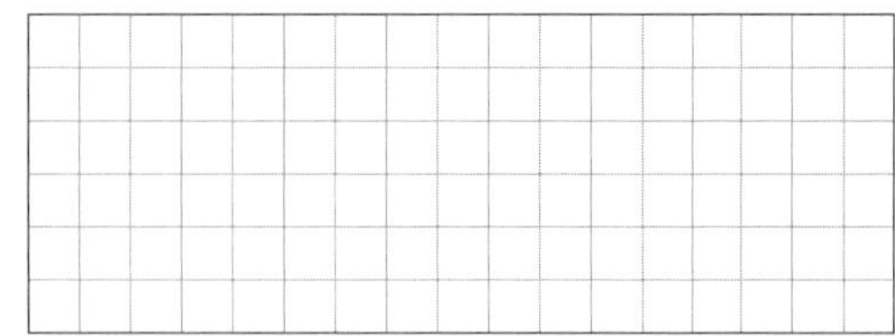

**18.** Elise had the following scores on her spelling tests: 78, 84, 94, 98, 62, 96, 89, 94, 92.
For this set of data, find ...
- **a.** the maximum 98
- **b.** the minimum 62
- **c.** the range 36
- **d.** the mode 94
- **e.** the median 92

**19.** Caitlin's great-grandmother was born in 1919. Her family had a big party for her on her 75th birthday. There were 52 family members at the party. In what year did they have the party?
- **a.** List the numbers needed to solve the problem. 1919 and 75
- **b.** Describe what you want to find. The year of the birthday party
- **c.** Open sentence: $1919 + 75 = p$
- **d.** Solution: 1994
- **e.** Answer: 1994

◇ *Math Masters,* p. 383

## ◆ Written Assessment
(*Math Masters,* pp. 381–383)

INDEPENDENT ACTIVITY 

Depending on the needs of students, you may want to work through an example together, reading a problem aloud, discussing it, and providing additional examples as necessary before students work the problem independently.

For your convenience, each of the problems is listed below and paired with one or more of this unit's learning goals.

- Find the sums and differences of multidigit whole numbers and decimals. (Problems 1–6) **Goal 2f**
- Round numbers to the nearest hundred, one, tenth, and ten. (Problems 7–10) **Goal 2b**
- Identify place value to billions and thousandths. (Problem 11) **Goal 2e**
- Find the product of multidigit whole numbers. (Problem 12) **Goal 2d**
- Explain why making a quick estimate of the answer before solving a problem would be helpful. (Problem 13) **Goal 2c**
- Make a magnitude estimate and find the products of multidigit whole numbers and decimals. (Problems 14–17) **Goals 2c and 2d**
- Find the maximum, minimum, range, mode, and median for a set of data. (Problem 18) **Goal 2g**
- Write and solve open sentences for number stories. (Problem 19) **Goal 2a**

Circulate and assist as students work.

## ◆ ALTERNATIVE ASSESSMENT OPTION
## Write Place-Value Puzzles
(*Math Masters,* p. 13)

INDEPENDENT ACTIVITY 

Students write a place-value puzzle like those on *Math Masters,* page 13. Collect the puzzles to assess students' understanding of place value.

## ✦ ALTERNATIVE ASSESSMENT OPTION

### Play *Subtraction Target Practice*

(*Student Reference Book,* p. 292)

PARTNER ACTIVITY

Have students keep a record of at least one round of play. Collect this record to assess students' subtraction skills. The instructions appear on the *Student Reference Book* page shown in Lesson 2.3.

## ✦ ALTERNATIVE ASSESSMENT OPTION

### Play *Number Top-It*

(*Student Reference Book,* p. 287; *Math Masters,* pp. 22 and 23)

PARTNER ACTIVITY

In each round, have students record their five numbers in order from least to greatest. Collect this record at the end of five rounds to assess students' ability to compare and order large numbers. The instructions appear on the *Student Reference Book* page shown in Lesson 2.10.

# 2 Build Background for Unit 3

### ✦ Math Boxes 2.11 (*Math Journal 1,* p. 59)

INDEPENDENT ACTIVITY 

**Mixed Review** The skills in Problems 1–4 are prerequisites for Unit 3.

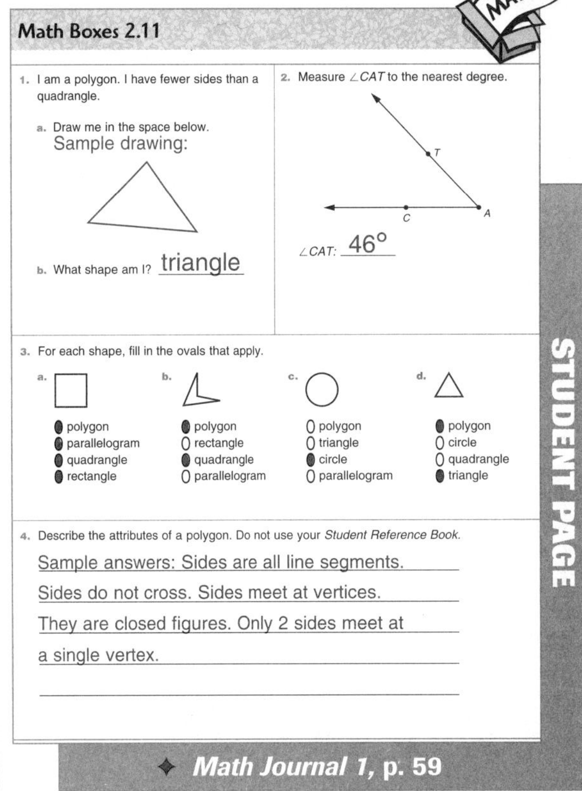

Math Boxes 2.11

1. I am a polygon. I have fewer sides than a quadrangle.
   a. Draw me in the space below.
   Sample drawing:
   b. What shape am I? triangle

2. Measure ∠CAT to the nearest degree.
   ∠CAT: 46°

3. For each shape, fill in the ovals that apply.

| a. (square) | b. | c. (circle) | d. (triangle) |
|---|---|---|---|
| ● polygon | ● polygon | ○ polygon | ● polygon |
| ● parallelogram | ○ rectangle | ○ triangle | ○ circle |
| ● quadrangle | ● quadrangle | ● circle | ○ quadrangle |
| ● rectangle | ○ parallelogram | ○ parallelogram | ● triangle |

4. Describe the attributes of a polygon. Do not use your *Student Reference Book.*
   Sample answers: Sides are all line segments. Sides do not cross. Sides meet at vertices. They are closed figures. Only 2 sides meet at a single vertex.

STUDENT PAGE

✦ *Math Journal 1,* p. 59

### ✦ Study Link 2.11: Unit 3 Family Letter

(*Math Masters,* pp. 237–240)

**Home Connection** This Study Link is a four-page newsletter that introduces parents and guardians to Unit 3's topics and terms. The letter also offers ideas for mathematics activities that are supportive of classroom work and can be done at home.

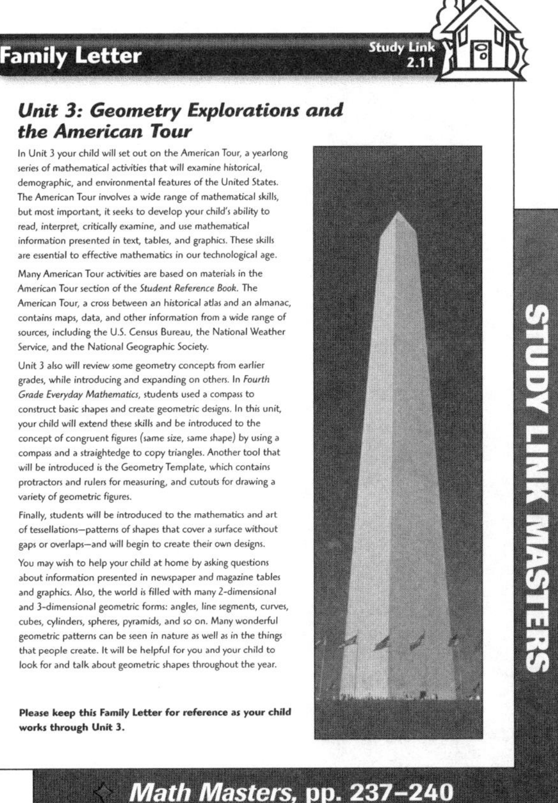

Family Letter

Study Link 2.11

***Unit 3: Geometry Explorations and the American Tour***

In Unit 3 your child will set out on the American Tour, a yearlong series of mathematical activities that will examine historical, demographic, and environmental features of the United States. The American Tour involves a wide range of mathematical skills, but most important, it seeks to develop your child's ability to read, interpret, critically examine, and use mathematical information presented in text, tables, and graphics. These skills are essential to effective mathematics in our technological age.

Many American Tour activities are based on materials in the American Tour section of the *Student Reference Book.* The American Tour, a cross between an historical atlas and an almanac, contains maps, data, and other information from a wide range of sources, including the U.S. Census Bureau, the National Weather Service, and the National Geographic Society.

Unit 3 also will review some geometry concepts from earlier grades, while introducing and expanding on others. In *Fourth Grade Everyday Mathematics,* students used a compass to construct basic shapes and create geometric designs. In this unit, your child will extend these skills and be introduced to the concept of congruent figures (same size, same shape) by using a compass and a straightedge to copy triangles. Another tool that will be introduced is the Geometry Template, which contains protractors and rulers for measuring, and cutouts for drawing a variety of geometric figures.

Finally, students will be introduced to the mathematics and art of tessellations—patterns of shapes that cover a surface without gaps or overlaps—and will begin to create their own designs.

You may wish to help your child at home by asking questions about information presented in newspaper and magazine tables and graphics. Also, the world is filled with many 2-dimensional and 3-dimensional geometric forms: angles, line segments, curves, cubes, cylinders, spheres, pyramids, and so on. Many wonderful geometric patterns can be seen in nature as well as in the things that people create. It will be helpful for you and your child to look for and talk about geometric shapes throughout the year.

**Please keep this Family Letter for reference as your child works through Unit 3.**

STUDY LINK MASTERS

✦ *Math Masters,* pp. 237–240

# Unit 3
# Geometry Explorations and the American Tour

## overview

Unit 3 has three main purposes. The first is to introduce the American Tour and to begin a yearlong series of lessons that will use information from the American Tour section of the *Student Reference Book.*

The second purpose of this unit is to examine properties of basic plane figures; to use tools such as compasses, rulers, and protractors; and to provide practice with the Geometry Template, a tool especially designed for *Everyday Mathematics.* These lessons deal explicitly with facts concerning the angle sums of triangles, quadrangles, and polygons in general; and the fact that, if two lines intersect, the sum of the measures of adjacent angles is 180 degrees and measures of vertical (opposite) angles are equal.

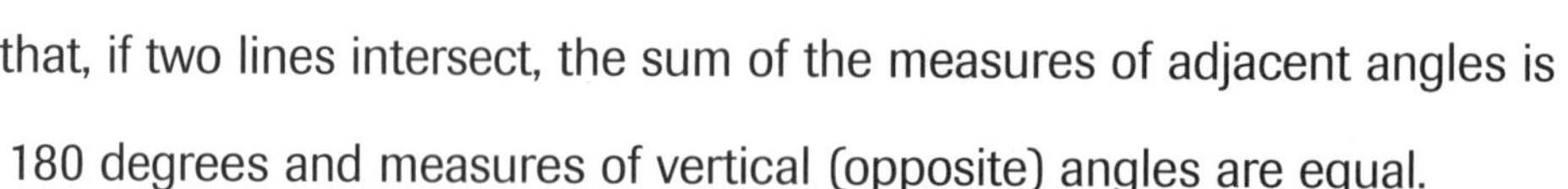

The third purpose of this unit is to explore tessellations with polygons.

# contents

UNIT 3

# learning goals in perspective

| | learning goals | links to the past | links to the future |
|---|---|---|---|
| 3a | **Developing Goal** Determine angle measures based on relationships between angles. **(Lessons 3.3 – 3.5 and 3.9)** | Grades 1-3: Define and demonstrate angles; including right angles; use straws to explore rotations and angles; determine that there are 360° in a circle.<br>Grade 4: Use a protractor to draw and measure angles; discover that the sum of measures of the angles of a triangle is 180°. | Grade 5: Applications and maintenance.<br>Grade 6: Explore the relationships between angles formed by intersecting lines and by parallel lines cut by a transversal; investigate angles in a parallelogram. |
| 3b | **Developing/Secure Goal** Estimate the measure of an angle. **(Lessons 3.6 and 3.8)** | Grades 1-3: Use straws, geoboards, and body turns to demonstrate rotations and angles.<br>Grade 4: Estimate angles as being acute, right obtuse, straight, or reflex. | Grades 5-6: Applications and maintenance. |
| 3c | **Developing/Secure Goal** Measure an angle to within 2°. **(Lessons 3.4 and 3.9)** | Grade 3: Construct an angle measure from a folded and labeled circle.<br>Grade 4: Use a full- and half-circle protractor to measure and draw angles. | Grades 5-6: Applications and maintenance.<br>Grade 6: Convert percents of circles to degrees, and then draw circle graphs with either a full- or half-circle protractor. |
| 3d | **Developing/Secure Goal** Identify types of angles. **(Lessons 3.4 and 3.5)** | Grade 3: Use a string to act out "square corners" (right angles) and other angles.<br>Grade 4: Define *acute, obtuse, straight,* and *reflex* angles. | Grades 5-6: Applications and maintenance. |
| 3e | **Developing/Secure Goal** Identify types of triangles. **(Lesson 3.6)** | Grades 1-4: Model triangles with straws and with geoboards; introduce notations for naming triangles. | Grades 5-6: Applications and maintenance.<br>Grade 6: Verify and use the Pythagorean Theorem for right triangles. |
| 3f | **Secure Goal** Identify place value in numbers to billions. **(Lesson 3.2)** | Grades 1-4: Develop place-value concepts using base-10 blocks, place-value books, slate routines, and games.<br>Grade 4: Extend place value to 100 millions; write place value as powers of 10.<br>Grade 5: Compare millions, billions, and trillions (Unit 2). | Grade 5: Review exponential notation; introduce negative exponents and scientific notation (Unit 7).<br>Grade 6: Extend place value to trillions and to thousandths; read and write both large and small numbers in scientific notation. |
| 3g | **Secure Goal** Know properties of polygons. **(Lesson 3.7)** | Grades 1-3: Explore polygons with straws, geoboards, and dot paper.<br>Grades 3-4: Practice naming polygons; introduce *regular, convex,* and *concave (non-convex)* polygons. | Grade 5: Explore transformations of polygons using a coordinate gride (Unit 9); use polygon names to classify prisms and pyramids (Unit 11).<br>Grade 6: Explore angle relationships for polygons; solve problems about polygons on a coordinate grid. |
| 3h | **Secure Goal** Define and create tessellations. **(Lesson 3.8)** | Grades 1-4: Solve spatial puzzles; create and complete patterns using dot paper, pattern blocks, and ruler and pattern-block template; tessellate pattern blocks to make large polygons. | Grade 6: Review regular tessellations; identify semi-regular tessellations; create non-polygonal Escher-type tessellations. |

# assessment

**ongoing • product • periodic**

## Informal Assessment

**Math Boxes** These *Math Journal* pages provide opportunities for cumulative review or assessment of concepts and skills.

**Ongoing Assessment: Kid Watching** Use the Ongoing Assessment suggestions in the following lessons to make quick, on-the-spot observations about students' understanding of:

- Operations and Computation **(Lesson 3.2, Part 2)**
- Data and Chance **(Lesson 3.4, Part 2)**
- Geometry **(Lesson 3.5, Part 1; Lesson 3.9, Part 1)**
- Patterns, Functions, and Algebra **(Lesson 3.9, Part 1)**
- Measurement and Reference Frames **(Lesson 3.3, Part 1; Lesson 3.4, Part 1; Lesson 3.5, Part 1)**

**Portfolio Ideas** Samples of students' work may be obtained from the following assignments:

- Inscribing a Regular Hexagon in a Circle **(Lesson 3.5)**
- Reading about Polygons **(Lesson 3.7)**
- Tessellating Quadrangles **(Lesson 3.9)**
- Solving Geometry Template Challenges **(Lesson 3.10)**
- Describe a Polygon **(Lesson 3.11)**

## Unit 3 Review and Assessment

**Slate Assessments** Use slate assessments during Lesson 3.11 to assess students' progress toward the following learning goals: **Goals 3b, 3d, and 3f**

**Written Assessment** Use a written review during Lesson 3.11 to assess students' progress toward the following learning goals: **Goals 3a–3h**

**Alternative Assessment Options** Use partner and independent alternative assessments in Lesson 3.11 to assess students' progress toward the following learning goals: **Goals 3b, 3c, and 3g**

# assessmenthandbook

For more information on how to use different types of assessment in Unit 3, see the Assessment Overview on pages 42–44 in the *Assessment Handbook*. The following Assessment Masters can be found in the *Math Masters* book:

- Unit 3 Checking Progress, pp. 384–386
- Unit 3 Individual Profile of Progress, p. 433
- Unit 3 Class Checklist, p. 432
- Class Progress Indicator, p. 471
- Math Logs, pp. 474 and 475
- Self-Assessment Forms, pp. 477 and 478
- Interest Inventories, pp. 472 and 473

# problemsolving

## *A process of modeling everyday situations using tools from mathematics*

Encourage students to use a variety of strategies when attacking a given problem—and to explain those strategies. *Strategies students might use in this unit:*

- Use data from tables
- Use estimation
- Act out the problem
- Use logical reasoning
- Use a graph
- Identify and use a pattern
- Draw a picture

**Four Problem-Solving REPRESENTATIONS**

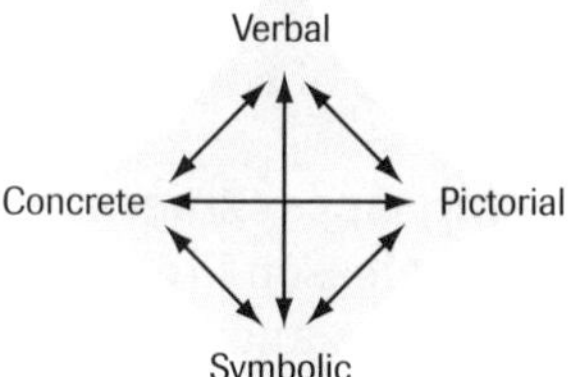


### Lessons that teach *through* problem solving, not just *about* problem solving

| Lesson | Activity | Lesson | Activity |
|---|---|---|---|
| 3.1 | Compare the 1790 U.S. Census with the 2000 U.S. Census | 3.4 | Find data landmark for television-watching data |
| 3.2 | Estimate populations of the original colonies | 3.8 | Find out which regular polygons tessellate |
| 3.3 | Find the measures of angles of the pattern block (without a protractor) | 3.9 | Devise a method for finding the sum of angle measures for any polygon |
| 3.3 | Solve addition and subtraction number stories | 3.10 | Solve geometry problems involving attributes and the Geometry Template |
| 3.4, 3.6 3.9 | Use special cases to define acute angles, obtuse angles, and types of triangles, and to solve attribute puzzles | | |

For more information about problem solving in *Everyday Mathematics,* see the *Teacher's Reference Manual.*

# cross-curricularlinks

### literature

- Students read about different polygons in *The Greedy Triangle* by Marilyn Burns. **(Lesson 3.7)**
- Students read about shapes that tessellate in *A Cloak for the Dreamer* by Aileen Friedman. **(Lesson 3.8)**
- Students read about tangram puzzles in *Grandfather Tang's Story* by Ann Tompert. **(Lesson 3.10)**

### art

- Students inscribe a regular hexagon in a circle. **(Lesson 3.5)**
- Students create tessellating patterns. **(Lesson 3.8)**

### language arts

- Students discover the nonmathematical meanings of the words *acute, obtuse, adjacent,* and *vertical.* **(Lesson 3.5)**

### social studies

- Students discuss the meaning of the word *census.* Conduct a classroom census. **(Lesson 3.1)**
- Students use census tables to learn about early American colonial populations. **(Lesson 3.2)**
- Students use the American Tour section of the *Student Reference Book* to learn about history and geography. **(Lessons 3.1 and 3.2)**

# meeting INDIVIDUAL needs

UNIVERSAL ACCESS

## ✦ RETEACHING

The following features provide some additional instructional support:

**Adjusting the Activity**

- **Lesson 3.1, Part 1**
- **Lesson 3.2, Part 1**
- **Lesson 3.4, Part 1**
- **Lesson 3.5, Part 1**
- **Lesson 3.6, Part 1**
- **Lesson 3.7, Part 1**
- **Lesson 3.9, Part 1**

**Options for Individualizing**

- **Lesson 3.3** Reviewing Ways to Name Angles
- **Lesson 3.4** Playing *Robot*
- **Lesson 3.7** Sorting Attribute Blocks by Two Properties
- **Lesson 3.10** Solving Tangram Puzzles

## ✦ ENRICHMENT

The following features suggest enrichment and extension activities:

**Adjusting the Activity**

- **Lesson 3.3, Part 1**
- **Lesson 3.4, Part 1**
- **Lesson 3.6, Part 1**

**Options for Individualizing**

- **Lesson 3.1** Reporting on Census Information
- **Lesson 3.2** Ranking States by Their Native-American Populations
- **Lesson 3.4** Exploring the Geometry Template
- **Lesson 3.5** Solving a Baseball Challenge
- **Lesson 3.5** Inscribing a Regular Hexagon in a Circle
- **Lesson 3.7** Reading about Polygons
- **Lesson 3.8** Reading about Polygons That Tessellate
- **Lesson 3.9** Tessellating Quadrangles
- **Lesson 3.10** Solving Geometry Template Challenges

## ✦ LANGUAGE DIVERSITY

The following features suggest ways to support students who are acquiring proficiency in English:

**Options for Individualizing**

- **Lesson 3.4** Creating a Geometry Dictionary
- **Lesson 3.5** Building Background for Mathematics Words

## ✦ MULTIAGE CLASSROOM

The following chart lists related lessons from Grades 4 and 6 that can help you meet your instructional needs:

| | | | | | | | | | | |
|---|---|---|---|---|---|---|---|---|---|---|
| **Grade 4** | 2.1 | | 1.3 | 1.2<br>1.3<br>6.7<br>6.8 | 1.2<br>1.3<br>1.6 | 1.3 | 1.3<br>1.5 | | 1.5 | |
| **Grade 5** | 3.1 | 3.2 | 3.3 | 3.4 | 3.5 | 3.6 | 3.7 | 3.8 | 3.9 | 3.10 |
| **Grade 6** | | | 5.1<br>5.2<br>5.9 | 5.3 | 5.7<br>5.8 | | | 10.1<br>10.2 | | |

# materials

| lesson | math masters pages | manipulative kit items | other items |
|---|---|---|---|
| **3.1** | Study Link Master, p. 241<br>Teaching Master, p. 24 | | Probability Meter; stick-on notes<br>computer with Internet access<br>***See* Advance Preparation, p. 144** |
| **3.2** | Study Link Master, p. 242<br>***See* Advance Preparation, p. 149** | | overhead transparency of a Place-Value Chart (optional) |
| **3.3** | Study Link Master, p. 243<br>***See* Advance Preparation, p. 154** | | *Power Polygons*™ (optional)<br>slate; pattern blocks<br>Geometry Template (optional) |
| **3.4** | Study Link Master, p. 244<br>transparencies of Teaching Masters, pp. 25 and 27 (optional)<br>Assessment Master, p. 479 | | Geometry Template<br>***See* Advance Preparation, p. 158** |
| **3.5** | Study Link Master, p. 245<br>Teaching Masters, pp. 28 and 29<br>***See* Advance Preparation, p. 165** | | Geometry Template<br>1 sheet of paper about 2 feet square (for demonstration purposes)<br>compass; straightedge |
| **3.6** | Study Link Master, p. 246<br>transparency of Teaching Master, p. 25 (optional) | straws and connectors (or masking tape and cardstock strips)<br>***See* Advance Preparation, p. 171** | Geometry Template<br>compass, protractor, and meterstick for demonstration purposes<br>slate; compass; straightedge |
| **3.7** | Study Link Master, p. 247<br>transparency of Teaching Master, p. 30 (optional) | | *The Greedy Triangle* by Marilyn Burns<br>attribute blocks<br>***See* Advance Preparation, p. 177** |
| **3.8** | Study Link Master, p. 248<br>Teaching Master, p. 31<br>***See* Advance Preparation, p. 181** | | pattern blocks<br>Geometry Template (or protractor and straightedge)<br>*A Cloak for the Dreamer* by Aileen Friedman |
| **3.9** | Study Link Master, p. 249<br>Teaching Master, p. 33<br>transparency of Teaching Master, p. 32 (optional)<br>Assessment Master, p. 479 (optional) | | Geometry Template (or protractor and straightedge)<br>paper ($8\frac{1}{2}$" x 11")<br>cardstock (optional)<br>***See* Advance Preparation, p. 185** |
| **3.10** | Study Link Master, p. 250<br>Teaching Masters, pp. 34–37<br>***See* Advance Preparation, p. 191** | | Geometry Template<br>2 sharp pencils<br>1 sheet of paper at least 17" square (optional)<br>*Polygon Capture* Pieces and Property Cards (*Math Journals 1 and 2,* Activity Sheets 4 and 5)<br>cardstock (optional)<br>*Grandfather Tang's Story* by Ann Tompert |
| **3.11** | Study Link Masters, pp. 251–254<br>Assessment Masters, pp. 384-386<br>***See* Advance Preparation, p. 197** | | Geometry Template (or protractor and straightedge)<br>slate<br>*Polygon Capture* Pieces and Property Cards (*Math Journals 1 and 2,* Activity Sheets 4 and 5) |

# planningtips

## Pacing

Pacing depends on a number of factors, such as students' individual needs and how long your school has been using *Everyday Mathematics*. At the beginning of Unit 3, review your Content by Strand Poster to help you set a monthly pace.

| | ← MOST CLASSROOMS → | |
|---|---|---|
| SEPTEMBER | OCTOBER | NOVEMBER |

## Home Communication

Share Study Links 3.1–3.10 with families to help them understand the content and procedures in this unit. At the end of the unit, use Study Link 3.11 to introduce Unit 4. Supplemental information can be found in the *Home Connection Handbook.*

## NCTM Standards

| Standard | 1 | 2 | 3 | 4 | 5 | 6 | 7 | 8 | 9 | 10 |
|---|---|---|---|---|---|---|---|---|---|---|
| Unit 3 Lessons | 3.1–, 3.5, 3.7 | 3.9, 3.10 | 3.3–3.10 | 3.4, 3.5, 3.8 | 3.1, 3.4 | 3.1–3.11 | 3.1–3.11 | 3.1–3.11 | 3.1–3.11 | 3.1–3.11 |

**Content Standards**
1 Number and Operations
2 Algebra
3 Geometry
4 Measurement
5 Data Analysis and Probability

**Process Standards**
6 Problem Solving
7 Reasoning and Proof
8 Communication
9 Connections
10 Representation

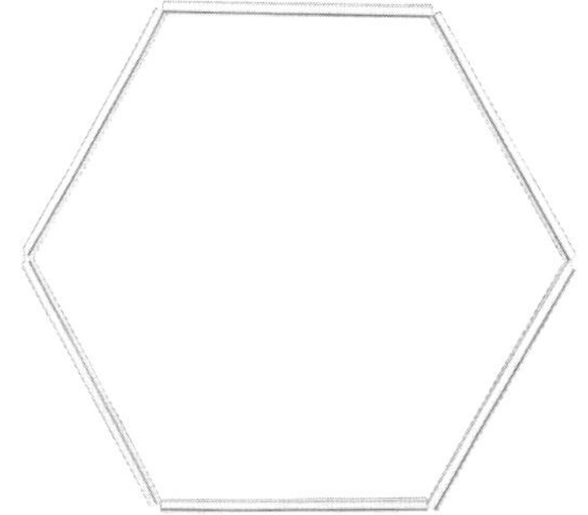

## PRACTICE through Games

*Everyday Mathematics* uses games to help students develop good fact power and other math skills.

- *Angle Tangle* to practice estimating and then using a protractor to measure angles **(Lessons 3.6, 3.8, and 3.11)**
- *Polygon Capture* to practice identifying the properties of polygons **(Lessons 3.7, 3.10, and 3.11)**

# unit 3 content highlights

*The discussion below highlights the major content ideas presented in Unit 3 and may help you establish instructional priorities.*

## The American Tour (Lessons 3.1 and 3.2)

Students begin a yearlong American Tour, on which they will visit mathematical aspects of the history, demographics, politics, and environment of the United States. The American Tour will also provide connections to other subjects and the world outside the classroom. Most subsequent units will have one or two American Tour lessons.

The American Tour section of the *Student Reference Book* is filled with fascinating information and is fun to read at any time.

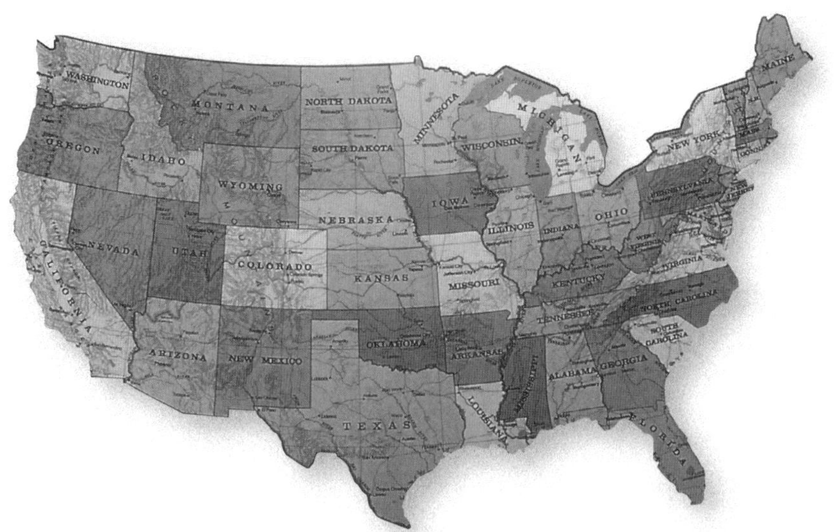


## Tools for Measuring and Drawing (Lessons 3.3–3.6 and 3.10)

Students are introduced to the Geometry Template in Lesson 3.4. They use the half-circle protractor to draw and measure angles from 0 to 180 degrees, and the full-circle protractor to measure angles from 0 to 360 degrees. The terms for various kinds of angles are introduced, along with conventions for naming angles. There are more activities involving the Geometry Template in Lesson 3.10.

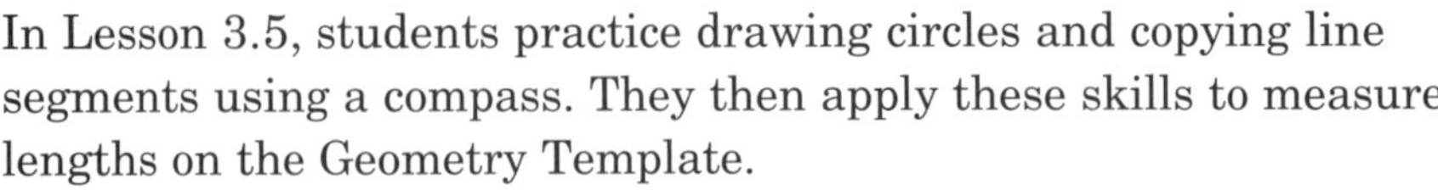

In Lesson 3.5, students practice drawing circles and copying line segments using a compass. They then apply these skills to measure lengths on the Geometry Template.

The concept of congruent figures is introduced in Lesson 3.6. Students copy triangles using their measuring and drawing tools. In some instances, certain tools are not allowed. The classic congruence theorems of plane geometry (such as Side-Side-Side) are hinted at, but are not presented explicitly.

## Polygons (Lessons 3.7 and 3.9)

Students consider the properties of a variety of polygons, and they play the game *Polygon Capture* to develop their ability to classify and sort polygons. They learn how to find the sum of the angle measures for triangles, quadrangles, and pentagons; and then for polygons in general by imagining the polygons divided into triangles.

## Tessellations (Lesson 3.8)

Students examine and create patterns with figures that cover a surface without gaps or overlaps. They discover criteria that determine whether a figure will tessellate, and they identify the regular polygons that will tessellate.

## Review and Assessment (Lesson 3.11)

The Unit 3 assessment in Lesson 3.11 includes a written assessment of the following concepts and skills:

- ▷ determining angle measures based on relationships among angles
- ▷ estimating and measuring angles
- ▷ identifying types of angles and triangles
- ▷ identifying place value in numbers to billions
- ▷ recognizing properties of polygons
- ▷ defining and creating tessellations

If you are planning a quarterly assessment for Units 1–3, you may want to refer to the *Assessment Handbook*. The quarterly learning goals Class Checklist and Individual Profile of Progress checklist (*Math Masters,* pages 452–455) are useful tools for keeping track of students' progress.

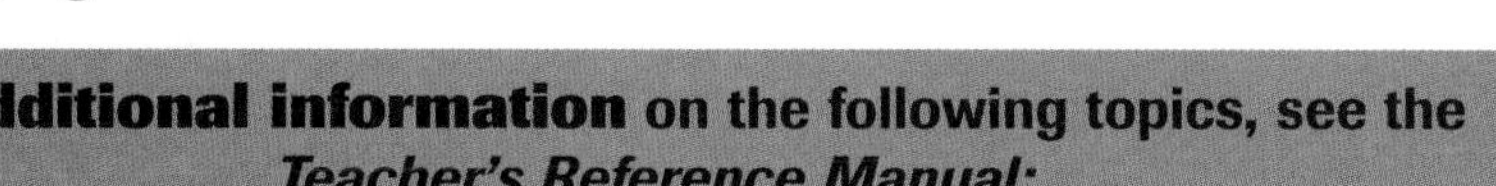

For **additional information** on the following topics, see the *Teacher's Reference Manual:*

- angles and rotations
- compass and straightedge
- straws and connectors
- Geometry Templates
- polygons
- relationships among angles
- tessellations

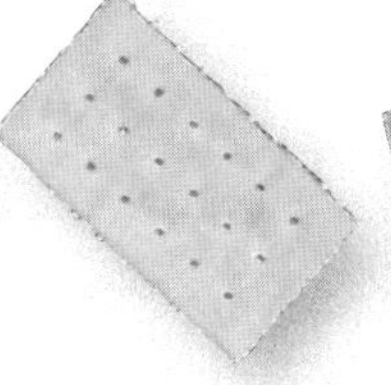

# 3.1 Introduction to the American Tour

**OBJECTIVES** **To introduce the American Tour; to learn about the U.S. Census and conduct a classroom census; and to use the Probability Meter.**

| summaries | materials |
|---|---|
| **1 Teaching the Lesson** | |
| Students are given an overview of the American Tour section of the *Student Reference Book.* [Data and Chance]<br>Students read and answer questions about the U.S. Census; complete abbreviated census forms; and post actual census results on the Probability Meter. [Data and Chance; Numeration] | □ *Math Journal 1,* p. 60<br>□ *Student Reference Book,* pp. 327 and 328<br>□ Teaching Master (*Math Masters,* p. 24)<br>□ Probability Meter<br>□ stick-on notes<br>***See* Advance Preparation** |
| **2 Ongoing Learning & Practice** | |
| Students learn and use a mental strategy for multiplying a number that ends in 9. [Operations and Computation]<br>Students practice and maintain skills through Math Boxes and Study Link activities. | □ *Math Journal 1,* pp. 61 and 62<br>□ Study Link Master (*Math Masters,* p. 241) |
| **3 Options for Individualizing** | |
| **Enrichment** Students visit the web site for the U.S. Bureau of the Census, obtain information, and write a brief report about a topic of interest. [Data and Chance; Numeration] | □ computer with Internet access |

## Additional Information

**Advance Preparation** For the activity in Part 1 on taking a classroom census, make a copy of *Math Masters,* page 24 for each student, including students who are absent. Provide a collection box for the census forms students will hand in.

You may want to set up an American Tour corner where students can post American Tour projects and data displays throughout the year. You can provide additional reference materials in this area, such as almanacs, maps, and historical atlases.

If you have not already done so, assemble the Probability Meter and hang it in a prominent place. See Lesson 2.6 for more information.

**Vocabulary** • **census**

# Getting Started

## Mental Math and Reflexes

Dictate large numbers for students to write and mark on their slates.

*Suggestions:*

- Write 3,497,128. Circle the tens digit. Underline the hundred-thousands digit. 3,497,1(2)8
- Write 15,024,367. Circle the ten-thousands digit. Underline the millions digit. 15,0(2)4,367
- Write 435,180,241. Circle the thousands digit. Underline the ten-millions digit. 435,18(0),241

Continue as time allows.

## Math Message

*Read about the U.S. Census on page 327 of the* Student Reference Book.

# 1 Teaching the Lesson

## ✦ Math Message Follow-Up

WHOLE-CLASS DISCUSSION

**Social Studies Link** Discuss the meaning of the word ***census.*** A census is a count or list, one-by-one, of every member of a population. A census may collect other information too, such as age and occupation.

Tell students that they will take a census of their class. This census will count and collect information about every student in the class.

## ✦ Examining the American Tour (*Student Reference Book*)

WHOLE-CLASS ACTIVITY

**Social Studies Link** The American Tour section of the *Student Reference Book* will be used throughout the year to show how mathematics can help students understand the history, geography, and population of the United States. Spend a few minutes leafing through the pages and naming the titles of the parts.

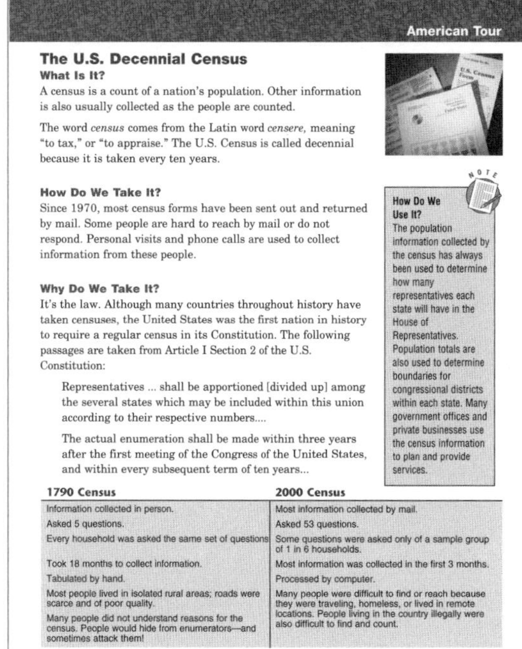

American Tour

### The U.S. Decennial Census

**What Is It?**

A census is a count of a nation's population. Other information is also usually collected as the people are counted.

The word *census* comes from the Latin word *censere,* meaning "to tax," or "to appraise." The U.S. Census is called decennial because it is taken every ten years.

**How Do We Take It?**

Since 1970, most census forms have been sent out and returned by mail. Some people are hard to reach by mail or do not respond. Personal visits and phone calls are used to collect information from these people.

**Why Do We Take It?**

It's the law. Although many countries throughout history have taken censuses, the United States was the first nation in history to require a regular census in its Constitution. The following passages are taken from Article I Section 2 of the U.S. Constitution:

> Representatives ... shall be apportioned [divided up] among the several states which may be included within this union according to their respective numbers....
>
> The actual enumeration shall be made within three years after the first meeting of the Congress of the United States, and within every subsequent term of ten years...

NOTE

**How Do We Use It?**
The population information collected by the census has always been used to determine how many representatives each state will have in the House of Representatives. Population totals are also used to determine boundaries for congressional districts within each state. Many government offices and private businesses use the census information to plan and provide services.

| 1790 Census | 2000 Census |
|---|---|
| Information collected in person. | Most information collected by mail. |
| Asked 5 questions. | Asked 53 questions. |
| Every household was asked the same set of questions | Some questions were asked only of a sample group of 1 in 6 households. |
| Took 18 months to collect information. | Most information was collected in the first 3 months. |
| Tabulated by hand. | Processed by computer. |
| Most people lived in isolated rural areas; roads were scarce and of poor quality. | Many people were difficult to find or reach because they were traveling, homeless, or lived in remote locations. People living in the country illegally were also difficult to find and count. |
| Many people did not understand reasons for the census. People would hide from enumerators—and sometimes attack them! | |

three hundred twenty-seven SRB 327

STUDENT PAGE

✦ *Student Reference Book*, p. 327

STUDENT PAGE

### U.S. Census Questions

Use the information on pages 328 and 332 of the *Student Reference Book* to compare the 1790 census with the 2000 census.

1. a. Which census asked more questions? The 2000 census
   b. How many more? 48 more questions
2. Which census took longer to collect its information? The 1790 census
3. About how much longer did it take? Sample answer: About 15 months longer
4. a. Which state reported the largest total population in the 1790 census? Virginia
   b. Which state reported the smallest total population in the 1790 census? Tennessee
5. What was the reported total population in 1790? 3,893,635; with a separate total of 35,691 for the Southwest Territory (Tennessee)
6. a. Were slaves counted in the 1790 Census? yes
   b. Which state had the most slaves? Virginia
   c. Which states had less than 100 slaves? Vermont, Maine, and Massachusetts
7. a. How many free white males were reported in Vermont in the 1790 Census? 44,763
   b. Is this more or less than the number of free white females reported? More

✦ *Math Journal 1*, p. 60

TEACHING MASTER

### U.S. Census Questions

Here are some of the questions from both the short and long forms of the U.S. Census. Answer the questions *for yourself.* Mark and fill in the boxes with your answers. Then put this sheet in the collection box.

1. What is this person's sex? Mark one box.
   ☐ Male ☐ Female
2. a. What is this person's date of birth? *Print numbers in boxes.*
   Month ☐☐ Day ☐☐
   Year of birth ☐☐☐☐
   b. What was this person's age on April 1 of this year? ☐☐☐
3. Where was this person born?
   ☐ In the United States—*Print name of state.*
   ☐ Outside the United States—*Print name of foreign country, or Puerto Rico, Guam, etc.*
4. a. Does this person speak a language other than English at home?
   ☐ Yes ☐ No → *Skip to 5.*
   b. What is this language?
   *(For example: Korean, Italian, Spanish, Vietnamese)*
5. Is there telephone service available in this house, apartment, or mobile home from which you can both make and receive calls?
   ☐ Yes ☐ No

✦ *Math Masters*, p. 24

Ask students to imagine that all of the paragraphs of text in the American Tour were removed or blanked out. *Which things would be left on the pages?* U.S. maps of many kinds, tables of data, and bar graphs are the most frequently included visual items.

## ✦ Comparing the 1790 Census with the 2000 Census (*Math Journal 1,* p. 60; *Student Reference Book,* pp. 327 and 328)

PARTNER ACTIVITY

Have students read the table at the bottom of page 327 of the *Student Reference Book*. Then they answer the questions on the journal page. For Problems 4–7, students refer to the official 1790 census report shown on page 328 of the *Student Reference Book.* Discuss as necessary.

## ✦ Taking a Classroom Census (*Math Masters,* p. 24)

INDEPENDENT ACTIVITY 

Distribute a copy of *Math Masters,* page 24 to each student. The actual U.S. Census has two forms—a short form that every household fills out, and a long form that only a sample of households fills out. Point out that the form students have contains questions from both forms. (Questions 1 and 2 are on both forms; Questions 3–5 are on the long form only.)

Have each student fill out the form and deposit it in the collection box. Point out that there is no place for their name so they do not need to write it on the form. Students who are absent should fill out the same form when they return. Since this is to be a classroom census, *all* students must be counted and answer the questions.

## ✦ Posting U.S. Census Results on the Probability Meter (*Math Masters,* p. 24)

WHOLE-CLASS ACTIVITY

Ask students to estimate (or guess) the following figures as collected in the 2000 census. Do not give the actual percents until students have arrived at their own figures.

▷ The percent of people living in the United States who were born in a foreign country (U.S. Census Question 3) About 10% of the people in the U.S. were born in a foreign country.

▷ The percent of people who speak a language other than English at home (U.S. Census Question 4) About 15% of the people in the U.S. speak a language other than English at home.

▷ The percent of houses and apartments that have a telephone (U.S. Census Question 5) About 95% of all houses and apartments have a telephone.

Ask students if they find any of the actual percents surprising.

**Adjusting the Activity** If students have difficulty with percents, ask them to estimate the number of people out of 100 who answered Question 3 with a foreign country, or Question 4 or 5 with "yes." For example, *For every hundred persons, how many do you think were born in a foreign country?*

Record the actual census results on stick-on notes and post them on the left side of the Probability Meter, with a corner pointing to the correct mark on the meter *(see the margin).*

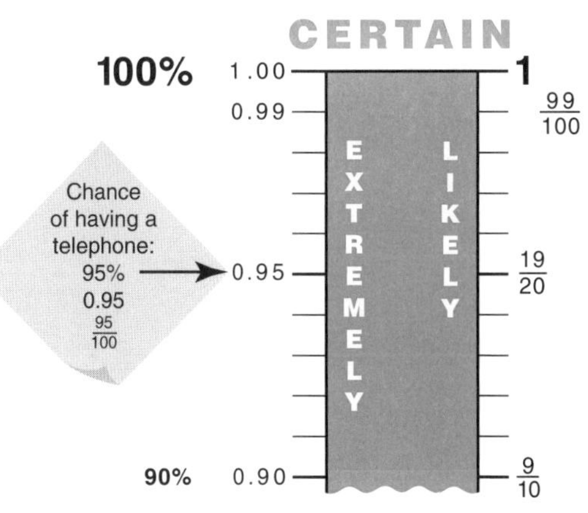


## 2 Ongoing Learning & Practice

### ✦ Multiplying Numbers That End in 9 (*Math Journal 1,* p. 61)

INDEPENDENT ACTIVITY 

Have students read the journal page and use the mental strategy given to answer the questions on the page. If necessary, read and discuss Example 1 as a class.

**A Mental Calculation Strategy** 

When you multiply a number that ends in 9, you can simplify the calculation by changing it into an easier problem. Then adjust the result.

*Example 1* 2 * 99 = ?

- Change 2 * 99 into 2 * 100.
- Find the answer: 2 * 100 = 200.
- Ask, "How is the answer to 2 * 100 different from the answer to 2 * 99?" 100 is 1 more than 99, and you multiplied by 2. So 200 is 2 more than the answer to 2 * 99.
- Adjust the answer to 2 * 100 to find the answer to 2 * 99: 200 − 2 = 198. So 2 * 99 = 198.

*Example 2* 3 * 149 = ?

- Change 3 * 149 into 3 * 150.
- Find the answer: 3 * 150 = (3 * 100) + (3 * 50) = 450.
- Ask, "How is the answer to 3 * 150 different from the answer to 3 * 149?" 150 is 1 more than 149, and you multiplied by 3. So 450 is 3 more than the answer to 3 * 149.
- Adjust: 450 − 3 = 447. So 3 * 149 = 447.

Use this strategy to calculate these products mentally.

1. 5 * 49 = 245
2. 5 * 99 = 495
3. 8 * 99 = 792
4. 4 * 199 = 796
5. 2 * 119 = 238
6. 3 * 98 = 294

STUDENT PAGE

✦ *Math Journal 1,* p. 61

### ✦ Math Boxes 3.1 (*Math Journal 1,* p. 62)

INDEPENDENT ACTIVITY 

**Mixed Review** Math Boxes in this lesson are paired with Math Boxes in Lesson 3.3. The skill in Problem 1 is a prerequisite for Unit 4.

### ✦ Study Link 3.1 (*Math Masters,* p. 241)

**Home Connection** Students use a table of census information about income and education levels to answer and write questions.

## Math Boxes 3.1

1. Round 14.762 to the nearest ...
   a. tenth. 14.8
   b. whole number. 15
   c. hundredth. 14.76

SRB 30 45 46

2. Find an object in the room that has a length of about 30 centimeters.
   Answers vary.

SRB 169

3. Solve.

   a. 209.0 − 73.5 = 135.5
   b. 9,825 − 7,982 = 1,843
   c. $30.49 − $8.51 = $21.98
   d. 7,675 + 3,082 = 10,757
   e. 4.339 + 6.671 = 11.010
   f. 5,946 + 8,217 = 14,163

4. a. Make up a set of at least twelve numbers that have the following landmarks.
   Maximum: 18 Range: 13 Mode: 7 Median: 12
   Sample answer: 5, 6, 7, 7, 7, 7, 12, 14, 15, 16, 16, 18, 18
   b. Make a bar graph of the data. Sample answer:

0 1 2 3 4

5 6 7 8 9 10 11 12 13 14 15 16 17 18

SRB 113 116

STUDENT PAGE

✦ *Math Journal 1,* p. 62

## Education and Earnings

Study Link 3.1

The table below contains information from surveys by the U.S. Census Bureau. The information describes Householders who were at least 25 years old. A *Householder* is the person in whose name a home is owned or rented. If a house is owned jointly by a husband and wife, the Householder could be either the husband or the wife.

SRB 327

| | 1990 | | | 1980 | | |
|---|---|---|---|---|---|---|
| Years of School Completed | Number of Householders (thousands) | Percent of House-holders | Median Income | Number of House-holders (thousands) | Percent of House-holders | Median Income |
| Elementary (less than 9 years) | 10,146 | 11% | $13,523 | 14,012 | 18% | $ 8,875 |
| High School (1–3 years) | 10,007 | 11% | $18,191 | 10,547 | 14% | $13,213 |
| High School (4 years) | 32,043 | 36% | $28,744 | 25,454 | 34% | $19,638 |
| College (1–3 years) | 16,451 | 19% | $35,724 | 11,480 | 15% | $21,740 |
| College (4 years) | 11,443 | 13% | $47,083 | 7,862 | 10% | $27,339 |
| College (5 or more years) | 9,269 | 10% | $54,636 | 6,661 | 9% | $30,684 |
| **Total** | 89,359 | 100% | $30,757 | 76,016 | 100% | $18,383 |

*Source: March Current Population Survey,* prepared by Income Statistics Branch/HHES Division U.S. Bureau of the Census

Use the table to answer the following questions.

1. Describe the relationship between number of years of education and income.
   Sample answer: The more years of school completed, the higher the median income.
2. In which year do you think a higher percentage of Householders were high school graduates—1990 or 2000? Explain your answer.
   Answers vary.
3. On the back of this page, write one question that can be answered using the information in the table. Answers vary.

STUDY LINK MASTER

✦ *Math Masters,* p. 241

# 3 Options for Individualizing

## ✦ ENRICHMENT Reporting on Census Information

SMALL-GROUP ACTIVITY  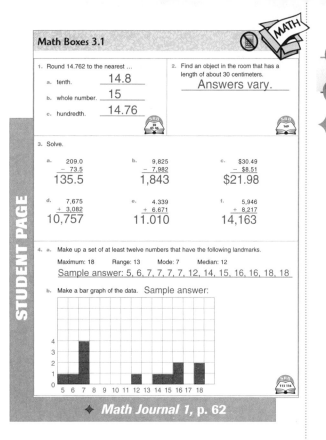 **30+ min** 

Students visit the Web site for the U.S. Bureau of the Census at the following address: www.census.gov/. They research the information found there on population, housing, and related areas, and write a brief report on a topic of interest.

### PLANNING AHEAD

When the classroom census forms have been returned by every student in the class, ask several students to tabulate the returns. Post the results in an American Tour display. Make, or have students make, a table for the display like the one shown below. Only the Number column should be filled in at this time. The Fraction, Decimal, and Percent columns will be filled in later.

| Classroom Census Results | | | | | |
|---|---|---|---|---|---|
| | | Number | Fraction | Decimal | Percent |
| Total students in classroom | | | | | 100% |
| Female | | | | | |
| Male | | | | | |
| Age | 9 | | | | |
| | 10 | | | | |
| | 11 | | | | |
| Born in this state | | | | | |
| Born in another state | | | | | |
| Born in another country | | | | | |
| Speak a language other than English at home | | | | | |
| Have telephone at home | | | | | |

# 3.2 American Tour: Population Estimates

**OBJECTIVE** **To read and interpret a table of population estimates.**

| summaries | materials |
|---|---|
| **1 Teaching the Lesson** | |
| Students use a table of state population estimates for the years 1610 to 1790; they discuss the sources and reliability of the data, and answer questions about the data. [Data and Chance; Numeration]<br><br>Students practice reading large numbers and review place value. [Numeration] | □ *Math Journal 1,* pp. 64 and 65<br>□ *Student Reference Book,* pp. 307 and 329<br>□ Study Link 3.1<br>□ overhead transparency of a Place-Value Chart (optional)<br>***See* Advance Preparation** |
| **2 Ongoing Learning & Practice** | |
| Students estimate and calculate sums and differences. [Operations and Computation]<br><br>Students practice and maintain skills through Math Boxes and Study Link activities. | □ *Math Journal 1,* pp. 63 and 66<br>□ Study Link Master (*Math Masters,* p. 242) |
| **3 Options for Individualizing** | |
| **Enrichment** Students use a color-coded map to rank states by their Native-American populations. [Numeration] | □ *Student Reference Book,* p. 301 |

## Additional Information

**Advance Preparation** For Part 1, draw a Place-Value Chart from ones to hundred-millions on the board or on an overhead transparency. *For example:*

| Millions | | | Thousands | | | Ones | | |
|---|---|---|---|---|---|---|---|---|
| 100 M | 10 M | 1 M | 100 K | 10 K | 1 K | 100 | 10 | 1 |
| | | | | | | | | |

## Getting Started

### Mental Math and Reflexes

Pose multiplication problems like the following:

- 3 ∗ 40 120 30 ∗ 40 1,200 300 ∗ 40 12,000
- 5 ∗ 80 400 50 ∗ 80 4,000 500 ∗ 800 400,000
- 9 ∗ 60 540 90 ∗ 60 5,400 90 ∗ 600 54,000

Continue as time allows.

### Math Message

*What is the largest number in the table on page 329 of the* Student Reference Book?

### Study Link 3.1 Follow-Up

Have a volunteer describe the relationship between the number of years of education and income. The more years of education, the higher the median income Then have students share whether they think there was a higher percentage of Householders who were high school graduates in 1990, or in 2000. Expect answers like the following:

- Combine the first two rows in the table. In 1980, 32% did *not* finish high school. In 1990, 22% did *not* finish high school. This shows a strong trend. In 2000, the percent who did *not* finish high school was probably less than 20%.
- The rows in the table for High School (4 years) and College all show higher percents in 1990 than in 1980. If that trend continued, there would be a higher percentage of high school graduates in 2000 than in 1990.
- Since you only have information for two different years (1980 and 1990), you can't tell if there is a trend or not.

Have the class try to answer questions that students wrote about the information in the table.

STUDENT PAGE

American Tour

**Population Estimates for Colonial and Continental Periods, 1610–1790**

| Year | Vermont | New Hampshire[1] | Maine | Massachusetts[1] | Rhode Island[1] | Connecticut[1] | New York[1] | New Jersey[1] | Pennsylvania[1] | Delaware[1] | Maryland[1] | Virginia[1] | Kentucky | North Carolina[1] | South Carolina[1] | Georgia[1] | Tennessee | TOTAL |
|---|---|---|---|---|---|---|---|---|---|---|---|---|---|---|---|---|---|---|
| 1610 | — | — | — | — | — | — | — | — | — | — | — | 210 | — | — | — | — | — | 210 |
| 1620 | — | — | — | 100 | — | — | — | — | — | — | — | 2,400 | — | — | — | — | — | 2,500 |
| 1630 | — | 500 | 400 | 1,300 | — | — | 500 | — | — | — | — | 3,000 | — | — | — | — | — | 5,700 |
| 1640 | — | 800 | 700 | 14,000 | 300 | 2,000 | 1,000 | — | — | — | 1,500 | 7,600 | — | — | — | — | — | 28,000 |
| 1650 | — | 1,400 | 1,000 | 18,000 | 800 | 6,000 | 3,000 | — | — | — | 4,500 | 17,000 | — | — | — | — | — | 52,000 |
| 1660 | — | 2,300 | [3] | 25,000[3] | 1,500 | 8,000 | 6,000 | — | — | — | 8,000 | 33,000 | — | 1,000 | — | — | — | 65,000 |
| 1670 | — | 3,000 | [3] | 30,000[3] | 2,500 | 10,000 | 9,000 | 2,500 | — | — | 15,000 | 40,000 | — | 2,500 | — | — | — | 115,000 |
| 1680 | — | 4,000 | [3] | 40,000[3] | 4,000 | 13,000 | 14,000 | 8,000 | — | 500 | 20,000 | 49,000 | — | 4,000 | 1,100 | — | — | 156,000 |
| 1690 | — | 5,000 | [3] | 54,000[3] | 5,000 | 18,000 | 20,000 | 9,000 | 12,000[4] | [4] | 25,000 | 58,000 | — | 3,000 | 4,500 | — | — | 214,000 |
| 1700 | — | 6,000 | [3] | 70,000[3] | 6,000 | 24,000 | 19,000 | 14,000 | 20,000[4] | [4] | 31,000 | 72,000 | — | 5,000 | 8,000 | — | — | 275,000 |
| 1710 | — | 7,500 | [3] | 80,000[3] | 8,000 | 31,000 | 26,000 | 20,000 | 35,000[4] | [4] | 43,000 | 87,000 | — | 7,000 | 13,000 | — | — | 358,000 |
| 1720 | — | 9,500 | [3] | 92,000[3] | 11,000 | 40,000 | 36,000 | 26,000 | 48,000[4] | [4] | 62,000 | 116,000 | — | 13,000 | 21,000 | — | — | 474,000 |
| 1730 | [2] | 12,000 | [3] | 125,000[3] | 17,000 | 55,000 | 49,000[2] | 37,000 | 65,000[4] | [4] | 82,000 | 153,000 | — | 30,000 | 30,000 | — | — | 655,000 |
| 1740 | [2] | 22,000 | [3] | 158,000[3] | 24,000 | 70,000 | 63,000[2] | 52,000 | 100,000[4] | [4] | 105,000 | 200,000 | — | 50,000 | 45,000 | — | — | 889,000 |
| 1750 | [2] | 31,000 | [3] | 180,000[3] | 35,000 | 100,000 | 80,000[2] | 66,000 | 150,000[4] | [4] | 137,000 | 275,000 | — | 80,000 | 68,000 | 5,000 | — | 1,207,000 |
| 1760 | [2] | 38,000 | [3] | 235,000[3] | 44,000 | 142,000 | 113,000[2] | 91,000 | 220,000[4] | [4] | 162,000 | 346,000 | — | 115,000 | 95,000 | 9,000 | — | 1,610,000 |
| 1770 | 25,000 | 60,000 | 34,000 | 265,000 | 55,000 | 175,000 | 160,000 | 110,000 | 250,000 | 25,000 | 200,000 | 450,000[5] | [5] | 230,000 | 140,000 | 26,000 | — | 2,205,000 |
| 1780 | 40,000 | 85,000 | 56,000 | 307,000 | 52,000 | 203,000 | 200,000 | 137,000 | 335,000 | 37,000 | 250,000 | 520,000 | 45,000 | 300,000 | 160,000 | 55,000 | — | 2,781,000 |
| 1790 | 86,000 | 142,000 | 97,000 | 379,000 | 69,000 | 238,000 | 340,000 | 184,000 | 434,000 | 59,000 | 320,000 | 748,000 | 74,000 | 394,000 | 249,000 | 83,000 | 36,000 | 3,929,000 |

[1]Original colony
[2]Vermont was included with New York, 1730–1760. Vermont was admitted to statehood in 1791.
[3]Maine was included with Massachusetts, 1660–1760. Maine was admitted to statehood in 1820.
[4]Delaware was included with Pennsylvania, 1690–1760.
[5]Kentucky was included with Virginia in 1770. Kentucky became a state in 1792.

Most estimates in the table have been rounded to the nearest thousand.

The bottom line of the table shows the state totals given in the 1790 Census report. The census counts have been rounded to the nearest thousand.

three hundred twenty-nine SRB 329

✦ *Student Reference Book*, p. 329

# 1 Teaching the Lesson

## ✦ Math Message Follow-Up
(*Student Reference Book*, p. 329)

WHOLE-CLASS DISCUSSION

The largest number in the table is 3,929,000. This was the total U.S. population in 1790.

## ✦ Estimating Colonial Populations
(*Student Reference Book*, pp. 307 and 329)

WHOLE-CLASS DISCUSSION

**Social Studies Link** The table on page 329 of the *Student Reference Book* gives population estimates. It shows the total number of European settlers and African Americans living in each of the original 13 colonies and in four regions that later became separate states. Data is given at 10-year intervals following the settlement of the colonies through 1790.

The original 13 colonies are identified by a raised number 1 following their names.

Briefly show how the table works. To find the population of a colony in a specific year, find the row for that year and follow it to the column for the colony. Students will be able to read the table more easily if they lay a ruler or sheet of paper across the table, just beneath the row for the year they want to find information about.

Have students find a few populations. *For example:*

▷ The population of New York in 1710 26,000

▷ The total U.S. population in 1770 2,205,000

▷ The population of Maine in 1700 Can't tell. The footnote says that Maine's population was combined with the population of Massachusetts.

**Adjusting the Activity** If students have difficulty reading larger numbers, display the populations in a Place-Value Chart. Name the digit in each place and ask students for the value of that digit.

Ask questions like the following:

- Do the population figures tell exactly how many people lived in the colonies? No. They are estimates to the nearest hundred or nearest thousand. The population figures do include slaves, but do not include Native Americans.
- Is the first year for which a population is given the same as the year the colony was settled? No. Data is given at ten-year intervals. All we know is that the colony was settled during the given year or previously. Show students how to find the dates when a colony was first explored and first settled using the map on page 307 of the *Student Reference Book*.
- The first official census was not conducted until 1790. How were the earlier population figures obtained? They are estimates by historians who have examined records from the time, such as birth and death certificates, lists of passengers on ships, and local censuses.

## ✦ Using the Population Table to Answer Questions (*Math Journal 1,* pp. 64 and 65; *Student Reference Book,* p. 329)

PARTNER ACTIVITY 

Students work with partners or alone to answer the questions on the journal pages. Discuss as necessary.

**Adjusting the Activity** Continue to write population figures in the Place-Value Chart on the board if students have difficulty reading large numbers or need additional place-value practice.

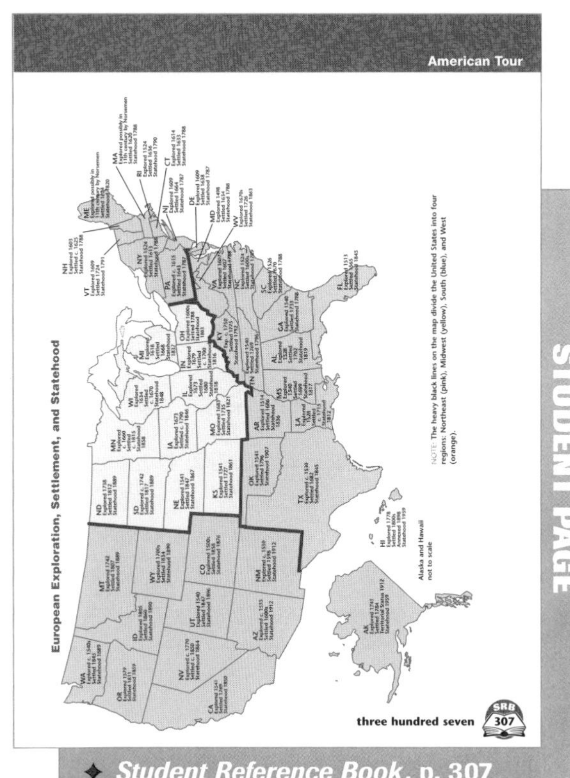


✦ *Student Reference Book,* p. 307

**State Populations, 1610–1790**

Use the population table on page 329 of the *Student Reference Book* to answer the following.

1. What was the population of Pennsylvania in 1780? 335,000
2. What was the total population of all states in 1760? 1,610,000
3. a. Which colony started with the smallest population?
   Name of colony Massachusetts
   Year 1620
   Population 100
   b. What was the population of this state in the census of 1790? 379,000
4. Which colony was the first to have a population of more than 100,000?
   Name of colony Virginia
   Year 1720
   Population 116,000
5. a. In what year was the total population of all states greater than 1 million for the first time? 1750
   b. In what year was the total population of all states greater than 2 million for the first time? 1770
6. In 1790, which state had the largest population?
   Name of state Virginia
   Population 748,000

STUDENT PAGE

✦ *Math Journal 1,* p. 64

STUDENT PAGE

**State Populations, 1610–1790** (cont.)

7. In 1790, which states had smaller populations than Rhode Island?
Delaware and Tennessee

8. Below, fill in the total U.S. populations for 1780 and 1790. Then find how much the population increased during that 10-year period.
Population in 1790 3,929,000
Population in 1780 2,781,000
Increase 1,148,000

**Challenge**

9. The table gives the population of Connecticut in 1750 as 100,000. Make a mark in front of the statement that best describes the population of Connecticut in 1750.

_____ It was exactly 100,000.
_____ It was most likely between 99,000 and 101,000.
✓ It was most likely between 95,000 and 105,000.

Explain your answer.
The population was most likely between 95,000 and 105,000 because 10 years earlier in 1740 the population was 70,000 and 10 years later in 1760 the population was 142,000. So the population was actually growing an average of 3,000 to 4,000 every year and the population grew within 1760 as well.

✦ *Math Journal 1*, p. 65

The Challenge problem concerns Connecticut's population in 1750. The table shows a population of 100,000. The first official census for the entire state was not conducted until 1790. The population estimate for 1750 is an estimate made by historians who used local census reports and other records from that time. It is very likely that the historians' estimate is off by several thousand, so the last choice is the best answer.

STUDENT PAGE

**Practicing Addition and Subtraction**

First, estimate the answer for each problem. Then use your favorite algorithms to calculate answers for problems whose estimated sums or differences are greater than 500.

| Problem | Estimate | Exact answer |
|---|---|---|
| 1. 289 + 245 | 500 | 534 |
| 2. 1,013 − 867 | 100 | |
| 3. 105 + 327 | 400 | |
| 4. 941 − 327 | 600 | 614 |
| 5. 824 − 109 | 700 | 715 |
| 6. 214 + 182 | 400 | |
| 7. 463 + 2,078 | 2,600 | 2,541 |
| 8. 1,532 − 176 | 1,300 | 1,356 |
| 9. 5,046 − 2,491 | 2,500 | 2,555 |

✦ *Math Journal 1*, p. 66

## 2 Ongoing Learning & Practice

### ✦ Estimating and Calculating Sums and Differences (*Math Journal 1*, p. 66)

INDEPENDENT ACTIVITY 

Students estimate the answers to multidigit addition and subtraction problems. Students then calculate answers for problems whose estimated sum or difference is greater than 500.

**ONGOING ASSESSMENT**
On a half-sheet of paper, have students explain in words how to solve a problem using their favorite addition or subtraction algorithm. Collect the papers to assess students' understanding of the algorithms.

### ✦ Math Boxes 3.2 (*Math Journal 1*, p. 63)

INDEPENDENT ACTIVITY 

**Mixed Review** Math Boxes in this lesson are paired with Math Boxes in Lesson 3.4. The skill in Problem 1 is a prerequisite for Unit 4.

### ✦ Study Link 3.2 (*Math Masters*, p. 242)

**Home Connection** Students use information from an "unofficial" census showing the number of people who believe that different sayings are true. Students order and calculate with large numbers.

# Options for Individualizing

## ✦ ENRICHMENT Ranking States by Their Native-American Populations
(*Student Reference Book,* p. 301)

SMALL-GROUP ACTIVITY  **15–30 min** 

Briefly discuss the color-coded map on page 301 of the *Student Reference Book.*

▷ The number printed within each state is the number (in thousands) of Native Americans in that state. For example, there were 51,000 Native Americans in Florida in 2000.

▷ The map key shows four colors. States colored tan have the largest numbers of Native Americans (100,000 or more). States colored orange have the next-largest numbers of Native Americans (50,000 to 99,000).

Ask students to list the 10 states that have the greatest numbers of Native Americans beginning with the state with the largest Native-American population. Students list the state with the second-largest Native-American population next, and so on. (See below.)

| Native-American Populations | |
|---|---|
| California | 292,000 |
| Oklahoma | 281,000 |
| Arizona | 262,000 |
| New Mexico | 169,000 |
| Washington | 107,000 |
| Texas | 95,000 |
| North Carolina | 94,000 |
| Alaska | 93,000 |
| New York | 73,000 |
| Minnesota | 64,000 |

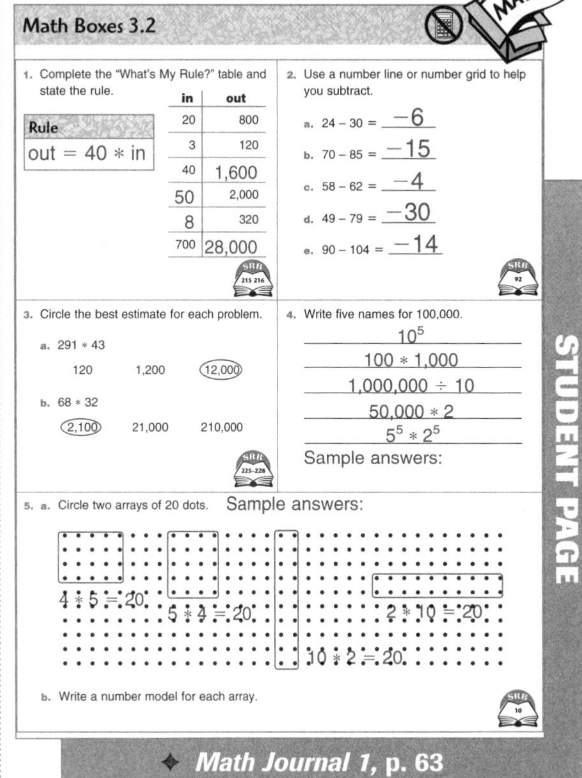

Math Boxes 3.2

1. Complete the "What's My Rule?" table and state the rule.

Rule: out = 40 * in

| in | out |
|---|---|
| 20 | 800 |
| 3 | 120 |
| 40 | 1,600 |
| 50 | 2,000 |
| 8 | 320 |
| 700 | 28,000 |

2. Use a number line or number grid to help you subtract.
a. 24 − 30 = −6
b. 70 − 85 = −15
c. 58 − 62 = −4
d. 49 − 79 = −30
e. 90 − 104 = −14

3. Circle the best estimate for each problem.
a. 291 * 43: 120 1,200 (12,000)
b. 68 * 32: (2,100) 21,000 210,000

4. Write five names for 100,000.
$10^5$
100 * 1,000
1,000,000 ÷ 10
50,000 * 2
$5^5 * 2^5$
Sample answers:

5. a. Circle two arrays of 20 dots. Sample answers:
4 * 5 = 20
5 * 4 = 20
2 * 10 = 20
10 * 2 = 20
b. Write a number model for each array.

STUDENT PAGE

✦ Math Journal 1, p. 63

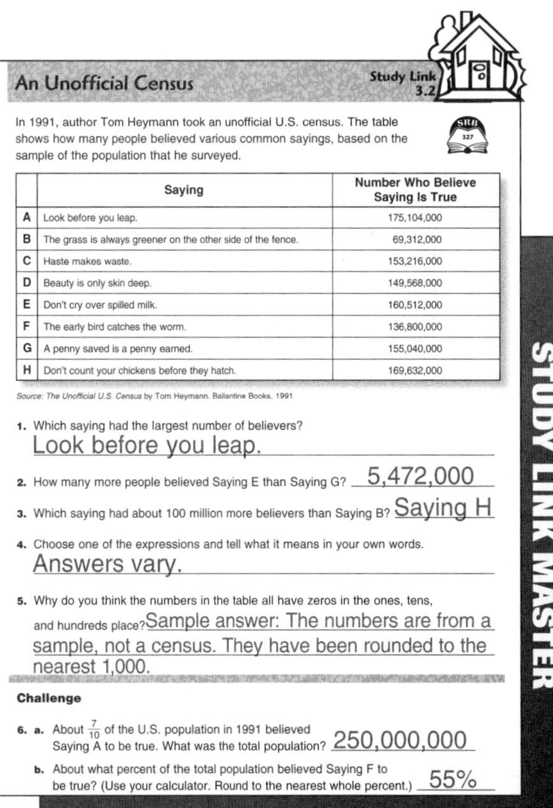

An Unofficial Census — Study Link 3.2

In 1991, author Tom Heymann took an unofficial U.S. census. The table shows how many people believed various common sayings, based on the sample of the population that he surveyed.

| | Saying | Number Who Believe Saying Is True |
|---|---|---|
| A | Look before you leap. | 175,104,000 |
| B | The grass is always greener on the other side of the fence. | 69,312,000 |
| C | Haste makes waste. | 153,216,000 |
| D | Beauty is only skin deep. | 149,568,000 |
| E | Don't cry over spilled milk. | 160,512,000 |
| F | The early bird catches the worm. | 136,800,000 |
| G | A penny saved is a penny earned. | 155,040,000 |
| H | Don't count your chickens before they hatch. | 169,632,000 |

Source: *The Unofficial U.S. Census* by Tom Heymann. Ballantine Books, 1991

1. Which saying had the largest number of believers? Look before you leap.
2. How many more people believed Saying E than Saying G? 5,472,000
3. Which saying had about 100 million more believers than Saying B? Saying H
4. Choose one of the expressions and tell what it means in your own words. Answers vary.
5. Why do you think the numbers in the table all have zeros in the ones, tens, and hundreds place? Sample answer: The numbers are from a sample, not a census. They have been rounded to the nearest 1,000.

Challenge

6. a. About $\frac{7}{10}$ of the U.S. population in 1991 believed Saying A to be true. What was the total population? 250,000,000
b. About what percent of the total population believed Saying F to be true? (Use your calculator. Round to the nearest whole percent.) 55%

STUDY LINK MASTER

✦ Math Masters, p. 242

# 3.3 Exploring Angle Measures

**OBJECTIVE** **To find the degree measures of angles using relationships between angles and circles.**

| summaries | materials |
| --- | --- |
| **1 Teaching the Lesson** | |
| Students use what they know about the total number of degrees in a circle and the relationships among angles to determine the size of various angles. [Geometry; Operations and Computation] | ☐ *Math Journal 1,* p. 67<br>☐ Study Link 3.2<br>☐ *Power Polygons*™ (optional)<br>☐ pattern blocks<br>***See* Advance Preparation** |
| **2 Ongoing Learning & Practice** | |
| Students use favorite algorithms and number models to solve number stories. [Operations and Computation]<br>Students practice and maintain skills through Math Boxes and Study Link activities. | ☐ *Math Journal 1,* pp. 68 and 69<br>☐ Study Link Master (*Math Masters,* p. 243)<br>☐ Geometry Template (optional) |
| **3 Options for Individualizing** | |
| **Reteaching** Students review different ways to name an angle. [Geometry] | |

### Additional Information

**Advance Preparation** For Part 1, students will need a supply of pattern blocks. You may want to arrange students in small groups and provide a collection of pattern blocks for each group.

**Power Polygons™** is a set of transparent, plastic polygons which includes the six pattern-block shapes plus other related shapes.

## Getting Started

### Mental Math and Reflexes

Dictate numbers for students to write and mark on their slates. *Suggestions:*

- Write 345,082. Circle the digit in the tens place. Put an X through the digit in the hundreds place. 345,0̸(8)2
- Write 7,803,596. Circle the digit in the hundred-thousands place. Underline the digit in the thousands place. 7,(8)0<u>3</u>,596
- Write 24.06. Circle the digit in the tenths place. Underline the digit in the tens place. <u>2</u>4.(0)6
- Write 140.7. Circle the digit in the hundreds place. Put an X through the digit in the tenths place. (1)40.7̸

Continue as time allows.

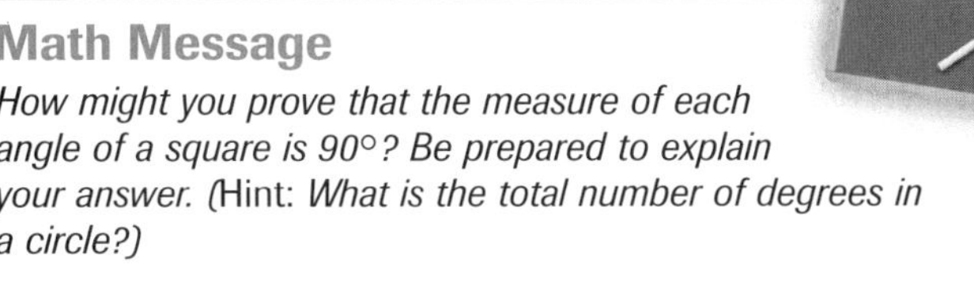

## Math Message

*How might you prove that the measure of each angle of a square is 90°? Be prepared to explain your answer.* (Hint: *What is the total number of degrees in a circle?)*

## Study Link 3.2 Follow-Up

Briefly review answers. For the Challenge problem, have students who solved the problems explain their strategies. Sample answers: Divide 175 million by 7 and multiply the result by 10, getting 250 million as the total population. Divide 136,800,000 by 250,000,000; getting about 55%.

# 1 Teaching the Lesson

## Math Message Follow-Up

WHOLE-CLASS DISCUSSION

Have volunteers share their explanations.

Have each student (or partnership, depending on your supply of pattern blocks) take four square pattern blocks and put them together to form a larger square. Ask them how many squares meet at the point in the center. 4 squares Draw a circle on the board. Ask what is the total number of degrees in the circle. 360° Divide the circle into four equal parts with perpendicular lines. Ask what the degree measure of each quarter-circle is. 90° Each quarter of the circle represents an angle from the square, so each angle of the square measures 90°. *(See the margin.)*

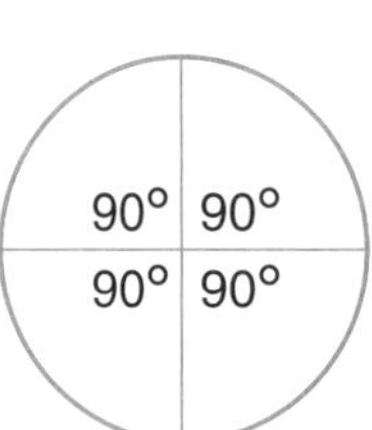

## Finding Pattern-Block Angle Measures (*Math Journal 1,* p. 67)

PARTNER ACTIVITY

Have students turn to the journal page. Remind them of the following:

▷ The symbol ∠ means "angle."

▷ Sometimes an angle is named with a single capital letter, which also names the vertex of the angle. Sometimes an angle is named with three letters: The middle letter names the vertex and the other two letters name points, one on each side of the angle.

Also point out symbols on the page such as m ∠*B*, which is an abbreviation for the "measure of angle *B*."

**Pattern-Block Angles**

For each pattern block below, tell the degree measure of the angle and explain how you found the measure. Do not use a protractor.

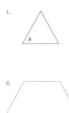

1. measure of ∠*A* = 60 °
Explain. Sample answer: Fit 6 triangles together at a point. The circle around that point has 360°. So each angle measures 360° / 6, or 60°.

2. 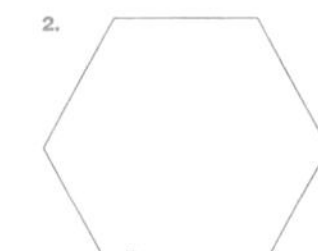
m ∠*B* = 120 ° ("m ∠*B*" means "measure of angle *B*.")
Explain. Sample answer: Two triangles fit together and exactly cover angle *B*. Each angle of the triangle measures 60°. So angle *B* measures 2 ∗ 60°, or 120°.

3. 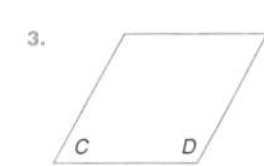
m ∠*C* = 60 ° m ∠*D* = 120 °
Explain. Sample answer: Angle *C* has the same measure as angle *A* of the triangle in Problem 1, or 60°. Angle *D* has the same measure as angle *B* of the hexagon in Problem 2, or 120°.

4. 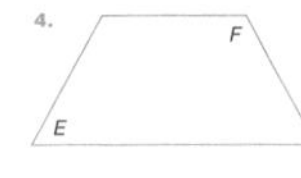
m ∠*E* = 60 ° m ∠*F* = 120 °
Explain. Sample answer: Angle *E* has the same measure as angle *A* of the triangle in Problem 1, or 60°. Angle *F* has the same measure as angle *B* of the hexagon in Problem 2, or 120°.

STUDENT PAGE

◆ *Math Journal 1,* p. 67

STUDENT PAGE

**Addition and Subtraction Number Stories**

For each problem, fill in the blanks and solve the problem.

1. Jeanne practiced her multiplication facts for 3 weeks. The first week she practiced for 45 minutes, the second week for 37 minutes, and the third week for 32 minutes. How many minutes did she practice in all?
   a. List the numbers needed to solve the problem. 45, 37, and 32
   b. Describe what you want to find. How many minutes Jeanne practiced in 3 weeks
   c. Open sentence: $45 + 37 + 32 = m$
   d. Solution: 114 e. Answer: 114 minutes (unit)
2. The shortest book Martha read one summer was 57 pages. The longest book was 243 pages. She read a total of 36 books. How many pages longer was the longest book than the shortest book?
   a. List the numbers needed to solve the problem. 57 and 243
   b. Describe what you want to find. How many more pages in the longer book than the shorter book
   c. Open sentence: $243 - 57 = p$
   d. Solution: 186 e. Answer: 186 pages (unit)
3. Chesa collects marbles. He had 347 marbles. Then he played in two tournaments. He lost 34 marbles in the first tournament. He won 23 marbles in the second tournament. How many marbles did he have after playing in both tournaments?
   a. List the numbers needed to solve the problem. 347, 34, and 23
   b. Describe what you want to find out. How many marbles Chesa had left after the two tournaments
   c. Open sentence: $347 - 34 + 23 = m$
   d. Solution: 336 e. Answer: 336 marbles (unit)

◆ *Math Journal 1*, p. 68

STUDENT PAGE

**Math Boxes 3.3**

1. Round 30.089 to the nearest ...
   a. tenth. 30.1
   b. whole number. 30
   c. hundredth. 30.09
2. Find an object in the room that has a length of about 18 inches. Answers vary.
3. Add or subtract. Show your work.
   a. $572 + 943 =$ 1,515
   b. $\$15.04 + \$23.97 =$ $39.01
   c. $2,094 - 878 =$ 1,216
   d. $421.6 - 5.97 =$ 415.63
4. a. Make up a set of at least twelve numbers that have the following landmarks.
   Maximum: 8 Range: 6 Mode: 6 Median: 5
   Sample answer: 2, 2, 2, 3, 4, 5, 5, 6, 6, 6, 6, 8, 8
   b. Make a bar graph of the data.
   Sample answer:

◆ *Math Journal 1*, p. 69

Students complete the page alone or with a partner. In addition to using the fact that the total number of degrees in a circle is 360°, they may also use relationships between pattern-block angles. For example, two trapezoids fit into a hexagon. Since each hexagon angle is 120°, the larger angle of the trapezoid is also 120°. Since two of the smaller trapezoid angles fit into one hexagon angle, the smaller angle of the trapezoid is half the size of the hexagon angle or 60°.

**Adjusting the Activity** Challenge students to find the angle measurements for the small pattern-block rhombus. Use Power Polygons™, if you have them, to determine angle measures based on known relationships.

**ONGOING ASSESSMENT**

**This is an exploration of angle relationships between circles and polygons. Do not expect all students to completely understand the process. These relationships will be further explored in future lessons. Have volunteers share their strategies for finding the angle measurements.**

## 2 Ongoing Learning & Practice

### ◆ Solving Number Stories (*Math Journal 1*, p. 68)

INDEPENDENT ACTIVITY 

Students use favorite algorithms to solve addition and subtraction number stories. This format for solving number stories was first used in Lesson 2.4. Refer students back to journal page 36 if they need a reminder about how to fill in the blanks on the page.

### ◆ Math Boxes 3.3 (*Math Journal 1*, p. 69)

INDEPENDENT ACTIVITY 

**Mixed Review** Math Boxes in this lesson are paired with Math Boxes in Lesson 3.1. The skill in Problem 1 is a prerequisite for Unit 4.

## ✦ Study Link 3.3 (*Math Masters,* p. 243)

**Home Connection** Students figure out the angle measures of tessellated polygons using the relationship between the angles and a circle.

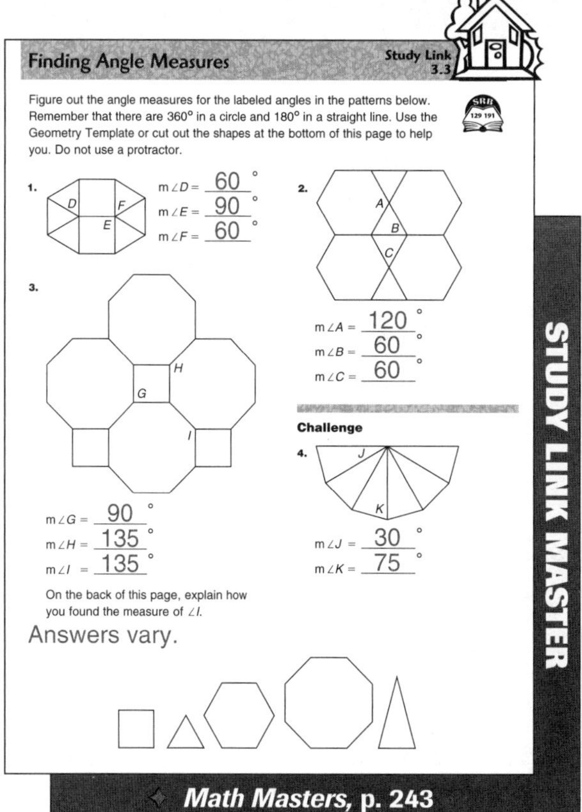

**Finding Angle Measures** — Study Link 3.3

Figure out the angle measures for the labeled angles in the patterns below. Remember that there are 360° in a circle and 180° in a straight line. Use the Geometry Template or cut out the shapes at the bottom of this page to help you. Do not use a protractor.

1. m∠D = 60°; m∠E = 90°; m∠F = 60°
2. m∠A = 120°; m∠B = 60°; m∠C = 60°
3. m∠G = 90°; m∠H = 135°; m∠I = 135°

On the back of this page, explain how you found the measure of ∠I.
Answers vary.

**Challenge**

4. m∠J = 30°; m∠K = 75°

Math Masters, p. 243

STUDY LINK MASTER

# 3 Options for Individualizing

## ✦ RETEACHING Reviewing Ways to Name Angles

INDEPENDENT ACTIVITY **5–15 min**

Some students may benefit from a brief review of the ways in which an angle can be named. *Suggestions:*

▷ Ask students to draw ∠*BAC*. Sample answer:

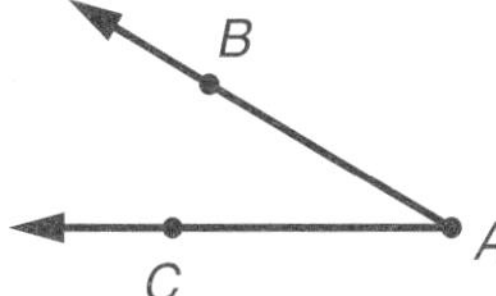


Pose the following questions:

- What are two other ways to name this angle? ∠*CAB* and ∠*A*
- What is the vertex of the angle? Point *A*

▷ Draw the following angle on the board:

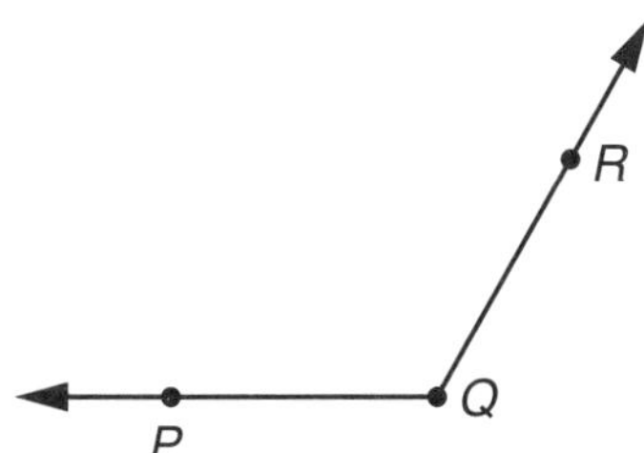


Ask students whether or not they agree with the following statement: *The name of this angle is* ∠*QRP.* Have them explain their reasoning. When using three points to name an angle, the vertex is named between the points on the sides of the angle.

# 3.4 Using a Protractor

**OBJECTIVES** **To review types of angles; to introduce the Geometry Template; and to measure and draw angles.**

| summaries | materials |
| --- | --- |
| **1 Teaching the Lesson** | |
| Students write definitions for acute and obtuse angles, and review other types of angles. They are introduced to the Geometry Template, measure angles using the half-circle and full-circle protractors, and draw angles with the half-circle protractor. [Geometry; Measurement and Reference Frames] | ☐ *Math Journal 1,* pp. 70 and 71<br>☐ *Student Reference Book,* pp. 152 and 153<br>☐ Study Link 3.3 ☐ Geometry Template<br>☐ Transparencies (*Math Masters,* pp. 25–27; optional)<br>☐ Assessment Master (*Math Masters,* p. 479; optional)<br>***See* Advance Preparation** |
| **2 Ongoing Learning & Practice** | |
| Students find the landmarks of data represented by a bar graph. [Data and Chance; Operations and Computation]<br>Students practice and maintain skills through Math Boxes and Study Link activities. | ☐ *Math Journal 1,* pp. 72 and 73<br>☐ Study Link Master (*Math Masters,* p. 244) |
| **3 Options for Individualizing** | |
| **Reteaching** Students play *Robot* to review and practice making rotations of a given size. [Geometry]<br>**Enrichment** Students explore the Geometry Template by making repeating designs. [Geometry]<br>**Language Diversity** Students write and illustrate a geometry dictionary. [Geometry] | ☐ *Student Reference Book,* pp. 152 and 153<br>☐ Geometry Template |

### Additional Information

**Advance Preparation** If the Geometry Templates were not distributed earlier, decide how you will manage them in your classroom before beginning the lesson. Experienced *Everyday Mathematics* teachers suggest writing student ID numbers on the templates with a permanent marker before distributing them to students.

**Vocabulary • acute angle • obtuse angle • right angle • straight angle • reflex angle • Geometry Template**

## Getting Started

### Mental Math and Reflexes

Students stand and follow directions related to angle measures or fractions of a turn. *Suggestions:*

- Rotate 180° to the right.
- Make a quarter-turn to the right.
- Turn 360° to the left.
- Make a half-turn to the left.

### Math Message

*Complete Problems 1 and 2 at the top of journal page 70 without using your* Student Reference Book.

## Study Link 3.3 Follow-Up

Briefly review angle measures. For each angle, have a volunteer describe a strategy for finding the measure. Expect a variety of responses, such as the following:

- Problem 1: The angles in the triangles are all the same. Six triangles fit together around a point, so each angle of the triangle must be 360° / 6, or 60°. In the pattern, the sides of two squares form a straight line. So each square angle must be 180° / 2, or 90°.
- Problem 2: Three hexagons fit together around a point, so each hexagon angle is $\frac{1}{3}$ of 360°, or 120°. In the pattern, a side of a hexagon and a side of a triangle form a straight line. So the triangle angle must be 180° − 120°, or 60°.
- Problem 3: One square and two octagons fit together around a point. A square angle is 90° (because two square sides make a straight line). The two angles of the octagons must total 360° − 90°, or 270°. So each octagon angle must be 270° / 2, or 135°.
- Problem 4: Three of the smaller angles of the triangle fit together to form a square angle. Each of the smaller angles must be 90° / 3, or 30°. Two of the larger angles fit together with a smaller one between them to form a straight line. Two of the larger angles must total 180° − 30°, or 150°. So each of the larger angles must be 150° / 2, or 75°.

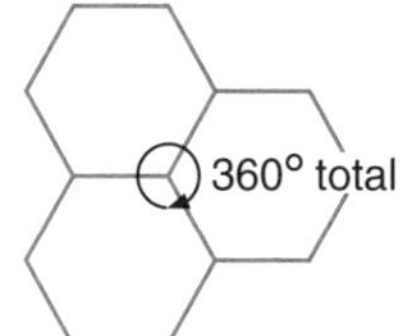


Problem 2

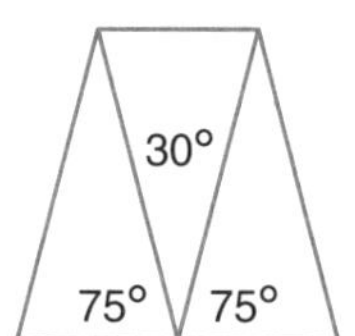


Problem 4

# 1 Teaching the Lesson

## Math Message Follow-Up
(*Math Journal 1,* p. 70)

WHOLE-CLASS DISCUSSION 

An **acute angle** is an angle whose measure is greater than 0° and less than 90°. An **obtuse angle** is an angle whose measure is greater than 90° and less than 180°. For each type of angle, compare the students' definitions, and if there are differences, try to arrive at one common definition that the class can agree on.

NOTE: Working with mathematical definitions helps students build logical thinking skills that are critical to success in higher mathematics. Definitions are closely related to classification schemes. The types of angles defined in this lesson, for example, make up a classification scheme for all angles: Every angle with a measure greater than 0° is either acute, right, obtuse, straight, or reflex.

Use incomplete or incorrect definitions to highlight the importance of definitions in mathematics. For example, discuss why "narrow" and "wide" are not acceptable definitions for acute and obtuse. Ask if an angle can be both acute and obtuse, and why or why not.

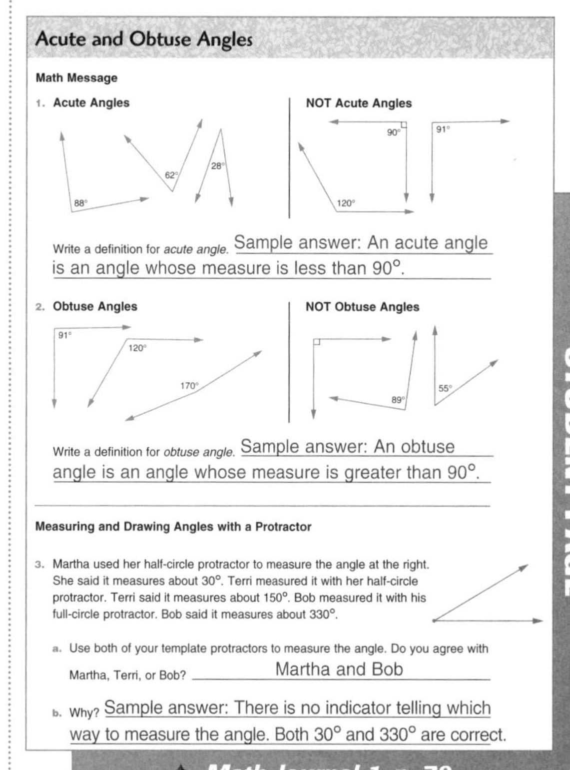

**Acute and Obtuse Angles**

**Math Message**

1. **Acute Angles** | **NOT Acute Angles**



Write a definition for *acute angle.* Sample answer: An acute angle is an angle whose measure is less than 90°.

2. **Obtuse Angles** | **NOT Obtuse Angles**



Write a definition for *obtuse angle.* Sample answer: An obtuse angle is an angle whose measure is greater than 90°.

**Measuring and Drawing Angles with a Protractor**

3. Martha used her half-circle protractor to measure the angle at the right. She said it measures about 30°. Terri measured it with her half-circle protractor. Terri said it measures about 150°. Bob measured it with his full-circle protractor. Bob said it measures about 330°.

   a. Use both of your template protractors to measure the angle. Do you agree with Martha, Terri, or Bob? Martha and Bob

   b. Why? Sample answer: There is no indicator telling which way to measure the angle. Both 30° and 330° are correct.

STUDENT PAGE

*Math Journal 1,* p. 70

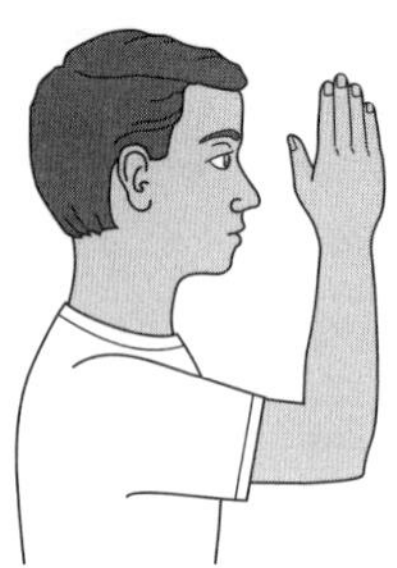

**Adjusting the Activity** *Skew lines* are lines that do not intersect and are not parallel. They lie in different planes. For example, a north-south line on the floor and an east-west line on the ceiling would be skew lines. Explain skew lines and challenge students to illustrate them with two pencils.

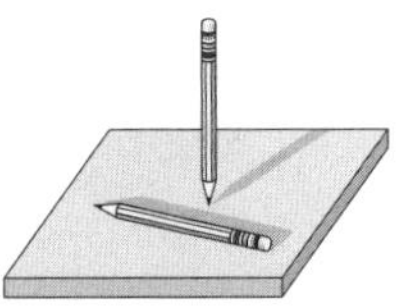

STUDENT PAGE

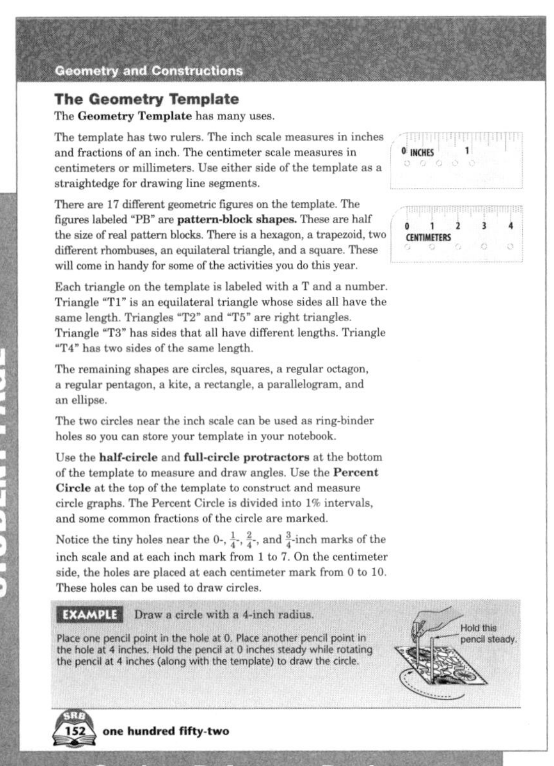

Geometry and Constructions

**The Geometry Template**

The **Geometry Template** has many uses.

The template has two rulers. The inch scale measures in inches and fractions of an inch. The centimeter scale measures in centimeters or millimeters. Use either side of the template as a straightedge for drawing line segments.

There are 17 different geometric figures on the template. The figures labeled "PB" are **pattern-block shapes.** These are half the size of real pattern blocks. There is a hexagon, a trapezoid, two different rhombuses, an equilateral triangle, and a square. These will come in handy for some of the activities you do this year.

Each triangle on the template is labeled with a T and a number. Triangle "T1" is an equilateral triangle whose sides all have the same length. Triangles "T2" and "T5" are right triangles. Triangle "T3" has sides that all have different lengths. Triangle "T4" has two sides of the same length.

The remaining shapes are circles, squares, a regular octagon, a regular pentagon, a kite, a rectangle, a parallelogram, and an ellipse.

The two circles near the inch scale can be used as ring-binder holes so you can store your template in your notebook.

Use the **half-circle** and **full-circle protractors** at the bottom of the template to measure and draw angles. Use the **Percent Circle** at the top of the template to construct and measure circle graphs. The Percent Circle is divided into 1% intervals, and some common fractions of the circle are marked.

Notice the tiny holes near the 0-, $\frac{1}{4}$-, $\frac{2}{4}$-, and $\frac{3}{4}$-inch marks of the inch scale and at each inch mark from 1 to 7. On the centimeter side, the holes are placed at each centimeter mark from 0 to 10. These holes can be used to draw circles.



**EXAMPLE** Draw a circle with a 4-inch radius.

Place one pencil point in the hole at 0. Place another pencil point in the hole at 4 inches. Hold the pencil at 0 inches steady while rotating the pencil at 4 inches (along with the template) to draw the circle.



SRB 152 one hundred fifty-two

✦ *Student Reference Book,* p. 152

Remind students that a 90° angle is called a **right angle.** Point out that a small square is often marked in the corner of a right angle to indicate that it is a "square corner."

Mention that a 180° angle is called a **straight angle** because the two sides of the angle form a straight line. A **reflex angle** is an angle whose measure is greater than 180° and less than 360°.

Ask students to stand by their desks and show various angles. They can bend one arm to form a 90° angle, an angle smaller than 90°, an angle between 90° and 180°, and a 180° angle—naming these as *right, acute, obtuse,* and *straight,* respectively. *(See the margin.)*

Then ask students to use their arms to illustrate the following terms: *parallel, perpendicular,* and *intersecting*.

## ✦ Introducing the Geometry Template (*Student Reference Book,* pp. 152 and 153; *Math Masters,* p. 25)

WHOLE-CLASS ACTIVITY

If possible, display the **Geometry Template,** either by putting the template on the overhead or by using an overhead transparency of *Math Masters,* page 25.

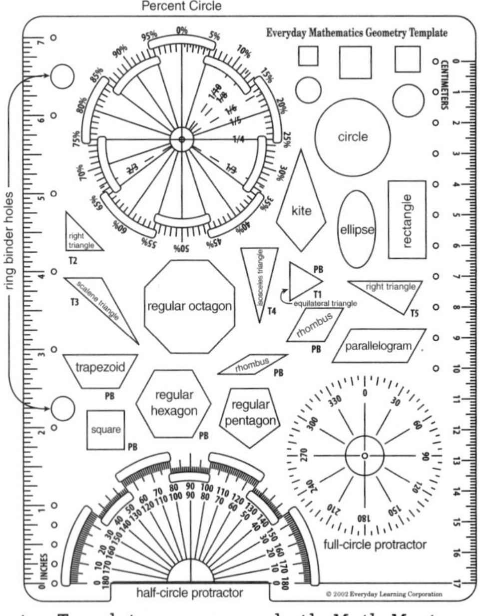



The Geometry Template appears on both *Math Masters,* page 25 and *Student Reference Book,* page 153.

Ask students to turn to pages 152 and 153 of the *Student Reference Book*. Refer to these pages as you discuss these features of the Geometry Template:

▷ There is an inch ruler along the left edge and a centimeter ruler along the right edge.

- ▷ There are six pattern-block shapes on the template—equilateral triangle, square, trapezoid, two rhombuses, and regular hexagon—labeled PB. You might ask students to compare the template shapes with actual pattern blocks. They will discover that the edges of the template shapes are half as long as the edges of the pattern blocks. The regular pentagon and octagon on the template are not pattern-block shapes.
- ▷ Have students use their templates to verify that the sides of the pentagon, octagon, and five pattern-block shapes are all the same length. Three sides of the pattern-block trapezoid are this length as well, and the fourth side of the trapezoid is twice as long. Any two figures can be compared by tracing them so that they are adjacent and share a common side, *as shown in the margin.*
- ▷ Some of the other shapes have some sides the same length as the pattern-block shapes.
- ▷ The squares and circles of various sizes can be used to draw figures quickly.
- ▷ The half-circle protractor can be used to measure and draw angles. The full-circle protractor can be used to measure angles, but it is difficult to draw angles with this protractor because there are no slots for placing points around the protractor.

The triangles on the Geometry Template will be discussed in Lesson 3.6. The Percent Circle is used to read and make circle (pie) graphs and will be discussed in Lessons 5.10 and 5.11 of Unit 5.

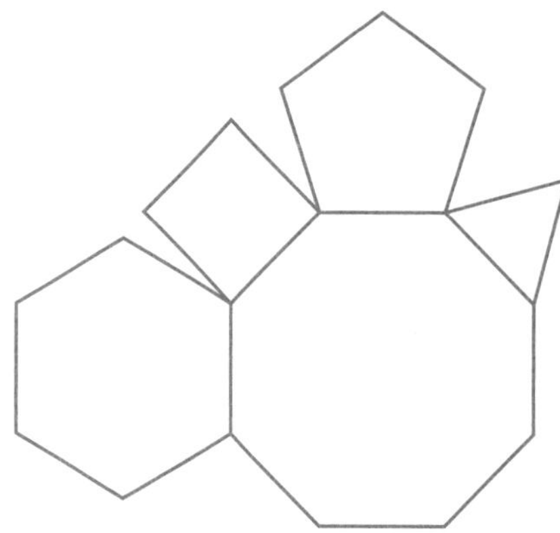

By comparing them with the octagon, the tracing shows that all regular polygons on the Geometry Template have sides of the same length. Other shapes can be compared in the same way.

## ✦ Assessing Students' Understanding of Angle Measurement (*Math Journal 1*, p. 70)

PARTNER ACTIVITY

Partners work on Problem 3 at the bottom of the journal page. Allow 5 to 10 minutes, and then discuss students' answers. Stop sooner if many students are having trouble.

Martha's and Bob's answers are both correct, because no angle is indicated on the drawing, and they measured different angles. Bob interpreted the angle to be a reflex angle (the angle larger than 180°). Terri used the wrong scale on her half-circle protractor.

Tell students that when they measure an angle in *Everyday Mathematics*, they will normally measure the smaller angle, not the reflex angle. When they are supposed to measure the reflex angle, it is indicated with an arc.

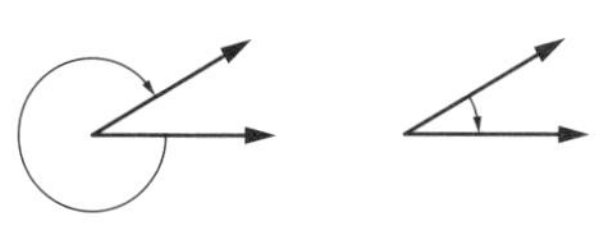

330° angle 30° angle

## ONGOING ASSESSMENT

In *Fourth Grade Everyday Mathematics,* students used both the full-circle and half-circle protractors.

With half-circle protractors, expect students to be able to measure to within about 2° more or less than the exact answer. With the full-circle protractor, expect that students might be less precise—perhaps within 3° or even to the nearest 5°.

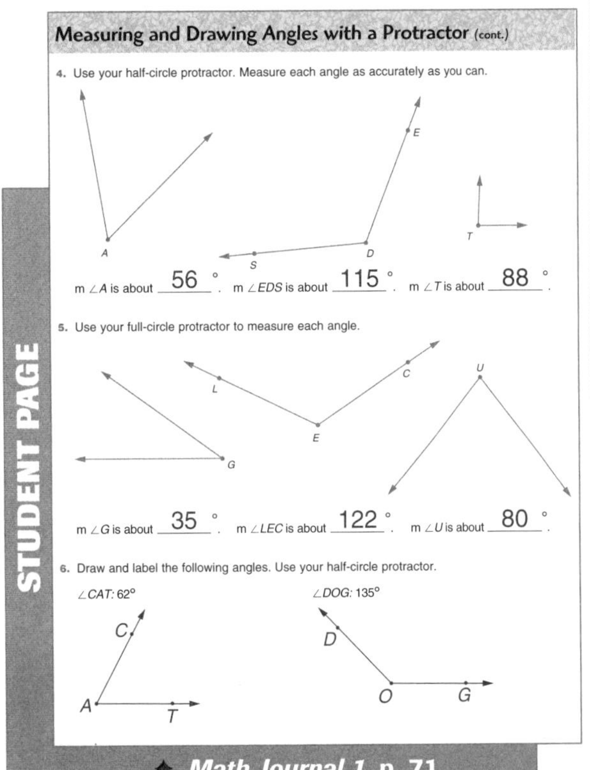

STUDENT PAGE

**Measuring and Drawing Angles with a Protractor** (cont.)

4. Use your half-circle protractor. Measure each angle as accurately as you can.

m ∠A is about 56°. m ∠EDS is about 115°. m ∠T is about 88°.

5. Use your full-circle protractor to measure each angle.

m ∠G is about 35°. m ∠LEC is about 122°. m ∠U is about 80°.

6. Draw and label the following angles. Use your half-circle protractor.

∠CAT: 62° ∠DOG: 135°



✦ *Math Journal 1,* p. 71

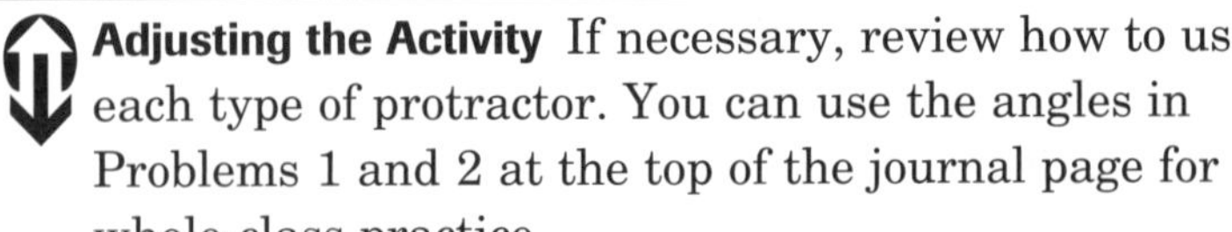

**Adjusting the Activity** If necessary, review how to use each type of protractor. You can use the angles in Problems 1 and 2 at the top of the journal page for whole-class practice.

- ▷ The key to using the half-circle protractor is to know which scale to read.
- ▷ The key to using the full-circle protractor is to note that the scale runs clockwise. The 0° mark must be lined up with one side of the angle so that to find the measure, you move from 0° in the clockwise direction.

Before measuring, students should always estimate whether the angle is more or less than 90°. If they develop this good habit, they will seldom read the wrong scale or move in the wrong direction.

Students will practice measuring angles throughout the year in Math Boxes problems and in Ongoing Learning & Practice activities.

## ✦ Practicing Measuring and Drawing Angles (*Math Journal 1,* p. 71; *Math Masters,* pp. 25–27, and 479)

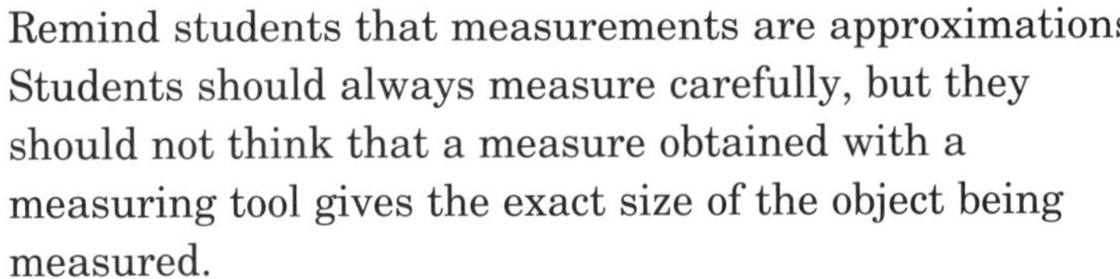

PARTNER ACTIVITY

Remind students that measurements are approximations. Students should always measure carefully, but they should not think that a measure obtained with a measuring tool gives the exact size of the object being measured.

Assign the journal page. Remind students to use the half-circle protractor to complete Problems 4 and 6, and the full-circle protractor to complete Problem 5. It is important that students practice with both types of protractors. Circulate and assist as necessary.

When most students have finished, go over the answers. Select at least one measuring problem and the drawing problem (Problem 6), and ask students to describe their methods. You might want to display an overhead transparency of the journal pages (*Math Masters,* pages 26 and 27) and have students demonstrate with an overhead transparency of the Geometry Template (*Math Masters,* page 25).

## ONGOING ASSESSMENT

**Ask students to write answers to one of the following questions on an Exit Slip or half-sheet of paper:**

- ▷ **How did you measure $\angle T$ in Problem 4?**
- ▷ **Which is easier to use—the full-circle protractor or the half-circle protractor? Why?**

**Angle *T* is difficult to measure because the figure is so small. Suggest that students extend the angle's sides with a straightedge before they measure the angle with a protractor. You might illustrate the pitfalls of extending the sides without using a straightedge.**

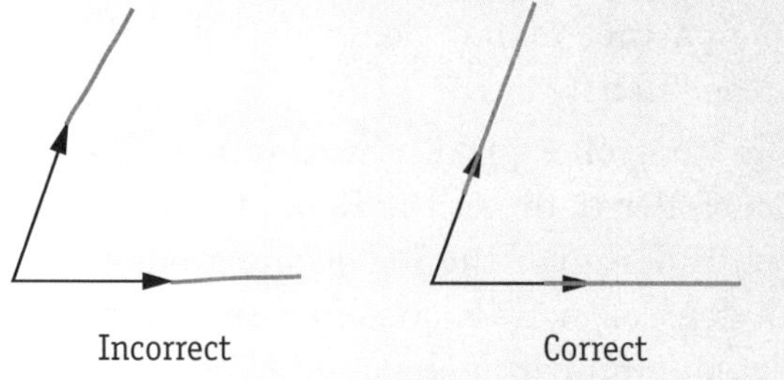


Extending the sides of an angle

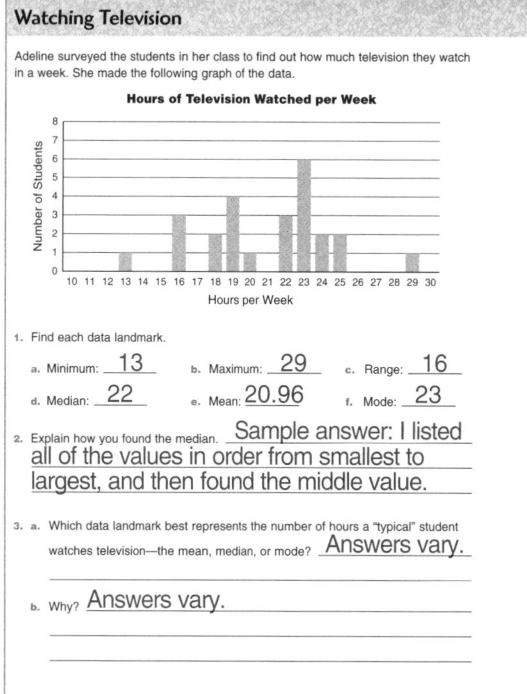

**Watching Television**

Adeline surveyed the students in her class to find out how much television they watch in a week. She made the following graph of the data.



1. Find each data landmark.
   - a. Minimum: 13
   - b. Maximum: 29
   - c. Range: 16
   - d. Median: 22
   - e. Mean: 20.96
   - f. Mode: 23
2. Explain how you found the median. Sample answer: I listed all of the values in order from smallest to largest, and then found the middle value.
3. a. Which data landmark best represents the number of hours a "typical" student watches television—the mean, median, or mode? Answers vary.

   b. Why? Answers vary.

STUDENT PAGE

✦ *Math Journal 1*, p. 72

# 2 Ongoing Learning & Practice

## ✦ Interpreting a Bar Graph (*Math Journal 1,* p. 72)

INDEPENDENT ACTIVITY 

Students find the landmarks of the data represented by the bar graph on the journal page. Refer them to the *Student Reference Book* if they need to review data landmarks.

## ONGOING ASSESSMENT

**Use journal page 72 to determine students' understanding of landmarks. Expect that some students will still struggle with finding the mean.**

## ✦ Math Boxes 3.4 (*Math Journal 1,* p. 73)

INDEPENDENT ACTIVITY 

**Mixed Review** Math Boxes in this lesson are paired with Math Boxes in Lesson 3.2. The skill in Problem 1 is a prerequisite for Unit 4.

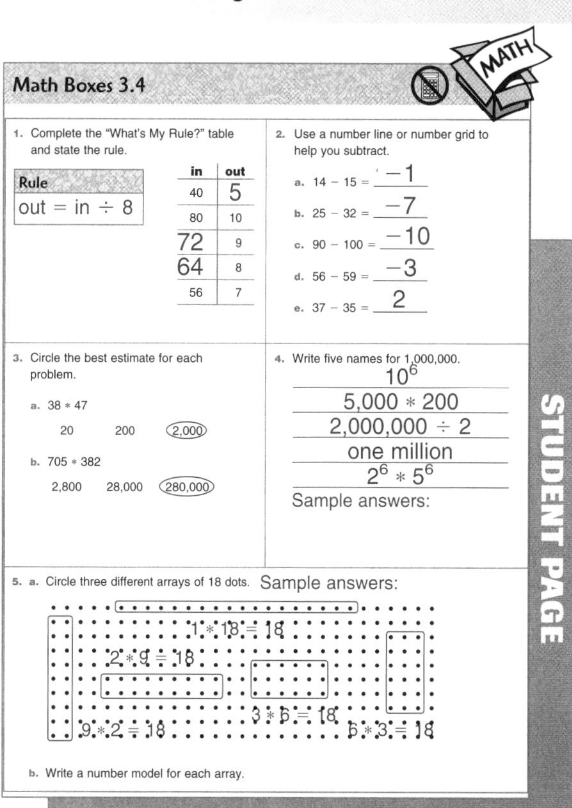

**Math Boxes 3.4**



1. Complete the "What's My Rule?" table and state the rule.

   Rule: out = in ÷ 8

| in | out |
|---|---|
| 40 | 5 |
| 80 | 10 |
| 72 | 9 |
| 64 | 8 |
| 56 | 7 |

2. Use a number line or number grid to help you subtract.
   - a. 14 − 15 = −1
   - b. 25 − 32 = −7
   - c. 90 − 100 = −10
   - d. 56 − 59 = −3
   - e. 37 − 35 = 2
3. Circle the best estimate for each problem.
   - a. 38 ∗ 47: 20, 200, (2,000)
   - b. 705 ∗ 382: 2,800, 28,000, (280,000)
4. Write five names for 1,000,000.
   - $10^6$
   - 5,000 ∗ 200
   - 2,000,000 ÷ 2
   - one million
   - $2^6 * 5^6$

   Sample answers:
5. a. Circle three different arrays of 18 dots. Sample answers:

   1 ∗ 18 = 18; 2 ∗ 9 = 18; 9 ∗ 2 = 18; 3 ∗ 6 = 18; 6 ∗ 3 = 18

   b. Write a number model for each array.

STUDENT PAGE

✦ *Math Journal 1*, p. 73

## ✦ Study Link 3.4 (*Math Masters,* p. 244)

**Home Connection** Students practice measuring angles with half-circle and full-circle protractors. Remind students to read the problems carefully.

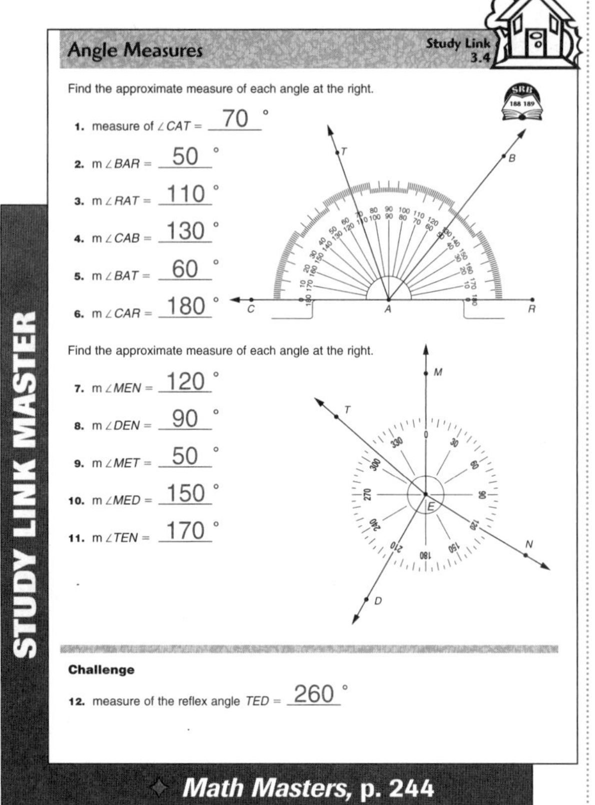
**STUDY LINK MASTER**

**Angle Measures** — Study Link 3.4

SRB 188 189

Find the approximate measure of each angle at the right.

1. measure of ∠CAT = 70 °
2. m∠BAR = 50 °
3. m∠RAT = 110 °
4. m∠CAB = 130 °
5. m∠BAT = 60 °
6. m∠CAR = 180 °

Find the approximate measure of each angle at the right.

7. m∠MEN = 120 °
8. m∠DEN = 90 °
9. m∠MET = 50 °
10. m∠MED = 150 °
11. m∠TEN = 170 °

**Challenge**

12. measure of the reflex angle TED = 260 °

*Math Masters,* p. 244

# 3 Options for Individualizing

## ✦ RETEACHING Playing *Robot*

PARTNER ACTIVITY 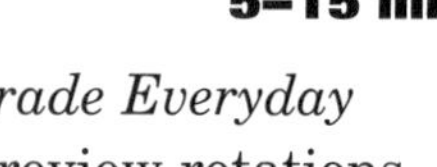 **5–15 min**

*Robot* was introduced in *Third Grade Everyday Mathematics.* It is a good way to review rotations of a given size.

One partner is the "Controller" and the other is the "Robot."

The Controller picks a destination. The goal is for the Controller to direct the Robot to the destination. The Controller gives the Robot directions to make turns (in degrees or fractions of a turn), and then to take a given number of steps.

Example: *Make a half-turn. Go forward 5 steps. Now turn 90° to the left. Go forward 3 steps.*

If the Robot is unclear about the instructions, he or she should ask for new directions.

## ✦ ENRICHMENT Exploring the Geometry Template

(*Student Reference Book,* pp. 152 and 153)

INDEPENDENT ACTIVITY  **5–15 min** 

Students do free drawings with the Geometry Template. Encourage them to make repeating designs or tessellations. See if they can figure out how to use the various features of the template. The Geometry Template is discussed in the *Student Reference Book* on pages 152 and 153.

## ✦ LANGUAGE DIVERSITY Creating a Geometry Dictionary

SMALL-GROUP ACTIVITY  **30+ min** 

Unit 3 is particularly rich in vocabulary. Consider pairing a student who is learning English with a proficient English speaker to create a Geometry Words Dictionary. For each word, students include a definition and an illustration. If students are familiar with the concept and know the equivalent word in another language, they should add it to the dictionary entry.

# 3.5 Using a Compass

**OBJECTIVES** **To use a compass to draw a circle and copy a line segment; and to measure and investigate angles formed by intersecting lines.**

| summaries | materials |
|---|---|
| **1 Teaching the Lesson** | |
| Students practice compass skills, including drawing a circle, copying line segments, and using a compass to estimate lengths. Students measure angles formed by intersecting lines and identify relationships between pairs of vertical angles and between pairs of adjacent angles. [Geometry; Measurement and Reference Frames] | □ *Math Journal 1,* pp. 74 and 75<br>□ *Student Reference Book,* p. 155 (optional)<br>□ Study Link 3.4 □ compass<br>□ 1 sheet of paper about 2 feet by 2 feet (for demonstration purposes)<br>□ Geometry Template<br>***See* Advance Preparation** |
| **2 Ongoing Learning & Practice** | |
| Students practice and maintain skills through Math Boxes and Study Link activities. | □ *Math Journal 1,* p. 76<br>□ Study Link Master (*Math Masters,* p. 245) |
| **3 Options for Individualizing** | |
| **Enrichment** Students solve a baseball challenge problem dealing with angle measures. [Geometry; Operations and Computation]<br>**Language Diversity** Students look up alternate meanings of *acute, obtuse, adjacent,* and *vertical* in a dictionary and write sentences using the alternate meanings. [Geometry]<br>**Enrichment** Students inscribe a hexagon in a circle, reproduce a design based on this construction, and make their own designs. [Geometry] | □ Teaching Masters (*Math Masters,* pp. 28 and 29)<br>□ *Student Reference Book,* p. 158<br>□ compass<br>□ straightedge<br>□ dictionary |

## Additional Information

**Background Information** Before beginning the lesson, read the information about the merits of various types of compasses in the *Teacher's Reference Manual.*

**Advance Preparation** For the Math Message Follow-Up, prepare a sheet of paper about 2 feet by 2 feet.

**Vocabulary** • **radius** • **center** • **diameter** • **vertical (*or* opposite) angles** • **adjacent angles**

# Getting Started

## Mental Math and Reflexes

Pose problems such as the following:

- 7 * 8 56
  70 * 8 560
  70 * 80 5,600
  700 * 80 56,000
- 6 * 7 42
  60 * 7 420
  60 * 70 4,200
  600 * 70 42,000
- 8 * 9 72
  80 * 9 720
  80 * 90 7,200
  800 * 90 72,000

## Math Message

*Draw the largest and the smallest circle you can draw with your compass. What is the radius of the largest circle?*

## Study Link 3.4 Follow-Up

Briefly review the answers. Have volunteers explain how to measure with the half-circle protractor and the full-circle protractor. Ask someone to explain what a reflex angle is.

# 1 Teaching the Lesson

## ✦ Math Message Follow-Up

WHOLE-CLASS DISCUSSION

Most students probably opened their compasses as far as possible. Remind students that a **radius** of a circle is any line segment from the **center** of the circle to any point on the circle. Thus the length of a radius is the distance between the anchor and pencil point of a compass.

The **diameter** of a circle is any line segment that passes through the center of the circle and has its endpoints on the circle. Thus the length of a diameter is twice the length of a radius.

NOTE: The terms *radius* and *diameter* are also used to name the lengths of these line segments; for example, *The radius of the circle is 2 inches. The diameter is 4 inches.*

STUDENT PAGE

### Copying Line Segments and Finding Lengths

1. Use your compass and straightedge to copy line segment *AB.* Do not measure the line segment with a ruler. Label the endpoints of the new line segment as points *M* and *N.* Line segment *MN* should be the same length as line segment *AB.*

   A ———— B

   M ———— N

2. Three line segments are shown below:

   A ——— B C ——— D E ——— F

   Use your compass and straightedge. Construct one line segment that is as long as the three segments joined together end to end. Label the two endpoints of the long line segment *X* and *Y.*

   X ———————— Y

Use your compass to find the lengths of different parts of the Geometry Template.

*Example* Find the length of the longer side of the rectangle on the Geometry Template.

**Step 1** Open the compass to the length of the longer side.

**Step 2** Don't change the opening on your compass. Hold the compass against the inch ruler with the anchor at 0. Read the length. The length is about 1 inch.

3. The length of the longer side of the trapezoid is about 1 inch(es).
4. The diameter of the full-circle protractor is about 2 inch(es).
5. The distance between the center of the full-circle protractor and the center of the Percent Circle is about $4\frac{3}{4}$ inch(es).
6. Use your compass and a ruler to find two other lengths. Be sure to include units.

| Part Measured | Length |
|---|---|
| | |
| | |

✦ *Math Journal 1, p. 74*

Demonstrate how to obtain an even larger separation by adjusting the pencil. Clamp a full-length pencil in the compass with the eraser as close to the clamp as possible (see below). Now open the compass to its largest separation, and draw a very large circle on your 2-foot by 2-foot sheet of paper. You can draw a circle with an 8-inch radius (16-inch diameter) this way, even with a small compass.

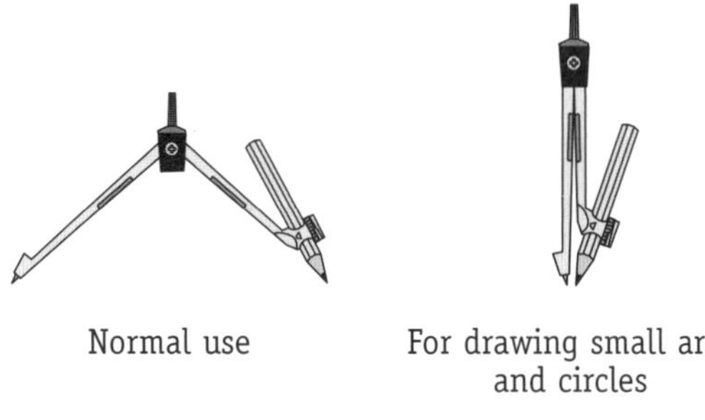

Normal use

For drawing small arcs and circles

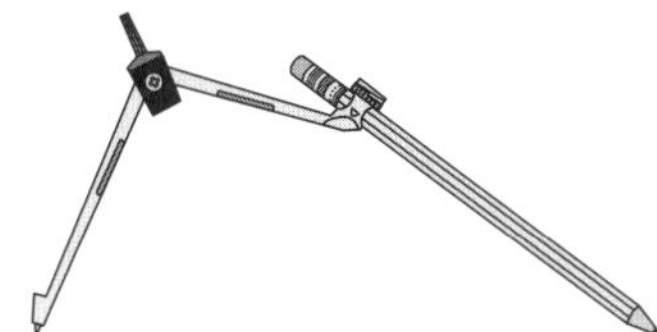

For drawing large arcs and circles

**Adjusting the Activity** In *Fourth Grade Everyday Mathematics,* students used a compass to draw circles and copy line segments. However, drawing circles with a compass requires practice. Drawing very small circles is more difficult than one might think. If students are struggling, review the two methods for drawing circles explained on page 154 of the *Student Reference Book,* and have students practice for a few minutes.

## ✦Copying Line Segments (*Math Journal 1,* p. 74)

PARTNER ACTIVITY

Explain to the class that in mathematics, the words *ruler* and *straightedge* have different meanings.

▷ A ruler has a scale along one or more edges so that it can be used to measure lengths.

▷ A straightedge is a tool for drawing straight lines, but not for measuring.

▷ A ruler can be used as a straightedge, but an activity may specify that it not be used to measure at the same time.

Students complete Problems 1 and 2 on the journal page. If they need to review the procedure for copying a line segment, have them read the directions on page 155 of the *Student Reference Book.*

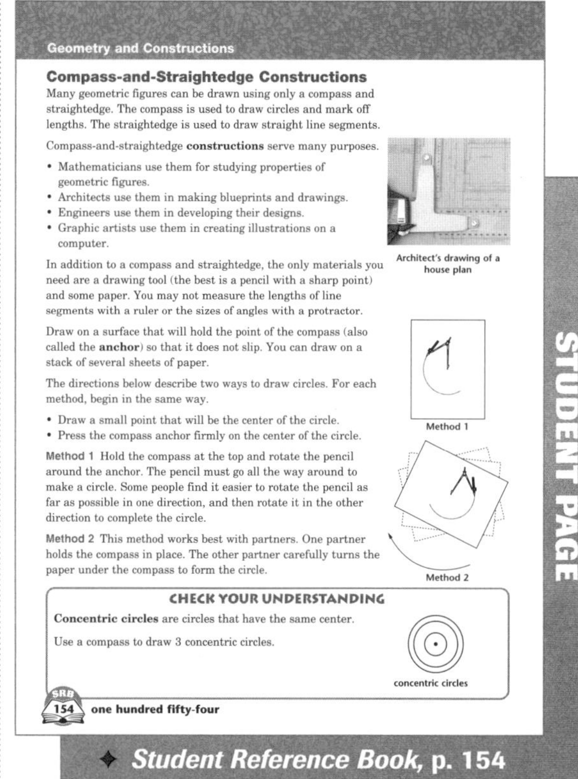

Geometry and Constructions

**Compass-and-Straightedge Constructions**

Many geometric figures can be drawn using only a compass and straightedge. The compass is used to draw circles and mark off lengths. The straightedge is used to draw straight line segments.

Compass-and-straightedge **constructions** serve many purposes.

- Mathematicians use them for studying properties of geometric figures.
- Architects use them in making blueprints and drawings.
- Engineers use them in developing their designs.
- Graphic artists use them in creating illustrations on a computer.

Architect's drawing of a house plan

In addition to a compass and straightedge, the only materials you need are a drawing tool (the best is a pencil with a sharp point) and some paper. You may not measure the lengths of line segments with a ruler or the sizes of angles with a protractor.

Draw on a surface that will hold the point of the compass (also called the **anchor**) so that it does not slip. You can draw on a stack of several sheets of paper.

The directions below describe two ways to draw circles. For each method, begin in the same way.

- Draw a small point that will be the center of the circle.
- Press the compass anchor firmly on the center of the circle.

Method 1

Method 1 Hold the compass at the top and rotate the pencil around the anchor. The pencil must go all the way around to make a circle. Some people find it easier to rotate the pencil as far as possible in one direction, and then rotate it in the other direction to complete the circle.

Method 2 This method works best with partners. One partner holds the compass in place. The other partner carefully turns the paper under the compass to form the circle.

Method 2

CHECK YOUR UNDERSTANDING

**Concentric circles** are circles that have the same center.

Use a compass to draw 3 concentric circles.

concentric circles

SRB 154 one hundred fifty-four

STUDENT PAGE

✦ *Student Reference Book,* p. 154

▼ Journal page 75 accompanies the *Measuring Angles Formed by Intersecting Lines* activity on the following page.

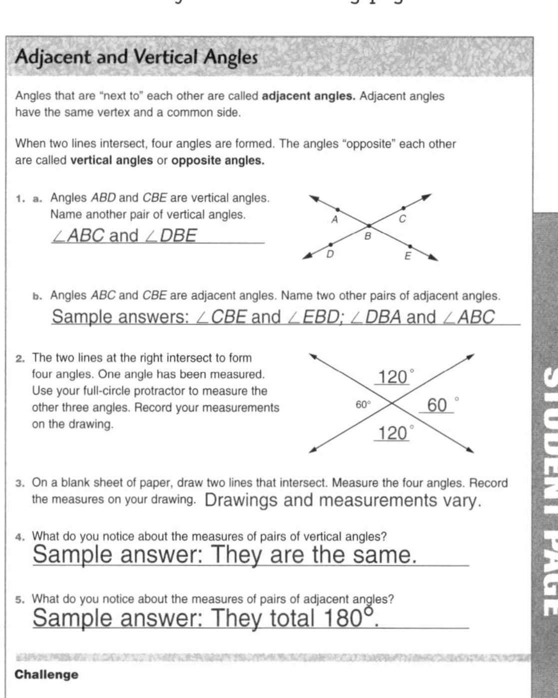

Adjacent and Vertical Angles

Angles that are "next to" each other are called **adjacent angles.** Adjacent angles have the same vertex and a common side.

When two lines intersect, four angles are formed. The angles "opposite" each other are called **vertical angles** or **opposite angles.**

1. a. Angles *ABD* and *CBE* are vertical angles. Name another pair of vertical angles.
   ∠ABC and ∠DBE

   b. Angles *ABC* and *CBE* are adjacent angles. Name two other pairs of adjacent angles.
   Sample answers: ∠CBE and ∠EBD; ∠DBA and ∠ABC

2. The two lines at the right intersect to form four angles. One angle has been measured. Use your full-circle protractor to measure the other three angles. Record your measurements on the drawing.
   120°, 60°, 60°, 120°

3. On a blank sheet of paper, draw two lines that intersect. Measure the four angles. Record the measures on your drawing. Drawings and measurements vary.

4. What do you notice about the measures of pairs of vertical angles?
   Sample answer: They are the same.

5. What do you notice about the measures of pairs of adjacent angles?
   Sample answer: They total 180°.

Challenge

6. For any pair of adjacent angles formed by two intersecting lines, the sum of the measures is always 180°. Explain why. Sample answer: The adjacent angles form a straight angle which always measures 180°.

STUDENT PAGE

✦ *Math Journal 1,* p. 75

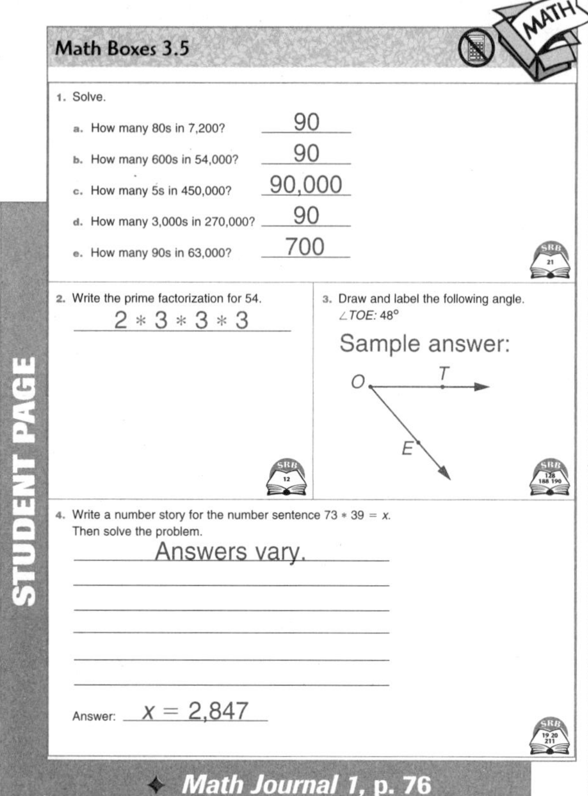

STUDENT PAGE

**Math Boxes 3.5**

1. Solve.
   a. How many 80s in 7,200? 90
   b. How many 600s in 54,000? 90
   c. How many 5s in 450,000? 90,000
   d. How many 3,000s in 270,000? 90
   e. How many 90s in 63,000? 700

2. Write the prime factorization for 54.
   $2 * 3 * 3 * 3$

3. Draw and label the following angle.
   $\angle TOE$: 48°
   Sample answer:

4. Write a number story for the number sentence $73 * 39 = x$.
   Then solve the problem.
   Answers vary.
   Answer: $x = 2,847$

✦ *Math Journal 1,* p. 76

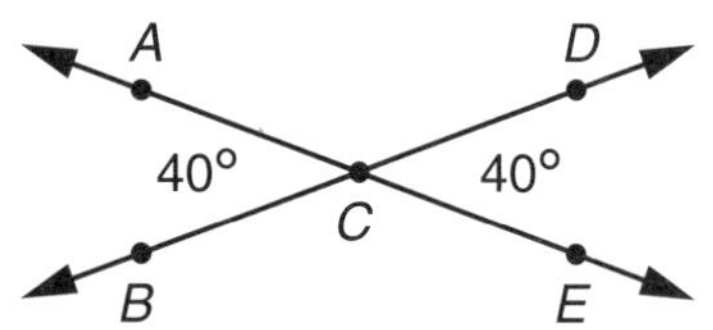


Opposite or vertical angles

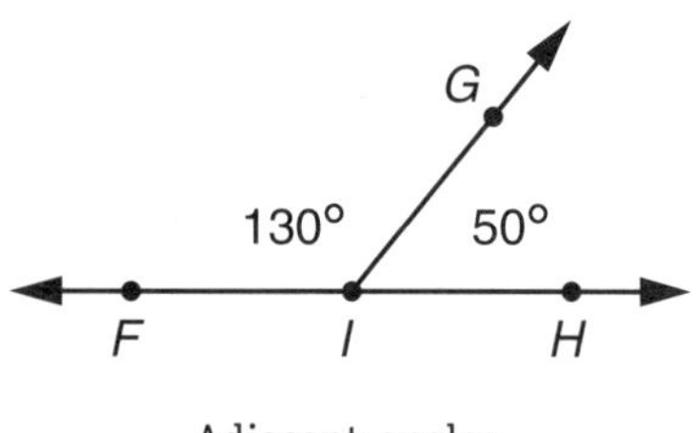


Adjacent angles

**ONGOING ASSESSMENT**

Use answers to Problem 6 on journal page 75 to assess students' understanding of angle measures and straight angles. Since this is an early exposure to adjacent, vertical, and straight angles, expect that many students may still struggle with these concepts.

The construction for Problem 2 can be done as follows: Draw a line segment that is longer than the three line segments arranged end to end. Then copy each of the three line segments onto the longer line segment, end to end.

## ✦ Finding Lengths with a Compass (*Math Journal 1,* p. 74)

PARTNER ACTIVITY

For Problems 3–6 on the journal page, students measure lengths and distances with a compass and a ruler. Work through the example with the class and make sure students understand what they are to do. Each measurement is a two-step operation:

1. Set the compass opening to the length that is to be measured.
2. Hold the compass against the inch ruler with the anchor at 0. Measure the length of the compass opening. This is the desired length.

Circulate and assist. The technique of transferring lengths with a compass is important for many compass-and-straightedge constructions, so make sure students do not solve these problems by measuring with a ruler.

## ✦ Measuring Angles Formed by Intersecting Lines (*Math Journal 1,* p. 75)

PARTNER ACTIVITY

Have students work with partners to complete the journal page. Circulate and assist as needed.

Bring the class together to share results. Most students will observe that when two lines intersect, the measures of the angles opposite each other are equal. Such angles are called **vertical angles** or **opposite angles.** Angles that are next to each other and have a common side are called **adjacent angles.** *(See the margin.)*

For Problem 6, point out that when two lines intersect, the sum of the measures of two adjacent angles is 180°. Ask students how they might confirm that this is true without measuring the angles. When two lines intersect, two adjacent angles form a straight angle, and the measure of a straight angle is 180°.

If students need additional practice with vertical and adjacent angles, discuss the example on page 129 of the *Student Reference Book* and assign the Check Your Understanding problems.

**Angles in Figures** — Study Link 3.5

SRB 128 129

Circle *acute, right,* or *obtuse* for each angle in triangle *ABC*. Then measure each angle.

1. ∠*ABC* (acute) right obtuse m∠*ABC* = 12°
2. ∠*CAB* (acute) right obtuse m∠*CAB* = 65°
3. ∠*BCA* acute right (obtuse) m∠*BCA* = 103°

Use the figure at the right to do Problems 4–6. Sample answers given for Problems 4–6.

4. Name a pair of adjacent angles. ∠D and ∠E
5. Name a pair of vertical angles. ∠D and ∠F
6. Name a pair of opposite angles. ∠D and ∠F

**Challenge**

7. a. The measure of ∠*F* is 110°. What is the measure of ∠*D*? 110°
   b. Explain how you know. ∠F and ∠D are vertical (or opposite) angles; vertical angles are equal in measure.

STUDY LINK MASTER

Math Masters, p. 245

# 2 Ongoing Learning & Practice

## ✦ Math Boxes 3.5 (*Math Journal 1,* p. 76)

INDEPENDENT ACTIVITY 

**Mixed Review** Math Boxes in this lesson are paired with Math Boxes in Lessons 3.7 and 3.9. The skill in Problem 1 is a prerequisite for Unit 4.

## ✦ Study Link 3.5 (*Math Masters,* p. 245)

**Home Connection** Students identify acute, obtuse, and right angles. Students identify vertical (or opposite) and adjacent angles.

# 3 Options for Individualizing

## ✦ ENRICHMENT Solving a Baseball Challenge (*Math Masters,* p. 28)

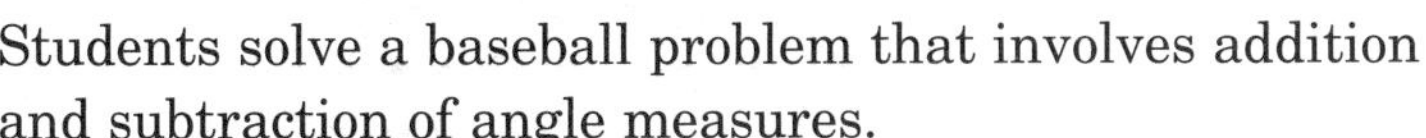

INDEPENDENT ACTIVITY  **15–30 min**

Students solve a baseball problem that involves addition and subtraction of angle measures.

As students complete the assignment, discuss answers and strategies. The field has a 90° angle within which a batted ball is put in play. Each of the four infielders covers 13°, for a total of 4 ∗ 13°, or 52°, and the pitcher covers 6°. That leaves 90° − 52° − 6°, or 32°, uncovered, which suggests that a little more than one-third of hard-hit ground balls should get past the infield. Ask the baseball players and fans in the class whether that conclusion has been borne out in their experiences.

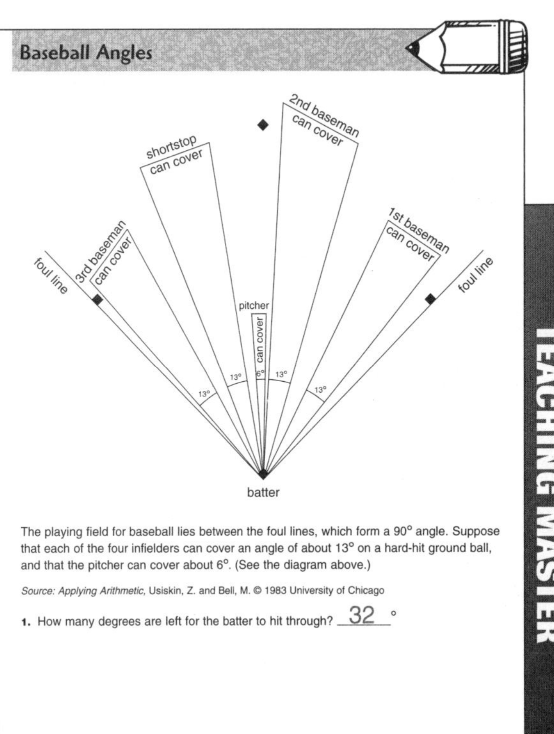


Math Masters, p. 28

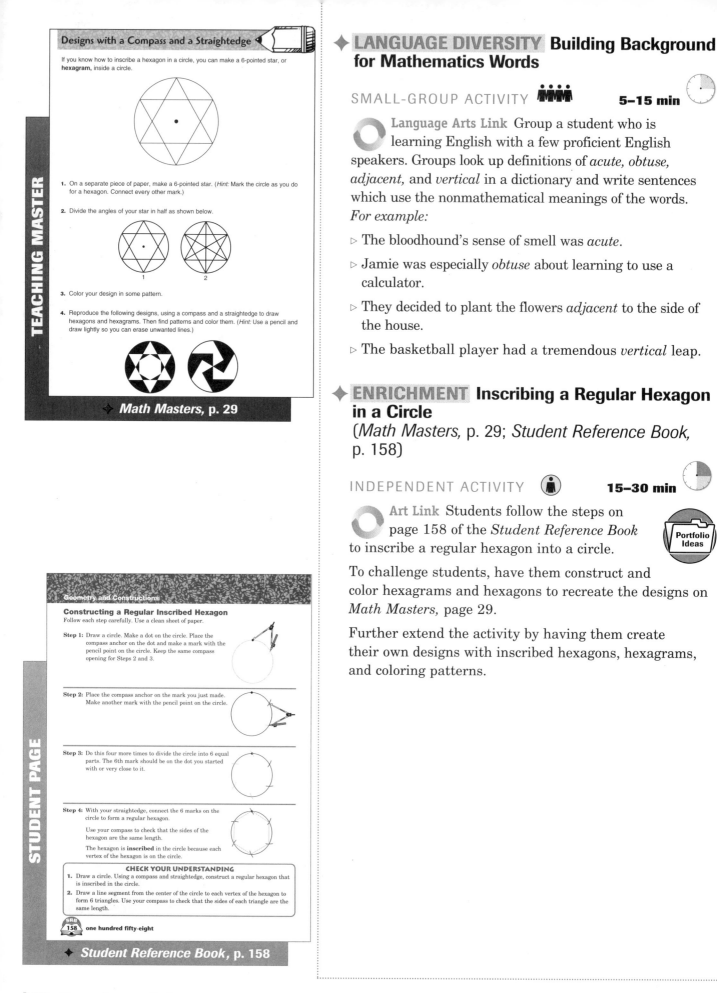

TEACHING MASTER

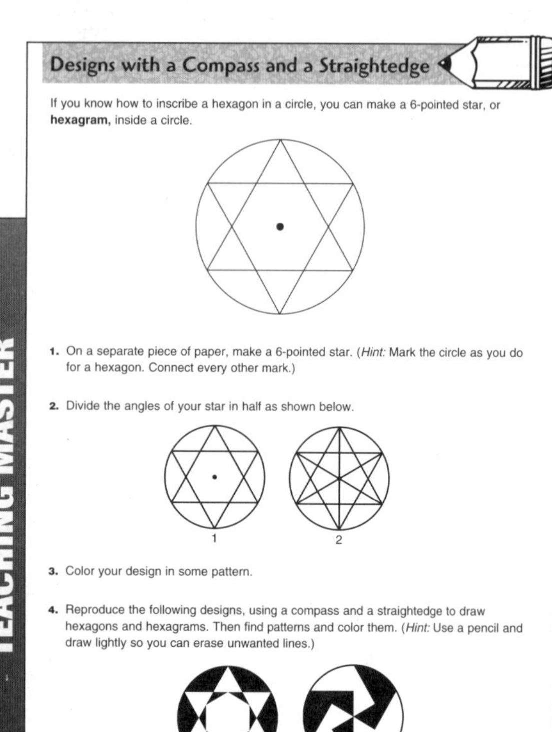

Designs with a Compass and a Straightedge

If you know how to inscribe a hexagon in a circle, you can make a 6-pointed star, or **hexagram,** inside a circle.

1. On a separate piece of paper, make a 6-pointed star. (*Hint:* Mark the circle as you do for a hexagon. Connect every other mark.)
2. Divide the angles of your star in half as shown below.
3. Color your design in some pattern.
4. Reproduce the following designs, using a compass and a straightedge to draw hexagons and hexagrams. Then find patterns and color them. (*Hint:* Use a pencil and draw lightly so you can erase unwanted lines.)

◆ *Math Masters,* p. 29

STUDENT PAGE

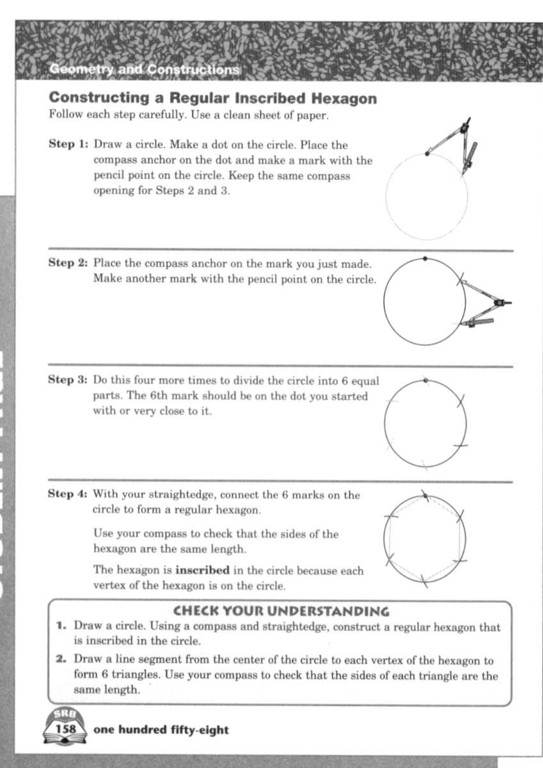

Geometry and Constructions

**Constructing a Regular Inscribed Hexagon**

Follow each step carefully. Use a clean sheet of paper.

**Step 1:** Draw a circle. Make a dot on the circle. Place the compass anchor on the dot and make a mark with the pencil point on the circle. Keep the same compass opening for Steps 2 and 3.

**Step 2:** Place the compass anchor on the mark you just made. Make another mark with the pencil point on the circle.

**Step 3:** Do this four more times to divide the circle into 6 equal parts. The 6th mark should be on the dot you started with or very close to it.

**Step 4:** With your straightedge, connect the 6 marks on the circle to form a regular hexagon.

Use your compass to check that the sides of the hexagon are the same length.

The hexagon is **inscribed** in the circle because each vertex of the hexagon is on the circle.

**CHECK YOUR UNDERSTANDING**

1. Draw a circle. Using a compass and straightedge, construct a regular hexagon that is inscribed in the circle.
2. Draw a line segment from the center of the circle to each vertex of the hexagon to form 6 triangles. Use your compass to check that the sides of each triangle are the same length.

SRB 158 one hundred fifty-eight

◆ *Student Reference Book,* p. 158

## ◆ LANGUAGE DIVERSITY Building Background for Mathematics Words

SMALL-GROUP ACTIVITY  **5–15 min** 

**Language Arts Link** Group a student who is learning English with a few proficient English speakers. Groups look up definitions of *acute, obtuse, adjacent,* and *vertical* in a dictionary and write sentences which use the nonmathematical meanings of the words. *For example:*

▷ The bloodhound's sense of smell was *acute.*

▷ Jamie was especially *obtuse* about learning to use a calculator.

▷ They decided to plant the flowers *adjacent* to the side of the house.

▷ The basketball player had a tremendous *vertical* leap.

## ◆ ENRICHMENT Inscribing a Regular Hexagon in a Circle

(*Math Masters,* p. 29; *Student Reference Book,* p. 158)

INDEPENDENT ACTIVITY  **15–30 min**

**Art Link** Students follow the steps on page 158 of the *Student Reference Book* to inscribe a regular hexagon into a circle.

To challenge students, have them construct and color hexagrams and hexagons to recreate the designs on *Math Masters,* page 29.

Further extend the activity by having them create their own designs with inscribed hexagons, hexagrams, and coloring patterns.

# 3.6 Congruent Triangles

**OBJECTIVES** **To define equilateral, isosceles, scalene, and congruent triangles; and to copy triangles.**

| summaries | materials |
| --- | --- |
| **1 Teaching the Lesson** | |
| Students define equilateral, isosceles, and scalene triangles; they explore methods for copying a triangle with a compass, ruler, and protractor, and then with a compass and straightedge only. [Geometry] | ☐ *Math Journal 1,* pp. 77–80<br>☐ *Student Reference Book,* p. 156<br>☐ Study Link 3.5<br>☐ Transparency (*Math Masters,* p. 25; optional)<br>☐ compass, protractor, and meterstick for demonstration purposes (optional)<br>☐ straws and connectors (or cardstock strips and masking tape)<br>☐ Geometry Template (or straightedge and protractor)<br>☐ compass<br>***See* Advance Preparation** |
| **2 Ongoing Learning & Practice** | |
| Students play *Angle Tangle* to practice estimating and measuring angles. [Geometry]<br>Students practice and maintain skills through Math Boxes and Study Link activities. | ☐ *Math Journal 1,* p. 81<br>☐ *Student Reference Book,* p. 258<br>☐ Study Link Master (*Math Masters,* p. 246)<br>☐ Geometry Template (or straightedge and protractor) |
| **3 Options for Individualizing** | |
| **Extra Practice** Students practice constructions. [Geometry] | ☐ *Student Reference Book,* pp. 157, 161, and 162<br>☐ compass ☐ straightedge |

## Additional Information

**Advance Preparation** For Part 1, students will need straws in three sizes—full length (about 8"), 6", and 4"—and connectors for the straws. If straws and connectors are not available, students can use cardstock cut in 8", 6", and 4" strips, connected with masking tape.

**Vocabulary** • **equilateral triangle** • **isosceles triangle** • **scalene triangle** • **congruent**

# Getting Started

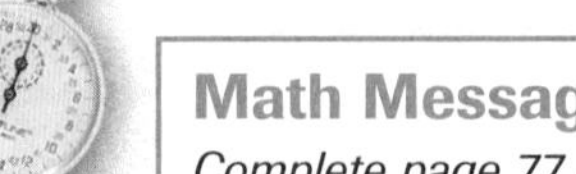

## Mental Math and Reflexes

Round to the nearest whole number.

- 15.7 16
- 209.82 210
- 32.06 32

Round to the nearest tenth.

- 81.39 81.4
- 376.14 376.1
- 546.96 547.0

Continue as time allows.

## Math Message

*Complete page 77 in your journal. Do not use your* Student Reference Book.

## Study Link 3.5 Follow-Up

Briefly review answers to problems and definitions for kinds of angles. Have students share their strategies for Problem 7. Expect answers like the following:

▷ I know that vertical angles have the same measure. If m $\angle F$ is 110°, then m $\angle D = 110°$.

▷ I know that the sum of the measures of adjacent angles formed by intersecting lines is 180°. m $\angle E$ + m $\angle F = 180°$, so m $\angle E = 70°$. I know that m $\angle E$ + m $\angle D = 180°$, so m $\angle D = 110°$.

# 1 Teaching the Lesson

## ✦ Math Message Follow-Up (*Math Journal 1,* p. 77)

WHOLE-CLASS DISCUSSION 

For each type of triangle, compare the students' definitions with the following. If there are differences, try to arrive at a definition that the class can agree on.

An **equilateral (ee-kwi-LAT-er-el) triangle** has three sides that are the same length.

An **isosceles (eye-SOS-e-leez) triangle** has at least two sides that are the same length.

A **scalene (SKAY-leen) triangle** has no sides of the same length.

Point out that an equilateral triangle is also an isosceles triangle. The reason is that the definition of an isosceles triangle requires that at least two sides be the same length. If all three sides are the same length, the triangle still fits the definition of *isosceles*.

You may need to clarify several points about the marks on the sides of some figures on the journal page.

▷ The marks can simply be called *marks*. Other names are *hatch marks, slash marks,* and *tick marks.*

▷ On the journal page, the marks indicate sides of the same length in the given figure. At other times, the marks may be used to indicate sides of the same length in two different figures.

STUDENT PAGE

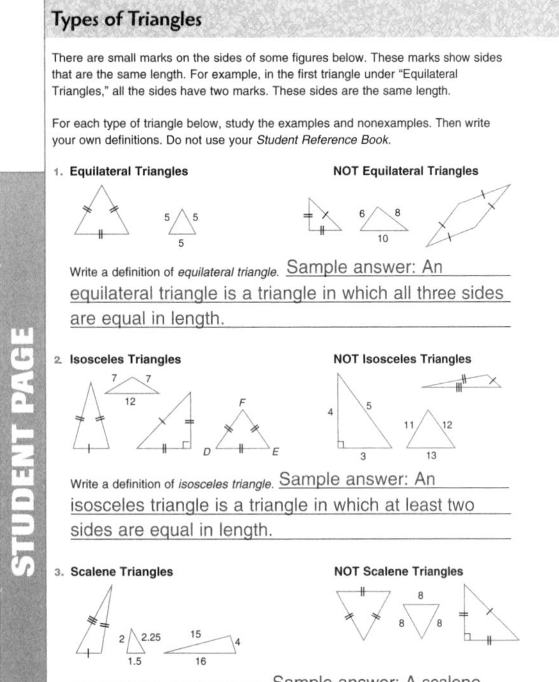

**Types of Triangles**

There are small marks on the sides of some figures below. These marks show sides that are the same length. For example, in the first triangle under "Equilateral Triangles," all the sides have two marks. These sides are the same length.

For each type of triangle below, study the examples and nonexamples. Then write your own definitions. Do not use your *Student Reference Book.*

1. **Equilateral Triangles** **NOT Equilateral Triangles**

Write a definition of *equilateral triangle.* Sample answer: An equilateral triangle is a triangle in which all three sides are equal in length.

2. **Isosceles Triangles** **NOT Isosceles Triangles**

Write a definition of *isosceles triangle.* Sample answer: An isosceles triangle is a triangle in which at least two sides are equal in length.

3. **Scalene Triangles** **NOT Scalene Triangles**

Write a definition of *scalene triangle.* Sample answer: A scalene triangle is a triangle in which no two sides are the same length.

✦ *Math Journal 1,* p. 77

▷ The number of marks has nothing to do with length. If a side has two marks, this does not mean it is longer than a side with one mark.

Ask students to examine the triangles on their Geometry Templates, and to classify them as equilateral, isosceles, or scalene. Use an overhead transparency of *Math Masters,* page 25 or an actual template to share answers.

**Adjusting the Activity** Draw triangles or other shapes on the board with different numbers of congruent sides. Use marks to indicate equal sides. For each figure, ask students how many sides are congruent.

## ✦ Copying a Triangle Using Any Available Tools (*Math Journal 1,* p. 78)

PARTNER ACTIVITY 

Students carefully copy $\Delta BIG$ on a blank sheet of paper. They can make the copy using any of their drawing and measuring tools, such as a protractor, ruler, straightedge, or compass. They are not allowed to trace the figure.

You might want to remind students that they used a compass to copy line segments in Lesson 3.5, and that this procedure is covered on page 155 of the *Student Reference Book.*

If a student copies $\Delta BIG$ correctly, the sides and angles of the copy should have the same measures as the sides and angles of the original triangle. Say that figures that are exact copies—the same size and shape—are called **congruent** figures. A student may verify that his or her copy is congruent to the original figure by cutting out the copy and laying it on top of the original. The two figures should match.

After about 10 minutes, bring students together to share results. Expect that students will have devised a variety of methods. Have them use a meterstick and the demonstration compass and protractor to show different methods, and assist them as needed.

NOTE: For board demonstrations, draw the triangle sides 10 times the given length—that is, 60 cm instead of 6 cm, 50 cm instead of 5 cm, and so on.

Here are some common solutions:

▷ Use a protractor to copy angle $B$. Label the vertex of the new angle as point $P$. Next, use a ruler to copy sides $\overline{BI}$ and $\overline{BG}$ onto the sides of the new angle, using $P$ as one endpoint for each segment. Label the two new endpoints $A$ and $L$. Finally, connect points $A$ and $L$.

▷ Use a ruler to draw a line segment the length of side $BG$. Label its endpoints $P$ and $L$. Use a protractor to draw angles at points $P$ and $L$ the same size as angles $B$ and $G$. Extend the sides of the angles at $P$ and $L$ so that they intersect. Label the point of intersection $A$.

**Adjusting the Activity** If students have trouble copying $\Delta BIG$, suggest they begin by using a protractor to copy one angle. Then they can use their ruler to measure the two sides adjacent to that angle. Connecting the endpoints of the two sides will complete the triangle.

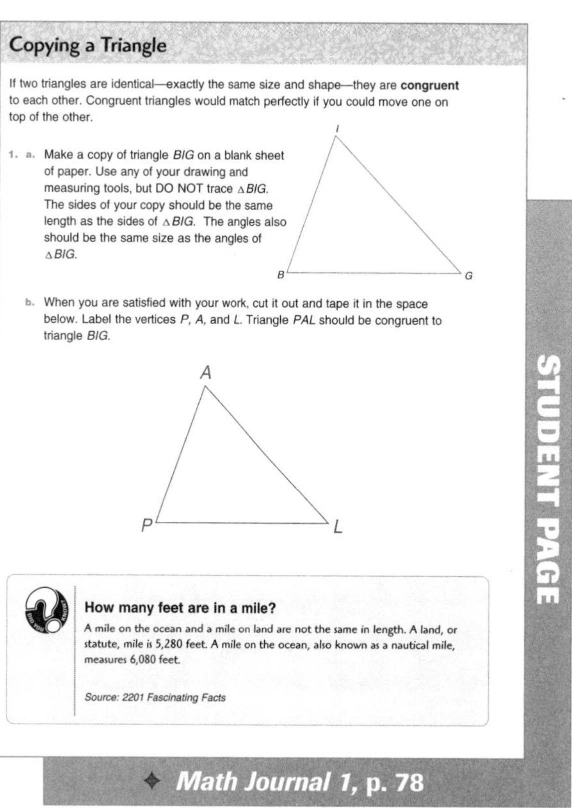

Copying a Triangle

If two triangles are identical—exactly the same size and shape—they are **congruent** to each other. Congruent triangles would match perfectly if you could move one on top of the other.

1. a. Make a copy of triangle *BIG* on a blank sheet of paper. Use any of your drawing and measuring tools, but DO NOT trace $\Delta BIG$. The sides of your copy should be the same length as the sides of $\Delta BIG$. The angles also should be the same size as the angles of $\Delta BIG$.

b. When you are satisfied with your work, cut it out and tape it in the space below. Label the vertices *P, A,* and *L.* Triangle *PAL* should be congruent to triangle *BIG.*



**How many feet are in a mile?**
A mile on the ocean and a mile on land are not the same in length. A land, or statute, mile is 5,280 feet. A mile on the ocean, also known as a nautical mile, measures 6,080 feet.

Source: 2201 Fascinating Facts

✦ *Math Journal 1,* p. 78

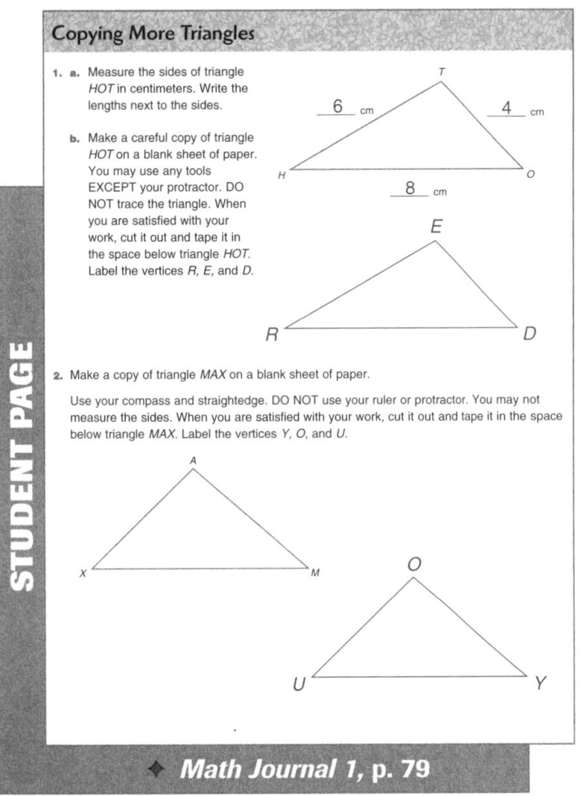

STUDENT PAGE

**Copying More Triangles**

1. a. Measure the sides of triangle *HOT* in centimeters. Write the lengths next to the sides.

   b. Make a careful copy of triangle *HOT* on a blank sheet of paper. You may use any tools EXCEPT your protractor. DO NOT trace the triangle. When you are satisfied with your work, cut it out and tape it in the space below triangle *HOT*. Label the vertices *R*, *E*, and *D*.



2. Make a copy of triangle *MAX* on a blank sheet of paper.

   Use your compass and straightedge. DO NOT use your ruler or protractor. You may not measure the sides. When you are satisfied with your work, cut it out and tape it in the space below triangle *MAX*. Label the vertices *Y*, *O*, and *U*.



✦ *Math Journal 1*, p. 79

NOTE: Students are not expected to master the triangle congruence theorems from plane geometry (such as Side-Angle-Side and Side-Side-Side), but they may notice that when some angle and side information is copied, the remainder of the construction is determined automatically.

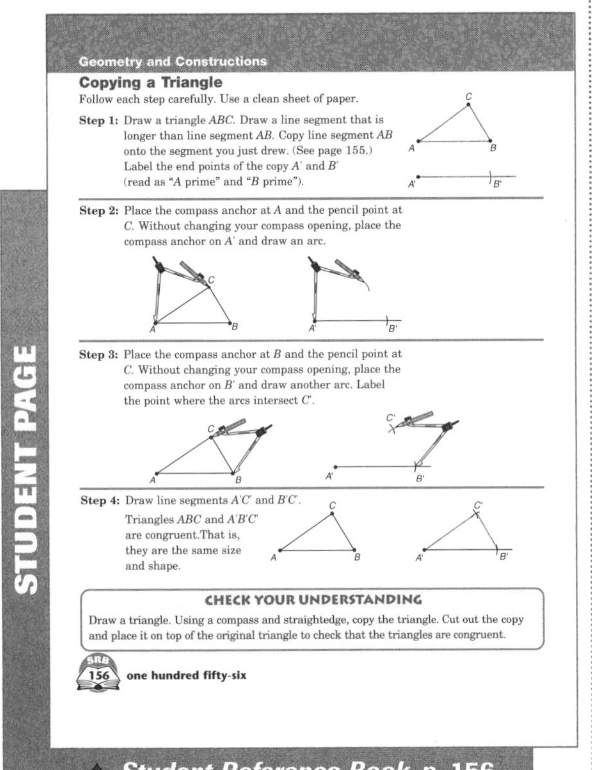

STUDENT PAGE

Geometry and Constructions

**Copying a Triangle**

Follow each step carefully. Use a clean sheet of paper.

**Step 1:** Draw a triangle *ABC*. Draw a line segment that is longer than line segment *AB*. Copy line segment *AB* onto the segment you just drew. (See page 155.) Label the end points of the copy *A'* and *B'* (read as "*A* prime" and "*B* prime").

**Step 2:** Place the compass anchor at *A* and the pencil point at *C*. Without changing your compass opening, place the compass anchor on *A'* and draw an arc.

**Step 3:** Place the compass anchor at *B* and the pencil point at *C*. Without changing your compass opening, place the compass anchor on *B'* and draw another arc. Label the point where the arcs intersect *C'*.

**Step 4:** Draw line segments *A'C'* and *B'C'*. Triangles *ABC* and *A'B'C'* are congruent. That is, they are the same size and shape.



**CHECK YOUR UNDERSTANDING**

Draw a triangle. Using a compass and straightedge, copy the triangle. Cut out the copy and place it on top of the original triangle to check that the triangles are congruent.

SRB 156 one hundred fifty-six

✦ *Student Reference Book*, p. 156

▷ Use a ruler to draw a line segment the length of side *BG*. Label its endpoints *P* and *L*. Use a protractor to draw an angle at point *P* the same size as angle *B*. Use a ruler to measure side *BI*. Extend the line segment at *P* so that it is the same length as segment *BI*. Label the endpoint of that segment *A*. Draw line segment *AL*.

▷ Draw a 6-cm line segment and label it *PL*. Draw a 71° angle at *P*. Extend the side of angle *P* 4.9 cm to point *A*. Draw a 63° angle at *A*, and extend the side of angle *A* 6.3 cm to point *L*. After the construction is complete, verify that angle *L* is 46°.

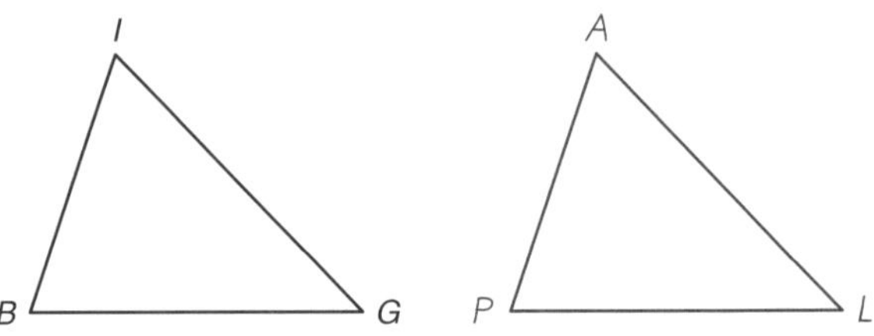


Triangles *BIG* and *PAL* are congruent.

Whichever solution students used, all sides and angles of both triangles should be measured to ensure that they have been copied correctly.

## ✦ Copying a Triangle without a Protractor

(*Math Journal 1*, p. 79)

PARTNER ACTIVITY

Assign Problem 1 on the journal page. Emphasize that this problem is similar to the previous one except students are NOT allowed to use a protractor this time. They may use a compass and a ruler or straightedge, but protractors and tracing are not allowed.

NOTE: Some students may remember from *Fourth Grade Everyday Mathematics* how to copy a triangle using a compass and straightedge only. The procedure is covered on page 156 of the *Student Reference Book.*

Each student works with a partner. Allow 5 to 10 minutes as a discovery period. If you have straws and connectors (or cardstock strips and masking tape) available, distribute several to each partnership. Students may cut the straws to create three pieces that have the same lengths as the sides of triangle *HOT*. The pieces will serve as a physical model for the problem and should facilitate discovery of a copying method. Circulate and provide assistance as needed.

## ◆ Modeling a Triangle (*Math Journal 1,* p. 79)

WHOLE-CLASS DISCUSSION 

Gather the class together to share results. Students can use the precut straws or cardstock strips to illustrate their methods at the board.

Be sure that the following method is demonstrated:

1. Tape one of the straws or strips on the board as the first side.
2. Hold or fasten the other two straws or strips to the first, one at each end.
3. Swing these two until their ends meet, and fasten the ends together.

The straws or cardstock strips have the same relative sizes as the sides of triangle *HOT,* which is to be copied. This demonstration illustrates the principle that two triangles are congruent if the sides of one are the same length as the sides of the other. This is the "Side-Side-Side" or "SSS" triangle congruence theorem from plane geometry.

## ◆ Copying a Triangle with Compass and Straightedge Only (*Math Journal 1,* pp. 79 and 80; *Student Reference Book,* p. 156)

PARTNER ACTIVITY 

Following this demonstration, have the class look at the method shown at the top of *Student Reference Book,* page 156. You may want to draw a triangle on the board and use your chalkboard compass and a meterstick to copy it as described.

Have partners work on Problem 2 on journal page 79. As you circulate, remind students to check their copies against the original before taping them in their journals.

**Adjusting the Activity** If students are experiencing difficulty copying line segment *AX* with only the compass and straightedge, you might want to review *Student Reference Book,* page 155 with them.

As students finish, assign journal page 80. Partners draw triangles, exchange drawings, and then practice the compass-and-straightedge method further by copying their partner's drawings.

**Adjusting the Activity** Students who finish early may want to try to construct an equilateral triangle using a compass and a straightedge only (no ruler).

### Copying a Partner's Triangle

1. Use a ruler to draw two triangles on a blank sheet of paper. Make your triangles fairly large, but leave enough room to draw a copy of each one. Then exchange drawings with your partner.
2. Copy your partner's triangles using only your compass and straightedge. Don't erase the arcs you make—they show how you made your copies. Measure the sides of the triangles and your copies of the triangles. Write the lengths next to the sides.
3. Cut out one of the triangles your partner drew, and cut out the copy you made. Tape them in the space below.

STUDENT PAGE

◆ *Math Journal 1,* p. 80

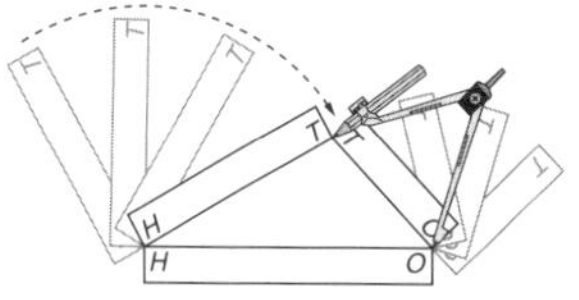


Putting three straws or strips together to make a triangle resembles the compass and straightedge procedure illustrated on page 156 of the *Student Reference Book.*

Games

***Angle Tangle***

**Materials** □ protractor
□ straightedge
□ blank sheets of paper

**Players** 2

**Directions**

In each round:

1. Player 1 uses a straightedge to draw an angle on a sheet of paper.
2. Player 2 estimates the degree measure of the angle.
3. Player 1 measures the angle with a protractor. Players agree on the measure.
4. Player 2's score is the difference between the estimate and the actual measure of the angle. (The difference will be a 0 or a positive number.)
5. Players trade roles and repeat Steps 1–4.

Players add their scores at the end of five rounds. The player with the lower total score wins the game.

**EXAMPLE**

| | Player 1 | | | Player 2 | | |
|---|---|---|---|---|---|---|
| | **Estimate** | **Actual** | **Score** | **Estimate** | **Actual** | **Score** |
| Round 1 | 120° | 108° | 12 | 50° | 37° | 13 |
| Round 2 | 75° | 86° | 11 | 85° | 87° | 2 |
| Round 3 | 40° | 44° | 4 | 15° | 19° | 4 |
| Round 4 | 60° | 69° | 9 | 40° | 56° | 16 |
| Round 5 | 135° | 123° | 12 | 150° | 141° | 9 |
| Total score | | | 48 | | | 44 |

Player 2 has the lower total score. Player 2 wins the game.

two hundred fifty-eight

STUDENT PAGE

◆ *Student Reference Book,* p. 258

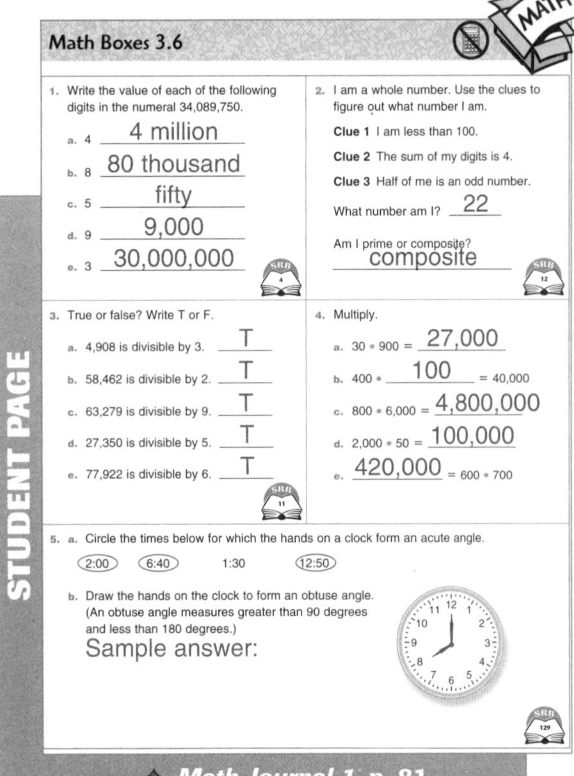

Math Boxes 3.6

1. Write the value of each of the following digits in the numeral 34,089,750.
   a. 4 4 million
   b. 8 80 thousand
   c. 5 fifty
   d. 9 9,000
   e. 3 30,000,000

2. I am a whole number. Use the clues to figure out what number I am.
   Clue 1 I am less than 100.
   Clue 2 The sum of my digits is 4.
   Clue 3 Half of me is an odd number.
   What number am I? 22
   Am I prime or composite? composite

3. True or false? Write T or F.
   a. 4,908 is divisible by 3. T
   b. 58,462 is divisible by 2. T
   c. 63,279 is divisible by 9. T
   d. 27,350 is divisible by 5. T
   e. 77,922 is divisible by 6. T

4. Multiply.
   a. 30 ∗ 900 = 27,000
   b. 400 ∗ 100 = 40,000
   c. 800 ∗ 6,000 = 4,800,000
   d. 2,000 ∗ 50 = 100,000
   e. 420,000 = 600 ∗ 700

5. a. Circle the times below for which the hands on a clock form an acute angle.
   (2:00) (6:40) 1:30 (12:50)
   b. Draw the hands on the clock to form an obtuse angle. (An obtuse angle measures greater than 90 degrees and less than 180 degrees.)
   Sample answer:

STUDENT PAGE

Math Journal 1, p. 81

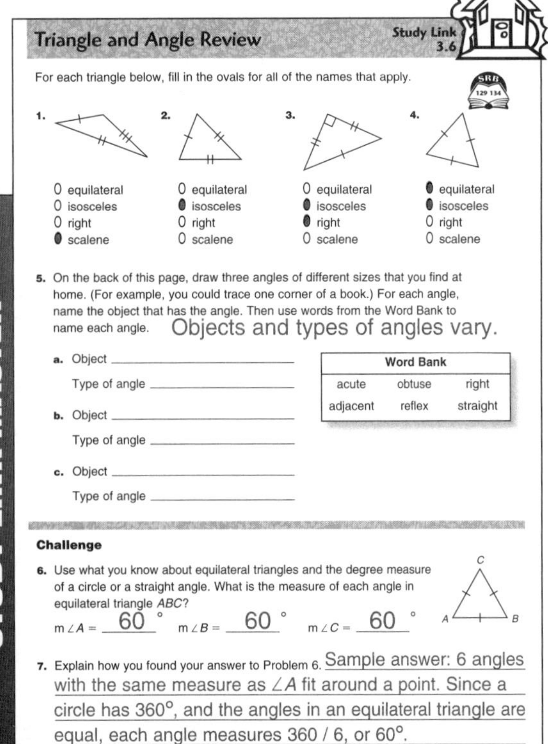

Triangle and Angle Review

Study Link 3.6

For each triangle below, fill in the ovals for all of the names that apply.

| 1. | 2. | 3. | 4. |
|---|---|---|---|
| O equilateral | O equilateral | O equilateral | ● equilateral |
| O isosceles | ● isosceles | ● isosceles | ● isosceles |
| O right | O right | ● right | O right |
| ● scalene | O scalene | O scalene | O scalene |

5. On the back of this page, draw three angles of different sizes that you find at home. (For example, you could trace one corner of a book.) For each angle, name the object that has the angle. Then use words from the Word Bank to name each angle. Objects and types of angles vary.
   a. Object ______
   Type of angle ______
   b. Object ______
   Type of angle ______
   c. Object ______
   Type of angle ______

| Word Bank | | |
|---|---|---|
| acute | obtuse | right |
| adjacent | reflex | straight |

Challenge

6. Use what you know about equilateral triangles and the degree measure of a circle or a straight angle. What is the measure of each angle in equilateral triangle *ABC*?
   m∠A = 60° m∠B = 60° m∠C = 60°

7. Explain how you found your answer to Problem 6. Sample answer: 6 angles with the same measure as ∠A fit around a point. Since a circle has 360°, and the angles in an equilateral triangle are equal, each angle measures 360 / 6, or 60°.

STUDY LINK MASTER

Math Masters, p. 246

# 2 Ongoing Learning & Practice

## ✦ Playing *Angle Tangle*
(*Student Reference Book,* p. 258)

PARTNER ACTIVITY 

*Angle Tangle* provides practice in measuring angles with a protractor and in estimating their measures.

## ✦ Math Boxes 3.6 (*Math Journal 1,* p. 81)

INDEPENDENT ACTIVITY 

**Mixed Review** Math Boxes in this lesson are paired with Math Boxes in Lessons 3.8 and 3.10. The skill in Problem 1 is a prerequisite for Unit 4.

## ✦ Study Link 3.6 (*Math Masters,* p. 246)

**Home Connection** Students classify triangles as scalene, isosceles, or equilateral. Students find three angles in objects at home; draw those angles; and identify each angle by type.

# 3 Options for Individualizing

## ✦ EXTRA PRACTICE Constructing Figures with a Compass and a Straightedge
(*Student Reference Book,* pp. 157, 161, and 162)

INDEPENDENT ACTIVITY  **15–30 min**

If students need practice with constructions, revisit constructions introduced in the second half of *Fourth Grade Everyday Mathematics.* Page 157 of the *Student Reference Book* has instructions for constructing a parallelogram. Pages 161 and 162 have instructions for constructing line segments perpendicular to a given line segment.

**PLANNING AHEAD**

Before Lesson 3.7, have students remove Activity Sheets 4 and 5 from their journals and cut out the 16 polygons and 16 Property Cards.

# 3.7 Properties of Polygons

**OBJECTIVE** **To classify and sort geometric shapes.**

| summaries | materials |
|---|---|
| **1 Teaching the Lesson** | |
| Students sort geometric shapes into sets according to various rules. They use geometric properties of polygons while playing *Polygon Capture.* [Geometry] | □ *Math Journals 1 and 2,* p. 82 and Activity Sheets 4 and 5<br>□ *Student Reference Book,* p. 289 □ Study Link 3.6<br>□ Transparency (*Math Masters,* p. 30; optional)<br>***See* Advance Preparation** |
| **2 Ongoing Learning & Practice** | |
| Students estimate products and then calculate exact answers. [Operations and Computation]<br>Students practice and maintain skills through Math Boxes and Study Link activities. | □ *Math Journal 1,* pp. 83 and 84<br>□ Study Link Master (*Math Masters,* p. 247) |
| **3 Options for Individualizing** | |
| **Reteaching** Students sort attribute blocks by two properties at a time. [Geometry]<br>**Enrichment** The class reads *The Greedy Triangle.* Students write a short story about what life would be like without a certain polygon, such as a triangle. [Geometry] | □ attribute blocks<br>□ *The Greedy Triangle*<br>***See* Advance Preparation** |

## Additional Information

**Advance Preparation** In Part 1, students cut out polygons from Activity Sheet 4 in *Math Journal 1* and Property Cards from Activity Sheet 5 in *Math Journal 2.* Experienced *Everyday Mathematics* teachers recommend making and cutting apart an overhead transparency of *Math Masters,* page 30, which has the same shapes as Activity Sheet 4. Play *Polygon Capture* to become familiar with the rules and materials.

For the optional Enrichment activity in Part 3, obtain the book *The Greedy Triangle* by Marilyn Burns (Scholastic, 1994).

# Getting Started

### Mental Math and Reflexes

Ask students to stand beside their desks or in an area where there is enough room for them to stretch out their arms. Give the following instructions:

- Hold your arms so that they are parallel to each other.
- Hold your left arm so that it is parallel to your right leg.
- Form a right angle (a 90° angle) with your arms.
- Form an acute angle (an angle between 0° and 90°) with your arms.
- Hold your arms so that both are perpendicular to the floor. (Point out that they form a right angle with the floor.)
- Hold your arms so that they form a right angle and are parallel to each other. *(This cannot be done. Ask students to explain why this is impossible.)*

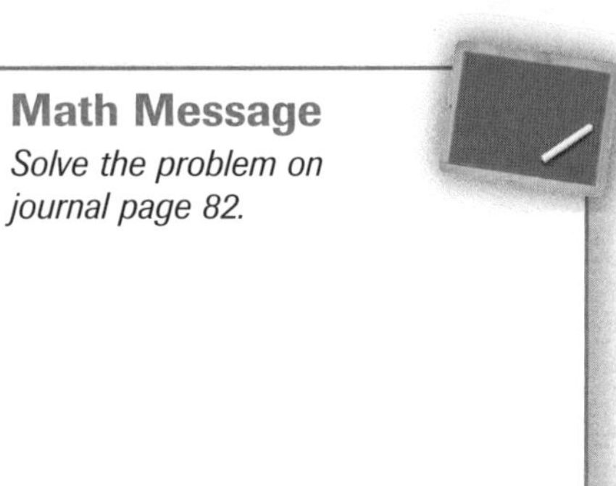

**Math Message**

*Solve the problem on journal page 82.*

**Study Link 3.6 Follow-Up**

Briefly review the answers. Have volunteers share where they found angles and what kind of angles they found. Consider making a class tally of how many of each kind of angle students found. Have students share strategies for the Challenge problem. Expect a variety of answers. Sample answers: The triangle has the same shape as the pattern-block triangle, and the angles of a pattern-block triangle have the same measure. So the angles of the triangle have the same measure. Since six triangles fit around a point and take up 360°, each angle must be 360° / 6, or 60°.

NOTE: Strictly speaking, a polygon consists of line segments. The interior (inside) of a polygon is not a part of the polygon. If the drawing of a polygon is cut out along its sides, the resulting shape consists of a polygon and its interior. Properly speaking, this is a polygonal region, not a polygon. This distinction need not be stressed.

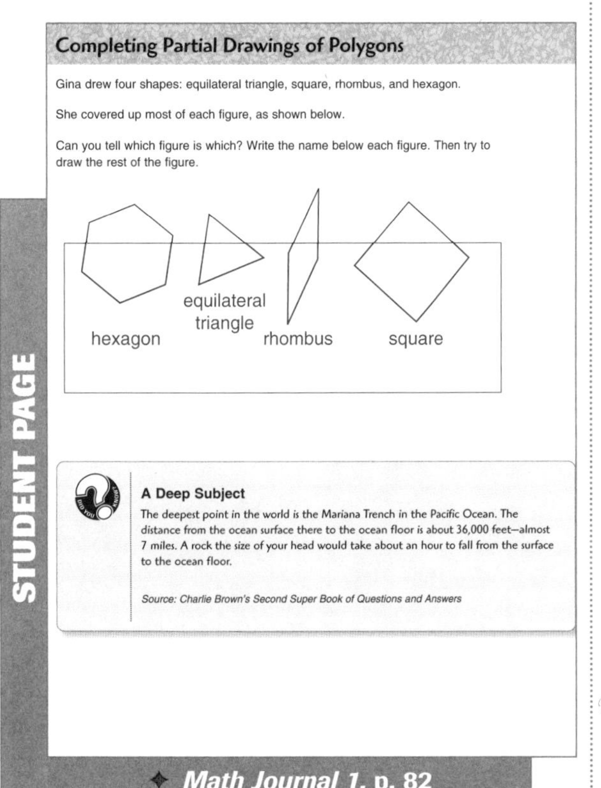

STUDENT PAGE

**Completing Partial Drawings of Polygons**

Gina drew four shapes: equilateral triangle, square, rhombus, and hexagon.

She covered up most of each figure, as shown below.

Can you tell which figure is which? Write the name below each figure. Then try to draw the rest of the figure.



**A Deep Subject**

The deepest point in the world is the Mariana Trench in the Pacific Ocean. The distance from the ocean surface there to the ocean floor is about 36,000 feet—almost 7 miles. A rock the size of your head would take about an hour to fall from the surface to the ocean floor.

*Source: Charlie Brown's Second Super Book of Questions and Answers*

◆ *Math Journal 1*, p. 82

# 1 Teaching the Lesson

## ◆ Math Message Follow-Up
(*Math Journal 1*, p. 82)

WHOLE-CLASS DISCUSSION

Ask students how they figured out the identities of the hidden geometric figures. Stress the geometric relationships and properties they used in their detection. For example: *I knew that the first three figures couldn't be squares, because they had angles that were not 90 degrees.*

## ◆ Sorting Polygons by Their Properties
(*Math Journal 1*, Activity Sheet 4)

WHOLE-CLASS ACTIVITY

If students have not already done so, they should remove Activity Sheet 4 from the back of their journals and cut out the 16 shapes. Ask students what these shapes are called. polygons

Ask each student to sort the 16 polygons into two or three different sets according to any rule that he or she makes up. You can demonstrate this by sorting polygons according to a stated rule or an unstated rule. See if the students can guess your unstated rule. *Suggested rules:*

- ▷ At least one pair of parallel sides versus no sides parallel
- ▷ Convex versus nonconvex
- ▷ At least one angle greater than 90 degrees versus all angles acute or right

After several minutes, ask a few students to show the sorting results for their rules. They might hold up the pieces in each set, or display them on the overhead projector or board. Have the class guess the rules.

## ◆ Playing *Polygon Capture* (*Math Journals 1* and *2*, Activity Sheets 4 and 5; *Student Reference Book*, p. 289)

PARTNER ACTIVITY

If students have not already done so, they should cut out the 16 Property Cards from Activity Sheet 5.

*Polygon Capture* is a geometry game for two players or two teams of two players each. The rules are on page 289 of the *Student Reference Book*.

Play a game or two against the class to help students learn the rules. You may want to display a set of polygons on the overhead projector while the students lay their own polygons in front of them.

**Adjusting the Activity** If students have trouble matching two properties, try one of the following variations:

- ▷ On each turn, the player draws one Property Card and takes all polygons with this property. If no polygons match, the player loses the turn. Play continues until fewer than three polygons are left.
- ▷ On each turn, the player draws one Property Card and takes all the polygons that have that property. Then the player draws another Property Card and puts back all of the polygons he or she just captured that DO NOT have the property on the second card.

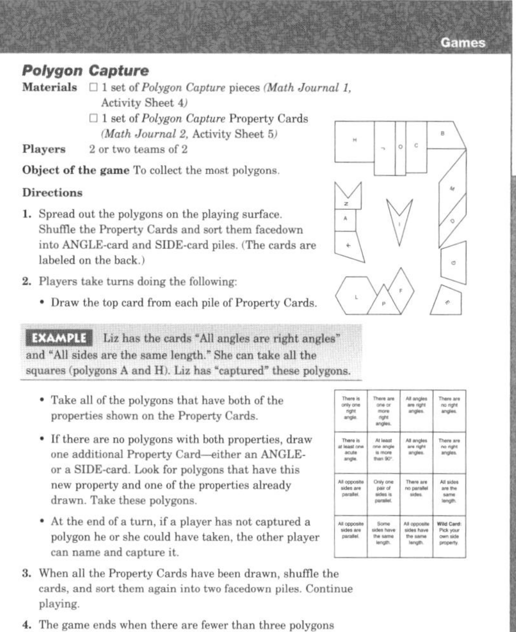

Games

**Polygon Capture**

**Materials** ☐ 1 set of *Polygon Capture* pieces (*Math Journal 1*, Activity Sheet 4)
☐ 1 set of *Polygon Capture* Property Cards (*Math Journal 2*, Activity Sheet 5)

**Players** 2 or two teams of 2

**Object of the game** To collect the most polygons.

**Directions**

1. Spread out the polygons on the playing surface. Shuffle the Property Cards and sort them facedown into ANGLE-card and SIDE-card piles. (The cards are labeled on the back.)
2. Players take turns doing the following:
   - Draw the top card from each pile of Property Cards.

**EXAMPLE** Liz has the cards "All angles are right angles" and "All sides are the same length." She can take all the squares (polygons A and H). Liz has "captured" these polygons.

   - Take all of the polygons that have both of the properties shown on the Property Cards.
   - If there are no polygons with both properties, draw one additional Property Card—either an ANGLE- or a SIDE-card. Look for polygons that have this new property and one of the properties already drawn. Take these polygons.
   - At the end of a turn, if a player has not captured a polygon he or she could have taken, the other player can name and capture it.
3. When all the Property Cards have been drawn, shuffle the cards, and sort them again into two facedown piles. Continue playing.
4. The game ends when there are fewer than three polygons left.
5. The winner is the player with the most polygons.

| | | | |
|---|---|---|---|
| There is only one right angle. | There are one or more right angles. | All angles are right angles. | There are no right angles. |
| There is at least one acute angle. | At least one angle is more than 90°. | All angles are right angles. | There are no right angles. |
| All opposite sides are parallel. | Only one pair of sides is parallel. | There are no parallel sides. | All sides are the same length. |
| All opposite sides are parallel. | Some sides have the same length. | All opposite sides have the same length. | **Wild Card:** Pick your own side property. |

two hundred eighty-nine

STUDENT PAGE

◆ *Student Reference Book*, p. 289

NOTE: Students can store the polygons and *Polygon Capture* Property Cards cut from Activity Sheets 4 and 5 in an envelope or fasten them together with rubber bands or paper clips.

# 2 Ongoing Learning & Practice

## ◆ Solving Multiplication Problems (*Math Journal 1*, p. 83)

INDEPENDENT ACTIVITY 

Students estimate the products and solve only those problems with an estimated product greater than 3,000.

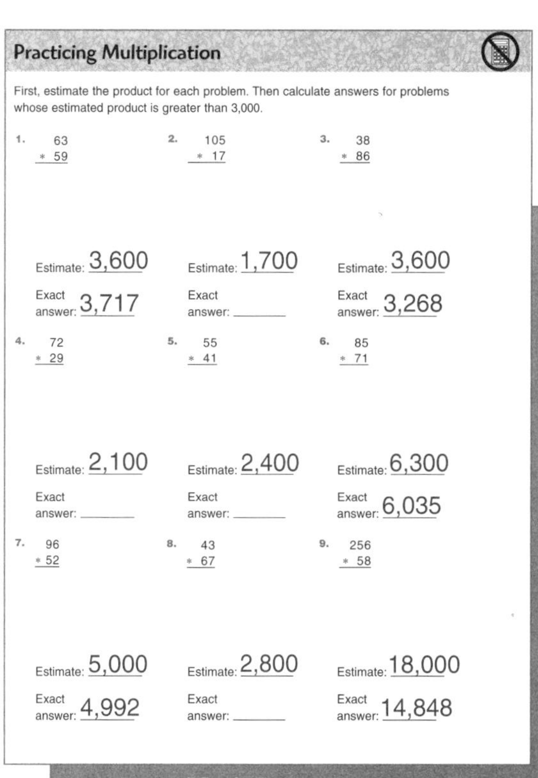

**Practicing Multiplication**

First, estimate the product for each problem. Then calculate answers for problems whose estimated product is greater than 3,000.

| Problem | Estimate | Exact answer |
|---|---|---|
| 1. 63 * 59 | 3,600 | 3,717 |
| 2. 105 * 17 | 1,700 | |
| 3. 38 * 86 | 3,600 | 3,268 |
| 4. 72 * 29 | 2,100 | |
| 5. 55 * 41 | 2,400 | |
| 6. 85 * 71 | 6,300 | 6,035 |
| 7. 96 * 52 | 5,000 | 4,992 |
| 8. 43 * 67 | 2,800 | |
| 9. 256 * 58 | 18,000 | 14,848 |

STUDENT PAGE

◆ *Math Journal 1*, p. 83

## ◆ Math Boxes 3.7 (*Math Journal 1*, p. 84)

INDEPENDENT ACTIVITY 

**Mixed Review** Math Boxes in this lesson are paired with Math Boxes in Lessons 3.5 and 3.9. The skill in Problem 1 is a prerequisite for Unit 4.

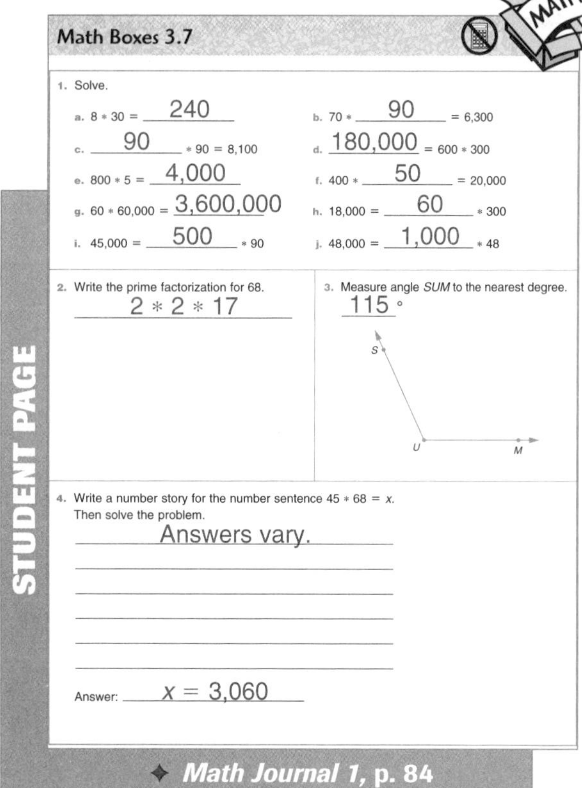

Math Boxes 3.7

1. Solve.

a. 8 * 30 = 240
b. 70 * 90 = 6,300
c. 90 * 90 = 8,100
d. 180,000 = 600 * 300
e. 800 * 5 = 4,000
f. 400 * 50 = 20,000
g. 60 * 60,000 = 3,600,000
h. 18,000 = 60 * 300
i. 45,000 = 500 * 90
j. 48,000 = 1,000 * 48

2. Write the prime factorization for 68.
2 * 2 * 17

3. Measure angle *SUM* to the nearest degree.
115 °

4. Write a number story for the number sentence 45 * 68 = *x*.
Then solve the problem.
Answers vary.

Answer: *x* = 3,060

STUDENT PAGE

Math Journal 1, p. 84

## Study Link 3.7 (*Math Masters*, p. 247)

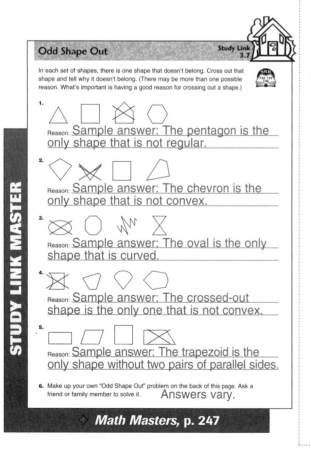

**Home Connection** Students solve "Odd Shape Out" problems, in which they identify one shape that is different from others in a set and tell why it is different. Students then make up their own "Odd Shape Out" problems.

# 3 Options for Individualizing

## RETEACHING Sorting Attribute Blocks by Two Properties

SMALL-GROUP ACTIVITY  **15–30 min** 

Have each student take an attribute block at random. Start with all students in the middle of the classroom. Ask students with thick blocks to go to one side of the room and students with thin blocks to go to the other side of the room. Then ask students with a circle to go to the front of the room, remaining on the same side of the room. Then ask students with a polygon to go to the back of the room, remaining on the same side of the room. There should now be four groups of students—thin polygons, thick polygons, thin circles, and thick circles.

Discuss the characteristics of each group. Repeat the exercise, sorting the blocks by other properties.

## ENRICHMENT Reading about Polygons

INDEPENDENT ACTIVITY  **15–30 min**

**Literature Link** Read the following book to the class, or have students read it on their own.

*The Greedy Triangle*

*Summary:* A dissatisfied triangle goes to the "Shapeshifter" and asks for one more angle and one more side. The shape then continually asks the Shapeshifter for one more angle and one more side.

Discuss the roles of various polygons. Students write a story about a day in the life of a certain polygon, focusing on where it appears in the world around them.

Students could instead write a story about a day in their lives without a certain polygon. For example, *How would a day be different without rectangles? What would your house look like?*

**Odd Shape Out** — Study Link 3.7

In each set of shapes, there is one shape that doesn't belong. Cross out that shape and tell why it doesn't belong. (There may be more than one possible reason. What's important is having a good reason for crossing out a shape.)

SRB 132 135 136

1. Reason: Sample answer: The pentagon is the only shape that is not regular.

2. Reason: Sample answer: The chevron is the only shape that is not convex.

3. Reason: Sample answer: The oval is the only shape that is curved.

4. Reason: Sample answer: The crossed-out shape is the only one that is not convex.

5. Reason: Sample answer: The trapezoid is the only shape without two pairs of parallel sides.

6. Make up your own "Odd Shape Out" problem on the back of this page. Ask a friend or family member to solve it. Answers vary.

STUDY LINK MASTER

Math Masters, p. 247

# 3.8 Regular Tessellations

**OBJECTIVES** **To introduce tessellations; and to discover which regular polygons tessellate and which do not.**

| summaries | materials |
|---|---|
| **1 Teaching the Lesson** | |
| Students are introduced to the history and concept of tessellations; they explore regular tessellations and decide which regular polygons tessellate and which do not. [Geometry] | ☐ *Math Journal 1,* pp. 86 and 87<br>☐ *Student Reference Book,* pp. 150 and 151<br>☐ Study Link 3.7<br>☐ Teaching Master (*Math Masters,* p. 31)<br>☐ Geometry Template ☐ scissors |
| **2 Ongoing Learning & Practice** | |
| Students play *Angle Tangle* to practice estimating and measuring angles. [Geometry; Measurement and Reference Frames]<br>Students practice and maintain skills through Math Boxes and Study Link activities. | ☐ *Math Journal 1,* p. 85<br>☐ *Student Reference Book,* p. 258<br>☐ Study Link Master (*Math Masters,* p. 248)<br>☐ Geometry Template (or protractor and straightedge)<br>***See* Advance Preparation** |
| **3 Options for Individualizing** | |
| **Extra Practice** Students make tessellations with pattern blocks and record them on paper. [Geometry]<br>**Enrichment** Students read and discuss a story about polygons that tessellate. [Geometry] | ☐ pattern blocks<br>☐ Geometry Template (optional)<br>☐ *A Cloak for the Dreamer*<br>***See* Advance Preparation** |

### Additional Information

**Advance Preparation** For the Study Link in Part 2, students are asked to collect examples for a Tessellation Museum. You may want to prepare a space in your classroom for this museum.

For the optional Enrichment activity in Part 3, you will need to obtain a copy of the book *A Cloak for the Dreamer* by Aileen Friedman (A Marilyn Burns Brainy Day Book, Scholastic, 1994).

**Vocabulary** • **regular polygon** • **tessellation** • **regular tessellation** • **tessellate**

## Getting Started

### Math Message

*Follow the directions on* Math Masters, *page 31.*

### Study Link 3.7 Follow-Up

Have students share their answers to the "Odd Shape Out" problems. If time permits, have several students pose the problems that they created.

### Mental Math and Reflexes

Students use estimation to answer questions like the following:

- Frieda has $12.00. Does she have enough money to buy 7 pounds of apples at $1.49 per pound? yes
- Jimmy reads about 47 pages an hour and reads 1 hour each day. Will he be able to finish a 283-page book in a week? yes
- Mark wants to take his two best friends to lunch. He has $20.00. Does he have enough to buy three hamburgers at $2.49 each, three large drinks at $1.59 each, and three orders of fries at $2.18 each? yes

Have volunteers share their strategies for solving the problems.

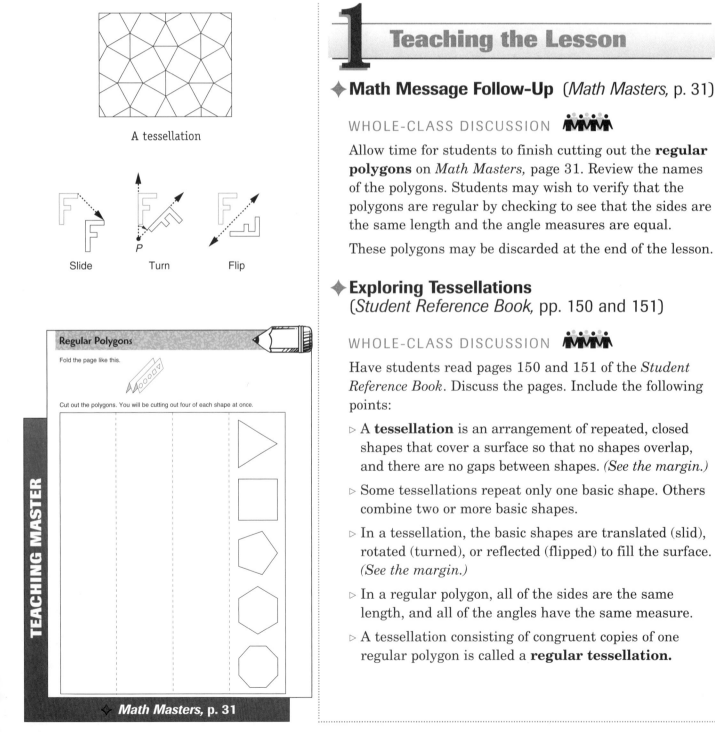

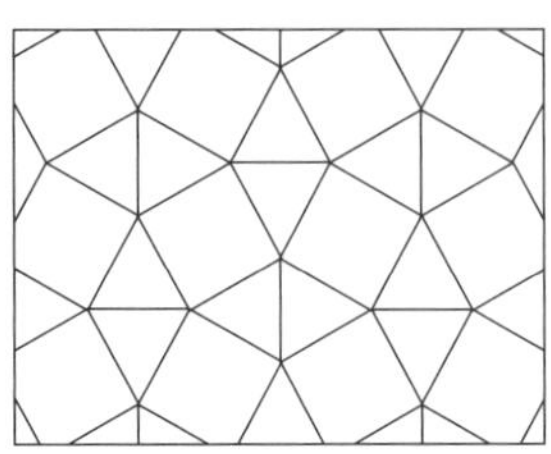

A tessellation

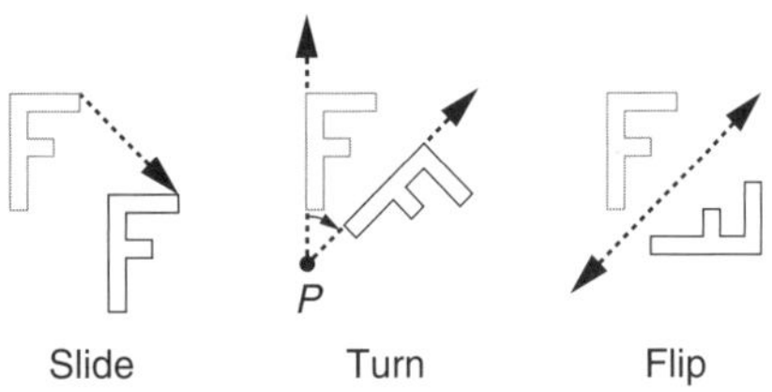


Slide Turn Flip

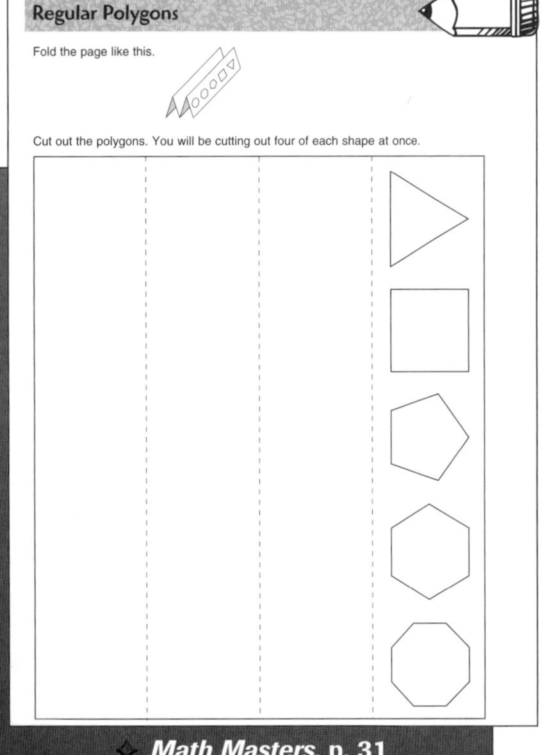

Regular Polygons

Fold the page like this.

Cut out the polygons. You will be cutting out four of each shape at once.

TEACHING MASTER

*Math Masters,* p. 31

# 1 Teaching the Lesson

## Math Message Follow-Up (*Math Masters,* p. 31)

WHOLE-CLASS DISCUSSION

Allow time for students to finish cutting out the **regular polygons** on *Math Masters,* page 31. Review the names of the polygons. Students may wish to verify that the polygons are regular by checking to see that the sides are the same length and the angle measures are equal.

These polygons may be discarded at the end of the lesson.

## Exploring Tessellations (*Student Reference Book,* pp. 150 and 151)

WHOLE-CLASS DISCUSSION

Have students read pages 150 and 151 of the *Student Reference Book*. Discuss the pages. Include the following points:

- A **tessellation** is an arrangement of repeated, closed shapes that cover a surface so that no shapes overlap, and there are no gaps between shapes. *(See the margin.)*
- Some tessellations repeat only one basic shape. Others combine two or more basic shapes.
- In a tessellation, the basic shapes are translated (slid), rotated (turned), or reflected (flipped) to fill the surface. *(See the margin.)*
- In a regular polygon, all of the sides are the same length, and all of the angles have the same measure.
- A tessellation consisting of congruent copies of one regular polygon is called a **regular tessellation.**

Have students identify tessellations that they see around them—in ceiling or floor tiles, carpet designs, designs on clothing, and so on. Ask which of these tessellations use only one shape, and whether any are made with regular polygons. (For example, the floor or ceiling may be tiled with squares.)

### ✦ Exploring the Basic Shapes in Regular Tessellations (*Math Journal 1,* pp. 86 and 87; *Math Masters,* p. 31)

PARTNER ACTIVITY

Students use the regular polygons that they cut out from *Math Masters,* page 31 to help them complete the tables on journal pages 86 and 87 and answer the questions on journal page 87.

For each of the given regular polygons, partners must decide whether the polygon can be used to create a regular tessellation. Have students use their Geometry Templates to draw an example of each tessellation. For polygons that do not tessellate, the drawing should show either an overlap or a gap in the design.

Students share their results from the journal page with the class. Verify that all students have discovered that only the triangle, square, and hexagon can be used to create regular tessellations. The other two regular polygons will not **tessellate.**

Have volunteers explain why they think there are only three regular tessellations. Each angle in a regular pentagon is 108°. No multiple of 108° equals 360°, so there will be overlaps or gaps if pentagons are arranged around a point. The angles in polygons with seven or more sides are too big. If three such polygons are arranged around a point, they will overlap. If only two are used, there will be a gap.

**Regular Tessellations**

1. A **regular polygon** is a polygon in which all sides are the same length and all angles have the same measure. Circle the regular polygons below.

2. In the table below, write the name of each regular polygon under its picture. Then, using the polygons that you cut out from Activity Sheet 4, decide whether each polygon can be used to create a regular tessellation. Record your answers in the middle column. In the last column, use your Geometry Template to draw examples showing how the polygons tessellate or don't tessellate. Record any gaps or overlaps.

| Polygon | Tessellates? (yes or no) | Draw an Example |
|---|---|---|
| triangle | yes | |
| square | yes | |
| pentagon | no | gap |

STUDENT PAGE

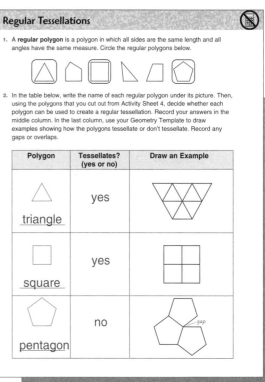

✦ *Math Journal 1,* p. 86

**Regular Tessellations** (cont.)

| Polygon | Tessellates? (yes or no) | Draw an Example |
|---|---|---|
| hexagon | yes | |
| octagon | no | overlap |

3. Which of the polygons can be used to create regular tessellations? Triangles, squares, and hexagons

4. Explain how you know that these are the only ones. Three pentagons leave a gap, and 4 pentagons create an overlap. For regular polygons that have 7 or more sides, 2 shapes leave a gap and 3 shapes create an overlap.

STUDENT PAGE

✦ *Math Journal 1,* p. 87

## 2 Ongoing Learning & Practice

### ✦ Playing *Angle Tangle* (*Student Reference Book,* p. 258)

PARTNER ACTIVITY

Students play *Angle Tangle* to practice estimating and measuring angles. For detailed instructions, see page 258 of the *Student Reference Book.*

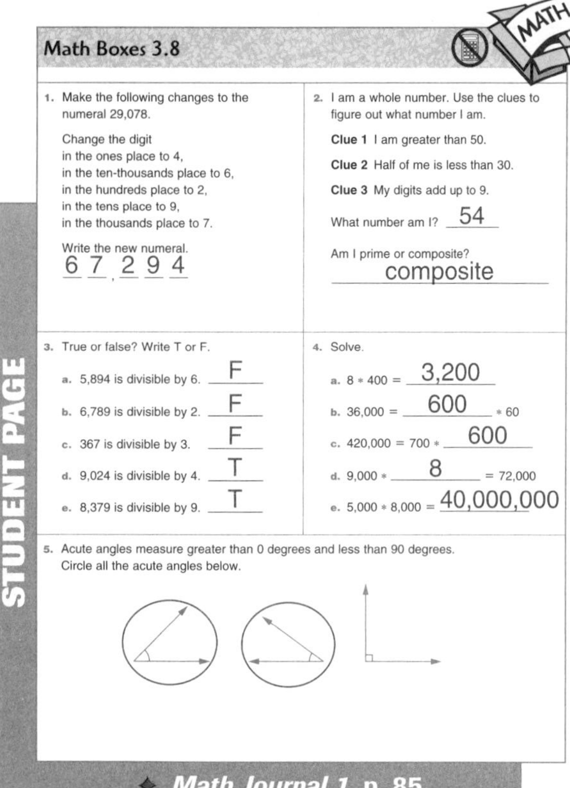

Math Boxes 3.8

1. Make the following changes to the numeral 29,078.

Change the digit
in the ones place to 4,
in the ten-thousands place to 6,
in the hundreds place to 2,
in the tens place to 9,
in the thousands place to 7.

Write the new numeral.
6 7 , 2 9 4

2. I am a whole number. Use the clues to figure out what number I am.

**Clue 1** I am greater than 50.

**Clue 2** Half of me is less than 30.

**Clue 3** My digits add up to 9.

What number am I? 54

Am I prime or composite? composite

3. True or false? Write T or F.

a. 5,894 is divisible by 6. F

b. 6,789 is divisible by 2. F

c. 367 is divisible by 3. F

d. 9,024 is divisible by 4. T

e. 8,379 is divisible by 9. T

4. Solve.

a. 8 * 400 = 3,200

b. 36,000 = 600 * 60

c. 420,000 = 700 * 600

d. 9,000 * 8 = 72,000

e. 5,000 * 8,000 = 40,000,000

5. Acute angles measure greater than 0 degrees and less than 90 degrees. Circle all the acute angles below.

STUDENT PAGE

◆ *Math Journal 1,* p. 85

# ◆ Math Boxes 3.8 (*Math Journal 1,* p. 85)

INDEPENDENT ACTIVITY 

**Mixed Review** Math Boxes in this lesson are paired with Math Boxes in Lessons 3.6 and 3.10. The skill in Problem 1 is a prerequisite for Unit 4.

# ◆ Study Link 3.8 (*Math Masters,* p. 248)

**Home Connection** Students collect tessellations. You may want to allow students more than one night to complete this assignment. Display their work in a Tessellation Museum.

NOTE: Several math-supply catalogs offer paper pattern blocks. These are already cut to the correct shapes and colors. They only need to be separated and glued down. Tessellmania™ is an excellent computer program for exploring tessellations.

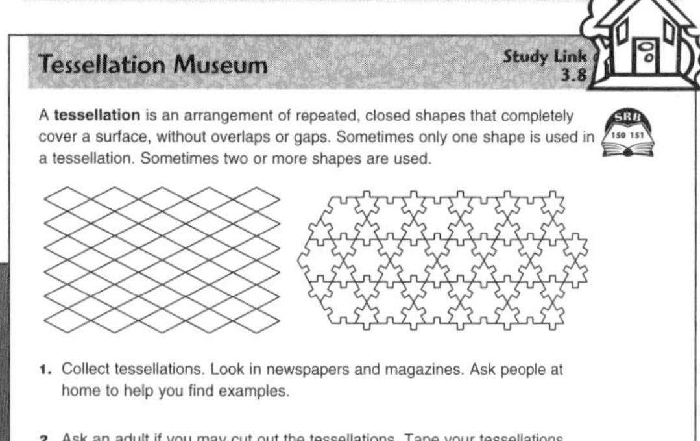

Tessellation Museum — Study Link 3.8

A **tessellation** is an arrangement of repeated, closed shapes that completely cover a surface, without overlaps or gaps. Sometimes only one shape is used in a tessellation. Sometimes two or more shapes are used.

SRB 150 151

1. Collect tessellations. Look in newspapers and magazines. Ask people at home to help you find examples.

2. Ask an adult if you may cut out the tessellations. Tape your tessellations onto this page in the space below.

3. If you can't find tessellations in newspapers or magazines, look around your home at furniture, wallpaper, tablecloths, or clothing. In the space below, sketch the tessellations you find.

STUDY LINK MASTER

◆ *Math Masters,* p. 248

# 3 Options for Individualizing

## ◆ EXTRA PRACTICE Making Tessellations with Pattern Blocks

INDEPENDENT ACTIVITY  **15–30 min** 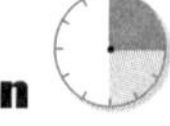

**Art Link** Students use pattern blocks to create tessellating patterns. They trace their patterns onto a piece of paper, either by tracing around the blocks or by using the Geometry Template. They might color their patterns in a way that emphasizes repeating elements.

## ◆ ENRICHMENT Reading about Polygons That Tessellate

SMALL-GROUP ACTIVITY  **5–15 min** 

**Literature Link** Read the following book with students.

***A Cloak for the Dreamer***

*Summary:* Tailors design patchwork cloaks made of rectangles, squares, triangles, and circles. The cloak made of circles is unacceptable because it has open spaces. The tailors think of a unique way to fix the cloak.

Discuss why the patchwork cloaks made of rectangles, squares, triangles, and hexagons did not have any open spaces. Ask, *Why was this not possible with the cloak made of circles?*

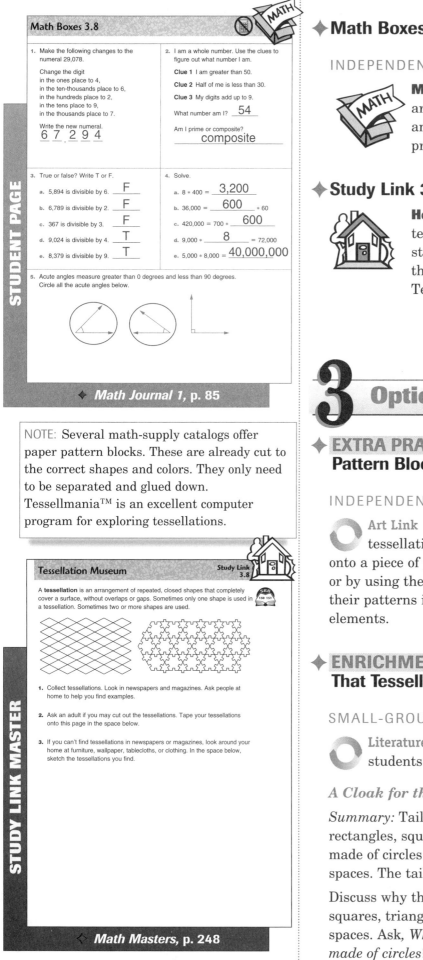

# 3.9 Angles of Polygons

**OBJECTIVE** **To find the sum of the measures of the angles in any polygon.**

| summaries | materials |
|---|---|
| **1 Teaching the Lesson** | |
| Students measure to find angle sums for triangles, quadrangles, pentagons, and hexagons; they use the pattern in these sums to devise a method for finding the angle sum for any polygon. [Geometry; Patterns, Functions, and Algebra] | □ *Math Journal 1,* pp. 88–92 □ Study Link 3.8<br>□ Transparency (*Math Masters,* p. 32; optional)<br>□ Assessment Master (*Math Masters,* p. 479; optional)<br>□ Geometry Template (or protractor and straightedge) |
| **2 Ongoing Learning & Practice** | |
| Students solve attribute puzzles. [Geometry; Patterns, Functions, and Algebra]<br>Students practice and maintain skills through Math Boxes and Study Link activities. | □ *Math Journal 1,* pp. 93 and 94<br>□ Study Link Master (*Math Masters,* p. 249) |
| **3 Options for Individualizing** | |
| **Enrichment** Students investigate whether all quadrangles will tessellate. [Geometry; Patterns, Functions, and Algebra] | □ Teaching Master (*Math Masters,* p. 33)<br>□ paper ($8\frac{1}{2}$" by 11")<br>□ cardstock (optional) □ scissors<br>***See*** **Advance Preparation** |

**Additional Information**

**Advance Preparation** For the optional Enrichment activity in Part 3, you may want to do the tessellation activity yourself with convex and nonconvex quadrangles, so that you can help students see how the angles fit together.

## Getting Started

### Mental Math and Reflexes

Students solve problems like the following:

- 70 [6s] 420
- 70 [60s] 4,200
- 70 [600s] 42,000
- 50 [9s] 450
- 50 [90s] 4,500
- 50 [900s] 45,000
- 80 [4s] 320
- 80 [40s] 3,200
- 80 [400s] 32,000

Continue as time allows.

### Math Message

*Use a straightedge to carefully draw a big triangle on a sheet of paper. Measure its angles. Find the sum of the angle measures.*

### Study Link 3.8 Follow-Up

Students share their tessellations with the class. Consider displaying their work in a Tessellation Museum.

# 1 Teaching the Lesson

## ✦ Math Message Follow-Up

WHOLE-CLASS DISCUSSION 

On the board, draw a line plot to record the sums of the angles found by students. Label it from about 175° to 185°.

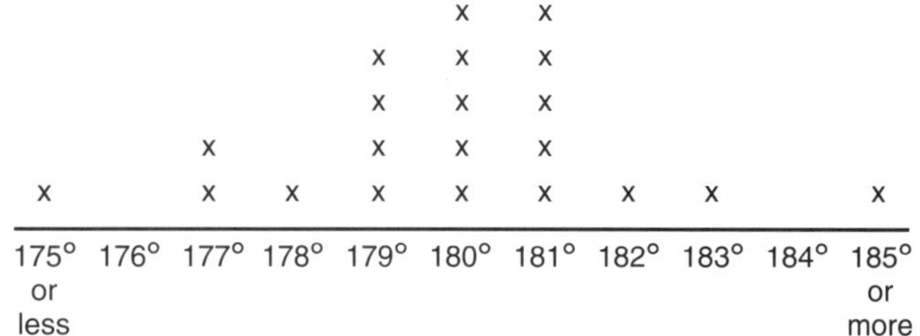


Sample data

- What is the maximum sum of the angles?
- What is the minimum sum of the angles?
- What is the median sum of the angles?

NOTE: Precise language would call for writing and saying "the sum of the measures of the angles" instead of "the sum of the angles." But it is common in mathematics to use the shorter phrase.

A range of sums is to be expected, because measurements are never exact and because some of the students' drawings may have sides that are not straight or do not meet exactly. Stress that if a triangle is accurately drawn and its angles are measured exactly, the sum of the angles will be 180°. To verify this, have students tear the three angles off their triangles as shown below.

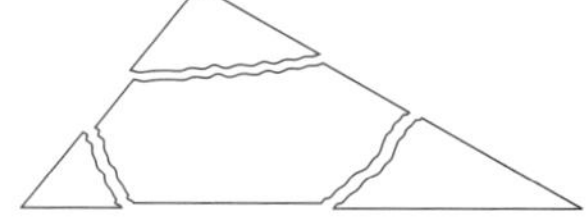

Next, have students arrange their three angles next to each other so that they line up as shown below. Ask what the measure of a straight angle is. 180° Therefore, the sum of the three angles is 180°. Have students check their neighbors' configurations so that they can see that various triangles all have a total angle measure of 180°.

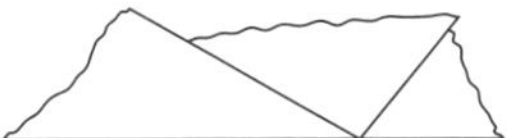

Students' angle measures may seem to total slightly more or less than 180°, since their original triangles may not be accurate.

## Finding the Sums of the Angles in Quadrangles, Pentagons, and Hexagons
(*Math Journal 1,* pp. 88 and 89)

SMALL-GROUP ACTIVITY

Students explore sums of angles in quadrangles and pentagons. After working in groups on either quadrangles or pentagons, students combine data from the whole class, find a pattern in the data, and use the pattern to make a prediction about the sum of the angles in a heptagon.

Results about angle measures in polygons refer to the measures of *interior* angles. In convex polygons, like the one shown below, this is probably obvious.

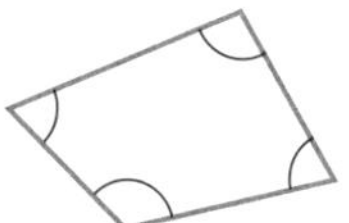

In nonconvex polygons, at least one of the interior angles in the sum is a reflex angle with a measure greater than 180°.

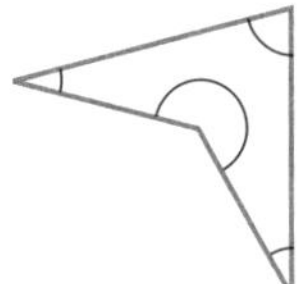

Students work in groups of three to five. Have some groups work on quadrangles and the others on pentagons. Students work through Problems 1–7 on journal pages 88 and 89. Allow time for enough students to do Problem 7 so that data on hexagons is also available for the following discussion.

**Angles in Quadrangles and Pentagons**

1. Circle the kind of polygon your group is working on.

   quadrangle pentagon

2. Below, use a straightedge to carefully draw the kind of polygon your group is working on. Your polygon should look different from the ones drawn by others in your group, but it should have the same number of sides.

   Drawings vary.

3. Measure the angles in your polygon. Write each measure in the angle.

   Answers vary for individual angle measurements.

4. Find the sum of the angles in your polygon. _____°

   Answers vary, but the total sum of the angles should be close to 360° for quadrangles and 540° for pentagons.

STUDENT PAGE

**Math Journal 1, p. 88**

**Angles in Quadrangles and Pentagons** (cont.)

5. Record your group's data below.

| Group Member's Name | Sketch of Polygon | Sum of Angles |
|---|---|---|
| | | |
| | | |
| | | |
| | | |
| | | |

Drawings of polygons vary. The sum of the angles vary but should be close to 360° for quadrangles and 540° for pentagons.

6. Find the median of the angle sums for your group. _____°

   Answers vary but should be close to 360° for quadrangles and 540° for pentagons.

7. If you have time, draw a hexagon. Measure its angles with a protractor. Find the sum.

   Sum of the angles in a hexagon = 720 °

STUDENT PAGE

**Math Journal 1, p. 89**

## Angles in Quadrangles and Pentagons (cont.)

8. Record the class data below.

| Sum of the Angles in a Quadrangle | |
|---|---|
| Group | Group Median |
| | |
| | |
| | |
| | |
| | |

| Sum of the Angles in a Pentagon | |
|---|---|
| Group | Group Median |
| | |
| | |
| | |
| | |
| | |

Answers vary but the group median should be close to 360° for a quadrangle and 540° for a pentagon.

9. Find the class median for each polygon. For the triangle, use the median from the Math Message.

| Sums of Polygon Angles | |
|---|---|
| Polygon | Class Median |
| triangle | |
| quadrangle | |
| pentagon | |
| hexagon | |

Answers vary, but the group median should be close to 180° for a triangle, 360° for a quadrangle, 540° for a pentagon, and 720° for a hexagon.

10. What pattern do you see in the Sums of Polygon Angles table?
Sample answer: As the number of sides increases by 1, the sum of the angle measures increases by 180°.

STUDENT PAGE

✦ *Math Journal 1,* p. 90

# ✦ Finding the Median for the Sums of the Angles in Triangles, Quadrangles, Pentagons, and Hexagons (*Math Journal 1,* p. 90)

WHOLE-CLASS DISCUSSION

Use the board or an overhead transparency of *Math Masters,* page 32 to collect each group's median angle sum. Have students enter this data in the group median tables in Problem 8 on journal page 90.

Next, fill in the "Sums of Polygon Angles" table in Problem 9.

▷ For a triangle, enter the class median from the Math Message.

▷ For a quadrangle, enter the median of the group medians for a quadrangle.

▷ Do the same for a pentagon.

▷ For a hexagon, collect data from students who did Problem 7 on journal page 89, find the median, and enter it in the table.

The class medians should be close to those shown in red *in the margin,* which are the exact sums.

Have students look for patterns in the Sums of Polygon Angles table and write about what they find in Problem 10.

**Adjusting the Activity** If students have trouble finding the pattern, suggest they look at multiples of 180.

## Angles in Heptagons

1. A heptagon is a polygon with 7 sides. Predict the sum of the angles in a heptagon. 900 °

2. Draw a heptagon below. Measure its angles with a protractor. Write each measure in the angle. Find the sum. Drawings vary.

Sum of the angles in a heptagon = 900 °

3. a. Is your measurement close to your prediction? Answers vary.

b. Why might your prediction and your measurement be different?
Sample answer: Because the angle measurement may not be exact for each angle in the heptagon.

STUDENT PAGE

✦ *Math Journal 1,* p. 91

# ✦ Finding Angle Sums by Dividing Polygons into Triangles (*Math Journal 1,* pp. 90 and 91)

WHOLE-CLASS DISCUSSION

Discuss the patterns students found in the Sums of Polygon Angles table. Ask if anyone can explain why the entries in the Class Median column are increasing by 180°. Suggest that to find an explanation, students think about the sum of the angles in a triangle.

If no one can explain the pattern, show how any quadrangle can be divided into two triangles.

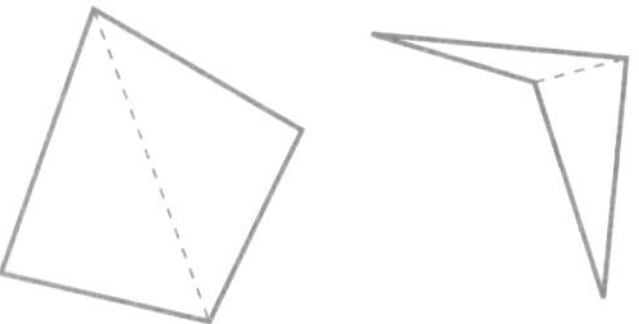

Since the sum of the angles in each triangle is 180°, the angles in the quadrangles must total 2 * 180°, or 360°. Any quadrangle can be divided into two triangles, so the sum of the angles of any quadrangle is 360°.

Similar arguments can be used to show that the sum of the angles in a pentagon must be 3 * 180°, or 540°, and in a hexagon 4 * 180°, or 720°.

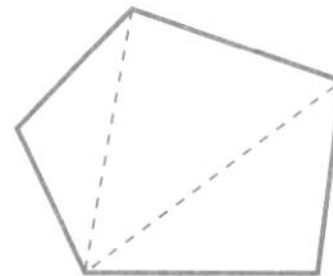

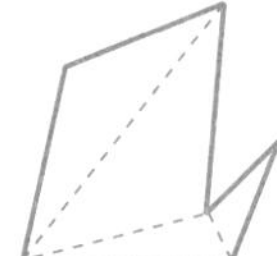

Have partners solve Problems 1–3 about heptagons on journal page 91. They can use the pattern in the table, or they might try dividing a heptagon into triangles to make their prediction. When most students have finished, bring the class together to discuss results.

### Finding Angle Sums for Any Polygon
(*Math Journal 1,* p. 92; *Math Masters,* p. 479)

PARTNER ACTIVITY 

Students complete the journal page. Problem 5 asks them to find the sum of the angles of a 50-gon. Although drawing such a polygon is impractical, one can imagine dividing a 50-gon into triangles. The number of triangles is 2 less than the number of sides, so there would be 48 triangles. Therefore, the sum of the angles would be 48 * 180°, or 8,640°.

**ONGOING ASSESSMENT**

**Use journal page 92 to assess whether students understand how to find the sum of the angles of a polygon. Alternatively, have students complete an Exit Slip explaining in their own words how to find the sum of the angles in a decagon.**

## 2 Ongoing Learning & Practice

### Solving Attribute Puzzles
(*Math Journal 1,* p. 93)

INDEPENDENT ACTIVITY 

Students identify members of a set based on attributes.

**Angles in Any Polygon**

1. Draw a line segment from vertex *A* of this octagon to each of the other vertices except *B* and *H*.

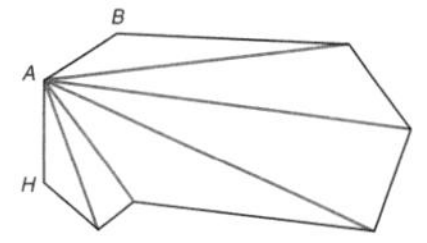

B
A
H

2. How many triangles did you divide the octagon into? 6
3. What is the sum of the angles in this octagon? 1,080 °
4. Ignacio said the sum of his octagon's angles is 1,440°. Below is the picture he drew to show how he found his answer. Explain Ignacio's mistake.
Ignacio should have drawn lines from one vertex to each of the other vertices in his octagon instead of drawing a line between each vertex and a point in the center of his octagon.

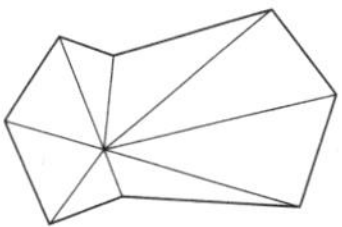

5. A 50-gon is a polygon with 50 sides. How could you find the sum of the angles in a 50-gon? A 50-gon can be divided into 48 triangles. The sum of the angles would be 48 * 180°.

Sum of the angles in a 50-gon = 8,640 °

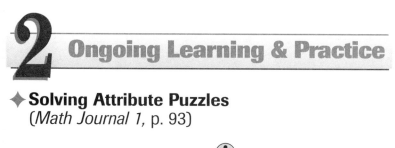

STUDENT PAGE

*Math Journal 1,* p. 92

**Attribute Puzzles**

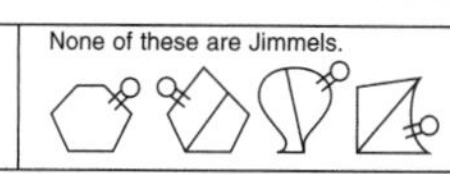

All of these are Jimmels.
None of these are Jimmels.

1. List some attributes of Jimmels. Sample answer: Each Jimmel is a triangle and a second polygon, joined along a common side. A plug figure is attached to one side of the polygon.
2. Circle the Jimmels below.

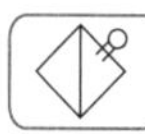   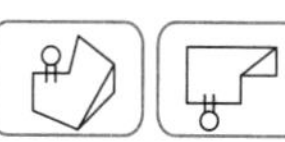

3. Draw your own Jimmel. Drawings vary. Sample drawing provided.

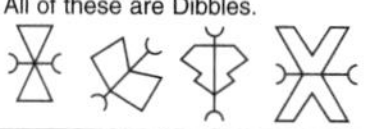

All of these are Dibbles.

None of these are Dibbles.

4. List some attributes of Dibbles. Sample answer: Each Dibble contains a line segment with half-circles at its ends, and includes congruent polygons on the sides of the segment.
5. Circle the Dibbles below.

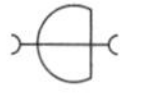   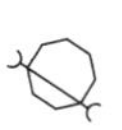 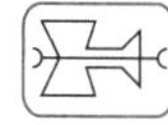

6. Draw your own Dibble. Drawings vary. Sample drawing provided.

STUDENT PAGE

*Math Journal 1,* p. 93

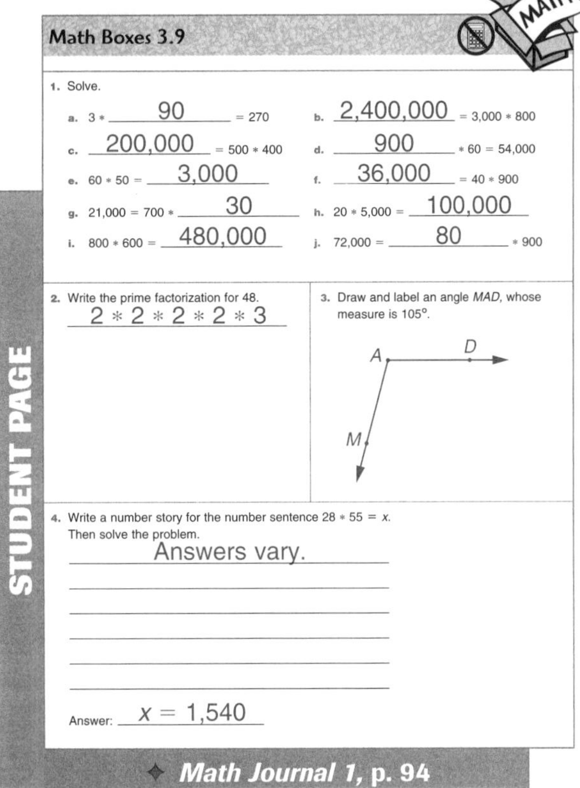
**Math Boxes 3.9**

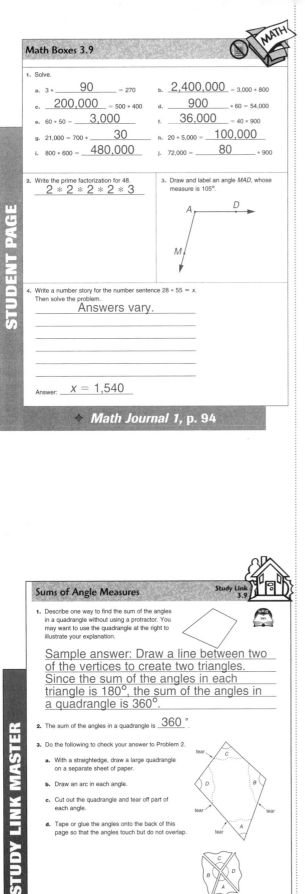

1. Solve.
   a. 3 * 90 = 270
   b. 2,400,000 = 3,000 * 800
   c. 200,000 = 500 * 400
   d. 900 * 60 = 54,000
   e. 60 * 50 = 3,000
   f. 36,000 = 40 * 900
   g. 21,000 = 700 * 30
   h. 20 * 5,000 = 100,000
   i. 800 * 600 = 480,000
   j. 72,000 = 80 * 900

2. Write the prime factorization for 48.
   2 * 2 * 2 * 2 * 3

3. Draw and label an angle *MAD*, whose measure is 105°.



4. Write a number story for the number sentence 28 * 55 = *x*. Then solve the problem.
   Answers vary.

   Answer: *x* = 1,540

STUDENT PAGE

✦ *Math Journal 1,* p. 94

**Sums of Angle Measures** — Study Link 3.9

1. Describe one way to find the sum of the angles in a quadrangle without using a protractor. You may want to use the quadrangle at the right to illustrate your explanation.
   Sample answer: Draw a line between two of the vertices to create two triangles. Since the sum of the angles in each triangle is 180°, the sum of the angles in a quadrangle is 360°.

2. The sum of the angles in a quadrangle is 360°.

3. Do the following to check your answer to Problem 2.
   a. With a straightedge, draw a large quadrangle on a separate sheet of paper.
   b. Draw an arc in each angle.
   c. Cut out the quadrangle and tear off part of each angle.
   d. Tape or glue the angles onto the back of this page so that the angles touch but do not overlap.

tear tear tear tear
C B D A

STUDY LINK MASTER

✦ *Math Masters,* p. 249

## ✦ Math Boxes 3.9 (*Math Journal 1,* p. 94)

INDEPENDENT ACTIVITY 

**Mixed Review** Math Boxes in this lesson are paired with Math Boxes in Lessons 3.5 and 3.7. The skill in Problem 1 is a prerequisite for Unit 4.

## ✦ Study Link 3.9 (*Math Masters,* p. 249)

**Home Connection** Students describe one way to find the sum of the angles of a quadrangle without using a protractor. They investigate finding the sum by tearing off the angles and putting them together around a point.

# 3 Options for Individualizing

## ✦ ENRICHMENT Tessellating Quadrangles (*Math Masters,* p. 33)

INDEPENDENT ACTIVITY  **15–30 min**

Since the sum of the angles in a quadrangle is equal to the number of degrees in a circle, it seems that all quadrangles should tessellate. In this activity, students investigate whether this is true.

Following directions on *Math Masters,* page 33 students cut out six identical quadrangles. They manipulate the quadrangles to see whether they will tessellate, and they tape their results onto a separate piece of paper.

Challenge students to tessellate nonconvex quadrangles. Nonconvex quadrangles will tessellate, but it is more difficult to place the pieces so that all four angles meet. Make sure all angles are correctly labeled to facilitate the process.

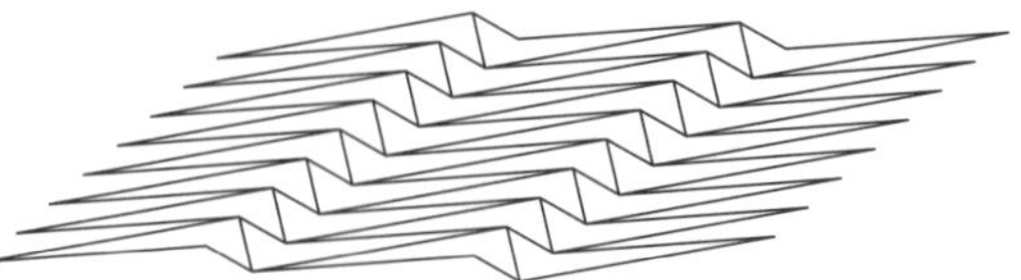

Tessellations with nonconvex quadrangles

Consider making a bulletin board of students' tessellations. Have students color their tessellations.

# 3.10 Solving Problems Using the Geometry Template

**OBJECTIVE** **To use the Geometry Template for problem solving and reviewing polygon attributes and vocabulary.**

| summaries | materials |
| --- | --- |
| **1 Teaching the Lesson** | |
| Students use their Geometry Templates to draw circles; students investigate geometric concepts by solving a variety of problems involving the Geometry Template. [Geometry] | □ *Math Journal 1,* pp. 95–99<br>□ Study Link 3.9<br>□ Geometry Template<br>□ 2 sharp pencils<br>□ sheet of paper at least 17" square (optional)<br>***See*** **Advance Preparation** |
| **2 Ongoing Learning & Practice** | |
| Students practice identifying attributes of polygons by playing *Polygon Capture.* [Geometry; Patterns, Functions, and Algebra]<br>Students practice and maintain skills through Math Boxes and Study Link activities. | □ *Math Journal 1,* p. 100<br>□ *Student Reference Book,* p. 289<br>□ Study Link Master (*Math Masters,* p. 250)<br>□ *Polygon Capture* Pieces and Property Cards (*Math Journals 1 and 2,* Activity Sheets 4 and 5) |
| **3 Options for Individualizing** | |
| **Enrichment** Students solve challenging problems with the Geometry Template. [Geometry]<br>**Reteaching** Students use spatial reasoning to solve tangram problems. [Geometry] | □ Teaching Masters (*Math Masters,* pp. 34–37)<br>□ Geometry Template<br>□ cardstock (optional)<br>□ *Grandfather Tang's Story* □ scissors<br>***See*** **Advance Preparation** |

## Additional Information

**Advance Preparation** Many teachers have found that this lesson can extend over two or more class periods. Many problems can be productively revisited over the next several weeks.

For the problems involving the Geometry Template in Part 1, solve some of the problems yourself first. This will help you to provide guidance and hints for successful strategies.

For the optional Reteaching activity in Part 3, you may want to copy *Math Masters,* page 37 (tangrams) on cardstock. You will need to obtain the book *Grandfather Tang's Story* by Ann Tompert (Crown Publishers, 1990).

**Vocabulary • radius • diameter • parallel • right angle • acute angle • obtuse angle • unit • perimeter • parallelogram • pentagon • kite**

# Getting Started

## Mental Math and Reflexes

Write numbers on the board and ask questions like the following to review rules of divisibility. Students show "thumbs up" if the number is divisible by the stated divisor, "thumbs down" if it is not divisible. If necessary, briefly review the divisibility rules from Lesson 1.5. *Suggestions:*

- Is 645 divisible by 2? down By 3? up By 5? up By 9? down
- Is 852 divisible by 2? up By 3? up By 4? up By 6? up
- Is 570 divisible by 2? up By 3? up By 5? up By 6? up By 9? down By 10? up

## Math Message

*Answer the three questions on the top of journal page 95.*

## Study Link 3.9 Follow-Up

Students share their work with the class. This construction shows that the sum of the angles of any quadrangle is 360°.

# 1 Teaching the Lesson

## ✦ Math Message Follow-Up (*Math Journal 1,* p. 95)

WHOLE-CLASS DISCUSSION 

Students are told to ignore some of the items on the Geometry Template and count the rest, which should yield a total of 24 shapes. $\frac{18}{24}$ or 75% of the shapes are polygons. The five circles and the ellipse are not polygons (nor are the protractor, Percent Circle, or the little holes next to the rulers). $\frac{10}{24}$ or about 42% of the shapes are quadrangles.

## ✦ Drawing Circles with the Geometry Template

WHOLE-CLASS ACTIVITY

Use the overhead projector to demonstrate how to use the circle guides to draw a circle of a specific radius. Since a focus of this lesson is on students' exploring the Geometry Template, spend a minimum amount of time on the demonstration.

1. Place the Geometry Template on a piece of paper.

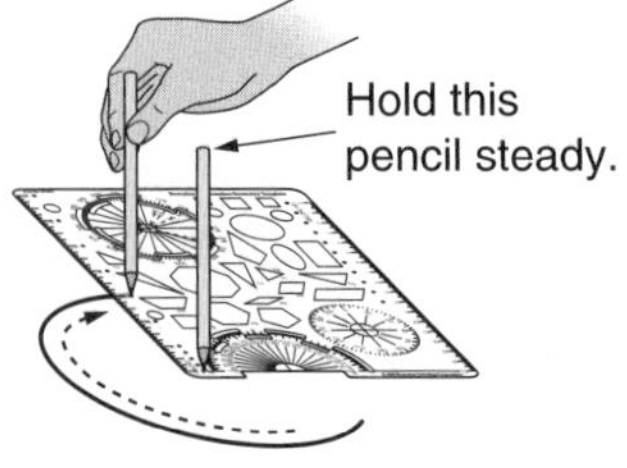
Hold this pencil steady.

STUDENT PAGE

**The Geometry Template**

**Math Message**

Answer the following questions about your Geometry Template. DO NOT count the protractors, Percent Circle, and little holes next to the rulers.

1. How many shapes are on the Geometry Template? 24
2. What fraction of these shapes are polygons? $\frac{3}{4}$
3. What fraction of the shapes are quadrangles? $\frac{10}{24}$

**Problems for the Geometry Template**

The problems on journal pages 96 and 98 are labeled Easy and Moderate. Each problem has been assigned a number of points according to its difficulty.

Complete as many of these problems as you can. Your Geometry Template and a sharp pencil are the only tools you may use. Record and label your answers on the page opposite the problems.

Some of the problems may seem confusing at first. Before asking your teacher for help, try the following:

- Look at the examples on the journal page. Do they help you understand what the problem is asking you to do?
- If you are not sure what a word means, look it up in the Glossary in your *Student Reference Book.* You might also look for help in the geometry section of the *Student Reference Book.*
- Find a classmate who is working on the same problem. Can the two of you work together to find a solution?
- Find a classmate who has completed the problem. Can she or he give you hints about how to solve it?

When the time for this activity has ended, you may want to total the number of points that you have scored. If you didn't have time to complete all these pages, you can continue working on them when you have free time.

Good luck and have fun!

✦ *Math Journal 1,* p. 95

2. Put one pencil in the circle guide at 0 inches and another pencil in the circle guide at 3 inches.
3. Use the pencil at the 0-inch mark as an anchor while you draw a circle around it with the pencil at the 3-inch mark.

This circle has a **radius** of 3 inches and a **diameter** of 6 inches.

Allow a few minutes for students to experiment with drawing circles of different diameters.

## ◆ Solving Problems Using the Geometry Template (*Math Journal 1,* pp. 96–99)

INDEPENDENT ACTIVITY 

Students choose the problems they want to solve on journal pages 96 and 98. Circulate and assist as necessary.

Some students may want to do these problems on their own, while others might prefer to work with a partner.

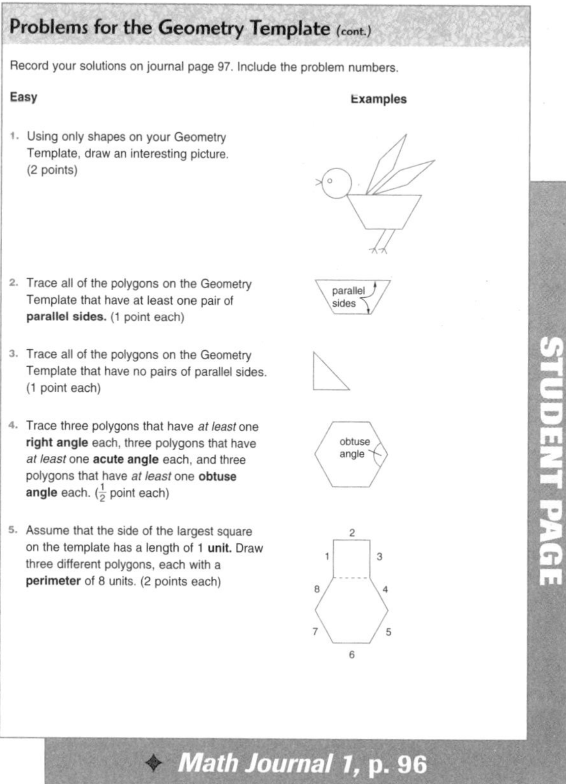

**Problems for the Geometry Template** (cont.)

Record your solutions on journal page 97. Include the problem numbers.

**Easy** — **Examples**

1. Using only shapes on your Geometry Template, draw an interesting picture. (2 points)
2. Trace all of the polygons on the Geometry Template that have at least one pair of **parallel sides.** (1 point each)
3. Trace all of the polygons on the Geometry Template that have no pairs of parallel sides. (1 point each)
4. Trace three polygons that have *at least* one **right angle** each, three polygons that have *at least* one **acute angle** each, and three polygons that have *at least* one **obtuse angle** each. ($\frac{1}{2}$ point each)
5. Assume that the side of the largest square on the template has a length of 1 **unit.** Draw three different polygons, each with a **perimeter** of 8 units. (2 points each)



STUDENT PAGE

◆ *Math Journal 1,* p. 96

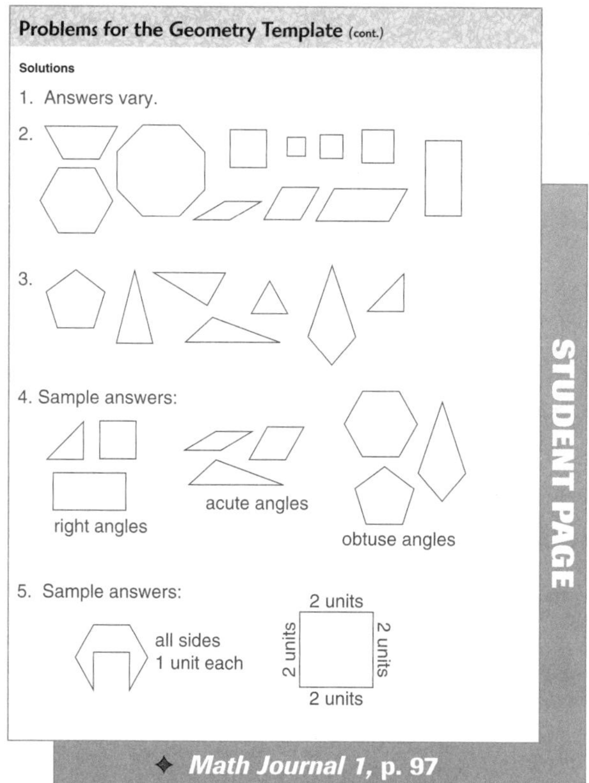

**Problems for the Geometry Template** (cont.)

**Solutions**

1. Answers vary.
2.
3.
4. Sample answers:
5. Sample answers:



STUDENT PAGE

◆ *Math Journal 1,* p. 97

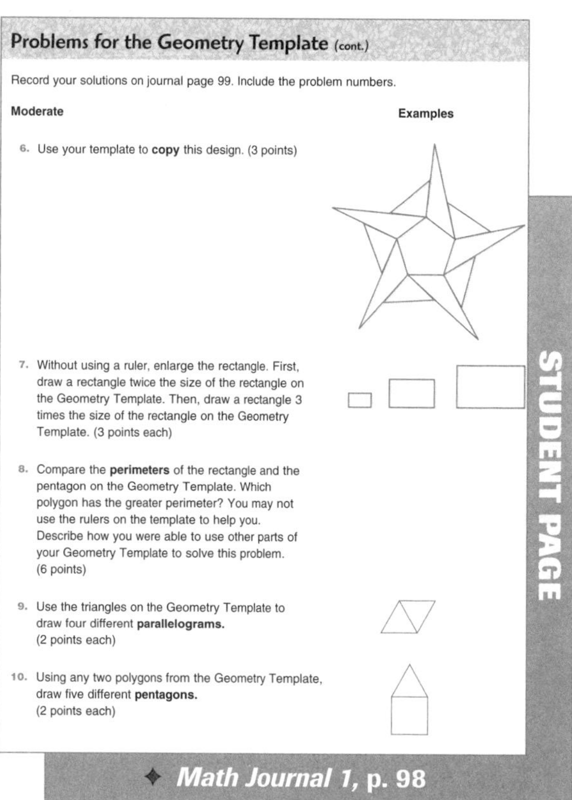

**Problems for the Geometry Template** (cont.)

Record your solutions on journal page 99. Include the problem numbers.

**Moderate** — **Examples**

6. Use your template to **copy** this design. (3 points)
7. Without using a ruler, enlarge the rectangle. First, draw a rectangle twice the size of the rectangle on the Geometry Template. Then, draw a rectangle 3 times the size of the rectangle on the Geometry Template. (3 points each)
8. Compare the **perimeters** of the rectangle and the pentagon on the Geometry Template. Which polygon has the greater perimeter? You may not use the rulers on the template to help you. Describe how you were able to use other parts of your Geometry Template to solve this problem. (6 points)
9. Use the triangles on the Geometry Template to draw four different **parallelograms.** (2 points each)
10. Using any two polygons from the Geometry Template, draw five different **pentagons.** (2 points each)

STUDENT PAGE

◆ *Math Journal 1,* p. 98

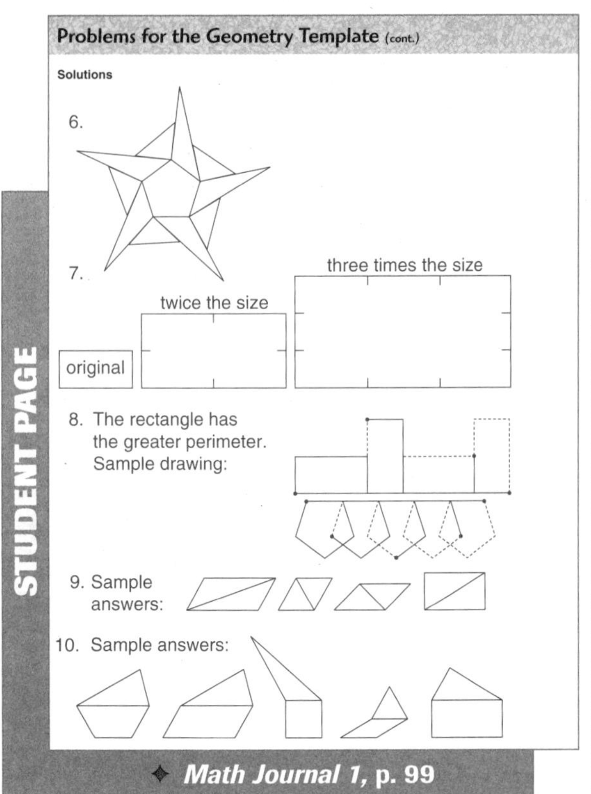
STUDENT PAGE

**Problems for the Geometry Template** (cont.)

Solutions

6.

7. original — twice the size — three times the size

8. The rectangle has the greater perimeter. Sample drawing:

9. Sample answers:

10. Sample answers:

◆ *Math Journal 1,* p. 99

Encourage students to jot down any additional discoveries that they make while using their Geometry Templates. Have students share these additional discoveries at the end of the lesson. Following are some comments on specific problems:

**Problem 7:** One method is to trace a side of the rectangle, slide the Geometry Template along the tracing, trace the same side again, and then trace the other sides in the same way. In this way both the length and the width are doubled. To draw a rectangle 3 times as large, trace each side 3 times.

**Problem 8:** One method is first to trace the five sides of the pentagon end to end, forming a line segment equal in length to the perimeter of the pentagon; and then trace the four sides of the rectangle in the same manner, above the line segment for the pentagon. It should be simple to determine which segment is longer and therefore which figure has the greater perimeter.

NOTE: As students devise solutions, ask them to copy them for a classroom display. Consider having the students add a description of how they obtained their solutions.

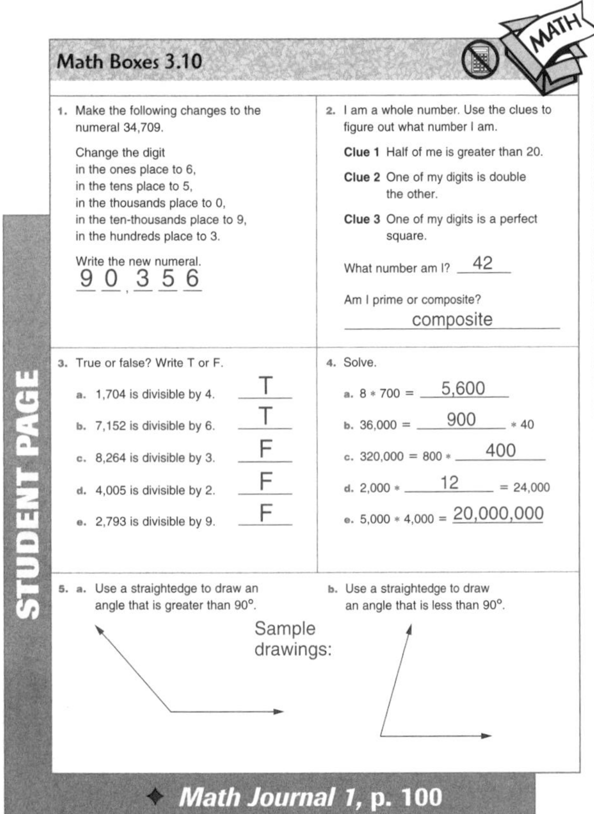
STUDENT PAGE

**Math Boxes 3.10**

1. Make the following changes to the numeral 34,709.

Change the digit
in the ones place to 6,
in the tens place to 5,
in the thousands place to 0,
in the ten-thousands place to 9,
in the hundreds place to 3.

Write the new numeral.
9 0 , 3 5 6

2. I am a whole number. Use the clues to figure out what number I am.

Clue 1 Half of me is greater than 20.

Clue 2 One of my digits is double the other.

Clue 3 One of my digits is a perfect square.

What number am I? 42

Am I prime or composite? composite

3. True or false? Write T or F.

a. 1,704 is divisible by 4. T

b. 7,152 is divisible by 6. T

c. 8,264 is divisible by 3. F

d. 4,005 is divisible by 2. F

e. 2,793 is divisible by 9. F

4. Solve.

a. 8 ∗ 700 = 5,600

b. 36,000 = 900 ∗ 40

c. 320,000 = 800 ∗ 400

d. 2,000 ∗ 12 = 24,000

e. 5,000 ∗ 4,000 = 20,000,000

5. a. Use a straightedge to draw an angle that is greater than 90°.

b. Use a straightedge to draw an angle that is less than 90°.

Sample drawings:

◆ *Math Journal 1,* p. 100

# 2 Ongoing Learning & Practice

## ◆ Playing *Polygon Capture*

(*Math Journals 1 and 2,* Activity Sheets 4 and 5; *Student Reference Book,* p. 289)

PARTNER ACTIVITY 

Students practice identifying attributes of polygons by playing *Polygon Capture.*

## ◆ Math Boxes 3.10 (*Math Journal 1,* p. 100)

INDEPENDENT ACTIVITY 

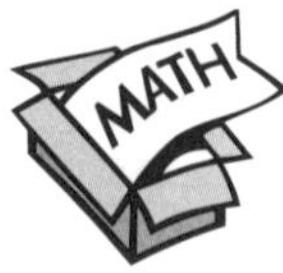


**Mixed Review** Math Boxes in this lesson are paired with Math Boxes in Lessons 3.6 and 3.8. The skill in Problem 1 is a prerequisite for Unit 4.

## ◆ Study Link 3.10 (*Math Masters,* p. 250)

**Home Connection** Students review some of the major concepts of the unit. They draw polygons with specific attributes, find missing angle measurements in two figures, measure a line segment, add angles, and identify a type of polygon.

# 3 Options for Individualizing

## ✦ ENRICHMENT Solving Geometry Template Challenges (*Math Masters,* pp. 34 and 35)

INDEPENDENT ACTIVITY  **15–30 min** 

Portfolio Ideas

Students solve more difficult problems based on the Geometry Template.

**Problem 1:** This problem is similar to Problem 7 on journal page 98, except that there are eight sides instead of four. Also, maintaining the angles might be a bit more difficult.

**Problem 2:** To draw a kite using one of the triangles on the Geometry Template, trace the triangle, flip the template over, and trace the triangle again to get a mirror image of the first tracing.

**Problem 3:** Use the circle guides at the 0-centimeter and 0-inch marks (diagonally across from each other) to draw the largest possible circle.

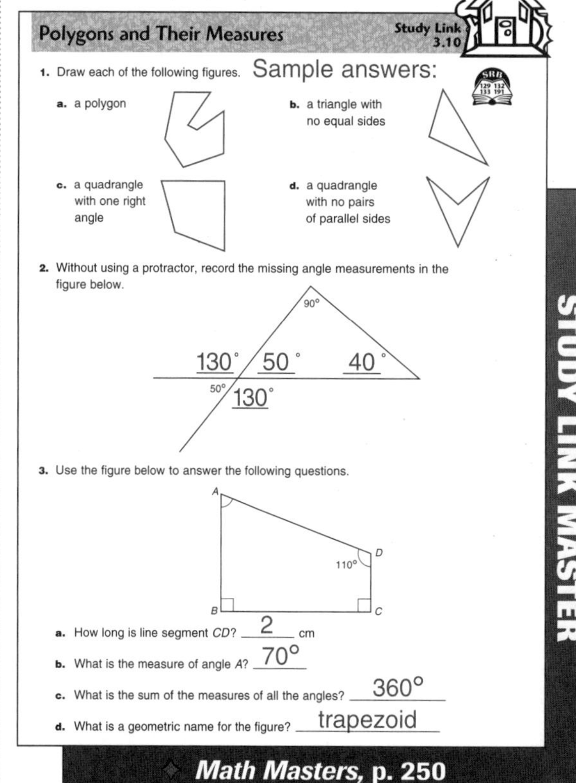

**Polygons and Their Measures** — Study Link 3.10

1. Draw each of the following figures. Sample answers:
   - a. a polygon
   - b. a triangle with no equal sides
   - c. a quadrangle with one right angle
   - d. a quadrangle with no pairs of parallel sides
2. Without using a protractor, record the missing angle measurements in the figure below.



3. Use the figure below to answer the following questions.



   - a. How long is line segment *CD*? 2 cm
   - b. What is the measure of angle *A*? 70°
   - c. What is the sum of the measures of all the angles? 360°
   - d. What is a geometric name for the figure? trapezoid

STUDY LINK MASTER

*Math Masters,* p. 250

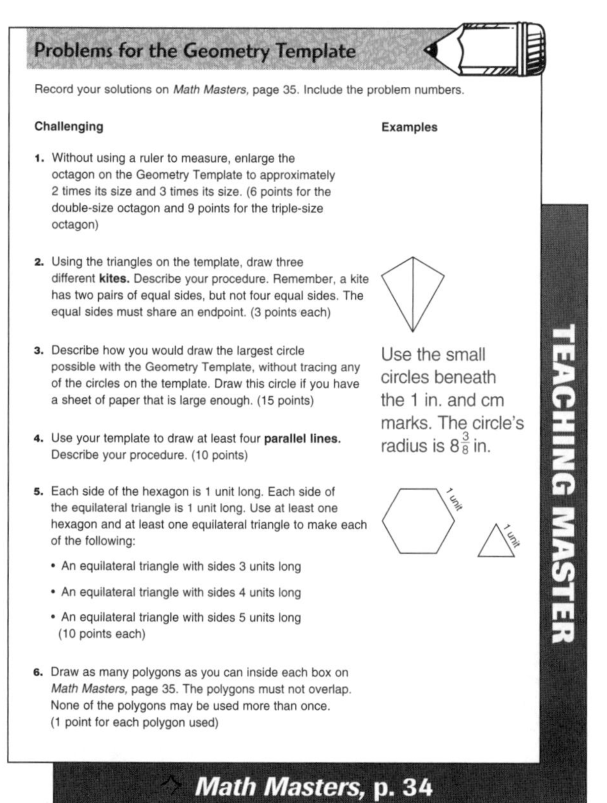

**Problems for the Geometry Template**

Record your solutions on *Math Masters,* page 35. Include the problem numbers.

**Challenging** | **Examples**

1. Without using a ruler to measure, enlarge the octagon on the Geometry Template to approximately 2 times its size and 3 times its size. (6 points for the double-size octagon and 9 points for the triple-size octagon)
2. Using the triangles on the template, draw three different **kites.** Describe your procedure. Remember, a kite has two pairs of equal sides, but not four equal sides. The equal sides must share an endpoint. (3 points each)
3. Describe how you would draw the largest circle possible with the Geometry Template, without tracing any of the circles on the template. Draw this circle if you have a sheet of paper that is large enough. (15 points)
   Use the small circles beneath the 1 in. and cm marks. The circle's radius is $8\frac{3}{8}$ in.
4. Use your template to draw at least four **parallel lines.** Describe your procedure. (10 points)
5. Each side of the hexagon is 1 unit long. Each side of the equilateral triangle is 1 unit long. Use at least one hexagon and at least one equilateral triangle to make each of the following:
   - An equilateral triangle with sides 3 units long
   - An equilateral triangle with sides 4 units long
   - An equilateral triangle with sides 5 units long (10 points each)



6. Draw as many polygons as you can inside each box on *Math Masters,* page 35. The polygons must not overlap. None of the polygons may be used more than once. (1 point for each polygon used)

TEACHING MASTER

*Math Masters,* p. 34

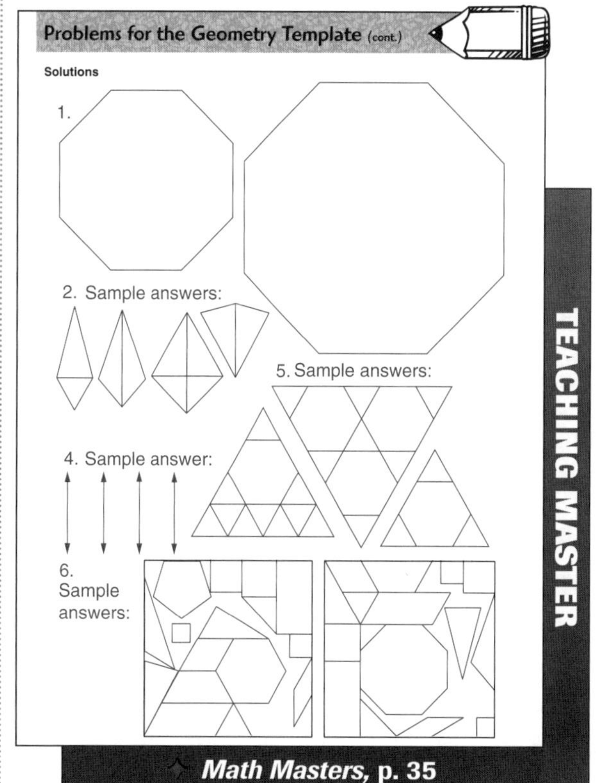

**Problems for the Geometry Template** (cont.)

**Solutions**



TEACHING MASTER

*Math Masters,* p. 35

*Math Masters*, p. 36

**Problem 4:** Use a side of the Geometry Template to draw a line segment. Place a side of one of the template triangles on this segment. Trace one of the other sides of the triangle. Slide the triangle along the first line segment that you drew and trace the same side of the triangle as before. The two tracings should be parallel.

Continue in this manner to create a series of parallel tracings. Put arrowheads on the ends of the tracings, and they will represent parallel lines.

## ✦ RETEACHING Solving Tangram Puzzles
(*Math Masters*, pp. 36 and 37)

PARTNER ACTIVITY  **15–30 min**

Students cut out tangram shapes and solve tangram puzzles.

**Literature Link** Read the following story to the class, or have students read it to themselves.

***Grandfather Tang's Story***

*Summary:* A tale of two foxes who try to outdo each other by changing themselves into different animals. Each fox is represented by the seven tangram pieces.

*Math Masters*, p. 37

# 3.11 Unit 3 Review and Assessment

**OBJECTIVE** **To review and assess students' progress on the material covered in Unit 3.**

## 1 Assess Progress

| learning goals | activities |
|---|---|
| 3a **Developing Goal** Determine angle measures based on relationships between angles. **(Lessons 3.3–3.5 and 3.9)** | ❑ Written Assessment, Problems 1–3 |
| 3b **Developing/Secure Goal** Estimate the measure of an angle. **(Lessons 3.6 and 3.8)** | ❑ Slate Assessment, Problem 5<br>❑ Written Assessment, Problems 8, 17, and 18 |
| 3c **Developing/Secure Goal** Measure an angle to within 2°. **(Lessons 3.4 and 3.9)** | ❑ Written Assessment, Problems 4–6 |
| 3d **Developing/Secure Goal** Identify types of angles. **(Lessons 3.4 and 3.5)** | ❑ Slate Assessment, Problem 5<br>❑ Written Assessment, Problems 4–8, 17, and 18 |
| 3e **Developing/Secure Goal** Identify types of triangles. **(Lesson 3.6)** | ❑ Written Assessment, Problems 10–14 |
| 3f **Secure Goal** Identify place value in numbers to billions. **(Lesson 3.2)** | ❑ Slate Assessment, Problem 3<br>❑ Written Assessment, Problem 9 |
| 3g **Secure Goal** Know properties of polygons. **(Lesson 3.7)** | ❑ Written Assessment, Problems 13–14, 17, and 18 |
| 3h **Secure Goal** Define and create tessellations. **(Lesson 3.8)** | ❑ Written Assessment, Problems 15 and 16 |

**materials**

- ☐ *Math Journal 1,* p. 101
- ☐ Study Link 3.10
- ☐ *Student Reference Book,* pp. 258 and 289
- ☐ Assessment Masters (*Math Masters,* pp. 384–386)
- ☐ *Polygon Capture* Pieces and Property Cards (*Math Journals 1 and 2,* Activity Sheets 4 and 5)
- ☐ slate
- ☐ Geometry Template (or protractor and straightedge)

## 2 Build Background for Unit 4

| summaries | materials |
|---|---|
| Students practice and maintain skills through Math Boxes and Study Link activities. | ☐ *Math Journal 1,* p. 102<br>☐ Study Link Masters (*Math Masters,* pp. 251–254) |

Each **learning goal** listed above indicates a level of performance that might be expected at this point in the *Everyday Mathematics* K–6 curriculum. For a variety of reasons, the levels indicated may not accurately portray your class's performance.

### Additional Information

**Advance Preparation** For additional information on assessment for Unit 3, see the *Assessment Handbook,* pages 42–44. For assessment checklists, see *Math Masters,* pages 432, 433, and 469–471.

# Getting Started

**Math Message**

*Complete the Time to Reflect questions on journal page 101.*

**Study Link 3.10 Follow-Up**

Briefly review answers.

NOTE: Some of these assessment suggestions relate to learning goals that have been addressed in previous units. Now is a good time to evaluate students' progress toward those goals.

STUDENT PAGE

**Time to Reflect**

1. Look back through your journal. Then describe what you liked most in this unit.

2. This unit was about geometry. Based on the lessons you did in this unit, how would you describe geometry to someone?

Answers vary for Problems 1–2.

✦ *Math Journal 1*, p. 101

# 1 Assess Progress

## ✦ Math Message Follow-Up (*Math Journal 1*, p. 101)

WHOLE-CLASS DISCUSSION 

Students share their responses to questions about the unit.

## ✦ Slate Assessment

WHOLE-CLASS ACTIVITY

If the suggested problems below are not appropriate for your class's level of performance, adjust the numbers or the problems themselves to better assess your students' abilities.

1. Round numbers.
   - 472 to the nearest ten. 470
   - 3,804 to the nearest ten. 3,800
   - 76.7 to the nearest whole number. 77
   - 29.08 to the nearest tenth. 29.1
   - 140.23 to the nearest tenth. 140.2
   - 653.09 to the nearest whole number. 653
2. Complete.
   - 4 [50s] = ? 200 40 [50s] = ? 2,000 400 [50s] = ? 20,000
   - 90 [6s] = ? 540 90 [60s] = ? 5,400 900 [60s] = ? 54,000
   - 7 [80s] = ? 560 70 [80s] = ? 5,600 700 [80s] = ? 56,000
3. Dictate numbers for students to write and mark on their slates.
   - Write 5,008,724. Circle the digit in the ten-thousands place. Underline the digit in the hundred-thousands place. 5,0(0)8,724

- Write 19,430,201,155. Circle the digit in the thousands place. Underline the digit in the hundred-thousands place. 19,430,201,155

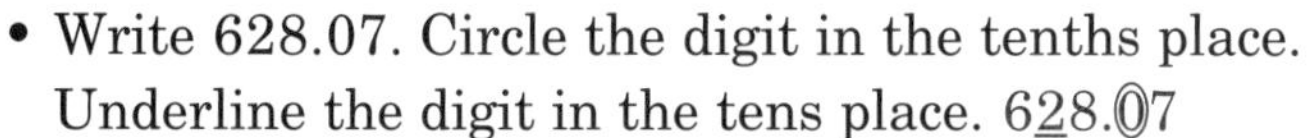

- Write 628.07. Circle the digit in the tenths place. Underline the digit in the tens place. 628.07
- Write 523.19. Circle the hundredths digit. Underline the tenths digit. 523.19 **Goal 3f**

4. Write numbers on the board. Students show "thumbs up" if the number is divisible by the stated divisor and "thumbs down" if it is not divisible.
   - Is 1,263 divisible by 2? down By 3? up By 5? down By 9? down
   - Is 476 divisible by 2? up By 3? down By 4? up By 6? down
   - Is 750 divisible by 2? up By 3? up By 5? up By 6? up By 9? down By 10? up
5. Students show types of angles with their arms: obtuse, right, acute, straight, reflex, about 45°, about 135°. Continue as time allows **Goals 3b and 3d**

## Written Assessment
(*Math Masters,* pp. 384–386)

INDEPENDENT ACTIVITY 

Depending on the needs of students, you may want to work through an example together, reading a problem aloud, discussing it, and providing additional examples as necessary before students work the problem independently.

- Determine angles measures based on relationships between angles. (Problems 1–3) **Goal 3a**
- Measure angles and identify types of angles. (Problems 4–6) **Goals 3c and 3d**
- Identify types of angles. (Problem 7) **Goal 3d**
- Identify types of angles and estimate the measure of angles. (Problem 8) **Goals 3b and 3d**
- Identify place value in numbers to billions. (Problem 9) **Goal 3f**
- Draw types of triangles. (Problems 10–12) **Goal 3e**
- Identify types of triangles and compare properties of triangles. (Problems 13 and 14) **Goals 3e and 3g**

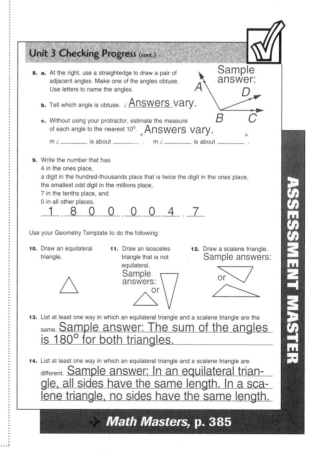

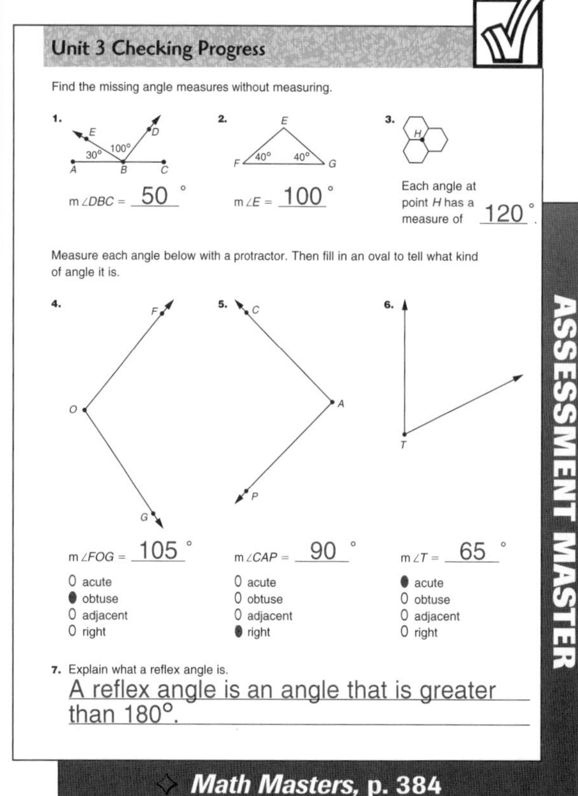

**Unit 3 Checking Progress**

Find the missing angle measures without measuring.

1. m∠DBC = 50°
2. m∠E = 100°
3. Each angle at point H has a measure of 120°.

Measure each angle below with a protractor. Then fill in an oval to tell what kind of angle it is.

4. m∠FOG = 105° (obtuse)
5. m∠CAP = 90° (right)
6. m∠T = 65° (acute)

7. Explain what a reflex angle is. A reflex angle is an angle that is greater than 180°.

ASSESSMENT MASTER

*Math Masters,* p. 384

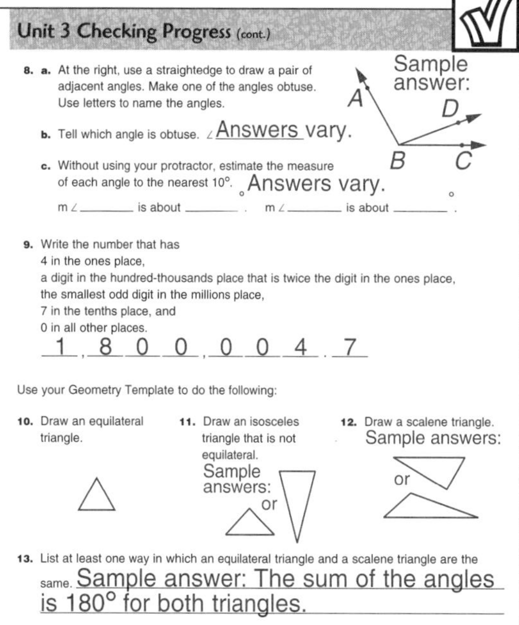

**Unit 3 Checking Progress** (cont.)

8. a. At the right, use a straightedge to draw a pair of adjacent angles. Make one of the angles obtuse. Use letters to name the angles. Sample answer:
   b. Tell which angle is obtuse. ∠Answers vary.
   c. Without using your protractor, estimate the measure of each angle to the nearest 10°. Answers vary.
   m∠_____ is about _____°. m∠_____ is about _____°.

9. Write the number that has
4 in the ones place,
a digit in the hundred-thousands place that is twice the digit in the ones place,
the smallest odd digit in the millions place,
7 in the tenths place, and
0 in all other places.
1,800,004.7

Use your Geometry Template to do the following:

10. Draw an equilateral triangle.
11. Draw an isosceles triangle that is not equilateral. Sample answers:
12. Draw a scalene triangle. Sample answers:

13. List at least one way in which an equilateral triangle and a scalene triangle are the same. Sample answer: The sum of the angles is 180° for both triangles.

14. List at least one way in which an equilateral triangle and a scalene triangle are different. Sample answer: In an equilateral triangle, all sides have the same length. In a scalene triangle, no sides have the same length.

ASSESSMENT MASTER

*Math Masters,* p. 385

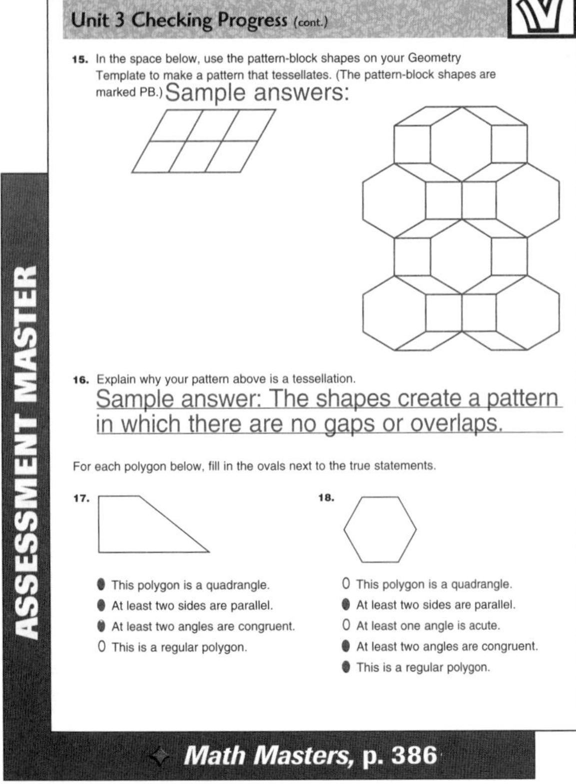
Unit 3 Checking Progress (cont.)

15. In the space below, use the pattern-block shapes on your Geometry Template to make a pattern that tessellates. (The pattern-block shapes are marked PB.) Sample answers:

16. Explain why your pattern above is a tessellation.
Sample answer: The shapes create a pattern in which there are no gaps or overlaps.

For each polygon below, fill in the ovals next to the true statements.

17.
- ● This polygon is a quadrangle.
- ● At least two sides are parallel.
- ● At least two angles are congruent.
- O This is a regular polygon.

18.
- O This polygon is a quadrangle.
- ● At least two sides are parallel.
- O At least one angle is acute.
- ● At least two angles are congruent.
- ● This is a regular polygon.

ASSESSMENT MASTER

*Math Masters,* p. 386

- Create and define tessellations. (Problems 15 and 16) **Goal 3h**
- Estimate the measure of an angle; identify types of angles; and compare the properties of polygons. (Problems 17 and 18) **Goals 3b, 3d, and 3g**

Circulate and assist as students work.

## ALTERNATIVE ASSESSMENT OPTION

### Play *Angle Tangle*
(*Student Reference Book,* p. 258)

PARTNER ACTIVITY 

Use this game to assess students' ability to estimate and measure angles. For detailed instructions, see Lesson 3.6.

NOTE: You may want to make up a master for the game *Angle Tangle*. Prepare the master so it can be cut in half. On each half-sheet, put a name blank at the top, leave the middle open, and put answer blanks at the bottom:

Estimate _____°

Actual _______°

Score ________

## ALTERNATIVE ASSESSMENT OPTION

### Play *Polygon Capture*
(*Math Journals 1 and 2,* Activity Sheets 4 and 5; *Student Reference Book,* p. 289)

PARTNER ACTIVITY 

Use this game to assess students' understanding of the properties of polygons. For detailed instructions, see Lesson 3.7.

## ALTERNATIVE ASSESSMENT OPTION

### Describe a Polygon

INDEPENDENT ACTIVITY 

Have students list as many polygon characteristics as they can without referring to the *Student Reference Book*. Below the list, have students label a section of the paper Polygons and another section Not Polygons. Have them draw at least three figures for each category. Collect the polygon record to assess students' familiarity with the attributes of polygons.

Portfolio Ideas

# Build Background for Unit 4

## ◆ Math Boxes 3.11 (*Math Journal 1*, p. 102)

INDEPENDENT ACTIVITY 

**Mixed Review** The skills in Problems 1–5 are prerequisites for Unit 4.

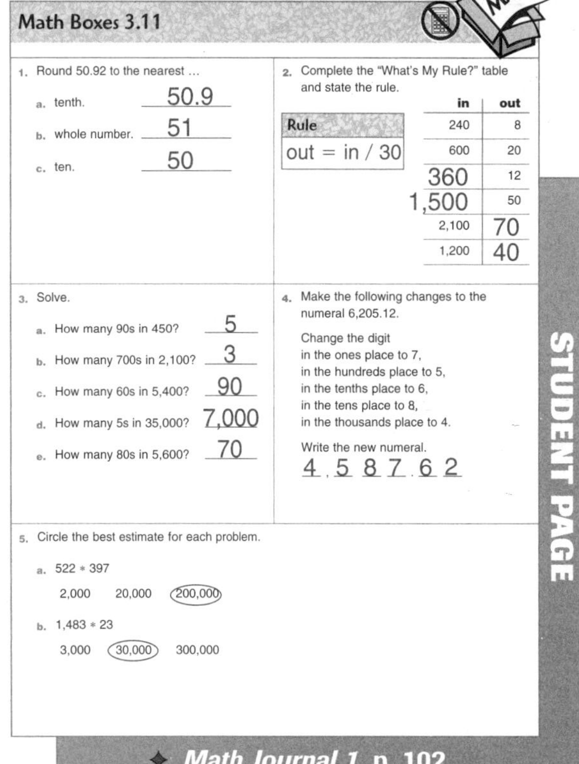

**Math Boxes 3.11**

1. Round 50.92 to the nearest …
   a. tenth. 50.9
   b. whole number. 51
   c. ten. 50

2. Complete the "What's My Rule?" table and state the rule.

Rule: out = in / 30

| in | out |
|---|---|
| 240 | 8 |
| 600 | 20 |
| 360 | 12 |
| 1,500 | 50 |
| 2,100 | 70 |
| 1,200 | 40 |

3. Solve.
   a. How many 90s in 450? 5
   b. How many 700s in 2,100? 3
   c. How many 60s in 5,400? 90
   d. How many 5s in 35,000? 7,000
   e. How many 80s in 5,600? 70

4. Make the following changes to the numeral 6,205.12.
   Change the digit
   in the ones place to 7,
   in the hundreds place to 5,
   in the tenths place to 6,
   in the tens place to 8,
   in the thousands place to 4.
   Write the new numeral. 4,587.62

5. Circle the best estimate for each problem.
   a. 522 * 397
      2,000  20,000  (200,000)
   b. 1,483 * 23
      3,000  (30,000)  300,000

STUDENT PAGE

◆ *Math Journal 1*, p. 102

## ◆ Study Link 3.11: Unit 4 Family Letter (*Math Masters*, pp. 251–254)

**Home Connection** This Study Link is a four-page newsletter that introduces parents and guardians to Unit 4's topics and terms. The letter also offers ideas for mathematics activities that are supportive of classroom work and can be done at home.

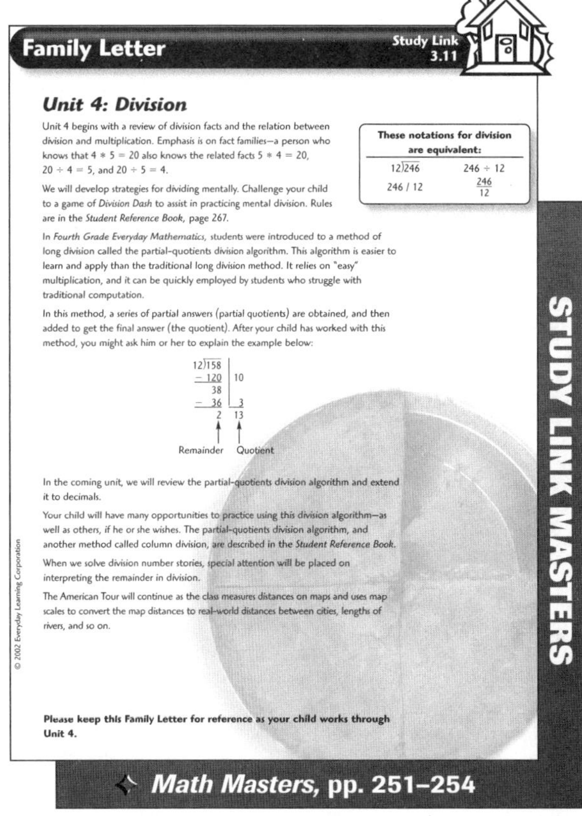

**Family Letter** Study Link 3.11

### Unit 4: Division

Unit 4 begins with a review of division facts and the relation between division and multiplication. Emphasis is on fact families—a person who knows that 4 * 5 = 20 also knows the related facts 5 * 4 = 20, 20 ÷ 4 = 5, and 20 ÷ 5 = 4.

**These notations for division are equivalent:**

| | |
|---|---|
| 12)246 | 246 ÷ 12 |
| 246 / 12 | $\frac{246}{12}$ |

We will develop strategies for dividing mentally. Challenge your child to a game of *Division Dash* to assist in practicing mental division. Rules are in the *Student Reference Book*, page 267.

In *Fourth Grade Everyday Mathematics*, students were introduced to a method of long division called the partial-quotients division algorithm. This algorithm is easier to learn and apply than the traditional long division method. It relies on "easy" multiplication, and it can be quickly employed by students who struggle with traditional computation.

In this method, a series of partial answers (partial quotients) are obtained, and then added to get the final answer (the quotient). After your child has worked with this method, you might ask him or her to explain the example below:

```
12)158  |
 - 120  | 10
    38  |
 -  36  |  3
     2    13
     ↑     ↑
Remainder  Quotient
```

In the coming unit, we will review the partial-quotients division algorithm and extend it to decimals.

Your child will have many opportunities to practice using this division algorithm—as well as others, if he or she wishes. The partial-quotients division algorithm, and another method called column division, are described in the *Student Reference Book*.

When we solve division number stories, special attention will be placed on interpreting the remainder in division.

The American Tour will continue as the class measures distances on maps and uses map scales to convert the map distances to real-world distances between cities, lengths of rivers, and so on.

**Please keep this Family Letter for reference as your child works through Unit 4.**



STUDY LINK MASTERS

◆ *Math Masters*, pp. 251–254

# Unit 4 Division

Unit 4 begins with a review of division facts, followed by a review of the "low stress" partial-quotients division algorithm for whole numbers, which was introduced in *Fourth Grade Everyday Mathematics*. The algorithm is extended to division of a decimal by a whole number. The unit then focuses on the meaning and treatment of remainders in problems that involve division. The American Tour lesson for the unit emphasizes map scales. The unit ends with a skills review through the game *First to 100.*

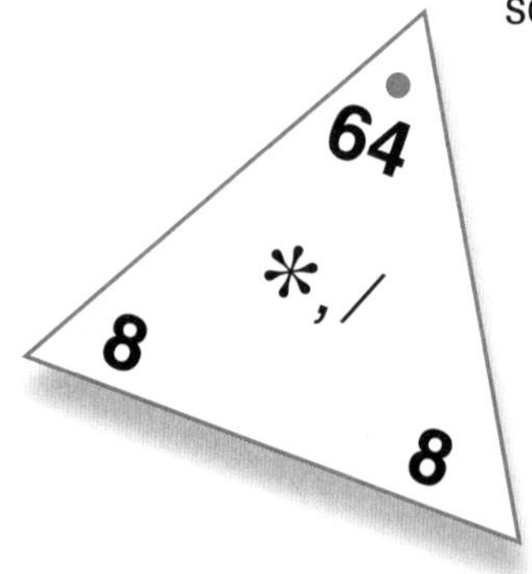


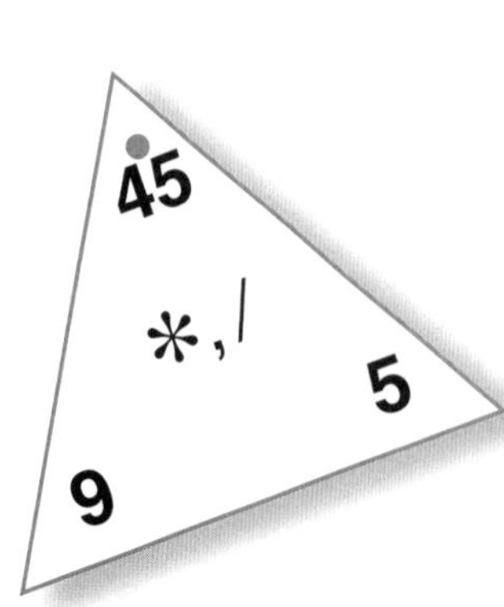

# contents



UNIT 4

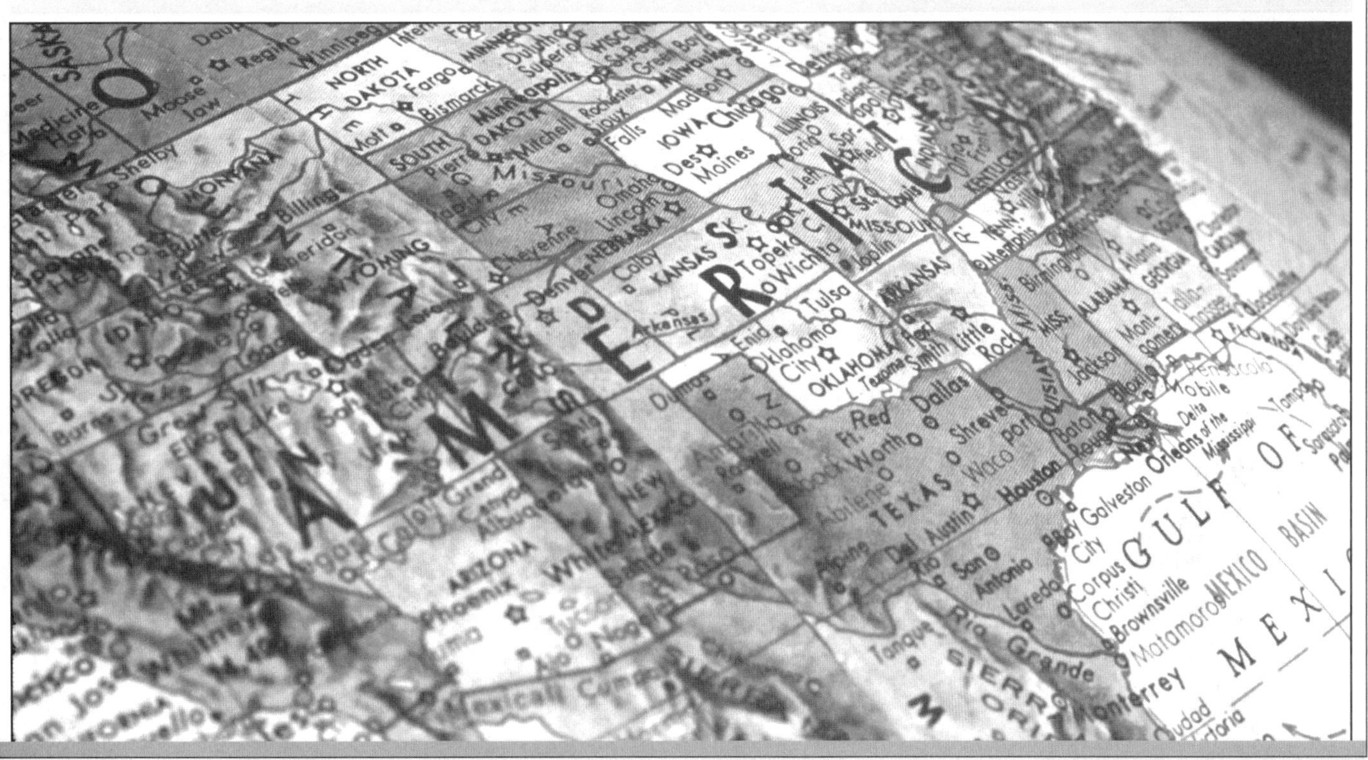

# learning goals in perspective

| learning goals | links to the past | links to the future |
|---|---|---|
| 4a **Beginning Goal** Divide decimal numbers by whole numbers with no remainders. **(Lessons 4.4 and 4.5)** | Grade 4: Extend the partial-quotients method to decimals divided by whole numbers, using estimation to place the decimal point. | Grade 6: Extend the partial-quotients method to decimal divisors. Use the method to find quotients to any given number of decimal places and to rename fractions as decimals. |
| 4b **Beginning/Developing Goal** Write and solve number sentences with variables for division number stories. **(Lessons 4.5 and 4.6)** | Grades 1-3: Solve open sentences in which the unknown is represented by a question mark, a blank, or a box.<br>Grade 4: Model division situations with multiplication/division diagrams and open number sentences. Solve open number sentences in which the unknown is represented by a letter variable. | Grade 5: Introduce a pan-balance approach to solving simple equations (Unit 10).<br>Grade 6: Extend the pan-balance approach to more complex equations. Solve open number sentences by trial and error, by the cover-up method, and by transforming them into simpler equivalent sentences. |
| 4c **Developing Goal** Find the quotient and remainder of a whole number divided by a 1-digit whole number. **(Lessons 4.1, 4.2, 4.4, and 4.5)** | Grades 1–3: Explore division as equal sharing. Solve division problems by modeling, arrays, and other direct methods.<br>Grade 4: Introduce the partial-quotients method for whole numbers as the focus algorithm for division. | Grades 4–6: Applications and maintenance to develop proficiency with the partial-quotients method for whole number and decimal division. |
| 4d **Developing Goal** Find the quotient and remainder of a whole number divided by a 2-digit whole number. **(Lessons 4.2, 4.4, and 4.5)** | See Goal 4c. | See Goal 4c. |
| 4e **Developing/Goal** Make magnitude estimates for quotients of whole and decimal numbers divided by whole numbers. **(Lessons 4.4 and 4.5)** | Grade 4: Estimate the magnitude of products of multidigit numbers. Use magnitude estimates to place decimal points in products and quotients.<br>Grade 5: Use magnitude estimates to place decimal points in products. (Unit 2) | Grade 6: Use magnitude estimates to place decimal points in quotients when decimals are divided by other decimals. |
| 4f **Developing Goal** Interpret the remainder in division number stories. **(Lesson 4.5)** | Grade 3: Introduce the meaning of the remainder in division.<br>Grade 4: Introduce division vocabulary: *dividend, divisor, quotient,* and *remainder.* Explore the relation between fractions and division. Express remainders as fractions or decimals. | Grade 5: Solve division number stories and interpret remainders (Unit 6).<br>Grade 6: Express answers to division problems as quotients and remainders or as mixed numbers or decimals as appropriate. |
| 4g **Developing Goal** Determine the value of a variable; use this value to complete a number sentence. **(Lesson 4.6)** | Grades 1–3: Find solutions for open number sentences in which the unknown is represented by a question mark, a blank, or a box.<br>Grade 4: Identify the solution of an open number sentence as a value for the variable that makes the sentence true.<br>Grade 5: Review variables and solutions of open sentences. (Unit 2) | Grade 5: Substitute a number for a variable in a problem and solve (Units 7 and 10). Use formulas containing variables (Units 9, 10, 11, 12).<br>Grade 6: Model general patterns with number sentences in one or more variables. Solve problems using formulas by substituting known values for the variables and solving the resulting equations. |
| 4h **Secure Goal** Know place value to hundredths. **(Lesson 4.1)** | Grades 1–4: Use decimal notation for money.<br>Grades 3–4: Use base-10 blocks to model decimals to hundredths; use conversions between metric measures to explore decimal numbers to thousandths.<br>Grade 5: Review place value for whole numbers and decimals (Unit 2). | Grade 5: Convert between fractions and decimals; use a 100-grid and fraction-stick chart to find decimal equivalents for fractions, to hundredths (Unit 5); review exponential notation and introduce negative exponents (Unit 7).<br>Grade 6: Read and write both large and small numbers in scientific notation. |

# assessment

## ongoing • product • periodic

### Informal Assessment

**Math Boxes** These *Math Journal* pages provide opportunities for cumulative review or assessment of concepts and skills.

**Ongoing Assessment: Kid Watching** Use the Ongoing Assessment suggestions in the following lessons to make quick, on-the-spot observations about students' understanding of:

- Operations and Computation **(Lesson 4.1, Part 1; Lesson 4.5, Part 1)**
- Geometry and Measurement and Reference Frames **(Lesson 4.3, Part 2)**

**Portfolio Ideas** Samples of students' work may be obtained from the following assignment:

- Writing Division Number Stories **(Lesson 4.5)**

### Unit 4 Review and Assessment

**Math Message** Use Time to Reflect Problem 1 in Lesson 4.7 to assess students' progress toward the following learning goals: **Goals 4b and 4f**

**Oral and Slate Assessments** Use slate assessments during Lesson 4.7 to assess students' progress toward the following learning goal: **Goal 4h**

**Written Assessment** Use a written review during Lesson 4.7 to assess students' progress toward the following learning goals: **Goals 4a–4g**

**Alternative Assessment Options** Use partner and independent alternative assessments in Lesson 4.7 to assess students' progress toward the following learning goals: **Goals 4c and 4g**

## assessment handbook

For more information on how to use different types of assessment in Unit 4, see the Assessment Overview on pages 45–48 in the *Assessment Handbook.* The following Assessment Masters can be found in the *Math Masters* book:

- Unit 4 Checking Progress, pp. 387 and 388
- Unit 4 Individual Profile of Progress, p. 435
- Unit 4 Class Checklist, p. 434
- Class Progress Indicator, p. 471
- Math Logs, pp. 474 and 475
- Self-Assessment Forms, pp. 477 and 478
- Interest Inventories, pp. 472 and 473

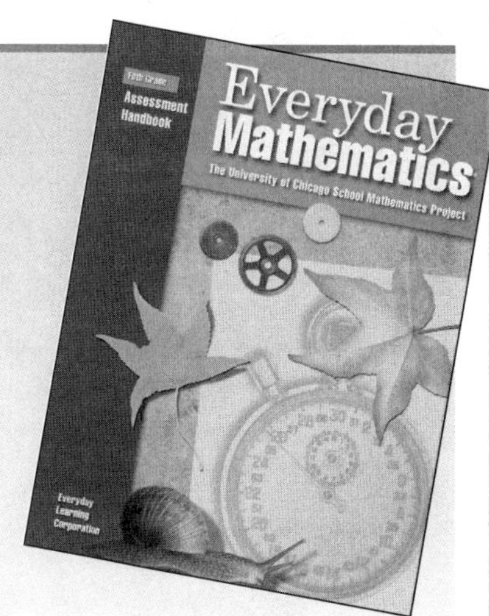

# problemsolving

## *A process of modeling everyday situations using tools from mathematics*

Encourage students to use a variety of strategies when attacking a given problem—and to explain those strategies. *Strategies students might use in this unit:*

- Draw a picture
- Use a diagram
- Use computation
- Write a number story
- Use logical reasoning
- Write a number sentence

**Four Problem-Solving REPRESENTATIONS**

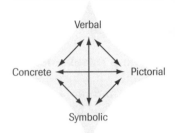

Verbal

Concrete

Pictorial

Symbolic

## Lessons that teach *through* problem solving, not just *about* problem solving

| Lesson | Activity | Lesson | Activity |
|---|---|---|---|
| **4.1, 4.2** | Solve number stories for a variety of situations by using division | **4.2, 4.5** | Solve number stories by using division and interpreting remainders within the context of the stories |
| **4.1** | Solve place-value puzzles | **4.6** | Use randomly generated numbers to replace variables in number stories; then solve the stories |
| **4.3** | Use a map scale to find straight-path and curved-path distances | | |

For more information about problem solving in *Everyday Mathematics,* see the *Teacher's Reference Manual.*

# cross-curricularlinks

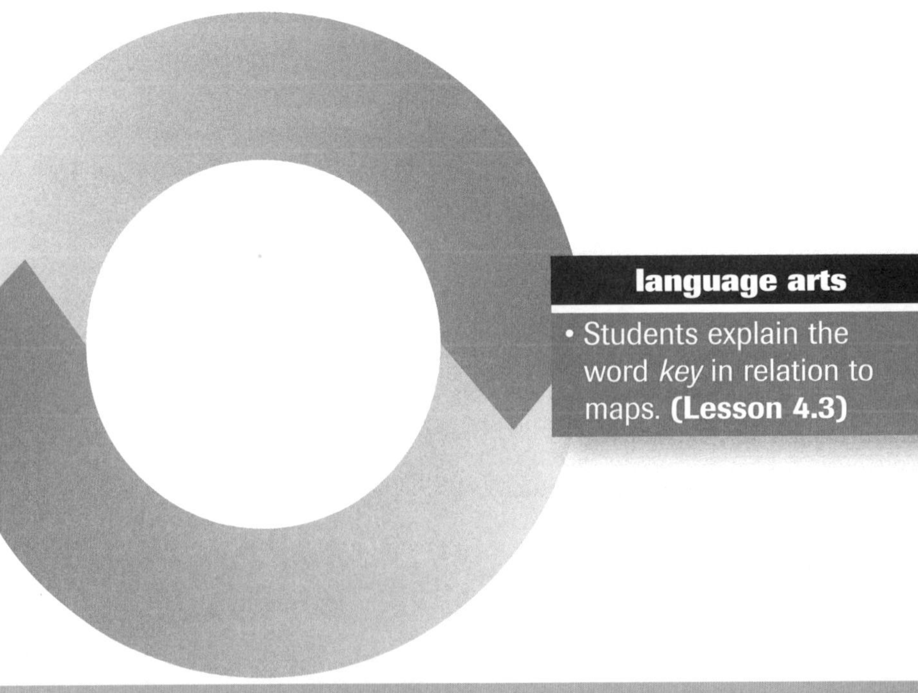

**social studies**

- Discuss symbols, markings, and colors on a migration map. **(Lesson 4.3)**
- If appropriate for your class, have students play *Algebra Election,* a game in which they travel through the United States capturing electoral votes by solving the problems on the *First to 100* cards. **(Lesson 4.6)**

**language arts**

- Students explain the word *key* in relation to maps. **(Lesson 4.3)**

# meeting INDIVIDUAL needs

UNIVERSAL ACCESS

## ✦ RETEACHING

The following features provide some additional instructional support:

**Adjusting the Activity**

- **Lesson 4.1, Part 1**
- **Lesson 4.2, Part 1**
- **Lesson 4.3, Part 1**
- **Lesson 4.4, Part 1**
- **Lesson 4.5, Part 2**

**Options for Individualizing**

- **Lesson 4.4** Modeling Division with Base-10 Blocks
- **Lesson 4.5** Illustrating Division Problems

## ✦ ENRICHMENT

The following features suggest enrichment and extension activities:

**Adjusting the Activity**

- **Lesson 4.1, Part 1**
- **Lesson 4.2, Part 1**
- **Lesson 4.5, Part 1**
- **Lesson 4.6, Part 1**

**Options for Individualizing**

- **Lesson 4.4** Exploring an Alternative Division Algorithm
- **Lesson 4.5** Writing Division Number Stories
- **Lesson 4.6** Playing *Algebra Election*

## ✦ LANGUAGE DIVERSITY

The following features suggest ways to support students who are acquiring proficiency in English:

**Options for Individualizing**

- **Lesson 4.2** Supporting Math Vocabulary Development
- **Lesson 4.5** Interpreting Remainders

## ✦ MULTIAGE CLASSROOM

The following chart lists related lessons from Grades 4 and 6 that can help you meet your instructional needs:

| | | | | | | |
|---|---|---|---|---|---|---|
| **Grade 4** | 3.5<br>4.6 | 6.2 | 3.6 | 9.9 | 6.4 | |
| **Grade 5** | 4.1 | 4.2 | 4.3 | 4.4 | 4.5 | 4.6 |
| **Grade 6** | 2.10 | 2.10 | | 2.11 | | |

# materials

| lesson | math masters pages | manipulative kit items | other items |
|---|---|---|---|
| **4.1** | Study Link Master, p. 255<br>Teaching Master, p. 38<br>***See* Advance Preparation, p. 214** | | calculator<br>overhead calculator for demonstration purposes (optional) |
| **4.2** | Study Link Master, p. 256<br>Teaching Masters, pp. 12 and 40; and p. 39 (optional)<br>***See* Advance Preparation, p. 219** | | Division Poster<br>***See* Advance Preparation, p. 219** |
| **4.3** | Study Link Master, p. 257<br>Teaching Master, p. 41 | | Geometry Template (or protractor)<br>slate<br>compass<br>string<br>ruler |
| **4.4** | Study Link Master, p. 258<br>Teaching Masters, p. 12 (optional); and pp. 42 and 43<br>***See* Advance Preparation, p. 230** | | slate<br>base-10 blocks: 6 flats, 22 longs and 40 cubes |
| **4.5** | Study Link Master, p. 259<br>Teaching Master, p. 12 (optional); and p. 44<br>Assessment Master, p. 479<br>***See* Advance Preparation, p. 235** | | |
| **4.6** | Study Link Master, p. 260<br>Teaching Masters, p. 45 (optional); and pp. 46–49<br>***See* Advance Preparation, p. 241** | 2 six-sided dice<br>1 six-sided die per group of 4 students | slate<br>calculator<br>envelope<br>Per group of 4 students:<br>32 *First to 100* Problem Cards (*Math Masters,* pp. 46 and 47)<br>4 pennies or other small counters<br>transparent tape<br>scratch paper<br>3"-by-5" index cards cut in half (optional) |
| **4.7** | Study Link Masters, pp. 261–264<br>Teaching Masters, pp. 38, 46, and 47<br>Assessment Masters, pp. 387 and 388 | 2 six-sided dice | calculator<br>*First to 100* Problem Cards (*Math Masters,* pp. 46 and 47) |

# planningtips

## Pacing

Pacing depends on a number of factors, such as students' individual needs and how long your school has been using *Everyday Mathematics*. At the beginning of Unit 4, review your Content by Strand Poster to help you set a monthly pace.

| | ← MOST CLASSROOMS → | |
|---|---|---|
| OCTOBER | NOVEMBER | DECEMBER |

## Home Communication

Share Study Links 4.1–4.6 with families to help them understand the content and procedures in this unit. At the end of the unit, use Study Link 4.7 to introduce Unit 5. Supplemental information can be found in the *Home Connection Handbook*.

## NCTM Standards

| Standard | 1 | 2 | 3 | 4 | 5 | 6 | 7 | 8 | 9 | 10 |
|---|---|---|---|---|---|---|---|---|---|---|
| Unit 4 Lessons | 4.1–4.6 | 4.6 | 4.3 | 4.3 | | 4.1–4.7 | 4.1–4.7 | 4.1–4.7 | 4.1–4.7 | 4.1–4.7 |

**Content Standards**
**1** Number and Operations
**2** Algebra
**3** Geometry
**4** Measurement
**5** Data Analysis and Probability

**Process Standards**
**6** Problem Solving
**7** Reasoning and Proof
**8** Communication
**9** Connections
**10** Representation

## PRACTICE through Games

*Everyday Mathematics* uses games to help students develop good fact power and other math skills.

- *Division Dash* to practice dividing 2-digit numbers by 1-digit numbers **(Lessons 4.1 and 4.7)**
- *First to 100* and *Algebra Election* to practice evaluating expressions after substituting values for variables. The expressions provide mixed practice involving multiple strands. **(Lessons 4.6 and 4.7)**
- *Algebra Election* is played in the context of a presidential election and winning electoral votes. **(Lesson 4.6)**

# unit 4 content highlights

*The discussion below highlights the major content ideas presented in Unit 4 and may help you establish instructional priorities.*

NOTE: Having instant recall of all the basic addition and multiplication facts is very helpful and important. For a few otherwise capable students, however, this may be unrealistic. For these students, possible alternatives include using tables, calculators, or mental-arithmetic strategies that rely on remembering only a few key facts rather than all the basic facts.

## Division Facts and Extensions (Lesson 4.1)

In *Everyday Mathematics,* instant recall of basic addition and multiplication facts is emphasized, and then used in strategies for getting answers to basic subtraction and division facts and "extended facts." For example, a student who knows by reflex that $7 * 8 = 56$ can use fact-family knowledge to find $56 \div 7$ and $56 \div 8$, and can apply extended-fact strategies to find $70 * 80$ and to tell how many 7s are in 560. Lesson 4.1 provides students with an opportunity to refresh their division-fact and extended-fact knowledge and to use it to solve division problems in a variety of contexts. A strategy for mental division is introduced, in which the dividend is broken into two or more "friendly" parts that are easy to divide. Students learn a new game, *Division Dash,* in which they generate 2-digit dividends and 1-digit divisors at random on a calculator, and then divide mentally.

## A Division Algorithm (Lesson 4.2)

In the adult world, the usual procedure used to solve any moderately complicated division problem is to reach for a calculator. Students, however, need to know how to solve some division problems without calculators. Students gain an understanding of the meanings of division by considering paper-and-pencil computation procedures.

Lesson 4.2 reteaches a method for division, the partial-quotients division algorithm, which was introduced in Unit 6 of *Fourth Grade Everyday Mathematics.* This "low stress algorithm" takes much of the mystery out of long division. It is a conceptually revealing alternative to the traditional U.S. long-division algorithm, which research has shown to be difficult for many students to learn and apply.

Division is a way of answering the question, "How many of these are in that?" or "How many $n$'s are in $m$?" The algorithm taught in this unit encourages students to ask a series of "How many..." questions. Using multiples of the divisor, they build up a series of interim answers, or partial quotients. At each step, if not enough $n$'s have been taken from the $m$'s, more are taken. When all possible $n$'s have been taken, the partial quotients are added.

The partial-quotients division algorithm is described in detail in the teacher's commentary for Lesson 4.2 and on pages 22 and 23 of the *Student Reference Book*. For example, 158 ÷ 12 = ? can be thought of as, "How many 12s are in 158?" The dividend and divisor are first written in the traditional way. Then multiples of the divisor, 12, are subtracted from the dividend, 158. When the difference is less than the divisor, the process stops. The partial quotients are added. *(See the margin.)*

| 12)158 | |
|---|---|
| −120 | 10 |
| 38 | |
| −36 | 3 |
| 2 | 13 |
| ↑ Remainder | ↑ Quotient |

It is important to note that students can use different partial quotients to obtain the correct answer. For example, a student could use 2 [12s] in the second step (2 ∗ 12 = 24), leaving 14. Then the student would take away another 12, leaving a remainder of 2. Thus the student would reach the final answer in three steps rather than two. One way is not better than another.

One advantage of this algorithm is that students can use numbers that are easy to work with. Students who are confident of their extended multiplication facts will need only a few multiples of the divisor to arrive at the quotient, while others will be more comfortable taking smaller steps. More important than the course a student follows is that he or she understands how and why this algorithm works and can use it to get an accurate answer.

In Lesson 4.1, division is limited to division of a larger whole number by a smaller whole number. The terms **quotient** and **remainder** are used.

The authors consider the partial-quotients division algorithm as a **focus algorithm,** to be learned by all students. If, however, students know another algorithm and prefer it to the one taught in the lesson, they should feel free to use it. If parents or siblings insist on the superiority of the algorithm they learned, it can easily be accommodated as an alternative. Similarly, if you want to teach another algorithm, please feel free to do so.

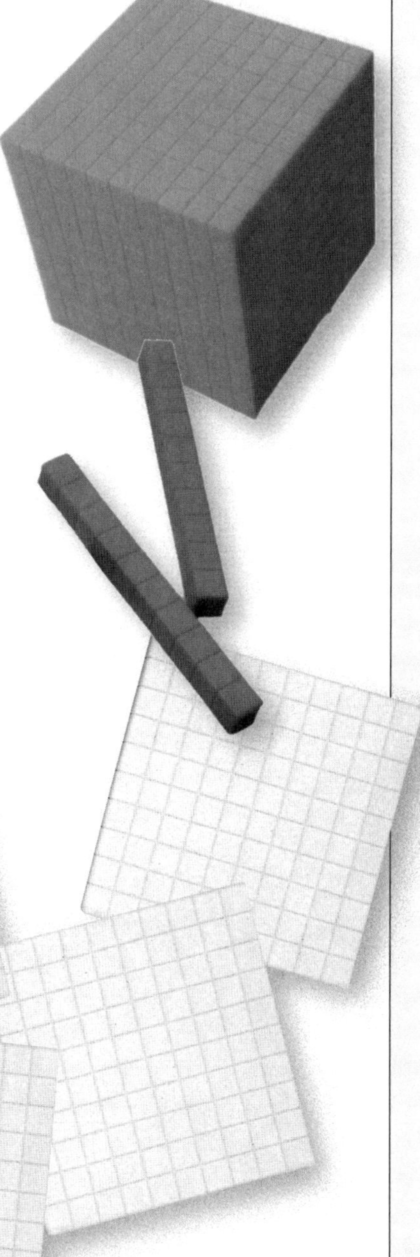

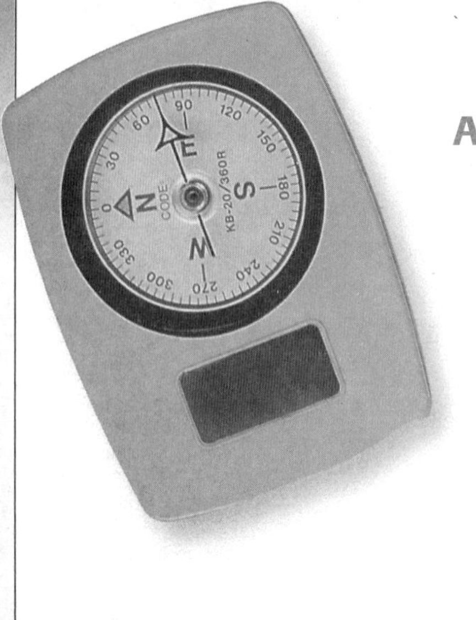

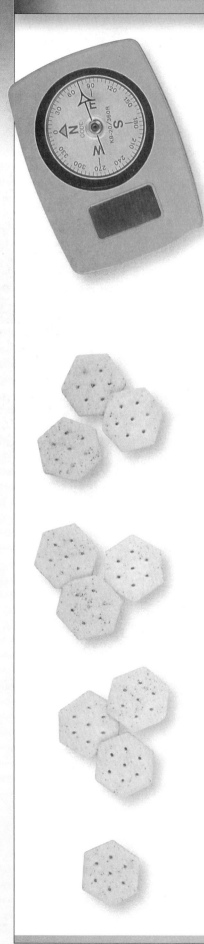

## American Tour: Finding Distances on a Map (Lesson 4.3)

A good mathematics education allows teachers to integrate mathematics into other disciplines, as well as incorporate other subjects into mathematics. The American Tour section of the *Student Reference Book,* for example, provides links among social studies, United States history, and mathematics. In this unit, students use maps in the American Tour to develop their skills of measuring distances and, using map scales, convert these into real-world distances.

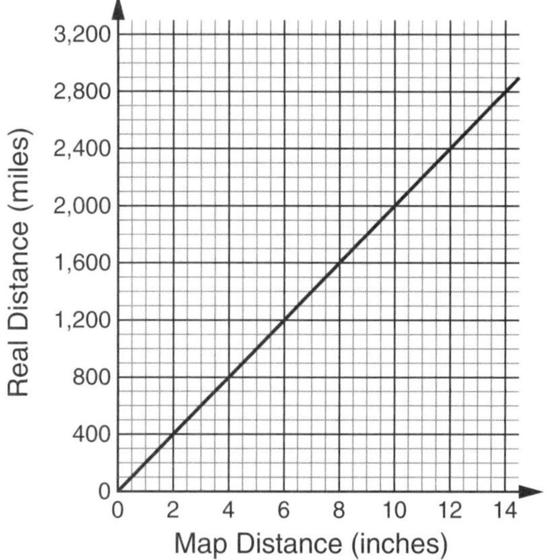

## Division of Decimal Numbers (Lesson 4.4)

In Lesson 4.4, the partial-quotients division algorithm is extended to division of a decimal number by a whole number. The strategy is first to make a magnitude estimate of the quotient. Will it be in the 0.1s, 1s, 10s, or 100s? For example, estimate the quotient of $67.2 \div 3$ by rounding the dividend to an "easy" number—for example, 60. $60 \div 3 = 20$, so the quotient is in the 10s. Then ignore the decimal point and use the algorithm to divide, getting 224. Use the magnitude estimate to insert the decimal point: 22.4.

## Interpreting the Remainder (Lesson 4.5)

Students use the division algorithm that was introduced in Lesson 4.2 and focus on interpreting remainders within problem contexts. Depending on the situation, a remainder is handled in different ways:

- The remainder might represent a "leftover" amount that cannot be further split up. For example, leftover people or cars can't easily be split up.

- ▷ The remainder might be regarded as a fractional or decimal part of the whole. For example, leftover parts of a dollar can be converted into cents.
- ▷ The remainder might indicate that the quotient should be rounded up to the next larger whole number to obtain the answer. For example, if 30 people need to be transported in vans that hold 8 people each, it makes sense to order 4 vans rather than 3.75 vans.
- ▷ The remainder might be ignored, and the answer is the quotient. If CDs are $9 and I have $50, I can only buy 5 CDs.

## Skills Review with *First to 100* (Lesson 4.6)

Students play the game *First to 100,* which exercises a variety of skills and develops the mathematical concept of a variable (a letter or other symbol whose value can vary). Players take turns drawing cards containing problems such as $(3x + 4) - 8 = ?$ At each turn, the player rolls two dice and finds the product of the numbers on the top faces. The player substitutes the product just calculated for the $x$ or $x$'s in the problem(s) on the card. The player solves the problem(s) mentally or with paper and pencil, and offers the answer(s). The other player checks the answer(s) with a calculator.

## Review and Assessment (Lesson 4.7)

The Unit 4 assessment in Lesson 4.7 includes a written assessment of the following concepts and skills:

- ▷ dividing whole and decimal numbers
- ▷ writing number sentences with variables to represent division number stories
- ▷ solving division number stories and interpreting the remainder

**For additional information on the following topics, see the *Teacher's Reference Manual:***

- algorithm and procedures
- division algorithms
- estimates in calculations
- linear measures in geography
- maps and model scales
- mental arithmetic

# 4.1 Division Facts and Extensions

**OBJECTIVES** **To review division facts and extended division facts; and to mentally divide 2-digit numbers by 1-digit numbers.**

| summaries | materials |
|---|---|
| **1 Teaching the Lesson** | |
| Students review links between multiplication facts and division facts, and use these links to practice division facts and extended facts. [Operations and Computation]<br>Students solve problems with 1-digit divisors by partitioning the dividend into "friendly" numbers; students play *Division Dash* to practice this mental strategy. [Operations and Computation] | ☐ *Math Journal 1,* p. 103<br>☐ *Student Reference Book,* p. 267<br>☐ calculator<br>☐ overhead calculator for demonstration purposes (optional)<br>***See* Advance Preparation** |
| **2 Ongoing Learning & Practice** | |
| Students practice place-value skills by solving place-value puzzles. [Numeration; Operations and Computation]<br>Students practice and maintain skills through Math Boxes and Study Link activities. | ☐ *Math Journal 1,* pp. 104 and 105<br>☐ Study Link Master (*Math Masters,* p. 255) |
| **3 Options for Individualizing** | |
| **Extra Practice** Students complete Fact Triangles and write the related fact families. [Operations and Computation] | ☐ Teaching Master (*Math Masters,* p. 38)<br>***See* Advance Preparation** |

## Additional Information

**Advance Preparation** In Part 1, you will need to become familiar with the rules and scoring for *Division Dash.* An overhead calculator will be useful for demonstrating the game.

For the optional Extra Practice activity in Part 3, fill in an appropriate product in the correct position on each of the four Fact Triangles on *Math Masters,* page 38. Then copy the master. If students need more practice with extended facts, the products might include numbers like 1,200; 2,400; 3,600; and 4,000.

**Vocabulary • divisor • dividend • quotient • remainder**

# Getting Started

## Mental Math and Reflexes

Present a variety of division facts and their extensions, such as the following:

- How many 5s in 25? 5 How many 50s in 250? 5 How many 5s in 250? 50
- How many 3s in 21? 7 How many 30s in 210? 7 How many 3s in 210? 70
- How many 7s in 49? 7 How many 70s in 490? 7 How many 7s in 490? 70
- About how many 4s are in 21? About 5 About how many 40s in 210? About 5 About how many 4s in 210? About 50

## Math Message

*For each of the following multiplication facts, write two related division facts.*

$8 * 7 = 56$ $9 * 6 = x$

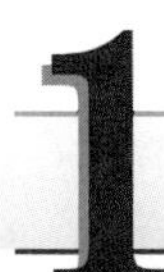

# Teaching the Lesson

## Math Message Follow-Up

WHOLE-CLASS DISCUSSION 

Briefly discuss students' answers. $56 / 7 = 8$, $56 / 8 = 7$; $x / 9 = 6$, $x / 6 = 9$

## Practicing Division Facts and Extended Division Facts

WHOLE-CLASS ACTIVITY

Practice division facts and their extensions. Stress the use of related multiplication facts. Ask students to share answers to questions such as the following:

- How many 6s are there in 42? *(Think: 6 times what number equals 42?)* 7
- How many 20s are there in 140? *(Think: 20 times what number equals 140?)* 7

Pose division problems like the following orally. Have students write the problems and their answers on paper. Vary your language; for example, sometimes ask: *What is 42 divided by 7?* At other times, ask: *How many 7s are there in 42?* If necessary, give a clue, such as, *Think: 7 times what number equals 42?*

- 42 / 7 6 — 270 / 30 9 — 48 / 4 12
- 64 / 8 8 — 1,000 / 10 100 — 200 / 20 10
- 120 / 10 12 — 20 / 5 4 — 350 / 50 7

NOTE: Instant recall of division facts is useful but is not an objective of *Everyday Mathematics*. Understanding the link between multiplication and division is important, however. Students who have instant recall of the multiplication facts should, after a few seconds' thought, be able to state related division facts.

### A Mental Division Strategy

If you want to divide 56 by 7 in your head, think: *How many 7s are there in 56?* or *7 times what number equals 56?*

Since $7 * 8 = 56$, you know that there are 8 [7s] in 56. So, 56 divided by 7 equals 8.

Fact knowledge can also help you find how many times a 1-digit number will divide any number. Just break the larger number into two or more "friendly" numbers—numbers that are easy to divide by the 1-digit number.

*Example 1* 96 divided by 3

Break 96 into smaller, "friendly" numbers, such as the following:

- 90 and 6. Ask yourself: *How many 3s in 90?* (30) *How many 3s in 6?* (2) Total = 30 + 2 = 32.
- 60 and 36. Ask yourself: *How many 3s in 60?* (20) *How many 3s in 36?* (12) Total = 20 + 12 = 32.

So, 96 divided by 3 equals 32. Check the result: $3 * 32 = 96$.

*Example 2* How many 4s in 71?

Break 71 into smaller, "friendly" numbers, such as the following:

- 40 and 31. Ask yourself: *How many 4s in 40?* (10) *How many 4s in 31?* (7 and 3 left over) (Think: *What multiplication fact for 4 has a product near 31?* $4 * 7 = 28$.) Total = 17 and 3 left over.
- 20, 20, 20, and 11. Ask yourself: *How many 4s in 20?* (5) *How many 4s in three 20s?* (15) *How many 4s in 11?* (2 and 3 left over) Total = 17 and 3 left over.

So, 71 divided by 4 equals 17 with 3 left over.

Use this method to mentally find or estimate the following. Remember to break the number being divided into two or more friendly parts.

1. 42 divided by 3 equals 14.
   30 and 12 (friendly parts for 42)
2. 57 divided by 3 equals 19.
   30 and 27 (friendly parts for 57)
3. 96 divided by 8 equals 12.
   80 and 16 (friendly parts for 96)
4. 99 divided by 7 equals 14 with 1 left over.
   70 and 29 (friendly parts for 99)

STUDENT PAGE

Math Journal 1, p. 103

**Adjusting the Activity** Extend the division facts activity by presenting some problems in a missing factor format. *Suggestions:*

30 * _____ = 240 8

50 * _____ = 2,000 40

360 = _____ * 9 40

_____ * 70 = 4,900 70

500 = _____ * 25 20

NOTE: The notation 13 [3s] was introduced in *Third Grade Everyday Mathematics*. It is read as "thirteen threes." Encourage students to think and say *13 threes*, not *13 times 3*.

**ONGOING ASSESSMENT**

Use students' answers to Problems 1–4 on journal page 103 to assess their recognition of and facility with division facts. If students have a difficult time finding "friendly" numbers, use Fact Triangles and *Division Dash* to encourage more fact practice.

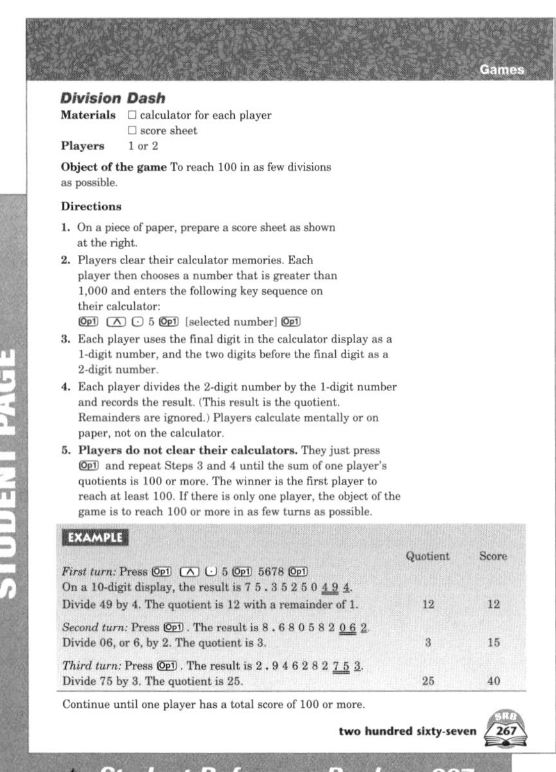

Games

***Division Dash***

**Materials** ☐ calculator for each player

☐ score sheet

**Players** 1 or 2

**Object of the game** To reach 100 in as few divisions as possible.

**Directions**

1. On a piece of paper, prepare a score sheet as shown at the right.
2. Players clear their calculator memories. Each player then chooses a number that is greater than 1,000 and enters the following key sequence on their calculator:
   Op1 ^ . 5 Op1 [selected number] Op1
3. Each player uses the final digit in the calculator display as a 1-digit number, and the two digits before the final digit as a 2-digit number.
4. Each player divides the 2-digit number by the 1-digit number and records the result. (This result is the quotient. Remainders are ignored.) Players calculate mentally or on paper, not on the calculator.
5. **Players do not clear their calculators.** They just press Op1 and repeat Steps 3 and 4 until the sum of one player's quotients is 100 or more. The winner is the first player to reach at least 100. If there is only one player, the object of the game is to reach 100 or more in as few turns as possible.

**EXAMPLE**

| | Quotient | Score |
|---|---|---|
| *First turn:* Press Op1 ^ . 5 Op1 5678 Op1<br>On a 10-digit display, the result is 7 5 . 3 5 2 5 0 4 9 4.<br>Divide 49 by 4. The quotient is 12 with a remainder of 1. | 12 | 12 |
| *Second turn:* Press Op1. The result is 8 . 6 8 0 5 8 2 0 6 2.<br>Divide 06, or 6, by 2. The quotient is 3. | 3 | 15 |
| *Third turn:* Press Op1. The result is 2 . 9 4 6 2 8 2 7 5 3.<br>Divide 75 by 3. The quotient is 25. | 25 | 40 |

Continue until one player has a total score of 100 or more.

two hundred sixty-seven SRB 267

STUDENT PAGE

*Student Reference Book*, p. 267

Let students correct their own work. Collect and examine the results. If the majority of students are having trouble with extended facts, hold frequent but brief oral reviews throughout the unit.

## Using a Mental Division Strategy
(*Math Journal 1*, p. 103)

WHOLE-CLASS ACTIVITY

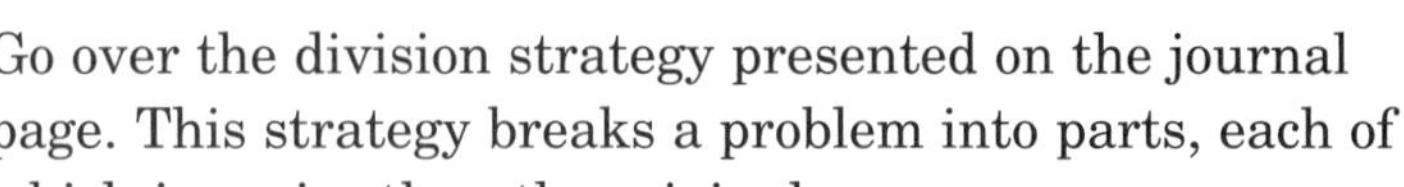

Go over the division strategy presented on the journal page. This strategy breaks a problem into parts, each of which is easier than the original.

Have students do Problems 1–4. Then ask them to explain how they broke the numbers into "friendly" parts.

Some students may propose breaking the larger number nearly in half. For example, *To find 42 divided by 3, I split 42 into 20 and 22. There are 6 [3s] in 20 and 7 [3s] in 22, for a total of 13 [3s].* This approach is useful for finding an estimate, but it can produce a result that is not the exact answer. Suggest that students identify at least one number that is evenly divisible by the divisor, and then adjust the result. For example, *I know that 3 times 7 equals 21, and 21 + 21 is 42, so there must be 14 [3s] in 42.*

You or your students can pose additional problems.

**Adjusting the Activity** A strategy to help struggling students is to break the dividend into two "friendly" numbers. One "friendly" number is the divisor times 10 and the other "friendly" number is the remaining part. For 42 divided by 3, use 3 * 10, or 30, as the first "friendly" number and 12 as the second.

For larger dividends, it may be necessary to use the divisor times a multiple of 10. For 132 divided by 3, use 3 * 40, or 120, as the first "friendly" number and 12 as the second.

## Introducing *Division Dash*
(*Student Reference Book*, p. 267)

WHOLE-CLASS ACTIVITY

Have all students clear their calculator memories by pressing the keys On/Off and Clear simultaneously, and then pressing Clear. Ask students to key in the following sequence: Op1 ^ . 5 Op1. The Op1 key will then function as a square root key until the calculator memory is cleared—even if the calculator is turned off.

Students can verify that the Op1 key now functions as a square root key. Enter 256 (Op1) and the display reads 16; 16 is the square root of 256, since 16 * 16 = 256. Press (Op1) a second time and the display reads 4, which is the square root of 16.

The purpose of using the Op1 key so that it functions as a square root key is to obtain random values for the **divisor** and **dividend.** To play *Division Dash,* students enter any initial number and then repeatedly press the Op1 key to obtain a new divisor and dividend.

*Example:* Enter 345. Press the Op1 key. The display shows 18.574175<u>56</u><u>2</u>. In *Division Dash,* the 1-digit divisor is 2, and the 2-digit dividend is 56. Now press the Op1 key a second time. The display shows 4.3097767<u>74</u><u>8</u>. The 1-digit divisor is now 8, and the 2-digit dividend is now 74.

Discuss the example on the *Student Reference Book* page. You may want to demonstrate it on an overhead calculator. Then have the class play a round of *Division Dash* together. Volunteers choose the first number, find the square root using their calculators, and identify the dividend and the divisor. Ask the whole class to attempt the division. Remind students that in *Division Dash,* only the whole-number part (the **quotient**) is recorded; the leftover part (the **remainder**) is ignored. In some cases, the quotient will be 0 (when the dividend begins with 0 and is less than the divisor).

Although students use calculators to generate random numbers, they perform the divisions mentally or on paper. Remind students to use the mental division strategy that they just learned, and to break the numbers into "friendly" parts.

## ✦ Playing *Division Dash*
## (*Student Reference Book,* p. 267)

PARTNER ACTIVITY 

Once students understand the rules, have partners play the game for the rest of the period. They can record their results on scratch paper. Pair students who have a good understanding of division with those who don't. Circulate and assist.

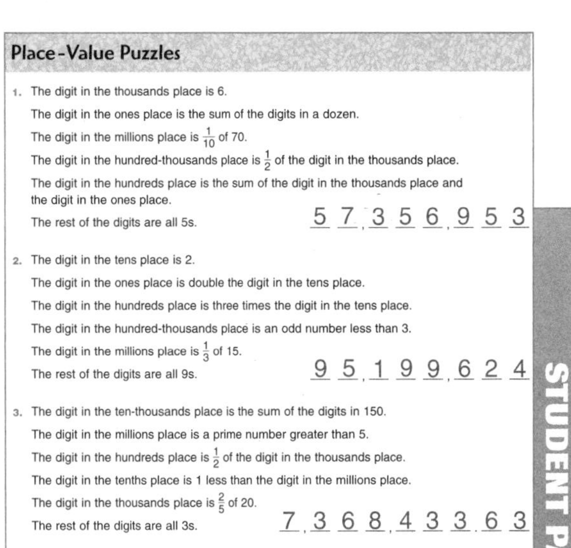

**Place-Value Puzzles**

1. The digit in the thousands place is 6.
The digit in the ones place is the sum of the digits in a dozen.
The digit in the millions place is $\frac{1}{10}$ of 70.
The digit in the hundred-thousands place is $\frac{1}{2}$ of the digit in the thousands place.
The digit in the hundreds place is the sum of the digit in the thousands place and the digit in the ones place.
The rest of the digits are all 5s. 5 7 , 3 5 6 , 9 5 3

2. The digit in the tens place is 2.
The digit in the ones place is double the digit in the tens place.
The digit in the hundreds place is three times the digit in the tens place.
The digit in the hundred-thousands place is an odd number less than 3.
The digit in the millions place is $\frac{1}{3}$ of 15.
The rest of the digits are all 9s. 9 5 , 1 9 9 , 6 2 4

3. The digit in the ten-thousands place is the sum of the digits in 150.
The digit in the millions place is a prime number greater than 5.
The digit in the hundreds place is $\frac{1}{2}$ of the digit in the thousands place.
The digit in the tenths place is 1 less than the digit in the millions place.
The digit in the thousands place is $\frac{2}{5}$ of 20.
The rest of the digits are all 3s. 7 , 3 6 8 , 4 3 3 . 6 3

**Challenge**

4. The digit in the thousands place is the smallest square number greater than 1.
The digit in the tens place is the same as the digit in the place 1,000 times greater.
The digit in the ten-thousands place is $\frac{1}{2}$ of the digit in the ten-millions place.
The digit in the ten-millions place is two more than the digit in the thousands place.
The digit in the hundreds place is 1 greater than double the digit in the ten-thousands place.
The rest of the digits are all 2s. 6 2 , 2 3 4 , 7 3 2

STUDENT PAGE

✦ *Math Journal 1,* p. 104

NOTE: The instructions given here for taking repeated square roots are for the Texas Instruments TI-15. For other calculators, check the instruction booklet.

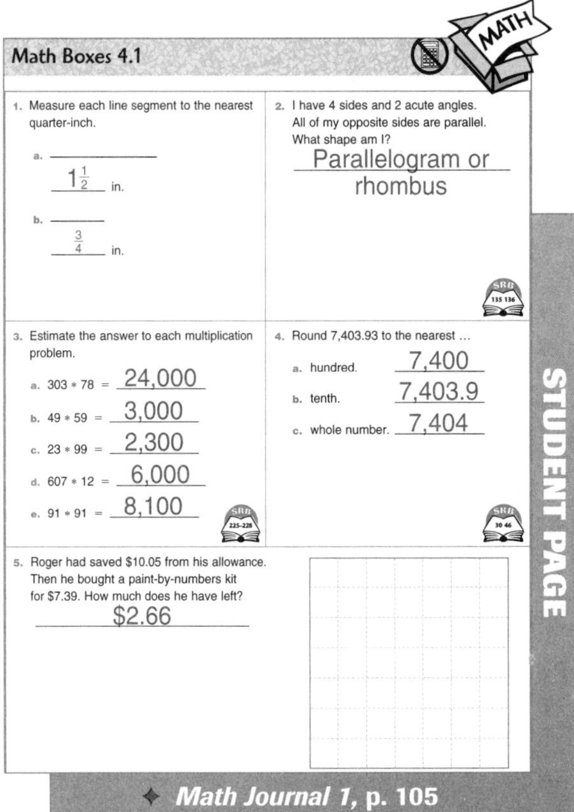

**Math Boxes 4.1**

1. Measure each line segment to the nearest quarter-inch.
a. $1\frac{1}{2}$ in.
b. $\frac{3}{4}$ in.

2. I have 4 sides and 2 acute angles. All of my opposite sides are parallel. What shape am I?
Parallelogram or rhombus

3. Estimate the answer to each multiplication problem.
a. 303 * 78 = 24,000
b. 49 * 59 = 3,000
c. 23 * 99 = 2,300
d. 607 * 12 = 6,000
e. 91 * 91 = 8,100

4. Round 7,403.93 to the nearest ...
a. hundred. 7,400
b. tenth. 7,403.9
c. whole number. 7,404

5. Roger had saved $10.05 from his allowance. Then he bought a paint-by-numbers kit for $7.39. How much does he have left?
$2.66

STUDENT PAGE

✦ *Math Journal 1,* p. 105

## Uses of Division

Study Link 4.1

Use what you know about division facts to solve the following problems. (Think: *How many of these are in that?*) Include units in your answers when appropriate.

SRB 11 21

1. Fifteen-year-old oak trees are often about 25 feet tall. Rose, a 15-year-old girl, is about 5 feet tall. How many times taller are the trees than Rose? 5 times taller
2. The job of interviewing 500 students in a school is to be divided equally among 10 interviewers. How many students should each interviewer talk to? 50 students
3. At an average speed of 50 miles per hour, about how long will a 400-mile trip take? 8 hours
4. A summer camp serves 180 gallons of milk per month to 90 campers. About how much milk, on average, does each camper drink per month? 2 gallons
5. The diameter of Earth is about 4 times the diameter of the Moon. Earth's diameter is about 8,000 miles. What is the approximate diameter of the Moon? 2,000 miles

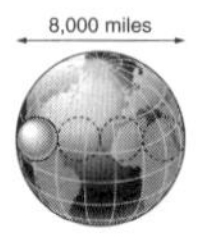


**Challenge**

Problems 6 and 7 were given to eighth graders on a test used to measure the progress of students in the United States. See how well you can do.

6. Jill needs to earn \$45 for a class trip. She earns \$2 each day on Mondays, Tuesdays, and Wednesdays. She earns \$3 each day on Thursdays, Fridays, and Saturdays. She does not work on Sundays. How many weeks will it take her to earn \$45? 3 weeks
7. The weight of an object on the Moon would be $\frac{1}{6}$ of its weight on Earth. An object that weighs 30 pounds on Earth would weigh how many pounds on the Moon? 5 pounds

Problem 6 was solved correctly by 59% of the eighth graders who tried it. Problem 7 was solved correctly by 49%.

STUDY LINK MASTER

Math Masters, p. 255

NOTE: The TI-15 calculator can be used to practice basic and extended division facts. For further information, see *Math Masters,* pages 480 and 481 and the *Teacher's Reference Manual.*

## Fact Families

Complete each Fact Triangle. Write the fact family for each Fact Triangle.

1. $*,/$
2. $*,/$
3. $*,/$
4. $*,/$

TEACHING MASTER

Math Masters, p. 38

# 2 Ongoing Learning & Practice

### Solving Place-Value Puzzles (*Math Journal 1,* p. 104)

INDEPENDENT ACTIVITY 

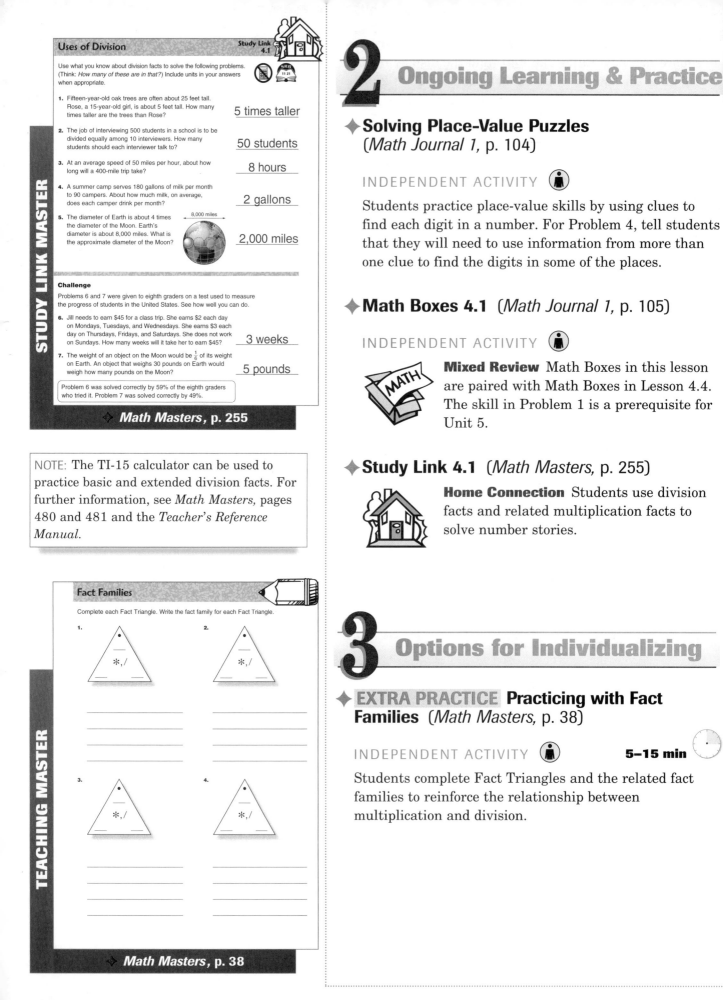

Students practice place-value skills by using clues to find each digit in a number. For Problem 4, tell students that they will need to use information from more than one clue to find the digits in some of the places.

### Math Boxes 4.1 (*Math Journal 1,* p. 105)

INDEPENDENT ACTIVITY 

**Mixed Review** Math Boxes in this lesson are paired with Math Boxes in Lesson 4.4. The skill in Problem 1 is a prerequisite for Unit 5.

### Study Link 4.1 (*Math Masters,* p. 255)

**Home Connection** Students use division facts and related multiplication facts to solve number stories.

# 3 Options for Individualizing

### EXTRA PRACTICE Practicing with Fact Families (*Math Masters,* p. 38)

INDEPENDENT ACTIVITY  **5–15 min**

Students complete Fact Triangles and the related fact families to reinforce the relationship between multiplication and division.

# 4.2 The Partial-Quotients Division Algorithm

**OBJECTIVE** **To review and practice the partial-quotients division algorithm for dividing a whole number by a whole number.**

| summaries | materials |
|---|---|
| **1 Teaching the Lesson** | |
| Students review and practice a paper-and-pencil algorithm for division in which they find partial quotients by using "easy" multiples of the divisor. [Operations and Computation] | □ *Math Journal 1,* pp. 106 and 107<br>□ *Student Reference Book,* pp. 22–23<br>□ Study Link 4.1<br>□ Teaching Masters (*Math Masters,* p. 12; and p. 39, optional)<br>***See* Advance Preparation** |
| **2 Ongoing Learning & Practice** | |
| Students practice and maintain skills through Math Boxes and Study Link activities. | □ *Math Journal 1,* p. 108<br>□ Study Link Master (*Math Masters,* p. 256) |
| **3 Options for Individualizing** | |
| **Extra Practice** Students solve division problems with 1-and 2-digit divisors by using the partial-quotients division algorithm. [Operations and Computation]<br>**Language Diversity** Students use a poster to review different formats for writing a division problem and the vocabulary for the parts of a division problem. [Operations and Computation] | □ Teaching Master (*Math Masters,* p. 40)<br>□ Division Poster<br>***See* Advance Preparation** |

## Additional Information

**Background Information** The partial-quotients division algorithm was introduced in fourth grade (Lesson 6.2) as the focus division algorithm for *Everyday Mathematics.* It resembles the traditional U.S. long-division algorithm, but it is simpler because students build up the quotient by working with "easy" multiples of the divisor. (It could also be called the ladder division algorithm because of its appearance.) It is a "low stress" algorithm. This algorithm will be extended to division of decimals by whole numbers in Lesson 4.5; division in fourth grade was limited to division of whole numbers by whole numbers.

**Advance Preparation** If the partial-quotients division algorithm is new to you, try a few problems and experiment with partial quotients.

In Part 1, you will need to make 1 or 2 copies of the computation grid (*Math Masters,* page 12) for each student.

For the optional Extra Practice activity in Part 3, fill in four division problems before copying *Math Masters,* page 40. For struggling students, write problems with 1-digit divisors and 2- or 3-digit dividends. Cross out multiples other than 100 *, 10 *, and 1 *. For more challenging practice, write problems with 2-digit divisors and 3- or 4-digit dividends.

Before beginning the optional Language Diversity activity, you will need to prepare a Division Poster. See instructions on page 223.

**Vocabulary • dividend • divisor • partial quotient • quotient • remainder**

# Getting Started

### Mental Math and Reflexes

Pose multiplication and division problems like the following:

- How many 5s are in 45? 9 What number times 9 equals 27? 3 What is 3 times 120? 360
- How many 4s are in 32? 8 What number times 8 equals 40? 5 Multiply 5 times 80. 400
- What number times 7 equals 35? 5 How many 5s are in 60? 12 Multiply 12 by 4. 48
- 10 times what number equals 120? 12 How many 12s are in 36? 3 Multiply 55 by 3. 165

### Math Message

*Amy is 127 days older than Bob. How many weeks is that?*

### Study Link 4.1 Follow-Up

Briefly review answers.

NOTE: Expressing remainders as fractions, which was introduced in fourth grade, will be reviewed in Lesson 4.5.

## 1 Teaching the Lesson

### ✦Math Message Follow-Up

WHOLE-CLASS ACTIVITY

Have students share their solution strategies. Expect that some students will suggest breaking 127 into "friendly" numbers such as 70 and 57. There are 10 [7s] in 70 and another 8 [7s] in 57. The remainder is 1.

### ✦Reviewing the Partial-Quotients Division Algorithm (*Math Masters,* p. 12)

WHOLE-CLASS ACTIVITY

Point out that to answer the Math Message question, students needed to figure out how many 7s are in 127. Model the partial-quotients division algorithm on the board or an overhead transparency, while students copy the steps on a computation grid.

1. Write the problem in the traditional form: $7\overline{)127}$. Point out that the **dividend**—the number that is being divided—is 127. The **divisor**—the number that the dividend is being divided by—is 7.
2. Draw a vertical line that will separate subtractions from partial-quotients. *(See the margin.)*
3. Suggest that one way to proceed is to use a series of "at least . . . not more than" multiples of the divisor. A good strategy is to start with easy numbers, such as 100 times the divisor or 10 times the divisor. Give students the following questions or directions:
   - Are there at least 100 [7s] in 127? No, because $100 * 7 = 700$, which is more than 127.

- Are there at least 10 [7s] in 127? Yes, because $10 * 7 = 70$, which is less than 127. Are there at least 20 [7s]? No, because $20 * 7 = 140$, which is more than 127.
- So there are at least 10 [7s] but not more than 20 [7s]. Try 10.

  Write $10 * 7$, or 70, under 127. Write 10 at the right. 10 is the first **partial quotient.** Partial quotients will be used to build up the final quotient.

| 7)127 | | |
|---|---|---|
| 70 | 10 | The first partial quotient. $10 * 7 = 70$ |

4. The next step is to find out how much is left to divide. Subtract 70 from 127.

| 7)127 | | |
|---|---|---|
| − 70 | 10 | The first partial quotient. $10 * 7 = 70$ |
| 57 | | Subtract. 57 is left to divide. |

5. Now find the number of 7s in 57. Following are two ways to do this:

▷ Use a fact family. $8 * 7 = 56$, so there are at least 8 [7s] in 57. Record as follows:

| 7)127 | | |
|---|---|---|
| − 70 | 10 | The first partial quotient. $10 * 7 = 70$ |
| 57 | | Subtract. 57 is left to divide. |
| 56 | 8 | The second partial quotient. $8 * 7 = 56$ |

▷ Continue to use "at least . . . not more than" multiples with easy numbers. For example, ask:

- Are there at least 10 [7s] in 57? No, because $10 * 7 = 70$.
- Are there at least 5 [7s]? Yes, because $5 * 7 = 35$.

Next, subtract 35 from 57 and continue by asking:

- How many 7s are in 22? 3

| 7)127 | | |
|---|---|---|
| − 70 | 10 | The first partial quotient. $10 * 7 = 70$ |
| 57 | | Subtract. 57 is left to divide. |
| − 35 | 5 | The second partial quotient. $5 * 7 = 35$ |
| 22 | | Subtract. 22 is left to divide. |
| 21 | 3 | The third partial quotient. $3 * 7 = 21$ |

6. In both cases, the division is complete when the subtraction leaves a number less than the divisor (7 in this example). The final step is to add the partial quotients—the numbers of 7s that were subtracted.

| 7)127 | |
|---|---|
| − 70 | 10 |
| 57 | |
| − 56 | 8 |
| 1 | 18 |

| 7)127 | |
|---|---|
| − 70 | 10 |
| 57 | |
| − 35 | 5 |
| 22 | |
| − 21 | 3 |
| 1 | 18 |

**Adjusting the Activity** Some students may have difficulty with the multiples used in this division method. Suggest that they first make a list of "easy" multiples of the divisor. For example, if the divisor is 7, students might make the following list:

$200 * 7 = 1,400$
$100 * 7 = 700$
$50 * 7 = 350$
$20 * 7 = 140$
$10 * 7 = 70$
$5 * 7 = 35$

Depending on the students and the divisor, the list can be extended or reduced.

Students can use their list of "easy" multiples to take the guesswork out of successive multiples and focus on solving the division problem.

Students will realize that they can work more quickly if they begin with a more extensive list of multiples. *Math Masters,* page 39 provides an optional form for writing multiples.

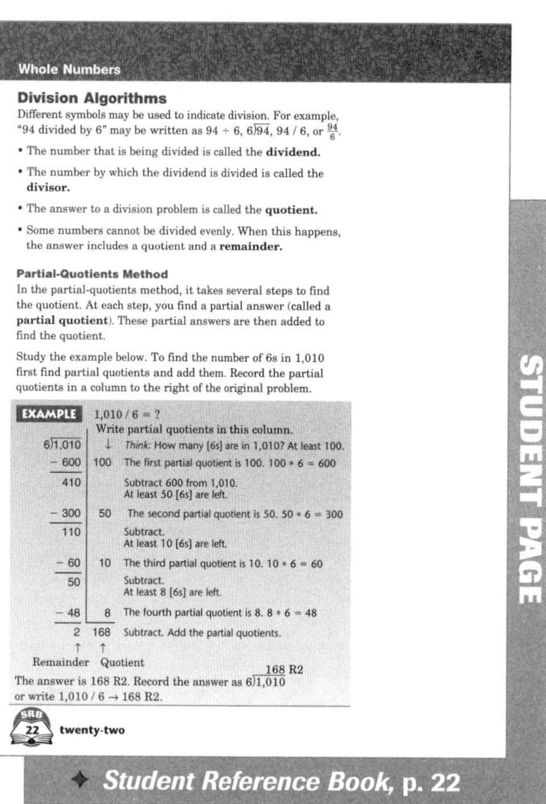

Whole Numbers

**Division Algorithms**

Different symbols may be used to indicate division. For example, "94 divided by 6" may be written as 94 ÷ 6, 6)94, 94 / 6, or $\frac{94}{6}$.

- The number that is being divided is called the **dividend.**
- The number by which the dividend is divided is called the **divisor.**
- The answer to a division problem is called the **quotient.**
- Some numbers cannot be divided evenly. When this happens, the answer includes a quotient and a **remainder.**

**Partial-Quotients Method**

In the partial-quotients method, it takes several steps to find the quotient. At each step, you find a partial answer (called a **partial quotient**). These partial answers are then added to find the quotient.

Study the example below. To find the number of 6s in 1,010 first find partial quotients and add them. Record the partial quotients in a column to the right of the original problem.

**EXAMPLE** 1,010 / 6 = ?

| | Write partial quotients in this column. | |
|---|---|---|
| 6)1,010 | ↓ | *Think:* How many [6s] are in 1,010? At least 100. |
| − 600 | 100 | The first partial quotient is 100. $100 * 6 = 600$ |
| 410 | | Subtract 600 from 1,010. At least 50 [6s] are left. |
| − 300 | 50 | The second partial quotient is 50. $50 * 6 = 300$ |
| 110 | | Subtract. At least 10 [6s] are left. |
| − 60 | 10 | The third partial quotient is 10. $10 * 6 = 60$ |
| 50 | | Subtract. At least 8 [6s] are left. |
| − 48 | 8 | The fourth partial quotient is 8. $8 * 6 = 48$ |
| 2 | 168 | Subtract. Add the partial quotients. |
| ↑ Remainder | ↑ Quotient | |

The answer is 168 R2. Record the answer as 6)1,010 with 168 R2 above, or write 1,010 / 6 → 168 R2.

SRB 22 twenty-two

STUDENT PAGE

✦ Student Reference Book, p. 22

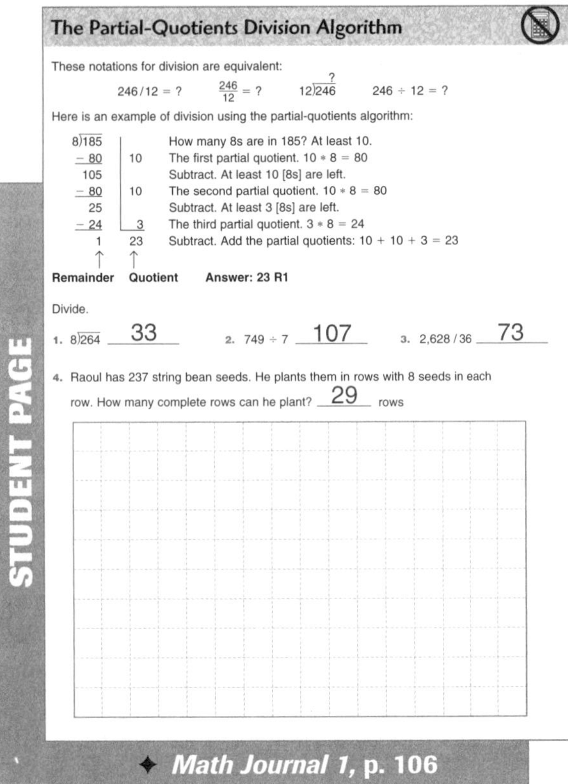
STUDENT PAGE

**The Partial-Quotients Division Algorithm**

These notations for division are equivalent:

246 / 12 = ?  $\frac{246}{12}$ = ?  $12\overline{)246}$ ?  246 ÷ 12 = ?

Here is an example of division using the partial-quotients algorithm:

| | | |
|---|---|---|
| $8\overline{)185}$ | | How many 8s are in 185? At least 10. |
| – 80 | 10 | The first partial quotient. 10 ∗ 8 = 80 |
| 105 | | Subtract. At least 10 [8s] are left. |
| – 80 | 10 | The second partial quotient. 10 ∗ 8 = 80 |
| 25 | | Subtract. At least 3 [8s] are left. |
| – 24 | 3 | The third partial quotient. 3 ∗ 8 = 24 |
| 1 | 23 | Subtract. Add the partial quotients: 10 + 10 + 3 = 23 |
| ↑ Remainder | ↑ Quotient | Answer: 23 R1 |

Divide.

1. $8\overline{)264}$ 33
2. 749 ÷ 7 107
3. 2,628 / 36 73
4. Raoul has 237 string bean seeds. He plants them in rows with 8 seeds in each row. How many complete rows can he plant? 29 rows

✦ *Math Journal 1,* p. 106

NOTE: Expect that some students may still struggle with the division algorithm. They will continue to practice the algorithm throughout the rest of this unit and in Math Boxes and Ongoing Learning & Practice activities throughout the year.

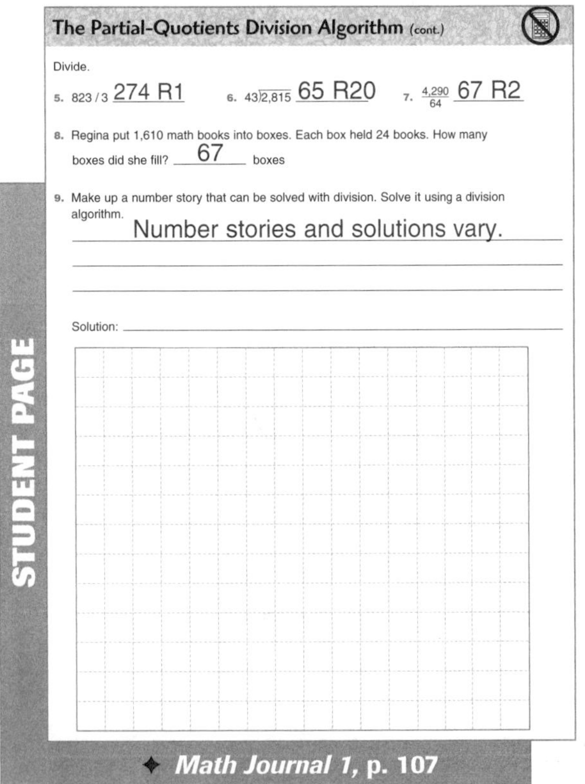
STUDENT PAGE

**The Partial-Quotients Division Algorithm** (cont.)

Divide.

5. 823 / 3 274 R1
6. $43\overline{)2,815}$ 65 R20
7. $\frac{4,290}{64}$ 67 R2
8. Regina put 1,610 math books into boxes. Each box held 24 books. How many boxes did she fill? 67 boxes
9. Make up a number story that can be solved with division. Solve it using a division algorithm. Number stories and solutions vary.

Solution:

✦ *Math Journal 1,* p. 107

7. Steps 1–6 show that there are 18 [7s] in 127. 18 is the **quotient.** There is 1 left over. 1 is the **remainder.**
8. Answers to division problems with remainders are usually written in the form "quotient R remainder"—in the example, 18 R1. Have students record the final answer in the traditional position above the dividend:

$$\begin{array}{r} 18\ \text{R1} \\ 7\overline{)127}\ | \end{array}$$

9. Conclude by interpreting the answer: Amy is 18 weeks and 1 day older than Bob.

Lead students through several more problems on the board. Ask: *How many n's are there in m?* The *n*'s should be 1- or 2-digit numbers; the *m*'s should be 2- or 3-digit numbers. When students seem to be catching on, ask them to work with partners. Have the class pose a division problem and ask the partnerships to attempt to find the answer. They may use computation grid paper.

After the partnerships have worked for a few minutes, ask volunteers to share their work with the class. Look for students who got the same result in different ways. Emphasize the following:

- ▷ Students should use multiples that are not too large and are easy to work with. Using such multiples may require more steps, but it will make the work go faster.
- ▷ Students should not be concerned if they pick a multiple that is too large. If that happens, they will quickly realize that they have a subtraction problem with a larger number being subtracted from a smaller number.

## ✦ Using the Division Algorithm
(*Math Journal 1,* pp. 106 and 107)

INDEPENDENT ACTIVITY 

Students work alone or with a partner. Circulate and assist, especially with the problems involving 2-digit divisors. Students can use pages 22 and 23 in the *Student Reference Book* to review the steps in this algorithm.

**Adjusting the Activity** Extend the activity for capable students. Review the idea that the remainder can be written as a fraction. You can compare this to rewriting a division problem in fraction format and finding the mixed number equivalent. Writing remainders as fractions will be addressed in Lesson 4.5.

## Ongoing Learning & Practice

### Math Boxes 4.2 (*Math Journal 1,* p. 108)

INDEPENDENT ACTIVITY 

**Mixed Review** Math Boxes in this lesson are paired with Math Boxes in Lesson 4.5. The skill in Problem 1 is a prerequisite for Unit 5.

### Study Link 4.2 (*Math Masters,* p. 256)

**Home Connection** Students practice the division algorithm. Problem 4 will provide some information about students' ability to interpret remainders. Interpreting remainders will be covered in Lesson 4.5.

## Options for Individualizing

### EXTRA PRACTICE Practicing Division (*Math Masters,* p. 40)

INDEPENDENT ACTIVITY  **5–15 min** 

Students complete a page of practice problems. Before copying the master, fill in four division problems based on your class's ability.

### LANGUAGE DIVERSITY Supporting Math Vocabulary Development

SMALL-GROUP ACTIVITY  **15–30 min**

Make a poster showing a division problem written in different formats. Label the different parts of the problem so that students can refer to the poster to help them with vocabulary. If students are keeping a dictionary of words with illustrations, they should add this to their dictionary.

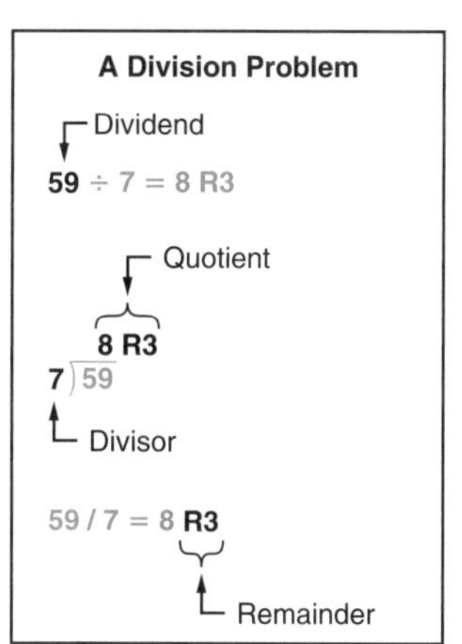


**Math Boxes 4.2**

1. Measure the length and width of each of the following objects to the nearest half inch. Answers vary.
   a. piece of paper length ______ in. width ______ in.
   b. dictionary length ______ in. width ______ in.
   c. palm of your hand length ______ in. width ______ in.
   d. ______ (your choice) length ______ in. width ______ in.

2. Do the following multiplication problems mentally.
   a. $89 * 5 =$ 445
   b. $199 * 12 =$ 2,388
   c. 1,596 $= 4 * 399$
   d. $29 * 15 =$ 435
   e. 1,770 $= 59 * 30$

3. Write the following numbers in order from least to greatest.
   2.05 2.70 2.57 2.07 2.5
   2.05
   2.07
   2.5
   2.57
   2.70

4. Measure each angle to the nearest degree.
   a. The measure of ∠B is about 105°.
   b. The measure of ∠E is about 47°.

STUDENT PAGE

*Math Journal 1,* p. 108

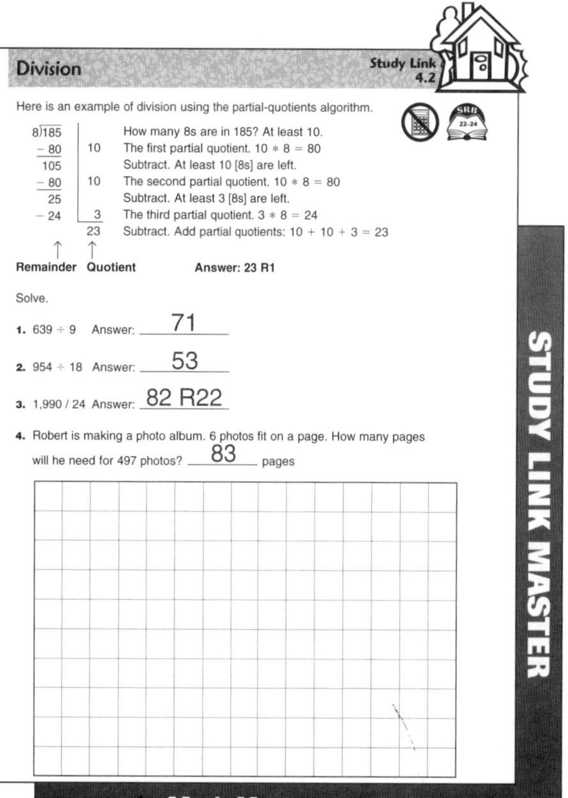

**Division** Study Link 4.2

Here is an example of division using the partial-quotients algorithm.

| | | |
|---|---|---|
| 8)185 | | How many 8s are in 185? At least 10. |
| − 80 | 10 | The first partial quotient. $10 * 8 = 80$ |
| 105 | | Subtract. At least 10 [8s] are left. |
| − 80 | 10 | The second partial quotient. $10 * 8 = 80$ |
| 25 | | Subtract. At least 3 [8s] are left. |
| − 24 | 3 | The third partial quotient. $3 * 8 = 24$ |
| 1 | 23 | Subtract. Add partial quotients: $10 + 10 + 3 = 23$ |

Remainder Quotient Answer: 23 R1

Solve.

1. 639 ÷ 9 Answer: 71
2. 954 ÷ 18 Answer: 53
3. 1,990 / 24 Answer: 82 R22
4. Robert is making a photo album. 6 photos fit on a page. How many pages will he need for 497 photos? 83 pages

STUDY LINK MASTER

*Math Masters,* p. 256

# 4.3 American Tour: Finding Distances on a Map

**OBJECTIVE** **To estimate distances using a map scale.**

| summaries | materials |
|---|---|
| **1 Teaching the Lesson** | |
| Students read about Native Americans in the American Tour and discuss parts of a map; students use map scales to estimate real distances along straight and curved paths. [Measurement and Reference Frames; Operations and Computation] | ☐ *Math Journal 1,* pp. 109 and 110<br>☐ *Student Reference Book,* pp. 195, 196, 299, 344, and 345<br>☐ Study Link 4.2<br>☐ ruler<br>☐ compass or string ☐ slate |
| **2 Ongoing Learning & Practice** | |
| Students classify and measure angles. [Geometry; Measurement and Reference Frames]<br>Students practice and maintain skills through Math Boxes and Study Link activities. | ☐ *Math Journal 1,* pp. 111 and 112<br>☐ Study Link Master (*Math Masters,* p. 257)<br>☐ Geometry Template or protractor |
| **3 Options for Individualizing** | |
| **Extra Practice** Students mark a route on a map and find its length. [Measurement and Reference Frames] | ☐ *Student Reference Book,* pp. 195 and 196<br>☐ Teaching Master (*Math Masters,* p. 41)<br>☐ ruler, compass, or string |

**Additional Information**

**Vocabulary** • **map legend or map key** • **direction symbol** • **map scale**

## Getting Started

### Mental Math and Reflexes

Students record on their slates whether given fractions are closer to 0, $\frac{1}{2}$, or 1. *Suggestions:*

$\frac{3}{8}, \frac{5}{6}, \frac{7}{12}, \frac{1}{5}, \frac{2}{5}, \frac{7}{9}$

Have volunteers share how they figured out their answers. Expect strategies such as the following:

- I know that $\frac{4}{8}$ equals $\frac{1}{2}$. Since $\frac{3}{8}$ is only $\frac{1}{8}$ away, $\frac{3}{8}$ is closer to $\frac{1}{2}$.
- I know that $\frac{4.5}{9}$ would be equal to $\frac{1}{2}$ and $\frac{9}{9}$ would be equal to 1. $\frac{7}{9}$ is closer to $\frac{9}{9}$ than to $\frac{4.5}{9}$.

Continue as time allows.

**Math Message**

*Begin reading about the First Americans on page 299 of your* Student Reference Book.

**Study Link 4.2 Follow-Up**

Briefly review answers. For Problem 4, students need to interpret the remainder in order to answer the question.

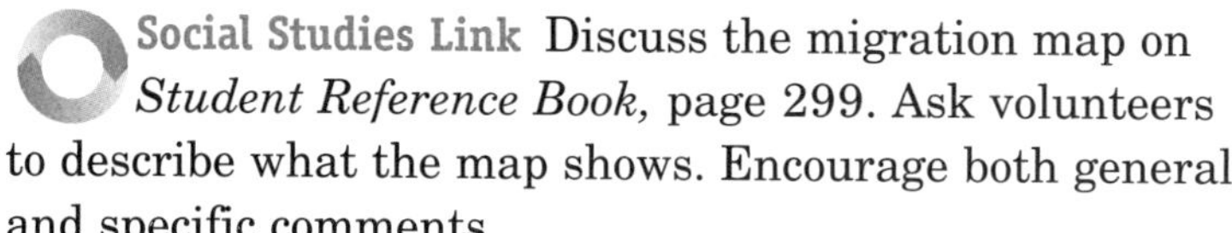


## ✦ Math Message Follow-Up
(*Student Reference Book*, p. 299)

WHOLE-CLASS DISCUSSION

**Social Studies Link** Discuss the migration map on *Student Reference Book,* page 299. Ask volunteers to describe what the map shows. Encourage both general and specific comments.

Refer to information such as the map title and labels. Point out that the map has three features found on most maps.

- ▷ A **map legend** or **map key** explains the symbols, markings, and colors on the map. The legend is one of the first places to look when examining a map.
- ▷ A **direction symbol** locates north, south, east, and west on the map. (If there is no direction symbol, north is usually understood to be at the top of the map.)
- ▷ A **map scale** compares distances on the map with real distances. The scale can be a ruler-like diagram *(see the margin)*, or words and symbols such as: *1 inch represents 100 miles, 1 inch = 100 miles, or 1 inch → 100 miles.*

**Language Arts Link** Have students look up the word *key* in a dictionary and share the definitions that they find. Ask a volunteer to explain why the legend on a map is also called a key. Sample answer: In a manner of speaking, the key "unlocks" the map by explaining what is depicted on the map as well as various map features.

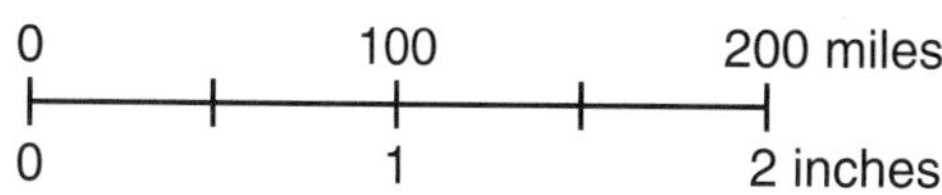


Notation such as "1 inch = 100 miles" is commonly used, but it violates the definition of an equation. *Everyday Mathematics* uses "1 inch represents 100 miles" or "1 inch → 100 miles."

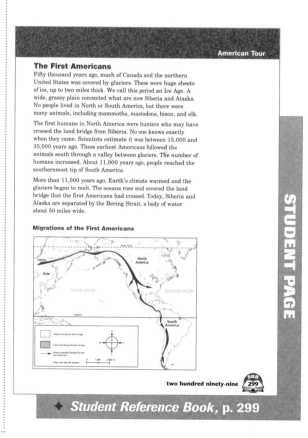

American Tour

**The First Americans**

Fifty thousand years ago, much of Canada and the northern United States was covered by glaciers. These were huge sheets of ice, up to two miles thick. We call this period an Ice Age. A wide, grassy plain connected what are now Siberia and Alaska. No people lived in North or South America, but there were many animals, including mammoths, mastodons, bison, and elk.

The first humans in North America were hunters who may have crossed the land bridge from Siberia. No one knows exactly when they came. Scientists estimate it was between 15,000 and 35,000 years ago. These earliest Americans followed the animals south through a valley between glaciers. The number of humans increased. About 11,000 years ago, people reached the southernmost tip of South America.

More than 11,000 years ago, Earth's climate warmed and the glaciers began to melt. The oceans rose and covered the land bridge that the first Americans had crossed. Today, Siberia and Alaska are separated by the Bering Strait, a body of water about 50 miles wide.

**Migrations of the First Americans**

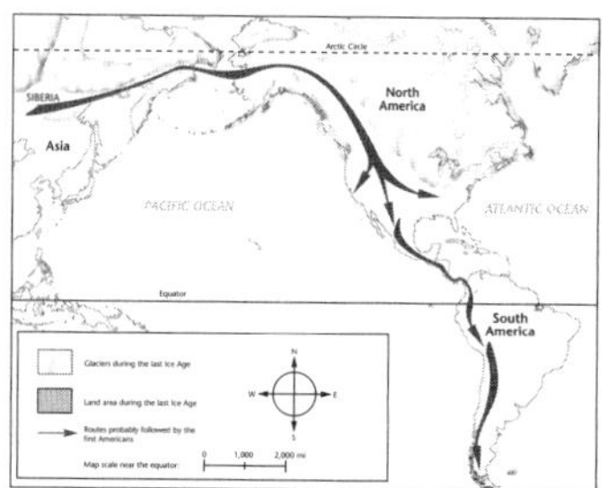


two hundred ninety-nine 

STUDENT PAGE

✦ *Student Reference Book,* p. 299

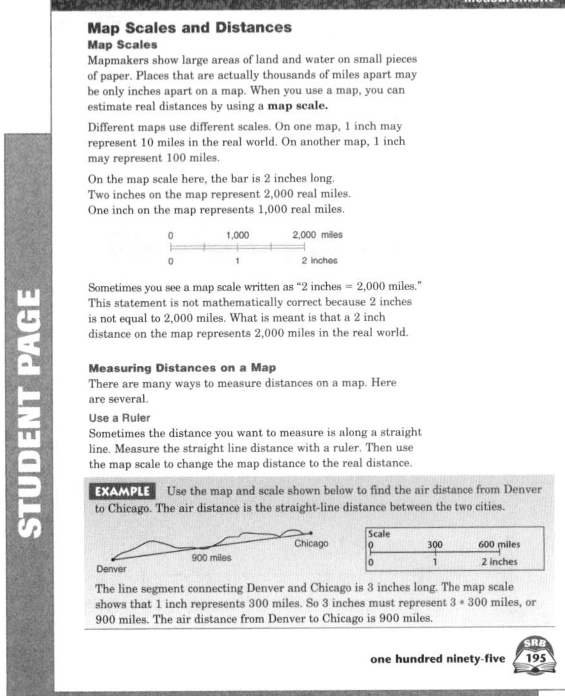

Measurement

### Map Scales and Distances

**Map Scales**

Mapmakers show large areas of land and water on small pieces of paper. Places that are actually thousands of miles apart may be only inches apart on a map. When you use a map, you can estimate real distances by using a **map scale.**

Different maps use different scales. On one map, 1 inch may represent 10 miles in the real world. On another map, 1 inch may represent 100 miles.

On the map scale here, the bar is 2 inches long. Two inches on the map represent 2,000 real miles. One inch on the map represents 1,000 real miles.



Sometimes you see a map scale written as "2 inches = 2,000 miles." This statement is not mathematically correct because 2 inches is not equal to 2,000 miles. What is meant is that a 2 inch distance on the map represents 2,000 miles in the real world.

**Measuring Distances on a Map**

There are many ways to measure distances on a map. Here are several.

Use a Ruler

Sometimes the distance you want to measure is along a straight line. Measure the straight line distance with a ruler. Then use the map scale to change the map distance to the real distance.

**EXAMPLE** Use the map and scale shown below to find the air distance from Denver to Chicago. The air distance is the straight-line distance between the two cities.



The line segment connecting Denver and Chicago is 3 inches long. The map scale shows that 1 inch represents 300 miles. So 3 inches must represent 3 ∗ 300 miles, or 900 miles. The air distance from Denver to Chicago is 900 miles.

one hundred ninety-five SRB 195

STUDENT PAGE

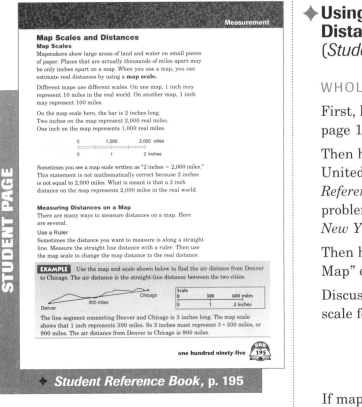

*Student Reference Book*, p. 195

## Using a Map Scale for Straight-Path Distances

(*Student Reference Book*, pp. 195, 344, and 345)

WHOLE-CLASS ACTIVITY

First, have students read "Map Scales" at the top of page 195 of the *Student Reference Book*.

Then have them locate the scale for the map of the United States on pages 344 and 345 of the *Student Reference Book*. Ask the class to suggest several distance problems—for example, *How far is it from Chicago to New York?* Write the students' problems on the board.

Then have students read "Measuring Distances on a Map" on page 195 of the *Student Reference Book*.

Discuss how to use a map to estimate distances. The scale for the map on pages 344 and 345 can be written:

1 inch represents 200 miles

or

1 in. → 200 miles

If map distances are in whole numbers of inches, then the real distances are not hard to find.

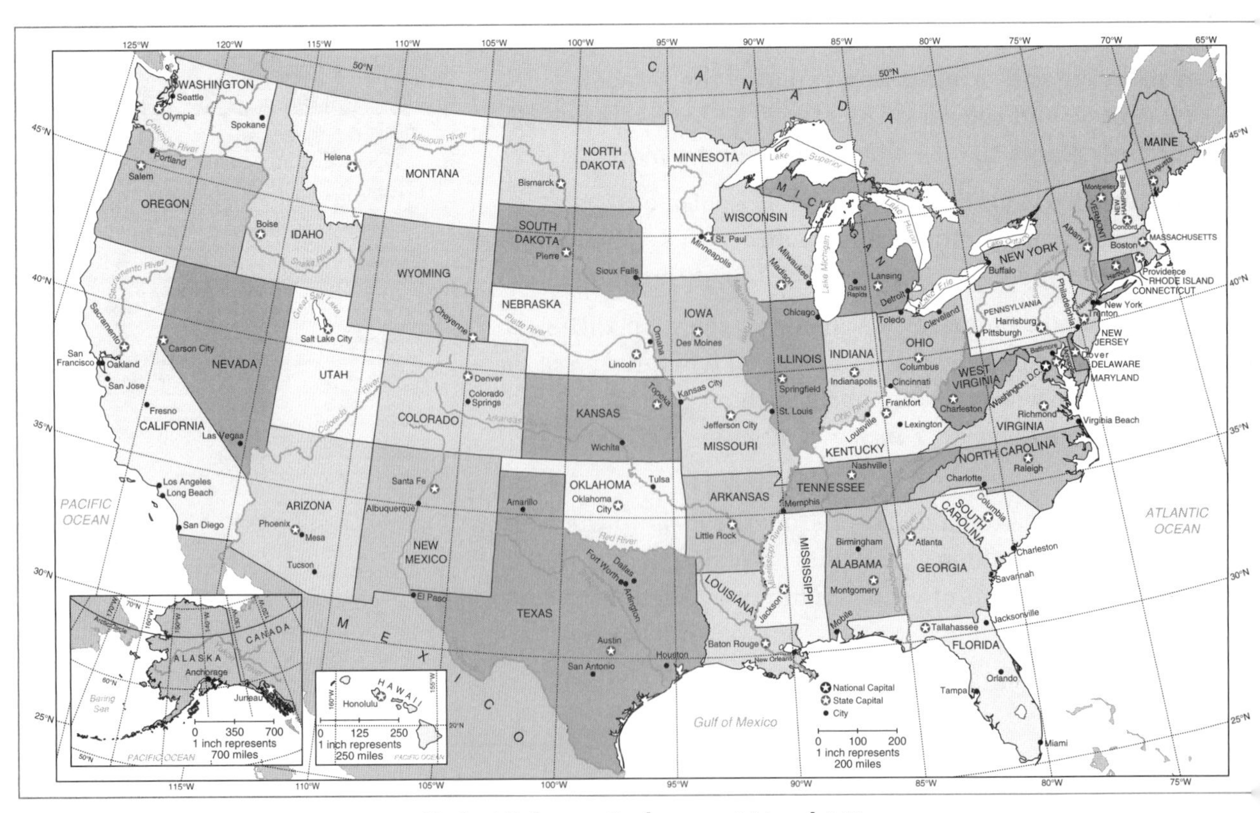


*Student Reference Book*, pages 344 and 345

*Example*

The map distance from Chicago to Pittsburgh is about 2 inches. Think: *1 inch represents 200 miles, so 2 inches represents 2 ∗ 200 miles. The real distance is approximately 2 ∗ 200 miles, or 400 miles.*

Write the following on the board. For each distance, ask students to measure the distance on the map as a whole number of inches, and then to give the real distance.

▷ Dallas, TX, to Nashville, TN 3 inches, 600 miles

▷ Lansing, MI, to Columbus, OH 1 inch, 200 miles

▷ Salt Lake City, UT, to Raleigh, NC 9 inches, 1,800 miles

▷ Boston, MA, to Washington, D.C. 2 inches, 400 miles

▷ Helena, MT, to Kansas City, MO 5 inches, 1,000 miles

However, most distances on maps are not whole numbers of inches. Such problems are harder to solve. Add the following to the list on the board:

▷ Chicago, IL, to New York, NY

Have students measure the distance on the map. It is a little more than $3\frac{1}{2}$ inches—about $3\frac{9}{16}$ inches. The problem can be simplified by rounding $3\frac{9}{16}$ inches to $3\frac{1}{2}$ inches. Since 1 inch represent 200 miles, 3 inches represents 3 ∗ 200 miles, or 600 miles. An additional $\frac{1}{2}$ inch would represent another 100 miles, for a total of 700 miles. The distance from Chicago to New York is a little more than 700 miles.

## ✦ Using a Map Scale to Find Distances in the United States

(*Math Journal 1,* p. 109; *Student Reference Book,* pp. 195, 344, and 345)

PARTNER ACTIVITY

After students demonstrate success with the problems on the board, have them answer the questions on the journal page.

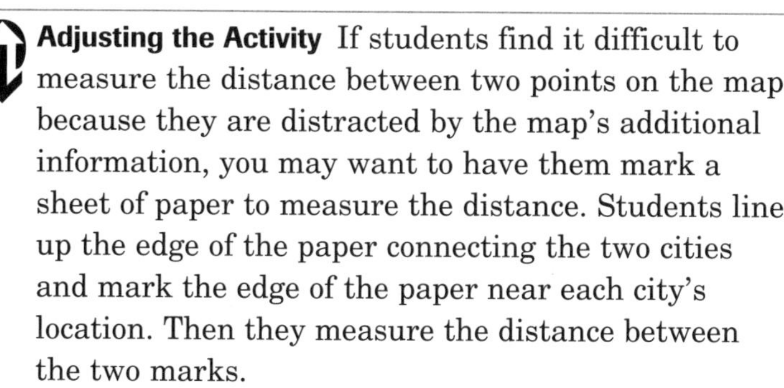

**Adjusting the Activity** If students find it difficult to measure the distance between two points on the map because they are distracted by the map's additional information, you may want to have them mark a sheet of paper to measure the distance. Students line up the edge of the paper connecting the two cities and mark the edge of the paper near each city's location. Then they measure the distance between the two marks.

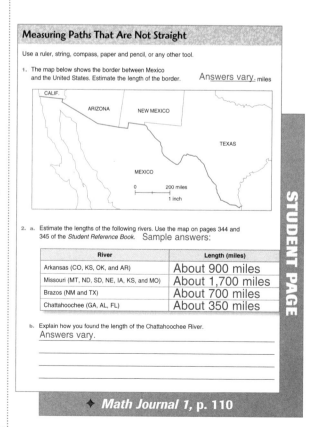

### Distances between U.S. Cities

1. Use the map of the United States on pages 344 and 345 of your *Student Reference Book* to estimate the distances between the following cities. Measure each map distance in inches. Complete the table. (Scale: 1 inch represents 200 miles)

| Cities | Map Distance (inches) | Real Distance (miles) |
|---|---|---|
| Chicago, IL, to Pittsburgh, PA | 2 inches | 400 miles |
| Little Rock, AR, to Jackson, MS | 1 inch | 200 miles |
| San Francisco, CA, to Salt Lake City, UT | 3 inches | 600 miles |
| Indianapolis, IN, to Raleigh, NC | $2\frac{1}{2}$ inches | 500 miles |
| Chicago, IL, to Boston, MA | $4\frac{1}{4}$ inches | 850 miles |
| San Antonio, TX, to Buffalo, NY | $7\frac{1}{4}$ inches | 1,450 miles |
| Salt Lake City, UT, to Pierre, SD | $3\frac{1}{4}$ inches | 650 miles |

2. Explain how you found the real distance from Salt Lake City, UT, to Pierre, SD.
Sample answer: I used a ruler to measure the distance from Salt Lake City to Pierre. The distance was $3\frac{1}{4}$ inches, to the nearest $\frac{1}{4}$ inch. 3 inches represents 600 miles. $\frac{1}{4}$ inch represents 50 miles. The distance is about 650 miles.

3. Explain who might use a map scale and why.
Sample answer: People on vacation might use a map scale to determine the distance that they need to drive to get to their next destination.

STUDENT PAGE

✦ *Math Journal 1,* p. 109

### Measuring Paths That Are Not Straight

Use a ruler, string, compass, paper and pencil, or any other tool.

1. The map below shows the border between Mexico and the United States. Estimate the length of the border. Answers vary. miles

2. a. Estimate the lengths of the following rivers. Use the map on pages 344 and 345 of the *Student Reference Book.* Sample answers:

| River | Length (miles) |
|---|---|
| Arkansas (CO, KS, OK, and AR) | About 900 miles |
| Missouri (MT, ND, SD, NE, IA, KS, and MO) | About 1,700 miles |
| Brazos (NM and TX) | About 700 miles |
| Chattahoochee (GA, AL, FL) | About 350 miles |

b. Explain how you found the length of the Chattahoochee River.
Answers vary.

STUDENT PAGE

✦ *Math Journal 1,* p. 110

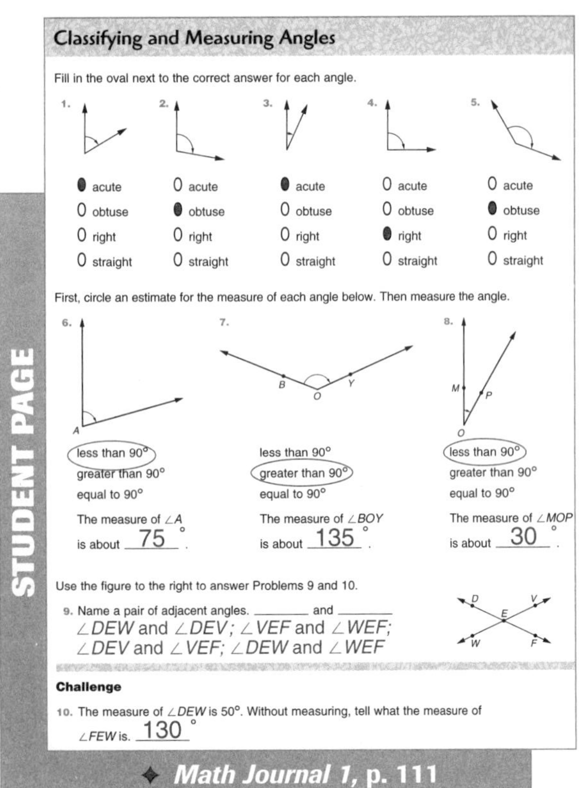

STUDENT PAGE

## Classifying and Measuring Angles

Fill in the oval next to the correct answer for each angle.

| 1. | 2. | 3. | 4. | 5. |
|---|---|---|---|---|
| ● acute | O acute | ● acute | O acute | O acute |
| O obtuse | ● obtuse | O obtuse | O obtuse | ● obtuse |
| O right | O right | O right | ● right | O right |
| O straight | O straight | O straight | O straight | O straight |

First, circle an estimate for the measure of each angle below. Then measure the angle.

| 6. | 7. | 8. |
|---|---|---|
| (less than 90°) | less than 90° | (less than 90°) |
| greater than 90° | (greater than 90°) | greater than 90° |
| equal to 90° | equal to 90° | equal to 90° |
| The measure of ∠A is about 75°. | The measure of ∠BOY is about 135°. | The measure of ∠MOP is about 30°. |

Use the figure to the right to answer Problems 9 and 10.

9. Name a pair of adjacent angles. ______ and ______
∠DEW and ∠DEV; ∠VEF and ∠WEF; ∠DEV and ∠VEF; ∠DEW and ∠WEF

**Challenge**

10. The measure of ∠DEW is 50°. Without measuring, tell what the measure of ∠FEW is. 130°

✦ *Math Journal 1,* p. 111

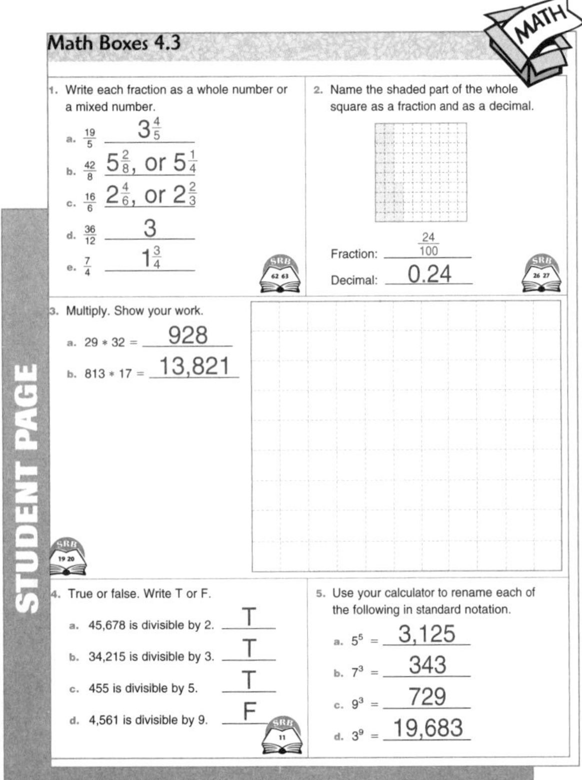

STUDENT PAGE

## Math Boxes 4.3

1. Write each fraction as a whole number or a mixed number.
   a. $\frac{19}{5}$ $3\frac{4}{5}$
   b. $\frac{42}{8}$ $5\frac{2}{8}$, or $5\frac{1}{4}$
   c. $\frac{16}{6}$ $2\frac{4}{6}$, or $2\frac{2}{3}$
   d. $\frac{36}{12}$ 3
   e. $\frac{7}{4}$ $1\frac{3}{4}$

2. Name the shaded part of the whole square as a fraction and as a decimal.
   Fraction: $\frac{24}{100}$
   Decimal: 0.24

3. Multiply. Show your work.
   a. 29 ∗ 32 = 928
   b. 813 ∗ 17 = 13,821

4. True or false. Write T or F.
   a. 45,678 is divisible by 2. T
   b. 34,215 is divisible by 3. T
   c. 455 is divisible by 5. T
   d. 4,561 is divisible by 9. F

5. Use your calculator to rename each of the following in standard notation.
   a. $5^5$ = 3,125
   b. $7^3$ = 343
   c. $9^3$ = 729
   d. $3^9$ = 19,683

✦ *Math Journal 1,* p. 112

## ✦ Estimating Curved-Path Distances

(*Math Journal 1,* p. 110; *Student Reference Book,* pp. 196, 344, and 345)

PARTNER ACTIVITY

When the path on a map is not straight, estimating the distance is harder. This problem may have come up already if one of the problems students suggested earlier was to find the length of a river or a curved boundary.

Read and discuss page 196 in the *Student Reference Book.* This page explains several methods for estimating distances that are not straight. In the compass method, straight-line segments are used to measure a curved path. Shorter segments will produce a more accurate answer.

Have students use the methods to estimate the length of the U.S.–Mexico border. Then have partners complete the journal page.

# 2 Ongoing Learning & Practice

## ✦ Classifying and Measuring Angles

(*Math Journal 1,* p. 111)

INDEPENDENT ACTIVITY 

Students classify angles as acute, right, obtuse, or straight. Then students measure angles.

**ONGOING ASSESSMENT**
**Use students' answers on journal page 111 to assess their familiarity with types of angles and their understanding about angle measurements. Watch to see that their estimates of angle size are reasonable, at least within the right quarter of the circle.**

## ✦ Math Boxes 4.3 (*Math Journal 1,* p. 112)

INDEPENDENT ACTIVITY 

**Mixed Review** Math Boxes in this lesson are paired with Math Boxes in Lesson 4.6. The skills in Problems 1 and 2 are prerequisites for Unit 5.

## ✦ Study Link 4.3 (*Math Masters,* p. 257)

**Home Connection** Students use a map scale to approximate distances. Remind students that they can use a compass or string to estimate the distances.

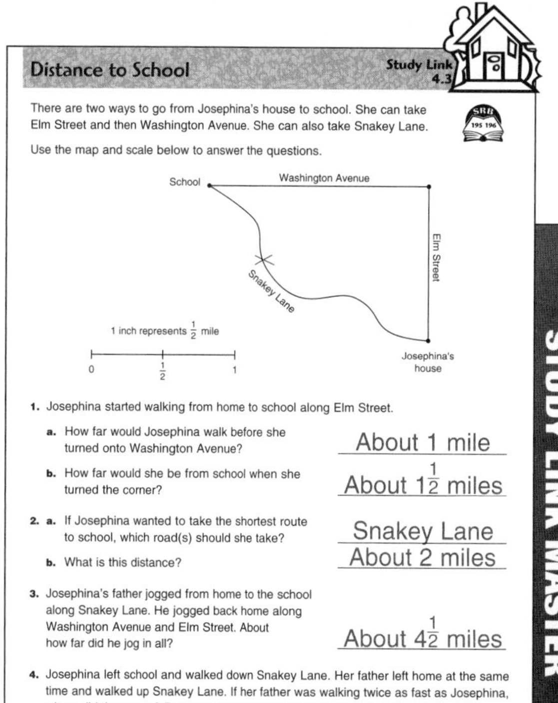

**Distance to School** — Study Link 4.3

There are two ways to go from Josephina's house to school. She can take Elm Street and then Washington Avenue. She can also take Snakey Lane.

Use the map and scale below to answer the questions.



1. Josephina started walking from home to school along Elm Street.
   a. How far would Josephina walk before she turned onto Washington Avenue? About 1 mile
   b. How far would she be from school when she turned the corner? About $1\frac{1}{2}$ miles
2. a. If Josephina wanted to take the shortest route to school, which road(s) should she take? Snakey Lane
   b. What is this distance? About 2 miles
3. Josephina's father jogged from home to the school along Snakey Lane. He jogged back home along Washington Avenue and Elm Street. About how far did he jog in all? About $4\frac{1}{2}$ miles
4. Josephina left school and walked down Snakey Lane. Her father left home at the same time and walked up Snakey Lane. If her father was walking twice as fast as Josephina, where did they meet? Put a mark on the road where they met. On the back of this page, explain how you found your answer.

Answers vary.

STUDY LINK MASTER

Math Masters, p. 257

# 3 Options for Individualizing

## ✦ EXTRA PRACTICE Estimating a Route Length

(*Student Reference Book,* pp. 195 and 196; *Math Masters,* p. 41)

INDEPENDENT ACTIVITY  **5–15 min**

Students pretend to travel by ship from New York, through the Panama Canal, to Los Angeles. They decide on a route, draw the route on a map, and then estimate the length of the route. Finally, they compare the length of this ship route with the straight-line distance from New York to Los Angeles.

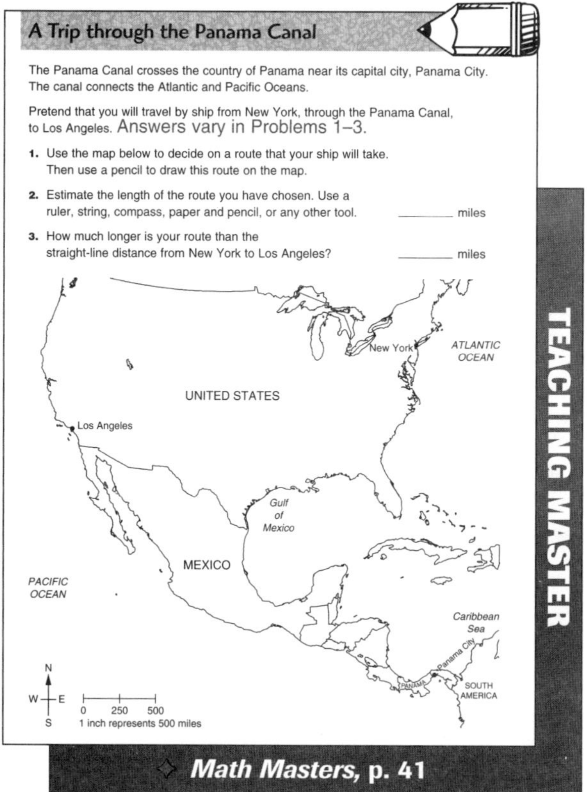

**A Trip through the Panama Canal**

The Panama Canal crosses the country of Panama near its capital city, Panama City. The canal connects the Atlantic and Pacific Oceans.

Pretend that you will travel by ship from New York, through the Panama Canal, to Los Angeles. Answers vary in Problems 1–3.

1. Use the map below to decide on a route that your ship will take. Then use a pencil to draw this route on the map.
2. Estimate the length of the route you have chosen. Use a ruler, string, compass, paper and pencil, or any other tool. ______ miles
3. How much longer is your route than the straight-line distance from New York to Los Angeles? ______ miles



TEACHING MASTER

Math Masters, p. 41

# 4.4 Division of Decimal Numbers

**OBJECTIVES** **To make magnitude estimates for quotients; and to use the partial-quotients division algorithm to divide decimals by whole numbers.**

| summaries | materials |
|---|---|
| **1 Teaching the Lesson** | |
| Students estimate whether quotients will be in the tenths, ones, tens, or hundreds; they mark estimates on a magnitude bar, divide the numbers ignoring the decimal point, and use their magnitude estimates to insert the decimal point in the answers. [Operations and Computation] | □ *Math Journal 1,* p. 113<br>□ Study Link 4.3<br>□ Teaching Master (*Math Masters,* p. 12; optional)<br>□ slate |
| **2 Ongoing Learning & Practice** | |
| Students practice multiplication facts with Fact Triangles or a favorite game. [Operations and Computation]<br>Students practice and maintain skills through Math Boxes and Study Link activities. | □ *Math Journal 1,* p. 114<br>□ Study Link Master (*Math Masters,* p. 258) |
| **3 Options for Individualizing** | |
| **Reteaching** Students model and solve division problems with base-10 blocks and with diagrams of base-10 blocks. [Operations and Computation]<br>**Enrichment** Students explore the column division algorithm, an alternative method of division. [Operations and Computation] | □ *Student Reference Book,* pp. 24 and 44<br>□ Teaching Masters (*Math Masters,* pp. 42 and 43)<br>□ base-10 blocks: 6 flats, 22 longs, 40 cubes<br>***See* Advance Preparation** |

### Additional Information

**Advance Preparation** For the optional Enrichment activity in Part 3, review the column division algorithm on *Math Masters,* page 43 and in the *Student Reference Book* on pages 24 and 44.

**Vocabulary** • **magnitude estimate**

## Getting Started

### Mental Math and Reflexes

Dictate decimal numbers for students to write and mark on their slates. *Suggestions:*

- Write 305.72. Circle the digit in the tens place. Underline the digit in the tenths place. 3⓪5.7̲2
- Write 18.09. Circle the digit in the tenths place. Underline the digit in the ones place. 18̲.⓪9
- Write 7,019.3. Circle the digit in the hundreds place. Underline the digit in the tenths place. 7,⓪19.3̲

Continue as time allows.

**Math Message**

*A rope is 87.6 meters long. You are to cut the rope into 12 pieces, all the same length.*

*About how long should each piece be? Do not calculate the exact answer.*

**Study Link 4.3 Follow-Up**

Briefly review answers. For Problem 4, point out to students that if Josephina's father is walking twice as fast as Josephina, he will cover twice the distance she covers in the same amount of time.

# 1 Teaching the Lesson

## ✦ Math Message Follow-Up
(*Math Masters,* p. 12)

WHOLE-CLASS ACTIVITY

Point out that this is an equal-sharing problem—the total length of 87.6 meters is equally shared (divided) among 12 pieces. The exact solution can be obtained by dividing 87.6 by 12.

Discuss students' strategies for estimating the quotient. *For example:*

- If the rope were 120 meters long, each piece would be 120 meters ÷ 12 = 10 meters long. So the answer is less than 10 meters.
- 2 ∗ 12 = 24. Double this: 4 ∗ 12 = 48. Double again: 8 ∗ 12 = 96, which is a little more than 87.6. Also, 7 ∗ 12 = 84, a little less than 87.6. So each piece is between 7 and 8 meters long.

Ask students to ignore the decimal point and divide 876 by 12, using the division algorithm they reviewed in Lesson 4.2. They can use a computation grid (*Math Masters,* page 12) to show their work. *(See the margin.)*

Ask: *Can 73 be the answer to the problem?* No. The estimated answer was in the range of 7 to 8 meters.

Ask students to use their previous estimates to insert a decimal point in 73 to get a correct answer to the problem. 7.3 meters Have students check their answer. 12 ∗ 7.3 = 87.6

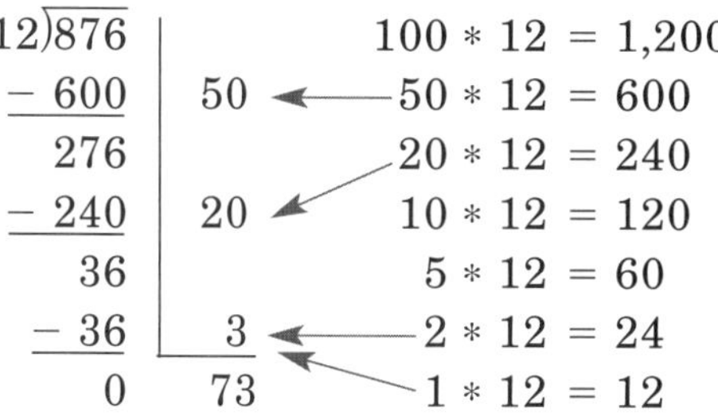


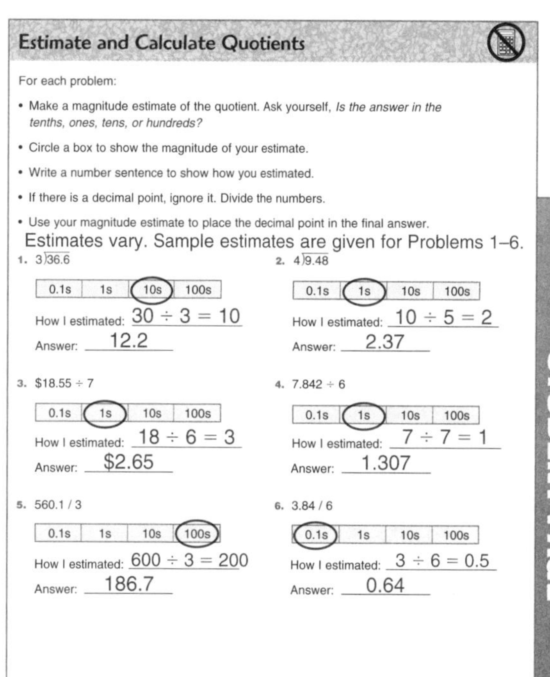

**Estimate and Calculate Quotients**

For each problem:

- Make a magnitude estimate of the quotient. Ask yourself, *Is the answer in the tenths, ones, tens, or hundreds?*
- Circle a box to show the magnitude of your estimate.
- Write a number sentence to show how you estimated.
- If there is a decimal point, ignore it. Divide the numbers.
- Use your magnitude estimate to place the decimal point in the final answer.

Estimates vary. Sample estimates are given for Problems 1–6.

1. 3)36.6 — 0.1s | 1s | (10s) | 100s — How I estimated: 30 ÷ 3 = 10 — Answer: 12.2
2. 4)9.48 — 0.1s | (1s) | 10s | 100s — How I estimated: 10 ÷ 5 = 2 — Answer: 2.37
3. $18.55 ÷ 7 — 0.1s | (1s) | 10s | 100s — How I estimated: 18 ÷ 6 = 3 — Answer: $2.65
4. 7.842 ÷ 6 — 0.1s | (1s) | 10s | 100s — How I estimated: 7 ÷ 7 = 1 — Answer: 1.307
5. 560.1 / 3 — 0.1s | 1s | 10s | (100s) — How I estimated: 600 ÷ 3 = 200 — Answer: 186.7
6. 3.84 / 6 — (0.1s) | 1s | 10s | 100s — How I estimated: 3 ÷ 6 = 0.5 — Answer: 0.64

STUDENT PAGE

✦ *Math Journal 1,* p. 113

NOTE: Students may have difficulty at first making magnitude estimates for problems with decimals. Some students may still be struggling with the division algorithm itself. Skills will develop as division is revisited throughout the year. Build in practice as necessary. Continue to play *Division Dash.*

How I estimated: 30 ÷ 3 = 10

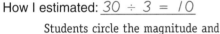

Students circle the magnitude and show their estimate.

"Easy" Multiples of 3

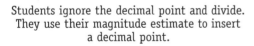

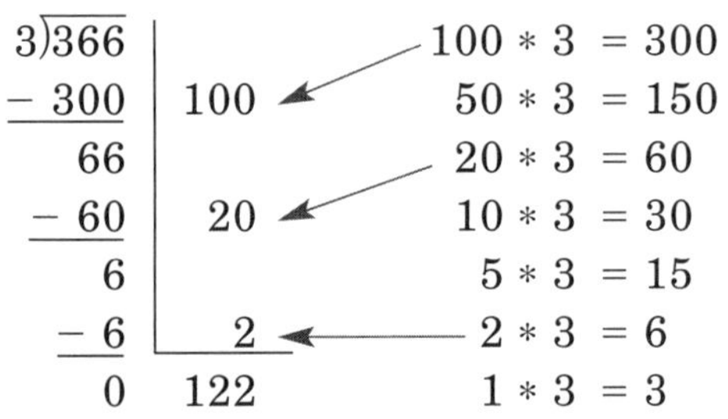


Students ignore the decimal point and divide. They use their magnitude estimate to insert a decimal point.

**Adjusting the Activity** For students who need more practice with whole-number division before tackling decimals, change the numbers in problems by truncating them (crossing off the digits after the decimal point) or by removing the decimal point.

## ◆Making Magnitude Estimates for Quotients
(*Math Journal 1,* p. 113)

WHOLE-CLASS ACTIVITY

When students work on a multiplication or division problem, whether with a calculator or a paper-and-pencil algorithm, they should first make a **magnitude estimate**—a rough estimate of the size of the answer. A magnitude estimate answers questions such as: *Is the answer in the tenths? Ones? Tens? Hundreds?*

NOTE: Students made magnitude estimates for multiplication in Lesson 2.7.

Ask the class to estimate the quotients for one or two problems on the journal page. Recommend the use of "friendly numbers" that are close to the numbers being divided and are easy to work with. Emphasize that students should estimate before finding the exact answer.

For example, in Problem 1, estimate the quotient for 3)36.6 by using a close number, 30, and dividing: 30 ÷ 3 = 10. There are 10 [3s] in 30, so there are a little more than 10 [3s] in 36.6. The quotient is in the 10s. Students record their answers on a magnitude bar and show how they made their estimates. *(See the margin.)*

## ◆Calculating Quotients
(*Math Journal 1,* p. 113; *Math Masters,* p. 12)

WHOLE-CLASS ACTIVITY

Complete Problem 1 by having students calculate the exact quotient. Tell them to ignore the decimal point and divide 366 by 3, using the division algorithm. *(See the margin.)* They write the result in the answer space, and then use their estimate to insert a decimal point for the correct answer. 366 ÷ 3 = 122; estimated answer is in the tens; 12.2 is the correct answer.

Students should use this same procedure to solve the rest of the problems on their own.

When most students have completed the page, write some of the problems on the board and ask students to show how they solved them. Discuss various solution strategies.

NOTE: Problems in this lesson use whole or decimal numbers divided by whole numbers. In each problem, the remainder is 0. Decimal division that leads to nonzero remainders, and division of a decimal by a decimal, will be treated in *Sixth Grade Everyday Mathematics.*

# 2 Ongoing Learning & Practice

## ✦ Practicing Multiplication Facts

PARTNER ACTIVITY 

If your students need more practice with multiplication facts, play a favorite multiplication game or practice with Fact Triangles.

## ✦ Math Boxes 4.4 (*Math Journal 1,* p. 114)

INDEPENDENT ACTIVITY 

**Mixed Review** Math Boxes in this lesson are paired with Math Boxes in Lesson 4.1. The skill in Problem 1 is a prerequisite for Unit 5.

## ✦ Study Link 4.4 (*Math Masters,* p. 258)

**Home Connection** Students make magnitude estimates for problems and then solve the problems. Remind students to use "easy numbers" to make their estimates. Students should ignore the decimal point as they do the actual division, and then use their estimate to place the decimal point in the answer.

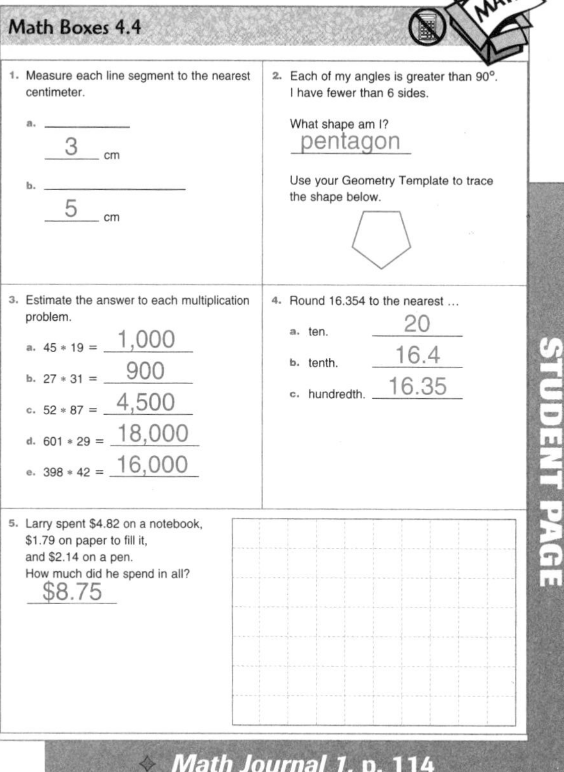

**Math Boxes 4.4**

1. Measure each line segment to the nearest centimeter.
   a. 3 cm
   b. 5 cm
2. Each of my angles is greater than 90°. I have fewer than 6 sides.
   What shape am I? pentagon
   Use your Geometry Template to trace the shape below.
3. Estimate the answer to each multiplication problem.
   a. 45 * 19 = 1,000
   b. 27 * 31 = 900
   c. 52 * 87 = 4,500
   d. 601 * 29 = 18,000
   e. 398 * 42 = 16,000
4. Round 16.354 to the nearest ...
   a. ten. 20
   b. tenth. 16.4
   c. hundredth. 16.35
5. Larry spent $4.82 on a notebook, $1.79 on paper to fill it, and $2.14 on a pen. How much did he spend in all? $8.75

STUDENT PAGE

✦ *Math Journal 1,* p. 114

NOTE: Students who need multiplication facts practice can use the Arithmetic Training mode of the TI-15 calculator. See *Math Masters,* pages 480 and 481.

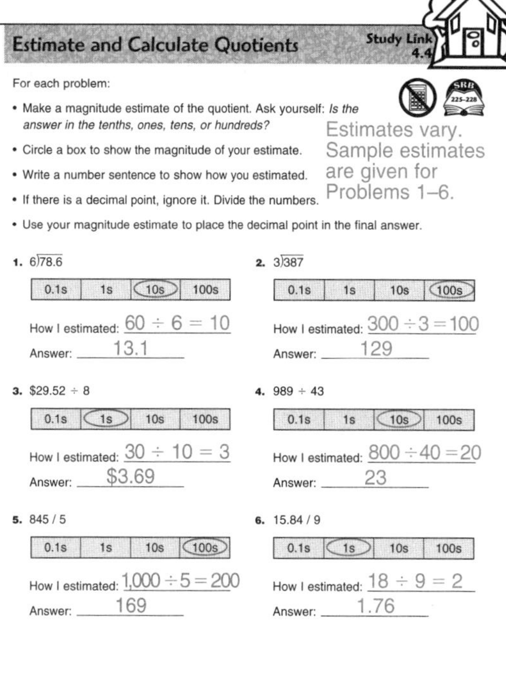

**Estimate and Calculate Quotients** Study Link 4.4

For each problem:

- Make a magnitude estimate of the quotient. Ask yourself: *Is the answer in the tenths, ones, tens, or hundreds?*
- Circle a box to show the magnitude of your estimate.
- Write a number sentence to show how you estimated.
- If there is a decimal point, ignore it. Divide the numbers.
- Use your magnitude estimate to place the decimal point in the final answer.

Estimates vary. Sample estimates are given for Problems 1–6.

1. 6)78.6 — 0.1s | 1s | (10s) | 100s
   How I estimated: 60 ÷ 6 = 10
   Answer: 13.1
2. 3)387 — 0.1s | 1s | 10s | (100s)
   How I estimated: 300 ÷ 3 = 100
   Answer: 129
3. $29.52 ÷ 8 — 0.1s | (1s) | 10s | 100s
   How I estimated: 30 ÷ 10 = 3
   Answer: $3.69
4. 989 ÷ 43 — 0.1s | 1s | (10s) | 100s
   How I estimated: 800 ÷ 40 = 20
   Answer: 23
5. 845 / 5 — 0.1s | 1s | 10s | (100s)
   How I estimated: 1,000 ÷ 5 = 200
   Answer: 169
6. 15.84 / 9 — 0.1s | (1s) | 10s | 100s
   How I estimated: 18 ÷ 9 = 2
   Answer: 1.76

STUDY LINK MASTER

✦ *Math Masters,* p. 258

# 3 Options for Individualizing

## ✦ RETEACHING Modeling Division with Base-10 Blocks (*Math Masters,* p. 42)

INDEPENDENT ACTIVITY  **15–30 min**

Pose the problem $4\overline{)623}$. Have students model the dividend (623) with base-10 blocks. Ask a volunteer to explain what it means to divide 623 blocks by 4. Sample answer: It means that the 623 blocks are to be grouped into 4 equal piles. Have students take four pieces of paper and distribute the blocks equally on the pieces of paper. They will need to make trades. For example, each of the four groups gets 1 flat, and 2 flats are left over.

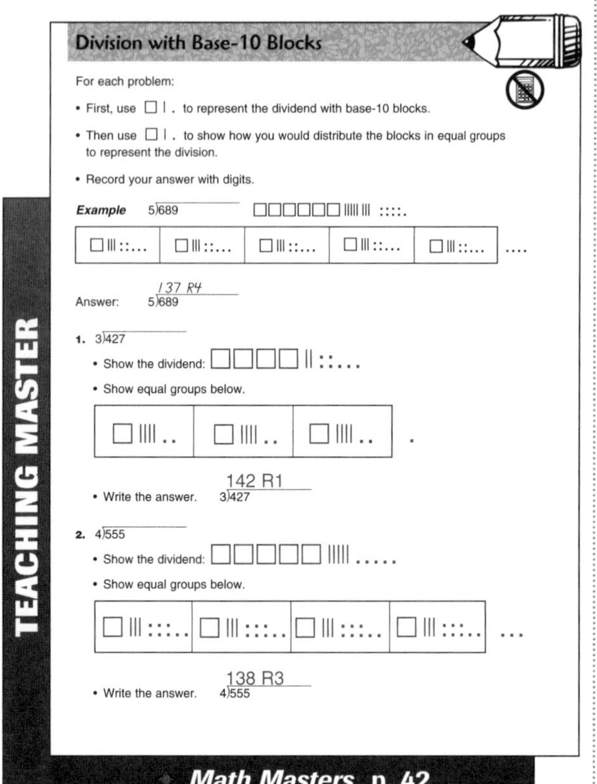

**Division with Base-10 Blocks**

For each problem:

- First, use □ | . to represent the dividend with base-10 blocks.
- Then use □ | . to show how you would distribute the blocks in equal groups to represent the division.
- Record your answer with digits.

*Example* 5)689 □□□□□□ ||||| ||| ::::.

□ ||| ::... | □ ||| ::... | □ ||| ::... | □ ||| ::... | □ ||| ::... ....

Answer: 137 R4 5)689

1. 3)427
   - Show the dividend: □□□□ || ::...
   - Show equal groups below.

   □ |||| .. | □ |||| .. | □ |||| .. .

   - Write the answer. 142 R1 3)427

2. 4)555
   - Show the dividend: □□□□□ ||||| .....
   - Show equal groups below.

   □ ||| :::.. | □ ||| :::.. | □ ||| :::.. | □ ||| :::.. ...

   - Write the answer. 138 R3 4)555

TEACHING MASTER

Math Masters, p. 42

Students trade these 2 flats for 20 longs. Then they distribute the 22 longs. Each of the four groups gets 5 longs, and 2 longs are left over. Students trade these 2 longs for 20 cubes. They distribute 20 of the 23 cubes evenly among the four groups. There are 3 cubes left over.

Have a volunteer interpret the answer. Each group has 155 cubes. There are 3 left over. So 623 divided by 4 is 155 with a remainder of 3.

Students work alone or with a partner to complete *Math Masters,* page 42. They represent base-10 blocks with symbols.

## ✦ ENRICHMENT Exploring an Alternative Division Algorithm

*(Student Reference Book,* pp. 24 and 44; *Math Masters,* p. 43)

INDEPENDENT ACTIVITY **15–30 min** 

You may want to introduce students who are good at long division to an alternative division algorithm. The column division algorithm is shown on *Math Masters,* page 43.

Students write an explanation of the algorithm on the master. This algorithm is discussed on pages 24 and 44 of the *Student Reference Book*.

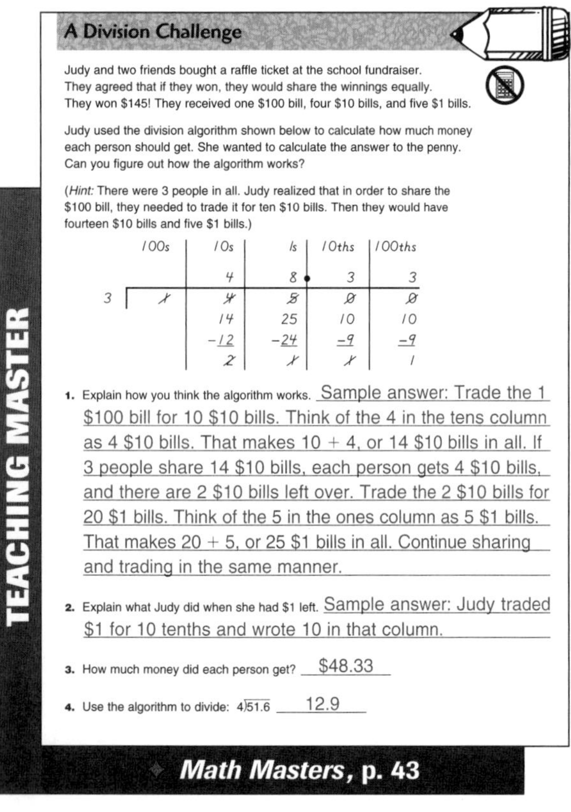

**A Division Challenge**

Judy and two friends bought a raffle ticket at the school fundraiser. They agreed that if they won, they would share the winnings equally. They won $145! They received one $100 bill, four $10 bills, and five $1 bills.

Judy used the division algorithm shown below to calculate how much money each person should get. She wanted to calculate the answer to the penny. Can you figure out how the algorithm works?

(*Hint:* There were 3 people in all. Judy realized that in order to share the $100 bill, they needed to trade it for ten $10 bills. Then they would have fourteen $10 bills and five $1 bills.)

| | 100s | 10s | 1s | 10ths | 100ths |
|---|---|---|---|---|---|
| | | 4 | 8 • | 3 | 3 |
| 3 | ~~1~~ | ~~4~~ | ~~5~~ | ~~0~~ | ~~0~~ |
| | | 14 | 25 | 10 | 10 |
| | | −12 | −24 | −9 | −9 |
| | | ~~2~~ | ~~1~~ | ~~1~~ | 1 |

1. Explain how you think the algorithm works. Sample answer: Trade the 1 $100 bill for 10 $10 bills. Think of the 4 in the tens column as 4 $10 bills. That makes 10 + 4, or 14 $10 bills in all. If 3 people share 14 $10 bills, each person gets 4 $10 bills, and there are 2 $10 bills left over. Trade the 2 $10 bills for 20 $1 bills. Think of the 5 in the ones column as 5 $1 bills. That makes 20 + 5, or 25 $1 bills in all. Continue sharing and trading in the same manner.
2. Explain what Judy did when she had $1 left. Sample answer: Judy traded $1 for 10 tenths and wrote 10 in that column.
3. How much money did each person get? $48.33
4. Use the algorithm to divide: 4)51.6 12.9

TEACHING MASTER

Math Masters, p. 43

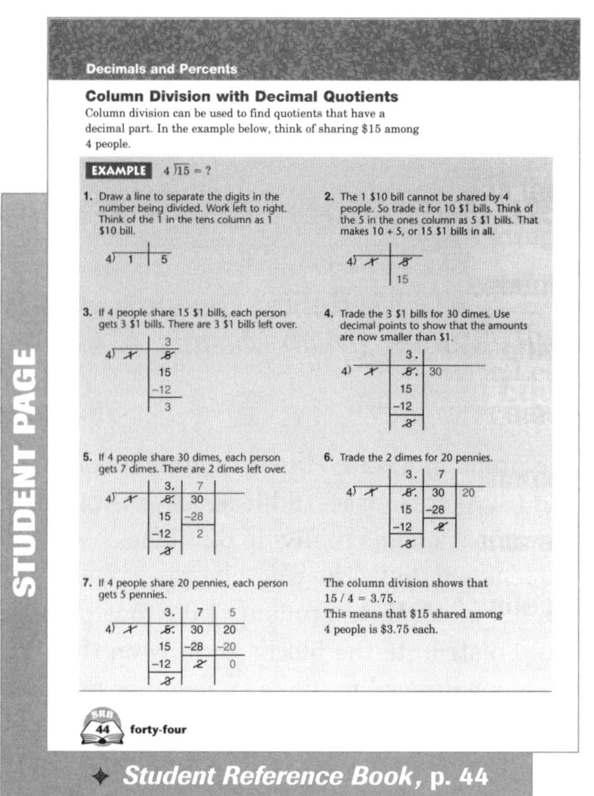

Decimals and Percents

**Column Division with Decimal Quotients**

Column division can be used to find quotients that have a decimal part. In the example below, think of sharing $15 among 4 people.

**EXAMPLE** 4)15 = ?

1. Draw a line to separate the digits in the number being divided. Work left to right. Think of the 1 in the tens column as 1 $10 bill.
2. The 1 $10 bill cannot be shared by 4 people. So trade it for 10 $1 bills. Think of the 5 in the ones column as 5 $1 bills. That makes 10 + 5, or 15 $1 bills in all.
3. If 4 people share 15 $1 bills, each person gets 3 $1 bills. There are 3 $1 bills left over.
4. Trade the 3 $1 bills for 30 dimes. Use decimal points to show that the amounts are now smaller than $1.
5. If 4 people share 30 dimes, each person gets 7 dimes. There are 2 dimes left over.
6. Trade the 2 dimes for 20 pennies.
7. If 4 people share 20 pennies, each person gets 5 pennies.

The column division shows that 15 / 4 = 3.75. This means that $15 shared among 4 people is $3.75 each.

44 forty-four

STUDENT PAGE

Student Reference Book, p. 44

# 4.5 Interpreting the Remainder

**OBJECTIVE** **To solve division number stories and interpret remainders within the context of the stories.**

| summaries | materials |
|---|---|
| **1 Teaching the Lesson** | |
| Students draw pictures and write number sentences that represent division number stories; they use a division algorithm to solve number stories; and they interpret remainders within the context of the number stories. [Operations and Computation; Patterns, Functions, and Algebra] | ☐ *Math Journal 1,* pp. 115 and 116<br>☐ Study Link 4.4<br>☐ Teaching Master (*Math Masters,* p. 12; optional)<br>☐ Assessment Master (*Math Masters,* p. 479; optional)<br>☐ calculator (optional)<br>***See* Advance Preparation** |
| **2 Ongoing Learning & Practice** | |
| Students review making magnitude estimates and calculating quotients. [Operations and Computation]<br>Students practice and maintain skills through Math Boxes and Study Link activities. | ☐ *Math Journal 1,* pp. 116 and 117<br>☐ Study Link Master (*Math Masters,* p. 259)<br>***See* Advance Preparation** |
| **3 Options for Individualizing** | |
| **Enrichment** Students write division number stories. [Operations and Computation]<br>**Language Diversity** Pairs of students review different ways to interpret remainders. [Operations and Computation]<br>**Reteaching** Students draw illustrations to represent and solve division problems. [Operations and Computation] | ☐ Teaching Master (*Math Masters,* p. 44) |

**Additional Information**

**Advance Preparation** You may wish to provide students with copies of the computation grid (*Math Masters,* page 12) as they do the activities in Parts 1 and 2.

## Getting Started

### Mental Math and Reflexes

Find $\frac{1}{10}$ of a number and 10 times a number. *Suggestions:*

| | | | |
|---|---|---|---|
| $\frac{1}{10}$ of 10 1 | $\frac{1}{10}$ of 18 1.8 | 10 ∗ 8 80 | 10 ∗ 0.7 7 |
| $\frac{1}{10}$ of 600 60 | $\frac{1}{10}$ of 305 30.5 | 10 ∗ 40 400 | 10 ∗ 0.79 7.9 |
| $\frac{1}{10}$ of 900 90 | $\frac{1}{10}$ of 234 23.4 | 10 ∗ 58 580 | 10 ∗ 90.6 906 |

**Math Message**

*There are 100 minutes of computer time for 8 students to share equally. How many minutes should each student get?*

**Study Link 4.4 Follow-Up**

Briefly review answers. Have volunteers share their strategies for placing the decimal point in Problem 3.

# 1 Teaching the Lesson

## ✦Math Message Follow-Up

WHOLE-CLASS ACTIVITY

NOTE: This same routine was used in Lesson 2.4 for solving addition and subtraction number stories.

Have students follow this routine for solving the number story:

1. Draw a simple picture to organize the given information and summarize the problem situation. Include the numbers that are known.

   Have several volunteers draw their pictures on the board. The problem is about equal sharing of 100 minutes by 8 people. Students' pictures should show 8 equal parts in some way. *(See the margin.)*

100 minutes

8 equal parts
How much in each?
Call it $M$.

$M = 100 \div 8$

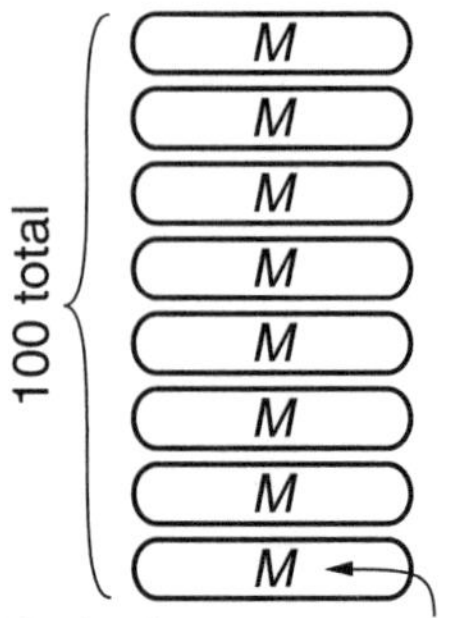


Find minutes per student.

$8 * M = 100$

2. Read the problem carefully and decide what is to be found. Write this on the picture in a word or short phrase. Use a letter variable for the missing number (such as $M$ for *number of minutes*).
3. Write a number sentence showing how the letter variable and other numbers in the problem are related.

   Students who view the problem as division of a figure into 8 equal parts are likely to write $M = 100 \div 8$. Students who view it as an array situation are more likely to "think multiplication" and write $8 * M = 100$. Both number sentences are fine.
4. Solve the number sentence.

   Students who wrote $M = 100 \div 8$ will know that they should divide. Students who wrote $8 * M = 100$ may need a prompt to notice that a related division fact is $M = 100 \div 8$, and that they should divide.

| | | |
|---|---|---|
| $8\overline{)100}$ | | How many 8s are in 100? At least 10. |
| $-\ 80$ | 10 | The first partial quotient. $10 * 8 = 80$ |
| 20 | | Subtract. At least 2 [8s] are left. |
| $-\ 16$ | 2 | The second partial quotient. $2 * 8 = 16$ |
| 4 | 12 | Subtract. Add the partial quotients. |
| ↑ Remainder | ↑ Quotient | |

**5.** Interpret the quotient and remainder. Decide what to do about the remainder.

Ask: *What do the quotient 12 and remainder 4 mean?* Each student can have 12 minutes of computer time, and 4 minutes will remain to be shared or left unused. Ask: *Should the 4 minutes be ignored?* No. That would waste valuable time. The context of the problem indicates that the remainder should be made part of the answer.

▷ One way to do this is to divide the remainder among the 8 students. The remainder is then reported as $\frac{4}{8}$ or $\frac{1}{2}$ or 0.5 of a minute per student.

▷ Another way is to change 4 minutes into 240 seconds. 240 seconds ÷ 8 = 30 seconds per student.

The solution is $12\frac{1}{2}$ minutes, or 12.5 minutes, or 12 minutes 30 seconds. Students can check the solution by substituting 12.5 for $M$ in their number sentences and using their calculators to divide or multiply. $100 \div 8 = 12.5$ and $8 * 12.5 = 100$ are true number sentences.

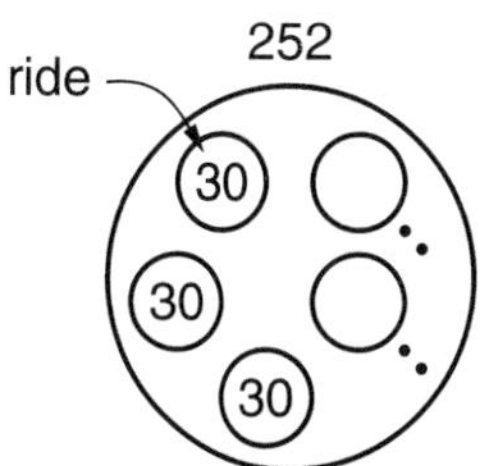

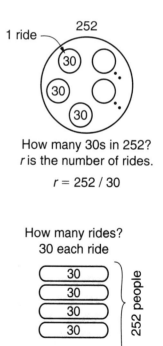

How many 30s in 252?
$r$ is the number of rides.

$r = 252 / 30$

## ✦ Solving Division Number Stories and Interpreting Remainders

WHOLE-CLASS ACTIVITY

***Example 1:*** A roller coaster holds 30 people. There are 252 people waiting for a ride. How many times will the roller coaster need to run so that all 252 people get a ride?

Students should follow the same routine used to solve the Math Message problem.

Expect that most students will think *How many 30s in 252?* and will write a number sentence like $252 \div 30 = r$ (where $r$ is the number of runs). Some may draw an array with 30 objects per row *(see the margin),* and write a number sentence like $r * 30 = 252$.

| | |
|---|---|
| $30\overline{)252}$ | |
| $-\ 150$ | 5 |
| 102 | |
| $-\ 90$ | 3 |
| 12 | 8 |

How many rides?
30 each ride

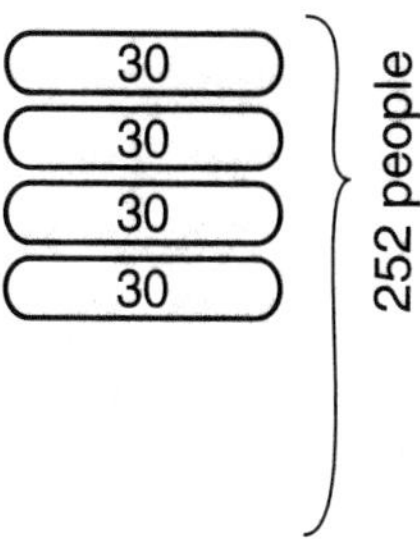


Let $r$ be the number of rides.

$r * 30 = 252$

Ask what the quotient, 8, and the remainder, 12, mean. Students should see that in 8 runs, 240 of the 252 people could ride. This would leave 12 people. The ride will need to run 9 times to take all 252 people.

The context of this problem indicates that the answer should be rounded up to the next whole number.

---

**Adjusting the Activity** To extend the activity, you may want to suggest that students can check their answers on the calculator by multiplying 30 ∗ 8 and adding the remainder of 12. Do not expect all students to understand why this works.

---

***Example 2:*** It costs $3 to rent a video. Bonita has $14. How many videos can she rent?

Encourage students to focus on interpreting the remainder within the context of the problem. The algorithm is shown below. Some students, however, may just use pictures, count by 3s, or use the fact, 4 ∗ 3 = 12, to find that there are 4 [3s] in 14 with 2 left over.

```
3)14  |
– 12  |_4
   2   4
```

Ask for a volunteer to share the solution. Bonita can rent 4 videos. She will have $2 left, but she won't be able to rent another video. In this situation, the remainder is ignored.

Students can check their answers by multiplying 3 ∗ 4 and adding the remainder of 2.

*Summary*

In the Math Message problem, the remainder was treated as a fraction of the whole and became part of the answer. The remainder was divided among the 8 students in order not to waste time.

In Example 1, the answer was rounded up. Otherwise, 12 people would not get a ride.

In Example 2, the remainder was ignored. The remainder indicated that there was not enough money to rent another video.

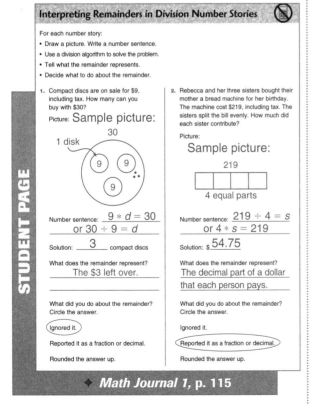

STUDENT PAGE

**Interpreting Remainders in Division Number Stories**

For each number story:

- Draw a picture. Write a number sentence.
- Use a division algorithm to solve the problem.
- Tell what the remainder represents.
- Decide what to do about the remainder.

1. Compact discs are on sale for $9, including tax. How many can you buy with $30?

Picture: Sample picture:

30

1 disk

9 9 9

Number sentence: 9 ∗ *d* = 30 or 30 ÷ 9 = *d*

Solution: 3 compact discs

What does the remainder represent? The $3 left over.

What did you do about the remainder? Circle the answer.

(Ignored it.)

Reported it as a fraction or decimal.

Rounded the answer up.

2. Rebecca and her three sisters bought their mother a bread machine for her birthday. The machine cost $219, including tax. The sisters split the bill evenly. How much did each sister contribute?

Picture:

Sample picture:

219

4 equal parts

Number sentence: 219 ÷ 4 = *s* or 4 ∗ *s* = 219

Solution: $54.75

What does the remainder represent? The decimal part of a dollar that each person pays.

What did you do about the remainder? Circle the answer.

Ignored it.

(Reported it as a fraction or decimal.)

Rounded the answer up.

✦ ***Math Journal 1*, p. 115**

## ✦ Interpreting Remainders in Division Number Stories

(*Math Journal 1,* pp. 115 and 116; *Math Masters,* p. 479)

INDEPENDENT ACTIVITY 

Have students complete Problems 1, 2, and 3 on the journal pages. Caution them to think about each remainder and the different ways in which it can be interpreted. Tell them that they will be asked to explain what each remainder represents and how they used the remainder to answer the question in the problem.

Circulate and help. When a majority of students have completed the pages, discuss the solutions as a class.

**ONGOING ASSESSMENT**

**Have students complete an Exit Slip for the following:** ***Choose Problem 1, 2, or 3 from journal pages 115–116. Describe how you used the remainder to answer the question in the problem.***

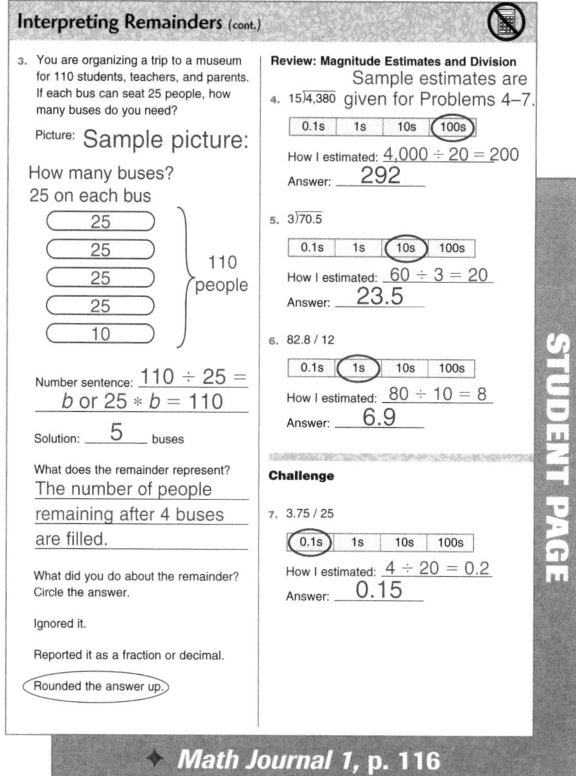

**Interpreting Remainders** (cont.)

3. You are organizing a trip to a museum for 110 students, teachers, and parents. If each bus can seat 25 people, how many buses do you need?

Picture: Sample picture:

How many buses?
25 on each bus

25, 25, 25, 25, 10 } 110 people

Number sentence: 110 ÷ 25 = b or 25 ∗ b = 110

Solution: 5 buses

What does the remainder represent? The number of people remaining after 4 buses are filled.

What did you do about the remainder? Circle the answer.

Ignored it.

Reported it as a fraction or decimal.

(Rounded the answer up.)

**Review: Magnitude Estimates and Division**

Sample estimates are given for Problems 4–7.

4. 15)4,380

0.1s | 1s | 10s | (100s)

How I estimated: 4,000 ÷ 20 = 200

Answer: 292

5. 3)70.5

0.1s | 1s | (10s) | 100s

How I estimated: 60 ÷ 3 = 20

Answer: 23.5

6. 82.8 / 12

0.1s | (1s) | 10s | 100s

How I estimated: 80 ÷ 10 = 8

Answer: 6.9

**Challenge**

7. 3.75 / 25

(0.1s) | 1s | 10s | 100s

How I estimated: 4 ÷ 20 = 0.2

Answer: 0.15

STUDENT PAGE

✦ *Math Journal 1,* p. 116

## Ongoing Learning & Practice

## ✦ Reviewing Making Magnitude Estimates and Calculating Quotients (*Math Journal 1,* p. 116)

INDEPENDENT ACTIVITY 

Students complete Problems 4–7 on journal page 116.

**Adjusting the Activity** For students who need more practice with whole number division, have them delete the decimal points in these problems.

## ✦ Math Boxes 4.5 (*Math Journal 1,* p. 117)

INDEPENDENT ACTIVITY 

**Mixed Review** Math Boxes in this lesson are paired with Math Boxes in Lesson 4.2. The skill in Problem 1 is a prerequisite for Unit 5.

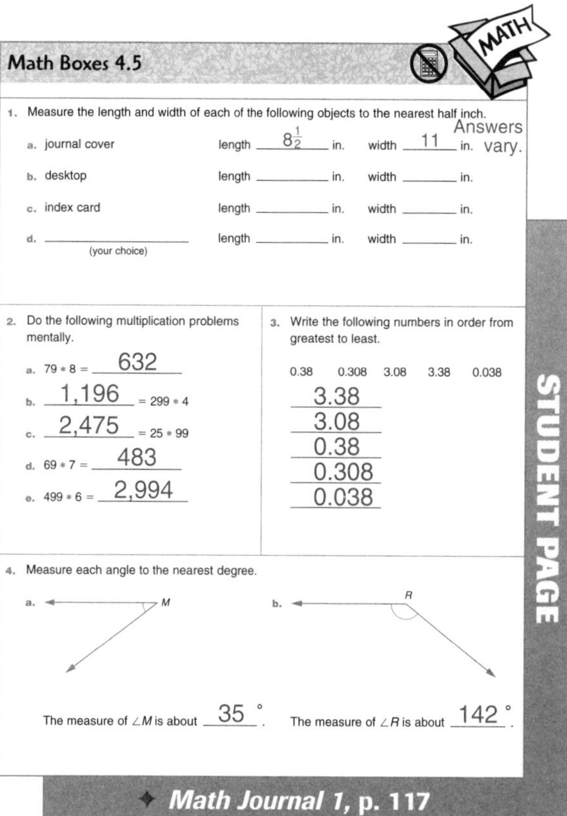

**Math Boxes 4.5**

1. Measure the length and width of each of the following objects to the nearest half inch. Answers vary.

a. journal cover — length $8\frac{1}{2}$ in. width 11 in.

b. desktop — length ____ in. width ____ in.

c. index card — length ____ in. width ____ in.

d. ____ (your choice) — length ____ in. width ____ in.

2. Do the following multiplication problems mentally.

a. 79 ∗ 8 = 632

b. 1,196 = 299 ∗ 4

c. 2,475 = 25 ∗ 99

d. 69 ∗ 7 = 483

e. 499 ∗ 6 = 2,994

3. Write the following numbers in order from greatest to least.

0.38 0.308 3.08 3.38 0.038

3.38
3.08
0.38
0.308
0.038

4. Measure each angle to the nearest degree.

a. The measure of ∠M is about 35 °.

b. The measure of ∠R is about 142 °.

STUDENT PAGE

✦ *Math Journal 1,* p. 117

## Division Number Stories with Remainders

Study Link 4.5

For each number story:
- Draw a picture and write a number sentence if you want.
- Use a division algorithm to solve the problem.
- Decide what to do about the remainder.
- Explain why you treated the remainder the way you did.

***Example***

You need to set up benches for a play. Each bench can seat 7 people. You expect 66 people to attend. How many benches do you need? 10 benches

What did you do about the remainder? Circle the answer.

Ignored it. Reported it as a fraction or decimal. (Rounded the answer up.)

Why? *9 benches seat 63 people. One more bench is needed for 3 remaining people.*

1. It costs $50.00 to be a member of a soccer team. The team plays 8 games during the season. What is the cost per game? $ 6.25

What did you do about the remainder? Circle the answer.

Ignored it. (Reported it as a fraction or decimal.) Rounded the answer up.

Why? Sample answer: $50.00 divided by 8 games is $6.00 per game with $2.00 left over. $2.00 divided by 8 games is $0.25 per game. $6.00 + $0.25 = $6.25

2. Lynn is having a party. Pizzas cost $8.00 each. How many pizzas can she buy with $60.00? 7 pizzas

What did you do about the remainder? Circle the answer.

(Ignored it.) Reported it as a fraction or decimal. Rounded the answer up.

Why? Sample answer: 7 pizzas cost $56.00. The remaining $4.00 is not enough to buy another pizza, and is ignored.

STUDY LINK MASTER

✦ **Math Masters, p. 259**

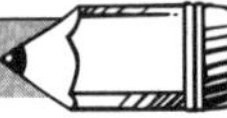

## Practice with Remainders

For each number story:
- Draw a picture to represent the problem. Make sure to show the remainder in your picture.
- Write a number sentence.
- Use a division algorithm to solve the problem.
- Decide what to do about the remainder and explain your decision.
- Record your solution to the problem.

1. Ms. Haag is rearranging her classroom. There are 30 students in the classroom. The students sit at tables. Four students can sit at each table. How many tables does she need?

Number sentence: $30 \div 4 = t$ or $4 * t = 30$

Explain what you did with the remainder. Sample answer: 7 tables seat 28 students. One more table is needed to seat the 2 remaining students. The answer was rounded up.

Solution: 8 tables

2. Marc needs 3 square yards of fabric to make a cape for a costume party. His friends want a cape to match his. If Marc has 17 square yards of fabric, how many capes can he make?

Number sentence: $17 \div 3 = c$ or $3 * c = 17$

Explain what you did with the remainder. Sample answer: Since the remainder represents extra material that is not enough to make another cape, the remainder was ignored.

Solution: 5 capes

TEACHING MASTER

✦ **Math Masters, p. 44**

## ✦ Study Link 4.5 (*Math Masters,* p. 259)

**Home Connection** Students use a division algorithm and interpret remainders to solve division number stories. Remind students of the three ways that a remainder can be used—as a fraction of the whole, ignored, or used to round up the quotient—depending upon how the remainder is interpreted for each problem.

# 3 Options for Individualizing

## ✦ ENRICHMENT Writing Division Number Stories

INDEPENDENT ACTIVITY  **5–15 min**

Have students write their own division number stories. These can be collected into a class book. The class book can be used as an additional resource for solving division number stories.

## ✦ LANGUAGE DIVERSITY Interpreting Remainders

PARTNER ACTIVITY  **5–15 min**

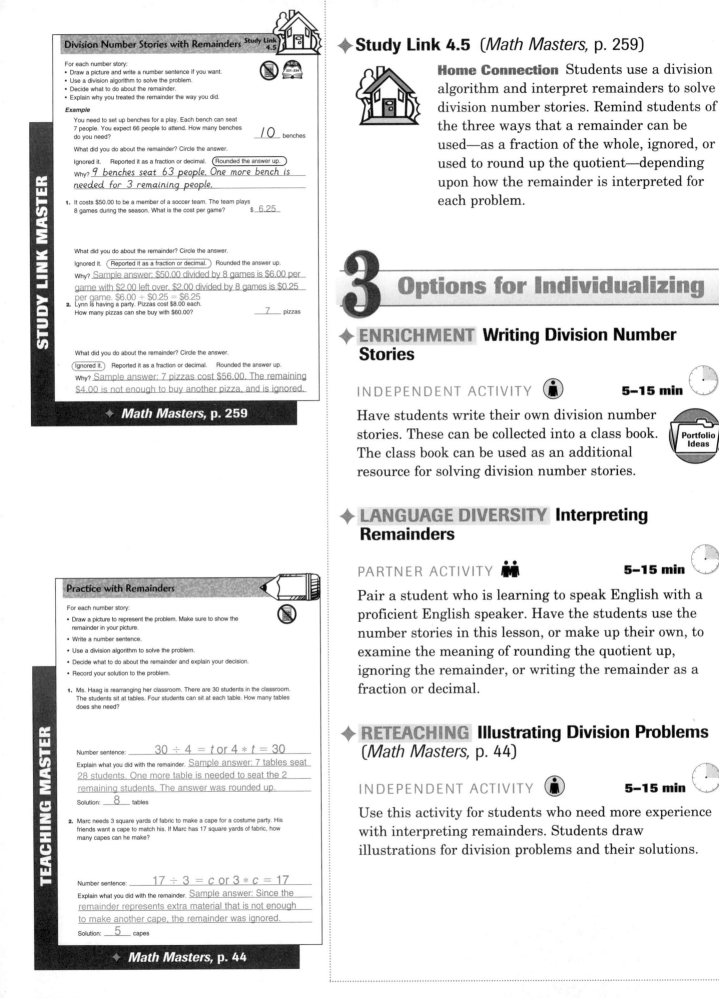

Pair a student who is learning to speak English with a proficient English speaker. Have the students use the number stories in this lesson, or make up their own, to examine the meaning of rounding the quotient up, ignoring the remainder, or writing the remainder as a fraction or decimal.

## ✦ RETEACHING Illustrating Division Problems (*Math Masters,* p. 44)

INDEPENDENT ACTIVITY  **5–15 min**

Use this activity for students who need more experience with interpreting remainders. Students draw illustrations for division problems and their solutions.

# 4.6 Skills Review with *First to 100*

**OBJECTIVES** **To investigate using a variable to represent a range of values; and to review a variety of mathematical skills.**

| summaries | materials |
|---|---|
| **1 Teaching the Lesson** | |
| Students play a new game, *First to 100,* which practices a variety of skills: using letter variables to represent a range of possible values, generating numbers, substituting numbers for variables in problems, and then solving the problems. [Patterns, Functions, and Algebra; Operations and Computation] | □ *Student Reference Book,* p. 273 □ Study Link 4.5<br>□ Teaching Masters (*Math Masters,* p. 45, optional; and pp. 46 and 47, per partnership)<br>Per partnership:<br>□ 2 six-sided dice □ calculator<br>□ envelope (for storing *First to 100* cards)<br>***See* Advance Preparation** |
| **2 Ongoing Learning & Practice** | |
| Students identify triangles as equilateral, isosceles, right, or scalene. [Geometry]<br>Students practice and maintain skills through Math Boxes and Study Link activities. | □ *Math Journal 1,* pp. 118 and 119<br>□ Study Link Master (*Math Masters,* p. 260) |
| **3 Options for Individualizing** | |
| **Enrichment** Students play *Algebra Election,* a variation of the game *First to 100* based on electoral votes for president of the United States. [Patterns, Functions, and Algebra; Operations and Computation]<br>**Extra Practice** Students practice writing and solving open number sentences. [Patterns, Functions, and Algebra; Operations and Computation] | □ slate<br>Per group of 4 students:<br>□ 32 *First to 100* Problem Cards (*Math Masters,* pp. 46 and 47)<br>□ *Student Reference Book,* pp. 256 and 257<br>□ Teaching Masters (*Math Masters,* pp. 48 and 49)<br>□ 4 pennies or other small counters; 3"-by-5" index cards cut in half (optional)<br>□ 1 six-sided die; scratch paper; calculator; transparent tape<br>***See* Advance Preparation** |

## Additional Information

**Advance Preparation** For the Math Message, you may want to use *Math Masters,* page 45. This page contains six copies of a form students can use to record their work. These copies can be cut apart and put near the Math Message. Familiarize yourself with the rules and scoring for *First to 100.* Read through the problems on the Problem Cards (*Math Masters,* pages 46 and 47).

For the optional Enrichment activity in Part 3, you or your students will need to tape together *Math Masters,* pages 48 and 49 to complete a map of the United States. Each group of 4 students will need one complete map.

**Vocabulary** • **variable** • **open number sentence**

# Getting Started

### Mental Math and Reflexes

Ask students to round decimals to the nearest whole number. *Suggestions:*

24.2 24   308.56 309   77.09 77

Ask students to round decimals to the nearest tenth. *Suggestions:*

17.63 17.6   109.14 109.1   239.86 239.9

### Math Message

*Roll 2 dice. Multiply the numbers shown by the dots on the top faces. Let the letter P stand for this product. Find the number 20 ∗ P. Record your work on the slips of paper that are near the Math Message.*

### Study Link 4.5 Follow-Up

Briefly review answers. Have volunteers tell how they decided what to do about the remainders.

| $P$ | $20 * P$ |
|---|---|
| 18 | $20 * 18 = 360$ |
| 12 | $20 * 12 = 240$ |
| 30 | $20 * 30 = 600$ |
| 16 | $20 * 16 = 320$ |
| 9 | $20 * 9 = 180$ |
| 15 | $20 * 15 = 300$ |
| 12 | $20 * 12 = 240$ |
| 4 | $20 * 4 = 80$ |
| 4 | $20 * 4 = 80$ |
| 20 | $20 * 20 = 400$ |

NOTE: In Lessons 2.4 and 4.5, letter variables were used in a different way. Students wrote number sentences such as $8 * M = 100$ to describe story problems. Here the letter $M$ stands for the specific missing number that makes the sentence true. In this example, 12.5 is the correct value of $M$, because it makes the sentence true. Any number not equal to 12.5 makes the sentence false, and is the wrong value for $M$.

**Adjusting the Activity** If interest is high, have students list all possible products when two dice are rolled. 1, 2, 3, 4, 5, 6, 8, 9, 10, 12, 15, 16, 18, 20, 24, 25, 30, and 36

# 1 Teaching the Lesson

## ✦ Math Message Follow-Up
(*Math Masters,* p. 45)

WHOLE-CLASS ACTIVITY

The Math Message problem previews the game *First to 100,* in which students generate problems by substituting numbers for letter variables.

Draw a table on the board to record students' answers. Write $P$ and $20 * P$ as the column headings. Record the responses of about 10 students in the table. *(See the margin.)*

Briefly discuss the Math Message problem. Ask questions like the following:

- Is there any right or wrong choice of a number to use in place of $P$? If Bob's product is 18 and Maria's product is 4, is 18 the correct value for $P$, and 4 is wrong? Or is 4 the correct value for $P$, and 18 is wrong? Neither. The letter $P$ stands for 18 when we talk about Bob's result after rolling the dice. The letter $P$ stands for 4 when we talk about Maria's result after rolling the dice.

A letter used to represent numbers is called a **variable.**

Ask: *What different numbers can the letter P stand for?* Any product of the numbers on 2 die faces.

## ✦ Introducing *First to 100*
(*Student Reference Book,* p. 273; *Math Masters,* pp. 46 and 47)

PARTNER ACTIVITY 

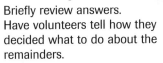

Have students cut apart the Problem Cards on *Math Masters,* pages 46 and 47. There are 32 cards, numbered

1–32. Cards numbered 25–32 will not be used today, and students should place these in their envelopes.

Together, read the rules for *First to 100* in the *Student Reference Book.*

## Playing *First to 100* (*Student Reference Book,* p. 273; *Math Masters,* pp. 46 and 47)

PARTNER ACTIVITY 

A player will typically need 6 to 10 turns to accumulate 100 points. Players record points won on a sheet of paper, updating their total when they win new points. It is wise to agree on a time limit for answering questions.

Encourage students to play *First to 100* during their free time. This game reviews a variety of skills. You can tailor it to address any skills you want to review (including skills covered on standardized tests) by writing a new set of Problem Cards.

**Adjusting the Activity** To make the game more challenging, have a player roll two dice and find the *sum* of the numbers on the top faces. This sum is then substituted for the *x* or *x*'s in the problem(s) on the Problem Card.

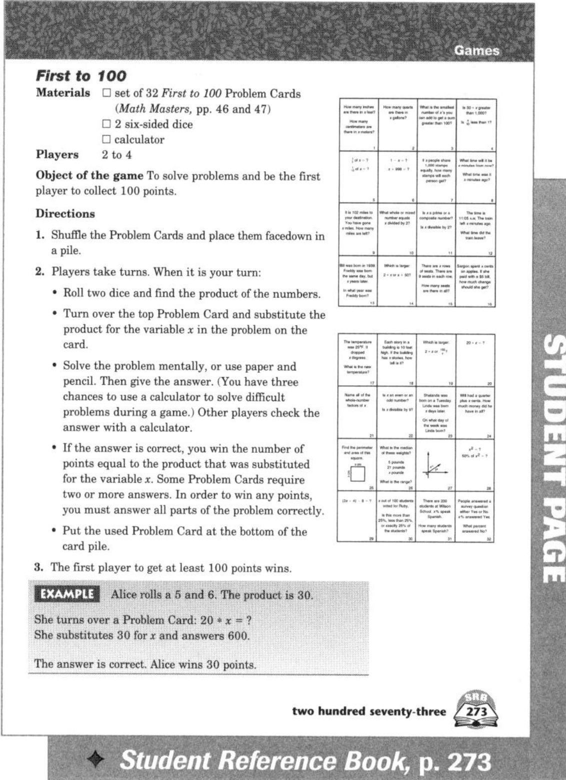

Games

***First to 100***

**Materials** ☐ set of 32 *First to 100* Problem Cards (*Math Masters,* pp. 46 and 47)
☐ 2 six-sided dice
☐ calculator

**Players** 2 to 4

**Object of the game** To solve problems and be the first player to collect 100 points.

**Directions**

1. Shuffle the Problem Cards and place them facedown in a pile.
2. Players take turns. When it is your turn:
   - Roll two dice and find the product of the numbers.
   - Turn over the top Problem Card and substitute the product for the variable *x* in the problem on the card.
   - Solve the problem mentally, or use paper and pencil. Then give the answer. (You have three chances to use a calculator to solve difficult problems during a game.) Other players check the answer with a calculator.
   - If the answer is correct, you win the number of points equal to the product that was substituted for the variable *x*. Some Problem Cards require two or more answers. In order to win any points, you must answer all parts of the problem correctly.
   - Put the used Problem Card at the bottom of the card pile.
3. The first player to get at least 100 points wins.

**EXAMPLE** Alice rolls a 5 and 6. The product is 30.
She turns over a Problem Card: $20 * x = ?$
She substitutes 30 for *x* and answers 600.
The answer is correct. Alice wins 30 points.

two hundred seventy-three SRB 273

STUDENT PAGE

*Student Reference Book,* p. 273

# 2 Ongoing Learning & Practice

## Reviewing Triangles (*Math Journal 1,* p. 118)

INDEPENDENT ACTIVITY 

Students identify equilateral, isosceles, right, and scalene triangles.

## Math Boxes 4.6 (*Math Journal 1,* p. 119)

INDEPENDENT ACTIVITY 

**Mixed Review** Math Boxes in this lesson are paired with Math Boxes in Lesson 4.3. The skills in Problems 1 and 2 are prerequisites for Unit 5.

The remaining *First to 100* cards are on *Math Masters,* page 47.

***First to 100* Problem Cards**

| | | | |
|---|---|---|---|
| How many inches are there in *x* feet? How many centimeters are there in *x* meters? 1 | How many quarts are there in *x* gallons? 2 | What is the smallest number of *x*'s you can add to get a sum greater than 100? 3 | Is $50 * x$ greater than 1,000? Is $\frac{x}{10}$ less than 1? 4 |
| $\frac{1}{2}$ of $x = ?$ $\frac{1}{10}$ of $x = ?$ 5 | $1 - x = ?$ $x + 998 = ?$ 6 | If *x* people share 1,000 stamps equally, how many stamps will each person get? 7 | What time will it be *x* minutes from now? What time was it *x* minutes ago? 8 |
| It is 102 miles to your destination. You have gone *x* miles. How many miles are left? 9 | What whole or mixed number equals *x* divided by 2? 10 | Is *x* a prime or a composite number? Is *x* divisible by 2? 11 | The time is 11:05 A.M. The train left *x* minutes ago. What time did the train leave? 12 |
| Bill was born in 1939. Freddy was born the same day, but *x* years later. In what year was Freddy born? 13 | Which is larger: $2 * x$ or $x + 50$? 14 | There are *x* rows of seats. There are 9 seats in each row. How many seats are there in all? 15 | Sargon spent *x* cents on apples. If she paid with a $5 bill, how much change should she get? 16 |

TEACHING MASTER

*Math Masters,* p. 46

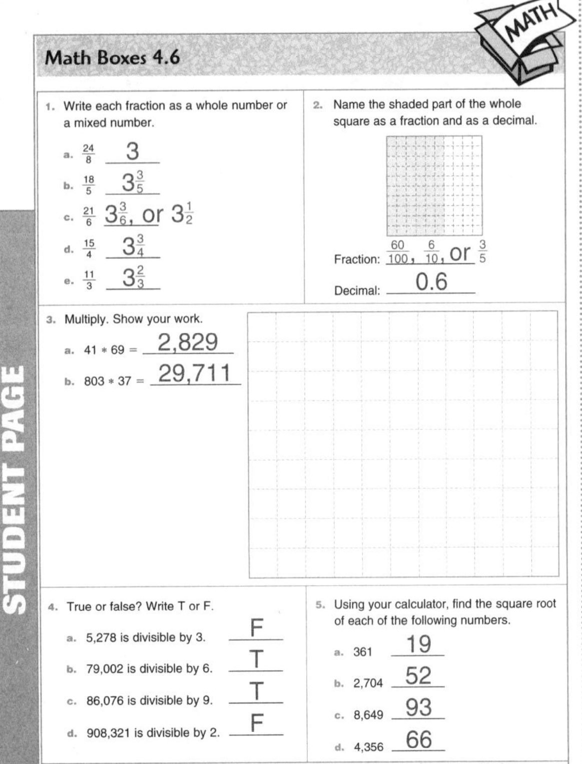
**Math Boxes 4.6**

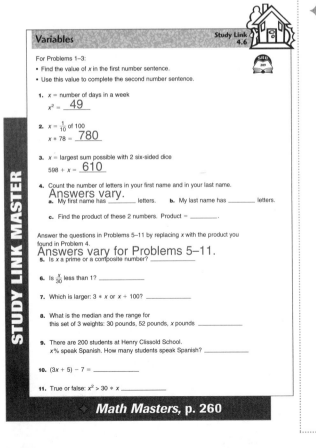

1. Write each fraction as a whole number or a mixed number.
   a. $\frac{24}{8}$ 3
   b. $\frac{18}{5}$ $3\frac{3}{5}$
   c. $\frac{21}{6}$ $3\frac{3}{6}$, or $3\frac{1}{2}$
   d. $\frac{15}{4}$ $3\frac{3}{4}$
   e. $\frac{11}{3}$ $3\frac{2}{3}$

2. Name the shaded part of the whole square as a fraction and as a decimal.
   Fraction: $\frac{60}{100}$, $\frac{6}{10}$, or $\frac{3}{5}$
   Decimal: 0.6

3. Multiply. Show your work.
   a. 41 * 69 = 2,829
   b. 803 * 37 = 29,711

4. True or false? Write T or F.
   a. 5,278 is divisible by 3. F
   b. 79,002 is divisible by 6. T
   c. 86,076 is divisible by 9. T
   d. 908,321 is divisible by 2. F

5. Using your calculator, find the square root of each of the following numbers.
   a. 361 19
   b. 2,704 52
   c. 8,649 93
   d. 4,356 66

STUDENT PAGE

Math Journal 1, p. 119

**Variables** Study Link 4.6

For Problems 1–3:
- Find the value of $x$ in the first number sentence.
- Use this value to complete the second number sentence.

1. $x$ = number of days in a week
   $x^2$ = 49
2. $x = \frac{1}{10}$ of 100
   $x * 78$ = 780
3. $x$ = largest sum possible with 2 six-sided dice
   $598 + x$ = 610
4. Count the number of letters in your first name and in your last name.
   Answers vary.
   a. My first name has ______ letters. b. My last name has ______ letters.
   c. Find the product of these 2 numbers. Product = ______.

Answer the questions in Problems 5–11 by replacing $x$ with the product you found in Problem 4.
Answers vary for Problems 5–11.

5. Is $x$ a prime or a composite number? ______
6. Is $\frac{x}{30}$ less than 1? ______
7. Which is larger: $3 * x$ or $x + 100$? ______
8. What is the median and the range for this set of 3 weights: 30 pounds, 52 pounds, $x$ pounds ______
9. There are 200 students at Henry Clissold School. $x$% speak Spanish. How many students speak Spanish? ______
10. $(3x + 5) - 7$ = ______
11. True or false: $x^2 > 30 * x$ ______

STUDY LINK MASTER

Math Masters, p. 260

## ✦ Study Link 4.6 (*Math Masters,* p. 260)

**Home Connection** Students find the values of variables and use these values to complete **open number sentences** and solve other problems.

# 3 Options for Individualizing

## ✦ ENRICHMENT Playing *Algebra Election* (*Student Reference Book,* pp. 256 and 257; *Math Masters,* pp. 46–49)

SMALL-GROUP ACTIVITY 

**Social Studies Link** If appropriate for your class, play *Algebra Election*—a variation of the *First to 100* game. In *Algebra Election,* students travel through the United States capturing electoral votes by solving the problems on the *First to 100* cards. It may take several periods for students to collect enough electoral votes to win.

You or the students can write additional Problem Cards on 3"-by-5" index cards that have been cut in half.

## ✦ EXTRA PRACTICE Solving Open Number Sentences

INDEPENDENT ACTIVITY 

**5–15 min**

Use this activity if students need more practice solving open number sentences. Write open sentences on the board or the overhead. Students write the solutions on their slates or on sheets of paper. *Suggestions:*

- ▷ $22 + a = 74$ 52
- ▷ $105 = 99 + n$ 6
- ▷ $30 * f = 360$ 12
- ▷ $7 * (4 + k) = 70$ 6
- ▷ $546 / w = 6$ 91
- ▷ $y - 36 = 58$ 94

Continue as time allows.

# 4.7 Unit 4 Review and Assessment

**OBJECTIVE** **To review and assess students' progress on the material covered in Unit 4.**

## 1 Assess Progress

| learning goals | activities |
|---|---|
| 4a **Beginning Goal** Divide decimal numbers by whole numbers with no remainders. **(Lessons 4.4 and 4.5)** | ❑ Written Assessment, Problems 7 and 8 |
| 4b **Beginning/Developing Goal** Write and solve number sentences with variables for division number stories. **(Lessons 4.5 and 4.6)** | ❑ Written Assessment, Problems 9, 10, and 13 |
| 4c **Developing Goal** Find the quotient and remainder of a whole number divided by a 1-digit whole number. **(Lessons 4.1, 4.2, 4.4, and 4.5)** | ❑ Written Assessment, Problems 1–4, 9, 10, and 13 |
| 4d **Developing Goal** Find the quotient and remainder of a whole number divided by a 2-digit whole number. **(Lessons 4.2, 4.4, and 4.5)** | ❑ Written Assessment, Problems 5 and 6 |
| 4e **Developing Goal** Make magnitude estimates for quotients of whole and decimal numbers divided by whole numbers. **(Lessons 4.4 and 4.5)** | ❑ Written Assessment, Problems 7 and 8 |
| 4f **Developing Goal** Interpret the remainder in division number stories. **(Lesson 4.5)** | ❑ Written Assessment, Problems 9 and 10 |
| 4g **Developing Goal** Determine the value of a variable; use this value to complete a number sentence. **(Lesson 4.6)** | ❑ Written Assessment, Problems 11 and 12 |
| 4h **Secure Goal** Know place value to hundredths. **(Lesson 4.1)** | ❑ Slate Assessment, Problems 1 and 3 |

**materials**

- ☐ *Math Journal 1,* p. 120
- ☐ Study Link 4.6
- ☐ *Student Reference Book,* pp. 267 and 273
- ☐ Teaching Master (*Math Masters,* p. 38)
- ☐ Assessment Masters (*Math Masters,* pp. 387 and 388)
- ☐ calculator; 2 six-sided dice
- ☐ *First to 100* Problem Cards (*Math Masters,* pp. 46 and 47)

## 2 Build Background for Unit 5

| summaries | materials |
|---|---|
| Students practice and maintain skills through Math Boxes and Study Link activities. | ☐ *Math Journal 1,* p. 121<br>☐ Study Link Masters (*Math Masters,* pp. 261–264) |

Each **learning goal** listed above indicates a level of performance that might be expected at this point in the *Everyday Mathematics* K-6 curriculum. For a variety of reasons, the levels indicated may not accurately portray your class's performance.

### Additional Information

**Advance Preparation** For additional information on assessment for Unit 4, see the *Assessment Handbook,* pages 45–48. For assessment checklists, see *Math Masters,* pages 434, 435, and 469–471.

# Getting Started

**Math Message**

*Complete the Time to Reflect questions on journal page 120.*

**Study Link 4.6 Follow-Up**

Briefly review answers.

NOTE: Some of these assessment suggestions relate to learning goals that have been addressed in previous units. Now is a good time to evaluate students' progress toward those goals.

**Time to Reflect**

1. Tell why you think it is important to be able to divide numbers. For what kind of problems do you need to use division?
   Answers vary.

2. Tell what part of this unit was the most difficult for you and why. Describe what you did to overcome any difficulties you had.
   Answers vary.

STUDENT PAGE

◆ *Math Journal 1,* p. 120

# 1 Assess Progress

## ◆ Math Message Follow-Up

WHOLE-CLASS DISCUSSION 

Students share their responses to questions about the unit.

## ◆ Slate Assessment

WHOLE-CLASS ACTIVITY

If the suggested problems below are not appropriate for your class's level of performance, adjust the numbers or the problems themselves to better assess your students' abilities.

1. Students round numbers. *Suggestions:*
   - 183 to the nearest ten. 180
   - 1,307 to the nearest ten. 1,310
   - 94.2 to the nearest whole number. 94
   - 36.58 to the nearest tenth. 36.6
   - 47.07 to the nearest tenth. 47.1
   - 305.96 to the nearest whole number. 306 **Goal 4h**
2. Students complete the following:
   - 8 [50s] = ? 400    80 [50s] = ? 4,000<br>800 [50s] = ? 40,000
   - 90 [7s] = ? 630    90 [70s] = ? 6,300<br>900 [70s] = ? 63,000
   - 7 [60s] = ? 420    70 [60s] = ? 4,200<br>700 [60s] = ? 42,000

3. Dictate numbers for students to write and mark on their slates. *Suggestions:*
   - Write 2,778,054. Circle the digit in the ten-thousands place. Underline the digit in the hundred-thousands place. 2,7⑦8,054
   - Write 507.38. Circle the digit in the tenths place. Underline the digit in the tens place. 507.③8
   - Write 849.62. Circle the hundredths digit. Underline the tenths digit. 849.6② **Goal 4h**
4. Pose problems like the following:
   - How many 5s are in 35? 7 What number times 7 equals 63? 9 Multiply 400 by 9. 3,600
   - How many 6s are in 36? 6 What number times 6 equals 60? 10 Multiply 10 by 4.5. 45
   - What number times 8 equals 56? 7 How many 7s are in 77? 11 Multiply 11 by 5. 55

## Written Assessment
(*Math Masters,* pp. 387 and 388)

INDEPENDENT ACTIVITY 

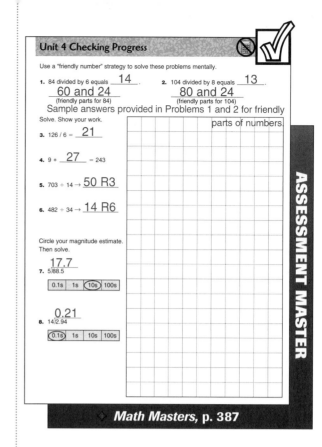

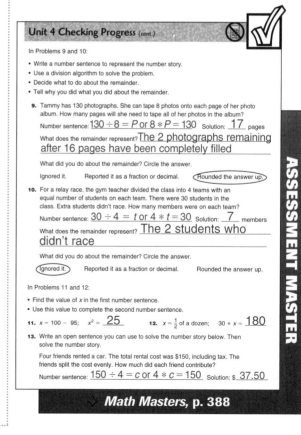

Depending on the needs of your students, you may wish to work through an example together, reading a problem aloud, discussing it, and providing additional examples as necessary before students work the problem independently. Each of the problems is listed below and paired with one or more of this unit's learning goals.

- Use a "friendly number" strategy to solve problems mentally. (Problems 1–2) **Goal 4c**
- Divide whole numbers by 1- and 2-digit whole numbers. (Problems 3–6) **Goals 4c and 4d**
- Make magnitude estimates and divide decimals by whole numbers. (Problems 7–8) **Goals 4a and 4e**
- Write a number sentence to represent a number story; use a division algorithm to solve the problem and interpret the remainder. (Problems 9–10) **Goals 4b, 4c, and 4f**
- Find the value of $x$ in a number sentence; then use the value to complete another number sentence. (Problems 11–12) **Goal 4g**
- Solve a division number story by writing a number sentence with a variable, and using a division algorithm. (Problem 13) **Goals 4b and 4c**

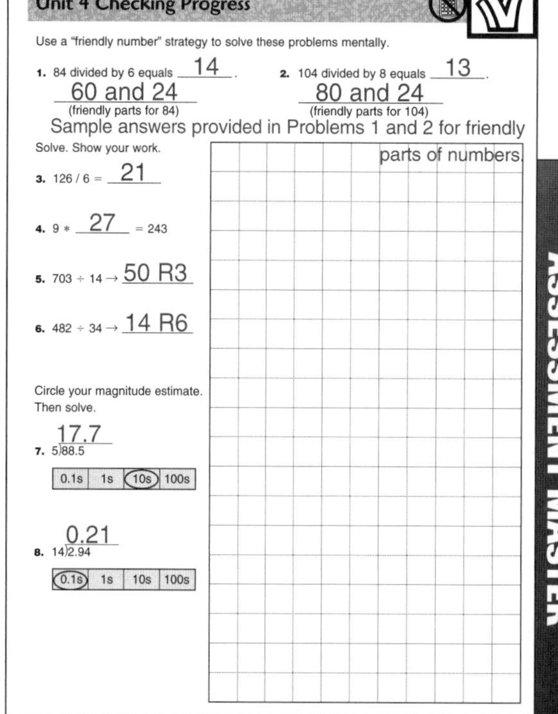
Unit 4 Checking Progress

Use a "friendly number" strategy to solve these problems mentally.

1. 84 divided by 6 equals 14.
60 and 24
(friendly parts for 84)

2. 104 divided by 8 equals 13.
80 and 24
(friendly parts for 104)

Sample answers provided in Problems 1 and 2 for friendly parts of numbers.

Solve. Show your work.

3. 126 / 6 = 21
4. $9 * 27 = 243$
5. 703 ÷ 14 → 50 R3
6. 482 ÷ 34 → 14 R6

Circle your magnitude estimate. Then solve.

7. 5)88.5 = 17.7 — 0.1s | 1s | (10s) | 100s
8. 14)2.94 = 0.21 — (0.1s) | 1s | 10s | 100s

ASSESSMENT MASTER

Math Masters, p. 387

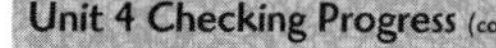

In Problems 9 and 10:

- Write a number sentence to represent the number story.
- Use a division algorithm to solve the problem.
- Decide what to do about the remainder.
- Tell why you did what you did about the remainder.

9. Tammy has 130 photographs. She can tape 8 photos onto each page of her photo album. How many pages will she need to tape all of her photos in the album?
Number sentence: $130 \div 8 = P$ or $8 * P = 130$ Solution: 17 pages
What does the remainder represent? The 2 photographs remaining after 16 pages have been completely filled
What did you do about the remainder? Circle the answer.
Ignored it. Reported it as a fraction or decimal. 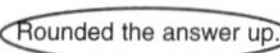 Rounded the answer up.

10. For a relay race, the gym teacher divided the class into 4 teams with an equal number of students on each team. There were 30 students in the class. Extra students didn't race. How many members were on each team?
Number sentence: $30 \div 4 = t$ or $4 * t = 30$ Solution: 7 members
What does the remainder represent? The 2 students who didn't race
What did you do about the remainder? Circle the answer.
 Ignored it. Reported it as a fraction or decimal. Rounded the answer up.

In Problems 11 and 12:

- Find the value of $x$ in the first number sentence.
- Use this value to complete the second number sentence.

11. $x = 100 - 95$; $x^2 = 25$
12. $x = \frac{1}{2}$ of a dozen; $30 * x = 180$

13. Write an open sentence you can use to solve the number story below. Then solve the number story.
Four friends rented a car. The total rental cost was $150, including tax. The friends split the cost evenly. How much did each friend contribute?
Number sentence: $150 \div 4 = c$ or $4 * c = 150$ Solution: $37.50

ASSESSMENT MASTER

Math Masters, p. 388

## ◆ ALTERNATIVE ASSESSMENT OPTION

### Practice with Fact Families

(*Math Masters,* p. 38)

INDEPENDENT ACTIVITY 

Use this activity from Lesson 4.1 to assess students' understanding of the relationship between multiplication and division.

## ◆ ALTERNATIVE ASSESSMENT OPTION

### Play *Division Dash*

(*Student Reference Book,* p. 267)

PARTNER ACTIVITY 

This game was introduced in Lesson 4.1. Have each student keep a record of the dividend, divisor, and quotient for 5 turns of play. Collect this record to assess the student's division skills.

## ◆ ALTERNATIVE ASSESSMENT OPTION

### Play *First to 100*

(*Student Reference Book,* p. 273; *Math Masters,* pp. 46 and 47)

PARTNER ACTIVITY 

This game was introduced in Lesson 4.6. In each round, have students record the problem, the value of $x$, and the solution. Collect students' records at the end of five rounds to assess their ability to solve open number sentences.

# 2 Build Background for Unit 5

## ✦ Math Boxes 4.7 (*Math Journal 1*, p. 121)

INDEPENDENT ACTIVITY 

**Mixed Review** The skills in Problems 1–6 are prerequisites for Unit 5.

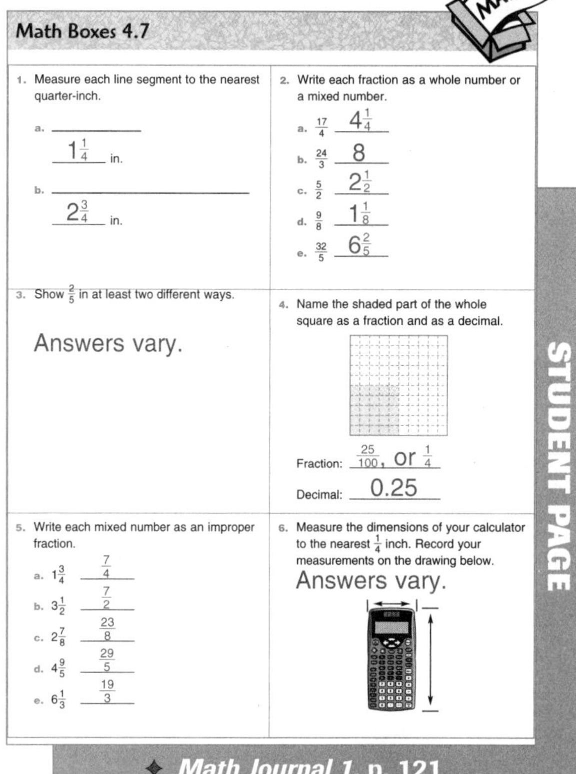

Math Boxes 4.7

1. Measure each line segment to the nearest quarter-inch.
   a. $1\frac{1}{4}$ in.
   b. $2\frac{3}{4}$ in.
2. Write each fraction as a whole number or a mixed number.
   a. $\frac{17}{4}$ $4\frac{1}{4}$
   b. $\frac{24}{3}$ 8
   c. $\frac{5}{2}$ $2\frac{1}{2}$
   d. $\frac{9}{8}$ $1\frac{1}{8}$
   e. $\frac{32}{5}$ $6\frac{2}{5}$
3. Show $\frac{2}{5}$ in at least two different ways.
   Answers vary.
4. Name the shaded part of the whole square as a fraction and as a decimal.
   Fraction: $\frac{25}{100}$, or $\frac{1}{4}$
   Decimal: 0.25
5. Write each mixed number as an improper fraction.
   a. $1\frac{3}{4}$ $\frac{7}{4}$
   b. $3\frac{1}{2}$ $\frac{7}{2}$
   c. $2\frac{7}{8}$ $\frac{23}{8}$
   d. $4\frac{9}{5}$ $\frac{29}{5}$
   e. $6\frac{1}{3}$ $\frac{19}{3}$
6. Measure the dimensions of your calculator to the nearest $\frac{1}{4}$ inch. Record your measurements on the drawing below.
   Answers vary.

STUDENT PAGE

✦ *Math Journal 1*, p. 121

## ✦ Study Link 4.7: Unit 5 Family Letter (*Math Masters*, pp. 261–264)

**Home Connection** This Study Link is a four-page newsletter that introduces parents and guardians to Unit 5's topics and terms. The letter also offers ideas for mathematics activities that are supportive of classroom work and can be done at home.

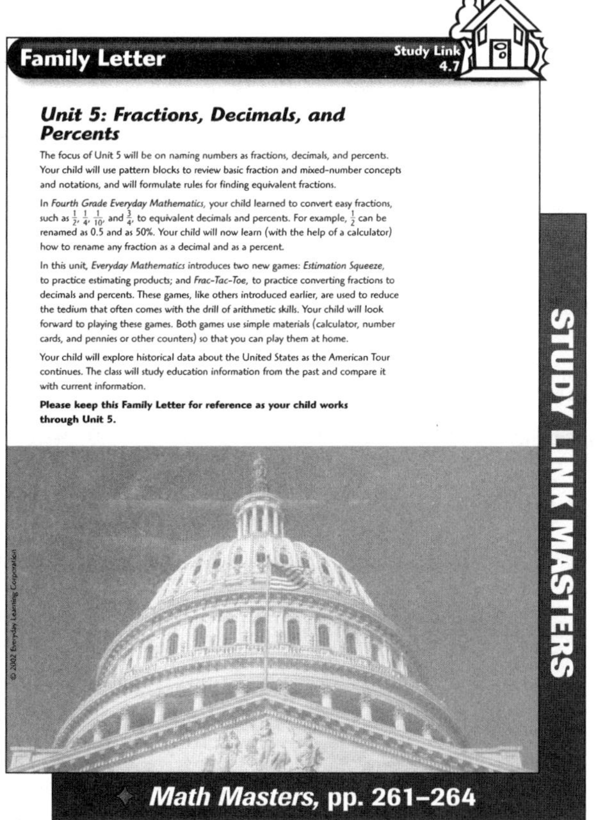

Family Letter — Study Link 4.7

***Unit 5: Fractions, Decimals, and Percents***

The focus of Unit 5 will be on naming numbers as fractions, decimals, and percents. Your child will use pattern blocks to review basic fraction and mixed-number concepts and notations, and will formulate rules for finding equivalent fractions.

In *Fourth Grade Everyday Mathematics*, your child learned to convert easy fractions, such as $\frac{1}{2}$, $\frac{1}{4}$, $\frac{1}{10}$, and $\frac{3}{4}$, to equivalent decimals and percents. For example, $\frac{1}{2}$ can be renamed as 0.5 and as 50%. Your child will now learn (with the help of a calculator) how to rename any fraction as a decimal and as a percent.

In this unit, *Everyday Mathematics* introduces two new games: *Estimation Squeeze*, to practice estimating products; and *Frac-Tac-Toe*, to practice converting fractions to decimals and percents. These games, like others introduced earlier, are used to reduce the tedium that often comes with the drill of arithmetic skills. Your child will look forward to playing these games. Both games use simple materials (calculator, number cards, and pennies or other counters) so that you can play them at home.

Your child will explore historical data about the United States as the American Tour continues. The class will study education information from the past and compare it with current information.

**Please keep this Family Letter for reference as your child works through Unit 5.**



STUDY LINK MASTERS

✦ *Math Masters*, pp. 261–264

# Unit 5 Fractions, Decimals, and Percents

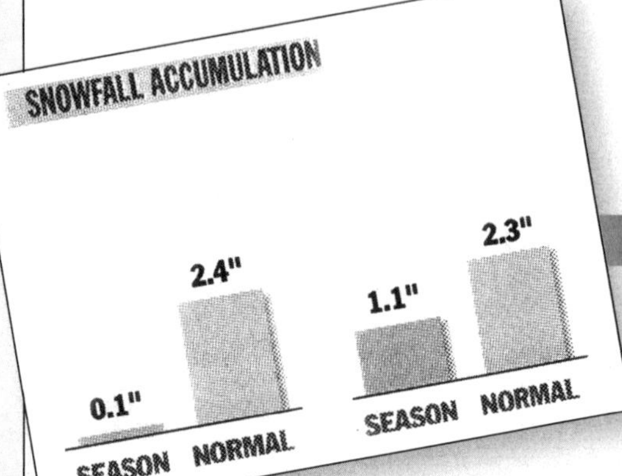


## overview

One of the main objectives of Unit 5 is to review the meanings of fraction, decimal, and percent notations for rational numbers. Another objective is to concentrate for an extended period of time on conversions among these notations, often emphasizing the fact that embedded in every fraction is a division problem. This freedom to convert among these notations is often important in solving problems in everyday life and in the occupations of many people, as illustrated by the data display exercises in Lessons 5.9–5.11 of this unit.

The equivalence of fractions, decimals, and percents was frequently dealt with in grades K–4 *Everyday Mathematics.* Beginning in this unit, *Fifth Grade Everyday Mathematics* emphasizes the relationships among these notations. The skills involved are not intended to be mastered in this unit, but they will be extensively practiced by all students and mastered by most students by the end of the fifth grade program.

SALE
SHOES
50% - 70%
OFF

# contents



UNIT 5

# learning goals in perspective

| learning goals | links to the past | links to the future |
|---|---|---|
| 5a **Beginning/Developing Goal** Add fractions with like denominators. **(Lesson 5.3)** | Grade 4: Add and subtract fractions using pattern blocks and clock faces. Estimate fraction sums. | Grade 5: Use a slide rule to add and subtract fractions. Use common denominators to add and subtract fractions with unlike denominators. (Unit 6) Add and subtract mixed numbers. (Unit 8)<br>Grade 6: Add, subtract, multiply, and divide fractions and mixed numbers with like or unlike denominators. |
| 5b **Developing Goal** Order and compare fractions. **(Lesson 5.3)** | Grades 1-3: Use concrete models to compare fractions.<br>Grade 4: Locate fractions on a number line. Compare and order fractions with like numerators, with like denominators, and with unlike numerators and denominators. Compare fractions to $\frac{1}{2}$. | Grade 5: Compare fractions by renaming them with a common denominator. (Units 6 and 8)<br>Grade 6: Compare fractions by renaming them as decimals. Compare ratios by renaming them as *n*-to-1 ratios. |
| 5c **Developing Goal** Convert between fractions and percents. **(Lesson 5.8)** | Grade 4: Shade 10-by-10 grids to represent percents, then rename each percent as a fraction and as a decimal. Rename "easy" fractions (fourths, fifths, and tenths) as decimals and percents. Use a calculator to rename fractions as decimals and as percents.<br>Grade 5: Use the Probability Meter to find equivalent fractions, decimals, and percents. (Unit 2) | Grade 5: Analyze data using equivalent fractions, decimals, and percents. (Project 5) Develop reflexes for fraction-decimal-percent equivalencies. Use the Percent Circle to graph data. (Unit 6)<br>Grade 6: Develop rules for converting between decimals and percents. Find equivalents for any fraction, decimal, or percent. |
| 5d **Developing Goal** Draw a circle graph for a set of data. **(Lesson 5.11)** | Grades 1-3: Construct bar graphs for data sets; name parts of a whole as fractions; compare circle sections equal to halves, fourths, and eighths.<br>Grade 4: Use full- and half-circle protractors to measure and draw angles. | Grade 5: Use circle graphs to investigate how sample size affects results. (Unit 6)<br>Grade 6: Measure, draw, and interpret circle graphs for more complicated contexts; convert percents of circles to degrees, and then draw circle graphs with either a full- or half-circle protractor. |
| 5e **Developing Goal** Measure pieces of a circle graph; interpret a circle graph. **(Lesson 5.10)** | See Goal 5d. | See Goal 5d. |
| 5f **Developing/Secure Goal** Convert between fractions and mixed numbers. **(Lesson 5.2)** | Grades 1-3: Introduce mixed numbers in measurement and in part-whole fractions.<br>Grade 4: Use improper fractions and mixed numbers to name numbers greater than or equal to 1. Express quotients as mixed numbers. | Grade 5: Rename fractions and mixed numbers in simplest form. (Unit 8)<br>Grade 6: Applications and maintenance. |
| 5g **Developing/Secure Goal** Find equivalent fractions. **(Lesson 5.4)** | Grades 1-3: Use name-collection boxes to study equivalent names for numbers. Use concrete models to explore equivalent fractions.<br>Grade 4: Develop the multiplication rule for finding equivalent fractions. Find equivalent rates. | Grade 5: Use clock faces and lists of equivalent fractions to find common denominators. (Unit 6)<br>Grade 6: Use cross multiplication to test equivalency of fractions. Use equivalent-fractions methods to solve proportions for rate and ratio problems. |

# assessment

## ongoing • product • periodic

### Informal Assessment

**Math Boxes** These *Math Journal* pages provide opportunities for cumulative review or assessment of concepts and skills.

**Ongoing Assessment: Kid Watching** Use the Ongoing Assessment suggestions in the following lessons to make quick, on-the-spot observations about students' understanding of:

- Numeration **(Lesson 5.4, Part 1; Lesson 5.6, Part 1; Lesson 5.7, Part 1; Lesson 5.8, Part 1)**
- Operations and Computation **(Lesson 5.1, Part 1)**
- Data and Chance **(Lesson 5.11, Part 1)**
- Measurement and Reference Frames **(Lesson 5.2, Part 2; Lesson 5.10, Part 1)**

**Portfolio Ideas** Samples of students' work may be obtained from the following assignments:

- Writing Parts-and-Whole Number Stories **(Lesson 5.1)**
- Finding Fractions of a Whole with Pattern Blocks **(Lesson 5.2)**
- Building Background for Mathematics Words **(Lesson 5.8)**
- Measuring Circle Graphs **(Lesson 5.10)**
- Converting Bar Graphs to Circle Graphs **(Lesson 5.11)**

### Unit 5 Review and Assessment

**Math Message** Use Time to Reflect Problem 5 in Lesson 5.13 to assess students' progress toward the following learning goal: **Goal 5c**

**Oral and Slate Assessments** Use slate assessments during Lesson 5.13 to assess students' progress toward the following learning goals: **Goals 5c, 5f, and 5g**

**Written Assessment** Use a written review during Lesson 5.13 to assess students' progress toward the following learning goals: **Goals 5a–5g**

**Alternative Assessment Options** Use independent alternative assessments in Lesson 5.13 to assess students' progress toward the following learning goals: **Goals 5c, 5e, and 5g**

## assessmenthandbook

For more information on how to use different types of assessment in Unit 5, see the Assessment Overview on pages 49–51 in the *Assessment Handbook.* The following Assessment Masters can be found in the *Math Masters* book:

- Unit 5 Checking Progress, pp. 389–391
- Unit 5 Individual Profile of Progress, p. 437
- Unit 5 Class Checklist, p. 436
- Class Progress Indicator, p. 471
- Math Logs, pp. 474 and 475
- Self-Assessment Forms, pp. 477 and 478
- Interest Inventories, pp. 472 and 473

# problem solving

***A process of modeling everyday situations using tools from mathematics***

Encourage students to use a variety of strategies when attacking a given problem—and to explain those strategies. *Strategies students might use in this unit:*

- Draw a picture
- Use a computation
- Act out the problem
- Use physical models
- Use estimation
- Use data in a table
- Use a graph

**Four Problem-Solving REPRESENTATIONS**

Verbal
Concrete
Pictorial
Symbolic

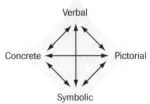

## Lessons that teach *through* problem solving, not just *about* problem solving

| Lesson | Activity | Lesson | Activity |
|---|---|---|---|
| **5.1** | Solve parts-and-whole and fraction of a whole problems | **5.7, 5.8** | Use fractions, decimals, and percents to rewrite data given in a table |
| **5.2** | Find the values of fractional parts of various blocks, designs, and rectangular regions | **5.8** | Solve number stories involving percents |
| **5.3** | Solve fraction number stories involving addition | **5.9, 5.11** | Make a bar graph and circle graph of after-school snack survey data |
| **5.5** | Examine situations that require rounding to a nearest place value or truncating after a place | **5.12** | Interpret information given as text and displays |
| **5.6** | Choose reasonable measures and best units for various measurements | | |

For more information about problem solving in *Everyday Mathematics,* see the *Teacher's Reference Manual.*

# cross-curricular links

### language arts

- Students learn the origin of the division term *vinculum.* **(Lesson 5.1)**
- Students relate the British slang term *bits* to dollars. **(Lesson 5.6)**
- Students discuss the word *percent.* **(Lesson 5.8)**

### science

- Students conduct a class experiment to determine which eye is dominant. **(Lesson 5.10)**

### social studies

- Students use a map to locate the 10 smallest countries in the world. **(Lesson 5.5)**
- Students read about the history of mathematics instruction and solve related problems. **(Lesson 5.12)**
- Students use library and Internet resources to find out about American history. **(Lesson 5.12)**

# meeting INDIVIDUAL needs

UNIVERSAL ACCESS

## ✦ RETEACHING

The following features provide some additional instructional support:

**Adjusting the Activity**

- **Lesson 5.1, Part 1**
- **Lesson 5.2, Parts 1, 2**
- **Lesson 5.3, Parts 1, 2**
- **Lesson 5.4, Part 1**
- **Lesson 5.5, Part 1**
- **Lesson 5.7, Part 1**
- **Lesson 5.9, Part 1**

**Options for Individualizing**

- **Lesson 5.1** Solving "Fraction-of" Problems
- **Lesson 5.2** Finding Fractions of a Whole with Pattern Blocks
- **Lesson 5.4** Making Equivalent Fractions
- **Lesson 5.5** Reviewing Rounding Decimals

## ✦ ENRICHMENT

The following features suggest enrichment and extension activities:

**Adjusting the Activity**

- **Lesson 5.2, Part 1**
- **Lesson 5.4, Part 1**
- **Lesson 5.5, Part 1**
- **Lesson 5.6, Part 1**
- **Lesson 5.7, Parts 1, 2**
- **Lesson 5.8, Part 1**
- **Lesson 5.11, Part 2**
- **Lesson 5.12, Part 1**
- **Lesson 5.13, Part 1**

**Options for Individualizing**

- **Lesson 5.4** Introducing "Fraction-of" Problems with Fraction Sticks
- **Lesson 5.7** Extending the Partial-Quotients Division Algorithm to Decimals
- **Lesson 5.9** Acting Out the Construction of a Circle Graph
- **Lesson 5.10** Conducting an Eye Test
- **Lesson 5.11** Making a Graph Museum
- **Lesson 5.12** Finding Out about American History

## ✦ LANGUAGE DIVERSITY

The following features suggest ways to support students who are acquiring proficiency in English:

**Adjusting the Activity**

- **Lesson 5.9, Part 1**

**Options for Individualizing**

- **Lesson 5.1** Writing Parts-and-Whole Number Stories
- **Lesson 5.8** Building Background for Mathematics Words

## ✦ MULTIAGE CLASSROOM

The following chart lists related lessons from Grades 4 and 6 that can help you meet your instructional needs:

| **Grade 4** | 7.1, 8.1 | 8.1 | 4.2, 8.1 | 7.7 | 4.1, 7.8 | 4.2, 7.8 | 4.3, 7.8 | 9.4, 9.5 | | 1.7 | 1.7 | |
|---|---|---|---|---|---|---|---|---|---|---|---|---|
| **Grade 5** | 5.1 | 5.2 | 5.3 | 5.4 | 5.5 | 5.6 | 5.7 | 5.8 | 5.9 | 5.10 | 5.11 | 5.12 |
| **Grade 6** | 4.1 | 4.4–4.5 | | 4.1 | | | | 10.1 | | 3.9 | 3.9 | |

# materials

| lesson | math masters pages | manipulative kit items | other items |
|---|---|---|---|
| **5.1** | Study Link Master, p. 265<br>transparency of Teaching Master, p. 50 (optional)<br>Assessment Master, p. 479 | | ruler or Geometry Template<br>slate<br>calculator<br>30 counters per partnership |
| **5.2** | Study Link Master, p. 266<br>Teaching Masters, pp. 51 and 52<br>***See* Advance Preparation, p. 268** | pattern blocks | Geometry Template |
| **5.3** | Study Link Master, p. 267<br>Teaching Master, p. 53<br>transparency of Teaching Master, p. 53 (optional) | | ruler<br>6 strips of 2" × $8\frac{1}{2}$" colored paper, $8\frac{1}{2}$" × 14" paper; (optional)<br>envelope (optional)<br>***See* Advance Preparation, p. 274** |
| **5.4** | Study Link Master, p. 268<br>Teaching Master, p. 5 or 6; optional | Everything Math Deck, if available | ruler<br>***See* Advance Preparation, p. 280** |
| **5.5** | Study Link Master, p. 269<br>Teaching Master, p. 56<br>transparencies of Teaching Masters, pp. 54 and 55; optional | | base-10 blocks<br>slate<br>calculator<br>***See* Advance Preparation, p. 286** |
| **5.6** | Study Link Master, p. 270<br>Teaching Masters, pp. 59 and 60<br>transparencies of Teaching Masters, pp. 57, 58, and 60; optional<br>Assessment Master, p. 479 | | Probability Meter<br>slate<br>straightedge<br>***See* Advance Preparation, p. 292** |
| **5.7** | Study Link Master, p. 271<br>Teaching Masters, pp. 61–64; and p. 65 (optional)<br>transparency of Teaching Master, p. 62 (optional)<br>Assessment Master, p. 479 | 4 each of the number cards 0–10 (from the Everything Math Deck, if available) per partnership | calculator per partnership<br>counters per partnership<br>***See* Advance Preparation, p. 298** |
| **5.8** | Study Link Master, p. 272<br>Teaching Masters, pp. 62, 66, 75, and 76<br>Assessment Master, p. 479<br>***See* Advance Preparation, p. 305** | 4 each of the number cards 0–10 (from the Everything Math Deck, if available) | counters (or pennies)<br>calculator |
| **5.9** | Study Link Master, p. 273<br>***See* Advance Preparation, p. 311** | | string; masking tape; ruler; paper circles<br>posterboard (optional) |
| **5.10** | Study Link Masters, pp. 274 and 275<br>Teaching Masters, pp. 77, 78, and 80; and p. 79 (optional)<br>transparencies of Teaching Masters, pp. 77 and 78; optional | | Geometry Template (optional)<br>calculator<br>***See* Advance Preparation, p. 316** |
| **5.11** | Study Link Master, p. 276<br>Teaching Masters, pp. 62, 67 or 68, and 77<br>***See* Advance Preparation, p. 322** | 4 each of the number cards 0–10 (from the Everything Math Deck, if available) for teacher only | Geometry Template<br>calculator; chalkboard compass; counters, coloring pencils, crayons, or markers (optional)<br>newspapers and magazines |
| **5.12** | Study Link Master, p. 277 | | slate; books and Internet access |
| **5.13** | Study Link Masters, pp. 278–281<br>Teaching Masters, pp. 62, 63, and 66; and pp. 64, 65, 69, and 72; optional<br>Assessment Masters, pp. 389–391 | 4 each of the number cards 0–10 (from the Everything Math Deck, if available)<br>pattern blocks | Geometry Template<br>slate, pennies, or 2-color counters<br>circle graphs from newspapers or magazines |

# planningtips

## Pacing

Pacing depends on a number of factors, such as students' individual needs and how long your school has been using *Everyday Mathematics.* At the beginning of Unit 5, review your Content by Strand Poster to help you set a monthly pace.

| ←MOST CLASSROOMS→ | | |
|---|---|---|
| DECEMBER | JANUARY | FEBRUARY |

## Using the Projects

Use Project 5, How Would You Spend $1,000,000, during or after Unit 5 to research and plan how to spend a million dollars; to compute with large numbers; to report on the plan; and to analyze and display data. The Projects can be found at the back of this book.

## Home Communication

Share Study Links 5.1–5.12 with families to help them understand the content and procedures in this unit. At the end of the unit, use Study Link 5.13 to introduce Unit 6. Supplemental information can be found in the *Home Connection Handbook.*

## NCTM Standards

| Standard | 1 | 2 | 3 | 4 | 5 | 6 | 7 | 8 | 9 | 10 |
|---|---|---|---|---|---|---|---|---|---|---|
| Unit 5 Lessons | 5.1–5.8, 5.10–5.12 | 5.5 | 5.6 | 5.10 | 5.9–5.12 | 5.1–5.13 | 5.1–5.13 | 5.1–5.13 | 5.1–5.13 | 5.1–5.13 |

**Content Standards**
1 Number and Operations
2 Algebra
3 Geometry
4 Measurement
5 Data Analysis and Probability

**Process Standards**
6 Problem Solving
7 Reasoning and Proof
8 Communication
9 Connections
10 Representation

## PRACTICE *through* Games

*Everyday Mathematics* uses games to help students develop good fact power and other math skills.

- *Factor Captor* to practice finding factors of a number **(Lesson 5.4)**
- *Multiplication Bull's-Eye* to practice estimation and multiplication skills **(Lesson 5.4)**
- *Estimation Squeeze* to practice estimating the square roots of numbers by naming decimals between two decimals **(Lesson 5.5)**
- *Frac-Tac-Toe* to practice renaming fractions as decimals or percents **(Lessons 5.7, 5.8, 5.11, and 5.13)**
- *Fraction/Percent Concentration* to practice recognizing fractions and percents that are equivalent **(Lesson 5.8)**

# unit 5 content highlights

*The discussion below highlights the major content ideas presented in Unit 5 and may help you establish instructional priorities.*

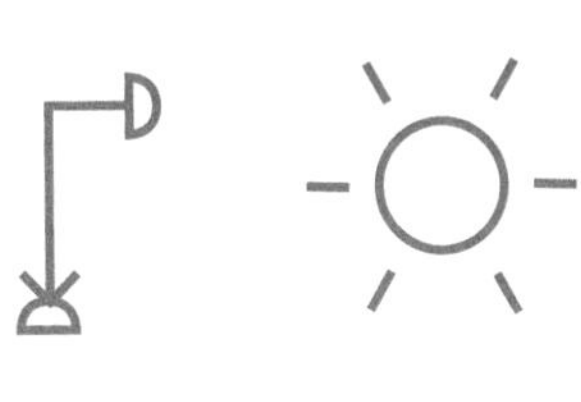

## Rational Numbers and Their Notations (Lessons 5.1–5.4)

The emphasis of this program with respect to fractions, decimals, and percents may be different from that of other fifth grade mathematics programs you may have used in the past. The emphasis is based on the fact that fractions, decimals, and percents have emerged as interchangeable notations for "rational numbers."

Every society throughout history has invented verbal counting, counting words, and counting systems. Many societies went beyond verbal counting to invent symbol systems for writing and calculating with whole numbers, including zero. As commerce and trade developed, many societies found that measures of length, capacity, and weight often needed numbers between whole numbers to express parts of whole measures. For this reason, people invented written notations for these "in-between numbers"—some with symbols that we recognize as precursors to fraction notation and some that we see as precursors to decimal notation. In the relatively recent development of mathematics, the rules for equivalence, order, and operations have been organized into what is called "the rational number system."

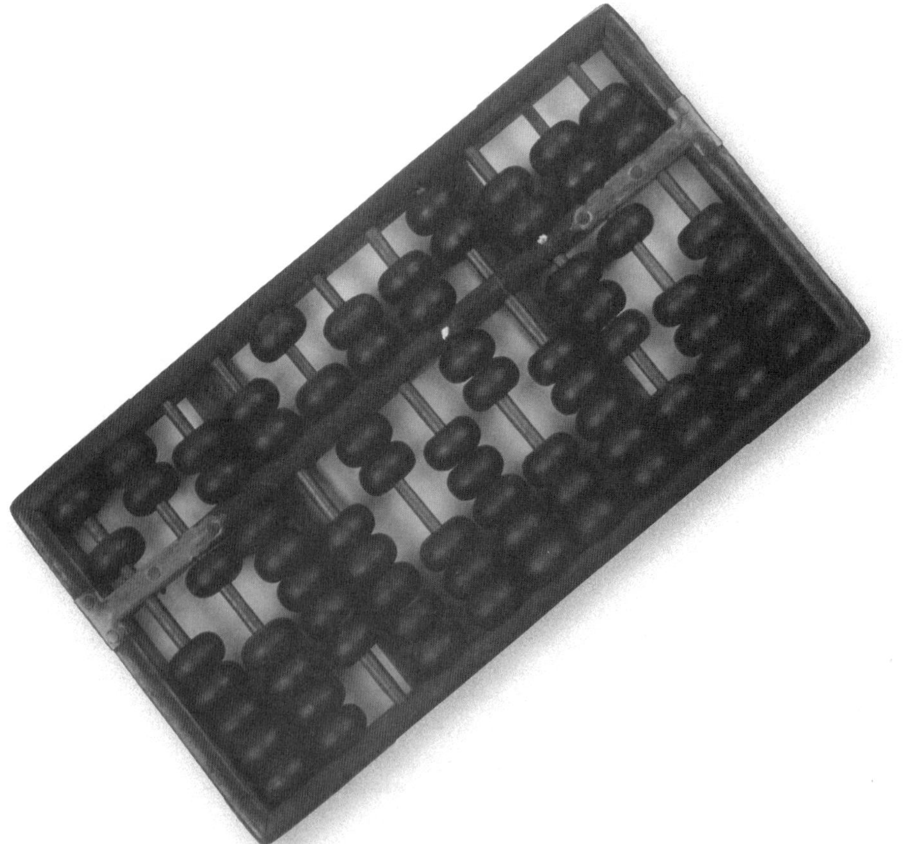

## Equivalence and Conversions among Fractions, Decimals, and Percents (Lessons 5.5–5.8)

Fraction and decimal notation systems invented in ancient times had ways of expressing order and equivalence within systems, but equivalencies between fraction and decimal notation systems (including endlessly repeating decimals) have been fully understood only in modern times. We now know that the three modern notations for rational numbers—fractions, decimals, and percents—are interchangeable. Any rational number written in one of these ways can be written in the other two ways, often by considering a fraction as a division problem, which is easily done with a calculator (Lesson 5.8).

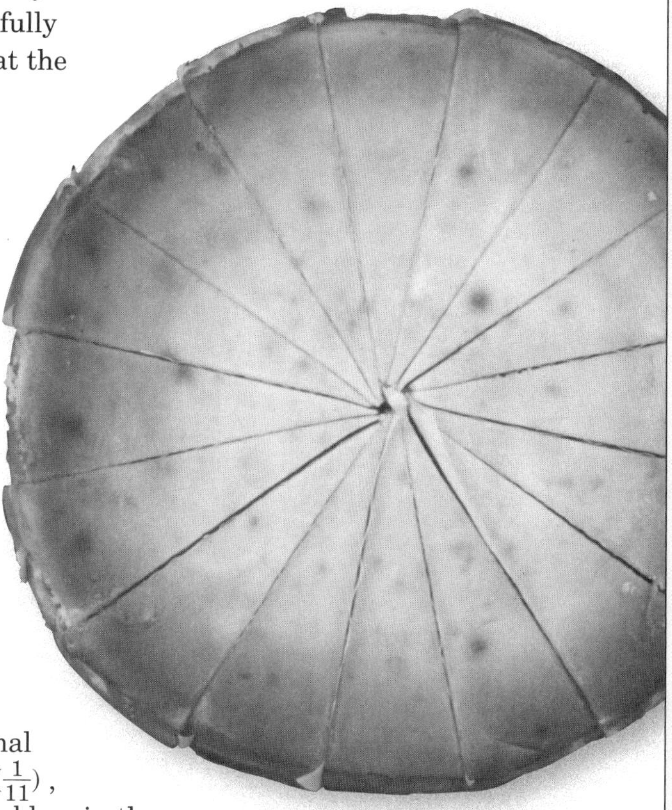

There are, however, practical difficulties in converting from one notation system to another, since many fractions written as decimals go on forever in a repeating pattern—such as $\frac{1}{3} = 0.333... = 0.\overline{3}$. This endless repetition poses no difficulty when going from fractions to decimals. We generally use a calculator for the division and then round the resulting decimal (which may be part of an endlessly repeating decimal) to however many significant figures we want. It is, however, more difficult to go from a repeating decimal such as $0.090909 = 0.\overline{09}$ to its fraction equivalent $(\frac{1}{11})$, and *Everyday Mathematics* does not address this problem in the fifth grade program.

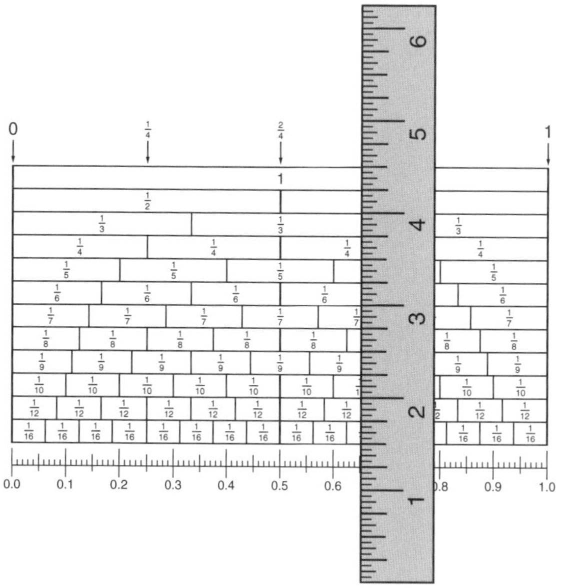

The Fraction-Stick Chart is one of the tools used to help students convert fractions to decimals.

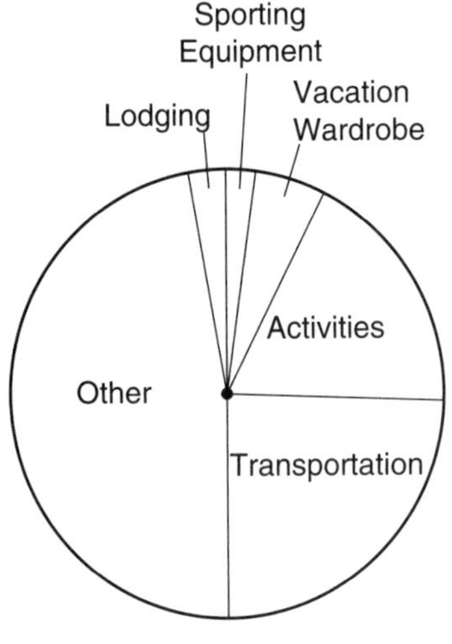

Students create circle graphs.

## Circle Graphs and the Percent Circle (Lessons 5.9–5.11)

Circle graphs are effective visual displays for certain kinds of information and are among the most common statistical displays encountered in newspapers and magazines. Circle graphs are often called "pie graphs" and are said to show how the "pie" is divided.

Preparing information for a circle graph involves expressing parts as fractions of a whole and then applying the fraction-to-percent conversion skills emphasized in these lessons. One then decides what part of 360° is needed to represent each part as a slice of the pie (circle) graph.

A protractor is used to draw angles that represent parts of a whole as parts of a full 360° rotation. Doing this over and over gets tedious (as does converting fractions to percents without a calculator), so the authors suggest using the Percent Circle, which is on the Geometry Template and also on *Math Masters,* pages 77 and 79 (ready to be cut out). The Percent Circle is like a full-circle protractor, except that the circumference is marked with percents instead of with degrees. You might want to practice using the Percent Circle before the lessons in which students use it.

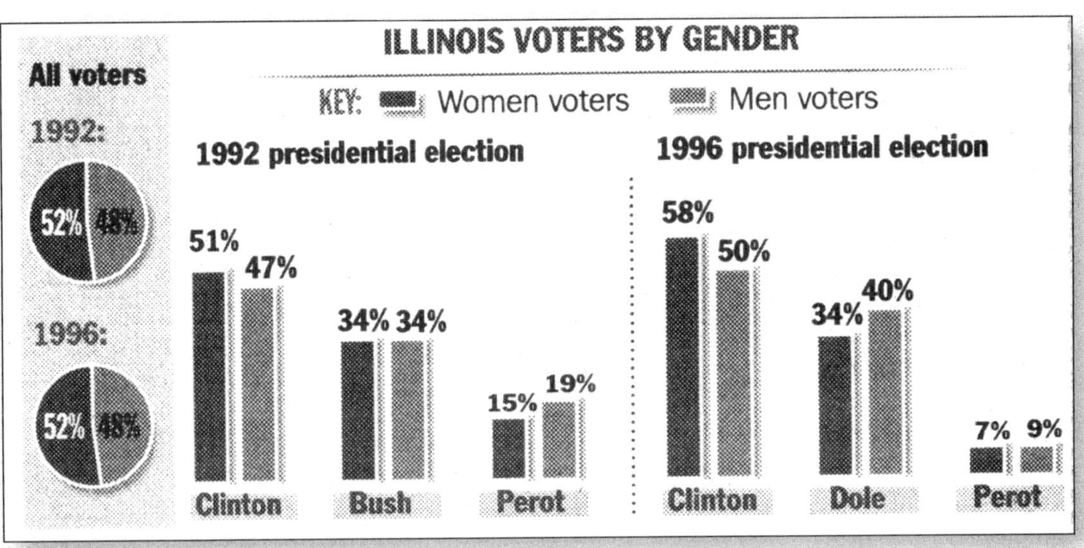

## American Tour: School Days (Lesson 5.12)

The American Tour continues as students read the article "School" in the American Tour section of the *Student Reference Book*. They answer questions that require them to interpret information about school attendance over the past 200 years. They also compare their skills with those of previous generations by solving problems that illustrate the changing emphases in mathematics instruction.

## Review and Assessment (Lesson 5.13)

The Unit 5 assessment in Lesson 5.13 includes a written assessment of the following concepts and skills:

- ▷ adding fractions
- ▷ finding equivalent fractions
- ▷ ordering and comparing fractions
- ▷ converting between fractions, decimals, and percents
- ▷ converting between fractions and mixed numbers
- ▷ drawing, measuring, and interpreting circle graphs

For **additional information** on the following topics, see the *Teacher's Reference Manual:*

- Fractions-Stick Charts and fraction sticks
- Percent Circles and protractors
- percents
- properties of rational numbers
- rational numbers and decimals
- uses of fraction notation
- fraction and decimal notation

# 5.1 Fraction Review

**OBJECTIVES** **To review fractions; and to find fractional parts of large whole numbers.**

| summaries | materials |
|---|---|
| **1 Teaching the Lesson** | |
| Students review key fractions concepts, solve a variety of parts-and-whole problems, and find fractional parts of large whole numbers. [Numeration; Operations and Computation] | ☐ *Math Journal 1,* pp. 122 and 123<br>☐ *Student Reference Book,* pp. 56–58<br>☐ Assessment Master (*Math Masters,* p. 479, optional)<br>☐ slate; calculator<br>☐ 20 counters per partnership |
| **2 Ongoing Learning & Practice** | |
| Students review the use of fractions when reading a ruler. [Measurement and Reference Frames]<br>Students practice and maintain skills through Math Boxes and Study Link activities. | ☐ *Math Journal 1,* pp. 124 and 125<br>☐ Transparency (*Math Masters,* p. 50; optional)<br>☐ Study Link Master (*Math Masters,* p. 265)<br>☐ ruler or Geometry Template |
| **3 Options for Individualizing** | |
| **Reteaching** Students find fractions of sets. [Operations and Computation]<br>**Language Diversity** Students write parts-and-whole number stories. [Numeration; Operations and Computation] | ☐ *Math Journal 1,* p. 123<br>☐ 30 counters per partnership |

**Additional Information**

**Vocabulary • whole (or ONE or unit) • denominator • numerator • unit fraction**

## Getting Started

### Mental Math and Reflexes

Pose problems such as the following either orally or on the board. Remind students of the tables of equivalent measures on page 355 of their *Student Reference Book.*

*Answer with a fraction.*

- An hour is what fraction of a day? $\frac{1}{24}$
- A minute is $\underline{\frac{1}{60}}$ of an hour.
- A second is $\underline{\frac{1}{60}}$ of a minute.
- Four days is $\underline{\frac{4}{7}}$ of a week.

*Answer with a whole number.*

- $\frac{1}{2}$ hour is how many minutes? 30
- $\frac{3}{4}$ of an hour is $\underline{45}$ minutes.
- $\frac{1}{3}$ of an hour is $\underline{20}$ minutes.
- $\frac{1}{6}$ of an hour is $\underline{10}$ minutes.

### Math Message

*Write any five fractions on your slate. Circle the greatest fraction and the least fraction in your set of fractions.*

# 1 Teaching the Lesson

## ✦ Math Message Follow-Up

WHOLE-CLASS DISCUSSION

Have students share their fractions with the class. You may wish to use some of their examples as you review basic fraction ideas and notation in the following discussion. Ask several students how they knew which fractions were least and greatest. (Ordering fractions is an important skill and a major focus of Lesson 5.3.)

## ✦ Reviewing Basic Fraction Ideas
(*Student Reference Book,* pp. 56–58)

WHOLE-CLASS DISCUSSION

Briefly review the meaning of fractions and their uses. Ask for suggestions from the students or give your own examples to illustrate important fraction ideas and uses, including those listed below.

- ▷ Fractions were invented to express numbers that are between whole numbers.
- ▷ Fractions can show measures between whole numbers on rulers and scales.
- ▷ Fractions can name part of a whole object (for example, part of a cake or pizza).
- ▷ Fractions can name part of a collection of objects (for example, part of the eggs in a carton).
- ▷ Fractions can compare two quantities as ratios or rates (for example, $\frac{1}{2}$ of the class are boys, the car's gas mileage was 100 miles / 4 gallons, or 25 mi/gal).
- ▷ Fractions can express chance or probability (for example, a probability of $\frac{1}{6}$ that a die will land with 6 up).
- ▷ Fractions can represent division (for example, $\frac{3}{4}$ is equivalent to $3 \div 4$ and $4\overline{)3}$).

Write several fractions and a "whole box" or "unit box" on the board. Use them to remind students of the meaning of fraction notation. *(See the margin.)*

- ▷ Most fractions are fractions of something. The "something" is referred to as the **whole,** the **ONE;** or with measures, as the **unit.** The whole box is a reminder of what is the whole when working with fractions.

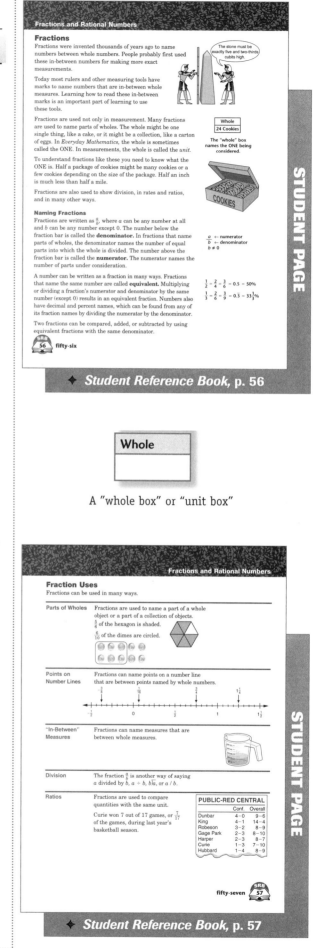

Fractions and Rational Numbers

### Fractions

Fractions were invented thousands of years ago to name numbers between whole numbers. People probably first used these in-between numbers for making more exact measurements.

The stone must be exactly five and two-thirds cubits high.

Today most rulers and other measuring tools have marks to name numbers that are in-between whole measures. Learning how to read these in-between marks is an important part of learning to use these tools.

Fractions are used not only in measurement. Many fractions are used to name parts of wholes. The whole might be one single thing, like a cake, or it might be a collection, like a carton of eggs. In *Everyday Mathematics,* the whole is sometimes called the ONE. In measurements, the whole is called the *unit.*

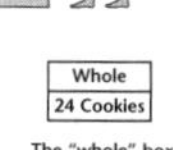

The "whole" box names the ONE being considered.

To understand fractions like these you need to know what the ONE is. Half a package of cookies might be many cookies or a few cookies depending on the size of the package. Half an inch is much less than half a mile.

Fractions are also used to show division, in rates and ratios, and in many other ways.

**Naming Fractions**

Fractions are written as $\frac{a}{b}$, where $a$ can be any number at all and $b$ can be any number except 0. The number below the fraction bar is called the **denominator.** In fractions that name parts of wholes, the denominator names the number of equal parts into which the whole is divided. The number above the fraction bar is called the **numerator.** The numerator names the number of parts under consideration.

$\frac{a}{b}$ ← numerator ← denominator, $b \neq 0$

A number can be written as a fraction in many ways. Fractions that name the same number are called **equivalent.** Multiplying or dividing a fraction's numerator and denominator by the same number (except 0) results in an equivalent fraction. Numbers also have decimal and percent names, which can be found from any of its fraction names by dividing the numerator by the denominator.

$\frac{1}{2} = \frac{2}{4} = \frac{3}{6} = 0.5 = 50\%$

$\frac{1}{3} = \frac{2}{6} = \frac{3}{9} = 0.\overline{3} = 33\frac{1}{3}\%$

Two fractions can be compared, added, or subtracted by using equivalent fractions with the same denominator.

fifty-six

STUDENT PAGE

✦ *Student Reference Book,* p. 56

| Whole |
|---|
| |

A "whole box" or "unit box"

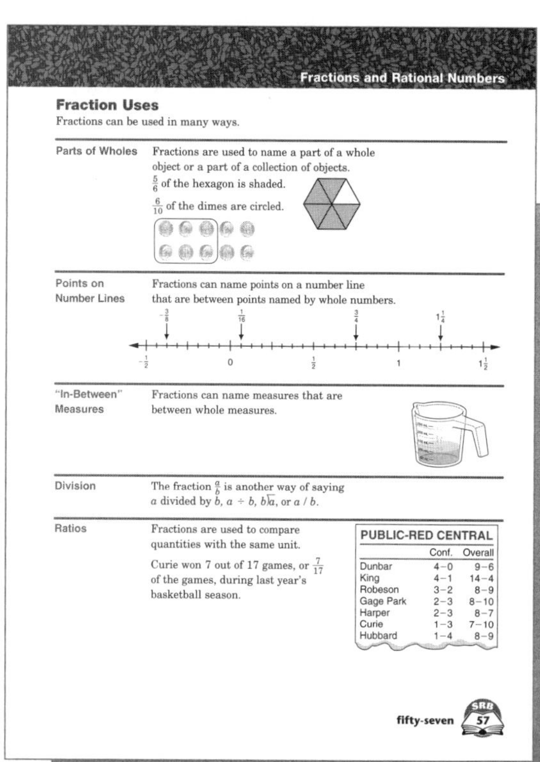

Fractions and Rational Numbers

### Fraction Uses

Fractions can be used in many ways.

**Parts of Wholes** — Fractions are used to name a part of a whole object or a part of a collection of objects.

$\frac{5}{6}$ of the hexagon is shaded.

$\frac{6}{10}$ of the dimes are circled.

**Points on Number Lines** — Fractions can name points on a number line that are between points named by whole numbers.



**"In-Between" Measures** — Fractions can name measures that are between whole measures.

**Division** — The fraction $\frac{a}{b}$ is another way of saying $a$ divided by $b$, $a \div b$, $b\overline{)a}$, or $a\,/\,b$.

**Ratios** — Fractions are used to compare quantities with the same unit.

Curie won 7 out of 17 games, or $\frac{7}{17}$ of the games, during last year's basketball season.

| PUBLIC-RED CENTRAL | Conf. | Overall |
|---|---|---|
| Dunbar | 4–0 | 9–6 |
| King | 4–1 | 14–4 |
| Robeson | 3–2 | 8–9 |
| Gage Park | 2–3 | 8–10 |
| Harper | 2–3 | 8–7 |
| Curie | 1–3 | 7–10 |
| Hubbard | 1–4 | 8–9 |

fifty-seven SRB 57

STUDENT PAGE

✦ *Student Reference Book,* p. 57

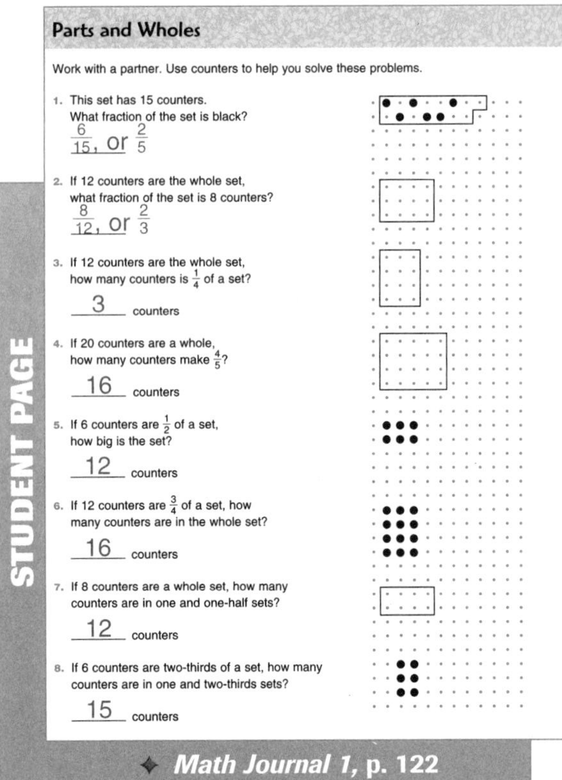
**Parts and Wholes**

Work with a partner. Use counters to help you solve these problems.

1. This set has 15 counters. What fraction of the set is black? $\frac{6}{15}$, or $\frac{2}{5}$
2. If 12 counters are the whole set, what fraction of the set is 8 counters? $\frac{8}{12}$, or $\frac{2}{3}$
3. If 12 counters are the whole set, how many counters is $\frac{1}{4}$ of a set? 3 counters
4. If 20 counters are a whole, how many counters make $\frac{4}{5}$? 16 counters
5. If 6 counters are $\frac{1}{2}$ of a set, how big is the set? 12 counters
6. If 12 counters are $\frac{3}{4}$ of a set, how many counters are in the whole set? 16 counters
7. If 8 counters are a whole set, how many counters are in one and one-half sets? 12 counters
8. If 6 counters are two-thirds of a set, how many counters are in one and two-thirds sets? 15 counters

STUDENT PAGE

✦ *Math Journal 1,* p. 122

NOTE: A unit fraction has 1 as its numerator. Throughout the year, encourage the "unit fraction" or "unit rate" method for solving fraction problems.

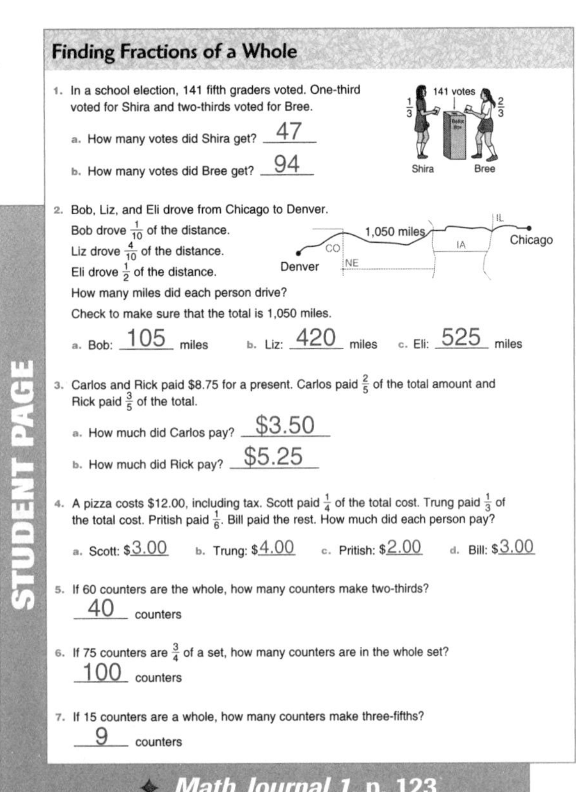
**Finding Fractions of a Whole**

1. In a school election, 141 fifth graders voted. One-third voted for Shira and two-thirds voted for Bree.
   a. How many votes did Shira get? 47
   b. How many votes did Bree get? 94



2. Bob, Liz, and Eli drove from Chicago to Denver.
   Bob drove $\frac{1}{10}$ of the distance.
   Liz drove $\frac{4}{10}$ of the distance.
   Eli drove $\frac{1}{2}$ of the distance.
   How many miles did each person drive?
   Check to make sure that the total is 1,050 miles.
   a. Bob: 105 miles b. Liz: 420 miles c. Eli: 525 miles



3. Carlos and Rick paid \$8.75 for a present. Carlos paid $\frac{2}{5}$ of the total amount and Rick paid $\frac{3}{5}$ of the total.
   a. How much did Carlos pay? \$3.50
   b. How much did Rick pay? \$5.25
4. A pizza costs \$12.00, including tax. Scott paid $\frac{1}{4}$ of the total cost. Trung paid $\frac{1}{3}$ of the total cost. Pritish paid $\frac{1}{6}$. Bill paid the rest. How much did each person pay?
   a. Scott: \$3.00 b. Trung: \$4.00 c. Pritish: \$2.00 d. Bill: \$3.00
5. If 60 counters are the whole, how many counters make two-thirds? 40 counters
6. If 75 counters are $\frac{3}{4}$ of a set, how many counters are in the whole set? 100 counters
7. If 15 counters are a whole, how many counters make three-fifths? 9 counters

STUDENT PAGE

✦ *Math Journal 1,* p. 123

- ▷ Fractions are written vertically as $\frac{a}{b}$, or horizontally as *a/b.*
- ▷ The number below (or to the right of) the fraction bar is called the **denominator.** The denominator names the number of equal parts into which the whole is divided.
- ▷ The number above (or to the left of) the fraction bar is called the **numerator.** The numerator names the number of parts under consideration.

**Language Arts Link** Students may be interested in knowing that the bar separating numerator from denominator is called a *vinculum,* from Latin *vinci,* to bind.

## ✦ Solving Parts-and-Whole Problems with Fractions (*Math Journal 1,* p. 122)

PARTNER ACTIVITY

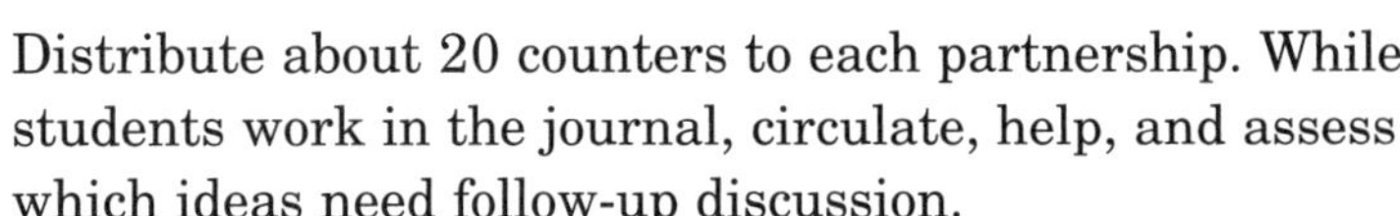

Distribute about 20 counters to each partnership. While students work in the journal, circulate, help, and assess which ideas need follow-up discussion.

Notice that there are three types of problems. Each kind of problem depends on the information given and what needs to be found.

1. In Problems 1 and 2, the whole and a part are given; the fraction needs to be named.
2. In Problems 3, 4, and 7, the whole is given and the fraction is named; the part needs to be found.
3. In Problems 5, 6, and 8, a part is given and the fraction is named; the whole needs to be found.

Depending on how easy this page was for your class, you may want to pose similar problems of these types and solve them as a group.

One important method for solving the third type of problem (Problems 5, 6, and 8) is to focus on the concept of unit fractions. When a whole is divided into equal parts, the **unit fraction** names *one* of those equal parts. Then the whole (or some other amount) can easily be found as a multiple of that unit fraction part:

- ▷ For Problem 5, if *one*-half is 6 counters, *two*-halves is 12 counters.

▷ For Problem 6, if *three*-fourths of the set is 12 counters, then *one*-fourth is 4. Since one-fourth is 4, the whole must be 16. A picture may help. Sketch a unit box divided into four sections, and fill three of the sections with 4 counters each. Filling in the fourth section shows that the full set has 16 counters.

▷ For Problem 8, if *two*-thirds is 6 counters, then *one*-third is 3 counters. The whole, or *three*-thirds, is 9 counters. One and two-thirds sets is 9 + 6, or 15 counters.

## ✦ Finding a Fraction of a Whole
(*Math Journal 1,* p. 123; *Math Masters,* p. 479)

PARTNER ACTIVITY

Ask students to solve the problems on the journal page. Allow them to use their calculators to solve some of the problems, if necessary.

**ONGOING ASSESSMENT**

**Have students complete an Exit Slip explaining how they solved Problem 2 or Problem 3 on the journal page. Use this explanation to assess students' understanding of fractions of a set and how well they can apply the concept of unit fractions. Do not expect all students to have these concepts mastered at this time. Students will continue to work on them in *Fifth Grade Everyday Mathematics* and *Sixth Grade Everyday Mathematics.***

Since the numbers involved are large, these number stories are more difficult to solve than the counter problems students solved earlier, even though the types of problems are the same. For example, in Problems 1–4 on this page, the *whole* and *fractions* are given and students need to find the *parts*.

▷ In Problem 1, focus on the unit fraction $\frac{1}{3}$. A set of 141 (votes) must be divided into thirds. Conceptually, this is the same as the problem of dividing 15 counters into thirds. Students can mentally or visually divide 15 into 3 equal shares.

▷ In Problem 3, \$8.75 (or 875 cents) must be divided into fifths. Focus on finding the unit fraction $\frac{1}{5}$. Having determined what $\frac{1}{5}$ of the total is, Carlos's portion ($\frac{2}{5}$) and Rick's portion ($\frac{3}{5}$) can easily be found. Students divide \$8.75 into 5 equal shares.

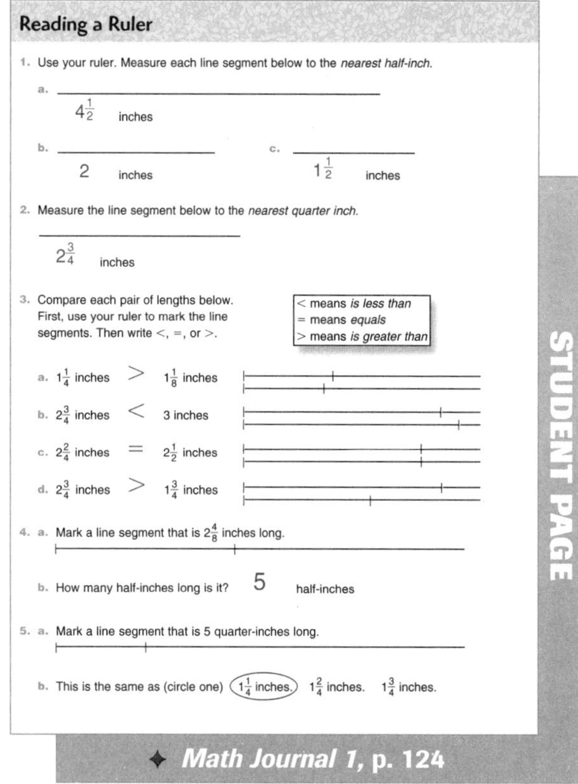

**Reading a Ruler**

1. Use your ruler. Measure each line segment below to the *nearest half-inch.*
   a. $4\frac{1}{2}$ inches
   b. 2 inches
   c. $1\frac{1}{2}$ inches
2. Measure the line segment below to the *nearest quarter inch.*
   $2\frac{3}{4}$ inches
3. Compare each pair of lengths below. First, use your ruler to mark the line segments. Then write <, =, or >.
   < means *is less than*
   = means *equals*
   > means *is greater than*
   a. $1\frac{1}{4}$ inches > $1\frac{1}{8}$ inches
   b. $2\frac{3}{4}$ inches < 3 inches
   c. $2\frac{2}{4}$ inches = $2\frac{1}{2}$ inches
   d. $2\frac{3}{4}$ inches > $1\frac{3}{4}$ inches
4. a. Mark a line segment that is $2\frac{4}{8}$ inches long.
   b. How many half-inches long is it? 5 half-inches
5. a. Mark a line segment that is 5 quarter-inches long.
   b. This is the same as (circle one) $1\frac{1}{4}$ inches. $1\frac{2}{4}$ inches. $1\frac{3}{4}$ inches.

STUDENT PAGE

✦ *Math Journal 1,* p. 124

Journal page 124 and *Math Masters,* page 50 accompany the *Using Fractions to Read a Ruler or Tape Measure* activity on the following page.

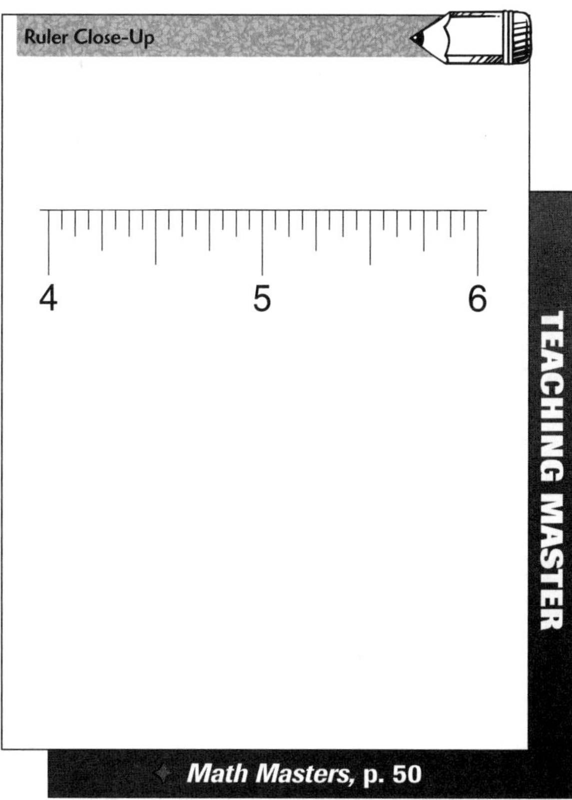


TEACHING MASTER

✦ *Math Masters,* p. 50

**Adjusting the Activity** If necessary, allow students to use calculators. The emphasis in this lesson is on the procedure for solving parts-and-whole problems. If students used calculators to divide 141 by 3 and to find $\frac{1}{5}$ of \$8.75, invite them to try mental arithmetic, and to share their procedures. *For example:*

- 3 [40s] is 120, and 3 [7s] is 21, so 3 [47s] is 120 + 21, or 141.
- 141 is near 150, and $\frac{1}{3}$ of 150 is 50. So $\frac{1}{3}$ of 141 is near 50. Since 141 is 9, or 3 [3s], less than 150, $\frac{1}{3}$ of 141 is 3 less than $\frac{1}{3}$ of 150. Since $\frac{1}{3}$ of 150 is 50, $\frac{1}{3}$ of 141 is 3 less than 50, or 47.
- 5 * \$1.50 is \$7.50, so another \$1.25 is needed. 5 * \$0.25 = \$1.25, so $\frac{1}{5}$ of \$8.75 is \$1.75.

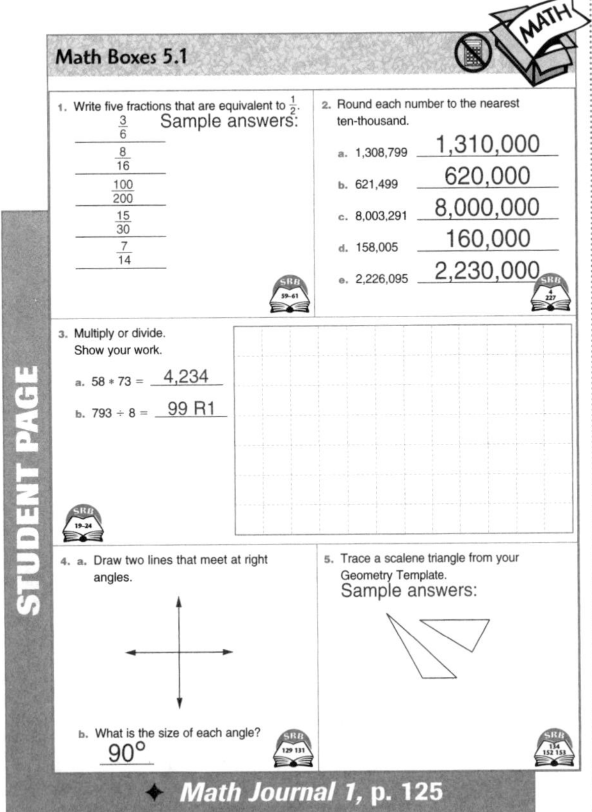
STUDENT PAGE

Math Boxes 5.1

1. Write five fractions that are equivalent to $\frac{1}{2}$.
Sample answers:
$\frac{3}{6}$
$\frac{8}{16}$
$\frac{100}{200}$
$\frac{15}{30}$
$\frac{7}{14}$

2. Round each number to the nearest ten-thousand.
a. 1,308,799 1,310,000
b. 621,499 620,000
c. 8,003,291 8,000,000
d. 158,005 160,000
e. 2,226,095 2,230,000

3. Multiply or divide. Show your work.
a. 58 * 73 = 4,234
b. 793 ÷ 8 = 99 R1

4. a. Draw two lines that meet at right angles.
b. What is the size of each angle? 90°

5. Trace a scalene triangle from your Geometry Template.
Sample answers:

✦ *Math Journal 1,* p. 125

▷ Problem 2 is similar to Problems 3 and 4. Students should be able to find $\frac{1}{2}$ and $\frac{1}{10}$ of 1,050 mentally. One strategy would be to add $\frac{1}{2}$ of 1,000 and $\frac{1}{2}$ of 50.

# 2 Ongoing Learning & Practice

## ✦ Using Fractions to Read a Ruler or Tape Measure (*Math Journal 1,* p. 124; *Math Masters,* p. 50)

WHOLE-CLASS DISCUSSION 

You may use an overhead transparency of *Math Masters,* page 50 to help students identify marks for inch, half-inch, quarter-inch, eighth-inch, and sixteenth-inch on their rulers. The longest lines on the ruler indicate inches. The shortest lines indicate sixteenth-inches.

Have partners complete journal page 124. Circulate and assist. Note that Problem 5 involves a fraction in which the numerator is greater than the denominator. Such *improper fractions* are taken up in the next lesson. Although fractions greater than 1 are called *improper fractions*, there is nothing "improper" about them. It is important for students to understand that it is acceptable and sometimes preferable to write fractions with numerators greater than the denominators. In algebra, students will often encounter and have to manipulate fractions written this way.

## ✦ Math Boxes 5.1 (*Math Journal 1,* p. 125)

INDEPENDENT ACTIVITY

**Mixed Review** Math Boxes in this lesson are paired with Math Boxes in Lesson 5.3. The skill in Problem 1 is a prerequisite for Unit 6.

## ✦ Study Link 5.1 (*Math Masters,* p. 265)

**Home Connection** Students use counters or draw pictures to help them solve parts-and-whole fraction problems.

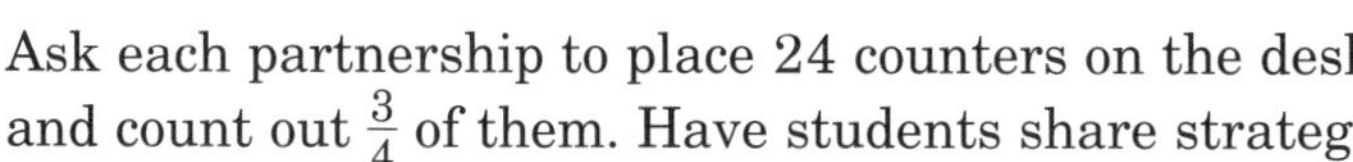

# 3 Options for Individualizing

## ✦ RETEACHING Solving "Fraction-of" Problems

PARTNER ACTIVITY **15–30 min**

Ask each partnership to place 24 counters on the desk and count out $\frac{3}{4}$ of them. Have students share strategies. Expect strategies like the following:

- First I separated the 24 pennies into four equal groups. I put three of the groups together to get three-fourths.
- I organized the 24 pennies into an array with four in each row. I pushed three of the four columns together and left the last column. The three columns are three-fourths of the total.
- I counted out three pennies to the left and one penny to the right. I repeated this until I had counted out all of the pennies.

Continue to pose problems as time allows. *Suggestions:*

- Find $\frac{3}{5}$ of 20. • Find $\frac{2}{3}$ of 18. • Find $\frac{5}{6}$ of 30.

## ✦ LANGUAGE DIVERSITY Writing Parts-and-Whole Number Stories (*Math Journal 1,* p. 123)

PARTNER ACTIVITY **15–30 min**

Pair a student learning English with a proficient English speaker. Have students write parts-and-whole number stories. Students can use journal page 123 for ideas about the kinds of problems to write.

The proficient English speaker can record their stories. The student learning English practices reading the stories. Consider having the proficient English speaker read back stories so that the nonproficient student can hear the correct language repeated. To extend the activity, collect student stories into a class book. Students can read and solve each other's stories.

**Parts-and-Whole Fraction Practice** Study Link 5.1

For the following problems, use counters or draw pictures to help you.

SRB 74 75

1. If 15 counters are the whole set, how many are $\frac{3}{5}$ of the set? 9 counters
2. If 18 counters are the whole set, how many are $\frac{7}{9}$ of the set? 14 counters
3. If 20 counters are the whole set, what fraction of the set is 16 counters? $\frac{4}{5}$
4. If 50 counters are the whole set, what fraction of the set is 45 counters? $\frac{9}{10}$
5. If 35 counters are half of a set, what is the whole set? 70 counters
6. If 12 counters are $\frac{3}{4}$ of a set, what is the whole set? 16 counters
7. Gerald and Michelle went on a 24-mile bike ride. They rode $\frac{1}{4}$ of the distance before stopping. By lunchtime, they rode $\frac{5}{8}$ of the total distance.
   a. How many miles did they have left to ride after lunch? 9 miles
   b. Explain what you did to solve the problem.
   Sample answer: They have $\frac{3}{8}$ of the distance left to ride. $\frac{1}{8}$ of 24 miles is 3 miles. So $\frac{3}{8}$ of 24 miles is $3 * 3 = 9$ miles.

**Challenge**

8. Jen and Heather went to lunch. When the bill came, Jen discovered she had only \$6. Luckily, Heather had enough money to pay the other part, or $\frac{3}{5}$, of the bill.
   a. How much did Heather pay? \$9 b. How much was the total bill? \$15
   c. Explain how you figured out Heather's portion of the bill.
   Sample answer: Since Heather paid $\frac{3}{5}$ of the bill, \$6 must be $\frac{2}{5}$ of the bill. If \$6 is 2 parts of the bill, then 1 part must be \$3 and 3 parts would be \$9.

STUDY LINK MASTER

✦ *Math Masters,* p. 265

# 5.2 Mixed Numbers

**OBJECTIVES** **To review the whole, or ONE; to explore mixed-number concepts; and to convert between mixed numbers and "improper" fractions.**

| summaries | materials |
|---|---|
| **1 Teaching the Lesson** | |
| Students use pattern blocks to review the role of the whole, or ONE, and to explore mixed-number concepts. They recognize and name mixed numbers and convert between mixed numbers and "improper" fractions. [Numeration] | ☐ *Math Journal 1,* pp. 126–128 ☐ Study Link 5.1<br>☐ Teaching Master (*Math Masters,* p. 51; optional)<br>☐ 13 pattern blocks: 2 yellow hexagons, 2 red trapezoids, 3 blue rhombuses, and 6 green triangles<br>***See* Advance Preparation** |
| **2 Ongoing Learning & Practice** | |
| Students label fractions on a ruler. [Numeration]<br>Students practice and maintain skills through Math Boxes and Study Link activities. | ☐ *Math Journal 1,* pp. 129 and 130<br>☐ Study Link Master (*Math Masters,* p. 266) |
| **3 Options for Individualizing** | |
| **Reteaching** Students practice finding fractional parts of a whole with pattern-block shapes.<br>**Extra Practice** Students represent ONE or a fraction of ONE with a pattern block, and calculate the value of various blocks and a design. [Numeration; Operations and Computation] | ☐ Teaching Masters (*Math Masters,* pp. 51 and 52)<br>☐ pattern blocks or Geometry Template |

### Additional Information

**Advance Preparation** For the teaching activities in Part 1, you may want to use *Math Masters,* page 51 and pattern blocks for the overhead projector.

**Vocabulary** • **improper fraction** • **mixed number**

## Getting Started

### Mental Math and Reflexes

Pose problems such as the following. Some students may find looking at a clock face helpful. Encourage them to express fractions in several forms, including the simplest.

What fraction of an hour is:

- 30 minutes? $\frac{1}{2}$
- 10 minutes? $\frac{10}{60}$, or $\frac{1}{6}$
- 45 minutes? $\frac{3}{4}$
- 15 minutes? $\frac{1}{4}$
- 50 minutes? $\frac{50}{60}$, or $\frac{5}{6}$
- 40 minutes? $\frac{2}{3}$

How many hours is:

- 120 minutes? 2
- 150 minutes? $2\frac{1}{2}$
- 90 minutes? $1\frac{1}{2}$
- 75 minutes? $1\frac{1}{4}$

### Math Message

*Take the following pattern blocks: 2 yellow hexagons, 2 red trapezoids, 3 blue rhombuses, and 6 green triangles.*

*If a trapezoid is worth $\frac{1}{2}$, what is a rhombus worth?*

### Study Link 5.1 Follow-Up

Briefly review answers. Have several students share their strategies for solving Problems 7 and 8. If no one suggests it, review how to find and use unit fractions to help solve the problems.

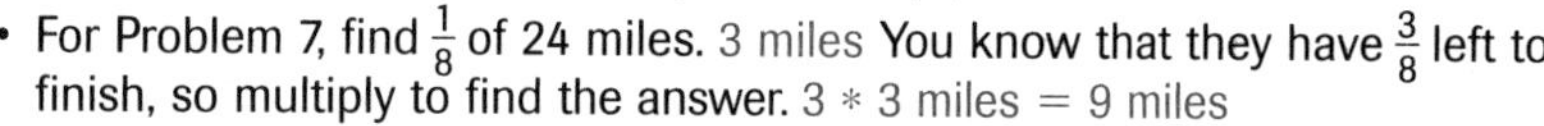

- For Problem 7, find $\frac{1}{8}$ of 24 miles. 3 miles You know that they have $\frac{3}{8}$ left to finish, so multiply to find the answer. 3 * 3 miles = 9 miles

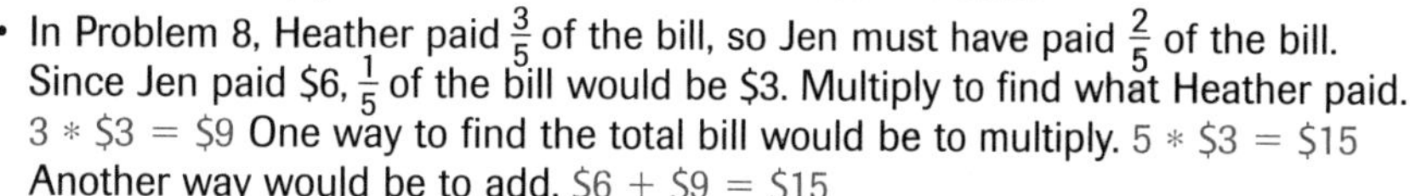

- In Problem 8, Heather paid $\frac{3}{5}$ of the bill, so Jen must have paid $\frac{2}{5}$ of the bill. Since Jen paid \$6, $\frac{1}{5}$ of the bill would be \$3. Multiply to find what Heather paid. 3 * \$3 = \$9 One way to find the total bill would be to multiply. 5 * \$3 = \$15 Another way would be to add. \$6 + \$9 = \$15

# 1 Teaching the Lesson

## Math Message Follow-Up

WHOLE-CLASS DISCUSSION

Discuss how students found the value of the rhombus. Probably the most common approach is first to find what the whole or ONE is (the hexagon) and then to find the value of the rhombus. $\frac{1}{3}$, since 3 rhombuses cover the hexagon.

Review the importance of the whole or ONE: In order to understand a fraction, it is necessary to know what ONE is. Half of a personal pizza is not the same as half of an extra-large pizza.

Pose problems like the following:

- If the triangle is $\frac{1}{3}$, what is the ONE? trapezoid
- If the triangle is $\frac{1}{3}$, what is the rhombus? $\frac{2}{3}$
- If the rhombus is $\frac{1}{3}$, what is the ONE? hexagon
- If the rhombus is $\frac{1}{3}$, what is the triangle? $\frac{1}{6}$
- If the triangle is $\frac{1}{2}$, what is the ONE? rhombus
- If the triangle is $\frac{1}{2}$, what is the trapezoid? $1\frac{1}{2}$, or $\frac{3}{2}$

Keep the pace brisk; these ideas are explored later in this lesson. The main point is that the meaning of fractions depends on what ONE is, so the whole must be clearly defined.

NOTE: Use overhead pattern blocks to model fractions throughout this lesson, use the blocks themselves, or draw them on the board.

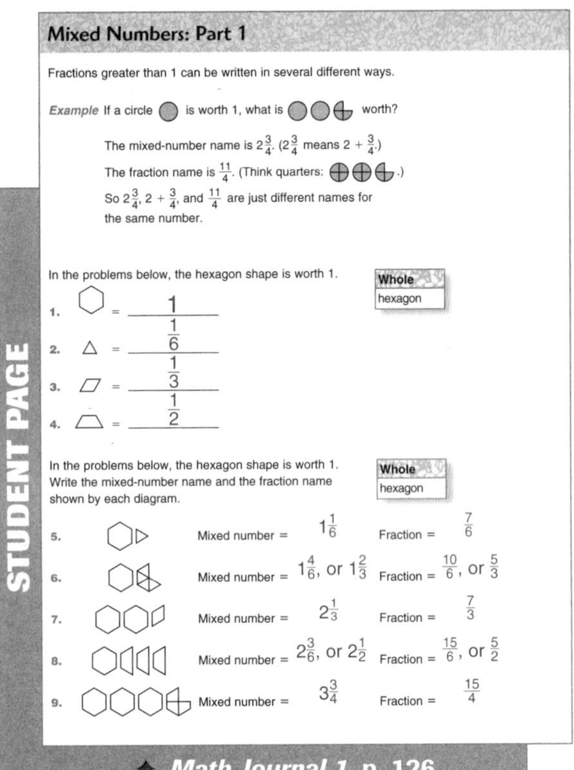

**Mixed Numbers: Part 1**

Fractions greater than 1 can be written in several different ways.

*Example* If a circle is worth 1, what is [three-circle diagram] worth?

The mixed-number name is $2\frac{3}{4}$. ($2\frac{3}{4}$ means $2 + \frac{3}{4}$.)

The fraction name is $\frac{11}{4}$. (Think quarters: [diagram].)

So $2\frac{3}{4}$, $2 + \frac{3}{4}$, and $\frac{11}{4}$ are just different names for the same number.

In the problems below, the hexagon shape is worth 1.

| Whole |
|---|
| hexagon |

1. [hexagon] = 1
2. [triangle] = $\frac{1}{6}$
3. [rhombus] = $\frac{1}{3}$
4. [trapezoid] = $\frac{1}{2}$

In the problems below, the hexagon shape is worth 1. Write the mixed-number name and the fraction name shown by each diagram.

| Whole |
|---|
| hexagon |

5. Mixed number = $1\frac{1}{6}$ Fraction = $\frac{7}{6}$
6. Mixed number = $1\frac{4}{6}$, or $1\frac{2}{3}$ Fraction = $\frac{10}{6}$, or $\frac{5}{3}$
7. Mixed number = $2\frac{1}{3}$ Fraction = $\frac{7}{3}$
8. Mixed number = $2\frac{3}{6}$, or $2\frac{1}{2}$ Fraction = $\frac{15}{6}$, or $\frac{5}{2}$
9. Mixed number = $3\frac{3}{4}$ Fraction = $\frac{15}{4}$

STUDENT PAGE

*Math Journal 1*, p. 126

| Whole |
|---|
| hexagon |

The hexagon is the whole, or ONE for this activity.

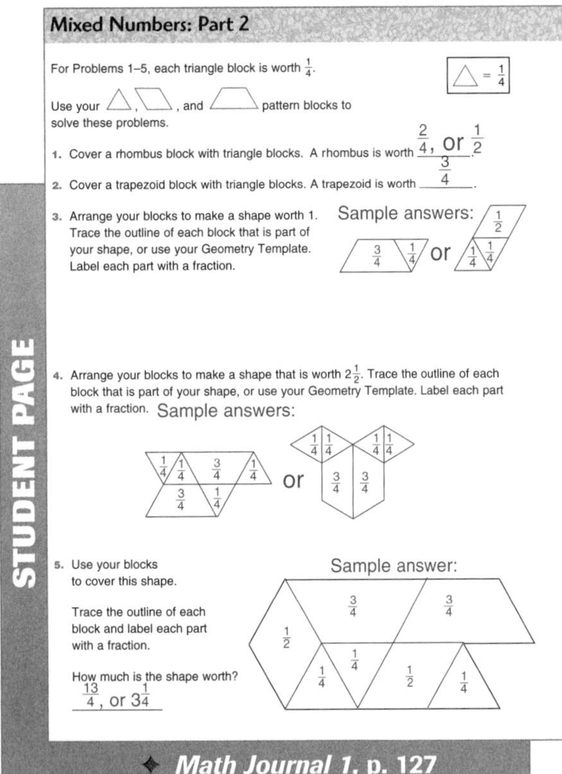

**Mixed Numbers: Part 2**

For Problems 1–5, each triangle block is worth $\frac{1}{4}$.

[triangle] = $\frac{1}{4}$

Use your [triangle], [rhombus], and [trapezoid] pattern blocks to solve these problems.

1. Cover a rhombus block with triangle blocks. A rhombus is worth $\frac{2}{4}$, or $\frac{1}{2}$.
2. Cover a trapezoid block with triangle blocks. A trapezoid is worth $\frac{3}{4}$.
3. Arrange your blocks to make a shape worth 1. Trace the outline of each block that is part of your shape, or use your Geometry Template. Label each part with a fraction.



4. Arrange your blocks to make a shape that is worth $2\frac{1}{2}$. Trace the outline of each block that is part of your shape, or use your Geometry Template. Label each part with a fraction.



5. Use your blocks to cover this shape.

Trace the outline of each block and label each part with a fraction.

How much is the shape worth? $\frac{13}{4}$, or $3\frac{1}{4}$



STUDENT PAGE

*Math Journal 1*, p. 127

## ✦ Using Pattern Blocks to Model Mixed Numbers

WHOLE-CLASS ACTIVITY

Announce that for this activity, the hexagon is the whole, the ONE. Then establish the fractional value for each pattern-block shape. Use the remaining shapes, one at a time, to cover a hexagon, and ask students to name the fractional value of each shape. Hexagon 1, trapezoid $\frac{1}{2}$, rhombus $\frac{1}{3}$, triangle $\frac{1}{6}$ Record the fractional values on the board or overhead transparency for reference.

**Adjusting the Activity** Make a poster of pattern-block shapes. Label each shape with its name. You may also want to have students underline the shape words on their journal pages with coloring pencils the same color as the blocks. For example, the word *trapezoid* would be underlined in red.

Display 8 rhombuses to show 8 thirds. Ask students to name the display in different ways. Some possible responses: $\frac{8}{3}$, $1\frac{5}{3}$, 2 and $\frac{2}{3}$, $2 + \frac{2}{3}$, 2 wholes and $\frac{2}{3}$, and the mixed number $2\frac{2}{3}$

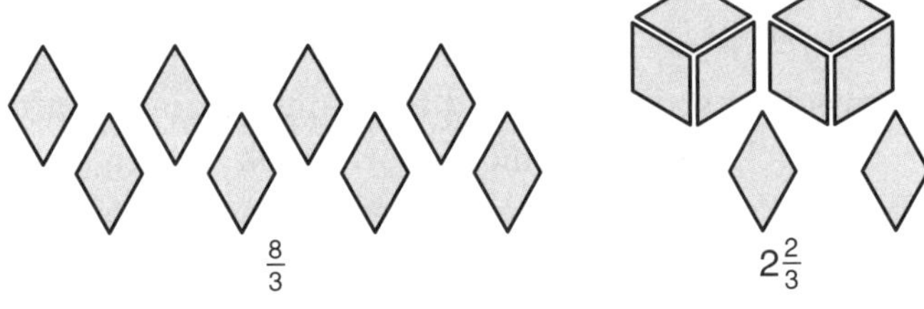


As noted in Lesson 5.1, fractions greater than 1, such as $\frac{8}{3}$, are often called **improper fractions,** although there is nothing "improper" about such fractions. They are perfectly acceptable, and are sometimes a preferable form of a fraction.

As students give various expressions of the mixed number, rearrange the rhombuses to show 2 wholes and a fractional part. A **mixed number** names a number of wholes and a part of a whole. Use the display to show that $\frac{8}{3} = \frac{3}{3} + \frac{3}{3} + \frac{2}{3} = 2 + \frac{2}{3} = 2\frac{2}{3}$.

Explain that $2 + \frac{2}{3}$ is usually written as $2\frac{2}{3}$. The two expressions name the same number. The + sign is left out, but it is understood.

Make other pattern-block displays to practice forming mixed numbers. For example, display $2\frac{1}{6}$ as 13 triangles, or $3\frac{1}{2}$ as 7 trapezoids.

Display 3 hexagons and 5 triangles to show $3\frac{5}{6}$. Ask:

- How should the display be changed to show the same value with a fraction? Replace the 3 hexagons with 18 triangles.
- What is the fraction name? $\frac{23}{6}$

Use the display to show that $3\frac{5}{6} = \frac{6}{6} + \frac{6}{6} + \frac{6}{6} + \frac{5}{6} = \frac{23}{6}$.

Make other pattern-block displays of mixed numbers, using the hexagon to represent the whole, the ONE. For example, display $\frac{9}{2}$ as 4 hexagons and 1 trapezoid.

For additional practice, write various fractions or mixed numbers on the board. Ask students how to represent each number with pattern blocks. For example, write $\frac{11}{6}$ on the board. Students may respond with either "1 hexagon plus 5 triangles" or "11 triangles." Some students may suggest "1 hexagon plus 1 trapezoid and 2 triangles."

## ✦ Modeling Mixed Numbers with Pattern Blocks (*Math Journal 1,* p. 126)

PARTNER ACTIVITY

Ask students to read the example at the top of the page before they do the problems on the page. Share their strategies as well as their answers. In Problem 8, the display for $2\frac{1}{2}$ is interesting because it also suggests the mixed number $1\frac{3}{2}$. The answers $2\frac{1}{2}$, $1\frac{3}{2}$, and $\frac{5}{2}$ are all correct and students should be comfortable with them.

## ✦ Changing the ONE with Fractions and Mixed Numbers (*Math Journal 1,* pp. 127 and 128)

PARTNER ACTIVITY

Point out that on these pages the hexagon is not ONE. The first thing students need to do is establish what ONE is and find the fractional value for each pattern-block shape. The same ONE is used for Problems 1–5. ONE changes for Problems 6–10, and changes again for Problem 11.

In several problems, students create arrangements of blocks to show specified totals. Many combinations of blocks are possible, and most of these combinations can be used to make a variety of shapes. Whatever their selection and arrangement of blocks, students should be able to justify that their blocks add to the required total. (The informal exploration of fraction addition, started here, continues in the fraction-stick activity of the following lesson. Algorithms for fraction operations will be developed in a later lesson.)

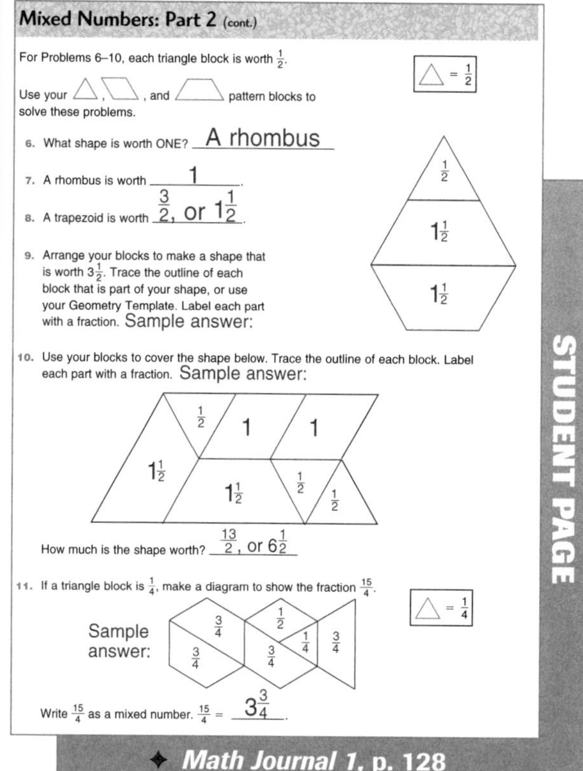
**Mixed Numbers: Part 2** (cont.)

For Problems 6–10, each triangle block is worth $\frac{1}{2}$. △ = $\frac{1}{2}$

Use your △, ▱, and ⏢ pattern blocks to solve these problems.

6. What shape is worth ONE? A rhombus
7. A rhombus is worth 1.
8. A trapezoid is worth $\frac{3}{2}$, or $1\frac{1}{2}$.
9. Arrange your blocks to make a shape that is worth $3\frac{1}{2}$. Trace the outline of each block that is part of your shape, or use your Geometry Template. Label each part with a fraction. Sample answer:



10. Use your blocks to cover the shape below. Trace the outline of each block. Label each part with a fraction. Sample answer:



How much is the shape worth? $\frac{13}{2}$, or $6\frac{1}{2}$

11. If a triangle block is $\frac{1}{4}$, make a diagram to show the fraction $\frac{15}{4}$. △ = $\frac{1}{4}$

Sample answer:



Write $\frac{15}{4}$ as a mixed number. $\frac{15}{4} = 3\frac{3}{4}$.

STUDENT PAGE

✦ *Math Journal 1,* p. 128

NOTE: Students have a limited supply of pattern blocks, but enough to complete the journal page activities if they share blocks.

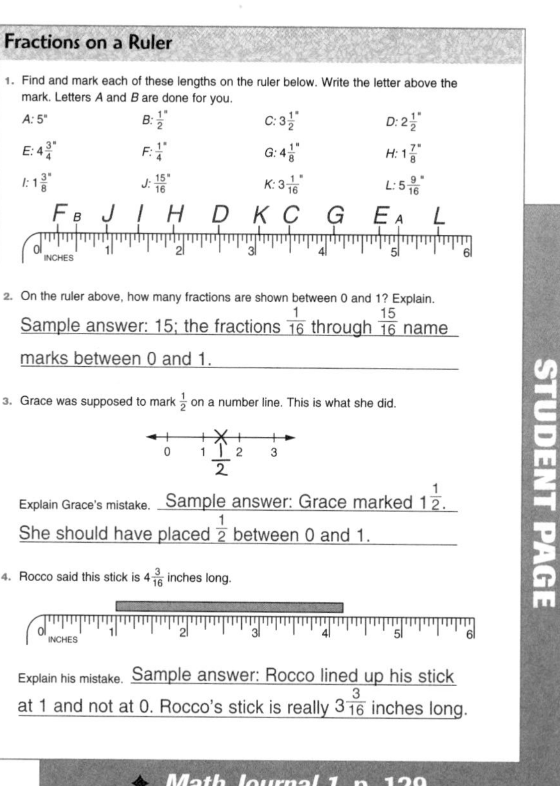
**Fractions on a Ruler**

1. Find and mark each of these lengths on the ruler below. Write the letter above the mark. Letters *A* and *B* are done for you.

| | | | |
|---|---|---|---|
| *A:* 5" | *B:* $\frac{1}{2}$" | *C:* $3\frac{1}{2}$" | *D:* $2\frac{1}{2}$" |
| *E:* $4\frac{3}{4}$" | *F:* $\frac{1}{4}$" | *G:* $4\frac{1}{8}$" | *H:* $1\frac{7}{8}$" |
| *I:* $1\frac{3}{8}$" | *J:* $\frac{15}{16}$" | *K:* $3\frac{1}{16}$" | *L:* $5\frac{9}{16}$" |



2. On the ruler above, how many fractions are shown between 0 and 1? Explain. Sample answer: 15; the fractions $\frac{1}{16}$ through $\frac{15}{16}$ name marks between 0 and 1.
3. Grace was supposed to mark $\frac{1}{2}$ on a number line. This is what she did.



Explain Grace's mistake. Sample answer: Grace marked $1\frac{1}{2}$. She should have placed $\frac{1}{2}$ between 0 and 1.

4. Rocco said this stick is $4\frac{3}{16}$ inches long.



Explain his mistake. Sample answer: Rocco lined up his stick at 1 and not at 0. Rocco's stick is really $3\frac{3}{16}$ inches long.

STUDENT PAGE

✦ *Math Journal 1,* p. 129

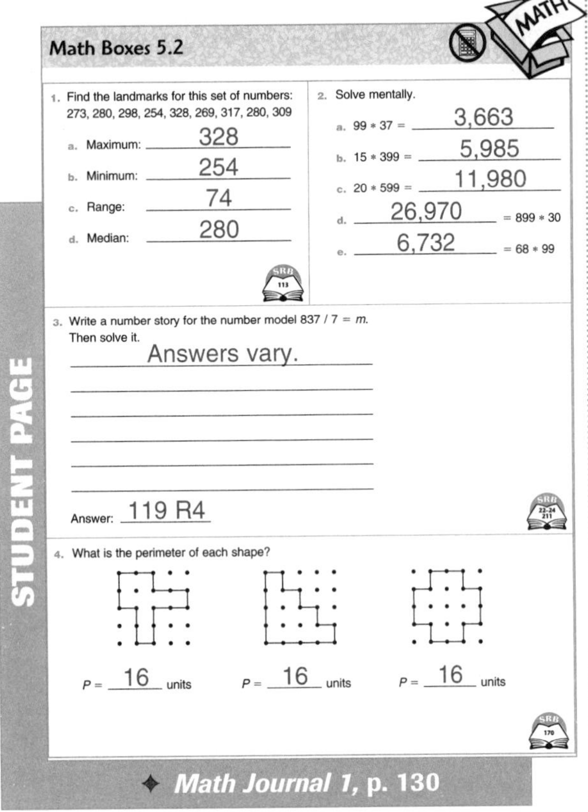

STUDENT PAGE

**Math Boxes 5.2**

1. Find the landmarks for this set of numbers: 273, 280, 298, 254, 328, 269, 317, 280, 309
   a. Maximum: 328
   b. Minimum: 254
   c. Range: 74
   d. Median: 280

2. Solve mentally.
   a. 99 * 37 = 3,663
   b. 15 * 399 = 5,985
   c. 20 * 599 = 11,980
   d. 26,970 = 899 * 30
   e. 6,732 = 68 * 99

3. Write a number story for the number model 837 / 7 = *m*. Then solve it.
   Answers vary.
   Answer: 119 R4

4. What is the perimeter of each shape?
   P = 16 units  P = 16 units  P = 16 units

✦ *Math Journal 1,* p. 130

# ONGOING ASSESSMENT

Use journal page 129 to assess students' understanding of measuring to the nearest fraction of an inch as well as to assess their general understanding of fractions on a number line.

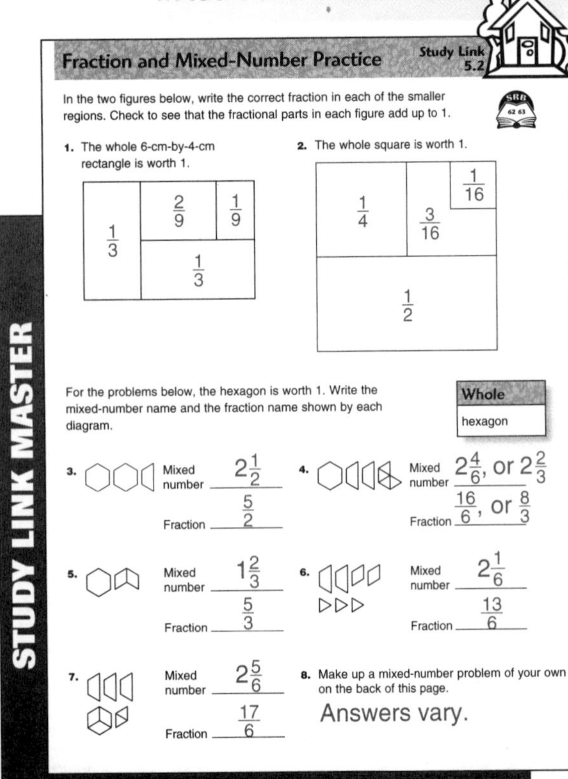

STUDY LINK MASTER

**Fraction and Mixed-Number Practice** Study Link 5.2

In the two figures below, write the correct fraction in each of the smaller regions. Check to see that the fractional parts in each figure add up to 1.

1. The whole 6-cm-by-4-cm rectangle is worth 1.
   $\frac{1}{3}$, $\frac{2}{9}$, $\frac{1}{9}$, $\frac{1}{3}$

2. The whole square is worth 1.
   $\frac{1}{4}$, $\frac{3}{16}$, $\frac{1}{16}$, $\frac{1}{2}$

For the problems below, the hexagon is worth 1. Write the mixed-number name and the fraction name shown by each diagram.

Whole: hexagon

3. Mixed number $2\frac{1}{2}$; Fraction $\frac{5}{2}$
4. Mixed number $2\frac{4}{6}$, or $2\frac{2}{3}$; Fraction $\frac{16}{6}$, or $\frac{8}{3}$
5. Mixed number $1\frac{2}{3}$; Fraction $\frac{5}{3}$
6. Mixed number $2\frac{1}{6}$; Fraction $\frac{13}{6}$
7. Mixed number $2\frac{5}{6}$; Fraction $\frac{17}{6}$
8. Make up a mixed-number problem of your own on the back of this page.
   Answers vary.

✦ *Math Masters,* p. 266

Students work with their partners and complete the problems and questions on journal pages 127 and 128. Circulate and assist.

**Adjusting the Activity** To extend this activity, ask students to write number models for Problems 3–5, 9–11.

For students having difficulty, be sure they identify what ONE is for each set of problems. Then have them identify the value of each of the pattern blocks based on that ONE.

When most students have finished the pages, review the answers. Have them share their solutions.

Review some of the main ideas in the lesson. Pose additional problems in which you first define ONE, name fractions greater than 1, and ask students to show these fractions by making diagrams like those in Problems 5–9 on journal page 126. Rewrite the fractions as mixed numbers. For example, you might define the trapezoid as ONE, ask students to show $\frac{9}{2}$ in several ways, and then rewrite $\frac{9}{2}$ as $4\frac{1}{2}$.

# 2 Ongoing Learning & Practice

## ✦ Reviewing Fractions on a Ruler

(*Math Journal 1,* p. 129)

PARTNER ACTIVITY 

Students locate fractions and mixed numbers on a ruler, and analyze mistakes in placing fraction labels on a number line.

**Adjusting the Activity** For students who are having difficulty reading the ruler, you may want to suggest that they use coloring pencils to highlight different markings. For example, they can trace the $\frac{1}{2}''$ marks with blue, the $\frac{1}{4}''$ marks with orange, and the $\frac{1}{8}''$ marks with green.

You may want to ask students if they can find a pattern for determining where $\frac{1}{4}''$ and $\frac{1}{8}''$ marks are located. The most important feature to notice is that the marks are different lengths. In addition, expect answers like the following: The fourths are always halfway between the halves and on the wholes and halves; the eighths are every other mark between the fourths (and on the fourths, halves, and wholes).

## ✦ Math Boxes 5.2 (*Math Journal 1*, p. 130)

INDEPENDENT ACTIVITY 

**Mixed Review** Math Boxes in this lesson are paired with Math Boxes in Lesson 5.4. The skill in Problem 1 is a prerequisite for Unit 6.

## ✦ Study Link 5.2 (*Math Masters*, p. 266)

**Home Connection** Students give the values of fractional parts of rectangular regions. They write mixed numbers and improper fractions for values of shapes made with pattern blocks.

# 3 Options for Individualizing

## ✦ RETEACHING Finding Fractions of a Whole with Pattern Blocks (*Math Masters*, p. 51)

PARTNER ACTIVITY  **15–30 min** 

Students practice finding fractional parts of a whole with pattern-block shapes.

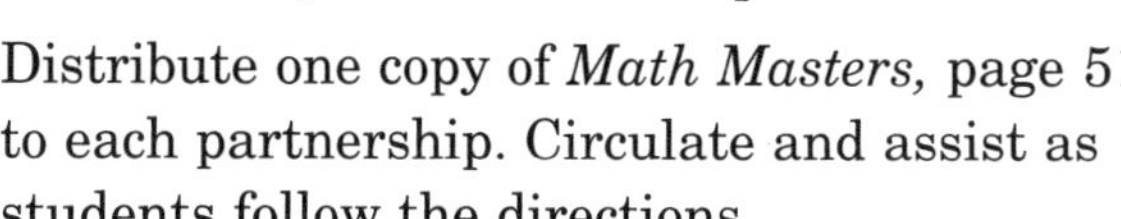

Distribute one copy of *Math Masters*, page 51 to each partnership. Circulate and assist as students follow the directions.

## ✦ EXTRA PRACTICE Solving Pattern-Block Puzzles (*Math Masters*, p. 52)

INDEPENDENT ACTIVITY  **15–30 min** 

Students choose a pattern block to represent ONE or a fraction of ONE. They then calculate the value of various blocks and a design.

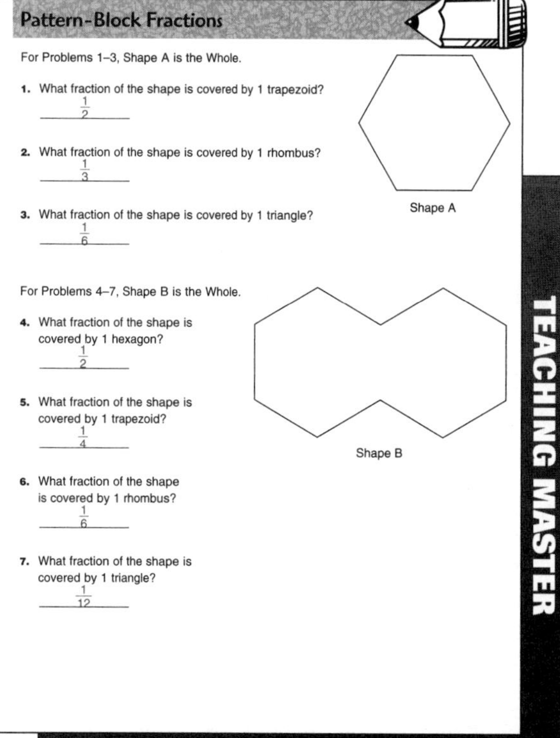

**Pattern-Block Fractions**

For Problems 1–3, Shape A is the Whole.

1. What fraction of the shape is covered by 1 trapezoid? $\frac{1}{2}$
2. What fraction of the shape is covered by 1 rhombus? $\frac{1}{3}$
3. What fraction of the shape is covered by 1 triangle? $\frac{1}{6}$

Shape A

For Problems 4–7, Shape B is the Whole.

4. What fraction of the shape is covered by 1 hexagon? $\frac{1}{2}$
5. What fraction of the shape is covered by 1 trapezoid? $\frac{1}{4}$
6. What fraction of the shape is covered by 1 rhombus? $\frac{1}{6}$
7. What fraction of the shape is covered by 1 triangle? $\frac{1}{12}$

Shape B

TEACHING MASTER

✦ *Math Masters*, p. 51

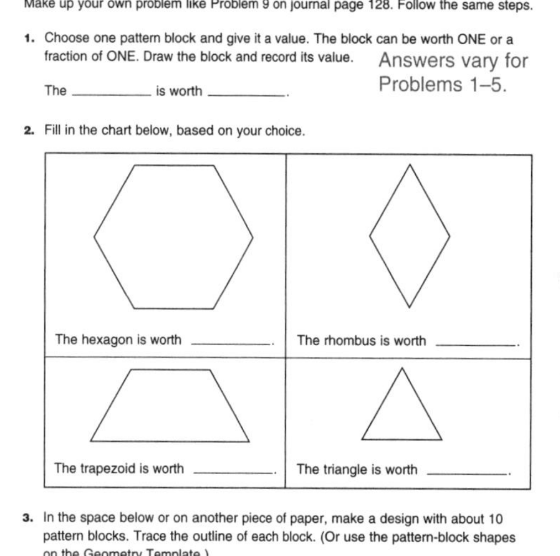

**Pattern Blocks and Fractions**

Make up your own problem like Problem 9 on journal page 128. Follow the same steps.

1. Choose one pattern block and give it a value. The block can be worth ONE or a fraction of ONE. Draw the block and record its value. Answers vary for Problems 1–5.

   The ________ is worth ________.

2. Fill in the chart below, based on your choice.

| | |
|---|---|
| The hexagon is worth ______. | The rhombus is worth ______. |
| The trapezoid is worth ______. | The triangle is worth ______. |

3. In the space below or on another piece of paper, make a design with about 10 pattern blocks. Trace the outline of each block. (Or use the pattern-block shapes on the Geometry Template.)
4. Label each part of your design with a fraction. How much is the design worth? ______
5. Write a number model to show how you calculated the value of the design.

TEACHING MASTER

✦ *Math Masters*, p. 52

# 5.3 Ordering Fractions

**OBJECTIVES** **To compare and order fractions; to review equivalent fractions; and to explore fraction addition.**

| summaries | materials |
| --- | --- |
| **1 Teaching the Lesson** | |
| Students use the Fraction-Stick Chart to find equivalent fractions; to determine which of two fractions is greater; and to compare fractions to 0, $\frac{1}{2}$, 1, and $1\frac{1}{2}$. [Numeration]<br>Students use the fraction-stick model to find equivalent fractions and to continue their exploration of fraction addition. [Numeration] | □ *Math Journal 1,* pp. 131–134 □ Study Link 5.2<br>□ Transparency (*Math Masters,* p. 53; optional)<br>□ ruler<br>***See* Advance Preparation** |
| **2 Ongoing Learning & Practice** | |
| Students practice and maintain skills through Math Boxes and Study Link activities. | □ *Math Journal 1,* p. 135<br>□ Study Link Master (*Math Masters,* p. 267) |
| **3 Options for Individualizing** | |
| **Extra Practice** Students make fraction strips. [Numeration] | □ 6 strips of colored paper, each 2″ by $8\frac{1}{2}$″; $8\frac{1}{2}$″ by 14″ paper (optional); envelope (optional)<br>***See* Advance Preparation** |

**Additional Information**

**Advance Preparation** For Part 1, review journal pages 131–134. Be sure to feel comfortable using the Fraction-Stick Chart.

For the optional activity in Part 3, each student will need 6 strips of colored paper, each 2″ by $8\frac{1}{2}$″. These can be prepared ahead of time or during the activity.

**Vocabulary** • **equivalent fractions** • **fraction stick**

## Getting Started

### Mental Math and Reflexes

Look at your ruler.

- Find $2\frac{1}{2}$ inches on the ruler. How many half-inches is that? 5
- Find $3\frac{1}{4}$ inches on the ruler. How many quarter-inches is that? 13
- Find $1\frac{3}{8}$ inches on the ruler. How many eighth-inches is that? 11
- Find $2\frac{4}{8}$ inches on the ruler. How many quarter-inches is that? 10

**Math Message**

*Complete Problems 1–5 on journal page 131.*

**Study Link 5.2 Follow-Up**

Briefly review answers. Have volunteers share their mixed-number problems.

# 1 Teaching the Lesson

## ✦ Math Message Follow-Up
(*Math Journal 1,* p. 131)

WHOLE-CLASS DISCUSSION

Discuss how students were able to put the fractions in order. Since $\frac{1}{8}$ inch is closest to 0 inches, it is the least fraction. Since $\frac{15}{16}$ inch is closest to 1 inch, it is the greatest. The other fractions, $\frac{5}{8}$ inch and $\frac{3}{8}$ inch, are both closest to $\frac{1}{2}$ inch, but since $\frac{3}{8}$ inch is less than $\frac{1}{2}$ inch and $\frac{5}{8}$ inch is greater than $\frac{1}{2}$ inch, they can easily be ordered.

## ✦ Comparing and Ordering Fractions
(*Math Journal 1,* p. 131)

PARTNER ACTIVITY

Students complete the journal page.

You may want to share some of the sample strategies listed below before they get started.

▷ Problem 6: Since the denominators are all the same, all of the pieces are the same size. Only the number of pieces (the numerators) need to be compared.

▷ Problem 7: Since all of the numerators are the same, there are the same number of pieces for each fraction. Only the size of the pieces (the denominators) needs to be compared. Remind students that the smaller the denominator, the larger the piece.

▷ Problem 8: First compare $\frac{1}{3}$ and $\frac{1}{4}$. They know that the smaller denominator will be the larger fraction. The remaining pair are both within one piece of 1—that is, $\frac{3}{4}$ is $\frac{1}{4}$ away from 1, and $\frac{2}{3}$ is $\frac{1}{3}$ away from 1. Since $\frac{1}{3}$ is greater than $\frac{1}{4}$, that makes $\frac{2}{3}$ farther away from 1.

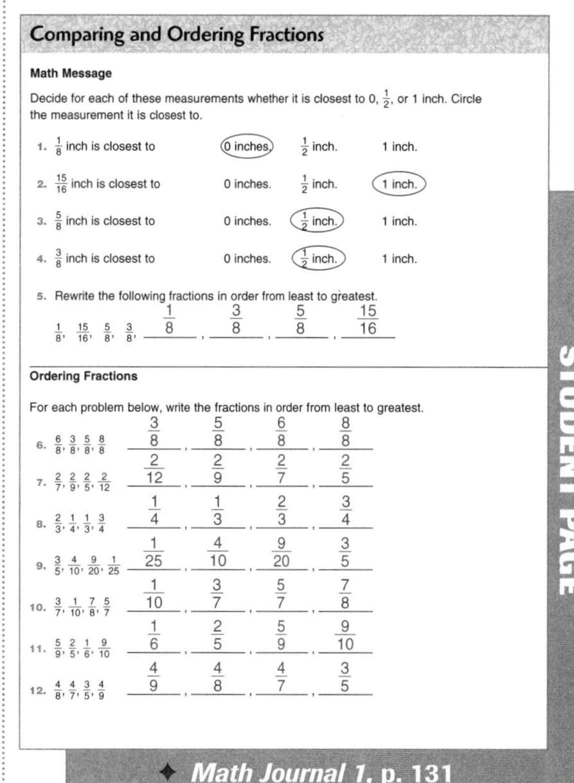

**Comparing and Ordering Fractions**

**Math Message**

Decide for each of these measurements whether it is closest to 0, $\frac{1}{2}$, or 1 inch. Circle the measurement it is closest to.

1. $\frac{1}{8}$ inch is closest to (0 inches.) $\frac{1}{2}$ inch. 1 inch.
2. $\frac{15}{16}$ inch is closest to 0 inches. $\frac{1}{2}$ inch. (1 inch.)
3. $\frac{5}{8}$ inch is closest to 0 inches. ($\frac{1}{2}$ inch.) 1 inch.
4. $\frac{3}{8}$ inch is closest to 0 inches. ($\frac{1}{2}$ inch.) 1 inch.
5. Rewrite the following fractions in order from least to greatest.
$\frac{1}{8}, \frac{15}{16}, \frac{5}{8}, \frac{3}{8}$ $\frac{1}{8}$, $\frac{3}{8}$, $\frac{5}{8}$, $\frac{15}{16}$

**Ordering Fractions**

For each problem below, write the fractions in order from least to greatest.

6. $\frac{6}{8}, \frac{3}{8}, \frac{5}{8}, \frac{8}{8}$ $\frac{3}{8}$, $\frac{5}{8}$, $\frac{6}{8}$, $\frac{8}{8}$
7. $\frac{2}{7}, \frac{2}{9}, \frac{2}{5}, \frac{2}{12}$ $\frac{2}{12}$, $\frac{2}{9}$, $\frac{2}{7}$, $\frac{2}{5}$
8. $\frac{2}{3}, \frac{1}{4}, \frac{1}{3}, \frac{3}{4}$ $\frac{1}{4}$, $\frac{1}{3}$, $\frac{2}{3}$, $\frac{3}{4}$
9. $\frac{3}{5}, \frac{4}{10}, \frac{9}{20}, \frac{1}{25}$ $\frac{1}{25}$, $\frac{4}{10}$, $\frac{9}{20}$, $\frac{3}{5}$
10. $\frac{3}{7}, \frac{1}{10}, \frac{7}{8}, \frac{5}{7}$ $\frac{1}{10}$, $\frac{3}{7}$, $\frac{5}{7}$, $\frac{7}{8}$
11. $\frac{5}{9}, \frac{2}{5}, \frac{1}{6}, \frac{9}{10}$ $\frac{1}{6}$, $\frac{2}{5}$, $\frac{5}{9}$, $\frac{9}{10}$
12. $\frac{4}{8}, \frac{4}{7}, \frac{3}{5}, \frac{4}{9}$ $\frac{4}{9}$, $\frac{4}{8}$, $\frac{4}{7}$, $\frac{3}{5}$

STUDENT PAGE

✦ *Math Journal 1,* p. 131

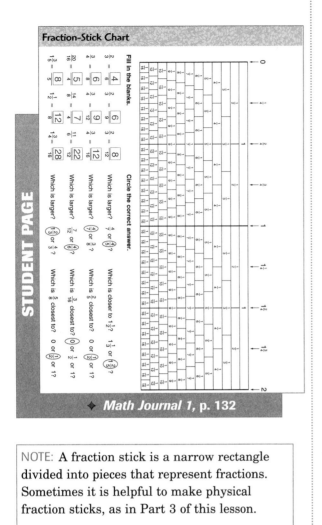

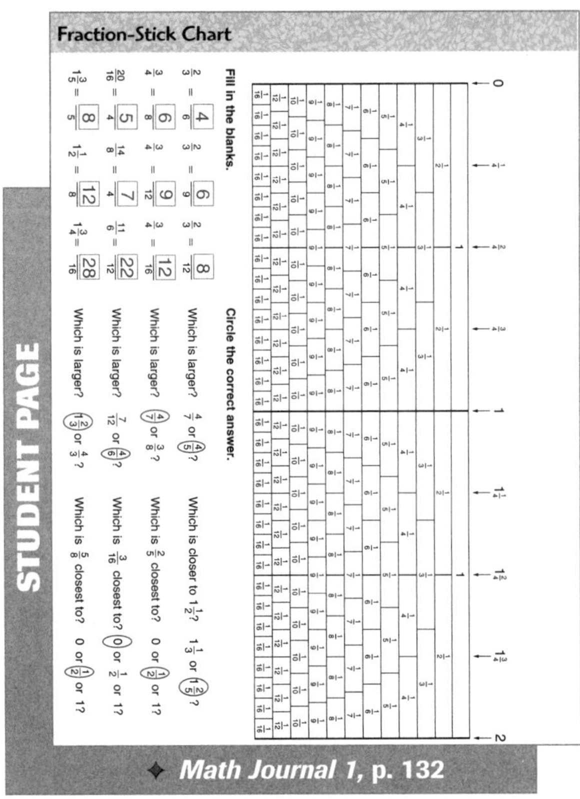

STUDENT PAGE

Math Journal 1, p. 132

NOTE: A fraction stick is a narrow rectangle divided into pieces that represent fractions. Sometimes it is helpful to make physical fraction sticks, as in Part 3 of this lesson.

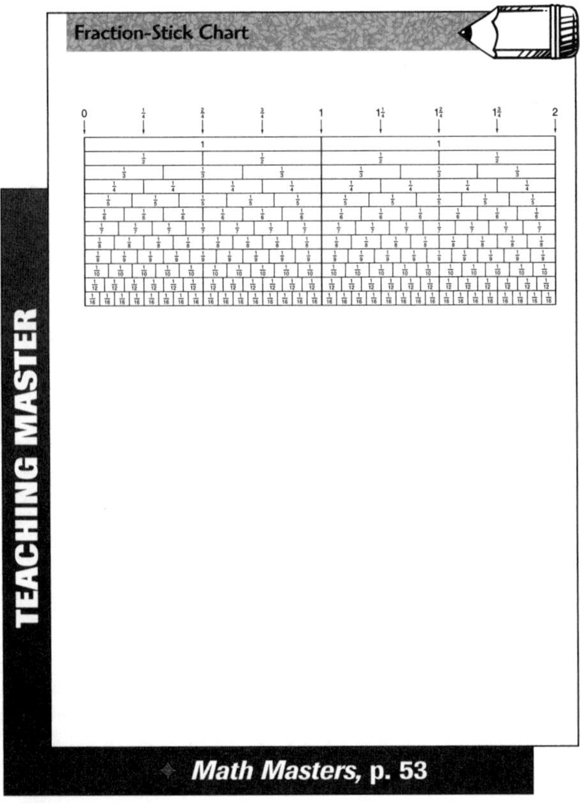

TEACHING MASTER

Math Masters, p. 53

If students have difficulty comparing these numbers, consider having them make a fraction strip for thirds and one for fourths.

- Problem 9: The least is $\frac{1}{25}$. That leaves the other three to compare. Change each to an equivalent fraction with a denominator of 20.
- Problem 10: One of these fractions is close to 0, one is close to 1, and the other two are close to $\frac{1}{2}$.
- Problem 11: Two of the fractions are greater than $\frac{1}{2}$. One is close to $\frac{1}{2}$ and the other is close to 1. One way to compare a fraction to $\frac{1}{2}$ is to see if the numerator is more or less than $\frac{1}{2}$ of the denominator. Of the two fractions that are less than $\frac{1}{2}$, the denominators are close to each other and one numerator is 2 times the numerator of the other.
- Problem 12: One fraction equals $\frac{1}{2}$. The others are close to $\frac{1}{2}$. $\frac{4}{9}$ is less than $\frac{1}{2}$. The other two are greater than $\frac{1}{2}$ but only by $\frac{1}{2}$ of a piece each—that is, $\frac{4}{7}$ is $\frac{1}{2}$ of a seventh greater than $\frac{1}{2}$ and $\frac{3}{5}$ is $\frac{1}{2}$ of a fifth greater than $\frac{1}{2}$. Since fifths are greater than sevenths, $\frac{3}{5}$ is greater than $\frac{4}{7}$.

## Introducing the Fraction-Stick Chart
(*Math Journal 1,* p. 132; *Math Masters,* p. 53)

WHOLE-CLASS ACTIVITY

You may use an overhead transparency of *Math Masters,* page 53 to demonstrate how the **Fraction-Stick** Chart can be used. The chart extends to 2 for practice with mixed numbers.

1. Explain that each row of sticks shows how the interval from 0 to 2 is divided into unit fractions for a particular denominator.

   *Example:* The third row shows two sticks each divided into thirds. There are 6 pieces in this row, each labeled $\frac{1}{3}$. The pieces can be used to count by thirds.

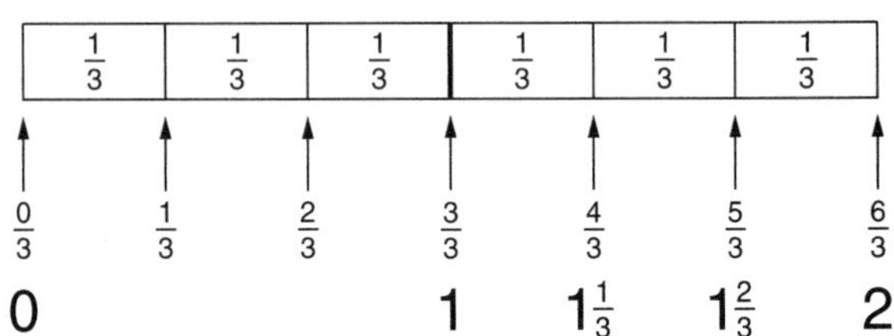


The third row of the Fraction-Stick Chart

2. Show how the chart can be used to find equivalent fractions. Review the concept that different fractions can name the same part of a whole. Fractions such as $\frac{1}{2}$ and $\frac{3}{6}$ are called **equivalent fractions.**

*Example:* Find equivalent fractions for $\frac{2}{3}$.

**Step 1:** Use the "thirds" stick to locate the fraction $\frac{2}{3}$. Count the pieces from left to right. The right edge of the second piece is $\frac{2}{3}$.

$\frac{2}{3}$ is both a length (the distance covered by two $\frac{1}{3}$ fraction sticks) and the point at the right edge of the second $\frac{1}{3}$ piece. This may be confusing to some students.

**Step 2:** Place one edge of a straightedge at $\frac{2}{3}$, that is, along the right edge of the second $\frac{1}{3}$ piece. The straightedge should be parallel to the sides of the Fraction-Stick Chart. *(See the margin.)*

**Step 3:** On the "sixths" stick, the straightedge touches the end of the fourth piece, which is $\frac{4}{6}$. So $\frac{4}{6} = \frac{2}{3}$.

**Step 4:** On the "ninths" stick, the straightedge touches the end of the sixth piece, which is $\frac{6}{9}$. So $\frac{6}{9} = \frac{2}{3}$.

**Step 5:** On the "twelfths" stick, the straightedge touches the end of the eighth piece, which is $\frac{8}{12}$. So $\frac{8}{12} = \frac{2}{3}$.

**Step 6:** On the other sticks, the straightedge cuts through some of the pieces, so $\frac{2}{3}$ cannot be written as an equivalent fraction using the pieces on those sticks.

**3.** Show how the chart can be used to compare fractions.

*Example:* Compare $\frac{4}{9}$ and $\frac{3}{8}$.

**Step 1:** Place one edge of a straightedge at $\frac{4}{9}$ (the right side of the fourth piece on the "ninths" stick). (See below.)

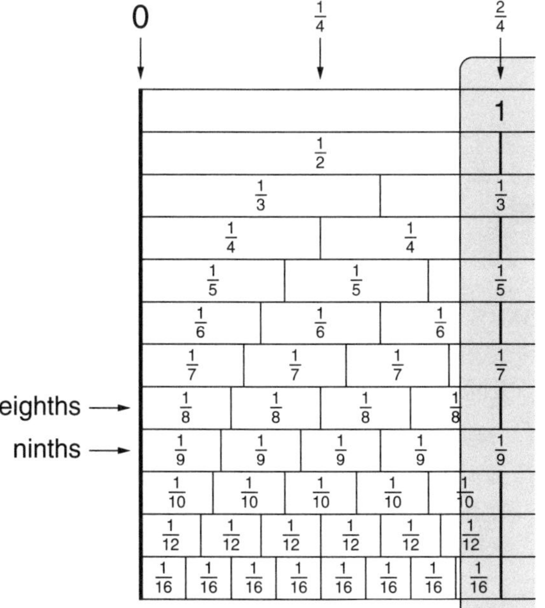


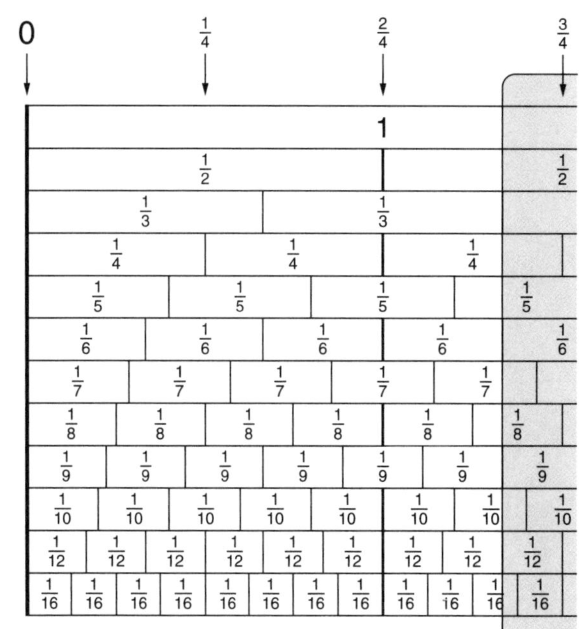


NOTE: Please do not provide students with rules for converting between mixed numbers and "improper" fractions. Introducing conversion rules at this stage might undermine conceptual understanding by reducing the process to a rote procedure. Formal rules for conversions will be covered in a later unit.

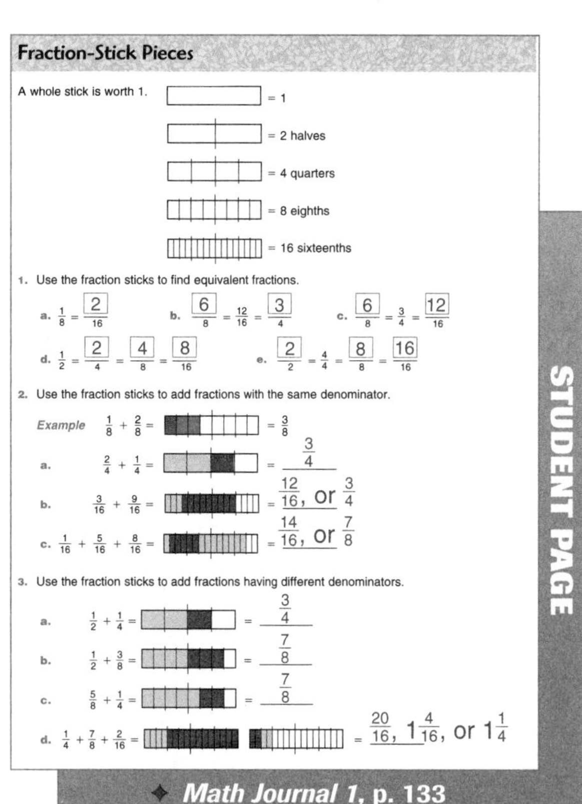
**Fraction-Stick Pieces**

A whole stick is worth 1. = 1

= 2 halves

= 4 quarters

= 8 eighths

= 16 sixteenths

1. Use the fraction sticks to find equivalent fractions.

a. $\frac{1}{8} = \frac{2}{16}$ b. $\frac{6}{8} = \frac{12}{16} = \frac{3}{4}$ c. $\frac{6}{8} = \frac{3}{4} = \frac{12}{16}$

d. $\frac{1}{2} = \frac{2}{4} = \frac{4}{8} = \frac{8}{16}$ e. $\frac{2}{2} = \frac{4}{4} = \frac{8}{8} = \frac{16}{16}$

2. Use the fraction sticks to add fractions with the same denominator.

*Example* $\frac{1}{8} + \frac{2}{8} = \frac{3}{8}$

a. $\frac{2}{4} + \frac{1}{4} = \frac{3}{4}$

b. $\frac{3}{16} + \frac{9}{16} = \frac{12}{16}$, or $\frac{3}{4}$

c. $\frac{1}{16} + \frac{5}{16} + \frac{8}{16} = \frac{14}{16}$, or $\frac{7}{8}$

3. Use the fraction sticks to add fractions having different denominators.

a. $\frac{1}{2} + \frac{1}{4} = \frac{3}{4}$

b. $\frac{1}{2} + \frac{3}{8} = \frac{7}{8}$

c. $\frac{5}{8} + \frac{1}{4} = \frac{7}{8}$

d. $\frac{1}{4} + \frac{7}{8} + \frac{2}{16} = \frac{20}{16}$, $1\frac{4}{16}$, or $1\frac{1}{4}$

STUDENT PAGE

Math Journal 1, p. 133

## Fraction Number Stories

Shade the fraction sticks to help you solve these fraction number stories. Write a number model for each story.

1. Chris made pizza dough with $\frac{5}{8}$ cup of white flour and $\frac{1}{4}$ cup of whole wheat flour.
   a. How much flour did he use in all? $\frac{7}{8}$ cup
   b. Number model: $\frac{5}{8} + \frac{1}{4} = \frac{7}{8}$
2. Sheryl's puppy weighed $1\frac{1}{2}$ pounds when it was born. After two weeks, the puppy had gained $\frac{3}{8}$ pounds.
   a. How much did the puppy weigh after two weeks? $1\frac{7}{8}$ pounds
   b. Number model: $1\frac{1}{2} + \frac{3}{8} = 1\frac{7}{8}$
3. Shade the fraction sticks to solve the number model. Then write a fraction number story that fits the number model.
   a. $\frac{3}{4} + \frac{5}{8} =$ $1\frac{3}{8}$
   b. Number story: Answers vary.
4. Make up your own fraction number story. Draw and shade fraction sticks to solve it. Write a number model for your story.
   a. Number story: Answers vary.
   b. Solution: ______
   c. Number model: ______

STUDENT PAGE

✦ *Math Journal 1*, p. 134

**Adjusting the Activity** For students who are having difficulty understanding how the Fraction-Stick Chart works, consider doing the fraction-strip activity in Part 3 on page 279.

## Math Boxes 5.3

1. Write five fractions that are equivalent to $\frac{3}{4}$. Sample answers:
   $\frac{12}{16}$, $\frac{33}{44}$, $\frac{6}{8}$, $\frac{45}{60}$, $\frac{42}{56}$
2. Round each number to the nearest thousand.
   a. 43,802 — 44,000
   b. 904,873 — 905,000
   c. 1,380,021 — 1,380,000
   d. 5,067 — 5,000
   e. 20,503 — 21,000
3. Multiply or divide. Show your work.
   a. 1,786 = 38 ∗ 47
   b. 142 R5 ← 857 / 6
4. a. Draw a quadrangle with two pairs of parallel sides. Sample answer:
   b. What kind of quadrangle is this? parallelogram
5. Trace the equilateral triangle from your Geometry Template.

STUDENT PAGE

✦ *Math Journal 1*, p. 135

**Step 2:** Locate $\frac{3}{8}$ (the right side of the third piece on the "eighths" stick). Since $\frac{3}{8}$ is to the left of $\frac{4}{9}$, $\frac{3}{8}$ is less than $\frac{4}{9}$.

Students work with their partners to complete journal page 132. Circulate and assist. When most of the students have completed the problems, briefly review the answers.

### ✦ Adding with Fraction-Stick Pieces (*Math Journal 1,* p. 133)

PARTNER ACTIVITY 

The fraction sticks divided into halves, quarters, eighths, and sixteenths will be used to formally introduce the concept of addition of fractions. The five fraction sticks at the top of journal page 133 furnish a length model for fraction work. Note that the denominators are restricted to 1, 2, 4, 8, and 16.

Expect students to have little difficulty with these problems, since they all can be solved "visually." The correct amount of shading for any fraction can be decided by using the appropriate fraction stick at the top of the page.

You may, however, want to work one or two additional problems similar to the example in Problem 2 as a whole-class activity.

### ✦ Solving Fraction Number Stories (*Math Journal 1,* p. 134)

INDEPENDENT ACTIVITY 

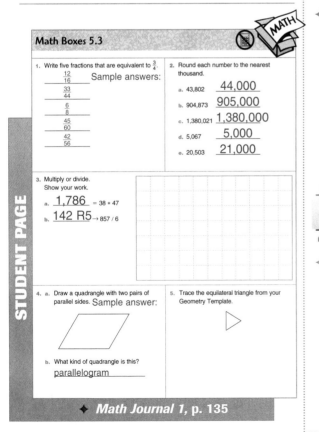

Students solve the fraction number stories on journal page 134. Circulate and assist. When most of the class has finished the page, briefly go over the answers.

## 2 Ongoing Learning & Practice

### ✦ Math Boxes 5.3 (*Math Journal 1*, p. 135)

INDEPENDENT ACTIVITY 

**Mixed Review** Math Boxes in this lesson are paired with Math Boxes in Lesson 5.1. The skill in Problem 1 is a prerequisite for Unit 6.

## Study Link 5.3 (*Math Masters*, p. 267)

**Home Connection** Students use fraction sticks to find equivalent fractions, as well as to add fractions. They also solve fraction number stories using fraction sticks.

**Adjusting the Activity** Problem 9 of the Study Link asks students to write a fraction number story. If your students have difficulty with such an open-ended task, you may want to suggest a specific kind of story. For example, suggest they write stories about something growing or stories about eating a cake.

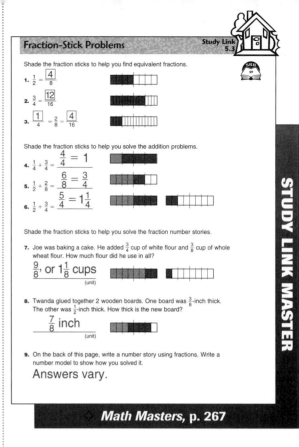

**Fraction-Stick Problems** — Study Link 5.3

Shade the fraction sticks to help you find equivalent fractions.

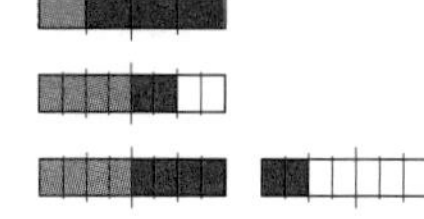

1. $\frac{1}{2} = \frac{4}{8}$
2. $\frac{3}{4} = \frac{12}{16}$
3. $\frac{1}{4} = \frac{2}{8} = \frac{4}{16}$

Shade the fraction sticks to help you solve the addition problems.

4. $\frac{1}{4} + \frac{3}{4} = \frac{4}{4} = 1$
5. $\frac{1}{2} + \frac{2}{8} = \frac{6}{8} = \frac{3}{4}$
6. $\frac{1}{2} + \frac{3}{4} = \frac{5}{4} = 1\frac{1}{4}$

Shade the fraction sticks to help you solve the fraction number stories.

7. Joe was baking a cake. He added $\frac{3}{4}$ cup of white flour and $\frac{3}{8}$ cup of whole wheat flour. How much flour did he use in all?
   $\frac{9}{8}$, or $1\frac{1}{8}$ cups (unit)
8. Twanda glued together 2 wooden boards. One board was $\frac{3}{8}$-inch thick. The other was $\frac{1}{2}$-inch thick. How thick is the new board?
   $\frac{7}{8}$ inch (unit)
9. On the back of this page, write a number story using fractions. Write a number model to show how you solved it.
   Answers vary.

STUDY LINK MASTER

*Math Masters*, p. 267

# 3 Options for Individualizing

## EXTRA PRACTICE Making a Fraction-Strip Poster

WHOLE-CLASS ACTIVITY  15–30 min 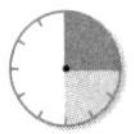

Students cut out 6 strips of colored paper, each 2″ by $8\frac{1}{2}$″, and then fold and label them with fractions to represent halves, thirds, fourths, fifths, sixths, and eighths.

- One strategy for folding into thirds is to fold one end in so that the doubled parts and the single part are the same size.

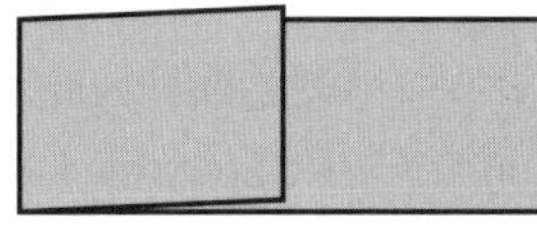

- To fold into sixths, fold a strip into thirds and then in half, or fold a strip in half and then into thirds.
- For fifths, fold the two outside edges of the strip in toward the middle, but do not bring them together. Instead, fold them so that the two doubled parts and the single part of the strip between them look like three equal parts.

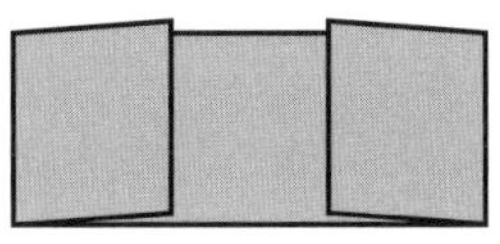

Instead of labeling strips with a fraction in each part, have students label the fractions on the folds. *(See the margin.)*

You may want to keep the strips loose, so that students can pick them up and compare them. If so, have students write their names on the strips and keep them in an envelope. If you want students to make fraction-stick posters, have them glue or tape the strips in order on an $8\frac{1}{2}$″ × 14″ sheet of paper.

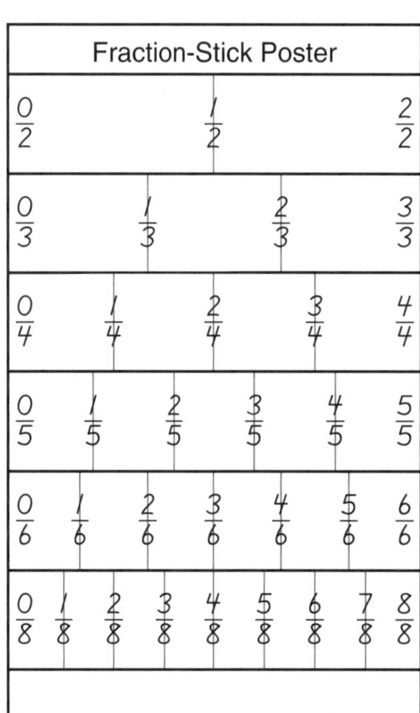

# 5.4 Two Rules for Finding Equivalent Fractions

**OBJECTIVES To use fraction sticks to find equivalent fractions; and to formulate multiplication and division rules for finding equivalent fractions.**

| summaries | materials |
| --- | --- |
| **1 Teaching the Lesson** | |
| Students split fraction sticks to show equivalent fractions. They formulate a multiplication rule and a division rule for finding equivalent fractions. [Numeration] | ☐ *Math Journal 1,* pp. 136 and 137<br>☐ Study Link 5.3<br>☐ ruler |
| **2 Ongoing Learning & Practice** | |
| Students play *Factor Captor* or *Multiplication Bull's-Eye.* [Numeration; Operations and Computation]<br>Students practice and maintain skills through Math Boxes and Study Link activities. | ☐ *Math Journal 1,* p. 138<br>☐ *Student Reference Book,* pp. 271 or 284<br>☐ Study Link Master (*Math Masters,* p. 268)<br>☐ *Factor Captor* Grid (*Math Masters,* p. 5 or 6); optional<br>***See* Advance Preparation** |
| **3 Options for Individualizing** | |
| **Reteaching** Students find equivalent fractions. [Numeration]<br>**Enrichment** Students use fraction sticks to solve "fraction-of" problems. [Numeration; Operations and Computation] | ☐ *Math Journal 1,* p. 136<br>☐ Everything Math Deck, if available |

**Additional Information**

**Advance Preparation** For Part 2, review the rules and materials needed to play *Factor Captor* and *Multiplication Bull's-Eye.*

**Vocabulary • equivalent fractions**

**Vocabulary (teacher) • simplest form (lowest terms)**

## Getting Started

### Mental Math and Reflexes

Write fractions as decimals.
*Suggestions:*

- $\frac{6}{10}$ = ? 0.6
- $\frac{3}{5}$ = ? 0.6
- $\frac{2}{3}$ = ? 0.67, or 0.667
- $\frac{4}{8}$ = ? 0.5
- $\frac{9}{12}$ = ? 0.75
- $\frac{9}{25}$ = ? 0.36

### Math Message

*Lisa has a 50-cent piece. Jamal has two quarters. Sam has five dimes. Hunter has ten nickels. Elliot has 50 pennies. Write a fraction to show what part of a dollar each person has. Who has the most money?*

### Study Link 5.3 Follow-Up

Briefly review the answers with the class. Provide time for students to share their fraction number story.

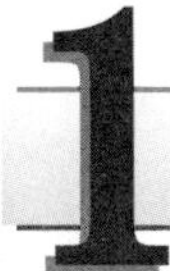

# Teaching the Lesson

## Math Message Follow-Up

WHOLE-CLASS DISCUSSION

Each person has $\frac{1}{2}$ dollar, but there are other fractions that represent their coins: Jamal, $\frac{2}{4}$ dollar; Sam, $\frac{5}{10}$ dollar; Hunter, $\frac{10}{20}$ dollar; and Elliot, $\frac{50}{100}$ dollar. Since all these are \$0.50, they all have the same amount.

Remind students that these fractions—$\frac{1}{2}$, $\frac{2}{4}$, $\frac{5}{10}$, $\frac{10}{20}$, and $\frac{50}{100}$—are equivalent. Ask them to name other fractions equivalent to these, and discuss how they know they are equivalent. Tell them that in today's lesson they will learn rules for finding equivalent fractions.

## Finding Equivalent Fractions

WHOLE-CLASS ACTIVITY

Demonstrate finding **equivalent fractions** by drawing rectangles on the board or overhead. For example, start with a rectangle showing $\frac{2}{3}$.

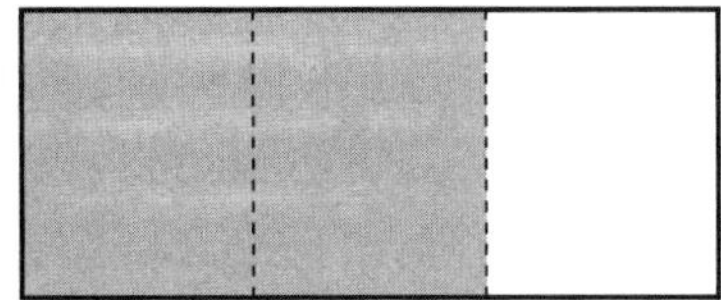

Point out that there are 3 parts in the rectangle, and that 2 are shaded. Write the fraction $\frac{2}{3}$.

Next, draw a horizontal line that divides each part of this rectangle into 2 parts.

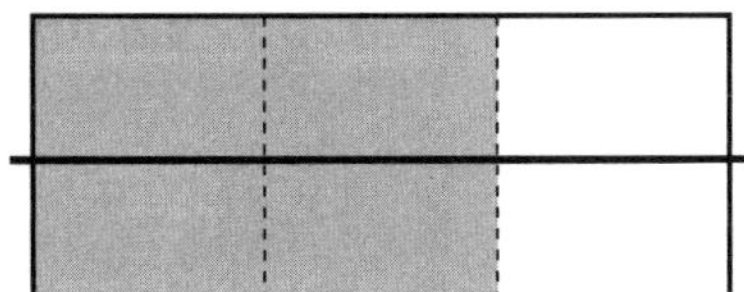

Point out that now there are 6 parts in the rectangle and that 4 are shaded. Write the fraction $\frac{4}{6}$. Since exactly the same amount of the rectangle is shaded, the fractions $\frac{2}{3}$ and $\frac{4}{6}$ are equivalent. Write $\frac{2}{3} = \frac{4}{6}$.

Now draw two more horizontal lines so that the whole rectangle is divided into 12 parts. *(See the margin.)*

There are 12 parts in all, of which 8 are shaded: $\frac{8}{12}$. So $\frac{2}{3}$, $\frac{4}{6}$, and $\frac{8}{12}$ are equivalent. This can be written $\frac{2}{3} = \frac{4}{6} = \frac{8}{12}$.

NOTE: Two or more fractions are called **equivalent fractions** if they represent the same amount. By now, most students should be very familiar with the idea of equivalent names for numbers, including the concept of equivalent fractions. The focus of this lesson is to help students formulate rules for finding equivalent fractions.

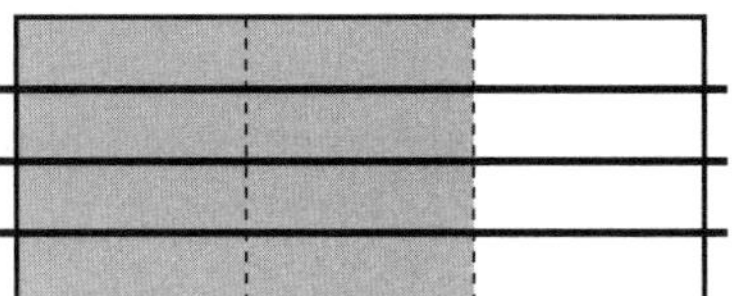

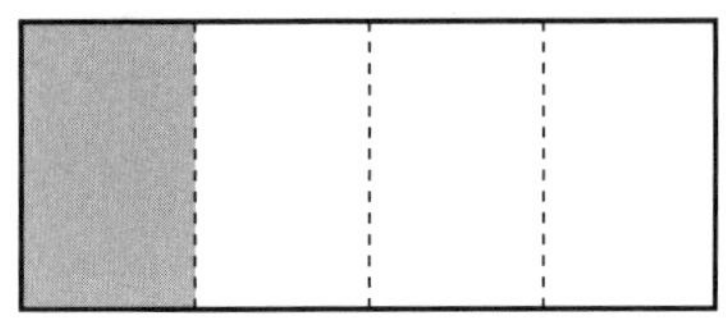

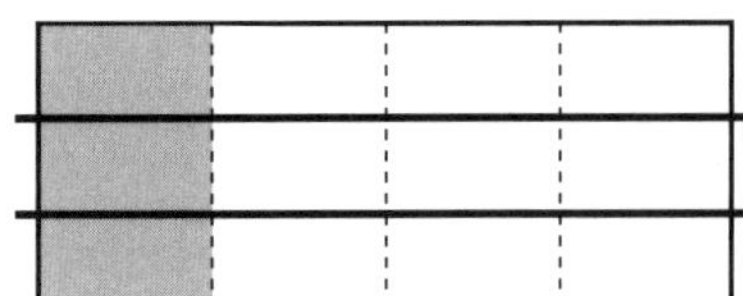

Ask students to draw a rectangle, divide it into fourths with vertical lines, and shade $\frac{1}{4}$. *(See the margin.)*

Then ask them to find a fraction equivalent to $\frac{1}{4}$ by drawing one or more evenly spaced horizontal lines to split each part of the rectangle into more pieces. For example, two evenly spaced horizontal lines split the rectangle into 12 pieces and show that $\frac{1}{4} = \frac{3}{12}$. *(See the margin.)*

Discuss several students' solutions.

**Adjusting the Activity** If students have difficulty visualizing that the shaded area is $\frac{1}{4}$ because of all of the lines, consider having them fold a strip of paper into fourths. They shade one of the fourths. Then they draw the horizontal dividing lines. These will be the only drawn lines on the page.

## ✦ Splitting Fraction Sticks to Make Equivalent Fractions (*Math Journal 1,* p. 136)

PARTNER ACTIVITY 

Briefly discuss the examples at the top of journal page 136. Assign the problems. Circulate, assess, and help as needed.

When students have completed the page, briefly go over the answers.

**Adjusting the Activity** Go beyond the models presented on the journal page. *For example:*

- What would a fraction stick representing $\frac{1}{3}$ show if each part were split into 5 equal parts? $\frac{1}{3} = \frac{5}{15}$
- What would a fraction stick representing $\frac{5}{6}$ show if each part were split into 3 equal parts? $\frac{5}{6} = \frac{15}{18}$

## ✦ Formulating Rules for Generating Equivalent Fractions

WHOLE-CLASS DISCUSSION

Focus on the mathematics just done with fraction sticks. Students should notice that, for a given unit, whenever the total number of equal parts is doubled (or tripled, or quadrupled), the number of shaded parts is also doubled (or tripled, or quadrupled). For example, start with a

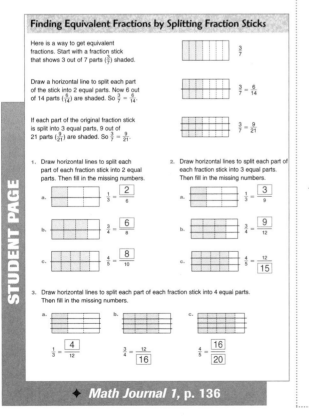

STUDENT PAGE

**Finding Equivalent Fractions by Splitting Fraction Sticks**

Here is a way to get equivalent fractions. Start with a fraction stick that shows 3 out of 7 parts ($\frac{3}{7}$) shaded. $\frac{3}{7}$

Draw a horizontal line to split each part of the stick into 2 equal parts. Now 6 out of 14 parts ($\frac{6}{14}$) are shaded. So $\frac{3}{7} = \frac{6}{14}$. $\frac{3}{7} = \frac{6}{14}$

If each part of the original fraction stick is split into 3 equal parts, 9 out of 21 parts ($\frac{9}{21}$) are shaded. So $\frac{3}{7} = \frac{9}{21}$. $\frac{3}{7} = \frac{9}{21}$

1. Draw horizontal lines to split each part of each fraction stick into 2 equal parts. Then fill in the missing numbers.
   a. $\frac{1}{3} = \frac{2}{6}$
   b. $\frac{3}{4} = \frac{6}{8}$
   c. $\frac{4}{5} = \frac{8}{10}$

2. Draw horizontal lines to split each part of each fraction stick into 3 equal parts. Then fill in the missing numbers.
   a. $\frac{1}{3} = \frac{3}{9}$
   b. $\frac{3}{4} = \frac{9}{12}$
   c. $\frac{4}{5} = \frac{12}{15}$

3. Draw horizontal lines to split each part of each fraction stick into 4 equal parts. Then fill in the missing numbers.
   a. $\frac{1}{3} = \frac{4}{12}$
   b. $\frac{3}{4} = \frac{12}{16}$
   c. $\frac{4}{5} = \frac{16}{20}$

✦ *Math Journal 1,* p. 136

fraction stick representing $\frac{3}{4}$. When each part of the stick is split into two equal parts, the total number of parts is doubled ($4 * 2 = 8$), and the number of shaded parts is also doubled ($3 * 2 = 6$).

Write this as $\frac{3 \text{ shaded} * 2}{4 \text{ total} * 2} = \frac{6 \text{ shaded}}{8 \text{ total}}$, and then just as $\frac{3 * 2}{4 * 2} = \frac{6}{8}$.

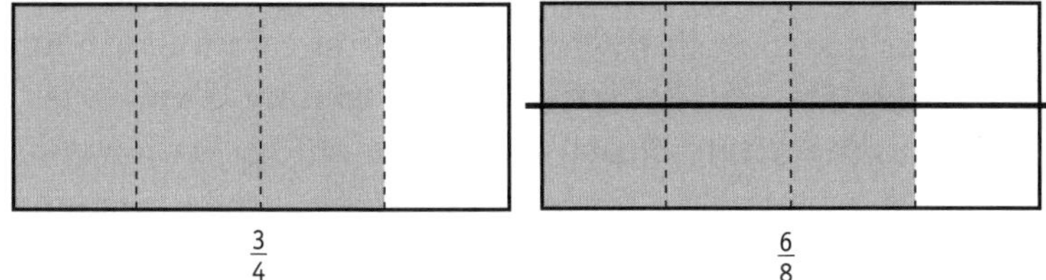


Repeat this strategy for the other fraction-stick models on journal page 136. Record the fractions for the models on the board. *(See the margin.)*

| Models for $\frac{1}{3}$ | Models for $\frac{3}{4}$ | Models for $\frac{4}{5}$ |
|---|---|---|
| $\frac{1 * 2}{3 * 2} = \frac{2}{6}$ | $\frac{3 * 2}{4 * 2} = \frac{6}{8}$ | $\frac{4 * 2}{5 * 2} = \frac{8}{10}$ |
| $\frac{1 * 3}{3 * 3} = \frac{3}{9}$ | $\frac{3 * 3}{4 * 3} = \frac{9}{12}$ | $\frac{4 * 3}{5 * 3} = \frac{12}{15}$ |
| $\frac{1 * 4}{3 * 4} = \frac{4}{12}$ | $\frac{3 * 4}{4 * 4} = \frac{12}{16}$ | $\frac{4 * 4}{5 * 4} = \frac{16}{20}$ |

Help students to formulate the following rule:

**Multiplication Rule**

To find an equivalent fraction, multiply both the numerator and the denominator of the fraction by the same number.

Now reverse the multiplication models to help students formulate the division rule. Since dividing a number by 1 results in the same number, if you divide both the numerator and the denominator of a fraction by the same number, the result is equivalent to the original fraction. (See below.)

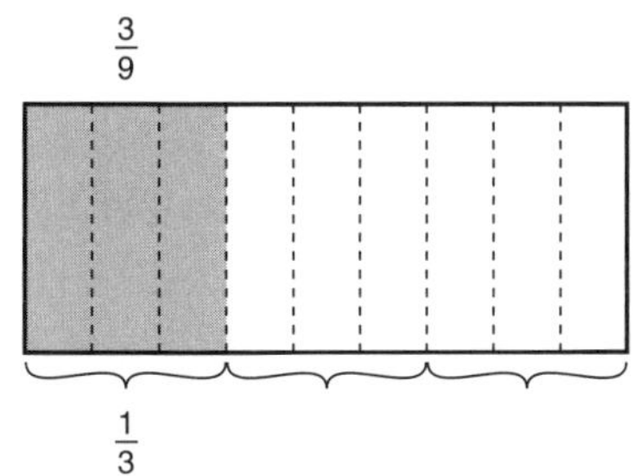


Use models suggested by the journal page.

$\frac{3 \div 3}{9 \div 3} = \frac{1}{3}$ $\quad \frac{12 \div 4}{16 \div 4} = \frac{3}{4}$ $\quad \frac{8 \div 2}{10 \div 2} = \frac{4}{5}$

**Division Rule**

To find an equivalent fraction, divide both the numerator and the denominator of the fraction by the same number.

NOTE: A fraction is said to be in **simplest form** or **lowest terms** if the division rule can't be applied to get an equivalent fraction (with a whole number numerator and denominator). It is traditional to think that fractions in simplest form are preferable, but there is little mathematical justification for this. What is desirable is the ability to shift to whatever form is most convenient for the problem at hand.

NOTE: In general, we recommend using "/" to show division, because that is the usual symbol for division in high school math courses and beyond, and because it reinforces the connection between division and fractions. We suggest that you use "÷" instead of "/" occasionally to remind students that it indicates division.

In working with the division rule for finding equivalent fractions, however, we recommend using "÷" instead of "/" in order to avoid confusion.

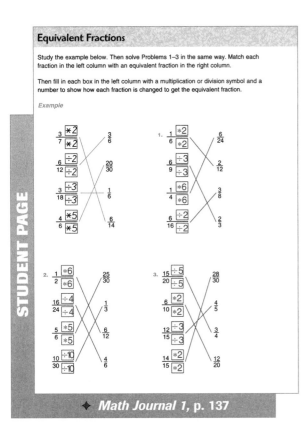

STUDENT PAGE

**Equivalent Fractions**

Study the example below. Then solve Problems 1–3 in the same way. Match each fraction in the left column with an equivalent fraction in the right column.

Then fill in each box in the left column with a multiplication or division symbol and a number to show how each fraction is changed to get the equivalent fraction.

*Example*

| | |
|---|---|
| $\frac{3 \; \boxed{*2}}{7 \; \boxed{*2}}$ | $\frac{3}{6}$ |
| $\frac{6 \; \boxed{\div 2}}{12 \; \boxed{\div 2}}$ | $\frac{20}{30}$ |
| $\frac{3 \; \boxed{\div 3}}{18 \; \boxed{\div 3}}$ | $\frac{1}{6}$ |
| $\frac{4 \; \boxed{*5}}{6 \; \boxed{*5}}$ | $\frac{6}{14}$ |

1.

| | |
|---|---|
| $\frac{1 \; \boxed{*2}}{6 \; \boxed{*2}}$ | $\frac{6}{24}$ |
| $\frac{6 \; \boxed{\div 3}}{9 \; \boxed{\div 3}}$ | $\frac{2}{12}$ |
| $\frac{1 \; \boxed{*6}}{4 \; \boxed{*6}}$ | $\frac{3}{8}$ |
| $\frac{6 \; \boxed{\div 2}}{16 \; \boxed{\div 2}}$ | $\frac{2}{3}$ |

2.

| | |
|---|---|
| $\frac{1 \; \boxed{*6}}{2 \; \boxed{*6}}$ | $\frac{25}{30}$ |
| $\frac{16 \; \boxed{\div 4}}{24 \; \boxed{\div 4}}$ | $\frac{1}{3}$ |
| $\frac{5 \; \boxed{*5}}{6 \; \boxed{*5}}$ | $\frac{6}{12}$ |
| $\frac{10 \; \boxed{\div 10}}{30 \; \boxed{\div 10}}$ | $\frac{4}{6}$ |

3.

| | |
|---|---|
| $\frac{15 \; \boxed{\div 5}}{20 \; \boxed{\div 5}}$ | $\frac{28}{30}$ |
| $\frac{6 \; \boxed{*2}}{10 \; \boxed{*2}}$ | $\frac{4}{5}$ |
| $\frac{12 \; \boxed{\div 3}}{15 \; \boxed{\div 3}}$ | $\frac{3}{4}$ |
| $\frac{14 \; \boxed{*2}}{15 \; \boxed{*2}}$ | $\frac{12}{20}$ |

✦ *Math Journal 1,* p. 137

## ✦ Finding Equivalent Fractions

(*Math Journal 1,* p. 137)

PARTNER ACTIVITY 

Have partners study the example and then solve Problems 1–3 in the same way.

Each problem lists two columns of fractions. Students must match each fraction in the first column with an equivalent fraction in the second column. They must also fill in the empty boxes—using the multiplication rule or the division rule—to show why the matched fractions are equivalent.

**ONGOING ASSESSMENT**

**Have students list at least three equivalent fractions for $\frac{4}{5}$. Then have them explain in writing how they found the equivalent fractions.**

# 2 Ongoing Learning & Practice

## ✦ Playing *Factor Captor* or *Multiplication Bull's-Eye*

(*Student Reference Book,* p. 271 or 284; *Math Masters,* p. 5 or 6)

PARTNER ACTIVITY 

Depending on the needs of your students, have them play either *Factor Captor* or *Multiplication Bull's-Eye.* These games were introduced in Lessons 1.4 or 2.7, respectively. *See the Student Reference Book,* pages 271 and 284 for detailed instructions.

Use this opportunity to help students who are having difficulty while the rest of the students play a game.

## ✦ Math Boxes 5.4 (*Math Journal 1,* p. 138)

INDEPENDENT ACTIVITY 

**Mixed Review** Math Boxes in this lesson are paired with Math Boxes in Lesson 5.2. The skill in Problem 1 is a prerequisite for Unit 6.

## ✦ Study Link 5.4 (*Math Masters,* p. 268)

**Home Connection** Students find equivalent fractions. Some problems make use of fraction sticks.

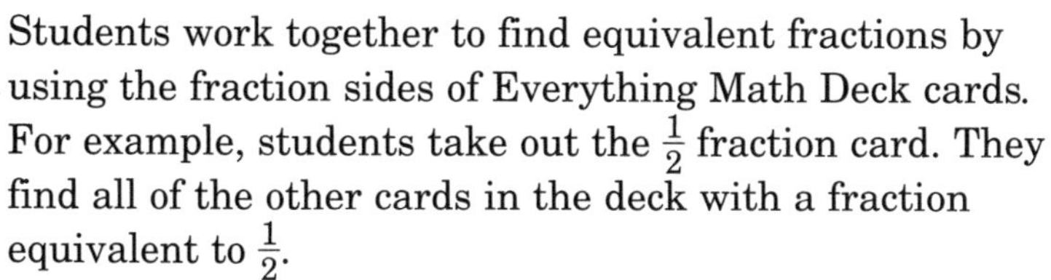


## ✦ RETEACHING Making Equivalent Fractions

PARTNER ACTIVITY **15–30 min**

Students work together to find equivalent fractions by using the fraction sides of Everything Math Deck cards. For example, students take out the $\frac{1}{2}$ fraction card. They find all of the other cards in the deck with a fraction equivalent to $\frac{1}{2}$.

Have students list all of the equivalents they can find for a given fraction, such as $\frac{1}{2}$, $\frac{1}{3}$, $\frac{1}{4}$, $\frac{1}{8}$, $\frac{2}{3}$, or $\frac{3}{4}$. Continue as need dictates and time allows.

## ✦ ENRICHMENT Introducing "Fraction-of" Problems with Fraction Sticks (*Math Journal 1,* p. 136)

INDEPENDENT ACTIVITY  **15–30 min**

This activity builds intuition for fraction multiplication.

Use the fraction-stick problems on journal page 136. Each time students split the fraction stick, they figure out what fraction is in one section of the shaded part of the stick. For example, Problem 1a instructs students to divide the thirds bar in half. Students figure out what $\frac{1}{2}$ of $\frac{1}{3}$ is by looking at the shaded area that is above the horizontal line they drew. $\frac{1}{6}$

Problem 1b instructs students to divide the fourths bar in half. Students figure out what $\frac{1}{2}$ of $\frac{3}{4}$ is by looking at the shaded area that is above the horizontal line they drew. $\frac{3}{8}$

Continue as time allows.

**Math Boxes 5.4** — MATH — STUDENT PAGE

1. Find the landmarks for this set of numbers: 99, 87, 85, 32, 57, 82, 85, 99, 85, 65, 78, 87, 85, 57, 85, 99
   a. Maximum: 99
   b. Minimum: 32
   c. Range: 67
   d. Median: 85

2. Solve mentally.
   a. 299 ∗ 50 = 14,950
   b. 1,999 ∗ 4 = 7,996
   c. 99 ∗ 72 = 7,128
   d. 2,320 = 80 ∗ 29
   e. 2,940 = 49 ∗ 60

3. Write a number story for the number model 743 / 8 = *n*. Then solve it.
   Answers vary.
   Answer: 92 R7

4. Draw two different rectangles on the grid below, each with a perimeter of 16 units.
   Sample answers:

✦ *Math Journal 1,* p. 138

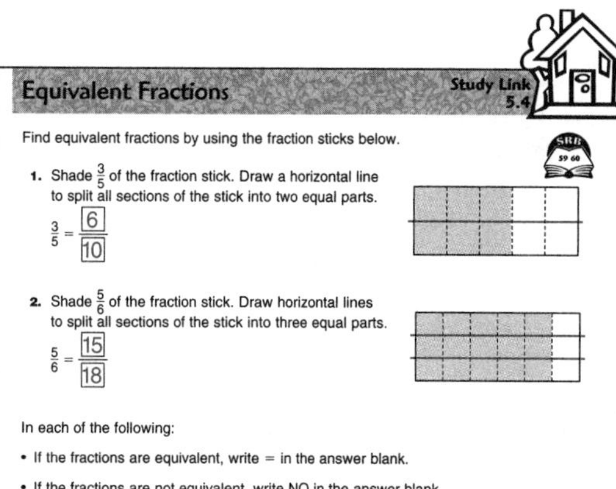
**Equivalent Fractions** — Study Link 5.4

Find equivalent fractions by using the fraction sticks below.

1. Shade $\frac{3}{5}$ of the fraction stick. Draw a horizontal line to split all sections of the stick into two equal parts.
   $\frac{3}{5} = \frac{6}{10}$

2. Shade $\frac{5}{6}$ of the fraction stick. Draw horizontal lines to split all sections of the stick into three equal parts.
   $\frac{5}{6} = \frac{15}{18}$

In each of the following:

- If the fractions are equivalent, write = in the answer blank.
- If the fractions are not equivalent, write NO in the answer blank.

3. $\frac{3}{4}$ = $\frac{9}{12}$
4. $\frac{3}{10}$ NO $\frac{1}{5}$
5. $\frac{7}{14}$ NO $\frac{8}{15}$
6. $\frac{36}{72}$ = $\frac{1}{2}$
7. $\frac{7}{12}$ = $\frac{21}{36}$
8. $\frac{16}{100}$ = $\frac{8}{50}$
9. $\frac{10}{12}$ = $\frac{5}{6}$
10. $\frac{9}{16}$ NO $\frac{45}{48}$
11. $\frac{8}{3}$ = $\frac{16}{6}$
12. $\frac{9}{36}$ NO $\frac{18}{108}$

Fill in the box to complete the equivalent fraction.

13. $\frac{3}{5} = \frac{6}{10}$
14. $\frac{44}{55} = \frac{4}{5}$
15. $\frac{35}{60} = \frac{7}{12}$
16. $\frac{2}{3} = \frac{14}{21}$
17. $\frac{12}{40} = \frac{3}{10}$
18. $\frac{2}{15} = \frac{6}{45}$

STUDY LINK MASTER

✦ *Math Masters,* p. 268

# 5.5 Fractions and Decimals: Part 1

**OBJECTIVES** **To rename simple fractions as decimals; to review rounding decimals; and to find decimals between pairs of numbers.**

| summaries | materials |
|---|---|
| **1 Teaching the Lesson** | |
| Students change fractions to equivalent fractions having denominators of 10 or 100, and then rename these fractions as decimals. [Numeration; Operations and Computation]<br>Students practice rounding decimal numbers up, down, or to the nearest specified place. [Numeration]<br>Students play *Estimation Squeeze* to practice finding decimals between two decimals. [Numeration] | □ *Math Journal 1,* pp. 139–141<br>□ *Student Reference Book,* p. 268<br>□ Study Link 5.4<br>□ Transparencies (*Math Masters,* pp. 54 and 55; optional)<br>□ calculator; base-10 blocks; slate<br>***See* Advance Preparation** |
| **2 Ongoing Learning & Practice** | |
| Students practice and maintain skills through Math Boxes and Study Link activities. | □ *Math Journal 1,* p. 142<br>□ Study Link Master (*Math Masters,* p. 269) |
| **3 Options for Individualizing** | |
| **Extra Practice** Students round whole numbers and decimals by completing number lines. [Numeration; Patterns, Functions, and Algebra]<br>**Reteaching** Students review rounding decimals and solve such problems in their *Student Reference Book.* [Numeration] | □ *Student Reference Book,* pp. 45 and 46<br>□ Teaching Master (*Math Masters,* p. 56) |

## Additional Information

**Advance Preparation** For Part 1, review the rules and materials needed to play *Estimation Squeeze.* Play a few games yourself to become familiar with the procedures.

**Vocabulary** • **round down** • **round up** • **round to the nearest ...**

# Getting Started

## Mental Math and Reflexes

Write each number as a fraction or mixed number, and then as a decimal.

- seven-tenths $\frac{7}{10}$; 0.7
- six-hundredths $\frac{6}{100}$; 0.06
- three and nine-tenths $3\frac{9}{10}$; 3.9
- three point nine $3\frac{9}{10}$; 3.9
- six and nine-hundredths $6\frac{9}{100}$; 6.09
- seven hundred eight thousandths $\frac{708}{1,000}$; 0.708
- forty-five hundredths $\frac{45}{100}$; 0.45
- nineteen-thousandths $\frac{19}{1,000}$; 0.019
- six and nineteen-thousandths $6\frac{19}{1,000}$; 6.019

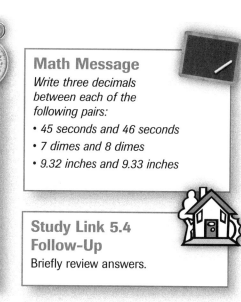

## Math Message

*Write three decimals between each of the following pairs:*

- *45 seconds and 46 seconds*
- *7 dimes and 8 dimes*
- *9.32 inches and 9.33 inches*

## Study Link 5.4 Follow-Up

Briefly review answers.

# 1 Teaching the Lesson

### ✦Math Message Follow-Up (*Math Masters,* p. 54)

WHOLE-CLASS DISCUSSION

Encourage students to share their answers. Expressing 7 dimes and 8 dimes in money notation, \$0.70 and \$0.80, makes writing decimals between the two amounts easier. Remind students that as the number of decimal places increases, the number of equal parts into which the whole has been divided also increases.

NOTE: Decimal numbers between 0 and 1 are usually written with a leading zero (0) in the ones place: .7 and .06 are acceptable, but 0.7 and 0.06 are preferred. The 0 emphasizes the decimal point and helps prevent confusion (for example, .7 could be mistaken for 7).

**Adjusting the Activity** If students need practice finding decimals between numbers, you may use an overhead transparency of *Math Masters,* page 54. Students mark the decimals they listed at their approximate places on the number lines.

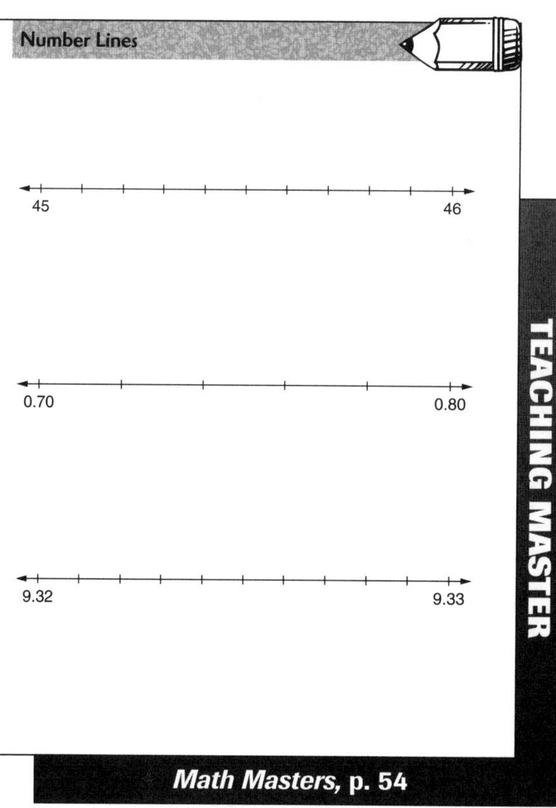


***Math Masters,* p. 54**

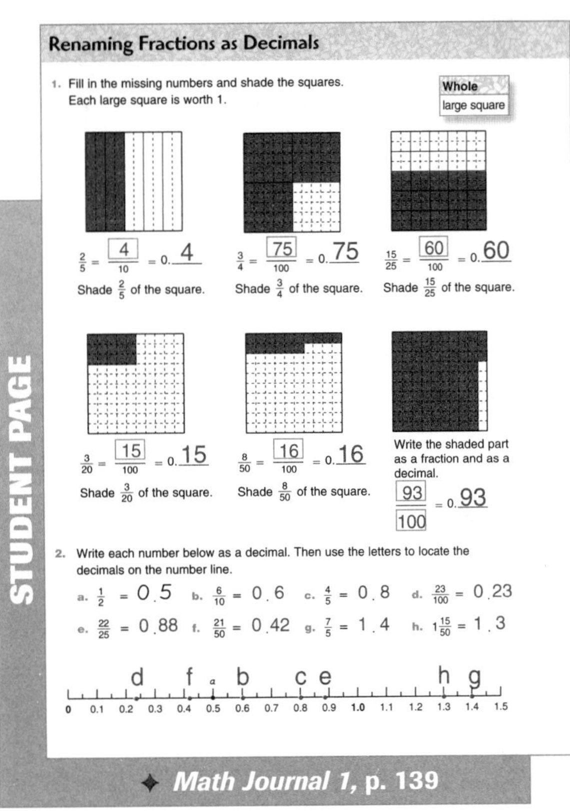
STUDENT PAGE

**Renaming Fractions as Decimals**

1. Fill in the missing numbers and shade the squares. Each large square is worth 1.

| Whole |
|---|
| large square |

$\frac{2}{5} = \frac{4}{10} = 0.4$ Shade $\frac{2}{5}$ of the square.

$\frac{3}{4} = \frac{75}{100} = 0.75$ Shade $\frac{3}{4}$ of the square.

$\frac{15}{25} = \frac{60}{100} = 0.60$ Shade $\frac{15}{25}$ of the square.

$\frac{3}{20} = \frac{15}{100} = 0.15$ Shade $\frac{3}{20}$ of the square.

$\frac{8}{50} = \frac{16}{100} = 0.16$ Shade $\frac{8}{50}$ of the square.

Write the shaded part as a fraction and as a decimal. $\frac{93}{100} = 0.93$

2. Write each number below as a decimal. Then use the letters to locate the decimals on the number line.

a. $\frac{1}{2} = 0.5$ b. $\frac{6}{10} = 0.6$ c. $\frac{4}{5} = 0.8$ d. $\frac{23}{100} = 0.23$

e. $\frac{22}{25} = 0.88$ f. $\frac{21}{50} = 0.42$ g. $\frac{7}{5} = 1.4$ h. $1\frac{15}{50} = 1.3$



✦ *Math Journal 1,* p. 139

## ✦Writing Fractions and Decimals

WHOLE-CLASS ACTIVITY

Extend the Mental Math and Reflexes activity with problems like the following. Allow time for students to share their strategies.

*Example*

Write each number as a fraction or a mixed number and then as a decimal.

▷ three-fourths $\frac{3}{4}$; 0.75

▷ four-fifths $\frac{4}{5}$; 0.8

▷ six-fiftieths $\frac{6}{50}$; 0.12

▷ five and one-half $5\frac{1}{2}$; 5.5

▷ two and nine twenty-fifths $2\frac{9}{25}$; 2.36

▷ seven and six-twentieths $7\frac{6}{20}$; 7.3

Students should have no difficulty in writing the fraction (or mixed number) form. Since the numbers are not expressed in tenths or hundredths, the decimal forms may not be easy to write.

If necessary, remind students to:

▷ Use the multiplication rule and the division rule for finding equivalent fractions.

▷ Change each fraction to an equivalent fraction having a denominator of 10 or 100, and then write the result as a decimal.

*Examples*

$\frac{3 * 25}{4 * 25} = \frac{75}{100} = 0.75$

$7\frac{6}{20} = 7\frac{6 * 5}{20 * 5} = 7\frac{30}{100} = 7.3$

Encourage mental calculation.

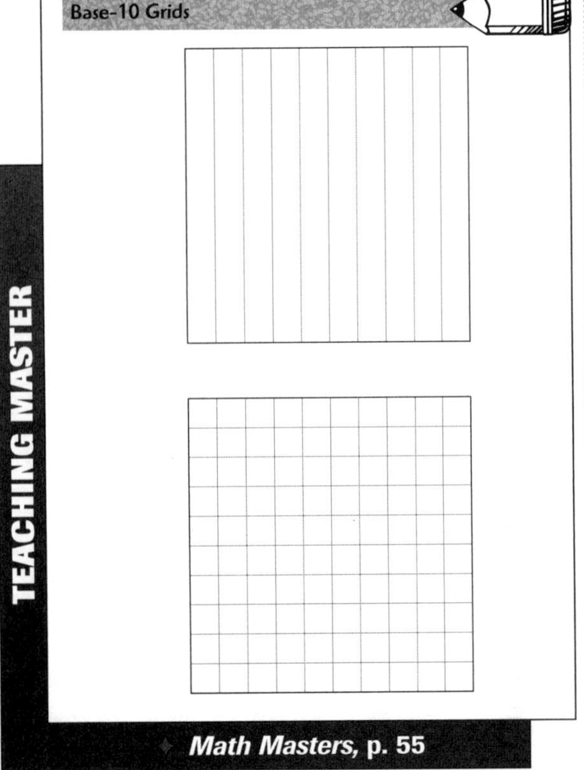


✦ *Math Masters,* p. 55

## ✦Renaming Fractions as Decimals

(*Math Journal 1,* p. 139; *Math Masters,* p. 55)

PARTNER ACTIVITY

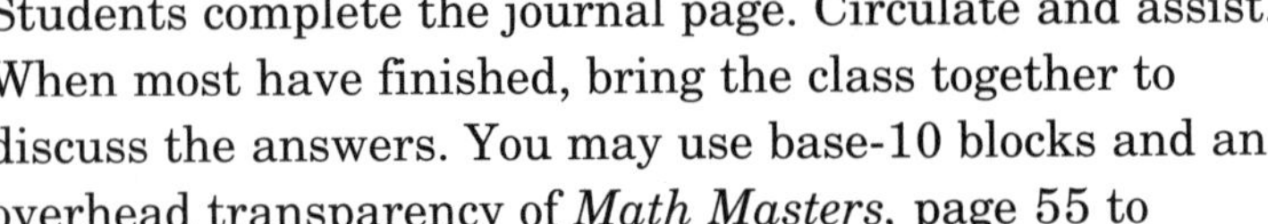

Students complete the journal page. Circulate and assist. When most have finished, bring the class together to discuss the answers. You may use base-10 blocks and an overhead transparency of *Math Masters,* page 55 to demonstrate.

Each fraction on the page can be changed to an equivalent fraction having a denominator of 10 or 100 by applying the multiplication rule for equivalent fractions.

Before locating the decimals in Problem 2 on the number line, ask students to name the decimals for the smallest marks on the number line. For example, *The mark between 0.2 and 0.3 represents 0.25.*

## Rounding Decimals in One of Three Ways
*(Math Journal 1,* pp. 140 and 141)

PARTNER ACTIVITY

Sometimes data are given with more decimal places than are needed. In some situations, too many decimal places imply that measurements are more precise than they actually are.

Such decimals are often rounded to a particular place in one of three ways: always **down,** always **up,** or to the **nearest** selected place.

## Playing *Estimation Squeeze*
*(Student Reference Book,* p. 268)

PARTNER ACTIVITY

This game provides practice in finding decimals between two decimals.

Explain the directions on page 268 of the *Student Reference Book*. Play a game against the class to be sure that students understand the directions.

NOTE: In *Estimation Squeeze,* players estimate the square root of a target number and then square the estimate to see how close they came. Some calculators, like the TI-15, do not have a squaring key $x^2$. The Op1 key may be converted to a squaring key as follows:

1. Press the On/Off and Clear keys simultaneously, and then press Clear. This clears the calculator memory.
2. Press Op1 ^ 2 Op1.

The Op1 key will now function as a squaring key.

**Adjusting the Activity** To extend the game, allow students to choose any number they like that is not a perfect square. Partners must agree on the range before beginning the game. For example, partners may agree that the number will be between 500 and 5,000.

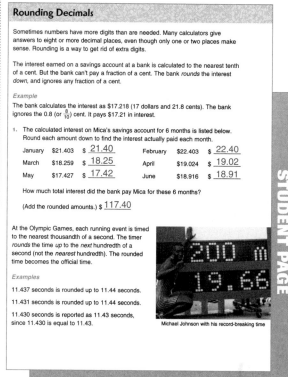

### Rounding Decimals

Sometimes numbers have more digits than are needed. Many calculators give answers to eight or more decimal places, even though only one or two places make sense. Rounding is a way to get rid of extra digits.

The interest earned on a savings account at a bank is calculated to the nearest tenth of a cent. But the bank can't pay a fraction of a cent. The bank *rounds* the interest *down,* and ignores any fraction of a cent.

*Example*

The bank calculates the interest as $17.218 (17 dollars and 21.8 cents). The bank ignores the 0.8 (or $\frac{8}{10}$) cent. It pays $17.21 in interest.

1. The calculated interest on Mica's savings account for 6 months is listed below. Round each amount down to find the interest actually paid each month.

| | | | | | |
|---|---|---|---|---|---|
| January | $21.403 | $ 21.40 | February | $22.403 | $ 22.40 |
| March | $18.259 | $ 18.25 | April | $19.024 | $ 19.02 |
| May | $17.427 | $ 17.42 | June | $18.916 | $ 18.91 |

How much total interest did the bank pay Mica for these 6 months?

(Add the rounded amounts.) $ 117.40

At the Olympic Games, each running event is timed to the nearest thousandth of a second. The timer *rounds* the time *up* to the *next* hundredth of a second (not the *nearest* hundredth). The rounded time becomes the official time.

*Examples*

11.437 seconds is rounded up to 11.44 seconds.

11.431 seconds is rounded up to 11.44 seconds.

11.430 seconds is reported as 11.43 seconds, since 11.430 is equal to 11.43.

Michael Johnson with his record-breaking time

STUDENT PAGE

Math Journal 1, p. 140

### Rounding Decimals (cont.)

2. Find the official times for these runs. s: second(s) min: minute(s)

| Electric Timer | Official Time | Electric Timer | Official Time |
|---|---|---|---|
| 10.752 s | 10.76 s | 20.001 s | 20.01 s |
| 11.191 s | 11.20 s | 43.505 s | 43.51 s |
| 10.815 s | 10.82 s | 49.993 s | 50.00 s |
| 21.970 s | 21.97 s | 1 min 55.738 s | 1 min 55.74 s |
| 20.092 s | 20.10 s | 1 min 59.991 s | 2 min 0.0 s |

3. Describe a situation involving money when the result of a computation might always be rounded up.
Sample answer: When someone owes a bank interest, the result might always be rounded up.

Supermarkets often show unit prices for items. This helps customers comparison shop. A unit price is found by dividing the price of an item (in cents, or dollars and cents) by the quantity of the item (often in pounds). When the quotient has more decimal places than are needed, it is *rounded to the nearest* tenth of a cent.

*Examples*

23.822 cents (per ounce) is rounded down to 23.8 cents.

24.769 cents is rounded up to 24.8 cents.

18.65 cents is halfway between 18.6 cents and 18.7 cents. It is rounded up to 18.7 cents.

4. Round these unit prices to the nearest tenth of a cent (per ounce).

| | | |
|---|---|---|
| a. 28.374¢ 28.4 ¢ | b. 19.796¢ 19.8 ¢ | c. 29.327¢ 29.3 ¢ |
| d. 16.916¢ 16.9 ¢ | e. 20.641¢ 20.6 ¢ | f. 25.583¢ 25.6 ¢ |
| g. 18.469¢ 18.5 ¢ | h. 24.944¢ 24.9 ¢ | i. 17.281¢ 17.3 ¢ |
| j. 23.836¢ 23.8 ¢ | k. 21.866¢ 21.9 ¢ | l. 22.814¢ 22.8 ¢ |

STUDENT PAGE

Math Journal 1, p. 141

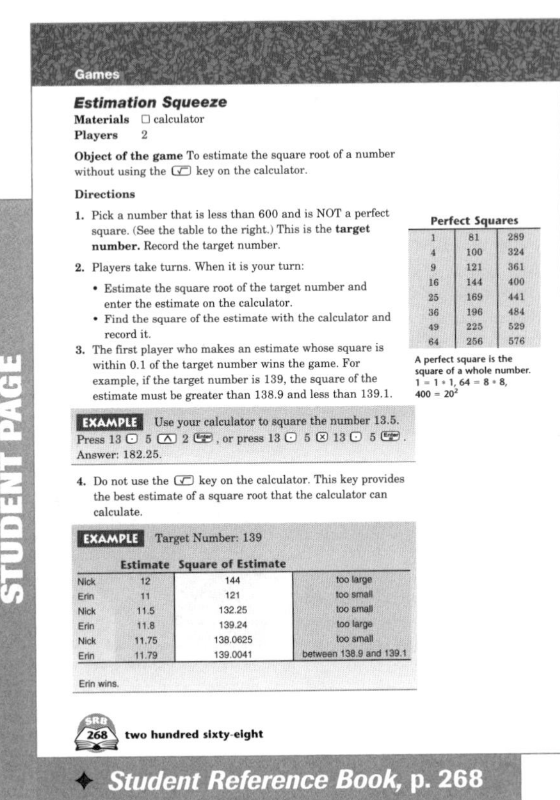

STUDENT PAGE

Games

**Estimation Squeeze**

**Materials** □ calculator

**Players** 2

**Object of the game** To estimate the square root of a number without using the [√] key on the calculator.

**Directions**

1. Pick a number that is less than 600 and is NOT a perfect square. (See the table to the right.) This is the **target number.** Record the target number.
2. Players take turns. When it is your turn:
   - Estimate the square root of the target number and enter the estimate on the calculator.
   - Find the square of the estimate with the calculator and record it.
3. The first player who makes an estimate whose square is within 0.1 of the target number wins the game. For example, if the target number is 139, the square of the estimate must be greater than 138.9 and less than 139.1.

**Perfect Squares**

| | | |
|---|---|---|
| 1 | 81 | 289 |
| 4 | 100 | 324 |
| 9 | 121 | 361 |
| 16 | 144 | 400 |
| 25 | 169 | 441 |
| 36 | 196 | 484 |
| 49 | 225 | 529 |
| 64 | 256 | 576 |

A perfect square is the square of a whole number. 1 = 1 * 1, 64 = 8 * 8, 400 = $20^2$

**EXAMPLE** Use your calculator to square the number 13.5. Press 13 [.] 5 [^] 2 [Enter], or press 13 [.] 5 [×] 13 [.] 5 [Enter]. Answer: 182.25.

4. Do not use the [√] key on the calculator. This key provides the best estimate of a square root that the calculator can calculate.

**EXAMPLE** Target Number: 139

| | Estimate | Square of Estimate | |
|---|---|---|---|
| Nick | 12 | 144 | too large |
| Erin | 11 | 121 | too small |
| Nick | 11.5 | 132.25 | too small |
| Erin | 11.8 | 139.24 | too large |
| Nick | 11.75 | 138.0625 | too small |
| Erin | 11.79 | 139.0041 | between 138.9 and 139.1 |

Erin wins.

SRB 268 two hundred sixty-eight

✦ *Student Reference Book,* p. 268

# 2 Ongoing Learning & Practice

## ✦ Math Boxes 5.5 (*Math Journal 1,* p. 142)

INDEPENDENT ACTIVITY

**Mixed Review** Math Boxes in this lesson are paired with Math Boxes in Lesson 5.7. The skill in Problem 1 is a prerequisite for Unit 6.

## ✦ Study Link 5.5 (*Math Masters,* p. 269)

**Home Connection** Students mark the location of decimal numbers on a number line. Then they round the areas of the 10 smallest countries to the nearest tenth of a square kilometer.

**Social Studies Link** Have students locate the 10 smallest countries on a map of the world.

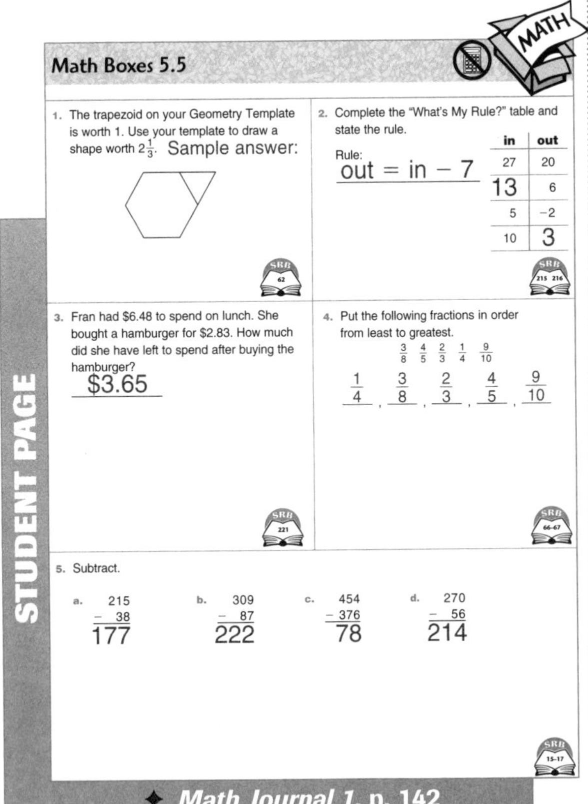

STUDENT PAGE

**Math Boxes 5.5**

1. The trapezoid on your Geometry Template is worth 1. Use your template to draw a shape worth $2\frac{1}{3}$. Sample answer:

2. Complete the "What's My Rule?" table and state the rule.

Rule: out = in − 7

| in | out |
|---|---|
| 27 | 20 |
| 13 | 6 |
| 5 | −2 |
| 10 | 3 |

3. Fran had $6.48 to spend on lunch. She bought a hamburger for $2.83. How much did she have left to spend after buying the hamburger? $3.65

4. Put the following fractions in order from least to greatest. $\frac{3}{8}$ $\frac{4}{5}$ $\frac{2}{3}$ $\frac{1}{4}$ $\frac{9}{10}$

$\frac{1}{4}$, $\frac{3}{8}$, $\frac{2}{3}$, $\frac{4}{5}$, $\frac{9}{10}$

5. Subtract.

a. 215 − 38 = 177 b. 309 − 87 = 222 c. 454 − 376 = 78 d. 270 − 56 = 214

✦ *Math Journal 1,* p. 142

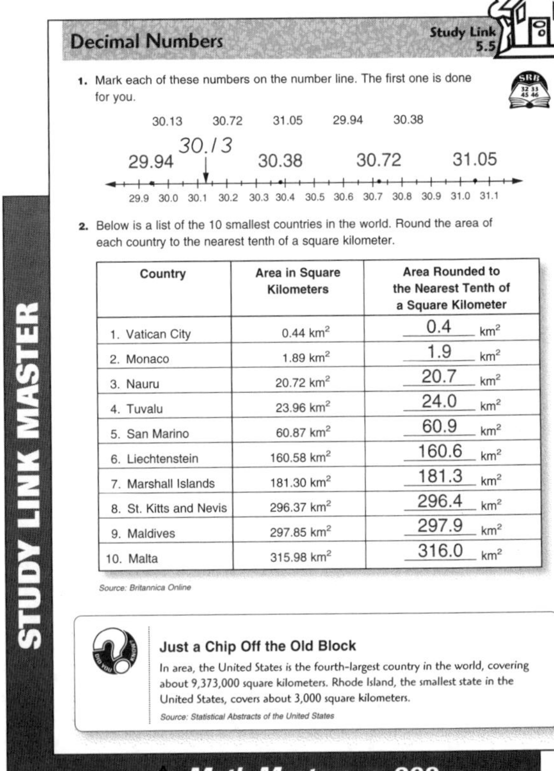

STUDY LINK MASTER

**Decimal Numbers** Study Link 5.5

1. Mark each of these numbers on the number line. The first one is done for you.

30.13 30.72 31.05 29.94 30.38



2. Below is a list of the 10 smallest countries in the world. Round the area of each country to the nearest tenth of a square kilometer.

| Country | Area in Square Kilometers | Area Rounded to the Nearest Tenth of a Square Kilometer |
|---|---|---|
| 1. Vatican City | 0.44 km² | 0.4 km² |
| 2. Monaco | 1.89 km² | 1.9 km² |
| 3. Nauru | 20.72 km² | 20.7 km² |
| 4. Tuvalu | 23.96 km² | 24.0 km² |
| 5. San Marino | 60.87 km² | 60.9 km² |
| 6. Liechtenstein | 160.58 km² | 160.6 km² |
| 7. Marshall Islands | 181.30 km² | 181.3 km² |
| 8. St. Kitts and Nevis | 296.37 km² | 296.4 km² |
| 9. Maldives | 297.85 km² | 297.9 km² |
| 10. Malta | 315.98 km² | 316.0 km² |

Source: *Britannica Online*

**Just a Chip Off the Old Block**

In area, the United States is the fourth-largest country in the world, covering about 9,373,000 square kilometers. Rhode Island, the smallest state in the United States, covers about 3,000 square kilometers.

Source: *Statistical Abstracts of the United States*

✦ *Math Masters,* p. 269

# 3 Options for Individualizing

## ◆ EXTRA PRACTICE Rounding Numbers (*Math Masters,* p. 56)

INDEPENDENT ACTIVITY  **15–30 min**

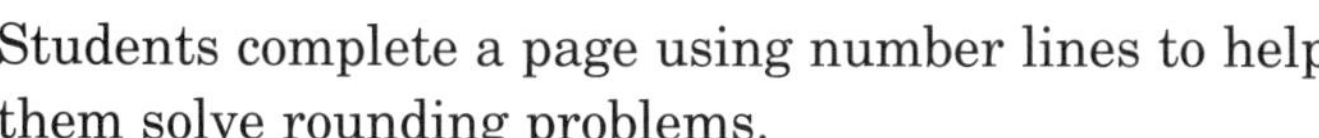

Students complete a page using number lines to help them solve rounding problems.

When most students have finished, briefly review answers and strategies.

NOTE: The T1-15 calculator can round numbers to any place from thousandths to thousands. See *Student Reference Book,* page 243.

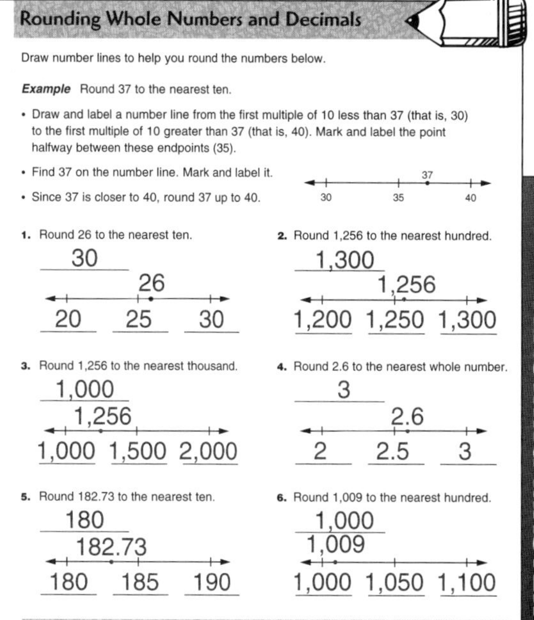

**Rounding Whole Numbers and Decimals**

Draw number lines to help you round the numbers below.

*Example* Round 37 to the nearest ten.

- Draw and label a number line from the first multiple of 10 less than 37 (that is, 30) to the first multiple of 10 greater than 37 (that is, 40). Mark and label the point halfway between these endpoints (35).
- Find 37 on the number line. Mark and label it.
- Since 37 is closer to 40, round 37 up to 40.



1. Round 26 to the nearest ten. 30 (number line: 20, 25, 30; 26)
2. Round 1,256 to the nearest hundred. 1,300 (number line: 1,200, 1,250, 1,300; 1,256)
3. Round 1,256 to the nearest thousand. 1,000 (number line: 1,000, 1,500, 2,000; 1,256)
4. Round 2.6 to the nearest whole number. 3 (number line: 2, 2.5, 3; 2.6)
5. Round 182.73 to the nearest ten. 180 (number line: 180, 185, 190; 182.73)
6. Round 1,009 to the nearest hundred. 1,000 (number line: 1,000, 1,050, 1,100; 1,009)

**Challenge**

7. Round 0.562 to the nearest hundredth. 0.56 (number line: 0.56, 0.565, 0.57; 0.562)

TEACHING MASTER

◆ *Math Masters,* p. 56

## ◆ RETEACHING Reviewing Rounding Decimals (*Student Reference Book,* pp. 45 and 46)

INDEPENDENT ACTIVITY  **15–30 min**

Ask students who are having difficulty with rounding decimals to read pages 45 and 46 in their *Student Reference Book* and solve the Check Your Understanding problems at the bottom of page 46.

Decimals and Percents

**Rounding Decimals**

Sometimes numbers have more digits than we need to use. This is especially true of decimals. When a calculator is used for a calculation, the display may show eight or more decimal places, even when only one or two places are needed to make sense.

Rounding is a way to get rid of unnecessary digits. There are three basic ways to round numbers: a number may be rounded down, rounded up, or rounded to a nearest place. (The examples here involve rounding to hundredths, but rounding to tenths, thousandths, or any other place is done in a similar way.)

**Rounding Down**

To round down to a given place, just drop all the digits to the right of the desired place.

When a bank computes the interest on a savings account, the interest is calculated to the nearest tenth of a cent. But the bank cannot pay a fraction of one cent. So the interest is **rounded down,** and any fraction of one cent is ignored.

**EXAMPLE** The bank calculates the interest earned as \$17.218. Round down to the next cent.

First, find the place you are rounding to: \$17.2**1**8.
Then, drop all the digits to the right of that place: \$17.21.

The bank pays \$17.21 in interest.

**Rounding Up**

To round up, look at all the digits to the right of the desired place. If any digit to the right of the desired place is not 0, then add 1 to the digit in the place you are rounding to. (You will have to do some trading if there is a 9 in that place.) If all the digits to the right of the desired place are 0, then leave the digit unchanged. Finally, drop all the digits to the right of the desired place.

Running events at the Olympic Games are timed with automatic electric timers. The electric timer records a time to the nearest thousandth of a second and automatically **rounds up** to the *next* hundredth of a second. The rounded time becomes the official time.

forty-five 

STUDENT PAGE

◆ *Student Reference Book,* p.45

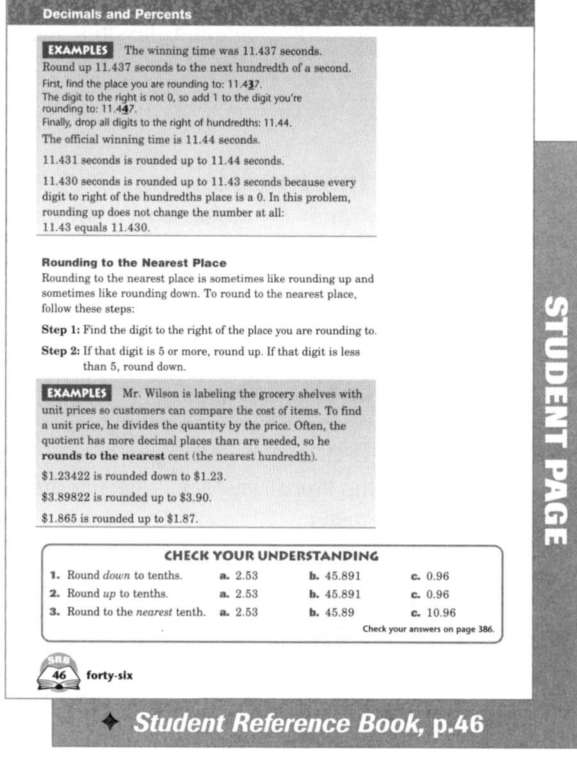

Decimals and Percents

**EXAMPLES** The winning time was 11.437 seconds. Round up 11.437 seconds to the next hundredth of a second.

First, find the place you are rounding to: 11.4**3**7.
The digit to the right is not 0, so add 1 to the digit you're rounding to: 11.4**4**7.
Finally, drop all digits to the right of hundredths: 11.44.
The official winning time is 11.44 seconds.

11.431 seconds is rounded up to 11.44 seconds.

11.430 seconds is rounded up to 11.43 seconds because every digit to right of the hundredths place is a 0. In this problem, rounding up does not change the number at all: 11.43 equals 11.430.

**Rounding to the Nearest Place**

Rounding to the nearest place is sometimes like rounding up and sometimes like rounding down. To round to the nearest place, follow these steps:

**Step 1:** Find the digit to the right of the place you are rounding to.

**Step 2:** If that digit is 5 or more, round up. If that digit is less than 5, round down.

**EXAMPLES** Mr. Wilson is labeling the grocery shelves with unit prices so customers can compare the cost of items. To find a unit price, he divides the quantity by the price. Often, the quotient has more decimal places than are needed, so he **rounds to the nearest** cent (the nearest hundredth).

\$1.23422 is rounded down to \$1.23.

\$3.89822 is rounded up to \$3.90.

\$1.865 is rounded up to \$1.87.

**CHECK YOUR UNDERSTANDING**

| | | | |
|---|---|---|---|
| 1. Round *down* to tenths. | a. 2.53 | b. 45.891 | c. 0.96 |
| 2. Round *up* to tenths. | a. 2.53 | b. 45.891 | c. 0.96 |
| 3. Round to the *nearest* tenth. | a. 2.53 | b. 45.89 | c. 10.96 |

Check your answers on page 386.

SRB 46 forty-six

STUDENT PAGE

◆ *Student Reference Book,* p.46

# 5.6 Fractions and Decimals: Part 2

**OBJECTIVES** **To use a Fraction-Stick Chart; to rename "easy" fractions as decimals; and to begin a table of decimal equivalents for fractions.**

| summaries | materials |
|---|---|
| **1 Teaching the Lesson** | |
| Students use a Fraction-Stick Chart to approximate decimal equivalents for fractions. They begin filling in a table of decimal equivalents. [Numeration] | ☐ *Math Journal 1,* pp. 143 and the inside back cover<br>☐ Study Link 5.5<br>☐ Transparencies (*Math Masters,* pp. 57 and 58; optional)<br>☐ Assessment Master (*Math Masters,* p. 479; optional)<br>☐ slate; Probability Meter; straightedge |
| **2 Ongoing Learning & Practice** | |
| Students practice measurement skills. [Measurement and Reference Frames]<br>Students practice and maintain skills through Math Boxes and Study Link activities. | ☐ *Math Journal 1,* pp. 144–146<br>☐ Study Link Master (*Math Masters,* p. 270) |
| **3 Options for Individualizing** | |
| **Extra Practice** Students write equivalent fractions and decimals for a shaded portion of a 100-grid. [Numeration] | ☐ Teaching Masters (*Math Masters,* pp. 59 and 60)<br>☐ Transparency (*Math Masters,* p. 60; optional)<br>***See* Advance Preparation** |

## Additional Information

**Advance Preparation** For the optional activity in Part 3, you can make an overhead transparency of *Math Masters,* page 60 for each group of six students. Cut apart the transparent grids.

## Getting Started

### Mental Math and Reflexes

Continue using the Probability Meter. Ask questions like the following, and have students find and point to numbers on the meter.

- Which is greater, $\frac{6}{10}$ or $\frac{5}{8}$? $\frac{5}{8}$
- Which is greater, $\frac{3}{8}$ or $\frac{1}{3}$? $\frac{3}{8}$
- Is $\frac{7}{8}$ closer to $\frac{7}{10}$ or to 1? 1
- Is $\frac{1}{6}$ closer to $\frac{1}{4}$ or to 0? $\frac{1}{4}$
- Is 0.36 closer to $\frac{1}{4}$ or to $\frac{1}{2}$? $\frac{1}{4}$
- Is 0.73 closer to 0.6 or 0.9? 0.6
- What fraction is about equal to 0.88? $\frac{7}{8}$ or $\frac{9}{10}$
- What fraction is about equal to 0.57? $\frac{6}{10}$
- What fraction is about equal to 0.06? $\frac{1}{20}$

## Math Message

*How would you use the Probability Meter to show someone what $\frac{1}{8}$ dollar is worth?*

## Study Link 5.5 Follow-Up

Briefly review the answers. You may want to use an overhead transparency of the page to show where the decimals fall on the number line.

Rounding the area of Malta to the nearest tenth may have been difficult for students. By rounding to the nearest tenth, students must round to the nearest whole number–316.0 square kilometers.

# Teaching the Lesson

## ✦ Math Message Follow-Up

WHOLE-CLASS DISCUSSION

The Probability Meter shows a number line from 0 to 1. Fraction, decimal, and percent numbers are all used as labels on the meter.

Ask students to think of the decimal labels as dollar notation in answering the Math Message.

The fraction $\frac{1}{4}$ is opposite the decimal 0.25, and $\frac{1}{4}$ dollar is \$0.25, or 25 cents. The fraction $\frac{1}{8}$ is opposite the decimal 0.125, so $\frac{1}{8}$ dollar must be worth \$0.125, or $12\frac{1}{2}$ cents.

What is $\frac{3}{8}$ dollar worth? \$0.375, or $37\frac{1}{2}$ cents What are $\frac{5}{8}$ dollar and $\frac{7}{8}$ dollar worth? \$0.625, or $62\frac{1}{2}$ cents, and \$0.875, or $87\frac{1}{2}$ cents

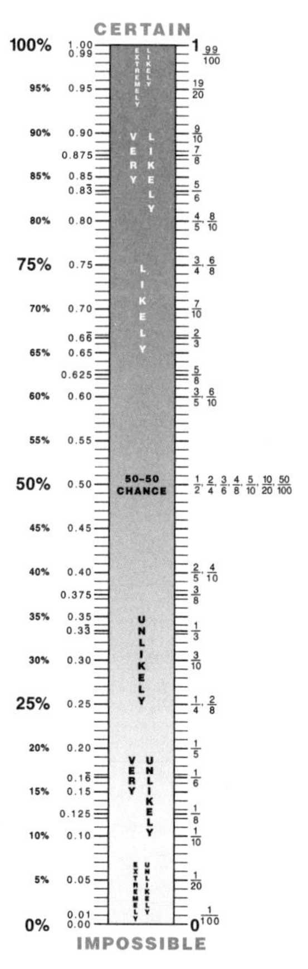

Probability Meter

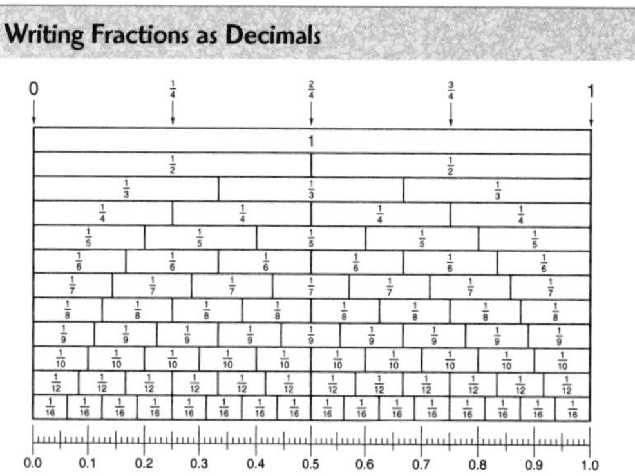

**Writing Fractions as Decimals**

Use a straightedge and the above chart to fill in the blanks to the right of each fraction below. Write a decimal that is equal to, or about equal to, the given fraction. Directions for filling in the blank to the left of each fraction will be given in the next lesson. Sample answers for blanks on the right:

| | | | |
|---|---|---|---|
| $0.\overline{333}$ | $\frac{1}{3}$ = 0. 3 3 | $0.\overline{666}$ | $\frac{2}{3}$ = 0. 6 7 |
| 0.4 | $\frac{4}{10}$ = 0. 4 0 | 0.8 | $\frac{4}{5}$ = 0. 8 0 |
| 0.125 | $\frac{1}{8}$ = 0. 1 3 | 0.625 | $\frac{5}{8}$ = 0. 6 3 |
| 0.75 | $\frac{9}{12}$ = 0. 7 5 | 0.917 | $\frac{11}{12}$ = 0. 9 2 |
| $1.\overline{333}$ | $1\frac{1}{3}$ = 1. 3 3 | 1.375 | $1\frac{3}{8}$ = 1. 3 8 |
| 3.875 | $3\frac{7}{8}$ = 3. 8 8 | $9.\overline{833}$ | $9\frac{5}{6}$ = 9 . 8 3 |

STUDENT PAGE

✦ *Math Journal 1*, p. 143

**Language Arts Link** "Two bits" is U.S. slang for 25 cents. Therefore, eight bits is worth $1.00, and 1 bit is worth $\frac{1}{8}$ dollar, or $12\frac{1}{2}$ cents. The term comes from British slang, which was applied in the South and West to a Mexican coin worth $12\frac{1}{2}$ cents.

## Using a Fraction-Stick Chart and Decimal Number Line to Write Fractions as Decimals

(*Math Journal 1,* p. 143; *Math Masters,* pp. 57 and 479)

WHOLE-CLASS ACTIVITY

You may use an overhead transparency of *Math Masters,* page 57 to demonstrate how the Fraction-Stick Chart can be used to approximate fractions with decimals. Show two or three examples of approximating fractions with decimals.

*Example:* Find a decimal for $\frac{2}{3}$.

**Step 1:** Use the thirds row, and locate the fraction $\frac{2}{3}$. Count the "$\frac{1}{3}$" bars from left to right: $\frac{2}{3}$ is the right side of the second bar.

**Step 2:** Place one edge of a straightedge at $\frac{2}{3}$, that is along the right edge of the second "$\frac{1}{3}$" bar. The straightedge should be vertical, perpendicular to the number line along the bottom.

NOTE: The Fraction-Stick Chart is a useful visual device, but it cannot be relied upon to furnish precise equivalencies between fractions and decimals. In Lesson 5.7, students will use their calculators to find decimal equivalents for fractions.

TEACHING MASTER

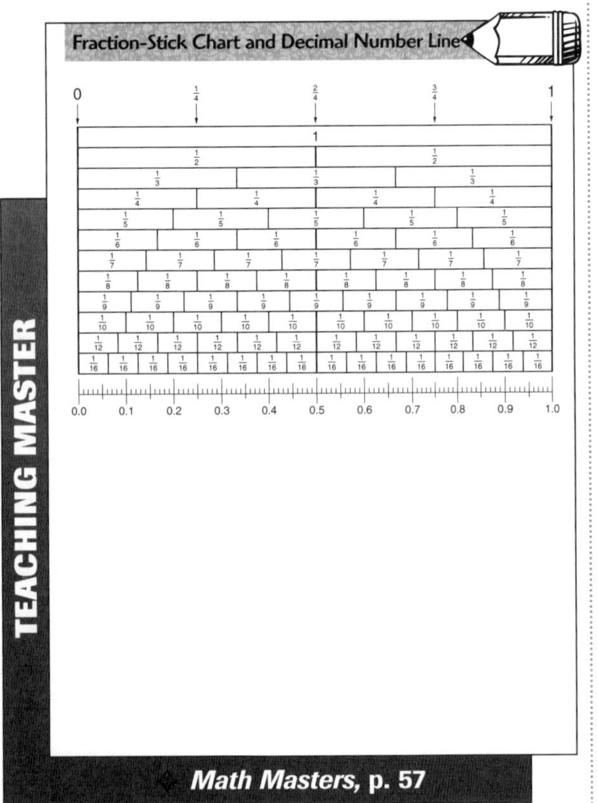


Math Masters, p. 57

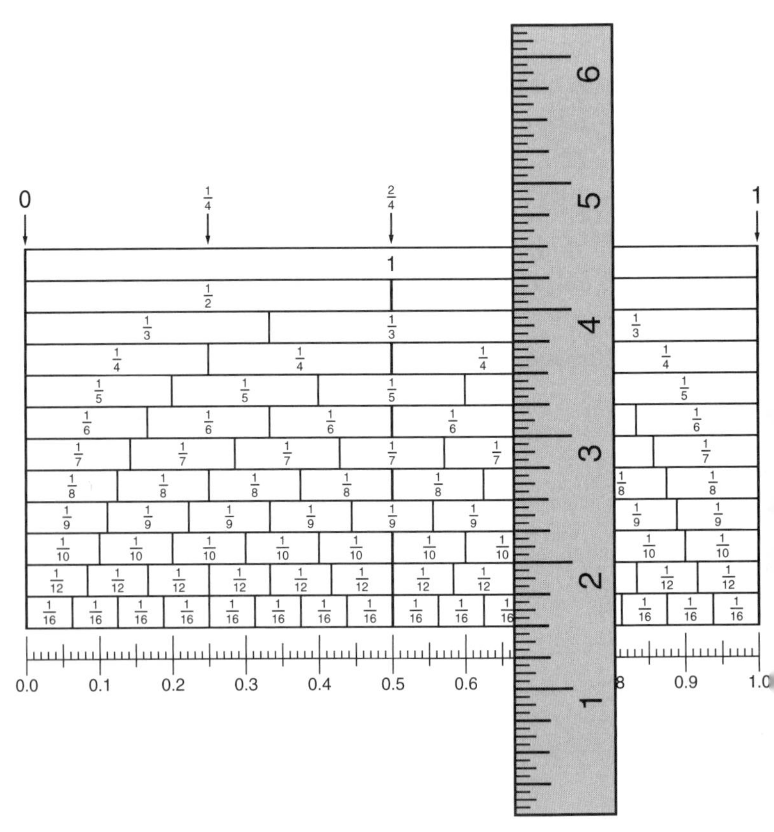

**Step 3:** Find where the straightedge crosses the number line. It crosses at about 0.67, so $\frac{2}{3}$ is about 0.67. Write the answer after the equals sign, to the right of the fraction.

Students complete the journal page. Circulate and assist. Bring the class together when most students have finished.

Several problems involve mixed numbers, but the Fraction-Stick Chart covers only the interval from 0 to 1. These problems may prove difficult for some students. Have a volunteer explain why it is only necessary to approximate the fraction part of a mixed number. They can simply copy over the whole number part when they write the decimal name.

**ONGOING ASSESSMENT**

**Have students complete an Exit Slip explaining in words how to use the Fraction-Stick Chart to find decimal approximations for fractions.**

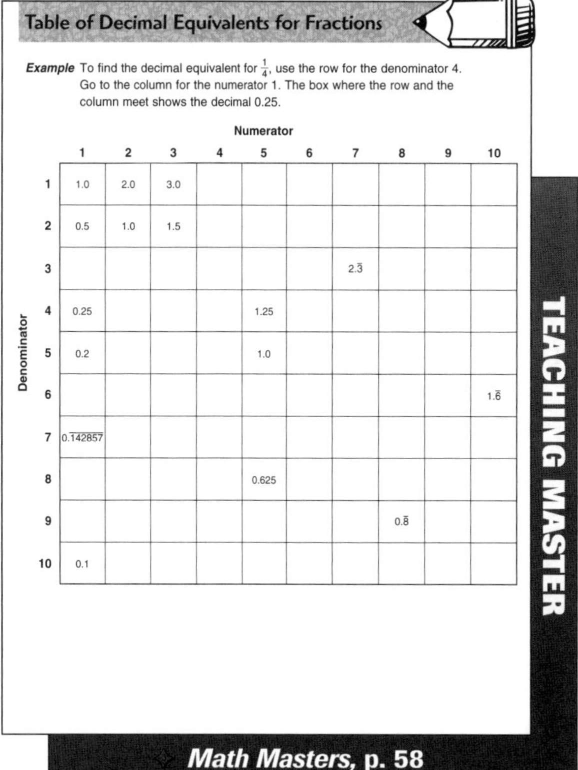

**Table of Decimal Equivalents for Fractions**

***Example*** To find the decimal equivalent for $\frac{1}{4}$, use the row for the denominator 4. Go to the column for the numerator 1. The box where the row and the column meet shows the decimal 0.25.

| Denominator \ Numerator | 1 | 2 | 3 | 4 | 5 | 6 | 7 | 8 | 9 | 10 |
|---|---|---|---|---|---|---|---|---|---|---|
| 1 | 1.0 | 2.0 | 3.0 | | | | | | | |
| 2 | 0.5 | 1.0 | 1.5 | | | | | | | |
| 3 | | | | | | | $2.\overline{3}$ | | | |
| 4 | 0.25 | | | | 1.25 | | | | | |
| 5 | 0.2 | | | | 1.0 | | | | | |
| 6 | | | | | | | | | | $1.\overline{6}$ |
| 7 | $0.\overline{142857}$ | | | | | | | | | |
| 8 | | | | | 0.625 | | | | | |
| 9 | | | | | | | | $0.\overline{8}$ | | |
| 10 | 0.1 | | | | | | | | | |

TEACHING MASTER

*Math Masters,* p. 58

## ✦ Filling in a Table of Decimal Equivalents for Fractions (*Math Journal 1,* inside back cover; *Math Masters,* p. 58)

PARTNER ACTIVITY 

A partially completed table of decimal equivalents for fractions appears on the inside back cover of the journal and on *Math Masters,* page 58.

You may use a transparency of *Math Masters,* page 58 to show students how the table works. Each number across the top of the table identifies the numerator of a fraction. Each number down the left side of the table identifies the denominator of a fraction. Once students have completed the table in the journal, it will serve as a handy and permanent reference throughout the school year.

For today, assign the denominators in rows 1 (whole numbers), 2 (halves), 4 (fourths), 5 (fifths), and 10 (tenths). Allow about 10 minutes for students to write in the decimal names.

Most of the fractions in the assigned rows are easy fractions. Students should know their decimal names or be able to calculate them mentally.

**Adjusting the Activity** Extend this activity by having students describe orally or in writing any patterns they see in the parts of the table they have completed.

**Measurement Review**

Fill in the oval next to the most reasonable answer.

1. About how long is a new pencil?
   ○ 2 inches ● 7 inches ○ 12 inches ○ 1 yard
2. About how high is the classroom door?
   ○ 6 inches ○ 4 feet ● 7 feet ○ 1 yard
3. About how tall is an adult?
   ○ 18 inches ○ 2 feet ● 2 yards ○ 4 yards
4. About what is the width of your journal?
   ○ 5 cm ○ 10 cm ● 20 cm ○ 50 cm

Fill in the oval next to the best unit to use for each measurement.

5. The weight of an ant
   ● ounce ○ kilogram ○ foot ○ cup
6. The amount of juice a 5-year-old drinks each day
   ○ ounce ○ kilogram ○ foot ● cup
7. The length of a boat
   ○ ounce ○ kilogram ● foot ○ cup
8. The weight of an elephant
   ○ ounce ● kilogram ○ foot ○ cup

STUDENT PAGE

✦ *Math Journal 1,* p. 144

STUDENT PAGE

**Measurement Review** (cont.)

Measure each line segment to the nearest $\frac{1}{8}$-inch.

9. ______ $2\frac{4}{8}$, or $2\frac{1}{2}$ inches

10. ______ $1\frac{6}{8}$, or $1\frac{3}{4}$ inches

Measure each line segment to the nearest $\frac{1}{16}$-inch.

11. ______ $1\frac{1}{16}$ inches

12. ______ $2\frac{6}{16}$ inches

Draw a line segment

13. 8 centimeters long.

14. 4.7 centimeters long.

◆ *Math Journal 1,* p. 145

# 2 Ongoing Learning & Practice

## ◆ Reviewing Measurement
(*Math Journal 1,* pp. 144–145)

INDEPENDENT ACTIVITY 

These journal pages provide a brief review of units of measure and measuring line segments.

## ◆ Math Boxes 5.6 (*Math Journal 1,* p. 146)

INDEPENDENT ACTIVITY 

**Mixed Review** Math Boxes in this lesson are paired with Math Boxes in Lesson 5.8. The skill in Problem 1 is a prerequisite for Unit 6.

## ◆ Study Link 5.6 (*Math Masters,* p. 270)

**Home Connection** Students practice converting among decimals, fractions, and mixed numbers.

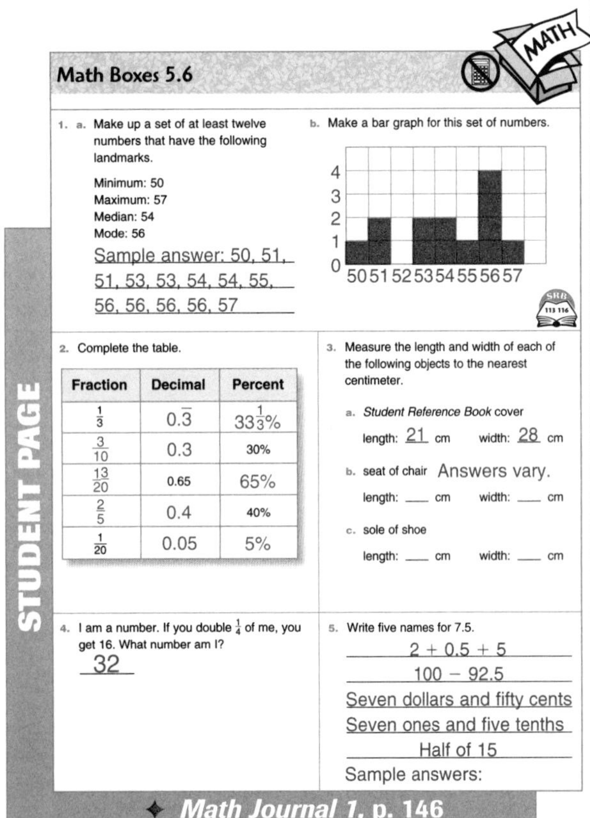

STUDENT PAGE

**Math Boxes 5.6**

1. a. Make up a set of at least twelve numbers that have the following landmarks.

Minimum: 50
Maximum: 57
Median: 54
Mode: 56

Sample answer: 50, 51, 51, 53, 53, 54, 54, 55, 56, 56, 56, 56, 57

b. Make a bar graph for this set of numbers.



2. Complete the table.

| Fraction | Decimal | Percent |
|---|---|---|
| $\frac{1}{3}$ | $0.\overline{3}$ | $33\frac{1}{3}\%$ |
| $\frac{3}{10}$ | 0.3 | 30% |
| $\frac{13}{20}$ | 0.65 | 65% |
| $\frac{2}{5}$ | 0.4 | 40% |
| $\frac{1}{20}$ | 0.05 | 5% |

3. Measure the length and width of each of the following objects to the nearest centimeter.

a. *Student Reference Book* cover
length: 21 cm width: 28 cm

b. seat of chair Answers vary.
length: ___ cm width: ___ cm

c. sole of shoe
length: ___ cm width: ___ cm

4. I am a number. If you double $\frac{1}{4}$ of me, you get 16. What number am I?
32

5. Write five names for 7.5.
2 + 0.5 + 5
100 − 92.5
Seven dollars and fifty cents
Seven ones and five tenths
Half of 15
Sample answers:

◆ *Math Journal 1,* p. 146

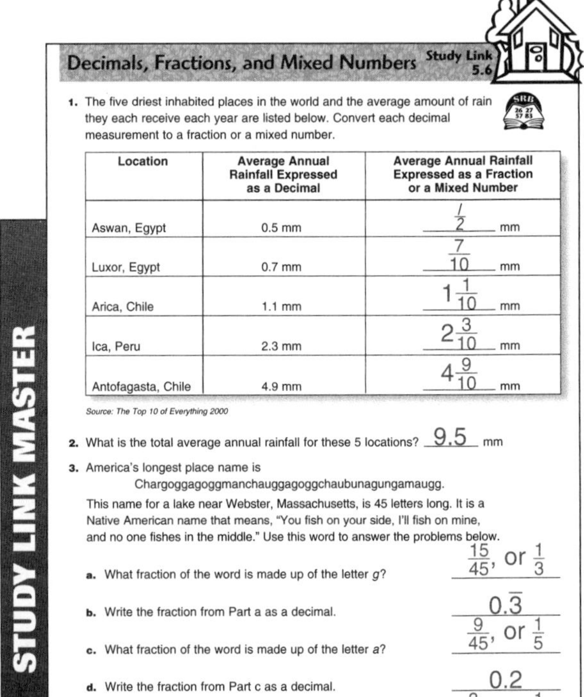

STUDY LINK MASTER

**Decimals, Fractions, and Mixed Numbers** Study Link 5.6

1. The five driest inhabited places in the world and the average amount of rain they each receive each year are listed below. Convert each decimal measurement to a fraction or a mixed number.

| Location | Average Annual Rainfall Expressed as a Decimal | Average Annual Rainfall Expressed as a Fraction or a Mixed Number |
|---|---|---|
| Aswan, Egypt | 0.5 mm | $\frac{1}{2}$ mm |
| Luxor, Egypt | 0.7 mm | $\frac{7}{10}$ mm |
| Arica, Chile | 1.1 mm | $1\frac{1}{10}$ mm |
| Ica, Peru | 2.3 mm | $2\frac{3}{10}$ mm |
| Antofagasta, Chile | 4.9 mm | $4\frac{9}{10}$ mm |

Source: *The Top 10 of Everything 2000*

2. What is the total average annual rainfall for these 5 locations? 9.5 mm

3. America's longest place name is
Chargoggagoggmanchauggagoggchaubunagungamaugg.
This name for a lake near Webster, Massachusetts, is 45 letters long. It is a Native American name that means, "You fish on your side, I'll fish on mine, and no one fishes in the middle." Use this word to answer the problems below.

a. What fraction of the word is made up of the letter *g*? $\frac{15}{45}$, or $\frac{1}{3}$

b. Write the fraction from Part a as a decimal. $0.\overline{3}$

c. What fraction of the word is made up of the letter *a*? $\frac{9}{45}$, or $\frac{1}{5}$

d. Write the fraction from Part c as a decimal. 0.2

e. What fraction of the word is made up of the letter *c*? $\frac{3}{45}$, or $\frac{1}{15}$

f. Write the fraction from Part e as a decimal. $0.0\overline{6}$

◆ *Math Masters,* p. 270

# Options for Individualizing

## ✦ EXTRA PRACTICE Writing Fraction and Decimal Equivalents for a Shaded 100-Grid

(*Math Masters,* pp. 59 and 60)

PARTNER ACTIVITY  **15–30 min**

Students write the fraction and decimal names for the shaded portions of squares, and then use a transparent 100-grid to check their answers. Extend the activity by having students shade a copy of *Math Masters,* page 60 to create their own designs. Then they estimate the fraction and decimal names for the shaded portions.

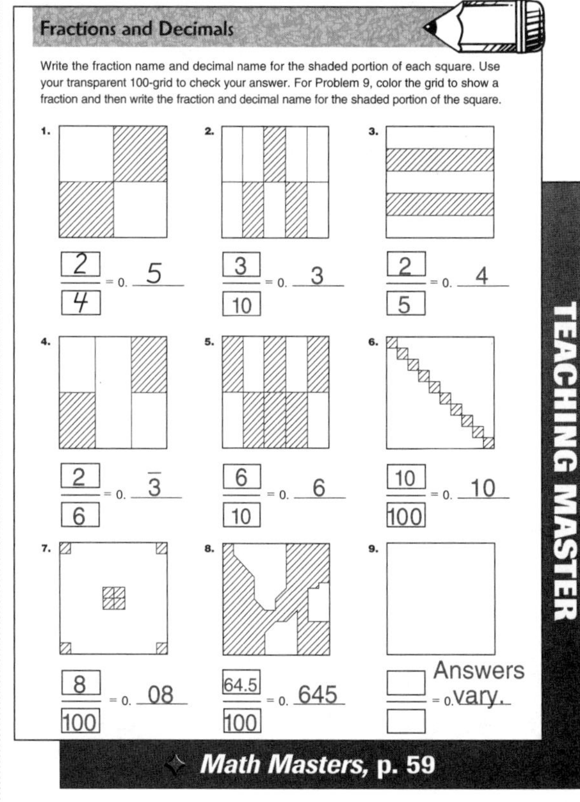

**Fractions and Decimals**

Write the fraction name and decimal name for the shaded portion of each square. Use your transparent 100-grid to check your answer. For Problem 9, color the grid to show a fraction and then write the fraction and decimal name for the shaded portion of the square.

1. $\frac{2}{4}$ = 0. 5
2. $\frac{3}{10}$ = 0. 3
3. $\frac{2}{5}$ = 0. 4
4. $\frac{2}{6}$ = 0. $\overline{3}$
5. $\frac{6}{10}$ = 0. 6
6. $\frac{10}{100}$ = 0. 10
7. $\frac{8}{100}$ = 0. 08
8. $\frac{64.5}{100}$ = 0. 645
9. Answers vary.

TEACHING MASTER

✦ *Math Masters,* p. 59

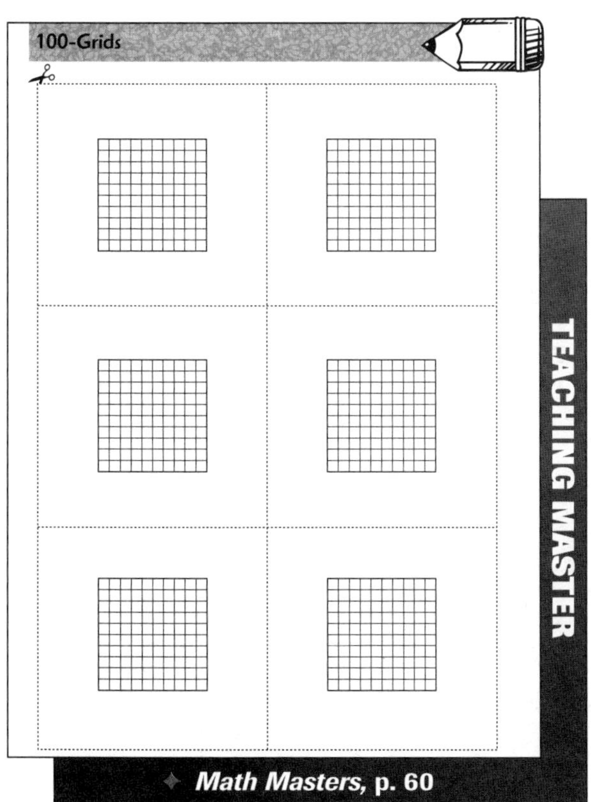

**100-Grids**

TEACHING MASTER

✦ *Math Masters,* p. 60

# 5.7 Fractions and Decimals: Part 3

**OBJECTIVE** **To use a calculator to find decimal equivalents for fractions.**

| summaries | materials |
| --- | --- |
| **1 Teaching the Lesson** | |
| Students rename fractions as decimals by dividing with a calculator. [Numeration; Operations and Computation]<br>Students play *Frac-Tac-Toe* to develop reflex recognition of fraction-decimal equivalents. [Numeration; Operations and Computation] | ☐ *Math Journal 1,* pp. 143 and 147<br>☐ *Student Reference Book,* pp. 88 and 274–276<br>☐ Study Link 5.6<br>☐ Teaching Master (*Math Masters,* pp. 62 and 63, 1 per partnership; and pp. 64 and 65, optional)<br>☐ Transparency (*Math Masters,* p. 62; optional)<br>☐ Assessment Master (*Math Masters,* p. 479; optional)<br>Per partnership:<br>☐ calculator; counters; 4 each of the number cards 0–10 (from the Everything Math Deck, if available)<br>***See* Advance Preparation** |
| **2 Ongoing Learning & Practice** | |
| Students fill in the decimals for thirds, sixths, and ninths in the Table of Decimal Equivalents. [Numeration; Operations and Computation]<br>Students practice and maintain skills through Math Boxes and Study Link activities. | ☐ *Math Journal 1,* p. 148 and the inside back cover<br>☐ Study Link Master (*Math Masters,* p. 271) |
| **3 Options for Individualizing** | |
| **Enrichment** Students explore the partial-quotients division algorithm to find decimal equivalents for fractions. [Operations and Computation]<br>**Extra Practice** Students practice ordering and comparing decimals. [Operations and Computation] | ☐ *Math Journal 1,* p. 147<br>☐ Teaching Master (*Math Masters,* p. 61) |

## Additional Information

**Advance Preparation** For Part 1, review the rules and materials needed to play *Frac-Tac-Toe* on *Student Reference Book,* pages 274–276. Play the *2-4-5-10,* Decimal Version, several times so that you understand the rules and scoring.

Each pair of students will need a deck of number cards to play *Frac-Tac-Toe.* The deck should consist of 44 cards, four each of the numbers 0 through 10. Use the number cards from the Everything Math Deck or modify a deck of ordinary playing cards by removing the Jacks, Kings, and Jokers, and then using a permanent marker to mark Aces with the number 1 and Queens with the number 0.

**Vocabulary • repeating decimal**

# Getting Started

## Mental Math and Reflexes

Students solve "fraction-of" problems. *Suggestions:*

- There are 12 counters in a set. How many counters are in $\frac{3}{4}$ of the set? 9
- There are 18 counters in a set. How many counters are in $\frac{2}{9}$ of the set? 4
- There are 24 counters in a set. How many counters are in $\frac{5}{6}$ of the set? 20
- There are 12 counters in $\frac{2}{3}$ of a set. How many counters are in the whole set? 18
- There are 15 counters in $\frac{3}{5}$ of a set. How many counters are in the whole set? 25

## Math Message

*Write $\frac{7}{16}$ as a decimal.*

0.4375

## Study Link 5.6 Follow-Up

Briefly review answers.

The name of the lake is pronounced *Char-gogg-a-gogg* (pause) *man-chaugg-a-gogg* (pause) *chau-bun-a-gung-a-maugg.*

# 1 Teaching the Lesson

## ✦ Math Message Follow-Up

WHOLE-CLASS DISCUSSION

Encourage students to share their strategies for converting $\frac{7}{16}$ to a decimal. They may have used a Fraction-Stick Chart, logical reasoning, or some other method. If any of the students used a calculator, praise them but put off discussing their approach for the moment. Discuss non-calculator methods first.

The Fraction-Stick Chart yields about 0.44 as the decimal equivalent of $\frac{7}{16}$, which is a good approximation but is not exact. To use logical reasoning, a student might begin with the fact that $\frac{1}{4} = 0.25$, so $\frac{1}{8} = 0.125$ and $\frac{1}{16} = 0.0625$. Also, since $\frac{1}{4} = \frac{4}{16}$ and $\frac{1}{8} = \frac{2}{16}$, $\frac{1}{4} + \frac{1}{8} + \frac{1}{16} = \frac{7}{16}$. So $\frac{7}{16} = 0.25 + 0.125 + 0.0625 = 0.4375$.

Neither method is completely satisfactory. The Fraction-Stick Chart approach is easy but not exact. Logical reasoning is exact but complicated. This lesson introduces using a calculator as an easy and accurate way to convert fractions to decimals.

*Student Reference Book,* page 88 accompanies the *Using a Calculator to Convert Fractions to Decimals* activity on the next page.

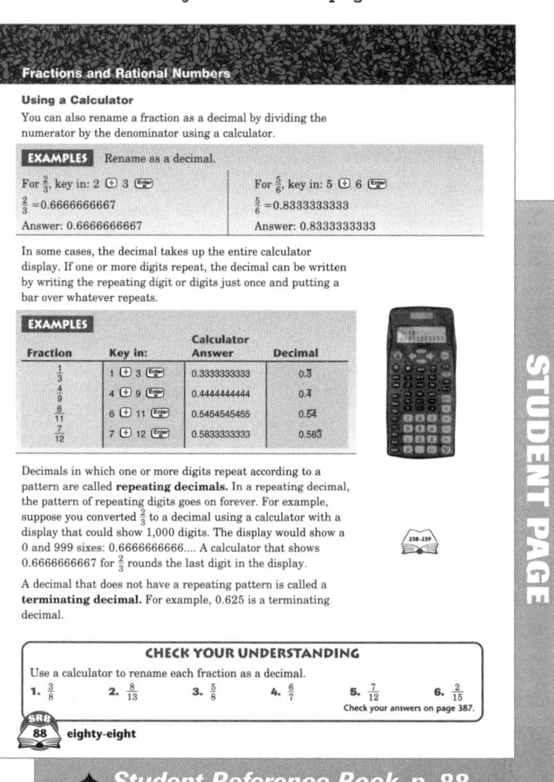

Fractions and Rational Numbers

**Using a Calculator**

You can also rename a fraction as a decimal by dividing the numerator by the denominator using a calculator.

**EXAMPLES** Rename as a decimal.

For $\frac{2}{3}$, key in: 2 ÷ 3 Enter
$\frac{2}{3}$ =0.6666666667
Answer: 0.6666666667

For $\frac{5}{6}$, key in: 5 ÷ 6 Enter
$\frac{5}{6}$ =0.8333333333
Answer: 0.8333333333

In some cases, the decimal takes up the entire calculator display. If one or more digits repeat, the decimal can be written by writing the repeating digit or digits just once and putting a bar over whatever repeats.

**EXAMPLES**

| Fraction | Key in: | Calculator Answer | Decimal |
|---|---|---|---|
| $\frac{1}{3}$ | 1 ÷ 3 Enter | 0.3333333333 | $0.\overline{3}$ |
| $\frac{4}{9}$ | 4 ÷ 9 Enter | 0.4444444444 | $0.\overline{4}$ |
| $\frac{6}{11}$ | 6 ÷ 11 Enter | 0.5454545455 | $0.\overline{54}$ |
| $\frac{7}{12}$ | 7 ÷ 12 Enter | 0.5833333333 | $0.58\overline{3}$ |

Decimals in which one or more digits repeat according to a pattern are called **repeating decimals.** In a repeating decimal, the pattern of repeating digits goes on forever. For example, suppose you converted $\frac{2}{3}$ to a decimal using a calculator with a display that could show 1,000 digits. The display would show a 0 and 999 sixes: 0.6666666666.... A calculator that shows 0.6666666667 for $\frac{2}{3}$ rounds the last digit in the display.

238–239

A decimal that does not have a repeating pattern is called a **terminating decimal.** For example, 0.625 is a terminating decimal.

**CHECK YOUR UNDERSTANDING**

Use a calculator to rename each fraction as a decimal.

**1.** $\frac{3}{8}$ **2.** $\frac{8}{13}$ **3.** $\frac{5}{8}$ **4.** $\frac{6}{7}$ **5.** $\frac{7}{12}$ **6.** $\frac{2}{15}$

Check your answers on page 387.

SRB 88 eighty-eight

STUDENT PAGE

✦ *Student Reference Book,* p. 88

## Writing Fractions as Decimals

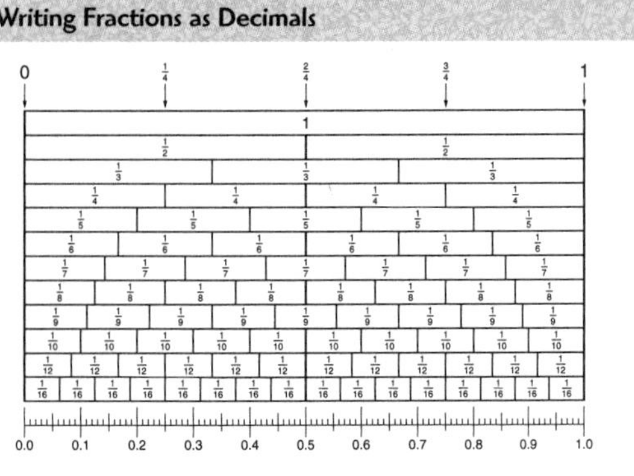


Use a straightedge and the above chart to fill in the blanks to the right of each fraction below. Write a decimal that is equal to, or about equal to, the given fraction. Directions for filling in the blank to the left of each fraction will be given in the next lesson. Sample answers for blanks on the right:

$0.33\overline{3}$ $\frac{1}{3} = 0.$ 3 3 $0.66\overline{6}$ $\frac{2}{3} = 0.$ 6 7

0.4 $\frac{4}{10} = 0.$ 4 0 0.8 $\frac{4}{5} = 0.$ 8 0

0.125 $\frac{1}{8} = 0.$ 1 3 0.625 $\frac{5}{8} = 0.$ 6 3

0.75 $\frac{9}{12} = 0.$ 7 5 0.917 $\frac{11}{12} = 0.$ 9 2

$1.33\overline{3}$ $1\frac{1}{3} = 1.$ 3 3 1.375 $1\frac{3}{8} = 1.$ 3 8

3.875 $3\frac{7}{8} = 3.$ 8 8 $9.83\overline{3}$ $9\frac{5}{6} =$ 9 . 8 3

STUDENT PAGE

◆ *Math Journal 1*, p. 143

NOTE: Most fraction-capable calculators have a special key for converting fractions to decimals, but do not let your students use it for this lesson. The goal here is to help students understand the connections between fractions, decimals, and division.

## More about Writing Fractions as Decimals

**How to Write a Repeating Decimal**

Some decimal numbers use up the entire calculator display. If a digit repeats, the decimal number can be written in a simple way by putting a bar over the repeating digit. Study these examples.

| Fraction | Divide Numerator by Denominator. Calculator Display: | Write the Decimal this Way: |
|---|---|---|
| $\frac{1}{3}$ | 0.3333333333 | $0.\overline{3}$ |
| $\frac{2}{3}$ | 0.6666666666 or 0.6666666667 (depending on the calculator) | $0.\overline{6}$ |
| $\frac{1}{12}$ | 0.0833333333 | $0.08\overline{3}$ |
| $\frac{8}{9}$ | 0.8888888888 or 0.8888888889 (depending on the calculator) | $0.\overline{8}$ |

Use your calculator to convert each fraction below to a decimal by dividing. If the result is a repeating decimal, write a bar over the digit or digits that repeat. Then circle the correct answer to each question.

1. Which is closer to 0.8? $\frac{6}{8}$ 0.75 or ($\frac{5}{6}$) $0.8\overline{3}$
2. Which is closer to 0.25? ($\frac{2}{9}$) $0.\overline{2}$ or $\frac{3}{9}$ $0.\overline{3}$
3. Which is closer to 0.6? $\frac{4}{7}$ 0.5714285714 or ($\frac{7}{12}$) $0.58\overline{3}$
4. Which is closer to 0.05? ($\frac{1}{30}$) $0.0\overline{3}$ or $\frac{1}{12}$ $0.08\overline{3}$
5. Which is closer to 0.39? ($\frac{3}{8}$) 0.375 or $\frac{7}{16}$ 0.4375

STUDENT PAGE

◆ *Math Journal 1*, p. 147

## ◆ Using a Calculator to Convert Fractions to Decimals (*Math Journal 1*, p. 143; *Student Reference Book*, p. 88)

WHOLE-CLASS ACTIVITY

Ask students if there is an easier way to divide 7 by 16. Someone will probably suggest using a calculator.

On the board or overhead, write several easy fractions that students know the decimal names for, such as $\frac{1}{2}$, $\frac{2}{4}$, $\frac{3}{6}$, $\frac{50}{100}$, $\frac{100}{200}$, $\frac{3}{10}$, $\frac{1}{4}$, and so on. Ask the class to say the decimal name for each. Then have them use their calculators to divide the numerator of each fraction by its denominator. Students should note that the calculator display confirms what they already know. Tell students that division works for all fractions, easy or hard.

*Summary*

- ▷ *Fact:* You can find the decimal name for any fraction by dividing the fraction's numerator by its denominator.
- ▷ *Reminder:* When you see a fraction, think "division": think of the bar between the numerator and denominator as though it was the slash, /, for division, and divide.

NOTE: In *Fourth Grade Everyday Mathematics,* the slash was introduced as an alternative to the traditional ÷ symbol for division. The use of the slash for division prepares students for the idea that a fraction represents a quotient. A fraction may be written as $\frac{a}{b}$ or $a/b$, and either form also means division.

Have students turn to journal page 143. Tell them to use their calculators to check their answers. They should divide numerators by denominators and write the decimal names in the spaces to the left of the fraction names. As they work, cover the following points:

- ▷ For mixed numbers, students only need to divide the fraction part. They can simply copy the whole number part when they write the decimal name.
- ▷ Several of the fractions involve eighths. Have students verify that dividing these fractions on a calculator gives the same decimals they noticed earlier on the Probability Meter.
- ▷ Several of the fractions, such as $\frac{1}{3}$, when divided fill up the calculator display with digits that would repeat forever if the calculator display went on forever. Such a decimal is a **repeating decimal.** Take a moment to show how to represent repeating decimals by drawing a bar over the digit or digits that repeat.

$$\frac{1}{3} = 0.333333333... = 0.\overline{3}$$

Have students turn to page 88 of the *Student Reference Book* and note the examples of repeating decimals.

**Adjusting the Activity** Help students who are having difficulty organizing the mixed number work by having them circle the fraction portion of each mixed number. Then they copy the part of the number that is not circled (the whole number part) into the answer blank and perform the division on the circled portion.

Expect some students to say they can't understand long decimal numbers. Assure students that a decimal with three decimal places (thousandths) will suffice for almost any problem they encounter.

## Converting Fractions to Decimals
(*Math Journal 1,* p. 147)

PARTNER ACTIVITY 

Students use calculators to convert fractions to decimals by dividing. Remind them to use the bar to write repeating decimals.

**Adjusting the Activity** To extend the activity, have students predict which fraction is greater before converting the fractions to decimals. Consider having students record their strategies for choosing the greater fraction, so that these can be shared later.

## Introducing *2-4-5-10 Frac-Tac-Toe*
(*Student Reference Book,* pp. 274–276; *Math Masters,* pp. 62, 63, and 479)

PARTNER ACTIVITY 

Pass out 1 copy each of *Math Masters,* page 62 (*Frac-Tac-Toe* Number-Card Board) and page 63 (*2-4-5-10 Frac-Tac-Toe,* Decimal Version, Gameboard) to each partnership.

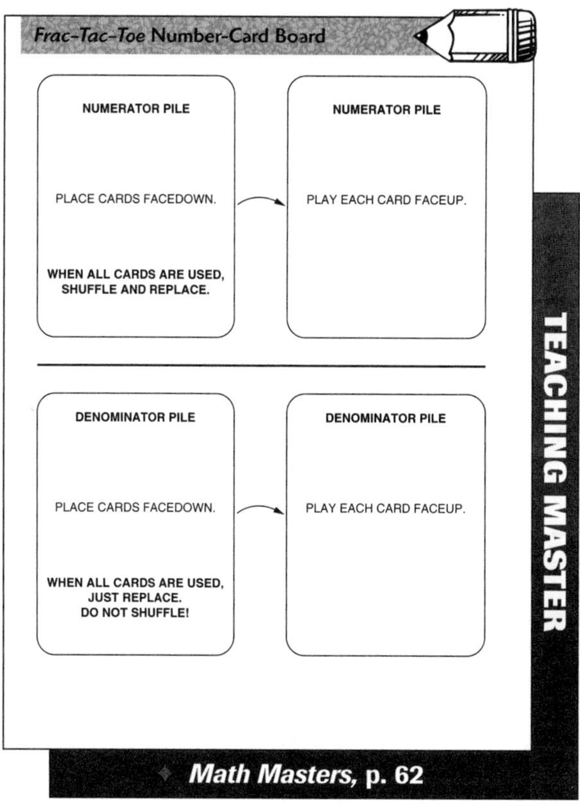
*Frac-Tac-Toe* Number-Card Board

NUMERATOR PILE
PLACE CARDS FACEDOWN.
WHEN ALL CARDS ARE USED, SHUFFLE AND REPLACE.

NUMERATOR PILE
PLAY EACH CARD FACEUP.

DENOMINATOR PILE
PLACE CARDS FACEDOWN.
WHEN ALL CARDS ARE USED, JUST REPLACE. DO NOT SHUFFLE!

DENOMINATOR PILE
PLAY EACH CARD FACEUP.

TEACHING MASTER

*Math Masters,* p. 62

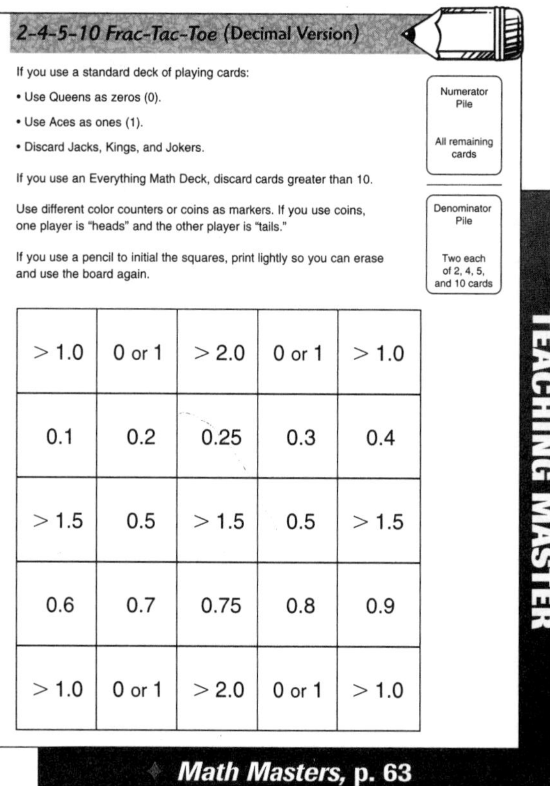
*2-4-5-10 Frac-Tac-Toe* (Decimal Version)

If you use a standard deck of playing cards:
- Use Queens as zeros (0).
- Use Aces as ones (1).
- Discard Jacks, Kings, and Jokers.

If you use an Everything Math Deck, discard cards greater than 10.

Use different color counters or coins as markers. If you use coins, one player is "heads" and the other player is "tails."

If you use a pencil to initial the squares, print lightly so you can erase and use the board again.

Numerator Pile
All remaining cards

Denominator Pile
Two each of 2, 4, 5, and 10 cards

| | | | | |
|---|---|---|---|---|
| > 1.0 | 0 or 1 | > 2.0 | 0 or 1 | > 1.0 |
| 0.1 | 0.2 | 0.25 | 0.3 | 0.4 |
| > 1.5 | 0.5 | > 1.5 | 0.5 | > 1.5 |
| 0.6 | 0.7 | 0.75 | 0.8 | 0.9 |
| > 1.0 | 0 or 1 | > 2.0 | 0 or 1 | > 1.0 |

TEACHING MASTER

*Math Masters,* p. 63

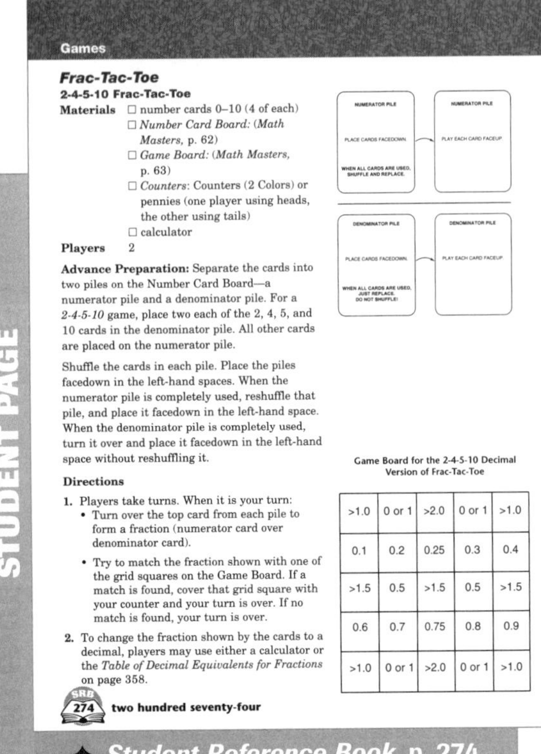

Games

*Frac-Tac-Toe*

**2-4-5-10 Frac-Tac-Toe**

**Materials**
- ☐ number cards 0–10 (4 of each)
- ☐ *Number Card Board:* (*Math Masters,* p. 62)
- ☐ *Game Board:* (*Math Masters,* p. 63)
- ☐ *Counters*: Counters (2 Colors) or pennies (one player using heads, the other using tails)
- ☐ calculator

**Players** 2

**Advance Preparation:** Separate the cards into two piles on the Number Card Board—a numerator pile and a denominator pile. For a *2-4-5-10* game, place two each of the 2, 4, 5, and 10 cards in the denominator pile. All other cards are placed on the numerator pile.

Shuffle the cards in each pile. Place the piles facedown in the left-hand spaces. When the numerator pile is completely used, reshuffle that pile, and place it facedown in the left-hand space. When the denominator pile is completely used, turn it over and place it facedown in the left-hand space without reshuffling it.



**Directions**

1. Players take turns. When it is your turn:
   - Turn over the top card from each pile to form a fraction (numerator card over denominator card).
   - Try to match the fraction shown with one of the grid squares on the Game Board. If a match is found, cover that grid square with your counter and your turn is over. If no match is found, your turn is over.
2. To change the fraction shown by the cards to a decimal, players may use either a calculator or the *Table of Decimal Equivalents for Fractions* on page 358.

Game Board for the 2-4-5-10 Decimal Version of Frac-Tac-Toe

| >1.0 | 0 or 1 | >2.0 | 0 or 1 | >1.0 |
|---|---|---|---|---|
| 0.1 | 0.2 | 0.25 | 0.3 | 0.4 |
| >1.5 | 0.5 | >1.5 | 0.5 | >1.5 |
| 0.6 | 0.7 | 0.75 | 0.8 | 0.9 |
| >1.0 | 0 or 1 | >2.0 | 0 or 1 | >1.0 |

SRB 274 two hundred seventy-four

✦ Student Reference Book, p. 274

**ONGOING ASSESSMENT**

Have students record on an Exit Slip something they learned while playing *Frac-Tac-Toe*. They might write about fraction-decimal equivalents or a strategy they used to win.

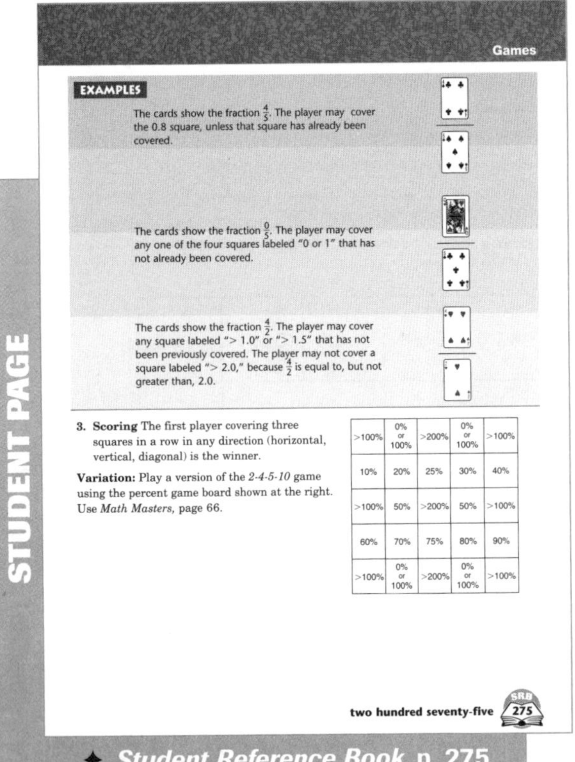

Games

**EXAMPLES**

The cards show the fraction $\frac{4}{5}$. The player may cover the 0.8 square, unless that square has already been covered.

The cards show the fraction $\frac{0}{5}$. The player may cover any one of the four squares labeled "0 or 1" that has not already been covered.

The cards show the fraction $\frac{4}{2}$. The player may cover any square labeled "> 1.0" or "> 1.5" that has not been previously covered. The player may not cover a square labeled "> 2.0," because $\frac{4}{2}$ is equal to, but not greater than, 2.0.

3. **Scoring** The first player covering three squares in a row in any direction (horizontal, vertical, diagonal) is the winner.

**Variation:** Play a version of the *2-4-5-10* game using the percent game board shown at the right. Use *Math Masters,* page 66.

| >100% | 0% or 100% | >200% | 0% or 100% | >100% |
|---|---|---|---|---|
| 10% | 20% | 25% | 30% | 40% |
| >100% | 50% | >200% | 50% | >100% |
| 60% | 70% | 75% | 80% | 90% |
| >100% | 0% or 100% | >200% | 0% or 100% | >100% |

two hundred seventy-five SRB 275

✦ Student Reference Book, p. 275

The *2-4-5-10,* Decimal Version, is the easiest *Frac-Tac-Toe* game. There are three variations of *Frac-Tac-Toe* (*2-4-5-10, 2-4-8,* and *3-6-9*), and four versions of each (Decimal, Percent, Decimal Bingo, and Percent Bingo), which will be introduced later. Gameboards are on *Math Masters,* pages 63–74.

Playing *Frac-Tac-Toe* regularly will promote reflex recognition of fraction, decimal, and percent equivalents. Students should always be permitted to use a calculator or a table of decimal equivalents when playing, but they will rely less and less on these resources as time goes by.

Play a practice game with the class. You play the cards for everybody. (The directions for *Frac-Tac-Toe* are on pages 274 and 275 of the *Student Reference Book.*)

1. Draw cards and name the fractions. Write the fractions on the board or an overhead transparency of the Number-Card Board.
2. Partners alternate and use the fractions you have drawn to play the game.
3. Play until there are a few winners and you are sure the students know how to play. As you play, check that students are using the "0 or 1" and the "greater than" grid squares correctly. (Devise a scheme for collecting and storing the Number-Card Boards and gameboards. They will be used many times throughout the school year and should be easily available for partner and whole-class use.)
4. There are 4 squares labeled "0 or 1." Any one of these squares, if not already marked, may be selected if the fraction is 0 or 1. If necessary, point out that a fraction equals 0 if the numerator is 0.
5. There are 9 squares with the "greater than" symbol (>). Fractions equal to 1, 1.5, or 2 may cause students some difficulty at first. For example, if the fraction is $\frac{3}{2}$ (= 1.5), grid squares marked "> 1.5" may not be selected, because $\frac{3}{2}$ is *not* greater than 1.5.

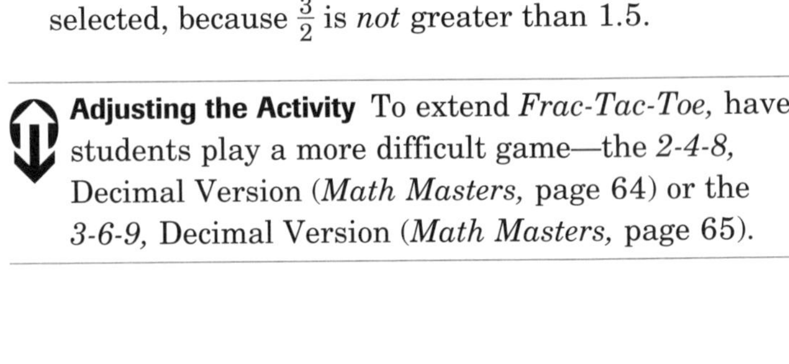

**Adjusting the Activity** To extend *Frac-Tac-Toe,* have students play a more difficult game—the *2-4-8,* Decimal Version (*Math Masters,* page 64) or the *3-6-9,* Decimal Version (*Math Masters,* page 65).

# 2 Ongoing Learning & Practice

## ✦ Finding Decimal Equivalents for Thirds, Sixths, and Ninths
(*Math Journal 1*, inside back cover)

PARTNER ACTIVITY 

Students continue to find and record decimal equivalents for fractions in the table on the inside back cover of the journal. Assign the denominators in rows 3 (thirds), 6 (sixths), and 9 (ninths).

Allow students to use calculators if necessary.

**Adjusting the Activity** To make the activity more challenging, allow students to use their calculators only for the first few entries in each row. Then have them identify and use the patterns to complete the rows.

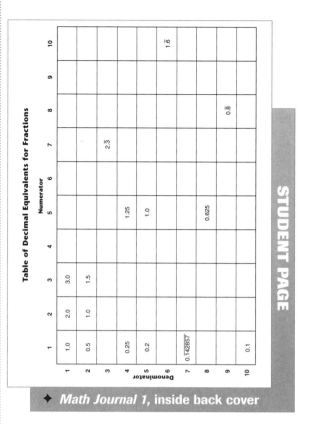

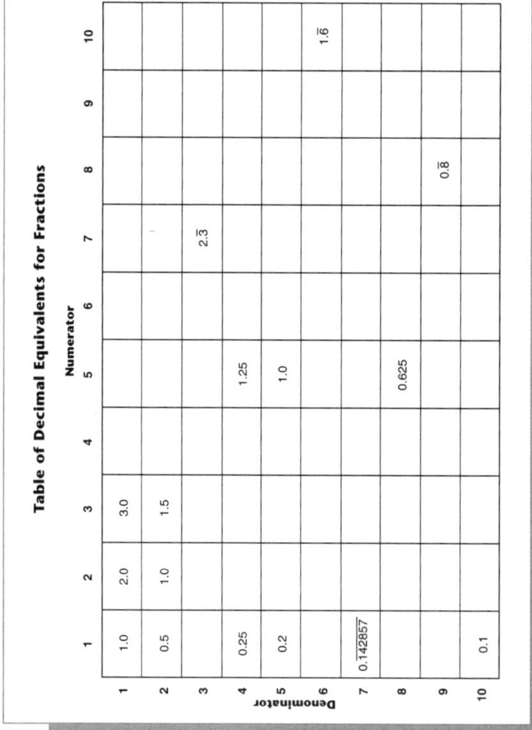

**Table of Decimal Equivalents for Fractions**

| Denominator \ Numerator | 1 | 2 | 3 | 4 | 5 | 6 | 7 | 8 | 9 | 10 |
|---|---|---|---|---|---|---|---|---|---|---|
| 1 | 1.0 | 2.0 | 3.0 | | | | | | | |
| 2 | 0.5 | 1.0 | 1.5 | | | | | | | |
| 3 | | | | | | | $2.\overline{3}$ | | | |
| 4 | 0.25 | | | | 1.25 | | | | | |
| 5 | 0.2 | | | | 1.0 | | | | | |
| 6 | | | | | | | | | | $1.\overline{6}$ |
| 7 | $0.\overline{142857}$ | | | | | | | | | |
| 8 | | | | | 0.625 | | | | | |
| 9 | | | | | | | | $0.\overline{8}$ | | |
| 10 | 0.1 | | | | | | | | | |

STUDENT PAGE

✦ *Math Journal 1*, inside back cover

## ✦ Math Boxes 5.7 (*Math Journal 1*, p. 148)

INDEPENDENT ACTIVITY 

**Mixed Review** Math Boxes in this lesson are paired with Math Boxes in Lesson 5.5. The skill in Problem 1 is a prerequisite for Unit 6.

**Math Boxes 5.7**

1. The large rhombus on your Geometry Template is worth 1. Use your Template to draw a shape worth $2\frac{1}{2}$.
   Sample answer:

2. Complete the "What's My Rule?" table and state the rule.
   Rule: out = in + 9

| in | out |
|---|---|
| 8 | 17 |
| 11 | 20 |
| 5 | 14 |
| −5 | 4 |

3. Sophie went to the ball game. She spent \$8.50 on the ticket, \$2.75 on a hot dog, \$1.99 on a soft drink, and \$0.15 on a souvenir pencil. How much did she spend in all?
   \$13.39

4. Put the following fractions in order from least to greatest.
   $\frac{3}{7}$ $\frac{3}{5}$ $\frac{2}{8}$ $\frac{8}{9}$ $\frac{5}{6}$
   $\frac{2}{8}$, $\frac{3}{7}$, $\frac{3}{5}$, $\frac{5}{6}$, $\frac{8}{9}$

5. Subtract.
   a. 727 − 47 = 680
   b. 503 − 65 = 438
   c. 248 − 176 = 72
   d. 2,403 − 764 = 1,639

STUDENT PAGE

✦ *Math Journal 1*, p. 148

## ✦ Study Link 5.7 (*Math Masters*, p. 271)

**Home Connection** Students convert information from a table about tennis titles into fractions and decimals.

## Champion Tennis Players

Study Link 5.7

The following table shows the number of times through 1999 that each of the following players won the four "Grand Slam" tennis tournaments.

| Player | Australian Open | Wimbledon | French Open | U.S. Open | Total |
|---|---|---|---|---|---|
| Chris Evert Lloyd | 2 | 3 | 7 | 6 | 18 |
| Monica Seles | 4 | 0 | 3 | 2 | 9 |
| Steffi Graf | 4 | 7 | 6 | 5 | 22 |
| Jimmy Connors | 1 | 2 | 0 | 5 | 8 |
| Pete Sampras | 2 | 6 | 0 | 6 | 14 |

Source: *The World Almanac and Book of Facts 1999*

1. a. How many times did Jimmy Connors win Wimbledon? 2
   b. What is the total number of times he won the four tournaments listed above? 8
   c. What fraction of this total were won at Wimbledon? $\frac{2}{8}$, or $\frac{1}{4}$
2. a. How many times did Chris Evert Lloyd win the U.S. Open? 6
   b. What is the total number of times she won the four tournaments listed above? 18
   c. What fraction of this total were won at the U.S. Open? $\frac{6}{18}$, or $\frac{1}{3}$
   d. Write the above fraction as a decimal. $0.\overline{3}$
3. a. How many times has Monica Seles won the Australian Open? 4
   b. What fraction is this of her total number of wins for these four tournaments? $\frac{4}{9}$
   c. Write the above fraction as a decimal. $0.\overline{4}$
4. a. How many times has Steffi Graf won the French Open? 6
   b. What fraction is this of her total number of wins for these four tournaments? $\frac{6}{22}$, or $\frac{3}{11}$
   c. Write the above fraction as a decimal. $0.\overline{27}$ or 0.27

STUDY LINK MASTER

Math Masters, p. 271

## Decimal Comparisons

1. Mark each of the following points on the ruler below. Write the letter above the point. Point *A* has been done for you.

*A*: 3.4 cm *B*: 0.7 cm *C*: 8.3 cm *D*: 1.5 cm *E*: 10.6 cm *F*: 6.8 cm

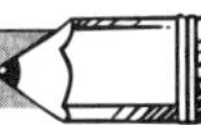

Write three numbers between each pair of numbers. Sample answers are given.

2. 0 and 1 — 0.25, 0.5, 0.75
3. 2 and 3 — 2.25, 2.5, 2.75
4. 0.6 and 0.8 — 0.65, 0.7, 0.775
5. 0.3 and 0.4 — 0.325, 0.35, 0.375
6. 0.06 and 0.05 — 0.051, 0.055, 0.059

Circle the correct answer to each question.

7. Which is closer to 0.6? 0.5 or (0.53)
8. Which is closer to 0.3? 0.02 or (0.2)
9. Which is closer to 0.8? (0.77) or 0.85
10. Which is closer to 0.75? 0.6 or ($0.\overline{8}$)
11. Which is closer to 0.04? 0.3 or (0.051)
12. Arrange the decimals below in order from least to greatest.

0.12 0.05 0.2 0.78 0.6 0.043 0.1

0.043, 0.05, 0.1, 0.12, 0.2, 0.6, 0.78

TEACHING MASTER

Math Masters, p. 61

# 3 Options for Individualizing

## ENRICHMENT Extending the Partial-Quotients Division Algorithm to Decimals (*Math Journal 1*, p. 147)

INDEPENDENT ACTIVITY  **15–30 min** 

Ask students to think of a way they could use the partial-quotients division algorithm to find decimal equivalents for fractions. Here is one strategy:

1. Decide how many decimal places there will be in the answer. If there are to be two decimal places, think of the numerator as a number of hundredths. Write "hundredths" in a unit box. Write that number of hundredths as the dividend. (Think of thousandths if the answer is to have three decimal places, ten-thousandths if four decimal places, and so on.)
2. Divide by the denominator.
3. Rewrite the quotient as the decimal named by the unit in the unit box.

*Example:* Change $\frac{2}{9}$ to a decimal.

| Unit |
|---|
| hundredths |

1. Change the numerator to hundredths. 2 is equal to 200 hundredths.
2. Do the division problem $9\overline{)200}$. The answer is 22 R2. The 22 stands for 22 hundredths (from the unit box).
3. Rewrite the quotient, 22 hundredths, as 0.22.

Have students convert the following fractions to decimals using the above strategy: $\frac{6}{8}$, $\frac{5}{6}$, and $\frac{4}{7}$. Students can check their work by comparing these quotients with the quotients found by using a calculator on journal page 147.

Have students convert the fractions in Problems 4 and 5 on journal page 147 to decimals using the division strategy above or one of their own.

## EXTRA PRACTICE Ordering and Comparing Decimals (*Math Masters*, p. 61)

INDEPENDENT ACTIVITY  **5–15 min**

Consider having students share their strategies for ordering and comparing decimals.

# 5.8 Using a Calculator to Convert Fractions to Percents

**OBJECTIVES** **To use a calculator to convert fractions to decimals and decimals to percents; and to discuss meanings and uses of percents.**

| summaries | materials |
| --- | --- |
| **1 Teaching the Lesson** | |
| Students convert fractions to decimals and decimals to percents with a calculator. [Numeration; Operations and Computation] | ☐ *Math Journal 1,* pp. 149 and 150<br>☐ Study Link 5.7<br>☐ Assessment Master (*Math Masters,* p. 479; optional)<br>☐ calculator |
| **2 Ongoing Learning & Practice** | |
| Students play *2-4-5-10 Frac-Tac-Toe* (Percent Version). [Numeration; Operations and Computation]<br>Students practice and maintain skills through Math Boxes and Study Link activities. | ☐ *Math Journal 1,* p. 151<br>☐ *Student Reference Book,* pp. 274–276<br>☐ Teaching Master (*Math Masters,* p. 66), 1 per partnership<br>☐ *Frac-Tac-Toe* Number-Card Board (*Math Masters,* p. 62), 1 per partnership<br>☐ Study Link Master (*Math Masters,* p. 272)<br>☐ counters (or pennies)<br>☐ calculator<br>☐ 4 each of the number cards 0–10 (from the Everything Math Deck, if available)<br>***See* Advance Preparation** |
| **3 Options for Individualizing** | |
| **Extra Practice** Students practice converting fractions to percents by playing *Fraction/Percent Concentration.* [Numeration; Operations and Computation]<br>**Language Diversity** Students list situations where quantities are reported in fractions, decimals, or percents. | ☐ *Student Reference Book,* p. 278<br>☐ Teaching Masters (*Math Masters,* pp. 75 and 76)<br>***See* Advance Preparation** |

## Additional Information

**Advance Preparation** For Part 2, familiarize yourself with the Percent Version of *2-4-5-10 Frac-Tac-Toe.*

For the optional Extra Practice activity in Part 3, students who play *Fraction/Percent Concentration* will need the fraction/percent tiles provided on *Math Masters,* pages 75 and 76. The masters should be used to make two-sided copies—the fronts and backs of the tiles. Then the tiles are cut out. Each partnership will need one set of 24 tiles.

**Vocabulary** • **percent**

# Getting Started

## Mental Math and Reflexes

Write decimals from dictation. Then round the decimals to a specified place. *Suggestions:*

- Three and twenty-four hundredths rounded to the nearest tenth 3.24; 3.2
- Twenty-one and one-hundred sixty-three thousandths rounded to the nearest hundredth 21.163; 21.16
- Sixty and three-hundred fifty-seven thousandths rounded to the nearest tenth 60.357; 60.4
- Sixteen and seventy-six thousandths rounded to the nearest hundredth 16.076; 16.08
- Twenty-five and three thousandths rounded to the nearest tenth 25.003; 25.0

## Math Message

*Using your calculator, find a way to rename $\frac{4}{7}$ as a percent. Do not use the percent key.*

## Study Link 5.7 Follow-Up

Briefly review the answers with the class. You may wish to pose additional problems similar to the following:

- How many times did Chris Evert Lloyd win the Australian Open? 2
- What fraction is this of her total number of titles? $\frac{2}{18}$, or $\frac{1}{9}$
- How would you express this fraction as a decimal? $0.\overline{1}$

NOTE: Examples of fraction-to-decimal conversions in this lesson are obtained from an 11-digit calculator (such as the TI-15) that rounds in the 11th place. Some calculators have 8-, 9-, or 10-digit displays. Please check to see how the calculators used by your class handle such problems, and make appropriate adjustments as you work through the lesson.

Many calculators have special percent keys, which sometimes work in ways that can be hard to understand. This lesson avoids these keys in favor of a more conceptual approach. (See *Student Reference Book,* page 237 for details about the percent keys on the T1-15.)

# 1 Teaching the Lesson

## ✦ Math Message Follow-Up

WHOLE-CLASS DISCUSSION 

A fraction can be renamed as an equivalent percent by first renaming the fraction as a decimal, and then multiplying the result by 100.

*Example:* Rename $\frac{4}{7}$ as a percent.

1. Divide 4 by 7. The calculator displays 0.5714285714.
2. Multiply the result by 100.
   $100 * 0.5714285714 = 57.14285714$.
3. Round to the nearest whole percent: 57%.

## ✦ Reviewing the Meaning of Percent

WHOLE-CLASS DISCUSSION 

**Language Arts Link** The word ***percent*** comes from the Latin *per centum: per* means "for" and *centum* means "one hundred."

Remind students that just as a fraction represents a fraction of something, so a percent represents a percent of something. The "something" is the whole (or ONE or unit). To understand a percent, you must know what ONE is: 50% of $1 is not the same as 50% of $1 million.

To assess students' understanding of percents, ask them to restate the following examples in a variety of ways.

*Example 1:* Allison scored 80% on a test.

Possible ways to restate this situation:

- If the test had exactly 100 questions, Allison answered 80 of them correctly.
- Allison answered $\frac{80}{100}$ questions correctly.
- If the test had more than 100 questions, Allison correctly answered 80 out of every 100 questions.
- For every 100 questions, Allison answered 80 correctly.

Ask: *How many questions did Allison answer correctly if there were 100 questions on the test?* 80 *If there were 50 questions?* 40 *10 questions?* 8 *20 questions?* 16

*Example 2:* Emily spent 18% of the money she earned baby-sitting last summer on school clothes.

Possible ways to restate this situation:

- For every 100 dollars earned, Emily spent 18 dollars on school clothes.
- If 100 baby-sitting dollars were spent, 18 of those dollars were spent on school clothes.
- Emily spent \$18 out of every \$100 earned on school clothes.
- Emily spent $\frac{18}{100}$ of her money on school clothes.

Emphasize that "18 out of 100" does not mean that exactly \$100 was spent, but that \$18 out of every \$100 was spent on school clothes. Ask, *How much would Emily have spent if she earned \$200?* \$36 *If she earned \$400?* \$72 *If she earned \$50?* \$9

## ✦ Exploring the Purpose of Percents

WHOLE-CLASS DISCUSSION 

Percents are useful for making comparisons between numbers when the whole is not the same. For example, 8 correct on a test could be worse than 4 correct on a different test, depending on how many questions were on each test—8 out of 20, or 40%, is worse than 4 out of 5, or 80%. Percent makes comparisons easier when the whole or ONE differs.

Use the following situation to emphasize that percents are useful when comparing quantities when the unit differs.

Kris earned \$167 setting up new computers for her neighbors. She spent \$43 on software. Clay earned \$219 teaching piano to children. He spent \$51 on sheet

### Converting Fractions to Decimals and Percents

*Example* Teneil used her calculator to rename the following fraction as a decimal and as a percent.

$\frac{14}{23}$ (Fraction) 14 ÷ 23 = 0.6086956522 (Decimal) 100 × 0.6086956522 = 60.86956522% (Percent)

Teneil only needed to work with a whole percent, so she rounded 60.86956522% to 61%.

1. Use your calculator to convert each fraction to a decimal. Write all of the digits shown in the display. Then write the equivalent percent rounded to the nearest whole percent. The first row has been done for you.

| Fraction | Decimal | Percent (rounded to the nearest whole percent) |
|---|---|---|
| $\frac{18}{35}$ | 0.5142857143 | 51% |
| $\frac{12}{67}$ | 0.1791044776 | 18% |
| $\frac{24}{93}$ | 0.2580645161 | 26% |
| $\frac{13}{24}$ | 0.5416666667 | 54% |
| $\frac{576}{1,339}$ | 0.43017177 | 43% |

2. Linell got 80% correct on a spelling test. If the test had 20 questions, how many did Linell get correct? 16 questions

3. Jamie spent 50% of his money on a baseball cap. The cap cost \$15. How much money did Jamie have at the beginning? \$30

4. Hunter got 75% correct on a music test. If he got 15 questions correct, how many questions were on the test? 20 questions

STUDENT PAGE

✦ Math Journal 1, p. 149

Journal pages 149 and 150 accompany the *Changing Fractions to Percents* activity on the following page.

### Converting Fractions to Decimals and Percents (cont.)

5. Below is a list of 10 animals and the average number of hours per day that each spends sleeping.

   Write the fraction of a day that each animal sleeps. Then calculate the equivalent decimal and percent (rounded to the nearest whole percent). You may use your calculator. The first row has been done for you.

| Animal | Average Hours of Sleep per Day | Fraction of Day Spent Sleeping | Decimal Equivalent | Percent of Day Spent Sleeping (to the nearest whole percent) |
|---|---|---|---|---|
| koala | 22 | $\frac{22}{24}$ | $0.91\overline{6}$ | 92% |
| sloth | 20 | $\frac{20}{24}$ | $0.8\overline{3}$ | 83% |
| armadillo and opossum | 19 | $\frac{19}{24}$ | $0.791\overline{6}$ | 79% |
| lemur | 16 | $\frac{16}{24}$ | $0.\overline{6}$ | 67% |
| hamster and squirrel | 14 | $\frac{14}{24}$ | $0.58\overline{3}$ | 58% |
| cat and pig | 13 | $\frac{13}{24}$ | $0.541\overline{6}$ | 54% |
| spiny anteater | 12 | $\frac{12}{24}$ | 0.5 | 50% |

*Source: The Top 10 of Everything 2000*

6. The total number of horses in the world is about 60,800,000. China is the country with the greatest number of horses (about 8,900,000). What percent of the world's horses live in China? About 15%

7. In the United States, about 45% of the population has blood type O. About how many people out of every 100 have blood type O? About 45 people

8. About 11 out of every 100 households in the United States has a parakeet. How would you express this as a percent? 11%

STUDENT PAGE

✦ Math Journal 1, p. 150

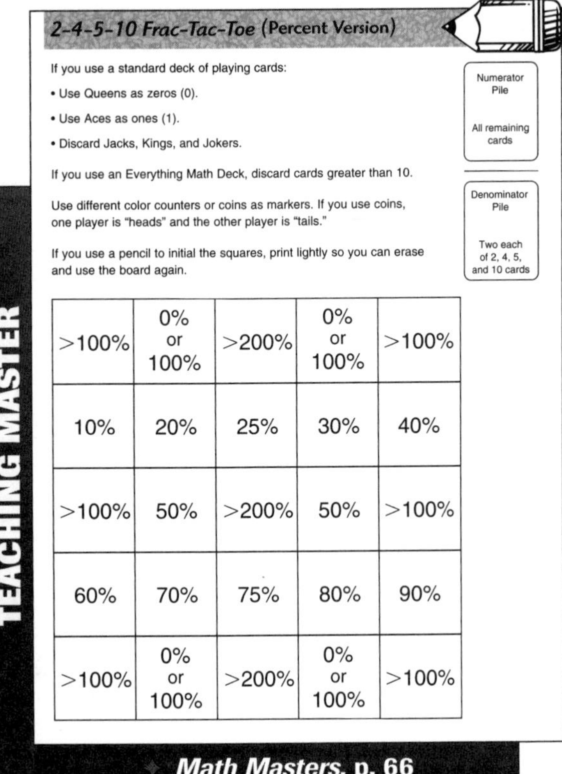

**2-4-5-10 Frac-Tac-Toe (Percent Version)**

If you use a standard deck of playing cards:

- Use Queens as zeros (0).
- Use Aces as ones (1).
- Discard Jacks, Kings, and Jokers.

If you use an Everything Math Deck, discard cards greater than 10.

Use different color counters or coins as markers. If you use coins, one player is "heads" and the other player is "tails."

If you use a pencil to initial the squares, print lightly so you can erase and use the board again.

Numerator Pile: All remaining cards

Denominator Pile: Two each of 2, 4, 5, and 10 cards

| | | | | |
|---|---|---|---|---|
| >100% | 0% or 100% | >200% | 0% or 100% | >100% |
| 10% | 20% | 25% | 30% | 40% |
| >100% | 50% | >200% | 50% | >100% |
| 60% | 70% | 75% | 80% | 90% |
| >100% | 0% or 100% | >200% | 0% or 100% | >100% |

TEACHING MASTER

*Math Masters,* p. 66

**Math Boxes 5.8**

1. a. Make up a set of at least twelve numbers that have the following landmarks.

   Minimum: 3
   Maximum: 9
   Median: 7
   Mode: 7

   Sample answer: 3, 3, 4, 5, 5, 7, 7, 7, 7, 7, 8, 9

   b. Make a bar graph for this set of numbers.

2. Complete the table.

| Fraction | Decimal | Percent |
|---|---|---|
| $\frac{19}{20}$ | 0.95 | 95% |
| $\frac{4}{5}$ | 0.80 | 80% |
| $\frac{3}{9}$ | $0.\overline{3}$ | $33\frac{1}{3}$% |
| $\frac{6}{8}$ | 0.75 | 75% |
| $\frac{2}{3}$ | $0.\overline{6}$ | $66\frac{2}{3}$% |

3. Measure the length and width of each of the following objects to the nearest centimeter. Answers vary.

   a. pinkie finger — length: ___ cm width: ___ cm

   b. notebook — length: ___ cm width: ___ cm

   c. pencil — length: ___ cm width: ___ cm

4. I am a number. If you double $\frac{1}{3}$ of me, you get 14. What number am I? 21

5. Write five names for 100.

   $10^2$
   $\frac{1}{2}$ of 200
   one tenth of one thousand
   (216 − 200) + 84
   C
   Sample answers:

STUDENT PAGE

*Math Journal 1,* p. 151

music. Who spent the larger portion of her or his earnings?

This situation illustrates why fractions are renamed so they have the same denominator (if that is easy to do), or fractions are converted to percents (if a common denominator is difficult to find). In effect, conversion to percents gives a "common denominator" of 100 to all such fractions, thereby making them easy to compare.

**Adjusting the Activity** Have students think about the use of fractions. Kris spent $\frac{43}{167}$ of her money, which is about $\frac{40}{160}$, or $\frac{1}{4}$. Clay spent $\frac{51}{219}$ of his money, which is about $\frac{50}{200}$, or $\frac{1}{4}$. They both spent about $\frac{1}{4}$ of their earnings. In order to answer the question, they need a more exact way to compare the portions spent.

To extend the activity, have students refine their fraction estimates. Ask, *Is $\frac{43}{167}$ more or less than $\frac{1}{4}$?* More, because 43 ∗ 4 is 172. *Is $\frac{51}{219}$ more or less than $\frac{1}{4}$?* Less, because 51 ∗ 4 is 204. *Can students think of a reason for finding a more exact way to compare the portions?* For example, if they had both been more than or less than $\frac{1}{4}$, it might have been difficult, if not impossible, to compare them further without computation. You might want to know how different the portions actually are.

## Changing Fractions to Percents

(*Math Journal 1,* pp. 149 and 150; *Math Masters,* p. 479)

PARTNER ACTIVITY

Answer the question posed in the above number story about Kris and Clay. Use a calculator to change $\frac{43}{167}$ and $\frac{51}{219}$ to decimals and then to percents. Mathematically, a comparison with decimals is equivalent to a comparison with percents, but in everyday situations, people usually prefer percents.

For $\frac{43}{167}$, an 11-digit display shows 0.2574850299. For $\frac{51}{219}$, the display shows 0.2328767123. These decimals can be easily changed to percents after rewriting them in hundredths. That can be done in either of two ways:

- Round to the nearest hundredth. 0.2574850299 becomes 0.26, or 26%, and 0.2328767123 becomes 0.23, or 23%.

▷ Truncate the decimals after the hundredths place. 0.2574850299 becomes 0.25, or 25%, and 0.2328767123 becomes 0.23, or 23%.

Kris spent $\frac{\$43}{\$167}$, or about 26%, and Clay spent $\frac{\$51}{\$219}$, or about 23%. So Kris spent a larger portion of her earnings than Clay did of his.

Some students may be unclear about how to interpret the calculator display when converting a decimal to a percent.

Review the example on page 149 with the class. Do additional problems if necessary.

Students work in partnerships to complete pages 149 and 150. Circulate and assist as necessary.

**ONGOING ASSESSMENT**

**Students complete an Exit Slip explaining in words the process for converting the fraction $\frac{18}{25}$ to a percent with or without a calculator.**

**Percent Problems** — Study Link 5.8

1. Convert the following fractions to decimals and percents. Round to the nearest whole percent.

| Fraction | Decimal | Percent (rounded to the nearest whole percent) |
|---|---|---|
| $\frac{3}{4}$ | 0.75 | 75% |
| $\frac{14}{16}$ | 0.875 | 88% |
| $\frac{15}{25}$ | 0.6 | 60% |
| $\frac{17}{20}$ | 0.85 | 85% |
| $\frac{3}{8}$ | 0.375 | 38% |

2. On the back of this page, explain how you could find the percent equivalent to $\frac{17}{20}$ without using a calculator. Answers vary.

3. Write the five fractions from Problem 1 in order from least to greatest.
$\frac{3}{8}$ $\frac{15}{25}$ $\frac{3}{4}$ $\frac{17}{20}$ $\frac{14}{16}$

4. Katie spent 50% of her money on shoes for soccer. The shoes cost $65. How much money did Katie start with? $130

5. Tom got 70% correct on a music test. If he got 7 questions correct, how many questions were on the test? 10 questions

6. Louis got 16 words correct on his vocabulary test. This was 80%. How many words did he miss? 4 words
Explain how you got your answer. Sample answer: If 80% is 16 words, then 10% is $\frac{1}{8}$ of 16 words, or 2 words. So 100% is 10 ∗ 2, or 20 words. The test had 20 words. Louis missed 20 − 16 = 4 words.

**Challenge**

7. Lincoln School raised $3,000 for charity. This is 30% of the school's goal. What is Lincoln School's goal? $10,000

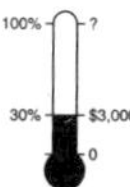


STUDY LINK MASTER

✦ Math Masters, p. 272

## Ongoing Learning & Practice

### ✦ Playing *2-4-5-10 Frac-Tac-Toe* (Percent Version)
(*Student Reference Book,* pp. 274–276; *Math Masters,* pp. 62 and 66)

PARTNER ACTIVITY 

Play the Percent Version of *2-4-5-10 Frac-Tac-Toe.* The game is like the Decimal Version played in Lesson 5.7, except that players convert fractions to percents. Distribute one of each of *Math Masters,* pages 62 and 66 to each partnership. Partners will also need counters (or pennies), a calculator, and 4 each of the number cards 0–10.

▼ *Student Reference Book,* page 278 accompanies the playing *Fraction/Percent Concentration* activity on the following page.

Games

***Fraction/Percent Concentration***

**Materials** ☐ 1 set of Fraction/Percent Tiles (*Math Masters,* pp. 75 and 76)
☐ calculator

**Players** 2 or 3

**Object of the game** To match equivalent fraction tiles and percent tiles.

**Directions**

1. Spread out the tiles facedown on the playing surface. Create two separate piles—a fraction pile and a percent pile. Mix up the tiles in each pile. The backs of the 12 fraction tiles should have the fraction $\frac{a}{b}$ showing. The backs of the 12 percent tiles should have the percent symbol % showing.
2. Players take turns. At each turn, a player turns over a fraction tile and a percent tile. If the fraction and percent are equivalent, the player keeps the tiles. If the tiles do not match, the player turns the tiles facedown.
3. Players may use a calculator to check each other's matches.
4. The game ends when all tiles have been taken. The player with the most tiles wins.

Fraction/Percent Tiles

| | | | |
|---|---|---|---|
| 10% | 20% | 25% | 30% |
| 40% | 50% | 60% | 70% |
| 75% | 80% | 90% | 100% |
| $\frac{1}{2}$ | $\frac{1}{4}$ | $\frac{3}{4}$ | $\frac{1}{5}$ |
| $\frac{2}{5}$ | $\frac{3}{5}$ | $\frac{4}{5}$ | $\frac{1}{10}$ |
| $\frac{3}{10}$ | $\frac{7}{10}$ | $\frac{9}{10}$ | $\frac{2}{2}$ |

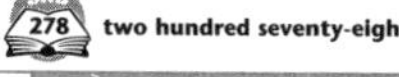


two hundred seventy-eight

STUDENT PAGE

✦ Student Reference Book, p. 278

### ✦ Math Boxes 5.8 (*Math Journal 1,* p. 151)

INDEPENDENT ACTIVITY 

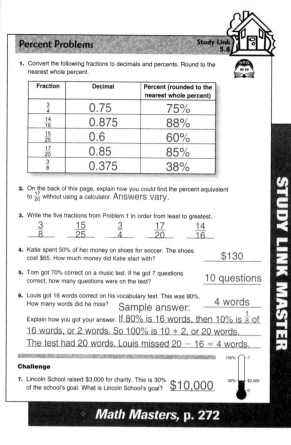

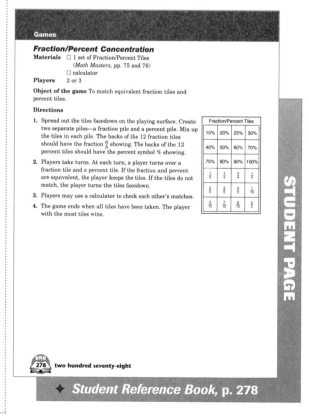

**Mixed Review** Math Boxes in this lesson are paired with Math Boxes in Lesson 5.6. The skill in Problem 1 is a prerequisite for Unit 6.

Fraction/Percent Concentration Tiles (front)

| 10% | 20% | 25% | 30% |
|---|---|---|---|
| 40% | 50% | 60% | 70% |
| 75% | 80% | 90% | 100% |
| $\frac{1}{2}$ | $\frac{1}{4}$ | $\frac{3}{4}$ | $\frac{1}{5}$ |
| $\frac{2}{5}$ | $\frac{3}{5}$ | $\frac{4}{5}$ | $\frac{1}{10}$ |
| $\frac{3}{10}$ | $\frac{7}{10}$ | $\frac{9}{10}$ | $\frac{2}{2}$ |

TEACHING MASTER

Math Masters, p. 75

Fraction/Percent Concentration Tiles (back)

| % | % | % | % |
|---|---|---|---|
| % | % | % | % |
| % | % | % | % |
| $\frac{a}{b}$ | $\frac{a}{b}$ | $\frac{a}{b}$ | $\frac{a}{b}$ |
| $\frac{a}{b}$ | $\frac{a}{b}$ | $\frac{a}{b}$ | $\frac{a}{b}$ |
| $\frac{a}{b}$ | $\frac{a}{b}$ | $\frac{a}{b}$ | $\frac{a}{b}$ |

TEACHING MASTER

Math Masters, p. 76

### ✦ Study Link 5.8 (*Math Masters,* p. 272)

**Home Connection** Students practice converting fractions to decimals and decimals to percents; comparing fractions by converting them to decimals and to percents; and using percents to solve number stories.

## 3 Options for Individualizing

### ✦ EXTRA PRACTICE Playing *Fraction/Percent Concentration*

(*Student Reference Book,* p. 278; *Math Masters,* pp. 75 and 76)

PARTNER ACTIVITY **15–30 min**

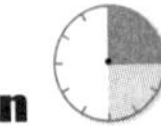

This game can be used to help students memorize some of the easy fraction/percent equivalencies.

### ✦ LANGUAGE DIVERSITY Building Background for Mathematics Words

PARTNER ACTIVITY **15–30 min**

Pair a student learning English with a proficient English speaker. Have students list situations where quantities are reported in fractions, in decimals, or in percents. *For example:*

| Fractions | Decimals | Percents |
|---|---|---|
| $\frac{2}{3}$ of a cup (not 0.66 of a cup) | \$0.75 (not 75% of a dollar) | 10% off (not $\frac{10}{100}$ of a dollar off) |
| $\frac{3}{4}$ of a tank of gas | 5.65 centimeters in length | 80% correct on a spelling test |

Extend the activity by having students record their lists on chart paper that can be displayed in the room.

# 5.9 Bar and Circle Graphs

**OBJECTIVES** **To construct and label bar graphs; and to discuss properties of circle graphs.**

| summaries | materials |
|---|---|
| **1 Teaching the Lesson** | |
| Students construct and label a bar graph that is based on class data. They begin a discussion of circle graphs and describe how a circle graph might be made. [Data and Chance] | □ *Math Journal 1,* p. 152<br>□ Study Link 5.8<br>***See*** **Advance Preparation** |
| **2 Ongoing Learning & Practice** | |
| Students use a multiplication algorithm of their choice to find products of multidigit whole numbers. [Operations and Computation]<br>Students practice and maintain skills through Math Boxes and Study Link activities. | □ *Math Journal 1,* pp. 153 and 154<br>□ Study Link Master *(Math Masters,* p. 273) |
| **3 Options for Individualizing** | |
| **Enrichment** Students act out the construction of a circle graph. [Data and Chance]<br>**Language Diversity** Students make a poster, labeling parts of a circle. [Data and Chance] | □ string; masking tape; ruler; paper circles<br>□ posterboard or poster paper (optional)<br>***See*** **Advance Preparation** |

### Additional Information

**Advance Preparation** Keep a record of the snack-survey data students collect in Part 1. You will need this data for Lesson 5.11.

Read the optional Enrichment activity in Part 3, and consider using it to begin the lesson. Many teachers have found it an effective introduction. Cut six 6-foot lengths of string and tie a small loop at one end of each (big enough to fit around the end of a pencil.) Use a compass to draw a circle, 7 inches in diameter, on unlined paper. Mark the center of the circle with a large dot. Make another circle, just like it, on another sheet of paper. You will also need masking tape (up to 40 feet) and a ruler.

**Vocabulary** • **bar graph** • **circle (or pie) graph**

## Getting Started

### Math Message

*Answer Problem 1 on journal page 152.*

## Mental Math and Reflexes

Students write decimal and percent equivalents for easy fractions without using a calculator. *Suggestions:*

- $\frac{1}{4}$ 0.25; 25%
- $\frac{3}{4}$ 0.75; 75%
- $\frac{3}{5}$ 0.6; 60%
- $\frac{14}{100}$ 0.14; 14%
- $\frac{6}{100}$ 0.06; 6%
- $\frac{7}{20}$ 0.35; 35%

## Study Link 5.8 Follow-Up

Briefly review answers. Have volunteers share strategies for converting $\frac{17}{20}$ to a percent with and without a calculator. Review strategies for solving Problems 4–7. Strategies might include the following:

- For Problem 4, double the amount to find the total.
- For Problem 5, notice that each question must be worth 10%, so there are 10 questions in 100%.
- For Problem 6, use equivalent fractions. 16 out of something is the same as 8 out of 10. Since 16 is 2 * 8, there would be 2 * 10, or 20 questions.
- For Problem 7, 30% is $3,000. 10% would be $1,000. There are ten [10%] in 100%, so the answer is $10,000.

# 1 Teaching the Lesson

## Math Message Follow-Up
(*Math Journal 1,* p. 152)

WHOLE-CLASS ACTIVITY 

Tally the results of the snack survey. On the board, the Class Data Pad, or a transparency, list the five snack choices and the total vote each received. Ask students to record these totals in Problem 2 in their journals and to find and record the total number of votes for all choices.

## Reviewing the Parts of Bar Graphs
(*Math Journal 1,* p. 152)

WHOLE-CLASS DISCUSSION 

Remind students that a **bar graph** should have the following parts:

1. A *title* that describes what is being graphed.
2. A list of the *groups* or *categories* for which bars are drawn.
3. A *number line with a scale.* The scale is used to draw bars of lengths that show the amount of data in each group or category. The scale is usually labeled.

## Graphing Class Snack-Survey Data
(*Math Journal 1,* p. 152)

PARTNER ACTIVITY 

Most students find that bar graphs are easy to read but difficult to construct. Ask students to work in pairs to

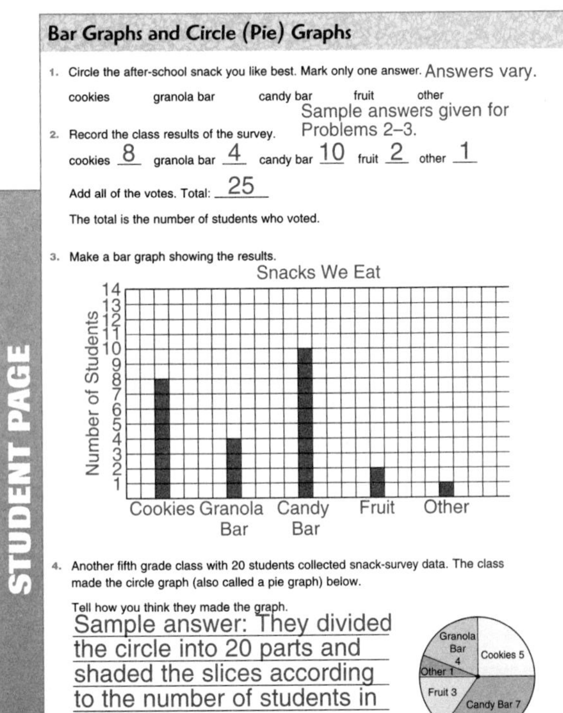

STUDENT PAGE

**Bar Graphs and Circle (Pie) Graphs**

1. Circle the after-school snack you like best. Mark only one answer. Answers vary.
   cookies granola bar candy bar fruit other
2. Record the class results of the survey. Sample answers given for Problems 2–3.
   cookies 8 granola bar 4 candy bar 10 fruit 2 other 1
   Add all of the votes. Total: 25
   The total is the number of students who voted.
3. Make a bar graph showing the results.



4. Another fifth grade class with 20 students collected snack-survey data. The class made the circle graph (also called a pie graph) below.
   Tell how you think they made the graph.
   Sample answer: They divided the circle into 20 parts and shaded the slices according to the number of students in each category.



✦ *Math Journal 1,* p. 152

make the bar graph in Problem 3. Remind them to label each part of their graphs and to give them titles. Circulate and assist as needed. After 5 to 10 minutes, bring the class together. Ask several students to explain their work.

Expect students to take a variety of approaches in graphing the snack-survey data. Some will use horizontal bars; others, vertical bars. Some will draw thick bars; others will draw thin ones, or perhaps draw lines instead of bars. In all cases, insist on good labeling and a title for each graph.

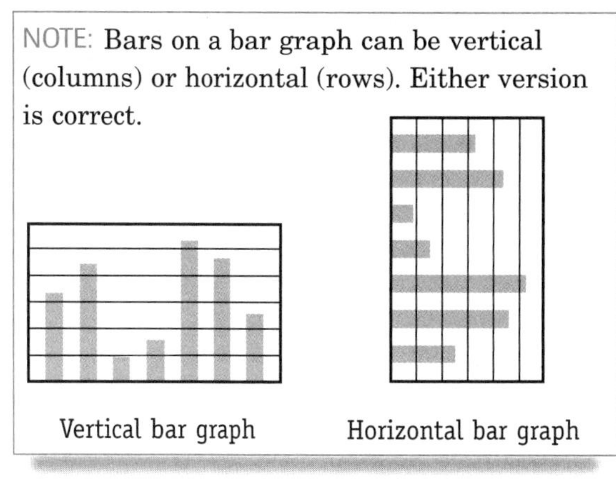

NOTE: Bars on a bar graph can be vertical (columns) or horizontal (rows). Either version is correct.
Vertical bar graph
Horizontal bar graph


## ✦ Discussing Properties of Circle Graphs
(*Math Journal 1,* p. 152)

WHOLE-CLASS DISCUSSION

Use Problem 4 on the journal page to begin a discussion of **circle graphs.** Ask plenty of questions, and encourage responses such as the following:

- What is the graph in Problem 4 called, and why? It's called a circle graph, because a circle has been divided to show each kind of snack. It's also called a **pie graph** because the circle is sliced up like a pie—one slice for each kind of snack.

NOTE: You and the students can decide whether *circle* or *pie* is the favorite term for use in class. Mention both names, however, because both are used extensively.

**Adjusting the Activity** If necessary, review vocabulary for circles: *circumference, radius, diameter,* and *center.* Invite students learning English to make a poster with the parts of a circle. Have them present their poster to the class.

- Why do you think the slices are different sizes? Popular snacks get bigger slices; less popular snacks get smaller slices.
- Do you notice any interesting slices or other features in the graph? For example, 5 students out of 20 picked cookies—that's $\frac{1}{4}$ of the students—and you can see that the Cookie part is $\frac{1}{4}$ of the pie. Look at Candy Bar and Fruit: half the students (10) picked one of those, and those two pieces together are half the pie.
- How do you think the graph was made? One way would have been to divide the circle into 20 slices of the same size, and then call 3 of the slices "Fruit," 7 of the slices "Candy Bar," and so on for the other snack choices.

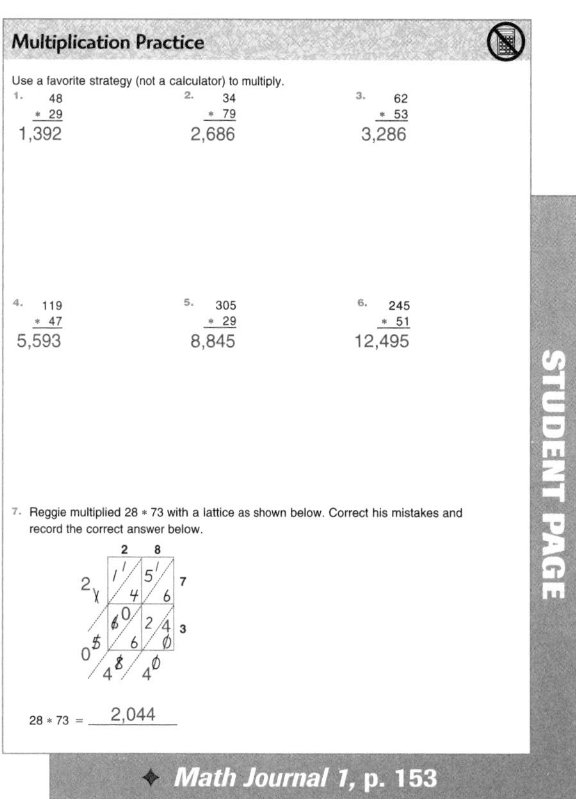
**Multiplication Practice**

Use a favorite strategy (not a calculator) to multiply.

1. 48 * 29 = 1,392
2. 34 * 79 = 2,686
3. 62 * 53 = 3,286
4. 119 * 47 = 5,593
5. 305 * 29 = 8,845
6. 245 * 51 = 12,495
7. Reggie multiplied 28 * 73 with a lattice as shown below. Correct his mistakes and record the correct answer below.

28 * 73 = 2,044

STUDENT PAGE

✦ *Math Journal 1,* p. 153

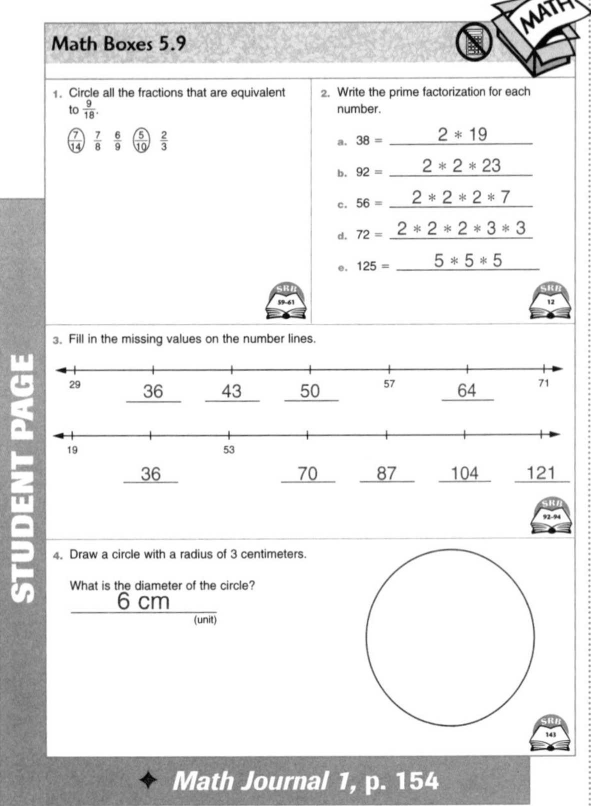

STUDENT PAGE

**Math Boxes 5.9**

1. Circle all the fractions that are equivalent to $\frac{9}{18}$.

$\frac{7}{14}$ $\frac{7}{8}$ $\frac{6}{9}$ $\frac{5}{10}$ $\frac{2}{3}$

2. Write the prime factorization for each number.
   a. 38 = 2 ∗ 19
   b. 92 = 2 ∗ 2 ∗ 23
   c. 56 = 2 ∗ 2 ∗ 2 ∗ 7
   d. 72 = 2 ∗ 2 ∗ 2 ∗ 3 ∗ 3
   e. 125 = 5 ∗ 5 ∗ 5

3. Fill in the missing values on the number lines.

29, 36, 43, 50, 57, 64, 71

19, 36, 53, 70, 87, 104, 121

4. Draw a circle with a radius of 3 centimeters.

What is the diameter of the circle? 6 cm (unit)

✦ *Math Journal 1,* p. 154

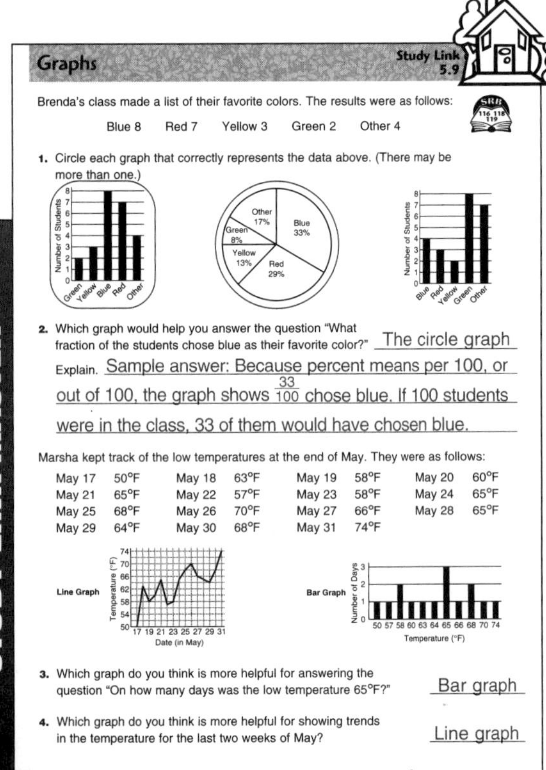

STUDY LINK MASTER

**Graphs** — Study Link 5.9

Brenda's class made a list of their favorite colors. The results were as follows:

Blue 8 Red 7 Yellow 3 Green 2 Other 4

1. Circle each graph that correctly represents the data above. (There may be more than one.)



2. Which graph would help you answer the question "What fraction of the students chose blue as their favorite color?" The circle graph

Explain. Sample answer: Because percent means per 100, or out of 100, the graph shows $\frac{33}{100}$ chose blue. If 100 students were in the class, 33 of them would have chosen blue.

Marsha kept track of the low temperatures at the end of May. They were as follows:

| | | | | | | | |
|---|---|---|---|---|---|---|---|
| May 17 | 50°F | May 18 | 63°F | May 19 | 58°F | May 20 | 60°F |
| May 21 | 65°F | May 22 | 57°F | May 23 | 58°F | May 24 | 65°F |
| May 25 | 68°F | May 26 | 70°F | May 27 | 66°F | May 28 | 65°F |
| May 29 | 64°F | May 30 | 68°F | May 31 | 74°F | | |



3. Which graph do you think is more helpful for answering the question "On how many days was the low temperature 65°F?" Bar graph

4. Which graph do you think is more helpful for showing trends in the temperature for the last two weeks of May? Line graph

*Math Masters,* p. 273

# 2 Ongoing Learning & Practice

## ✦ Practicing Multiplication of Whole Numbers (*Math Journal 1,* p. 153)

INDEPENDENT ACTIVITY 

Students use a multiplication algorithm of their choice to find products of multidigit whole numbers.

## ✦ Math Boxes 5.9 (*Math Journal 1,* p. 154)

INDEPENDENT ACTIVITY 

**Mixed Review** Math Boxes in this lesson are paired with Math Boxes in Lesson 5.11. The skill in Problem 1 is a prerequisite for Unit 6.

## ✦ Study Link 5.9 (*Math Masters,* p. 273)

**Home Connection** Students match graphs with data and choose the representation they feel best shows the results.

# 3 Options for Individualizing

## ✦ ENRICHMENT Acting Out the Construction of a Circle Graph

WHOLE-CLASS ACTIVITY **15–30 min**

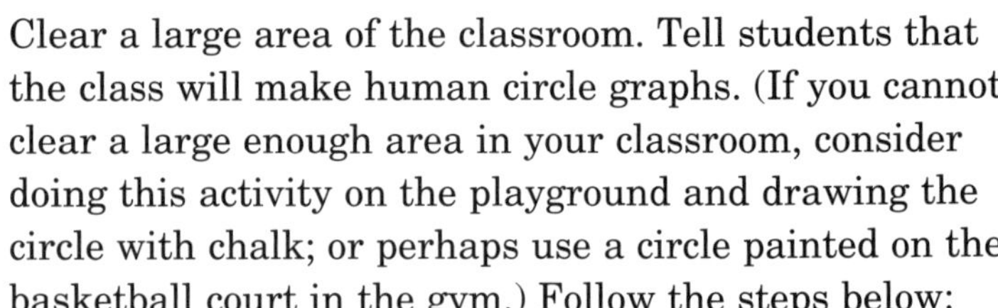

Clear a large area of the classroom. Tell students that the class will make human circle graphs. (If you cannot clear a large enough area in your classroom, consider doing this activity on the playground and drawing the circle with chalk; or perhaps use a circle painted on the basketball court in the gym.) Follow the steps below:

1. **First, make a large circle. This is the pie.**
   a. On the board, record the numbers of boys and girls in the class.
   b. Stick a small piece of tape to the floor. This will mark the center of the circle.
   c. Put a pencil through the loop end of one of the 6-foot lengths of string. This string compass will be

used to draw a 6-foot-radius circle. Ask, *What is the diameter of a circle whose radius is 6 feet?* 12 feet

d. One student holds the free end of the string to the floor, on top of the tape at the center of the circle.

e. A second student holds the pencil end of the string compass taut and uses it to slowly trace out a circle.

f. As the student traces out the circle, follow along and lay masking tape on the floor to create a circle of tape.

**2. Make a human circle graph for the boy-girl data.**

a. Boys stand together along one part of the circle. Girls stand together along another part of the circle.

b. Everyone faces the center of the circle. Students adjust their distances relative to one another until they are all equally spaced around the circle.

**3. Make a paper-and-pencil model for the human graph.**

a. Place one of the 7-inch-diameter paper circles so that its center is on top of the center of the human circle.

b. Put a pencil through the loop ends of two different 6-foot lengths of string.

c. Place the pencil point at the center of the circle.

d. Find a boy and girl who are standing next to each other and pull the free end of one string between them. Ask them to hold it taut.

e. Find the other boy and girl standing next to each other and repeat, using the other string.

f. Finally, ask any student who has a free hand to use a ruler to draw a line along each of the two strings from the center to the edge of the paper circle.

As students remain standing in the circle, help them to summarize the activity. Point out common features of the human graph and the paper-and-pencil graph. *For example:*

- There are 10 boys and 15 girls. So $\frac{10}{25}$ of the class are boys. Boys take up $\frac{10}{25}$ of the circumference of the human graph. The paper graph shows that, too. The slice of the pie representing boys is $\frac{10}{25}$ of the whole pie.
- Then ask, *What fraction of any class of fifth graders would you expect to be boys (or girls)?* About one-half *Does our class seem to be typical?* Answers vary by class.

NOTE: Laying a continuous strip of tape is faster than laying several smaller strips. But a continuous strip uses much more tape (about 40 feet). (The student should not mark the carpet or floor with the pencil. His or her objective is to trace out the path that you tape.)

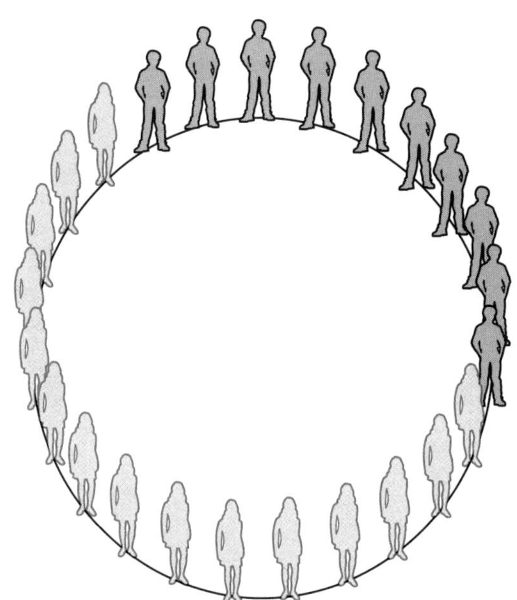

Human circle graph for boy-girl data

# 5.10 The Percent Circle: Reading Circle Graphs

**OBJECTIVE** **To use the Percent Circle to find the percents of circle graphs.**

| summaries | materials |
|---|---|
| **1 Teaching the Lesson** | |
| Students are introduced to the Percent Circle. They use the Percent Circle to find what percent of the area of a circle graph is represented by each piece. [Data and Chance; Measurement and Reference Frames] | □ *Math Journal 1,* pp. 155 and 156<br>□ Study Link 5.9<br>□ Teaching Masters (*Math Masters,* pp. 77 and 78), for teacher only<br>□ Teaching Master (*Math Masters,* p. 79; optional)<br>□ Transparencies (*Math Masters,* pp. 77 and 78; optional)<br>□ Geometry Template<br>***See* Advance Preparation** |
| **2 Ongoing Learning & Practice** | |
| Students practice dividing multidigit whole numbers by 1-digit whole numbers. [Operations and Computation]<br>Students practice and maintain skills through Math Boxes and Study Link activities. | □ *Math Journal 1,* pp. 157 and 158<br>□ Study Link Masters (*Math Masters,* pp. 274 and 275) |
| **3 Options for Individualizing** | |
| **Enrichment** Students conduct a class experiment to determine which eye is dominant. They post the class results on the Probability Meter. [Data and Chance]<br>**Extra Practice** Students use a Percent Circle to measure sectors in a circle graph. [Measurement and Reference Frames] | □ Teaching Masters (*Math Masters,* pp. 77 and 80)<br>□ calculator<br>***See* Advance Preparation** |

## Additional Information

**Advance Preparation** For Part 1, if you are not using an overhead projector, cut out a copy of the Percent Circle on *Math Masters,* page 77. Make a hole in the center of the circle. Cut out the circle graph on *Math Masters,* page 78 and tape it to the board.

For the optional Enrichment activity in Part 3, draw a circle with a 2-inch diameter on a piece of paper. Color the circle black and tape the paper to the board. Cut out a copy of the Percent Circle on *Math Masters,* page 77, and make a hole in the center of the circle (or use the one you cut out for Part 1). You will need the Probability Meter and a stick-on note. For the optional Extra Practice activity in Part 3, divide each circle into three or four sections and label the sections with a letter before copying the master. Note that you also enter the section letters in the boxes below the circle graph (to the left of the answer blanks).

**Vocabulary** • **Percent Circle**

## Getting Started

### Mental Math and Reflexes

Students stand in their places and rotate for given degrees and fractions of a circle. *Suggestions:*

- Turn $\frac{1}{4}$-turn to the right.
- Turn 90° to the right.
- Turn $\frac{1}{2}$-turn clockwise.
- Turn 60° to the left.
- Turn 30° to the left.
- Turn $\frac{3}{4}$-turn counter-clockwise.

### Math Message

*Look at the circle graph in Problem 1 on journal page 155. For each piece of the graph, estimate what fraction, and what percent of the whole circle, it is.*

### Study Link 5.9 Follow-Up

Students share their answers.

For Problem 2, expect a variety of answers. *For example:*

- With the bar graph, it is easy to tell exactly how many people liked each color.
- With the pie graph, the percents make it easy to name a fraction that tells what part of the whole class liked each color—for example, it looks like about $\frac{1}{3}$ of the class liked red the most, and about $\frac{1}{3}$ liked blue.

For Problem 3, the bar graph is more helpful for answering the question quickly. Expect that some students may say that they think that the line graph is best. Accept this answer, too, with a reasonable explanation.

For Problem 4, the best answer would be the line graph because it displays a trend: The low temperatures rose over the course of the two weeks.

# 1 Teaching the Lesson

### Math Message Follow-Up
(*Math Journal 1,* p. 155)

WHOLE-CLASS DISCUSSION

Ask a few students to share their estimates.

### Introducing the Percent Circle
(*Math Masters,* p. 79)

WHOLE-CLASS DISCUSSION

NOTE: If Geometry Templates are not available, students should cut a Percent Circle from *Math Masters,* page 79.

Ask students to describe in their own words the features of the **Percent Circle** on their Geometry Template. Be sure the following features are included in the discussion:

- There are 100 equally-spaced marks around the circle.
- The 100 marks show the edges of thin pieces, shaped like slices of pie, that divide the circle into 100 pieces.
- The area of each piece is $\frac{1}{100}$, or 1 percent (1%) of the total area of the circle.
- The complete circle includes all 100 pieces and represents 100%.

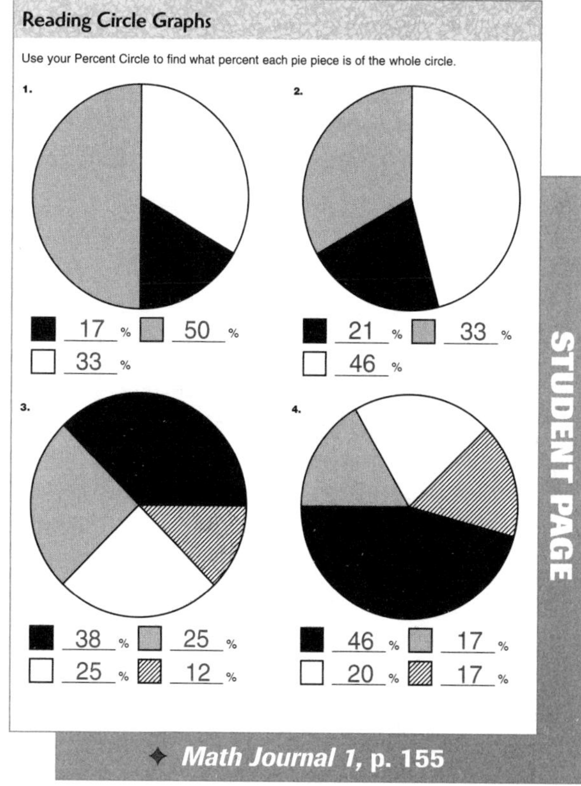

**Reading Circle Graphs**

Use your Percent Circle to find what percent each pie piece is of the whole circle.

1. ■ 17 % ▩ 50 % □ 33 %

2. ■ 21 % ▩ 33 % □ 46 %

3. ■ 38 % ▩ 25 % □ 25 % ▨ 12 %

4. ■ 46 % ▩ 17 % □ 20 % ▨ 17 %

STUDENT PAGE

✦ *Math Journal 1,* p. 155

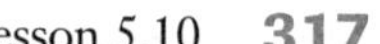

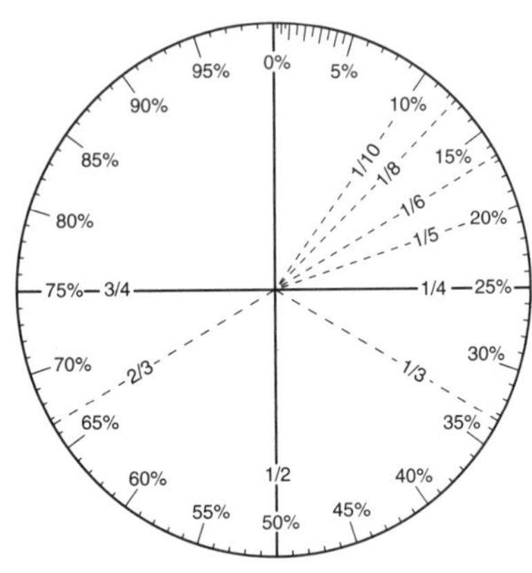


The Percent Circle from *Math Masters,* page 77

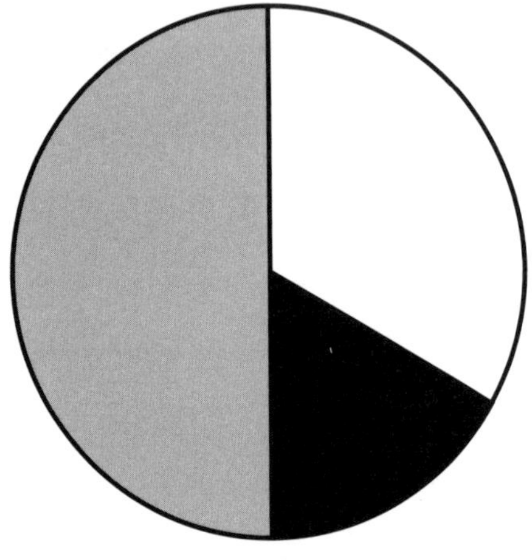

The circle graph from *Math Masters,* page 78

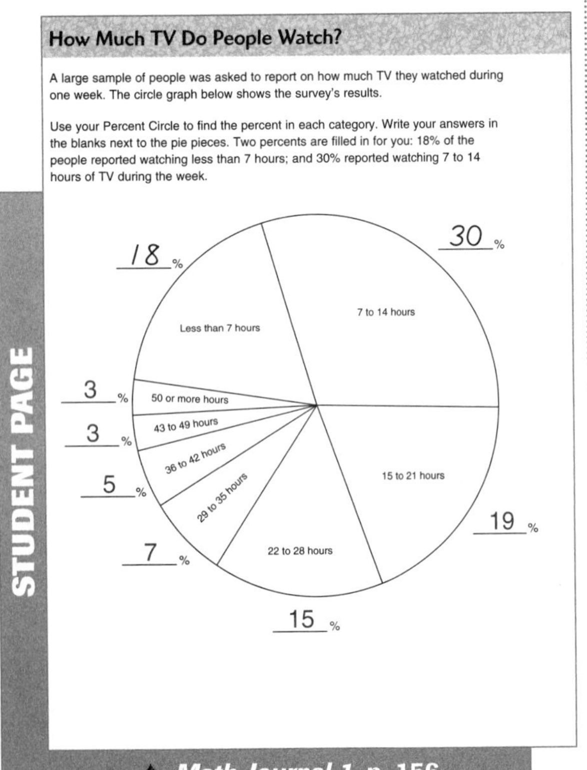

**How Much TV Do People Watch?**

A large sample of people was asked to report on how much TV they watched during one week. The circle graph below shows the survey's results.

Use your Percent Circle to find the percent in each category. Write your answers in the blanks next to the pie pieces. Two percents are filled in for you: 18% of the people reported watching less than 7 hours; and 30% reported watching 7 to 14 hours of TV during the week.



STUDENT PAGE

✦ *Math Journal 1,* p. 156

Point out that the arc from 0% to 5% has additional marks at the $\frac{1}{2}$ positions. Ask: *What percents do these marks represent?* They represent $\frac{1}{2}\%$, $1\frac{1}{2}\%$, $2\frac{1}{2}\%$, $3\frac{1}{2}\%$, and $4\frac{1}{2}\%$.

## ✦ Demonstrating Methods for Using a Percent Circle (*Math Journal 1,* p. 155; *Math Masters,* pp. 77 and 78)

WHOLE-CLASS DISCUSSION

Demonstrate how to use the Percent Circle for Problem 1 on the journal page, to find what percent of the whole graph each piece of the circle graph is. Use overhead transparencies or copies of *Math Masters,* pages 77 and 78. *(See the margin.)*

Two possible methods for using the Percent Circle are described below. Examples of the methods are shown.

**Method 1: Direct Comparison**

1. Center the Percent Circle over the center of the circle graph.
2. Aim the Percent Circle 0% mark at one of the dividing lines that separates two pieces.
3. Read the percent at the dividing line of the adjoining section (the adjoining section in the clockwise direction).
4. Move the 0% mark to the next dividing line and repeat.

**Method 1**

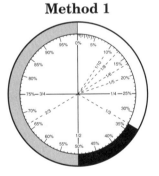

I put the 0% where the white piece begins. Then I read 33% for the white area. I read the percents for the black and gray areas in the same way.

**Method 2: Difference Comparison**

1. Center the Percent Circle over the center of the circle graph.
2. Aim the Percent Circle 0% mark at one of the dividing lines that separates two pieces.
3. Estimate the percent for each piece by finding the difference between Percent Circle readings of adjacent dividing lines.

**Method 2**

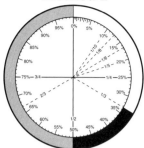

I put the 0% mark where the white piece begins. Then I read 33% for the white area. It goes from 33% to 50% for the black area. So that's 50 minus 33, or 17% for the black area. Gray goes from 50% to 100%. So that's 50% for gray.

## ✦ Reading Circle Graphs
(*Math Journal 1,* pp. 155 and 156)

PARTNER ACTIVITY

Ask students to look at Problems 2–4 on journal page 155 and estimate what fraction and what percent of the whole pie graph each piece is. After a few students have shared their estimates, have partners complete the remaining problems. Circulate and assist as needed. Discuss any problems or new strategies.

NOTE: You may want to introduce the word *sector* as the name for the pieces of a circle. A *sector* is a region bounded by two radiuses of a circle and the included arc. The word *wedge* is sometimes used instead of sector.

### ONGOING ASSESSMENT

**Expect that most students will be able to estimate the size of a section of the circle graph to the nearest quarter of a circle (0%, 25%, 50%, 75%, or 100%).**

**Many students may still have difficulty with measuring sections. Make sure students align the center of the Percent Circle with the center of the graph, align the 0% with the left edge of the sector they are measuring, and read the percent circle in a clockwise direction.**

Then assign journal page 156. Remind students to make an estimate for each piece of the pie graph before using their Percent Circles.

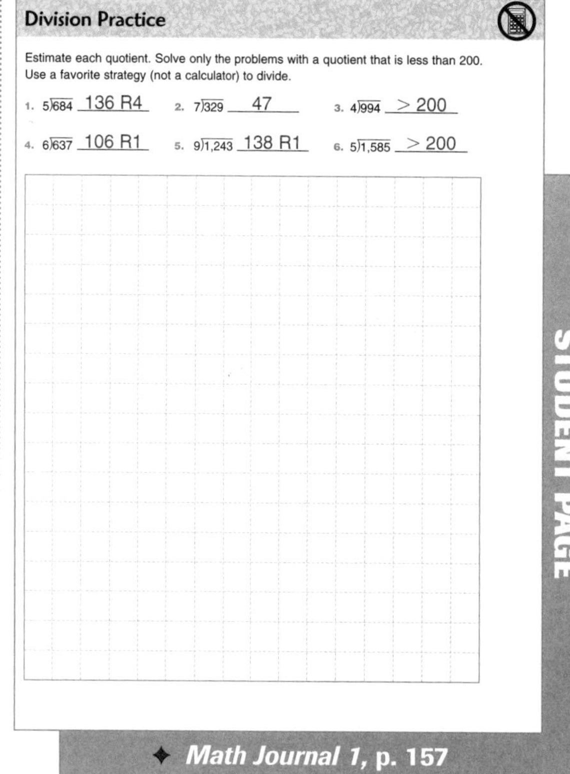

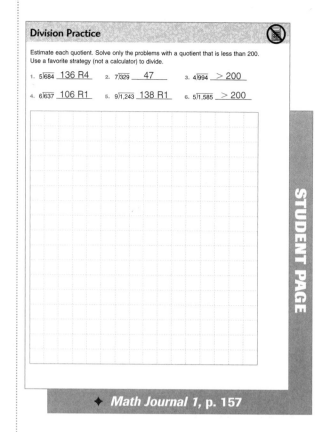

**Division Practice**

Estimate each quotient. Solve only the problems with a quotient that is less than 200. Use a favorite strategy (not a calculator) to divide.

1. 5)684 136 R4
2. 7)329 47
3. 4)994 > 200
4. 6)637 106 R1
5. 9)1,243 138 R1
6. 5)1,585 > 200

STUDENT PAGE

✦ *Math Journal 1,* p. 157

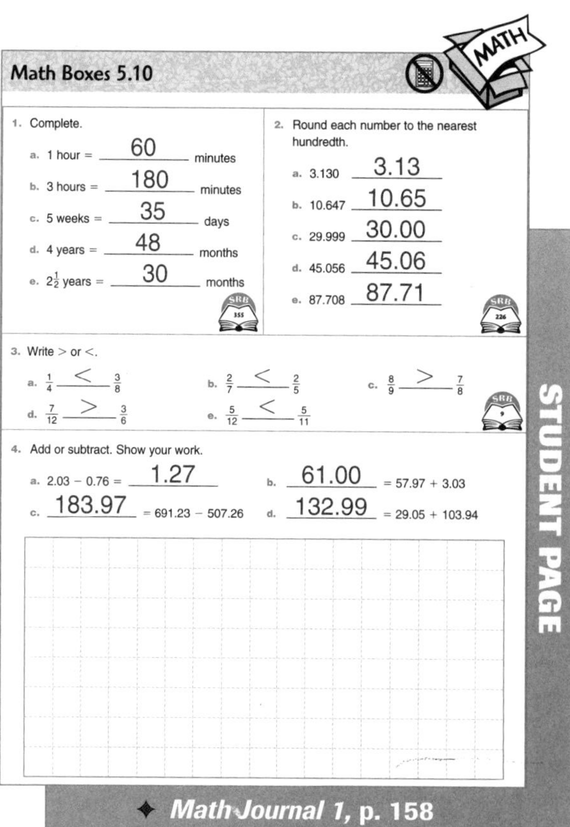

**Math Boxes 5.10**

1. Complete.
   a. 1 hour = 60 minutes
   b. 3 hours = 180 minutes
   c. 5 weeks = 35 days
   d. 4 years = 48 months
   e. $2\frac{1}{2}$ years = 30 months

2. Round each number to the nearest hundredth.
   a. 3.130 3.13
   b. 10.647 10.65
   c. 29.999 30.00
   d. 45.056 45.06
   e. 87.708 87.71

3. Write > or <.
   a. $\frac{1}{4}$ < $\frac{3}{8}$
   b. $\frac{2}{7}$ < $\frac{2}{5}$
   c. $\frac{8}{9}$ > $\frac{7}{8}$
   d. $\frac{7}{12}$ > $\frac{3}{6}$
   e. $\frac{5}{12}$ < $\frac{5}{11}$

4. Add or subtract. Show your work.
   a. 2.03 − 0.76 = 1.27
   b. 61.00 = 57.97 + 3.03
   c. 183.97 = 691.23 − 507.26
   d. 132.99 = 29.05 + 103.94

STUDENT PAGE

✦ *Math Journal 1,* p. 158

## Circle Graphs and Collecting Data

Study Link 5.10

**Estimating the Size of Pieces in a Circle Graph**

SRB 119 120

1. Estimate the percent of the circle for each piece of the graph at the right.
   a. A is about 50% of the circle.
   b. B is about 15% of the circle.
   c. C is about 35% of the circle.

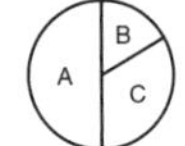


2. Draw a line connecting each data set with the most likely circle graph.

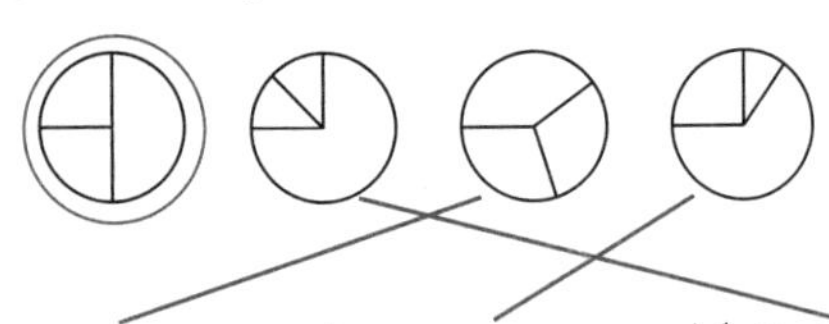

| | | |
|---|---|---|
| 30% of Michel's class walks to school. | 25% of Jeannene's toy cars are blue. | $\frac{1}{8}$ of Angelo's pants are jeans. |
| 30% of Michel's class rides the bus. | 10% of Jeannene's toy cars are striped. | $\frac{1}{8}$ of Angelo's pants are black dress pants. |
| 40% of Michel's class rides in a car or van. | 65% of Jeannene's toy cars are red. | $\frac{3}{4}$ of Angelo's pants are blue dress pants. |

**Challenge**

3. Circle the graph above that you did not use. Write a set of data to match that circle graph.
   Answers vary.

Continue on the next page.

◆ *Math Masters,* p. 274

STUDY LINK MASTER

## Circle Graphs and Collecting Data (cont.)

Study Link 5.10

**The Number of States We've Been In**

SRB 108

4. Talk with an adult at home and think of all the states you have ever been in. (Be sure to include the state you're living in.) Look at the map below to help you remember.
   Use a pencil or crayon to mark each state you have been in.
   Don't count any state that you have flown over in an airplane, unless the plane landed and you left the airport.
5. Count the number of states you have marked.
   I have been in ______ states in my lifetime.
6. Now ask the adult to mark the map to show the states he or she has been in, using a different color or mark from yours.
   Keep a tally as states are marked.
   The adult I interviewed has been in ______ states.

*Note:* Alaska and Hawaii are not shown to scale.

*Student and adult: This data is important for our next mathematics class. Please bring this completed Study Link back to school tomorrow.*

◆ *Math Masters,* p. 275

# 2 Ongoing Learning & Practice

## ◆ Practicing Division of Whole Numbers (*Math Journal 1,* p. 157)

INDEPENDENT ACTIVITY 

Students practice dividing multidigit whole numbers by 1-digit whole numbers.

## ◆ Math Boxes 5.10 (*Math Journal 1,* p. 158)

INDEPENDENT ACTIVITY 

**Mixed Review** Math Boxes in this lesson are paired with Math Boxes in Lesson 5.12. The skill in Problem 1 is a prerequisite for Unit 6.

## ◆ Study Link 5.10 (*Math Masters,* pp. 274 and 275)

**Home Connection** Note that this is a two-page Study Link. On the first page, students estimate the size of pieces of circle graphs. They match graphs with data sets. On the second page, they count the number of states they and an adult have visited. These data will be combined, organized, and discussed in Lesson 6.1.

# 3 Options for Individualizing

## ◆ ENRICHMENT Conducting an Eye Test (*Math Masters,* p. 77)

WHOLE-CLASS ACTIVITY  **15–30 min**

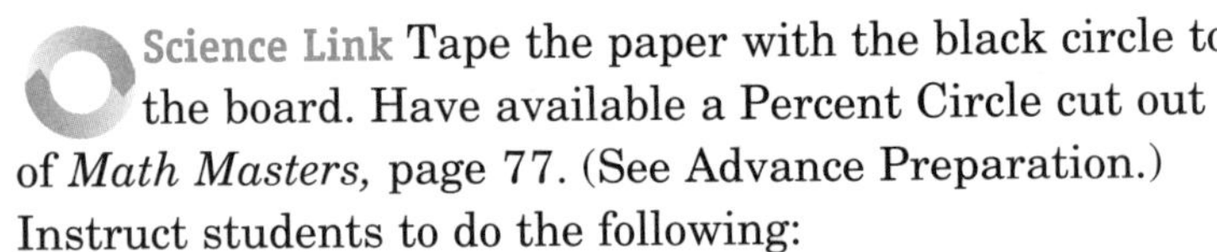

**Science Link** Tape the paper with the black circle to the board. Have available a Percent Circle cut out of *Math Masters,* page 77. (See Advance Preparation.) Instruct students to do the following:

1. Stand 5 to 10 feet away from the black circle. Look directly at the black circle with both eyes open.

2. Raise the cut-out Percent Circle and hold it where you can see the black circle through the hole in the Percent Circle with *both* eyes open.

3. Don't move the paper. Close your left eye. If you can still see the black circle, your *right eye is dominant.*

4. Don't move the paper. Open your left eye and close your right eye. If you see the black circle, your *left eye is dominant.*

Take a class count and tally the results on the board; for example, 17 right, 11 left.

Write the fraction of students whose right eye is dominant.
*Example:* $\frac{17}{28}$

Ask students to use a calculator to convert this fraction to a decimal and then write it as a percent. In the example, $\frac{17}{28} = 0.6071428571$, which is about 0.61, or 61%.

Write the result on a stick-on note and post it on the Probability Meter; for example, a note saying "Right eye dominant—61%."

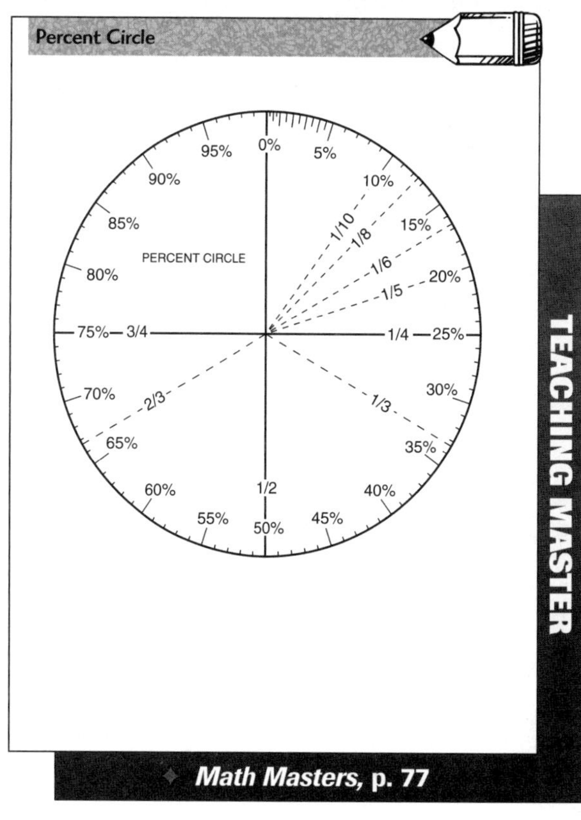

Math Masters, p. 77

## ✦ EXTRA PRACTICE Measuring Circle Graphs (*Math Masters,* p. 80)

INDEPENDENT ACTIVITY  **15–30 min**

Use this page for students who need more practice measuring sectors of a circle graph with their Percent Circle.

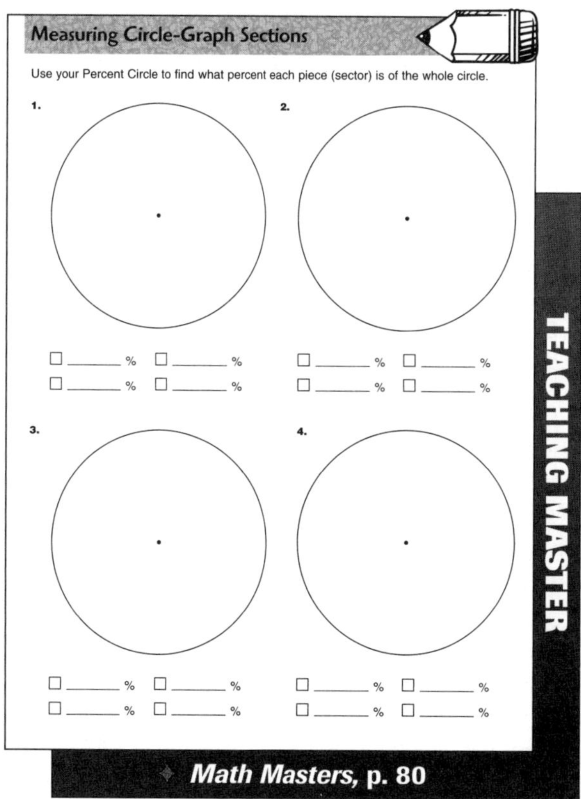

Measuring Circle-Graph Sections
Use your Percent Circle to find what percent each piece (sector) is of the whole circle.
1.
2.
3.
4.
TEACHING MASTER

Math Masters, p. 80

# 5.11 The Percent Circle: Making Circle Graphs

**OBJECTIVE** **To construct circle graphs with the Percent Circle.**

| summaries | materials |
|---|---|
| **1 Teaching the Lesson** | |
| Students use the Percent Circle to draw a circle graph. They construct a circle graph for the snack-survey data collected in Lesson 5.9. [Data and Chance] | □ *Math Journal 1,* pp. 152, 159, and 160<br>□ Study Link 5.10<br>□ Teaching Master (*Math Masters,* p. 77), for teacher only<br>□ Geometry Template<br>□ chalkboard compass for demonstration purposes<br>□ coloring pencils, crayons, or markers (optional)<br>***See* Advance Preparation** |
| **2 Ongoing Learning & Practice** | |
| Students fill in the decimals for sevenths and eighths in the Table of Decimal Equivalents. [Numeration; Operations and Computation]<br>Students play a Bingo Version of *Frac-Tac-Toe.* The Bingo Versions promote reflex recognition of equivalent fractions and decimals, and equivalent fractions and percents. [Operations and Computation]<br>Students practice and maintain skills through Math Boxes and Study Link activities. | □ *Math Journal 1,* p. 161 and the inside back cover<br>□ *Student Reference Book,* pp. 274–276<br>□ Study Link Master (*Math Masters,* p. 276)<br>□ *Frac-Tac-Toe* Number-Card Board (*Math Masters,* p. 62), for teacher only<br>□ *Frac-Tac-Toe* Gameboard (*Math Masters,* pp. 67 or 68)<br>□ 4 each of the number cards 0–10 (from the Everything Math Deck, if available), for teacher only<br>□ calculator<br>□ counters |
| **3 Options for Individualizing** | |
| **Enrichment** Students collect and interpret circle graphs from newspapers and magazines. [Data and Chance]<br>**Extra Practice** Students convert bar graphs into circle graphs. [Data and Chance] | □ newspapers and magazines<br>□ Geometry Template<br>□ calculator<br>***See* Advance Preparation** |

## Additional Information

**Advance Preparation** For Part 1, you will need the snack-survey data from Lesson 5.9. Each snack received a fraction of the total class votes. Convert each fraction to a percent, rounded to the nearest percent. For example, if 7 out of 27 students voted for cookies, rewrite $\frac{7}{27}$ as 26%. List the snacks and percents in a table on the board or Class Data Pad. You will need a chalkboard compass and a paper copy of the Percent Circle on *Math Masters,* page 77, or a compass for the overhead and a transparency of the Percent Circle.

For the optional Enrichment activity in Part 3, students will need newspapers and magazines from which they can cut graphs.

# Getting Started

### Mental Math and Reflexes

Rename percents as fractions. Encourage students to find fractions with denominators that are less than 100. *Suggestions:*

- 50% $\frac{1}{2}$
- $33\frac{1}{3}$% $\frac{1}{3}$
- 25% $\frac{1}{4}$
- 40% $\frac{4}{10}$, or $\frac{2}{5}$
- 20% $\frac{2}{10}$, or $\frac{1}{5}$
- 80% $\frac{8}{10}$, or $\frac{4}{5}$

If students are having difficulty, suggest that they write the percent as a decimal and then as a fraction.

### Math Message

*Turn to Problem 2 on journal page 152. Copy the number of votes for each snack into the second column of the table on journal page 160. Leave the rest of the table blank for now.*

### Study Link 5.10 Follow-Up

Briefly review answers. Have volunteers share their data sets for Problem 3.

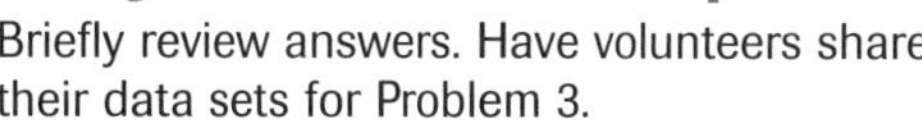

# 1 Teaching the Lesson

## ✦ Math Message Follow-Up (*Math Journal 1,* pp. 152 and 160)

INDEPENDENT ACTIVITY  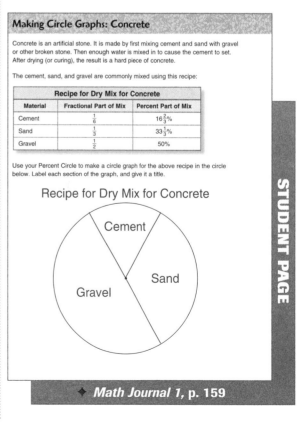

In Lesson 5.9, the class collected snack-survey data. Each snack received a certain number of the total class votes. Check to see that students have copied the data correctly.

In the third column of the table on journal page 160, have students write the number of votes for each snack as a fraction of the total number of votes.

## ✦ Constructing a Circle Graph Using the Percent Circle (*Math Journal 1,* p. 159)

WHOLE-CLASS ACTIVITY

Ask students to read about mixing concrete on journal page 159. Discuss their ideas for constructing a circle graph. Ask questions such as the following:

- How many pieces (sectors) must the graph have? Three, one for each dry ingredient (concrete, sand, and gravel)
- How should the pieces be labeled or colored? If the graph is labeled correctly, colors may help but are not necessary. Some students may suggest using symbols to mark the pieces.
- How can the Percent Circle be used to make each piece the correct size? Use marks on the Percent Circle to make pieces that are the same part of the circle as materials are part of the mix.

**Making Circle Graphs: Concrete**

Concrete is an artificial stone. It is made by first mixing cement and sand with gravel or other broken stone. Then enough water is mixed in to cause the cement to set. After drying (or curing), the result is a hard piece of concrete.

The cement, sand, and gravel are commonly mixed using this recipe:

| Recipe for Dry Mix for Concrete | | |
|---|---|---|
| Material | Fractional Part of Mix | Percent Part of Mix |
| Cement | $\frac{1}{6}$ | $16\frac{2}{3}$% |
| Sand | $\frac{1}{3}$ | $33\frac{1}{3}$% |
| Gravel | $\frac{1}{2}$ | 50% |

Use your Percent Circle to make a circle graph for the above recipe in the circle below. Label each section of the graph, and give it a title.

Recipe for Dry Mix for Concrete

Cement
Sand
Gravel

STUDENT PAGE

✦ *Math Journal 1,* p. 159

**Making Circle Graphs: Snack Survey**

Your class recently made a survey of favorite snacks. As your teacher tells you the percent of votes each snack received, record the data in the table at the right. Make a circle graph of the snack-survey data in the circle below. Remember to label each piece of the graph and give it a title.

Sample answers:

| Snack | Votes: Number | Votes: Fraction | Votes: Percent |
|---|---|---|---|
| Cookies | 8 | $\frac{8}{25}$ | 32% |
| Granola Bar | 4 | $\frac{4}{25}$ | 16% |
| Candy Bar | 10 | $\frac{10}{25}$ | 40% |
| Fruit | 2 | $\frac{2}{25}$ | 8% |
| Other | 1 | $\frac{1}{25}$ | 4% |
| Total | 25 | $\frac{25}{25}$ | About 100% |

Favorite-Snack Survey Results

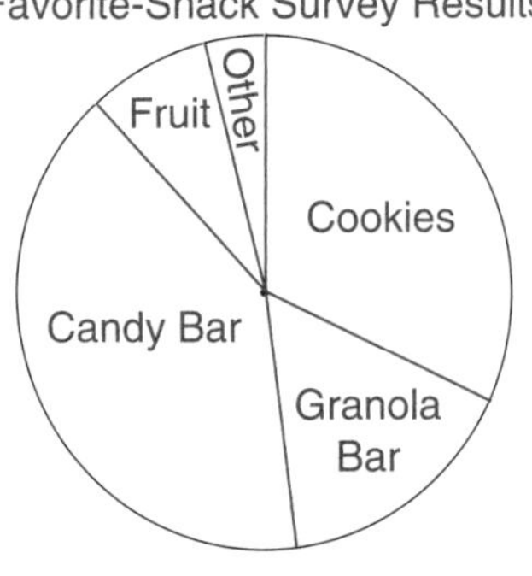


STUDENT PAGE

✦ *Math Journal 1,* p. 160

NOTE: Water is a necessary fourth ingredient in concrete. It is usually added to a dry mix of the other ingredients. About 5 to 7 gallons of water are used for a 94-pound bag of cement. When the concrete has dried (cured), the water is gone and the proportions of cement:sand:gravel are still 1:2:3.

**ONGOING ASSESSMENT**

**Expect that some students will have difficulty drawing the circle graphs on journal pages 159 and 160. Check that they keep the center of the Percent Circle over the center of the circle graphs on journal pages 159 and 160; that they read the percents in a clockwise direction; and that they line up the 0% mark on the Percent Circle with the side of the last piece drawn so that the next piece continues the clockwise movement around the circle.**

Have students demonstrate the methods they have devised, using a chalkboard compass and a large paper Percent Circle on the board, or a compass and transparency of the Percent Circle on the overhead. Have students take turns sketching sections of the circle. Then have them complete the circle graph on journal page 159.

If students have difficulty, demonstrate the following method:

1. Use the board compass to draw a circle with a diameter of 12 to 18 inches on the board. Mark the center with a dot.
2. If possible, use the fractions printed on the Percent Circle: $\frac{1}{10}$, $\frac{1}{8}$, $\frac{1}{6}$, $\frac{1}{5}$, $\frac{1}{4}$, $\frac{1}{3}$, $\frac{1}{2}$, $\frac{2}{3}$, and $\frac{3}{4}$. This makes it easy to mark fractional parts of a circle.
3. Place the center of the Percent Circle over the center of the circle on the board and make dots at the 0 and $\frac{1}{6}$ ($16\frac{2}{3}$%) marks.
4. Remove the Percent Circle and draw a line segment from the center of the circle to each dot. This $\frac{1}{6}$ section represents the proportion of cement in the mix.
5. Now place the 0% mark of the Percent Circle along the line segment just drawn through the $\frac{1}{6}$ mark. Make a dot at the $\frac{1}{3}$ ($33\frac{1}{3}$%) mark. Draw a line segment from the center to the dot to get the $\frac{1}{3}$ section representing the proportion of sand in the mix.
6. Measure the remaining section to verify that it is $\frac{1}{2}$ (50%) of the circle, representing the amount of gravel in the mix. Then label the graph and add a title.

## ✦ Constructing a Circle Graph for the Snack-Survey Data (*Math Journal 1,* p. 160)

PARTNER ACTIVITY 

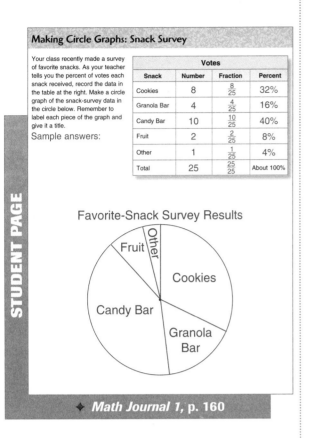

Have students write a fraction for each snack in column 3 of the table on journal page 160. Then ask them to copy the snack-survey percents from the board or Class Data Pad (see Advance Preparation) into column 4 of the table. You should calculate these percents for the students. Ask: *What should the total of the percents for all five snacks be?* The total should be 100%, but it may not be exactly 100 because of rounding.

Have students check the total and then begin working on a circle graph for the snack-survey data. Suggest that they begin by drawing the smallest piece of the circle graph first and work their way up to the largest. This way, if there is some error in their sections, it can be absorbed into the largest piece at the end. Circulate and assist as necessary.

# 2 Ongoing Learning & Practice

## ✦ Finding Decimal Equivalents for Sevenths and Eighths (*Math Journal 1,* inside back cover)

PARTNER ACTIVITY

Students continue to find and record decimal equivalents for fractions in the table on the inside back cover of the journal. Assign the denominators in rows 7 (sevenths) and 8 (eighths).

Allow students to use calculators if necessary.

**Adjusting the Activity** To make the activity more challenging, allow students to use their calculators only for the first few entries in each row. Then have them identify and use the patterns to complete the rows.

## ✦ Playing Bingo Versions of *2-4-5-10 Frac-Tac-Toe* (*Student Reference Book,* pp. 274–276; *Math Masters,* p. 62 and p. 67 or 68)

WHOLE-CLASS ACTIVITY

Play the *2-4-5-10,* Decimal or Percent Bingo Versions of *Frac-Tac-Toe.* The gameboard for the Bingo Version is like the ones used in Lesson 5.7, except that students fill in some of the numbers, as they wish. The class plays the game together. You can be the caller and turn over the number cards and name the fractions. Each student plays for himself or herself.

The only rule change for the Bingo Versions of *Frac-Tac-Toe* is the scoring. The first player to cover five squares in a row either horizontally, vertically, or diagonally is the winner.

## ✦ Math Boxes 5.11 (*Math Journal 1,* p. 161)

INDEPENDENT ACTIVITY 

**Mixed Review** Math Boxes in this lesson are paired with Math Boxes in Lesson 5.9. The skill in Problem 1 is a prerequisite for Unit 6.

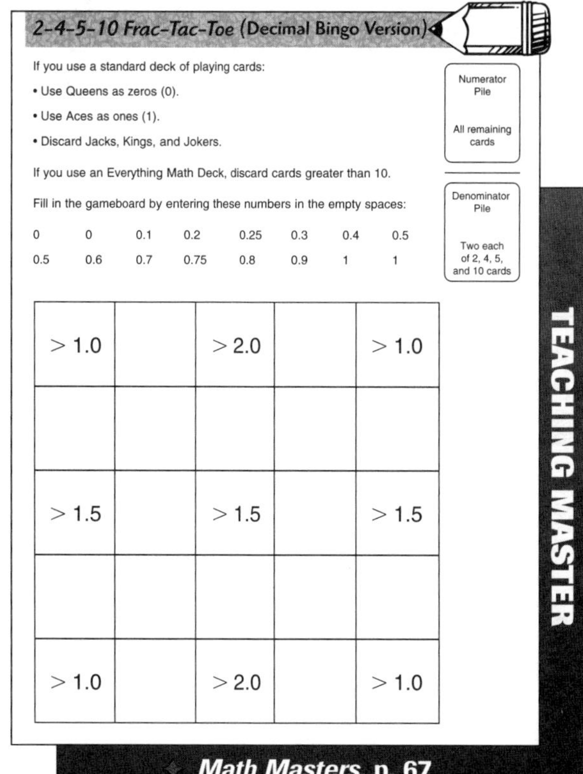

**2-4-5-10 Frac-Tac-Toe (Decimal Bingo Version)**

If you use a standard deck of playing cards:

- Use Queens as zeros (0).
- Use Aces as ones (1).
- Discard Jacks, Kings, and Jokers.

If you use an Everything Math Deck, discard cards greater than 10.

Fill in the gameboard by entering these numbers in the empty spaces:

0 0 0.1 0.2 0.25 0.3 0.4 0.5
0.5 0.6 0.7 0.75 0.8 0.9 1 1

Numerator Pile: All remaining cards

Denominator Pile: Two each of 2, 4, 5, and 10 cards

| > 1.0 | | > 2.0 | | > 1.0 |
|---|---|---|---|---|
| | | | | |
| > 1.5 | | > 1.5 | | > 1.5 |
| | | | | |
| > 1.0 | | > 2.0 | | > 1.0 |

TEACHING MASTER

✦ *Math Masters,* p. 67

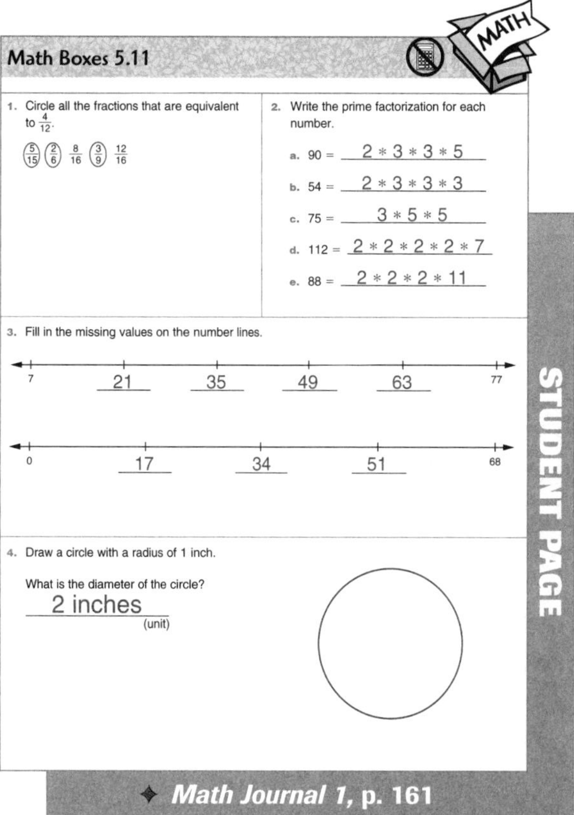

**Math Boxes 5.11**

1. Circle all the fractions that are equivalent to $\frac{4}{12}$.
$\frac{5}{15}$ $\frac{2}{6}$ $\frac{8}{16}$ $\frac{3}{9}$ $\frac{12}{16}$

2. Write the prime factorization for each number.
a. 90 = 2 * 3 * 3 * 5
b. 54 = 2 * 3 * 3 * 3
c. 75 = 3 * 5 * 5
d. 112 = 2 * 2 * 2 * 2 * 7
e. 88 = 2 * 2 * 2 * 11

3. Fill in the missing values on the number lines.
7, 21, 35, 49, 63, 77
0, 17, 34, 51, 68

4. Draw a circle with a radius of 1 inch.
What is the diameter of the circle?
2 inches (unit)

STUDENT PAGE

✦ *Math Journal 1,* p. 161

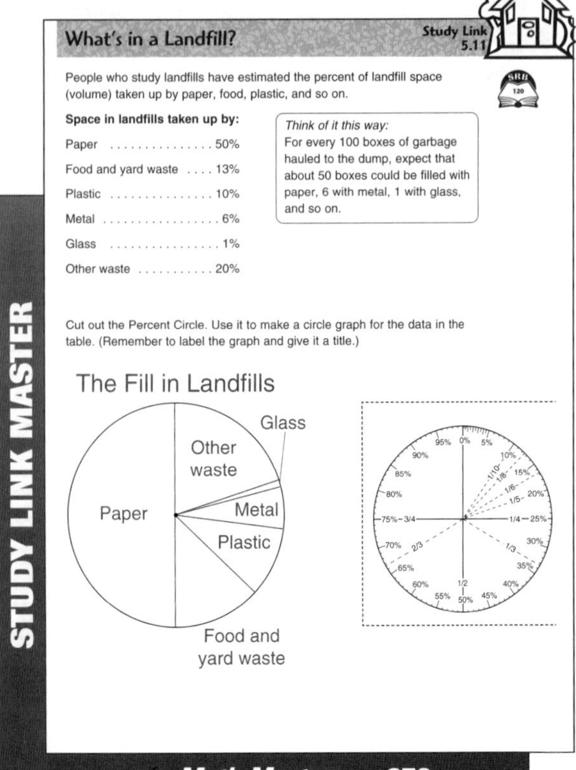

What's in a Landfill? Study Link 5.11

People who study landfills have estimated the percent of landfill space (volume) taken up by paper, food, plastic, and so on.

**Space in landfills taken up by:**

| | |
|---|---|
| Paper | 50% |
| Food and yard waste | 13% |
| Plastic | 10% |
| Metal | 6% |
| Glass | 1% |
| Other waste | 20% |

*Think of it this way:* For every 100 boxes of garbage hauled to the dump, expect that about 50 boxes could be filled with paper, 6 with metal, 1 with glass, and so on.

Cut out the Percent Circle. Use it to make a circle graph for the data in the table. (Remember to label the graph and give it a title.)

The Fill in Landfills

Paper
Other waste
Glass
Metal
Plastic
Food and yard waste

STUDY LINK MASTER

Math Masters, p. 276

## ✦ Study Link 5.11 (*Math Masters,* p. 276)

**Home Connection** Students use the Percent Circle to make a circle graph. They do not have to calculate any percents because all percents are given.

# 3 Options for Individualizing

## ✦ ENRICHMENT Making a Graph Museum

INDEPENDENT ACTIVITY  **15–30 min**

Have students collect bar graphs and circle graphs that they find in magazines and newspapers. (*USA Today* is a good source. Children's magazines, such as *GeoWorld,* also provide good examples.) Have students tape or glue each graph to a piece of paper and write a brief description of what the graph illustrates.

Display students' graphs on a bulletin board or collect them in a class book.

Extend the activity by having students write problems that can be answered using the graphs they found.

## ✦ EXTRA PRACTICE Converting Bar Graphs to Circle Graphs

PARTNER ACTIVITY  **15–30 min**

Students convert bar graphs from newspapers or magazines to circle graphs. The data may have to be converted to fractions and then to percents. Students may use their calculators.

Students should display the bar graph and the circle graph next to each other.

Extend the activity by discussing the advantages and disadvantages of the two representations.

*2-4-5-10 Frac-Tac-Toe* (Percent Bingo Version)

If you use a standard deck of playing cards:

- Use Queens as zeros (0).
- Use Aces as ones (1).
- Discard Jacks, Kings, and Jokers.

If you use an Everything Math Deck, discard cards greater than 10.

Numerator Pile — All remaining cards

Denominator Pile — Two each of 2, 4, 5, and 10 cards

Fill in the gameboard by entering these numbers in the empty spaces:

0% 0% 10% 20% 25% 30% 40% 50%
50% 60% 70% 75% 80% 90% 100% 100%

| | | | | |
|---|---|---|---|---|
| >100% | | >200% | | >100% |
| | | | | |
| >100% | | >200% | | >100% |
| | | | | |
| >100% | | >300% | | >100% |

TEACHING MASTER

Math Masters, p. 68

# 5.12 American Tour: School Days

**OBJECTIVES** **To interpret information from the American Tour; and to read about mathematics instruction and solve related historical problems.**

| summaries | materials |
|---|---|
| **1 Teaching the Lesson** | |
| Students read the article "School" in the American Tour section of the *Student Reference Book.* They answer questions that require them to interpret information in the text and displays. Students also read an essay and solve a series of problems about the changing emphases in mathematics instruction. [Data and Chance; Operations and Computation] | ☐ *Math Journal 1,* pp. 162–165<br>☐ *Student Reference Book,* pp. 318–320<br>☐ Study Link 5.11<br>☐ slate |
| **2 Ongoing Learning & Practice** | |
| Students practice and maintain skills through Math Boxes and Study Link activities. | ☐ *Math Journal 1,* p. 166<br>☐ Study Link Master (*Math Masters,* p. 277) |
| **3 Options for Individualizing** | |
| **Enrichment** Students explore resources on American history. [Data and Chance] | ☐ books and Internet access |

## Getting Started

### Mental Math and Reflexes

Students write equivalent decimals and percents for given fractions. *Suggestions:*

- $\frac{1}{2}$ 0.50; 50%
- $\frac{3}{4}$ 0.75; 75%
- $\frac{35}{50}$ 0.70; 70%
- $\frac{2}{5}$ 0.40; 40%
- $\frac{1}{4}$ 0.25; 25%
- $\frac{1}{8}$ 0.125; 12.5%
- $\frac{7}{20}$ 0.35; 35%
- $\frac{9}{25}$ 0.36; 36%
- $\frac{2}{3}$ $0.\overline{6}$; $66\frac{2}{3}$%

### Math Message

*Read pages 318–320, "School," in the American Tour section of your* Student Reference Book.

### Study Link 5.11 Follow-Up

Review the strategy for constructing a circle graph. Begin with the smallest piece first. Draw a radius to begin the first piece. Line up the center of the Percent Circle with the center of the graph. Line up the radius that forms the initial side of the first piece with 0 on the Percent Circle. Read the Percent Circle in a clockwise direction. Make a point at the appropriate percent mark. Connect the center of the circle and the point with a line segment. Continue in a clockwise direction to draw the remaining pieces.

American Tour

**School**

Throughout the history of the United States, schooling has been important.

The Northwest Ordinance of 1787 created the rules for forming new states. It also showed the nation's belief in the importance of schooling. It stated—

> Being necessary to good government and the happiness of mankind, schools and the means of education shall forever be preserved.

**Who Went to School in 1790?**

In the northern states, most children between the ages of 4 and 14 went to school for part of the year. In the southern states, many, but not all, white children of these ages went to school. African Americans who were slaves did not receive formal schooling. Often they were not allowed to learn how to read. Some, however, found ways to learn secretly.

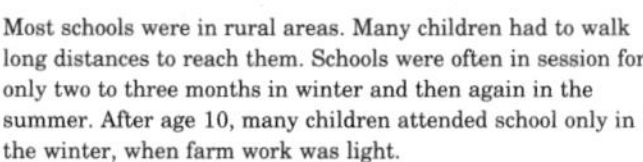

Most schools were in rural areas. Many children had to walk long distances to reach them. Schools were often in session for only two to three months in winter and then again in the summer. After age 10, many children attended school only in the winter, when farm work was light.

**Who Went to School in 1900?**

In 1900, parents reported to census takers that 80% of 10- to 14-year-olds had attended school at some point during the previous six months.

Three examples of early American schoolhouses.

Almost all children who went to school in 1900 attended elementary school, which usually had eight grades. Approximately 15 million students attended public school in 1900. Only about 500,000, or roughly 3%, were in high school.

In rural schools, students were usually not separated by age. Five- and 6-year-olds were often in the same elementary classroom with 15- and 16-year-olds. The older students were not slow learners. They had to do farm work and could only attend school part time.

three hundred eighteen

STUDENT PAGE

◆ Student Reference Book, p. 318

# 1 Teaching the Lesson

## ◆ Math Message Follow-Up (*Student Reference Book,* pp. 318–320)

WHOLE-CLASS DISCUSSION

Discuss students' overall impression of the essay. Ask if anything surprised them about American schooling in years past.

Spend a few minutes discussing the line graph on page 320 of the *Student Reference Book*. Be sure students can read the graph properly and understand the trends it shows. Increasing length of school year and decreasing number of days absent

NOTE: The stem-and-leaf display on page 319 of the *Student Reference Book*, "Days in School, 1900: State Averages," has the same data as the table above it.

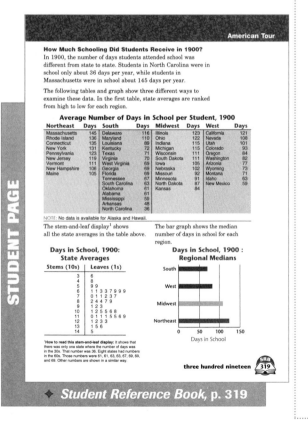

American Tour

**How Much Schooling Did Students Receive in 1900?**

In 1900, the number of days students attended school was different from state to state. Students in North Carolina were in school only about 36 days per year, while students in Massachusetts were in school about 145 days per year.

The following tables and graph show three different ways to examine these data. In the first table, state averages are ranked from high to low for each region.

**Average Number of Days in School per Student, 1900**

| Northeast | Days | South | Days | Midwest | Days | West | Days |
|---|---|---|---|---|---|---|---|
| Massachusetts | 145 | Delaware | 116 | Illinois | 123 | California | 121 |
| Rhode Island | 136 | Maryland | 110 | Ohio | 122 | Nevada | 108 |
| Connecticut | 135 | Louisiana | 89 | Indiana | 115 | Utah | 101 |
| New York | 131 | Kentucky | 72 | Michigan | 115 | Colorado | 93 |
| Pennsylvania | 123 | Texas | 71 | Wisconsin | 111 | Oregon | 84 |
| New Jersey | 119 | Virginia | 70 | South Dakota | 111 | Washington | 82 |
| Vermont | 111 | West Virginia | 69 | Iowa | 105 | Arizona | 77 |
| New Hampshire | 106 | Georgia | 69 | Nebraska | 102 | Wyoming | 73 |
| Maine | 105 | Florida | 69 | Missouri | 92 | Montana | 71 |
| | | Tennessee | 67 | Minnesota | 91 | Idaho | 63 |
| | | South Carolina | 63 | North Dakota | 87 | New Mexico | 59 |
| | | Oklahoma | 61 | Kansas | 84 | | |
| | | Alabama | 61 | | | | |
| | | Mississippi | 59 | | | | |
| | | Arkansas | 48 | | | | |
| | | North Carolina | 36 | | | | |

NOTE: No data is available for Alaska and Hawaii.

The stem-and-leaf display[1] shows all the state averages in the table above.

**Days in School, 1900: State Averages**

| Stems (10s) | Leaves (1s) |
|---|---|
| 3 | 6 |
| 4 | 8 |
| 5 | 9 9 |
| 6 | 1 1 3 3 7 9 9 9 |
| 7 | 0 1 1 2 3 7 |
| 8 | 2 4 4 7 9 |
| 9 | 1 2 3 |
| 10 | 1 2 5 5 6 8 |
| 11 | 0 1 1 1 5 5 6 9 |
| 12 | 1 2 3 3 |
| 13 | 1 5 6 |
| 14 | 5 |

[1]**How to read this stem-and-leaf display:** It shows that there was only one state where the number of days was in the 30s. That number was 36. Eight states had numbers in the 60s. Those numbers were 61, 61, 63, 63, 67, 69, 69, and 69. Other numbers are shown in a similar way.

The bar graph shows the median number of days in school for each region.

**Days in School, 1900 : Regional Medians**

South
West
Midwest
Northeast
0
50
100
150
Days in School

three hundred nineteen 319

STUDENT PAGE

◆ Student Reference Book, p. 319

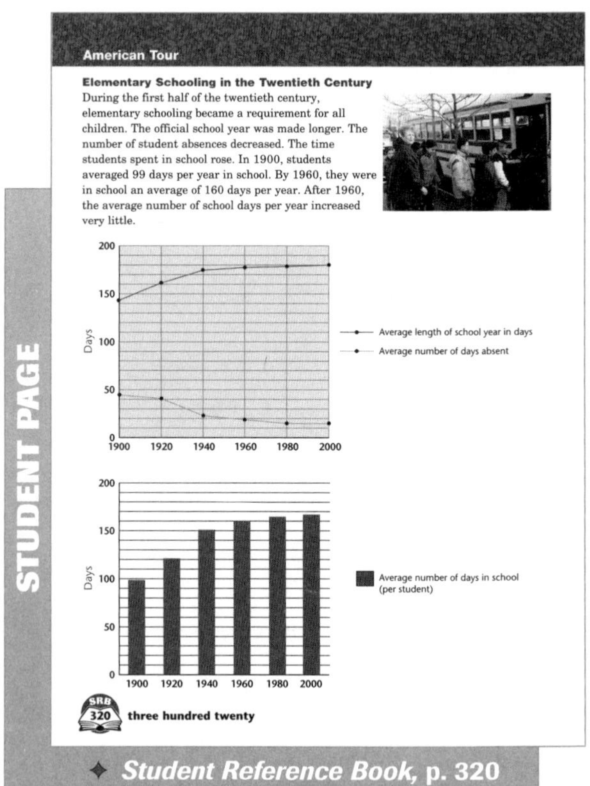
American Tour

**Elementary Schooling in the Twentieth Century**

During the first half of the twentieth century, elementary schooling became a requirement for all children. The official school year was made longer. The number of student absences decreased. The time students spent in school rose. In 1900, students averaged 99 days per year in school. By 1960, they were in school an average of 160 days per year. After 1960, the average number of school days per year increased very little.



three hundred twenty

STUDENT PAGE

◆ Student Reference Book, p. 320

## ✦ Interpreting Mathematics in Text and Graphics (*Math Journal 1,* pp. 162 and 163; *Student Reference Book,* pp. 318–320)

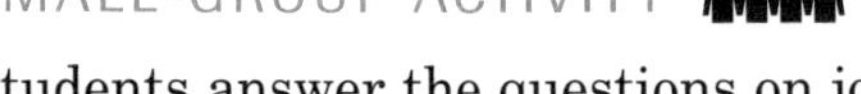

Students answer the questions on journal pages 162 and 163.

Students use information in the American Tour section of the *Student Reference Book* to decide whether statements are true or false. They support their decisions with evidence from the text and displays.

Try not to provide specific directions, such as "Look at the third paragraph to find the information you need." A goal of the lesson is to develop students' ability to locate and interpret mathematical information. Encourage students to ask each other for help.

After students have completed Problems 1 and 2 (which refer to page 318 of the American Tour), have them share their strategies and solutions. Then have them complete Problems 3–6 (which refer to pages 319 and 320) and share strategies and solutions.

**Adjusting the Activity** If some students finish quickly, have them do Challenge Problems 7–9 or find interesting information in the American Tour to share with the class. You may want to assign the Challenge items to all students. (For Problem 8, if you are in Alaska or Hawaii, choose another state.)

### School Days

Read the article "School" on pages 318–320 in the American Tour section of the *Student Reference Book.*

1. Tell whether the statement below is true or false. Support your answer with evidence from page 318 of the American Tour.

   In 1790, it was common for 11-year-olds to go to school fewer than 90 days a year.
   True. Sample answer: Many children after age 10 attended school for only the winter session, which was 2 to 3 months long.

2. About how many days will you go to school this year? About 180 days

   Write a fraction to compare the number of days you will go to school this year to the number of days an 11-year-old might have gone to school in 1790.
   Sample answer: $\frac{180}{60}$, $\frac{3}{1}$, or 3

3. Tell whether the statement below is true or false. Support your answer with evidence from page 319 of the American Tour.

   In 1900, students in some states spent twice as many days in school, on average, as students in some other states.
   True. Sample answer: In New Mexico and Idaho, students went to school for about 60 days. In Illinois, Pennsylvania, New Jersey, and California, students went to school for about twice as many days.

4. In 1900, in which region (Northeast, South, Midwest, or West) did students go to school …

   the greatest number of days per year? Northeast

   the fewest number of days per year? South

STUDENT PAGE

✦ *Math Journal 1,* p. 162

### School Days (cont.)

Tell whether each statement below is true or false. Support your answer with evidence from the graphs on page 320 of the American Tour.

5. On average, students in 2000 were absent from school about one-third as many days as students were absent in 1900.
   True. Sample answer: The top graph shows about 45 days absent in 1900, and about 15 days absent in 2000; 15 is one-third of 45.

6. The average number of days students spent in school per year has not changed much since 1960.
   True. The bottom graph shows about 160 days in school for 1960, and about 165 days in school for 1980 and 2000. An increase of 5 days is not a large change.

**Challenge**

7. Tell whether the statement below is true or false. Support your answer with evidence from the American Tour.

   From 1900 to 1980, the average number of days students spent in school per year more than doubled.
   False. Sample answer: The graph shows that the number increased from about 100 to about 165. Doubling would require an increase to about 200.

8. Locate your state in the table "Average Number of Days in School per Student, 1900" on page 319 of the American Tour. If you are in Alaska or Hawaii, choose another state.

   Was your state above or below the median for its region? Answers vary.

9. Locate the number of days in school for your state in the stem-and-leaf plot on page 319 of the American Tour.

   Was your state above or below the median for all states? Answers vary.

STUDENT PAGE

✦ *Math Journal 1,* p. 163

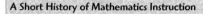

## A Short History of Mathematics Instruction

Throughout our nation's history, students have learned mathematics in different ways and have spent their time working on different kinds of problems. This is because people's views of what students can and should learn are constantly changing.

1. **1790s** If you went to elementary school in 1790, you were probably not taught mathematics. People believed that it was too hard to teach mathematics to children younger than 12.

   Older students spent most of their time solving problems about buying and selling goods. Here is a typical problem for a student in high school or college in the 1700s. Try to solve it.

   If 7 yards of cloth cost 21 shillings (a unit of money), how much do 19 yards of cloth cost? 57 shillings

2. **1840s** It was discovered that children could be very good at mental arithmetic, and students began to solve mental arithmetic problems as early as age 4. A school in Connecticut reported that its arithmetic champion could mentally multiply 314,521,325 by 231,452,153 in $5\frac{1}{2}$ minutes.

   After studying arithmetic two hours a day for 7 to 9 years, 94% of eighth graders in Boston in 1845 could solve the following problem. Try to solve it.

   What is $\frac{1}{2}$ of $\frac{1}{3}$ of 9 hours, 18 minutes? 93 minutes or 1 hour and 33 minutes

3. **1870s** Many textbooks were step-by-step guides on how to solve various problems. Students were given problems and answers. They had to show how the rules in the textbook could be used to produce the given answers.

   Here is a problem from around 1870 (without the answer) given to students at the end of 6 to 8 years of elementary arithmetic study. Try to solve it.

   I was married at the age of 21. If I live 19 years longer, I will have been married 60 years. What is my age now? 62 years (units)

STUDENT PAGE

◆ *Math Journal 1*, p. 164

## A Short History of Mathematics Instruction (cont.)

4. **1920s** Elementary mathematics emphasized skill with paper-and-pencil algorithms. People were needed to keep track of income, expenses, and profits for businesses. Clerks in stores had to add up sales, but there were no cheap, easy-to-use calculators. As a result, students spent much of their time doing exercises like the following. These problems are from a test for students in grades 5 through 8. Most students couldn't solve them until seventh grade. See how well you can do now (without a calculator).

| | |
|---|---|
| $ 0.49 | $ 8.00 |
| 0.28 | 5.75 |
| 0.63 | 2.33 |
| 0.95 | 4.16 |
| 1.69 | 0.94 |
| 0.22 | + 6.32 |
| 0.33 | $27.50 |
| 0.36 | |
| 1.01 | |
| + 0.56 | |
| $6.52 | |

5. **1990s** Today the emphasis is on solving problems and applying mathematics in the everyday world. The following problem was solved correctly by 47% of eighth graders on a test given in 1990. Try to solve it.

   The cost to rent a motorbike is given by the following formula:
   Cost = ($3 ∗ number of hours rented) + $2

   Complete the following table:

| Time | Cost |
|---|---|
| 1 hour | $5 |
| 4 hours | $ 14 |
| 5 hours | $17 |

STUDENT PAGE

◆ *Math Journal 1*, p. 165

## ◆ Reading about the History of Mathematics Instruction and Solving Related Problems (*Math Journal 1*, pp. 164 and 165)

WHOLE-CLASS ACTIVITY 

**Social Studies Link** Follow your usual group reading procedure to read the introduction to Problem 1 on journal page 164.

Students work alone, with a partner, or in a small group to solve Problem 1. Encourage discussion among students, and then have them share their solutions.

Continue with the remaining text and problems on journal pages 164 and 165. Encourage a feeling of exploration and challenge. At the times mentioned, people would not have expected fifth graders to be able to solve these problems.

# 2 Ongoing Learning & Practice

## ◆ Math Boxes 5.12 (*Math Journal 1*, p. 166)

INDEPENDENT ACTIVITY 

**Mixed Review** Math Boxes in this lesson are paired with Math Boxes in Lesson 5.10. The skill in Problem 1 is a prerequisite for Unit 6.

## ◆ Study Link 5.12 (*Math Masters*, p. 277)

**Home Connection** Students use equivalent fractions, decimals, and percents to rewrite expressions stated in an unusual way. They also identify numbers named by **equivalent forms** in name-collection boxes.

# 3 Options for Individualizing

## ✦ ENRICHMENT Finding Out about American History

INDEPENDENT ACTIVITY  **15–30 min** 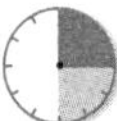

**Social Studies Link** A number of "outdoor museums" recreate the American past with buildings, costumes, crafts, exhibits, and programs. For example, Colonial Williamsburg in Virginia emphasizes the eighteenth century. Old Sturbridge Village in Massachusetts shows life in New England in the early nineteenth century. Old World Wisconsin recreates Midwest farms of the nineteenth century. If a visit to such a place isn't possible, students can use the Internet. As this book went to press, Web site addresses for these three places were:

http://www.colonialwilliamsburg.org

http://www.osv.org

http://www.shsw.wisc.edu

Many other sites are available. In addition to a "virtual tour," some offer readings, documents, lesson plans, and activities (for example, "Mathematics with a Mob Hat").

Your school or local library should have books on life that occurred about 200 years ago, and books on schools at that time. *Some possibilities are:*

- ▷ *Child Life in Colonial Days* by Alice Morse Earle (Berkshire House, 1993)
- ▷ *Everyday Life in Early America* by David Freeman Hawke (HarperCollins, 1989)
- ▷ *Colonial Times* by Walter A. Hazen (Celebration Press, 1999)
- ▷ *Children Everywhere: Dimensions of Childhood in Early 19th Century New England* by Jack Larkin (Old Sturbridge Village, 1988) Note that this is excerpted on the site listed above.
- ▷ *Going to School in 1776* by John J. Loeper (Atheneum, 1973)

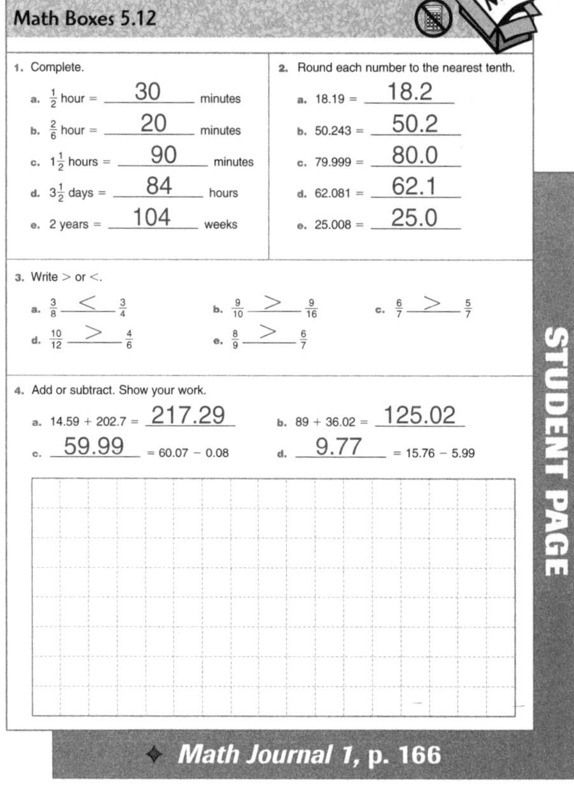

**Math Boxes 5.12**

1. Complete.
   a. $\frac{1}{2}$ hour = 30 minutes
   b. $\frac{2}{6}$ hour = 20 minutes
   c. $1\frac{1}{2}$ hours = 90 minutes
   d. $3\frac{1}{2}$ days = 84 hours
   e. 2 years = 104 weeks

2. Round each number to the nearest tenth.
   a. 18.19 = 18.2
   b. 50.243 = 50.2
   c. 79.999 = 80.0
   d. 62.081 = 62.1
   e. 25.008 = 25.0

3. Write > or <.
   a. $\frac{3}{8} < \frac{3}{4}$
   b. $\frac{9}{10} > \frac{9}{16}$
   c. $\frac{6}{7} > \frac{5}{7}$
   d. $\frac{10}{12} > \frac{4}{6}$
   e. $\frac{8}{9} > \frac{6}{7}$

4. Add or subtract. Show your work.
   a. 14.59 + 202.7 = 217.29
   b. 89 + 36.02 = 125.02
   c. 59.99 = 60.07 − 0.08
   d. 9.77 = 15.76 − 5.99

STUDENT PAGE

✦ *Math Journal 1*, p. 166

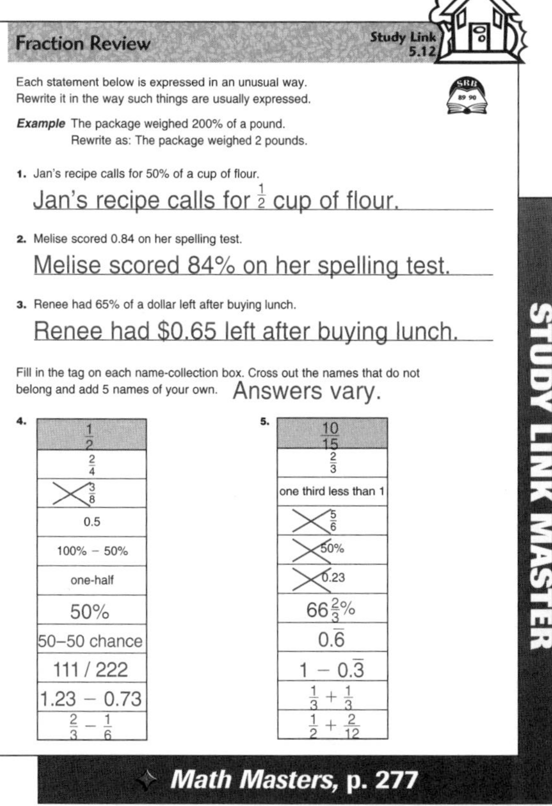

**Fraction Review** Study Link 5.12

Each statement below is expressed in an unusual way. Rewrite it in the way such things are usually expressed.

*Example* The package weighed 200% of a pound. Rewrite as: The package weighed 2 pounds.

1. Jan's recipe calls for 50% of a cup of flour.
   Jan's recipe calls for $\frac{1}{2}$ cup of flour.
2. Melise scored 0.84 on her spelling test.
   Melise scored 84% on her spelling test.
3. Renee had 65% of a dollar left after buying lunch.
   Renee had $0.65 left after buying lunch.

Fill in the tag on each name-collection box. Cross out the names that do not belong and add 5 names of your own. Answers vary.

4.

| $\frac{1}{2}$ |
|---|
| $\frac{2}{4}$ |
| ~~$\frac{3}{8}$~~ |
| 0.5 |
| 100% − 50% |
| one-half |
| 50% |
| 50–50 chance |
| 111 / 222 |
| 1.23 − 0.73 |
| $\frac{2}{3} - \frac{1}{6}$ |

5.

| $\frac{10}{15}$ |
|---|
| $\frac{2}{3}$ |
| one third less than 1 |
| ~~$\frac{5}{6}$~~ |
| ~~50%~~ |
| ~~0.23~~ |
| $66\frac{2}{3}\%$ |
| $0.\overline{6}$ |
| $1 - 0.\overline{3}$ |
| $\frac{1}{3} + \frac{1}{3}$ |
| $\frac{1}{2} + \frac{2}{12}$ |

STUDY LINK MASTER

✦ *Math Masters*, p. 277

# 5.13 Unit 5 Review and Assessment

**OBJECTIVE** **To review and assess students' progress on the material covered in Unit 5.**

## 1 Assess Progress

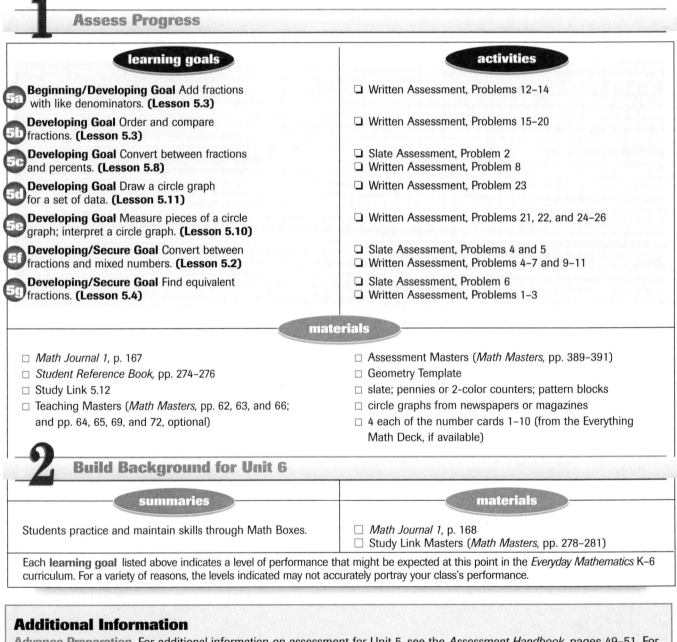

| learning goals | activities |
|---|---|
| 5a **Beginning/Developing Goal** Add fractions with like denominators. **(Lesson 5.3)** | ❑ Written Assessment, Problems 12–14 |
| 5b **Developing Goal** Order and compare fractions. **(Lesson 5.3)** | ❑ Written Assessment, Problems 15–20 |
| 5c **Developing Goal** Convert between fractions and percents. **(Lesson 5.8)** | ❑ Slate Assessment, Problem 2<br>❑ Written Assessment, Problem 8 |
| 5d **Developing Goal** Draw a circle graph for a set of data. **(Lesson 5.11)** | ❑ Written Assessment, Problem 23 |
| 5e **Developing Goal** Measure pieces of a circle graph; interpret a circle graph. **(Lesson 5.10)** | ❑ Written Assessment, Problems 21, 22, and 24–26 |
| 5f **Developing/Secure Goal** Convert between fractions and mixed numbers. **(Lesson 5.2)** | ❑ Slate Assessment, Problems 4 and 5<br>❑ Written Assessment, Problems 4–7 and 9–11 |
| 5g **Developing/Secure Goal** Find equivalent fractions. **(Lesson 5.4)** | ❑ Slate Assessment, Problem 6<br>❑ Written Assessment, Problems 1–3 |

**materials**

- ☐ *Math Journal 1,* p. 167
- ☐ *Student Reference Book,* pp. 274–276
- ☐ Study Link 5.12
- ☐ Teaching Masters (*Math Masters,* pp. 62, 63, and 66; and pp. 64, 65, 69, and 72, optional)
- ☐ Assessment Masters (*Math Masters,* pp. 389–391)
- ☐ Geometry Template
- ☐ slate; pennies or 2-color counters; pattern blocks
- ☐ circle graphs from newspapers or magazines
- ☐ 4 each of the number cards 1–10 (from the Everything Math Deck, if available)

## 2 Build Background for Unit 6

| summaries | materials |
|---|---|
| Students practice and maintain skills through Math Boxes. | ☐ *Math Journal 1,* p. 168<br>☐ Study Link Masters (*Math Masters,* pp. 278–281) |

Each **learning goal** listed above indicates a level of performance that might be expected at this point in the *Everyday Mathematics* K–6 curriculum. For a variety of reasons, the levels indicated may not accurately portray your class's performance.

### Additional Information

**Advance Preparation** For additional information on assessment for Unit 5, see the *Assessment Handbook,* pages 49–51. For assessment checklists, see *Math Masters,* pages 436, 437, and 469–471.

# Getting Started

**Math Message**

*Complete the Time to Reflect questions on journal page 167.*

**Study Link 5.12 Follow-Up**

Briefly review the answers. Have volunteers share the names they added to the name-collection boxes.

# 1 Assess Progress

## ◆ Math Message Follow-Up
(*Math Journal 1,* p. 167)

WHOLE-CLASS DISCUSSION 

Students share their responses to questions about the unit.

## ◆ Slate Assessments

WHOLE-CLASS ACTIVITY

If the list of suggested problems below is not appropriate for your class's level of performance, adjust the numbers in the problems or adjust the problems themselves to better assess your students' abilities.

*Slate Assessment Suggestions*

1. Write numbers from dictation. Round each number to the specified place.
   - 14.89 to the nearest tenth. 14.9
   - 1.028 to the nearest hundredth. 1.03
   - 62.54 to the nearest tenth. 62.5
   - 59.153 to the nearest tenth. 59.2
   - 3.781 to the nearest hundredth. 3.78
   - 203.81 to the nearest whole number. 204
2. Write an equivalent decimal and percent for each fraction.
   - $\frac{3}{4}$ 0.75; 75%
   - $\frac{5}{8}$ 0.625; 62.5%, or 63%
   - $\frac{3}{5}$ 0.6; 60%
   - $\frac{9}{10}$ 0.9; 90%
   - $\frac{11}{25}$ 0.44; 44%
   - $\frac{43}{50}$ 0.86; 86% **Goal 5c**

NOTE: Some of these assessment suggestions relate to learning goals that have been addressed in previous units. Now is a good time to evaluate students' progress toward those goals.

**Time to Reflect**

1. Name two places outside of school where people use fractions.
   Answers vary.

In some situations, parts of a whole are usually named with fractions.
In some situations, they are usually named with decimals.
In some situations, they are usually named with percents.
Give at least one example of each type of situation below.

2. Parts of a whole usually named with a fraction:
3. Parts of a whole usually named with a decimal:
4. Parts of a whole usually named with a percent:
5. Explain one advantage to reporting test scores as a percent instead of as a fraction.

STUDENT PAGE

◆ *Math Journal 1,* p. 167

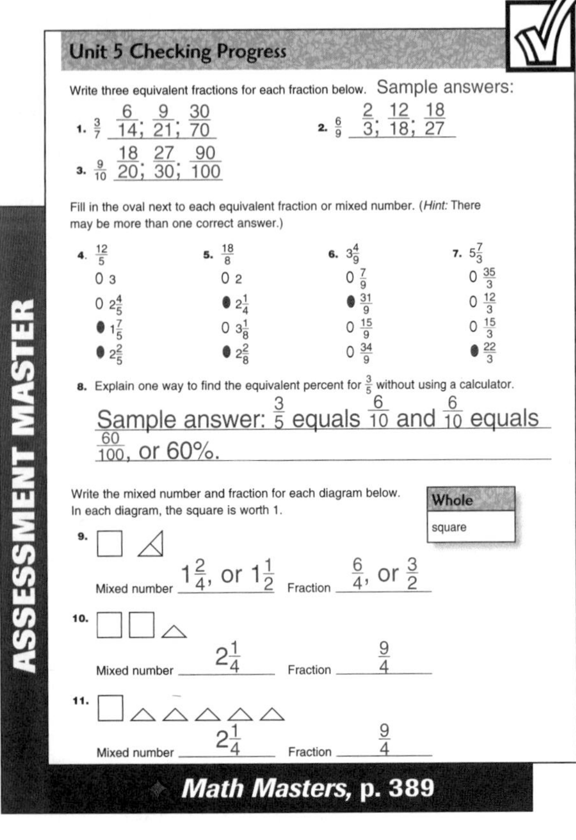
ASSESSMENT MASTER

Unit 5 Checking Progress

Write three equivalent fractions for each fraction below. Sample answers:

1. $\frac{3}{7}$ $\frac{6}{14}$; $\frac{9}{21}$; $\frac{30}{70}$

2. $\frac{6}{9}$ $\frac{2}{3}$; $\frac{12}{18}$; $\frac{18}{27}$

3. $\frac{9}{10}$ $\frac{18}{20}$; $\frac{27}{30}$; $\frac{90}{100}$

Fill in the oval next to each equivalent fraction or mixed number. (*Hint:* There may be more than one correct answer.)

4. $\frac{12}{5}$ — 0 3; 0 $2\frac{4}{5}$; ● $1\frac{7}{5}$; ● $2\frac{2}{5}$

5. $\frac{18}{8}$ — 0 2; ● $2\frac{1}{4}$; 0 $3\frac{1}{8}$; ● $2\frac{2}{8}$

6. $3\frac{4}{9}$ — 0 $\frac{7}{9}$; ● $\frac{31}{9}$; 0 $\frac{15}{9}$; 0 $\frac{34}{9}$

7. $5\frac{7}{3}$ — 0 $\frac{35}{3}$; 0 $\frac{12}{3}$; 0 $\frac{15}{3}$; ● $\frac{22}{3}$

8. Explain one way to find the equivalent percent for $\frac{3}{5}$ without using a calculator.

Sample answer: $\frac{3}{5}$ equals $\frac{6}{10}$ and $\frac{6}{10}$ equals $\frac{60}{100}$, or 60%.

Write the mixed number and fraction for each diagram below. In each diagram, the square is worth 1.

| Whole |
|---|
| square |

9. Mixed number $1\frac{2}{4}$, or $1\frac{1}{2}$ Fraction $\frac{6}{4}$, or $\frac{3}{2}$

10. Mixed number $2\frac{1}{4}$ Fraction $\frac{9}{4}$

11. Mixed number $2\frac{1}{4}$ Fraction $\frac{9}{4}$

Math Masters, p. 389

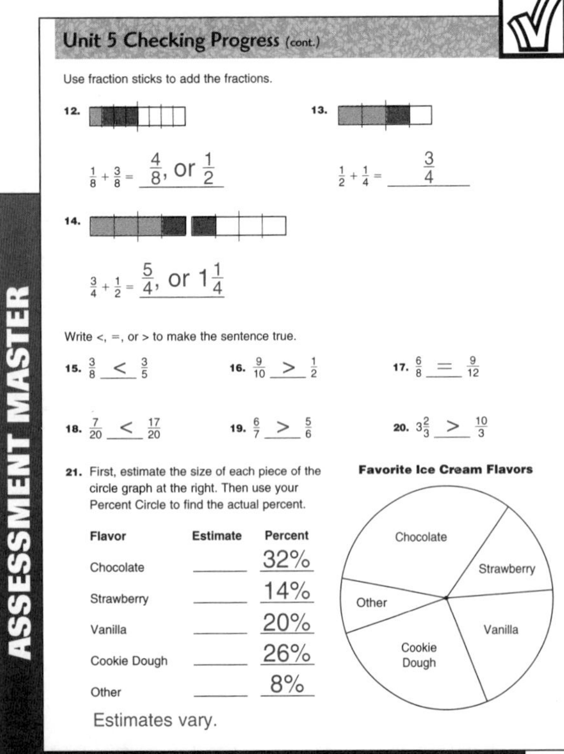
ASSESSMENT MASTER

Unit 5 Checking Progress (cont.)

Use fraction sticks to add the fractions.

12. $\frac{1}{8} + \frac{3}{8} = \frac{4}{8}$, or $\frac{1}{2}$

13. $\frac{1}{2} + \frac{1}{4} = \frac{3}{4}$

14. $\frac{3}{4} + \frac{1}{2} = \frac{5}{4}$, or $1\frac{1}{4}$

Write <, =, or > to make the sentence true.

15. $\frac{3}{8} < \frac{3}{5}$ 16. $\frac{9}{10} > \frac{1}{2}$ 17. $\frac{6}{8} = \frac{9}{12}$

18. $\frac{7}{20} < \frac{17}{20}$ 19. $\frac{6}{7} > \frac{5}{6}$ 20. $3\frac{2}{3} > \frac{10}{3}$

21. First, estimate the size of each piece of the circle graph at the right. Then use your Percent Circle to find the actual percent.

| Flavor | Estimate | Percent |
|---|---|---|
| Chocolate | | 32% |
| Strawberry | | 14% |
| Vanilla | | 20% |
| Cookie Dough | | 26% |
| Other | | 8% |

Estimates vary.



Math Masters, p. 390

3. Draw angles.
   - right angle, acute angle, obtuse angle, straight angle, reflex angle, angle about 45°, angle about 100°
4. Convert improper fractions to equivalent mixed numbers or whole numbers.
   - $\frac{18}{4}$ $4\frac{2}{4}$, or $4\frac{1}{2}$
   - $\frac{24}{5}$ $4\frac{4}{5}$
   - $\frac{9}{3}$ 3
   - $\frac{22}{8}$ $2\frac{6}{8}$, or $2\frac{3}{4}$
   - $\frac{55}{25}$ $2\frac{5}{25}$, or $2\frac{1}{5}$ **Goal 5f**
5. Convert mixed or whole numbers to equivalent improper fractions.
   - $2\frac{6}{7}$ $\frac{20}{7}$
   - $8\frac{1}{2}$ $\frac{17}{2}$
   - $2\frac{1}{6}$ $\frac{13}{6}$
   - $4\frac{5}{8}$ $\frac{37}{8}$
   - $9\frac{7}{3}$ $\frac{34}{3}$ **Goal 5f**
6. Write two equivalent fractions for each fraction.
   - $\frac{1}{2}$ $\frac{2}{4}$, $\frac{4}{8}$, …
   - $\frac{1}{3}$ $\frac{2}{6}$, $\frac{3}{9}$, …
   - $\frac{3}{4}$ $\frac{6}{8}$, $\frac{9}{12}$, …
   - $\frac{5}{6}$ $\frac{10}{12}$, $\frac{15}{18}$, …
   - $\frac{3}{8}$ $\frac{6}{16}$, $\frac{9}{24}$, …
   - $\frac{4}{7}$ $\frac{8}{14}$, $\frac{12}{21}$, …**Goal 5g**

## ✦Written Assessment
(*Math Masters*, pp. 389–391)

INDEPENDENT ACTIVITY 

Depending on the needs of students, you may want to work through an example together, reading a problem aloud, discussing it, and providing additional examples as necessary before students work the problem independently.

Each of the problems is listed below and paired with one or more of this unit's learning goals.

- Write equivalent fractions for a given fraction. (Problems 1–3) **Goal 5g**
- Convert fractions to equivalent mixed numbers and vice versa. (Problems 4–7) **Goal 5f**
- Convert from a fraction to a percent without using a calculator. (Problem 8) **Goal 5c**
- Convert between fractions and mixed numbers. (Problems 9–11) **Goal 5f**
- Use fraction sticks to add fractions. (Problems 12–14) **Goal 5a**
- Write <, =, or > to compare fractions. (Problems 15–20) **Goal 5b**
- Estimate and measure the size of each section of a circle graph. (Problem 21) **Goal 5e**
- Explain why it is helpful to make an estimate before measuring a section of a circle graph. (Problem 22) **Goal 5e**
- Make a circle graph for a survey on favorite types of books for fifth graders. (Problem 23) **Goal 5d**
- Interpret a circle graph. (Problems 24–26) **Goal 5e**

## ALTERNATIVE ASSESSMENT OPTION

### Play *2-4-5-10 Frac-Tac-Toe*

(*Student Reference Book,* pp. 274–276; *Math Masters,* pp. 62, 63, and 66)

PARTNER ACTIVITY 

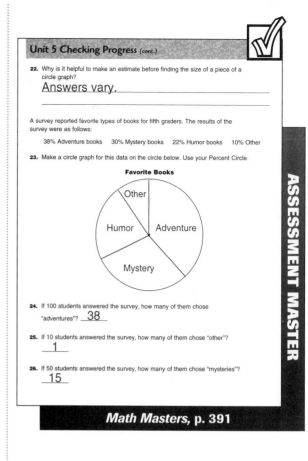

To assess students' ability to convert between fractions and decimals or fractions and percents, students play an appropriate version of *Frac-Tac-Toe.*

On a half-sheet of paper, have students keep a record of the fractions and the decimal or percent equivalents they cover on the gameboard. Collect their records to assess students' facility with the conversions.

**Adjusting the Activity** Challenge students by having them play the more difficult versions of *Frac-Tac-Toe,* such as *2-4-8* or *3-6-9* (*Math Masters,* pages 64, 65, 69, and 72).

---

**ASSESSMENT MASTER**

**Unit 5 Checking Progress** (cont.)

**22.** Why is it helpful to make an estimate before finding the size of a piece of a circle graph?

Answers vary.

A survey reported favorite types of books for fifth graders. The results of the survey were as follows:

38% Adventure books 30% Mystery books 22% Humor books 10% Other

**23.** Make a circle graph for this data on the circle below. Use your Percent Circle.

**Favorite Books**

**24.** If 100 students answered the survey, how many of them chose "adventures"? 38

**25.** If 10 students answered the survey, how many of them chose "other"? 1

**26.** If 50 students answered the survey, how many of them chose "mysteries"? 15

***Math Masters,* p. 391**

---

**TEACHING MASTER**

**2-4-5-10 *Frac-Tac-Toe* (Decimal Version)**

If you use a standard deck of playing cards:

- Use Queens as zeros (0).
- Use Aces as ones (1).
- Discard Jacks, Kings, and Jokers.

If you use an Everything Math Deck, discard cards greater than 10.

Use different color counters or coins as markers. If you use coins, one player is "heads" and the other player is "tails."

If you use a pencil to initial the squares, print lightly so you can erase and use the board again.

Numerator Pile — All remaining cards

Denominator Pile — Two each of 2, 4, 5, and 10 cards

| > 1.0 | 0 or 1 | > 2.0 | 0 or 1 | > 1.0 |
|---|---|---|---|---|
| 0.1 | 0.2 | 0.25 | 0.3 | 0.4 |
| > 1.5 | 0.5 | > 1.5 | 0.5 | > 1.5 |
| 0.6 | 0.7 | 0.75 | 0.8 | 0.9 |
| > 1.0 | 0 or 1 | > 2.0 | 0 or 1 | > 1.0 |

***Math Masters,* p. 63**

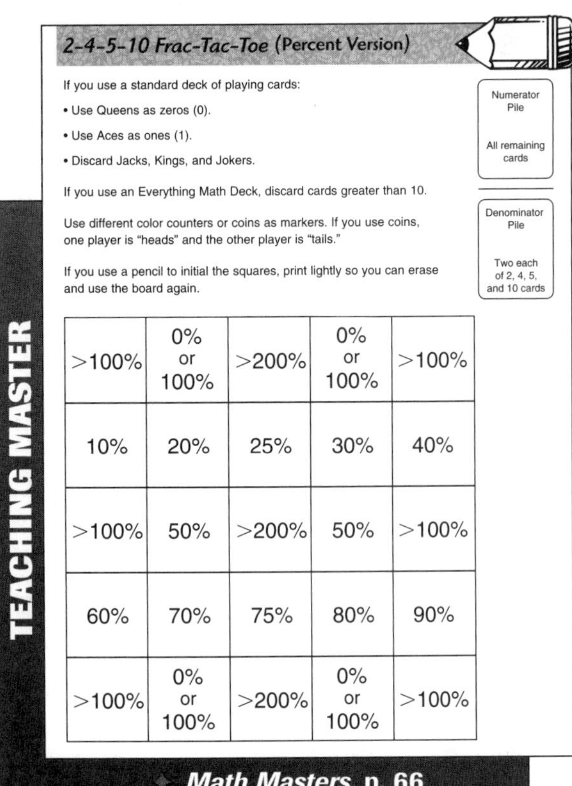

TEACHING MASTER

**2-4-5-10 *Frac-Tac-Toe* (Percent Version)**

If you use a standard deck of playing cards:

- Use Queens as zeros (0).
- Use Aces as ones (1).
- Discard Jacks, Kings, and Jokers.

If you use an Everything Math Deck, discard cards greater than 10.

Use different color counters or coins as markers. If you use coins, one player is "heads" and the other player is "tails."

If you use a pencil to initial the squares, print lightly so you can erase and use the board again.

Numerator Pile

All remaining cards

Denominator Pile

Two each of 2, 4, 5, and 10 cards

| >100% | 0% or 100% | >200% | 0% or 100% | >100% |
|---|---|---|---|---|
| 10% | 20% | 25% | 30% | 40% |
| >100% | 50% | >200% | 50% | >100% |
| 60% | 70% | 75% | 80% | 90% |
| >100% | 0% or 100% | >200% | 0% or 100% | >100% |

***Math Masters,* p. 66**

TEACHING MASTER

**2-4-8 *Frac-Tac-Toe* (Percent Version)**

If you use a standard deck of playing cards:

- Use Queens as zeros (0).
- Use Aces as ones (1).
- Discard Jacks, Kings, and Jokers.

If you use an Everything Math Deck, discard cards greater than 10.

Use different color counters or coins as markers. If you use coins, one player is "heads" and the other player is "tails."

If you use a pencil to initial the squares, print lightly so you can erase and use the board again.

Numerator Pile

All remaining cards

Denominator Pile

Two each of 2, 4, and 8 cards

| >200% | 0% or 100% | >150% | 0% or 100% | >200% |
|---|---|---|---|---|
| 150% | $12\frac{1}{2}$% | 25% | $37\frac{1}{2}$% | 150% |
| >100% | 50% | 25% or 75% | 50% | >100% |
| 200% | $62\frac{1}{2}$% | 75% | $87\frac{1}{2}$% | 200% |
| >200% | 0% or 100% | $112\frac{1}{2}$% | 0% or 100% | >200% |

***Math Masters,* p. 69**

## ✦ ALTERNATIVE ASSESSMENT OPTION
## Identify Fractions in Pattern-Block Designs

PARTNER ACTIVITY 

Use this activity, which is similar to the activity in Lesson 5.2 Part 3, to assess students' ability to identify fractional parts of a design and to convert between improper fractions and mixed numbers.

On a piece of paper, have students make a design with pattern blocks. They record only the outline of the design. They do not trace each individual block. Under their design, students record the value for one of the blocks.

Have students trade designs with a partner.

Students cover their partner's design exactly with pattern blocks, and trace the outlines of the blocks to record how they covered the design. Students then calculate the value of their partner's design both as a mixed number and as an improper fraction.

To assess their understanding of adding and subtracting fractions, have students write a number model to show how they calculated the value.

## ✦ ALTERNATIVE ASSESSMENT OPTION
## Write and Answer Questions about Circle Graphs

INDEPENDENT ACTIVITY 

Use this activity from Lesson 5.11 to assess students' ability to read and interpret circle graphs.

If you have already established a Graphs Museum, use graphs from the museum. If not, you or the students bring in circle graphs from magazines and newspapers. (*USA Today* and children's magazines, like *Geoworld,* provide good examples of circle graphs.)

If you did this activity in Lesson 5.11 and questions already exist, have students answer a set of questions for one graph. If students have not already written questions, have them write questions that can be answered using the graph.

The entire class may work with the same graph and questions, or each student may work with a different graph.

# 2 Build Background for Unit 6

## ◆ Math Boxes 5.13 (*Math Journal 1,* p. 168)

INDEPENDENT ACTIVITY 

**Mixed Review** The skills in Problems 1–5 are prerequisites for Unit 6.

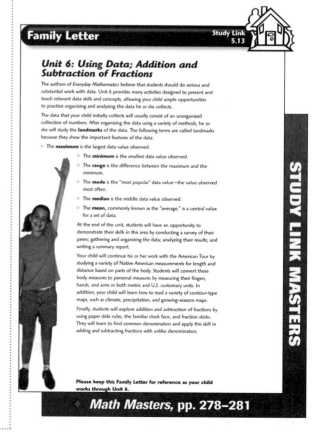

## ◆ Study Link 5.13: Unit 6 Family Letter (*Math Masters,* pp. 278–281)

**Home Connection** This Study Link is a four-page newsletter that introduces parents and guardians to Unit 6's topics and terms. The letter also offers ideas for mathematics activities that are supportive of classroom work and can be done at home.

### 3-6-9 *Frac-Tac-Toe* (Percent Version) 

If you use a standard deck of playing cards:

- Use Queens as zeros (0).
- Use Aces as ones (1).
- Discard Jacks, Kings, and Jokers.

If you use an Everything Math Deck, discard cards greater than 10.

Use different color counters or coins as markers. If you use coins, one player is "heads" and the other player is "tails."

If you use a pencil to initial the squares, print lightly so you can erase and use the board again.

Numerator Pile — All remaining cards

Denominator Pile — Two each of 3, 6, and 9 cards

| | | | | |
|---|---|---|---|---|
| >100% | 0% or 100% | 11.1% | 0% or 100% | >100% |
| $16\frac{2}{3}$% | 22.2% | $33\frac{1}{3}$% | 33.3% | 44.4% |
| >200% | 55.5% | >100% | 66.6% | >200% |
| $66\frac{2}{3}$% | 77.7% | $83\frac{1}{3}$% | 88.8% | $133\frac{1}{3}$% |
| >100% | 0% or 100% | $166\frac{2}{3}$% | 0% or 100% | >100% |

TEACHING MASTER

◆ *Math Masters,* p. 72

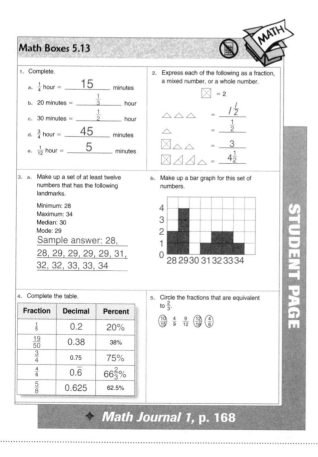

### Math Boxes 5.13

1. Complete.
   a. $\frac{1}{4}$ hour = 15 minutes
   b. 20 minutes = $\frac{1}{3}$ hour
   c. 30 minutes = $\frac{1}{2}$ hour
   d. $\frac{3}{4}$ hour = 45 minutes
   e. $\frac{1}{12}$ hour = 5 minutes

2. Express each of the following as a fraction, a mixed number, or a whole number.
   ☒ = 2
   △△△ = $1\frac{1}{2}$
   △ = $\frac{1}{2}$
   ☒△△ = 3
   ☒◺◺△ = $4\frac{1}{2}$

3. a. Make up a set of at least twelve numbers that has the following landmarks.
   Minimum: 28
   Maximum: 34
   Median: 30
   Mode: 29
   Sample answer: 28, 28, 29, 29, 29, 29, 31, 32, 32, 33, 33, 34

   b. Make up a bar graph for this set of numbers.
   (Bar graph: vertical axis 0–4; horizontal axis 28 29 30 31 32 33 34)

4. Complete the table.

| Fraction | Decimal | Percent |
|---|---|---|
| $\frac{1}{5}$ | 0.2 | 20% |
| $\frac{19}{50}$ | 0.38 | 38% |
| $\frac{3}{4}$ | 0.75 | 75% |
| $\frac{4}{6}$ | $0.\overline{6}$ | $66\frac{2}{3}$% |
| $\frac{5}{8}$ | 0.625 | 62.5% |

5. Circle the fractions that are equivalent to $\frac{2}{3}$.
   ($\frac{10}{15}$) $\frac{4}{9}$ $\frac{9}{12}$ ($\frac{12}{18}$) ($\frac{4}{6}$)

STUDENT PAGE

◆ *Math Journal 1,* p. 168

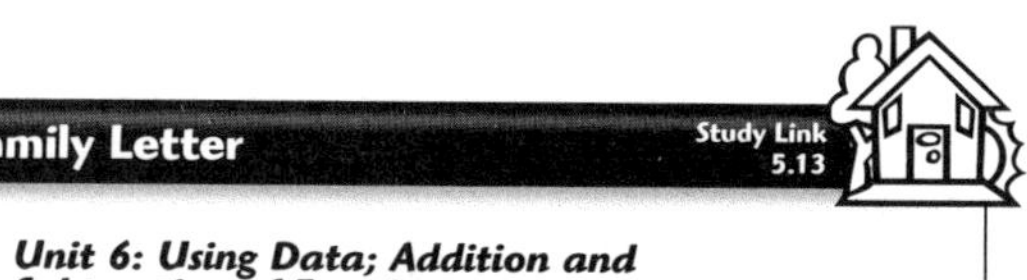


### *Unit 6: Using Data; Addition and Subtraction of Fractions*

The authors of *Everyday Mathematics* believe that students should do serious and substantial work with data. Unit 6 provides many activities designed to present and teach relevant data skills and concepts, allowing your child ample opportunities to practice organizing and analyzing the data he or she collects.

The data that your child initially collects will usually consist of an unorganized collection of numbers. After organizing the data using a variety of methods, he or she will study the **landmarks** of the data. The following terms are called landmarks because they show the important features of the data:

- The **maximum** is the largest data value observed.
- The **minimum** is the smallest data value observed.
- The **range** is the difference between the maximum and the minimum.
- The **mode** is the "most popular" data value—the value observed most often.
- The **median** is the middle data value observed.
- The **mean,** commonly known as the "average," is a central value for a set of data.

At the end of the unit, students will have an opportunity to demonstrate their skills in this area by conducting a survey of their peers; gathering and organizing the data; analyzing their results; and writing a summary report.

Your child will continue his or her work with the American Tour by studying a variety of Native American measurements for length and distance based on parts of the body. Students will convert these body measures to personal measures by measuring their fingers, hands, and arms in both metric and U.S. customary units. In addition, your child will learn how to read a variety of contour-type maps, such as climate, precipitation, and growing-seasons maps.

Finally, students will explore addition and subtraction of fractions by using paper slide rules, the familiar clock face, and fraction sticks. They will learn to find common denominators and apply this skill in adding and subtracting fractions with unlike denominators.

**Please keep this Family Letter for reference as your child works through Unit 6.**

STUDY LINK MASTERS

◆ *Math Masters,* pp. 278–281

# Unit 6
# Using Data; Additior and Subtraction of Fractions

## overview

In Lessons 5.9–5.11, students displayed data with line plots, line graphs, and circle graphs. Unit 6 continues this work with data. By using data from surveys, students revisit the standard landmarks, begin to use stem-and-leaf plots, and investigate the effect of sample size. In a new routine, they match "myst plots" with data that could have led to those plots. I the American Tour lesson, students read and us contour maps that show climate and growing-season data.

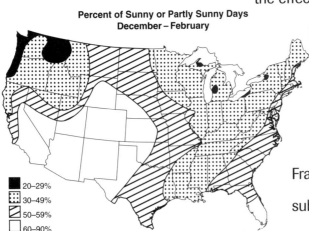

Percent of Sunny or Partly Sunny Days
December – February

20–29%
30–49%
50–59%
60–90%

Fractions are revisited in this unit. At first, students add subtract fractions with the help of various hands-on devices—slide rules, fraction sticks, and clock faces. Th they extend the idea that every fraction has many equivalent names to finding comm denominators, and apply this skill to paper-and-pencil computation.

# contents

# learning goals in perspective

| learning goals | links to the past | links to the future |
|---|---|---|
| 6a **Beginning/Developing Goal** Construct stem-and-leaf plots. **(Lesson 6.3)** | In Grade 5, students drew a circle graph for a set of data. In Grade 4, students displayed data with line plots, bar graphs, and tally charts. *(Related Grade 5 lessons: 5.11)* | In fifth grade, students will interpret mystery line plots and graphs. In sixth grade, students will interpret and construct step graphs, broken-line graphs, bar graphs, and circle graphs. *(Related Grade 5 lesson: 10.7)* |
| 6b **Beginning/Developing Goal** Read and interpret stem-and-leaf plots. **(Lesson 6.4)** | In Grade 5, students interpreted circle graphs. *(Related Grade 5 lesson: 5.10)* | In fifth grade, students will interpret mystery line plots and graphs. In sixth grade, students will interpret and construct step graphs, broke-line graphs, bar graphs, and circle graphs. *(Related Grade 5 lesson: 10.7)* |
| 6c **Developing Goal** Add and subtract fractions with like denominators. **(Lessons 6.8–6.10)** | In Grade 5, students added fractions with like denominators. *(Related Grade 5 lesson: 5.3)* | In fifth grade, students will add mixed numbers and fractions with unlike denominators; they will subtract and multiply fractions and mixed numbers. *(Related Grade 5 lessons: 8.2–8.9)* |
| 6d **Developing Goal** Add and subtract fractions with unlike denominators. **(Lessons 6.8–6.10)** | In Grade 5, students added fractions with like denominators. *(Related Grade 5 lesson: 5.3)* | In fifth grade, students will add mixed numbers and fractions with unlike denominators; they will subtract and multiply fractions and mixed numbers. *(Related Grade 5 lessons: 8.2–8.9)* |
| 6e **Developing Goal** Understand how sample size affects results. **(Lesson 6.5)** | In Grade 4, students examined data on the estimated number of times that the "average" person does something in a lifetime and they explored the validity of data. | In sixth grade, students will continue to study how sample size affects results in real-world situations. |
| 6f **Developing Goal** Find common denominators. **(Lessons 6.9 and 6.10)** | In Grade 4, students found fractions equivalent to a given fraction. | In sixth grade, students will find the least common multiple of two numbers. |
| 6g **Developing/Secure Goal** Convert between fractions, decimals, and percents. **(Lessons 6.5, 6.8, and 6.10)** | In Grade 5, students converted between fractions and percents. *(Related Grade 5 lesson: 5.8)* | In fifth grade, students will continue to work with converting among fractions, decimals, and percents. In sixth grade, students will rename numbers expressed by fractions, mixed numbers, decimals, and percents. *(Related Grade 5 lesson: 8.8)* |
| 6h **Secure Goal** Identify and use data landmarks. **(Lessons 6.1, 6.5, and 6.6)** | In Grades 4 and 5, students identified the *maximum, minimum, median, mode,* and *mean* for a data set. *(Related Grade 5 lesson: 2.5)* | In fifth grade, students will use data landmarks to interpret mystery line plots and graphs. In sixth grade, students will continue to find and use the data landmarks *maximum, minimum, median, mode,* and *mean* in real world situations. *(Related Grade 5 lesson: 10.7)* |

# assessment

## ongoing • product • periodic

### Informal Assessment

**Math Boxes** These *Math Journal* pages provide opportunities for cumulative review or assessment of concepts and skills.

**Ongoing Assessment: Kid Watching** Use the Ongoing Assessment suggestions in the following lessons to make quick, on-the-spot observations about students' understanding of:

- Operations and Computation **(Lesson 6.7, Part 2; Lesson 6.8, Part 1; Lesson 6.9, Part 1)**
- Data and Chance **(Lesson 6.3, Part 1; Lesson 6.4, Part 1; Lesson 6.5, Part 1; Lesson 6.10, Part 2)**
- Measurement and Reference Frames **(Lesson 6.2, Part 1)**

**Portfolio Ideas** Samples of students' work may be obtained from the following assignments:

- Measuring with a Ruler **(Lesson 6.2)**
- Interpreting Data in the News **(Lesson 6.6)**
- Finding Contour Maps **(Lesson 6.7)**
- Writing Elapsed Time Number Stories **(Lesson 6.9)**

### Unit 6 Review and Assessment

**Math Message** Use Time to Reflect Problems 1 and 2 in Lesson 6.11 to assess students' progress toward the following learning goals: **Goals 6b and 6e**

**Oral and Slate Assessments** Use oral or slate assessments during Lesson 6.11 to assess students' progress toward the following learning goal: **Goal 6g**

**Written Assessment** Use a written review during Lesson 6.11 to assess students' progress toward the following learning goals: **Goals 6a–6h**

**Alternative Assessment Options** Use independent alternative assessments in Lesson 6.11 to assess students' progress toward the following learning goals: **Goals 6c, 6d, and 6h**

## assessmenthandbook

For more information on how to use different types of assessment in Unit 6, see the Assessment Overview on pages 52–54 in the *Assessment Handbook*. The following Assessment Masters can be found in the *Math Masters* book:

- Unit 6 Checking Progress, pp. 392–394
- Unit 6 Individual Profile of Progress, p. 439
- Unit 6 Class Checklist, p. 438
- Class Progress Indicator, p. 471
- Math Logs, pp. 474 and 475
- Self-Assessment Forms, pp. 477 and 478
- Interest Inventories, pp. 472 and 473

# problemsolving

## *A process of modeling everyday situations using tools from mathematics*

Encourage children to use a variety of strategies when attacking a given problem—and to explain those strategies. *Strategies children might use in this unit:*

- Make a data display
- Use computation
- Use a ruler
- Use logical reasoning
- Use physical models (pattern blocks, slide ruler, clock)
- Use estimation

Four Problem-Solving **REPRESENTATIONS**

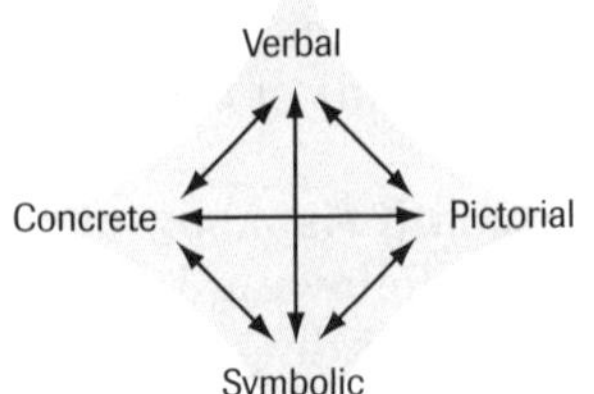


## Lessons that teach *through* problem solving, not just *about* problem solving

| Lesson | Activity | Lesson | Activity |
|---|---|---|---|
| **6.1, 6.3, 6.4** | Organize data and find landmarks for the number of states students and adults have visited, for hand measures and finger flexibility, for test scores, and student spending data | **6.4** | Identify mystery data displays |
| **6.1, 6.5, 6.7–6.9** | Solve number stories involving fractions and division | **6.5** | Examine how sample size affects predictions of colors of candy in a bow |
| **6.2** | Find personal measures for various body units | **6.7** | Use contour maps for precipitation and growing seasons to compare the climat of various U.S locations |
| **6.2–6.6** | Determine whether a game is a fair game | | |

For more information about problem solving in ***Everyday Mathematics,*** see the ***Teacher's Reference Manual***.

# cross-curricularlinks

### social studies

- Students analyze information about class members' visits to various states. **(Lesson 6.1)**
- Discuss ancient measures of length and weight. **(Lesson 6.2)**
- Students report on historical units of measures. **(Lesson 6.2)**
- Discuss the definition and purpose of a survey. **(Lesson 6.6)**

### language arts

- Students discuss meanings of the word *span.* **(Lesson 6.3)**

### science

- Discuss the purpose and parts of a contour map. Students investigate contour maps that show climate data. **(Lesson 6.7)**

# meeting INDIVIDUAL needs

## ✦ RETEACHING

The following features provide additional instructional support:

**Adjusting the Activity**

- **Lesson 6.1, Part 1**
- **Lesson 6.3, Part 1**
- **Lesson 6.4, Part 1**
- **Lesson 6.6, Part 1**
- **Lesson 6.8, Part 1**
- **Lesson 6.9, Part 1**

**Options for Individualizing**

- **Lesson 6.1** Making a Stick-On Note Graph
- **Lesson 6.2** Reviewing Metric Conversions
- **Lesson 6.8** Representing Patterns with Variables

## ✦ ENRICHMENT

The following features suggest enrichment and extension activities:

**Adjusting the Activity**

- **Lesson 6.1, Part 1**
- **Lesson 6.2, Part 1**
- **Lesson 6.5, Part 1**
- **Lesson 6.7, Part 1**
- **Lesson 6.9, Part 1**

**Options for Individualizing**

- **Lesson 6.1** Identifying States Visited by the Most Students
- **Lesson 6.2** Learning about Nonstandard Units of Measure
- **Lesson 6.3** Making a Stem-and-Leaf Plot
- **Lesson 6.5** Investigating How Sample Size Affects the Results of Chance Events
- **Lesson 6.6** Interpreting Data in the News
- **Lesson 6.7** Finding Contour Maps
- **Lesson 6.9** Writing Elapsed Time Number Stories

## ✦ LANGUAGE DIVERSITY

The following features suggest ways to support children who are acquiring proficiency in English:

**Adjusting the Activity**

- **Lesson 6.1, Part 1**

**Options for Individualizing**

- **Lesson 6.8** Adding and Subtracting Fractions with Pattern-Block Models

## ✦ MULTIAGE CLASSROOM

The following chart lists related lessons from Grades 4 and 6 that can help you meet your instructional needs:

| | | | | | | | | | | | |
|---|---|---|---|---|---|---|---|---|---|---|---|
| **Grade 4** | 2.5 | 4.8 | 2.5, 4.8 | | | | | 7.4, 9.1, 9.5 | 7.5 9.1 | 7.6 | |
| **Grade 5** | 6.1 | 6.2 | 6.3 | 6.4 | 6.5 | 6.6 | 6.7 | 6.8 | 6.9 | 6.10 | 6.11 |
| **Grade 6** | | | | 1.2 | | | | 4.3–4.5 | 4.3–4.5 | | |

# materials

| lesson | math masters pages | manipulative kit items | other items |
|---|---|---|---|
| **6.1** | Study Link Masters, pp. 275 and 282<br>***See* Advance Preparation, p. 350** | | stick-on notes<br>calculator<br>estimation jar and contents |
| **6.2** | Study Link Master, p. 283<br>Teaching Master, p. 81 | deck of cards, 4 each of the numbers 4–8 (from the Everything Math Deck, if available) | ruler<br>tape measure with metric and U.S. customary units<br>slate<br>***See* Advance Preparation, p. 356** |
| **6.3** | Study Link Master, p. 284<br>Assessment Master, p. 479<br>***See* Advance Preparation, p. 362** | deck of number cards (or the Everything Math Deck, If available) | protractor; ruler; protractor for demonstration purposes<br>newspapers and/or almanacs |
| **6.4** | Study Link Master, p. 285<br>Teaching Masters, pp. 82 and 83<br>Assessment Master, p. 479 | | protractor |
| **6.5** | Study Link Master, p. 286<br>Teaching Master, p. 84 (optional)<br>Assessment Master, p. 479 | | Geometry Template<br>crayons or markers (optional)<br>calculator<br>small pieces of colored candy<br>coins or dice<br>***See* Advance Preparation, p. 372** |
| **6.6** | Study Link Master, p. 287 | | calculator<br>newspapers and magazines<br>***See* Advance Preparation, p. 377** |
| **6.7** | Study Link Master, p. 288<br>Assessment Master, p. 476 | | physical and political map(s) of the United States for the classroom (optional)<br>contour maps |
| **6.8** | Study Link Master, p. 289<br>Teaching Masters, pp. 62–74 and 86<br>transparencies of Teaching Masters, pp. 25 and 85 (optional) | pattern blocks | slate<br>***See* Advance Preparation, p. 387** |
| **6.9** | Study Link Master, p. 290<br>Teaching Masters, pp. 87 and 88 | 2 six-sided dice per partnership | slide rule (*Math Journal 2,* Activity Sheet 6)<br>slate |
| **6.10** | Study Link Master, p. 291<br>Teaching Master, p. 89 | | slide rule (*Math Journal 2,* Activity Sheet 6)<br>slate |
| **6.11** | Study Link Masters, pp. 292–295<br>Teaching Master, p. 86<br>Assessment Masters, pp. 392–394 | pattern blocks | slate |

# planningtips

## Pacing

Pacing depends on a number of factors, such as students' individual needs and how long your school has been using *Everyday Mathematics*. At the beginning of Unit 6, review your Content by Strand Poster to help you set a monthly pace.

| ←MOST CLASSROOMS→ JANUARY | FEBRUARY | MARCH |
|---|---|---|

## Home Communication

Share Study Links 6.1–6.10 with families to help them understand the content and procedures in this unit. At the end of the unit, use Study Link 6.11 to introduce Unit 7. Supplemental information can be found in the *Home Connection Handbook*.

## NCTM Standards

| Standard | 1 | 2 | 3 | 4 | 5 | 6 | 7 | 8 | 9 | 10 |
|---|---|---|---|---|---|---|---|---|---|---|
| Unit 6 Lessons | 6.1, 6.5, 6.8, 6.10 | 6.8 | 6.9 | 6.2–6.4, 6.9 | 6.1, 6.3–6.7, 6.10 | 6.1–6.11 | 6.1–6.11 | 6.1–6.11 | 6.1–6.11 | 6.1–6.11 |

**Content Standards**
1 Number and Operations
2 Algebra
3 Geometry
4 Measurement
5 Data Analysis and Probability

**Process Standards**
6 Problem Solving
7 Reasoning and Proof
8 Communication
9 Connections
10 Representation

## PRACTICE *through* Games

*Everyday Mathematics* uses games to help students develop good fact power and other math skills.

- *First to 21* to determine if a game involving mental addition is a fair game **(Lessons 6.2–6.6)**
- *Frac-Tac-Toe* to practice renaming fractions as decimals or percents **(Lesson 6.8)**
- *Angle Tangle* to practice estimating and then using a protractor to measure angles **(Lesson 6.9)**
- *Fraction Capture* to practice naming equivalent fractions **(Lesson 6.9)**

# unit 6 content highlights

*The discussion below highlights the major content ideas presented in Unit 6 and may help you establish instructional priorities.*

## Landmarks in Data Sets (Lesson 6.1)

The data landmarks reviewed in this lesson have been a focus of informal work since *Kindergarten Everyday Mathematics*. Using data landmarks to make sense of data can serve five-year-olds as well as adults. The contexts may become more complicated; the data sets may grow larger and more difficult to collect; and more complex algorithms, procedures, and statistical tools may be needed, but the basic ideas remain the same.

## "Natural" Measures versus Standardized Measures (Lessons 6.2 and 6.3)

Almost every human society has invented systems for counting and measuring. Measure systems typically began with units of length based on body parts (the foot, the span, and so on) and with commonly used food or water containers for capacity. As people gathered into larger groups and commerce developed, they began to establish common standards for units of measure.

Lessons 6.2 and 6.3 remind students how measure systems developed in human history, and how natural measures became standardized measures. In addition to presenting important information about the development of measure in Native American cultures, the lessons also review data gathering, use of landmarks, and angle-measure skills.

## "Mystery Plots"—Establishing a New Routine (Lesson 6.4)

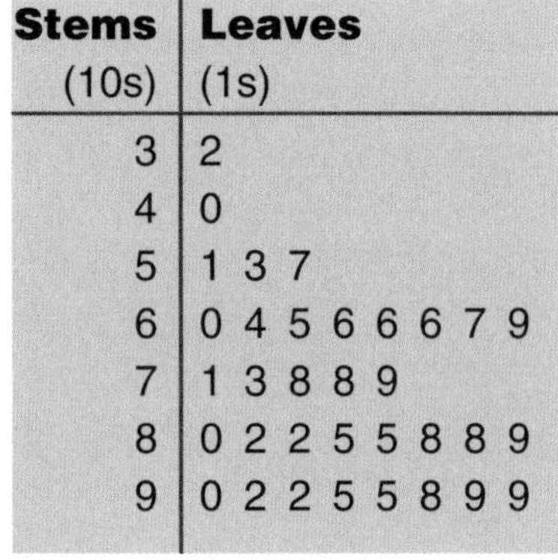

| **Stems** (10s) | **Leaves** (1s) |
|---|---|
| 3 | 2 |
| 4 | 0 |
| 5 | 1 3 7 |
| 6 | 0 4 5 6 6 6 7 9 |
| 7 | 1 3 8 8 9 |
| 8 | 0 2 2 5 5 8 8 9 |
| 9 | 0 2 2 5 5 8 9 9 |

Students act as consumers and critics of data and data displays, rather than as producers. They need to develop judgment, common sense, and a healthy skepticism in order to adjust to the data-filled world. The mystery-plots routine will recur in later lessons. You may want to use it with data or graphs that you or the students find in newspapers and other sources.

## Survey Design, Implementation, and Data Analysis (Lessons 6.5 and 6.6)

Much of the information used to make decisions today comes from surveys. Manufacturers survey consumers to find out what products to make or what to change in an existing product. Television stations survey viewers to learn what programs are popular. Politicians, newspapers, and magazines survey people to obtain opinions on issues or candidates.

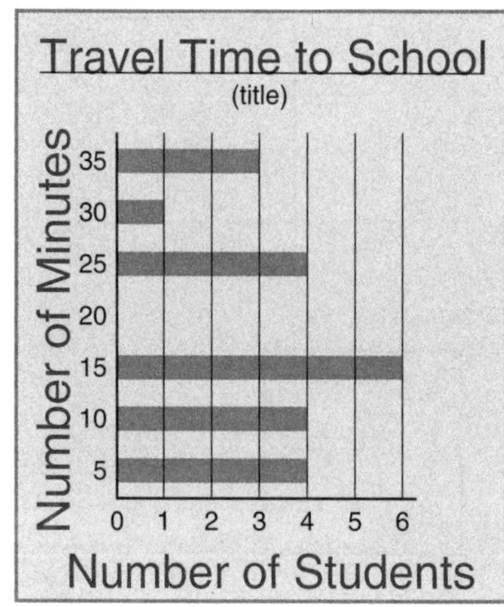


Sometimes the information needed comes from a small enough group so that everyone involved can be questioned. Even then the formulation of the questions is important, and so are the analysis of answers and displays of the resulting data. More often it is impossible to talk to everyone, and a representative sample of people is surveyed. The initial design of these surveys is crucial; a flawed design will yield either no results or questionable results. The size of the sample and the extent to which the sample represents the larger population are important. Students should keep in mind that:

- ▷ It is hazardous to draw conclusions from small samples of large populations.
- ▷ It is possible, with planning and precautions, to combine many small samples with unreliable and volatile results into large samples yielding reliable conclusions.

With the issue of sample size attended to, the important matters are to formulate the questions, gather the data, and analyze the results.

The examples in these lessons are drawn from a survey done by our field-test students. You and your students should feel free to survey on a topic that interests you. The particular topics don't matter; what's important is the process of formulating questions and gathering data to illuminate those questions.

Different ways of displaying data are appropriate for different questions, even in the same survey. Again, what is important is not finding one correct display, but considering and discussing the strengths and weaknesses of various displays.

## Contour Maps: Showing a Third Dimension on a 2-Dimensional Map (Lesson 6.7)

Most units include at least one lesson that makes use of the American Tour. In this unit, students will use climate maps in the American Tour, and interpret contour lines on the maps.

Nearly everyone has seen temperature contours on daily weather maps in newspapers and on television. Many people have used contour maps that show altitudes of mountains, hills, and valleys. Such 2-dimensional maps are much easier to produce and more convenient to put into a backpack or take to a construction job than are 3-dimensional models. With experience, the user can get as much information from a contour map as from a 3-dimensional model.

The important point of this lesson is that contour (or "equal measure") lines can convey many kinds of information. Again your students are cast in the roles of consumers and interpreters of data displays rather

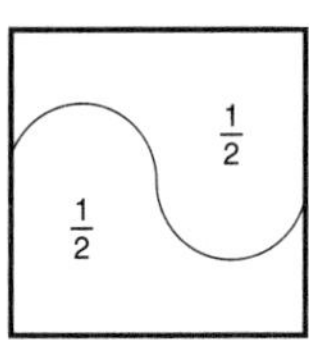


than of producers of data displays. Both roles are important, and, in fact, people are more often consumers than producers of data displays.

Mathematical modeling is again revisited. In this lesson, the maps model vast amounts of data collected over many years.

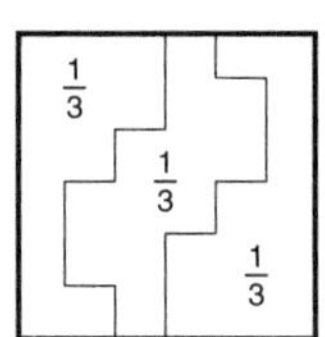


## A Slide Rule for Adding and Subtracting Fractions (Lesson 6.8)

Students model addition and subtraction by using a paper "slide rule." This slide rule demonstrates basic concepts of addition and subtraction of linear measures, as might actually be applied by carpenters, plumbers, mechanics, or laboratory technicians. Addition and subtraction of two numbers is acted out by finding the first number on a number line and then "moving ahead" by the amount of the second number (for addition) or "moving back" (for subtraction).

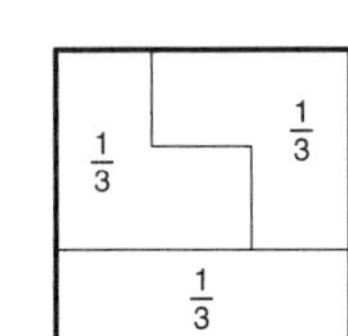


## Common Denominator Uses and Misconceptions (Lessons 6.9 and 6.10)

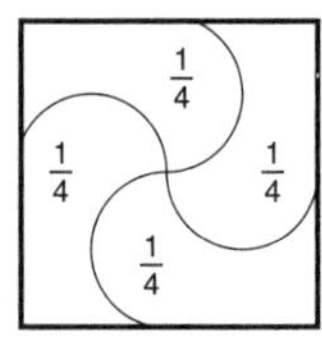


In principle, any two fractions can be rewritten as fractions with the same denominator, which can be found among the endless supply of equivalent names for each fraction. With common denominators, it is easy to add or subtract any two (or more) fractions. Hence, traditional school arithmetic has extensive teaching and practice in finding and using common denominators and especially in finding a "least common denominator" (LCD) for two or more fractions. The pervasive search in schools for *least* common denominators (LCDs) wastes time, and excessive attention to LCDs as the only permissible denominators is almost certainly harmful to later learning of algebra.

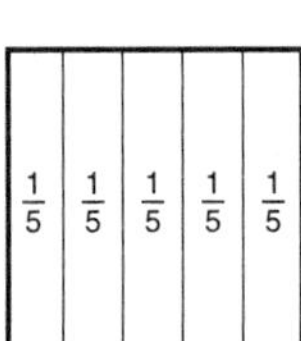


In adding, subtracting, or comparing fractions, any common denominator works as well as any other, and finding a "quick common denominator" (QCD) as the product of two denominators (Lesson 6.10) is very useful. Hence, finding QCDs is suggested as the preferred method whenever the fractions are complex enough that the least common denominator or other common denominators are not obvious. The algebra rule for adding fractions thus becomes

$$\frac{a}{b} + \frac{c}{d} = \frac{(a * d) + (c * d)}{b * d}$$

## Misconceptions Regarding Simplest Form, Mixed Numbers, and Fractions Greater Than One

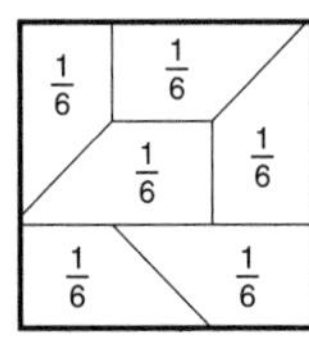

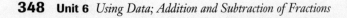

It is important to know how to exploit the fact that there are many equivalent names for any fraction. It is useful to know that among the names, there is a fraction in "simplest form"—that is, its numerator and denominator have no common factors except 1—and that the simplest form is a convenient label for the entire collection of equivalent fractions.

It is also useful to know that if the numerator is larger than the denominator, there are equivalent names that are "mixed numbers," some with the numerator still larger than the denominator, some with the fraction part in simplest form, and some with the fraction part not in simplest form.

It is not useful to insist that "simplest form" is preferred to all other equivalent names. In fact, flexibility in arithmetic is gained by freely using whatever form is most convenient or illuminating for the purpose at hand. Truly numerate people artfully use one form of a number rather than another to express what they want or need to say. Also, "reducing" ratios or rates to "simpler" forms may result in important information being lost. For example, saying that the fraction of people voting for a candidate was 7,500/10,000 conveys more information than giving the portion as $\frac{3}{4}$, or 75%.

School mathematics should promote flexibility in using numbers and in using fractions in particular. Standard forms have their place, but to acknowledge their use as the only method is harmful to learning.

## Review and Assessment (Lesson 6.11)

Like every unit in *Fifth Grade Everyday Mathematics,* Unit 6 ends with a review and assessment lesson. This lesson provides a list of unit goals, as well as suggested questions for oral and slate evaluation. Assessment Masters provide review items for students to complete in writing; each item is keyed to a unit goal.

If you are planning a quarterly assessment for Units 4–6, you may want to refer to the *Assessment Handbook.* The quarterly learning goals Class Checklist and Individual Profile of Progress checklist (*Math Masters,* pages 456–459) are useful tools for keeping track of students' progress.

**For additional information on the following topics, see the *Teacher's Reference Manual:***

- contour maps
- fraction addition and subtraction
- landmarks of data sets
- making predictions
- metric system
- personal measures
- stem-and-leaf plots
- U.S. customary system

# 6.1 Organizing Data

**OBJECTIVES** **To review methods for organizing data; and to describe prominent features of a data set.**

| summaries | materials |
|---|---|
| **1 Teaching the Lesson** | |
| Students organize and describe previously collected data on the number of states that they and adults have been in. They review common "landmarks" that are used to describe a data set, including the minimum, maximum, range, mode, median, and mean. [Data and Chance] | □ *Math Journal 1,* p. 160 (optional); and pp. 170 and 171<br>□ Study Link 5.10 (*Math Masters,* p. 275)<br>□ stick-on notes<br>□ calculator<br>***See*** **Advance Preparation** |
| **2 Ongoing Learning & Practice** | |
| Students solve problems by identifying fractional parts of a whole. They also solve a logic problem. [Operations and Computation]<br>Students practice and maintain skills through Math Boxes and Study Link activities. | □ *Math Journal 1,* pp. 169 and 172<br>□ Study Link Master (*Math Masters,* p. 282) |
| **3 Options for Individualizing** | |
| **Enrichment** Students identify the states that have been visited by the greatest number of classmates. [Data and Chance]<br>**Reteaching** Students organize and describe estimates of contents of an estimation jar. They then use stick-on notes to make a line-plot graph. [Data and Chance] | □ Study Link 5.10 (*Math Masters,* p. 275)<br>□ estimation jar and contents<br>□ stick-on notes |

## Additional Information

**Advance Preparation** Before beginning the lesson, make sure students have completed Study Link 5.10.

Draw two horizontal number lines labeled 0, 1, 2, 3, ... on the board. Leave enough room above each number line for small stick-on notes. One number line will be used to plot the number of states students have been in, the other to plot the number of states adults have been in. Because it is possible that some adults have visited all 50 states, the adult line may need to be much longer than the student line.

**Vocabulary** • **organizing data** • **landmark** • **minimum** • **maximum** • **range** • **mode** • **median** • **mean (average)** • **line plot**

# Getting Started

## Mental Math and Reflexes

Compare pairs of fractions, using <, >, or =.

*Suggestions:*

- $\frac{2}{3}$ < $\frac{4}{5}$
- $\frac{1}{16}$ < $\frac{1}{12}$
- $\frac{2}{8}$ < $\frac{3}{10}$
- $\frac{4}{7}$ > $\frac{5}{9}$
- $\frac{12}{20}$ > $\frac{3}{16}$
- $\frac{8}{16}$ = $\frac{4}{8}$

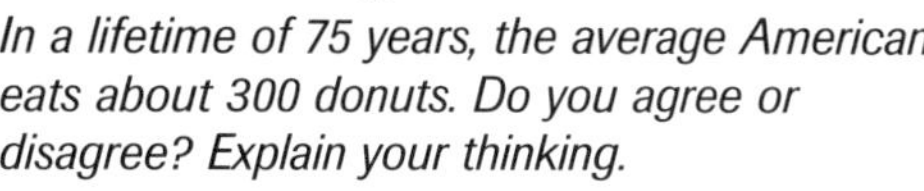

## Math Message

*In a lifetime of 75 years, the average American eats about 300 donuts. Do you agree or disagree? Explain your thinking.*

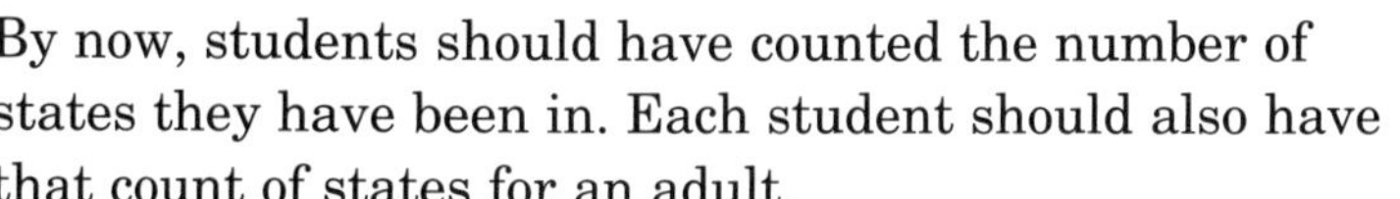

# 1 Teaching the Lesson

## ✦ Math Message Follow-Up

WHOLE-CLASS DISCUSSION

Have students show “thumbs up” if they agree with the statement and “thumbs down” if they disagree. Have a few volunteers on both sides of the question share their thinking. Expect answers like the following:

- 300 donuts in 75 years would only be about 4 donuts each year. I think most people eat more than 4 donuts per year, so I think that the average has to be higher.
- My family and I don’t eat many donuts. We probably do not even eat 4 donuts a year. Some people probably eat more than we do. I would say that 300 donuts is probably a reasonable average.

## ✦ Organizing the Class Data for the Number of States Students Have Visited

(*Math Journal 1,* p. 170; *Math Masters,* p. 275)

SMALL-GROUP ACTIVITY

By now, students should have counted the number of states they have been in. Each student should also have that count of states for an adult.

One at a time, ask students to report the number of states they have visited. List these on the board, the Class Data Pad, or an overhead transparency *in the order in which they are called out*. Students should also record these data on journal page 170.

**States Students Have Visited**

1. You and your classmates counted the number of states each of you has visited. As the counts are reported and your teacher records them, write them in the space below. When you finish, circle your own count in the list.
Answers vary.

2. Decide with your group how to organize the data you just listed. (For example, you might make a line plot or a tally table.) Then organize the data and show the results below. Answers vary.

3. Write two things you think are important about the data. Answers vary.
   a. ______
   b. ______

4. Compare your own count of states with those of your classmates.
Answers vary.

STUDENT PAGE

✦ *Math Journal 1,* p. 170

NOTE: Students' plots, tables, and other ways of organizing the data should be easy to make and easy to read. Unlike graphs for a report, they need not be carefully done or nicely labeled in order to be useful.

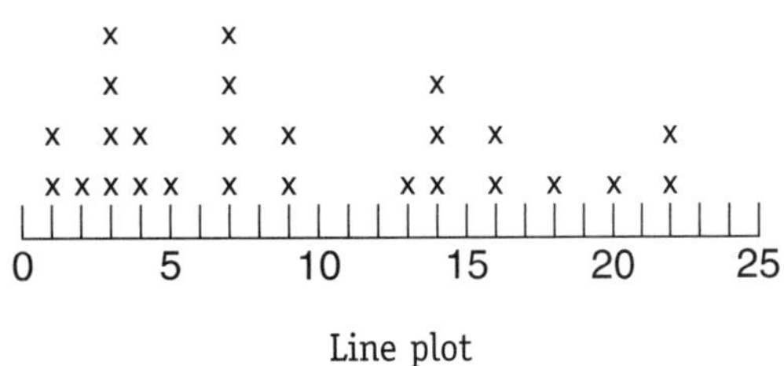

Line plot

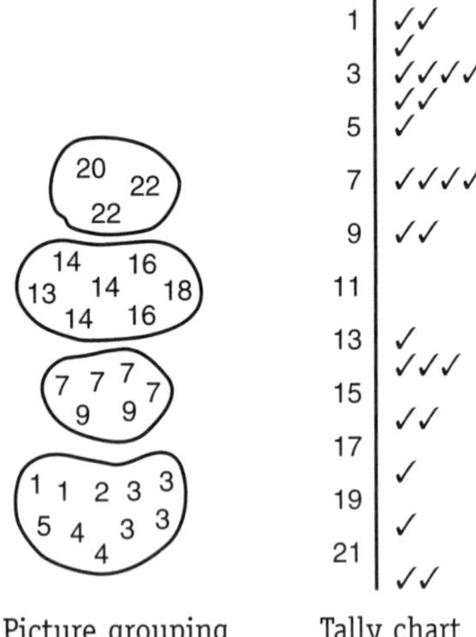
Picture grouping    Tally chart

NOTE: Students who have used *Everyday Mathematics* previously have seen stick-on note graphs before. Do not spend a lot of time reteaching the idea if it is review for most students. See Part 3 for a Reteaching suggestion.

Ask students how they might organize the class data. Remind them that **organizing data** helps people understand what is being presented. It is often easier to interpret a picture, graph, table, or list than it is to interpret an unorganized set of data.

Divide the class into small groups and ask each group to complete Problems 2 and 3. Each group should:

1. Decide on a method for organizing the data.
2. Use this method to organize the data.
3. Write two comments about the data.

Students record their group's conclusions on journal page 170. When most students have completed Problems 2 and 3, bring the class together to discuss the results.

## Describing the Data (*Math Journal 1,* p. 170)

WHOLE-CLASS DISCUSSION

Ask students to demonstrate their methods for organizing the data. Some methods you might expect from students are shown *in the margin*. Make sure several ways are presented.

Some groups may have arranged the data *in order*. Point out that putting data in order helps the viewer "see the data better."

Show students how to plot the data using stick-on notes. Point out the number line labeled "States Students Have Been In." Ask each student to print his or her personal count for states on a stick-on note and to attach it above the appropriate mark on the number line. If the stick-on notes are carefully stacked, the result models a bar graph.

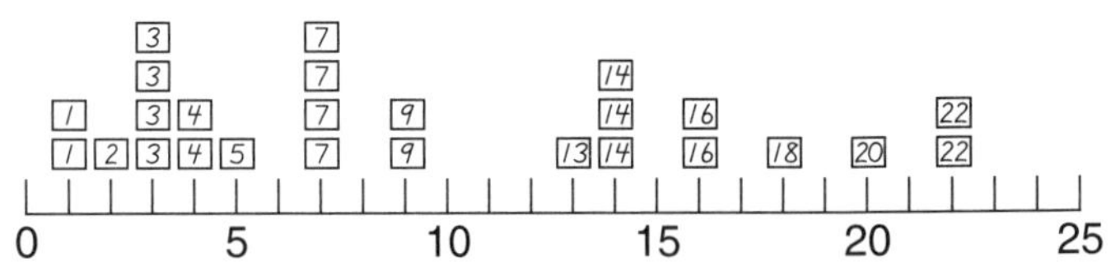

Check to see whether students used any common landmarks in organizing the data. Mark and label the maximum, minimum, mode(s), median, and range on the stick-on note graph.

**Adjusting the Activity** You may need to review the definitions of the **landmarks.** These are the prominent features of a data set.

**minimum** smallest value
**maximum** largest value
**range** difference between the minimum and the maximum
**mode** most frequent value or values
**median** middle value
**mean (average)** another middle value, found by dividing the sum of the numbers by the number of numbers

You might have students turn to *Student Reference Book,* pages 113, 114, and 115 to review definitions of landmarks and study worked examples. Or you could use the snack-survey data on journal page 160 to illustrate each definition.

To help students with data vocabulary, display a **line plot** with the landmarks identified and the definitions of landmarks listed.

Encourage students to describe the shape of the stick-on note graph. Informal terms such as "bunches," "bumps," and "far away from most" are fine. Expect good observations on the shape of the data plot as students compare their personal counts with the whole-class results.

Ask students to complete Problem 4 on the journal page.

## Organizing the Class Data for the Number of States Adults Have Visited

(*Math Journal 1,* pp. 170 and 171; *Math Masters,* p. 275)

PARTNER ACTIVITY

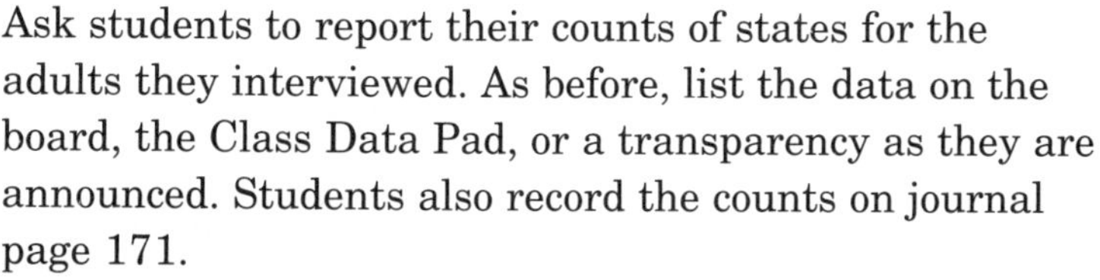

Ask students to report their counts of states for the adults they interviewed. As before, list the data on the board, the Class Data Pad, or a transparency as they are announced. Students also record the counts on journal page 171.

Have students work alone or with partners to complete the journal page. When most students have completed the page, bring the class together and use stick-on notes to make a "bar graph" of the adult data.

Discuss and compare the two stick-on note graphs. Compare landmarks for the two plots. Expect that adults will have a larger median (and mean). Ask students why this may be the case. Adults have lived longer and have traveled more.

**States Adults Have Visited**

1. You and your classmates each recorded the number of states that an adult had been in. As the numbers are reported and your teacher records them, write them in the space below. Answers vary.

2. Draw a line plot to organize the data you just listed. Answers vary.

3. Record landmarks for the data about adults and students in the table below.

| Landmark | Adults | Students |
|---|---|---|
| Minimum | Answers vary. | Answers vary. |
| Maximum | | |
| Mode(s) | | |
| Median | | |

4. How are the counts for adults and students different? Explain your answer.
Answers vary.

STUDENT PAGE

Math Journal 1, p. 171

NOTE: If available, have students explore using data analysis software to organize, record, and display their data, as well as to construct various kinds of graphs.

**Adjusting the Activity** Ask several volunteers to find the mean (average) number of states students have been in. They should use calculators to add the counts recorded in Problem 1 on journal page 170, and then divide by the number of counts. Ask other volunteers to find the mean number of states adults have been in, using the counts recorded in Problem 1 on journal page 171.

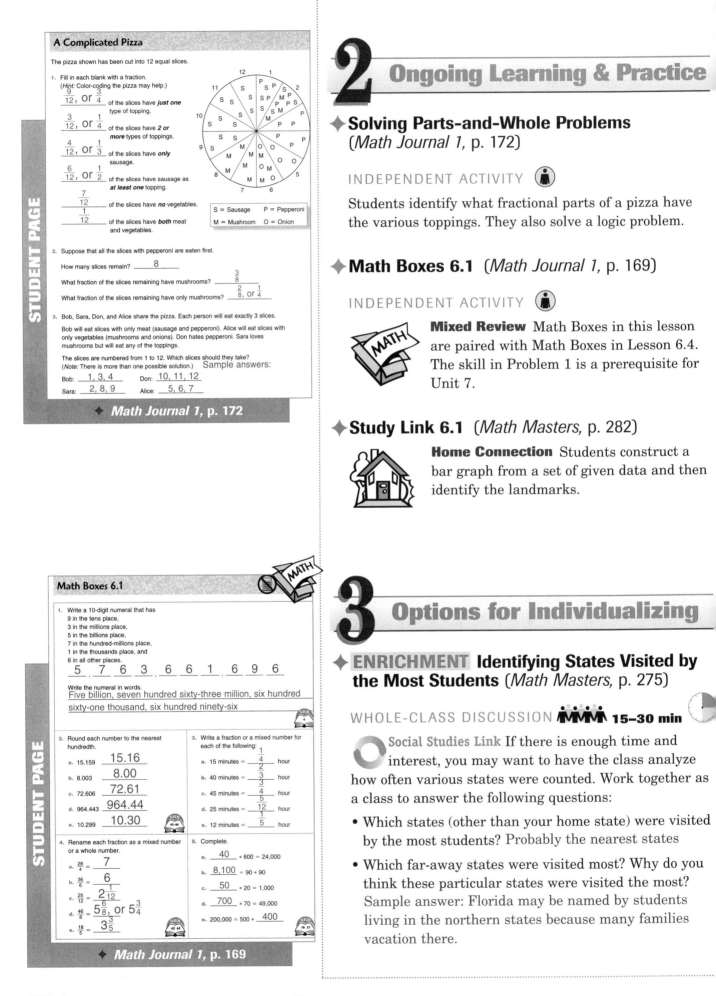

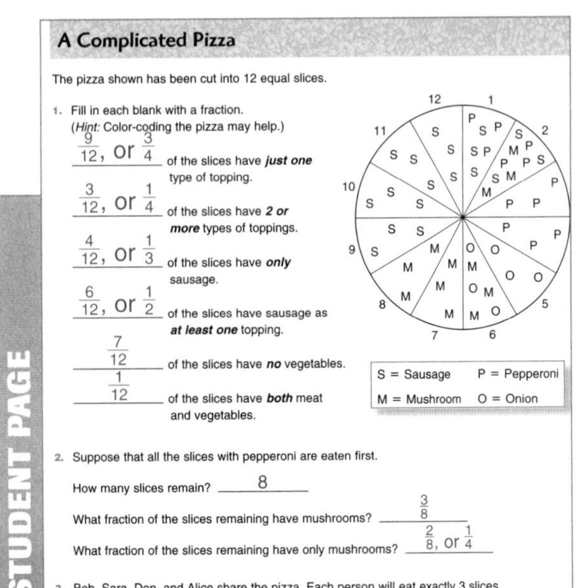

STUDENT PAGE

## A Complicated Pizza

The pizza shown has been cut into 12 equal slices.

1. Fill in each blank with a fraction. (*Hint:* Color-coding the pizza may help.)

$\frac{9}{12}$, or $\frac{3}{4}$ of the slices have *just one* type of topping.

$\frac{3}{12}$, or $\frac{1}{4}$ of the slices have *2 or more* types of toppings.

$\frac{4}{12}$, or $\frac{1}{3}$ of the slices have *only* sausage.

$\frac{6}{12}$, or $\frac{1}{2}$ of the slices have sausage as *at least one* topping.

$\frac{7}{12}$ of the slices have *no* vegetables.

$\frac{1}{12}$ of the slices have *both* meat and vegetables.

S = Sausage  P = Pepperoni
M = Mushroom  O = Onion

2. Suppose that all the slices with pepperoni are eaten first.

How many slices remain? 8

What fraction of the slices remaining have mushrooms? $\frac{3}{8}$

What fraction of the slices remaining have only mushrooms? $\frac{2}{8}$, or $\frac{1}{4}$

3. Bob, Sara, Don, and Alice share the pizza. Each person will eat exactly 3 slices.

Bob will eat slices with only meat (sausage and pepperoni). Alice will eat slices with only vegetables (mushrooms and onions). Don hates pepperoni. Sara loves mushrooms but will eat any of the toppings.

The slices are numbered from 1 to 12. Which slices should they take? (*Note:* There is more than one possible solution.) Sample answers:

Bob: 1, 3, 4  Don: 10, 11, 12
Sara: 2, 8, 9  Alice: 5, 6, 7

✦ *Math Journal 1,* p. 172

# 2 Ongoing Learning & Practice

## ✦ Solving Parts-and-Whole Problems (*Math Journal 1,* p. 172)

INDEPENDENT ACTIVITY 

Students identify what fractional parts of a pizza have the various toppings. They also solve a logic problem.

## ✦ Math Boxes 6.1 (*Math Journal 1,* p. 169)

INDEPENDENT ACTIVITY 

**Mixed Review** Math Boxes in this lesson are paired with Math Boxes in Lesson 6.4. The skill in Problem 1 is a prerequisite for Unit 7.

## ✦ Study Link 6.1 (*Math Masters,* p. 282)

**Home Connection** Students construct a bar graph from a set of given data and then identify the landmarks.

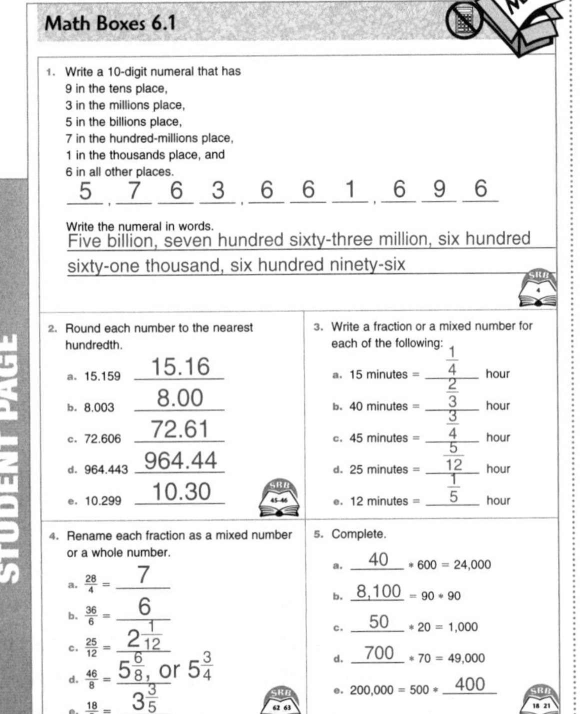

STUDENT PAGE

## Math Boxes 6.1

1. Write a 10-digit numeral that has 9 in the tens place, 3 in the millions place, 5 in the billions place, 7 in the hundred-millions place, 1 in the thousands place, and 6 in all other places.

5,763,661,696

Write the numeral in words.
Five billion, seven hundred sixty-three million, six hundred sixty-one thousand, six hundred ninety-six

2. Round each number to the nearest hundredth.

a. 15.159 15.16
b. 8.003 8.00
c. 72.606 72.61
d. 964.443 964.44
e. 10.299 10.30

3. Write a fraction or a mixed number for each of the following:

a. 15 minutes = $\frac{1}{4}$ hour
b. 40 minutes = $\frac{2}{3}$ hour
c. 45 minutes = $\frac{3}{4}$ hour
d. 25 minutes = $\frac{5}{12}$ hour
e. 12 minutes = $\frac{1}{5}$ hour

4. Rename each fraction as a mixed number or a whole number.

a. $\frac{28}{4}$ = 7
b. $\frac{36}{6}$ = 6
c. $\frac{25}{12}$ = $2\frac{1}{12}$
d. $\frac{46}{8}$ = $5\frac{6}{8}$, or $5\frac{3}{4}$
e. $\frac{18}{5}$ = $3\frac{3}{5}$

5. Complete.

a. 40 ∗ 600 = 24,000
b. 8,100 = 90 ∗ 90
c. 50 ∗ 20 = 1,000
d. 700 ∗ 70 = 49,000
e. 200,000 = 500 ∗ 400

✦ *Math Journal 1,* p. 169

# 3 Options for Individualizing

## ✦ ENRICHMENT Identifying States Visited by the Most Students (*Math Masters,* p. 275)

WHOLE-CLASS DISCUSSION **15–30 min**

**Social Studies Link** If there is enough time and interest, you may want to have the class analyze how often various states were counted. Work together as a class to answer the following questions:

- Which states (other than your home state) were visited by the most students? Probably the nearest states
- Which far-away states were visited most? Why do you think these particular states were visited the most? Sample answer: Florida may be named by students living in the northern states because many families vacation there.

## ✦ RETEACHING Making a Stick-on Note Graph

WHOLE-CLASS ACTIVITY  **15–30 min**

Have students estimate the number of objects contained in an estimation jar. Collect their estimates on a line plot. *Suggested estimation situations:*

▷ Fill the jar with large beans or colored candies.

▷ Fill a fraction of the jar ($\frac{1}{4}$ or $\frac{1}{3}$) with large beans or colored candies.

Once students' estimates are collected on the line plot, find the data landmarks: maximum, minimum, mode, range, and median. One strategy for locating the median is to remove stick-on notes in pairs—the highest and the lowest—until only one or two remain. If only one remains, that is the median. If two remain, the median is the value halfway between the two.

Compare actual counts with estimates.

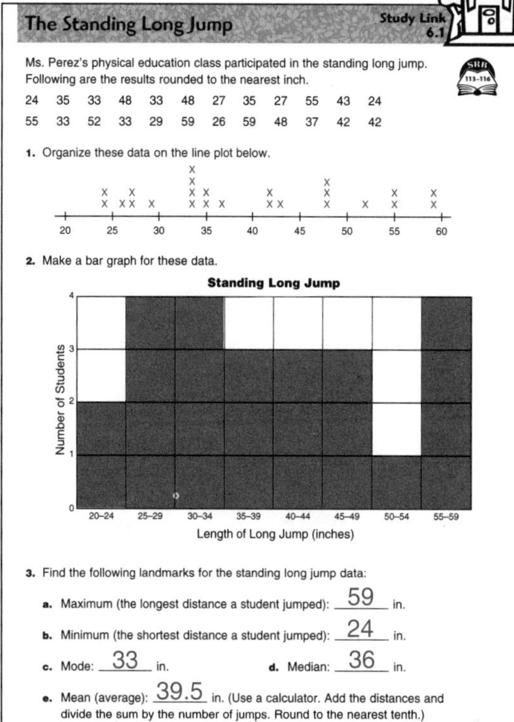

**The Standing Long Jump** — Study Link 6.1

Ms. Perez's physical education class participated in the standing long jump. Following are the results rounded to the nearest inch.

24 35 33 48 33 48 27 35 27 55 43 24

55 33 52 33 29 59 26 59 48 37 42 42

1. Organize these data on the line plot below.



2. Make a bar graph for these data.



3. Find the following landmarks for the standing long jump data:

a. Maximum (the longest distance a student jumped): 59 in.

b. Minimum (the shortest distance a student jumped): 24 in.

c. Mode: 33 in.

d. Median: 36 in.

e. Mean (average): 39.5 in. (Use a calculator. Add the distances and divide the sum by the number of jumps. Round to the nearest tenth.)

STUDY LINK MASTER

✦ *Math Masters,* p. 282

# 6.2 Natural Measures of Length

**OBJECTIVES** **To use metric and U.S. customary units of length; to measure the human body; and to begin investigating whether a game is a fair game.**

| summaries | materials |
|---|---|
| **1 Teaching the Lesson** | |
| Students find their own personal measures for various body units by measuring their fingers, hands, and arms in both metric and U.S. customary units. They begin an extended investigation to determine if the card game *First to 21* is a fair game. During the coming week, students will play the game repeatedly and keep records of the results. [Measurement and Reference Frames; Data and Chance] | ☐ *Math Journal 1,* pp. 174–177<br>☐ *Student Reference Book,* p. 166<br>☐ Study Link 6.1<br>☐ 4 each of the number cards 4–8 (from the Everything Math Deck, if available)<br>☐ ruler with metric and U.S. customary units<br>☐ tape measure with metric and U.S. customary units<br>***See* Advance Preparation** |
| **2 Ongoing Learning & Practice** | |
| Students practice and maintain skills through Math Boxes and Study Link activities. | ☐ *Math Journal 1,* p. 173<br>☐ Study Link Master (*Math Masters,* p. 283) |
| **3 Options for Individualizing** | |
| **Extra Practice** Students measure line segments to the nearest centimeter, millimeter, and $\frac{1}{8}$ inch. [Measurement and Reference Frames]<br>**Enrichment** Students look up information about nonstandard units of measure. [Measurement and Reference Frames]<br>**Reteaching** Students review metric conversions for lengths. [Measurement and Reference Frames] | ☐ Teaching Master (*Math Masters,* p. 81)<br>☐ ruler with metric and U.S. customary units<br>☐ slate |

## Additional Information

**Advance Preparation** For Part 1, prepare a tally sheet, consisting of Tables A and B (see pages 359 and 360 in this book), for recording class results as students play *First to 21.* Also draw the axes for a bar graph to represent daily class results (see page 360).

**Vocabulary** • **span** • **cubit** • **fathom** • **fair game**

# Getting Started

### Mental Math and Reflexes

Dictate numbers and have students write them in standard notation. *Suggestions:*

- Eighty-five hundredths 0.85
- Twenty-two thousandths 0.022
- Two and seven hundredths 2.07
- Sixteen and five tenths 16.5
- Ten and sixty-nine hundredths 10.69

### Math Message

*Read the essay on page 166 of your* Student Reference Book.

### Study Link 6.1 Follow-Up

Briefly go over the answers.

# 1 Teaching the Lesson

## ✦ Math Message Follow-Up
(*Student Reference Book,* p. 166)

WHOLE-CLASS DISCUSSION

**Social Studies Link** Discuss the essay on ancient measures of length and weight with the class. Make sure that the following points are mentioned.

▷ People have used a variety of units for length and distance that are based on the human body.

▷ Measures such as the **span, cubit,** and **fathom,** have been used since ancient times by many cultures, including Native American.

▷ The cubit is probably the most ancient unit of length. (The Latin word *cubitum* means "elbow.")

▷ None of these measures was originally an exact unit of length, because the lengths and shapes of body parts differ from person to person, between males and females, and between adults and children.

## ✦ Finding Personal Measures for Various Body Measures (*Math Journal 1,* pp. 174 and 175)

PARTNER ACTIVITY 

Working with partners, students measure their fingers, hands, and arms to find personal measures for the body measures listed. Students measure in both metric and U.S. customary units.

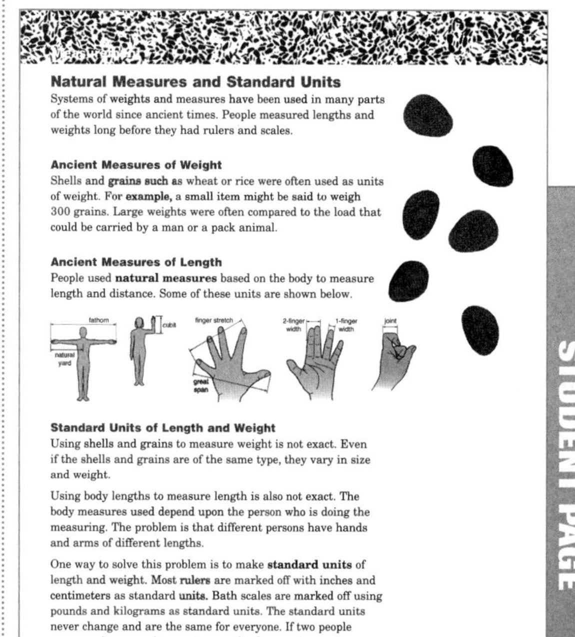

**Natural Measures and Standard Units**

Systems of weights and measures have been used in many parts of the world since ancient times. People measured lengths and weights long before they had rulers and scales.

**Ancient Measures of Weight**

Shells and **grains such as** wheat or rice were often used as units of weight. For **example,** a small item might be said to weigh 300 grains. Large weights were often compared to the load that could be carried by a man or a pack animal.

**Ancient Measures of Length**

People used **natural measures** based on the body to measure length and distance. Some of these units are shown below.



**Standard Units of Length and Weight**

Using shells and grains to measure weight is not exact. Even if the shells and grains are of the same type, they vary in size and weight.

Using body lengths to measure length is also not exact. The body measures used depend upon the person who is doing the measuring. The problem is that different persons have hands and arms of different lengths.

One way to solve this problem is to make **standard units** of length and weight. Most **rulers** are marked off with inches and centimeters as standard **units.** Bath scales are marked off using pounds and kilograms as standard units. The standard units never change and are the same for everyone. If two people measure the same object using standard units, their measurements will be the same or almost the same.

SRB 166 one hundred sixty-six

STUDENT PAGE

✦ *Student Reference Book,* p. 166

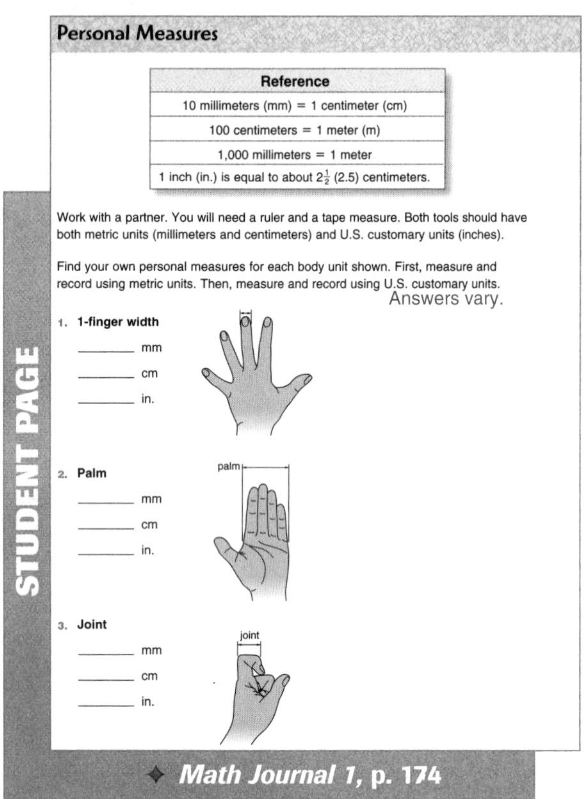
**Personal Measures**

| Reference |
|---|
| 10 millimeters (mm) = 1 centimeter (cm) |
| 100 centimeters = 1 meter (m) |
| 1,000 millimeters = 1 meter |
| 1 inch (in.) is equal to about $2\frac{1}{2}$ (2.5) centimeters. |

Work with a partner. You will need a ruler and a tape measure. Both tools should have both metric units (millimeters and centimeters) and U.S. customary units (inches).

Find your own personal measures for each body unit shown. First, measure and record using metric units. Then, measure and record using U.S. customary units.
Answers vary.

1. **1-finger width**
 ______ mm
 ______ cm
 ______ in.

2. **Palm**
 ______ mm
 ______ cm
 ______ in.

3. **Joint**
 ______ mm
 ______ cm
 ______ in.



Math Journal 1, p. 174

Ask students to measure as accurately as possible. For the smaller finger and hand measures, they should attempt to measure to the nearest millimeter and nearest $\frac{1}{8}$ or $\frac{1}{16}$ inch. For the natural yard, fathom, and cubit, measuring to the nearest centimeter and nearest $\frac{1}{2}$ or $\frac{1}{4}$ inch is sufficient.

**Adjusting the Activity** To extend the activity, ask students to explain why it is necessary to measure to the nearest $\frac{1}{16}$ inch or 1 millimeter for smaller measurements, but only to the nearest $\frac{1}{2}$ inch or 1 centimeter for the larger measurements. A small error is much more significant on the smaller measurements.

Mention these two methods for finding finger and hand measures:

▷ Use the illustration on the journal page as a guide. Arrange your fingers or hand on a sheet of paper as shown. Mark the ends of the desired length with a pencil. Then measure between the marks.

▷ Measure your partner's fingers or hand directly.

Let students use whichever method they like best. Circulate and assist. Verify that students are measuring the finger and hand measures precisely enough—to the nearest millimeter, and to the nearest $\frac{1}{8}$ or $\frac{1}{16}$ inch.

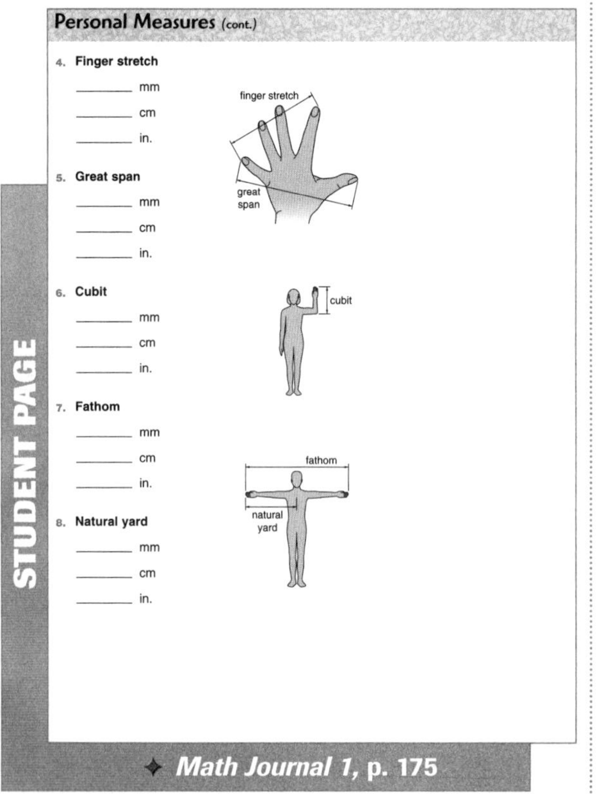
**Personal Measures** (cont.)

4. **Finger stretch**
 ______ mm
 ______ cm
 ______ in.

5. **Great span**
 ______ mm
 ______ cm
 ______ in.

6. **Cubit**
 ______ mm
 ______ cm
 ______ in.

7. **Fathom**
 ______ mm
 ______ cm
 ______ in.

8. **Natural yard**
 ______ mm
 ______ cm
 ______ in.



Math Journal 1, p. 175

### ONGOING ASSESSMENT

**Expect that most students will be able to measure to the nearest $\frac{1}{4}$ inch and to the nearest centimeter.**

**You may still have a few students who have difficulty measuring to the nearest $\frac{1}{8}$ inch and to the nearest millimeter. The Extra Practice activity in Part 3 provides more measurement work for these students. If necessary, review place value and conversions among metric units. See Part 3 for a suggested Reteaching activity on metric conversions for lengths.**

Bring the class together and discuss the results. Here are some suggested questions:

- How close were your personal measures for a natural yard to the standard yard of 3 feet? The average natural yard for a 10-year-old is about 28 inches.
- The cubit is usually thought of as 18 inches. Given the class's personal measures for the cubit, is this reasonable? The average cubit for a 10-year-old is about 15 inches.

- Would any measures by adults be about the same as measures by fifth graders? Probably not. The average measures for adults are all about 25% greater.

## Explaining the Challenge Questions for *First to 21* (*Math Journal 1*, pp. 176 and 177)

WHOLE-CLASS DISCUSSION

Go over the rules for playing *First to 21* on journal page 176 with the class. Have partners play a few practice games, as you circulate to make sure that students understand the rules.

Read and discuss the Estimation Challenge on journal page 177. Ask whether *First to 21* is a **fair game,** and what chance the first player has of winning.

Students are not able to answer these questions today. Each partnership should play the game at least 50 times over the next week. As results accumulate, students will be able to answer the questions with increasing certainty.

Although students work in pairs, they should each keep separate tallies of game results in the table on journal page 177.

NOTE: Students will soon realize that the game is *not* fair: The second player has an advantage. In order to estimate the chance that the first player will win, students need to play many games. If you have 25 students, and each plays 50 games, your class estimate will very likely be within 2% of the actual chance, and almost certainly within 4% of the actual chance.

Have each partnership play 2 or 3 games now and tally their results on journal page 177. Display the classroom tally sheet (Table A), the table for recording cumulative totals (Table B), and the graph that you have posted. Explain the routine you will use to record and update each day's results.

1. Whenever partners have finished a series of games during a day, one of the partners should enter the tally results for their game results on the classroom tally sheet (Table A).

**Table A**

| Date | First Player Wins | Second Player Wins |
|---|---|---|
| 2/6/01 | ~~////~~ ~~////~~ ~~////~~ / | ~~////~~ ~~////~~ ~~////~~ ~~////~~ ~~////~~ ~~////~~ /// |
| 2/7/01 | ~~////~~ ~~////~~ /// | ~~////~~ ~~////~~ ~~////~~ ~~////~~ ~~////~~ ~~////~~ ~~////~~ ~~////~~ / |

### *First to 21*

**Materials** A deck of cards, consisting of four of each of the numbers 4, 5, 6, 7, and 8 (Do not use any other cards.)

**Number of Players** 2

**Directions**

Decide who will go first. That person should then always play first, whenever you start a new game.

1. Shuffle the cards. Place the deck facedown.
2. The player going first turns over the top card and announces its value.
3. The player going second turns over the next card and announces the total value of the two cards turned over.
4. Partners continue to take turns turning over cards and announcing the total value of all the cards turned over so far.
5. The winner is the first player to correctly announce "21" or any number greater than 21.
6. Start a new game using the cards that are still facedown. If all of the cards are turned over during a game, shuffle the deck, place it facedown, and continue.

STUDENT PAGE

✦ *Math Journal 1*, p. 176

### Estimation Challenge

A **fair game** is one that each player has the same chance of winning. If there is an advantage or disadvantage in playing first, then the game is not fair.

With your partner, investigate whether *First to 21* is a fair game.

**Collect data by playing the game.**
Over the next week, play *First to 21* at least 50 times. Keep a tally each day. Show how many times the player going first wins, and how many times the player going second wins.

| Date | Player Going First Wins | Player Going Second Wins | Total Games to Date |
|---|---|---|---|
| | | | |
| | | | |
| | | | |
| | | | |
| | | | |
| | | | |
| | | | |
| | | | |

**Enter your results on the classroom tally sheet.**
Each day you play the game, record the results on the tally sheet for the whole class that your teacher has prepared.

**Each day you play, ask yourself:**

- What is my estimate for the chance that the player going first will win?
- What is my estimate for the chance that the player going second will win?
- Do my estimates change as more and more games are played?
- Does *First to 21* seem to be a fair game?

STUDENT PAGE

✦ *Math Journal 1*, p. 177

2. Appoint a "Statistician" and "Checker" for the day, who count the tallies in Table A for that day, and use these tallies to update the totals in Table B. Note that these totals are cumulative.

**Table B**

| | Totals to Date | | | | |
|---|---|---|---|---|---|
| | 2/6/01 | 2/7/01 | | | |
| First Player Wins | 16 | 29 | | | |
| Second Player Wins | 33 | 74 | | | |
| Games Played | 49 | 103 | | | |

3. The Statistician and Checker also update the bar graph. They use the most recent cumulative totals from Table B to calculate the percent of all games played to date that have been won by the player going first. They then draw a new bar on the graph to show this percent. (*See the margin.*)

Post a stick-on note on the Probability Meter each day to show the percent of all games played to date that have been won by the player going first.

NOTE: The cumulative results of the game will be used in Lesson 6.6.

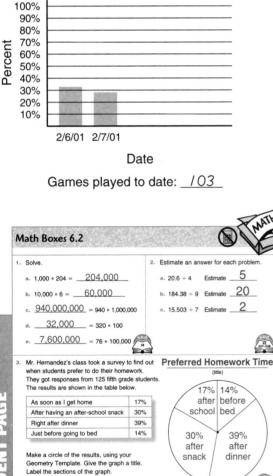

**Percent of Time Player Going First Wins**

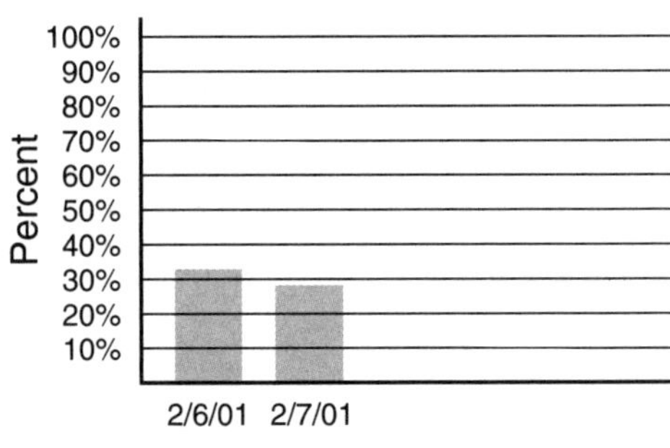


Games played to date: 103

**Math Boxes 6.2**

1. Solve.
   a. 1,000 * 204 = 204,000
   b. 10,000 * 6 = 60,000
   c. 940,000,000 = 940 * 1,000,000
   d. 32,000 = 320 * 100
   e. 7,600,000 = 76 * 100,000

2. Estimate an answer for each problem.
   a. 20.6 ÷ 4 Estimate 5
   b. 184.38 ÷ 9 Estimate 20
   c. 15.503 ÷ 7 Estimate 2

3. Mr. Hernandez's class took a survey to find out when students prefer to do their homework. They got responses from 125 fifth grade students. The results are shown in the table below.

| As soon as I get home | 17% |
|---|---|
| After having an after-school snack | 30% |
| Right after dinner | 39% |
| Just before going to bed | 14% |

Make a circle of the results, using your Geometry Template. Give the graph a title. Label the sections of the graph.
Answers vary.

Preferred Homework Time (title)

17% after school; 14% before bed; 30% after snack; 39% after dinner

4. Write the following numbers in order from least to greatest.
   $\frac{9}{2}$ 4.75 $\frac{13}{4}$ 4.8 $4\frac{7}{8}$
   $\frac{13}{4}$, $\frac{9}{2}$, 4.75, 4.8, $4\frac{7}{8}$

5. Rename each fraction as a decimal.
   a. $\frac{15}{40}$ = 0.375
   b. $\frac{9}{12}$ = 0.75
   c. $\frac{2}{100}$ = 0.02
   d. $\frac{33}{99}$ = $0.\overline{3}$
   e. $\frac{40}{50}$ = 0.8

STUDENT PAGE

Math Journal 1, p. 173

## 2 Ongoing Learning & Practice

### Math Boxes 6.2 (*Math Journal 1*, p. 173)

INDEPENDENT ACTIVITY 

**Mixed Review** Math Boxes in this lesson are paired with Math Boxes in Lesson 6.5. The skill in Problem 1 is a prerequisite for Unit 7.

## ✦ Study Link 6.2 (*Math Masters,* p. 283)

**Home Connection** Students find objects the size of given nonstandard units of measure. They give the unit of measure they would use to make various measurements.

# 3 Options for Individualizing

## ✦ EXTRA PRACTICE Measuring with a Ruler (*Math Masters,* p. 81)

INDEPENDENT ACTIVITY  **15–30 min** 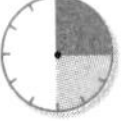

Students measure line segments to the nearest centimeter, millimeter, and $\frac{1}{8}$ inch.

## ✦ ENRICHMENT Learning about Nonstandard Units of Measure

PARTNER ACTIVITY  **30+ min** 

**Social Studies Link** Have students do research and report on other historical units of measure—for example, stones or drams.

## ✦ RETEACHING Reviewing Metric Conversions

SMALL-GROUP ACTIVITY  **5–15 min** 

Have students record conversions on their slates. *Suggestions:*

- How many millimeters in 5 cm? 50 mm
- How many millimeters in 8 m? 8,000 mm
- How many centimeters in 48 mm? 4.8 cm How many meters? 0.048 m
- How many meters in 7 cm? 0.07 m How many millimeters? 70 mm
- How many meters in 502 mm? 0.502 m How many centimeters? 50.2 cm

---

**Standard and Nonstandard Units** — Study Link 6.2

1. Use your body measures to find three objects that are about the size of each measurement below.

a. 1 cubit — Answers vary.
b. 1 great span — Answers vary.
c. 1 finger width — Answers vary.

2. For each problem below, mark the unit or units you *could* use to measure the object.

| | | | | |
|---|---|---|---|---|
| a. Height of your ceiling | ● cm | ● ft | ○ lb | ○ miles |
| b. Amount of milk in a pitcher | ○ cm | ● ounces | ● gal | ● liters |
| c. Depth of the ocean | ● m | ○ ounces | ○ gal | ● miles |
| d. Length of a bee | ● cm | ● ft | ● mm | ○ liters |
| e. Weight of a nickel | ○ in. | ● kg | ● lb | ● grams |

STUDY LINK MASTER

✦ *Math Masters,* p. 283

---

**Measuring Practice**

1. Measure each line segment below to the nearest centimeter.

a. 3 cm
b. 7 cm
c. 14 cm

2. Measure each line segment below to the nearest millimeter.

a. 6 mm
b. 12 mm
c. 10 mm

3. Measure each line segment below to the nearest $\frac{1}{8}$ inch.

a. $\frac{3}{8}$ in.
b. $\frac{7}{8}$ in.
c. $\frac{6}{8}$ in.
d. $1\frac{5}{8}$ in.

4. Draw line segments having the following lengths:

a. $2\frac{1}{8}$ inches
b. 9 centimeters
c. 22 millimeters

TEACHING MASTER

✦ *Math Masters,* p. 81

# 6.3 Stem-and-Leaf Plots for Hand and Finger Measures

**OBJECTIVES** **To use stem-and-leaf plots to organize data; to measure lengths in metric units; and to use a protractor.**

| summaries | materials |
|---|---|
| **1 Teaching the Lesson** | |
| Students use a ruler to measure their hand spans and a protractor to measure angles of finger separation. They make stem-and-leaf plots to display the combined class data. [Measurement and Reference Frames; Data and Chance] | ☐ *Math Journal 1,* pp. 178 and 179<br>☐ Study Link 6.2<br>☐ Assessment Master (*Math Masters,* p. 479)<br>☐ protractor ☐ ruler<br>☐ protractor for demonstration purposes<br>***See* Advance Preparation** |
| **2 Ongoing Learning & Practice** | |
| Students continue to collect data by playing *First to 21.* [Data and Chance]<br>Students practice and maintain skills through Math Boxes and Study Link activities. | ☐ *Math Journal 1,* pp. 176, 177, and 180<br>☐ Study Link Master (*Math Masters,* p. 284)<br>☐ deck of number cards (from the Everything Math Deck, if available) |
| **3 Options for Individualizing** | |
| **Enrichment** Students collect data and display the data in a stem-and-leaf plot. [Data and Chance] | ☐ newspapers and/or almanacs |

**Additional Information**

**Advance Preparation** For Part 1, copy the stem-and-leaf plot that appears on journal page 178 on the board.

**Vocabulary** • **span** • **normal span** • **great span** • **stem** • **leaf** • **stem-and-leaf plot** • **angle of separation**

## Getting Started

### Mental Math and Reflexes

Show "thumbs up" if the number is divisible by the given number and "thumbs down" if it is not divisible. *Suggestions:*

- Write 628 on the board. Is it divisible by 2? yes By 3? no By 4? yes By 9? no
- Write 723 on the board. Is it divisible by 3? yes By 5? no By 6? no By 9? no

### Math Message

*List as many meanings for the word* span *as you can.*

### Study Link 6.2 Follow-Up

Students report objects they found for each measurement. Briefly review the answers to Problem 2.

# 1 Teaching the Lesson

## Math Message Follow-Up

WHOLE-CLASS DISCUSSION

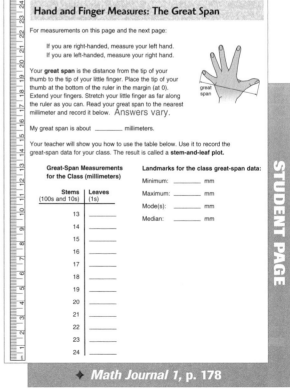

**Language Arts Link** The word *span* is used in several related ways. For a bridge, span means either the distance from one end to the other or the distance between major supports. The span of a bird or an airplane wing is the distance from wingtip to wingtip. A span of time is the length of time between one event and another; a life span is the length of time an organism is alive.

Many Native Americans used hand measures similar to what are called **spans** today.

- A **normal span** is the distance from the tip of the thumb to the tip of the first (index) finger, stretched as far apart as possible. *(See the margin.)*
- A **great span** is the distance from the tip of the thumb to the tip of the fourth (little) finger, stretched as far apart as possible. *(See the margin.)*

Neither span has a definite length, because different people have different-sized hands. Today, in the United States and in Great Britain, a standard span is sometimes defined as 9 inches (22.86 centimeters).

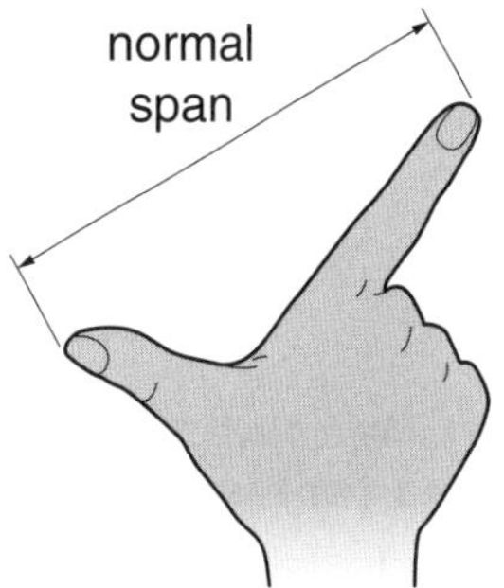


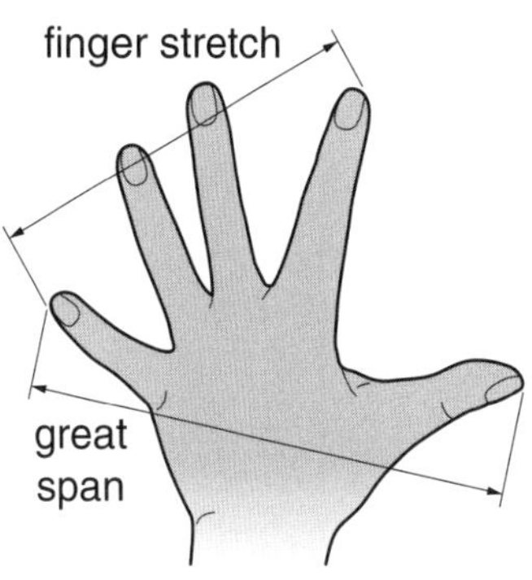


## Measuring the Great Span
(*Math Journal 1*, p. 178)

PARTNER ACTIVITY

Ask students why it might be interesting or important to know their hand spans, and how far apart they can separate their fingers. Sample answers: Span and finger separation angles determine how big a person's "grab" is. Span and flexibility are important in playing musical instruments, for handling sports balls, and for operating various triggers, grips, and switches.

Have students work with partners on journal page 178. They measure and record each other's great span to the nearest millimeter.

NOTE: If any students are unable to perform this activity, provide an alternative data set.

### Hand and Finger Measures: The Great Span

For measurements on this page and the next page:

If you are right-handed, measure your left hand.
If you are left-handed, measure your right hand.

Your **great span** is the distance from the tip of your thumb to the tip of your little finger. Place the tip of your thumb at the bottom of the ruler in the margin (at 0). Extend your fingers. Stretch your little finger as far along the ruler as you can. Read your great span to the nearest millimeter and record it below. Answers vary.

great span

My great span is about _______ millimeters.

Your teacher will show you how to use the table below. Use it to record the great-span data for your class. The result is called a **stem-and-leaf plot**.

**Great-Span Measurements for the Class (millimeters)**

| Stems (100s and 10s) | Leaves (1s) |
|---|---|
| 13 | |
| 14 | |
| 15 | |
| 16 | |
| 17 | |
| 18 | |
| 19 | |
| 20 | |
| 21 | |
| 22 | |
| 23 | |
| 24 | |

**Landmarks for the class great-span data:**

Minimum: _______ mm
Maximum: _______ mm
Mode(s): _______ mm
Median: _______ mm

STUDENT PAGE

*Math Journal 1*, p. 178

## ✦Organizing the Data in a Stem-and-Leaf Plot
(*Math Journal 1,* p. 178)

WHOLE-CLASS ACTIVITY

When all students have completed their measurements, call attention to the incomplete table on the board and on journal page 178. Introduce the stem-and-leaf plot as a way of organizing students' data on great spans.

To demonstrate, ask a student for her or his great span (for example, 186 millimeters). Write this number on the board.

1. Circle the hundreds and tens digits of the number you just wrote (in the example, 18). These digits are a **stem** in the plot. Find the stem in the left column of the table.
2. The ones digit of the number (in the example, 6) is the **leaf.** Record the leaf in the right column, after its stem.

Repeat this with two or three more great spans. Be sure students see that each one-digit leaf goes in the right column, after the corresponding two-digit stem. (The plot *in the margin* represents spans of 149, 186, and 180 millimeters.) Continue recording spans until all the class data are in the plot.

**Great-Span Measurements for the Class (millimeters)**

| Stems (100s and 10s) | Leaves (1s) |
|---|---|
| 13 | |
| 14 | 9 |
| 15 | |
| 16 | |
| 17 | |
| 18 | 6 0 |
| 19 | |
| 20 | |
| 21 | |
| 22 | |
| 23 | |
| 24 | |

NOTE: If available, have students explore using data analysis software to organize, record, and display their data, as well as to construct various kinds of graphs.

**Adjusting the Activity** For students who are struggling with how to organize the stem-and-leaf plot, read back each entry (combining each leaf with its stem) on the completed plot.

Ask students why they think this is called a **stem-and-leaf plot.** It's like a plant or tree. The stems are on the left. You put leaves (digits) on the right, making sure you put them on the correct stems.

Students should copy the data from the board onto the stem-and-leaf plot on journal page 178, but they should rearrange each row of leaves in numerical order. For example, the leaves 6 0 4 0 6 8 would be rewritten as 0 0 4 6 6 8.

Rewriting the data in order makes it easier to find the landmark spans: minimum, maximum, mode or modes, and median. Students record these on page 178.

After they finish, ask questions such as the following:

- Where is your span in this plot?
- Is your span near the middle or median?
- Is your span near the minimum?
- Which is closer to your span, the maximum span or the mode (the most common span)?
- How does your span compare with the median span? (Encourage difference or ratio comparisons.)
- How do you think the data on spans for our class would compare with the data on spans for a second grade class? For a professional basketball team?

## ✦ Measuring Finger-Separation Angles
(*Math Journal 1,* p. 179)

WHOLE-CLASS ACTIVITY

Students worked with half-circle protractors in Unit 3. Review use of this tool if necessary.

Demonstrate the following procedure for measuring the **angle of separation** for the thumb and first finger:

1. Spread your thumb and first finger as far apart as possible and trace them on the board.
2. Discuss how to "fit" an angle to the drawing. Where should the vertex be? Should the sides of the angle be entirely within the tracing?
3. Draw an angle that fits the drawing, and measure it with the board protractor. This is your thumb and first finger span.

Have students measure the angle between their thumb and first finger, and between their first and second fingers. They record these angle measures on journal page 179.

On the board or overhead transparencies, make separate stem-and-leaf plots for the two different finger-separation angle measurements. After recording all the class data, rewrite each row of leaves in numerical order.

Have students find the landmarks for each plot and record them on journal page 179.

**ONGOING ASSESSMENT**

On an Exit Slip have students complete a statement that begins with: "Stem-and-leaf plots are a good way to display data because...."

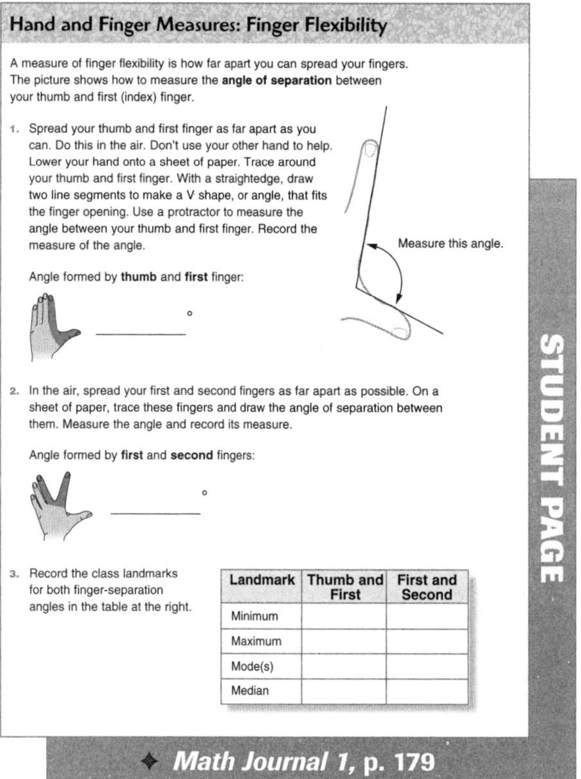

**Hand and Finger Measures: Finger Flexibility**

A measure of finger flexibility is how far apart you can spread your fingers. The picture shows how to measure the **angle of separation** between your thumb and first (index) finger.

1. Spread your thumb and first finger as far apart as you can. Do this in the air. Don't use your other hand to help. Lower your hand onto a sheet of paper. Trace around your thumb and first finger. With a straightedge, draw two line segments to make a V shape, or angle, that fits the finger opening. Use a protractor to measure the angle between your thumb and first finger. Record the measure of the angle.

   Measure this angle.

   Angle formed by **thumb** and **first** finger: ________°

2. In the air, spread your first and second fingers as far apart as possible. On a sheet of paper, trace these fingers and draw the angle of separation between them. Measure the angle and record its measure.

   Angle formed by **first** and **second** fingers: ________°

3. Record the class landmarks for both finger-separation angles in the table at the right.

| Landmark | Thumb and First | First and Second |
|---|---|---|
| Minimum | | |
| Maximum | | |
| Mode(s) | | |
| Median | | |

STUDENT PAGE

✦ *Math Journal 1,* p. 179

NOTE: Don't hurry the discussion about how to "fit" the angle. Fitting geometric figures to pictures is a very useful model, especially in data analysis. A key question about any fit is, "What is the best fit?"

**Thumb and First Finger Separation (degrees)**

| Stems (100s and 10s) | Leaves (1s) |
|---|---|
| 7 | |
| 8 | |
| 9 | |
| 10 | |
| 11 | |
| 12 | |
| 13 | |
| 14 | |
| 15 | |

**First and Second Finger Separation (degrees)**

| Stems (10s) | Leaves (1s) |
|---|---|
| 1 | |
| 2 | |
| 3 | |
| 4 | |
| 5 | |
| 6 | |
| 7 | |

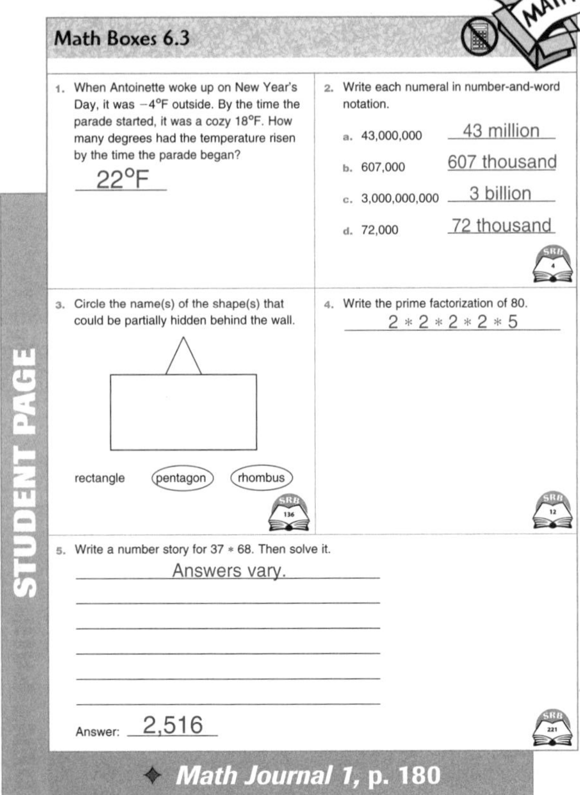

STUDENT PAGE

**Math Boxes 6.3**

1. When Antoinette woke up on New Year's Day, it was −4°F outside. By the time the parade started, it was a cozy 18°F. How many degrees had the temperature risen by the time the parade began?
   22°F

2. Write each numeral in number-and-word notation.
   a. 43,000,000 — 43 million
   b. 607,000 — 607 thousand
   c. 3,000,000,000 — 3 billion
   d. 72,000 — 72 thousand

3. Circle the name(s) of the shape(s) that could be partially hidden behind the wall.
   rectangle (pentagon) (rhombus)

4. Write the prime factorization of 80.
   2 ∗ 2 ∗ 2 ∗ 2 ∗ 5

5. Write a number story for 37 ∗ 68. Then solve it.
   Answers vary.
   Answer: 2,516

✦ *Math Journal 1,* p. 180

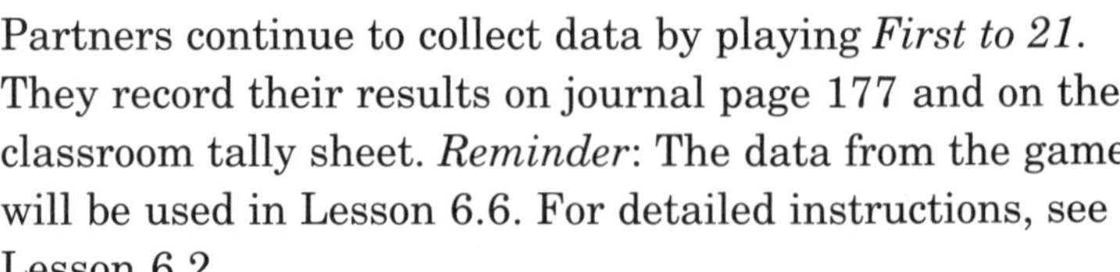

# 2 Ongoing Learning & Practice

## ✦ Playing *First to 21* (*Math Journal 1,* pp. 176 and 177)

PARTNER ACTIVITY

Partners continue to collect data by playing *First to 21*. They record their results on journal page 177 and on the classroom tally sheet. *Reminder*: The data from the game will be used in Lesson 6.6. For detailed instructions, see Lesson 6.2.

## ✦ Math Boxes 6.3 (*Math Journal 1,* p. 180)

INDEPENDENT ACTIVITY 

**Mixed Review** Math Boxes in this lesson are paired with Math Boxes in Lesson 6.6. The skill in Problem 1 is a prerequisite for Unit 7.

## ✦ Study Link 6.3 (*Math Masters,* p. 284)

**Home Connection** Students answer questions based on a stem-and-leaf plot.

STUDY LINK MASTER

**Reading a Stem-and-Leaf Plot** — Study Link 6.3

Use the information below to answer the questions.

Randy was growing sunflowers. After eight weeks, he measured the height of his sunflowers, in inches. He recorded the heights in the stem-and-leaf plot below.

**Height of Sunflowers (inches)**

| **Stems** (10s) | **Leaves** (1s) |
|---|---|
| 3 | 9 1 |
| 4 | 7 6 9 2 9 |
| 5 | 2 3 3 5 2 8 7 3 |
| 6 | 5 3 4 |
| 7 | 3 |

1. How tall is the tallest sunflower? 73 in.
   Which landmark is the height of the tallest flower? Circle its name.
   minimum mode (maximum) mean
2. How many sunflowers did Randy measure? 19 sunflowers
3. What is the mode for his measurements? 53 in.
4. Explain how you would find the median for his measurements.
   Sample answer: Cross off the highest and lowest values—31 and 73. Continue by crossing off the highest and lowest values remaining. Finally, only the number 53 remains. So 53 is the median.

**Challenge**

5. On the back of this page, describe how Randy made his stem-and-leaf plot once he had his measurements. Answers vary.

✦ *Math Masters,* p. 284

# 3 Options for Individualizing

## ✦ ENRICHMENT Making a Stem-and-Leaf Plot

PARTNER ACTIVITY  **15–30 min**

Have students choose a topic on which to collect data. The data should be numbers with at least two digits and should not have a large range. For example, the number of points scored by a favorite team for a number of games; the number of home runs hit by a baseball league leader in each of the past 20 years; the record high temperatures for the 50 states.

Students display these data in a stem-and-leaf plot. You may want to display the plots on a bulletin board.

Extend the activity by having students write questions about each plot and compare the plots.

# 6.4 Mystery Plots

**OBJECTIVE** **To interpret data in line plots and stem-and-leaf plots.**

| summaries | materials |
|---|---|
| **1 Teaching the Lesson** | |
| Students are given examples of data collected from a hypothetical class of fifth graders, and are asked to match descriptions with the line plots displayed. [Data and Chance] | □ *Math Journal 1,* pp. 182–184<br>□ Study Link 6.3<br>□ Assessment Master (*Math Masters,* p. 479; optional) |
| **2 Ongoing Learning & Practice** | |
| Students compare the flexibility of the hand they write with and their nonwriting hand. [Measurement and Reference Frames]<br>Students continue to collect data by playing *First to 21.* [Data and Chance]<br>Students practice and maintain skills through Math Boxes and Study Link activities. | □ *Math Journal 1,* pp. 176, 177, and 181<br>□ Teaching Master (*Math Masters,* p. 83)<br>□ Study Link Master (*Math Masters,* p. 285)<br>□ protractor |
| **3 Options for Individualizing** | |
| **Extra Practice** Students display data about states visited in a stem-and-leaf plot. [Data and Chance]<br>**Extra Practice** Students display data about a spelling test in a stem-and-leaf plot, find the median and mode, and discuss the advantages of using a stem-and-leaf plot. [Data and Chance] | □ *Math Journal 1,* pp. 170 and 171<br>□ Teaching Master (*Math Masters,* p. 82) |

## Getting Started

### Mental Math and Reflexes

Have students round numbers to a given place.
*Suggestions:*

- Thirty-two and six hundredths to the nearest whole number 32
- Four and thirty-eight hundredths to the nearest tenth 4.4
- Seven and eighteen hundredths to the nearest whole number 7
- Eighty-six and fifty-five hundredths to the nearest ten 90
- Nine hundredths to the nearest tenth 0.1

### Math Message

*Find the minimum, maximum, range, mode, and median for this stem-and-leaf plot.*

**Unit: inches**

| **Stems** (10s) | **Leaves** (1s) |
|---|---|
| 4 | 4 7 |
| 5 | 0 8 6 0 |
| 6 | 1 5 3 |

### Study Link 6.3 Follow-Up

Have volunteers share explanations of how to find the median and how to construct the stem-and-leaf plot.

Unit: inches

| Stems (10s) | Leaves (1s) |
|---|---|
| 4 | 4 7 |
| 5 | 0 0 6 8 |
| 6 | 1 3 5 |

Stem-and-leaf plot for the Math Message, with leaves in numerical order.

NOTE: Students will quickly see that the procedure for finding a median is the same for stem-and-leaf plots as it is for line plots. In each case, one counts from the smallest data value up to the middle one, or from the largest value down to the middle one.

**Mystery Plots**

There are five line plots on page 183. Each plot shows a different set of data about a fifth grade class.

Match each of the following four sets of data with one of the five plots. Then fill in the "Unit" for each matched graph on page 183.

1. The number of hours of TV each fifth grader watched last night Plot #2
2. The ages of the younger brothers and sisters of the fifth graders Plot #5
3. The heights, in inches, of some fifth graders Plot #1
4. The ages of some fifth graders' grandmothers Plot #3
5. Explain how you selected the line plot for Data Set 4.
Sample answer: Plot #1 and Plot #3 both show reasonable numbers for grandmothers' ages. But Plot #3 shows numbers in the 70s and 80s and is more reasonable for showing grandmothers' ages.
6. Tell why you think the other line plots are not correct for Data Set 4.
Sample answer: Some or all of the numbers in Plots #2, #4, and #5 are too small to represent ages of fifth graders' grandmothers. If Plot #3 represents fifth graders' heights, then 6 of them would be taller than 6 feet. So Plot #1 represents heights which means that Plot #3 must represent grandmothers' ages.

STUDENT PAGE

*Math Journal 1*, p. 182

# 1 Teaching the Lesson

## Math Message Follow-Up

WHOLE-CLASS DISCUSSION

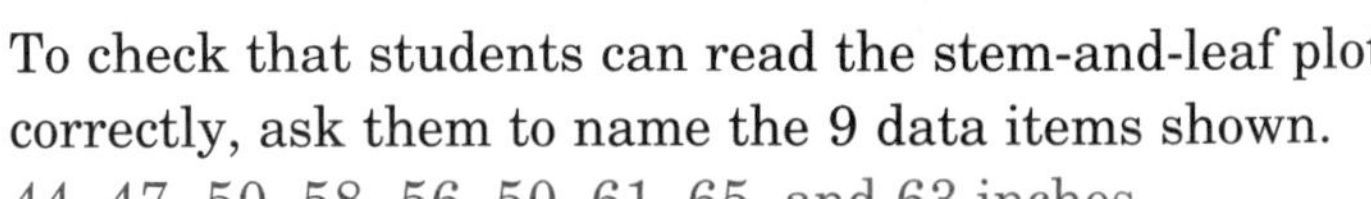

To check that students can read the stem-and-leaf plot correctly, ask them to name the 9 data items shown. 44, 47, 50, 58, 56, 50, 61, 65, and 63 inches

Draw a second version of the stem-and-leaf plot by rewriting each row of leaves in numerical order *(see the margin)*. Expect that most students will be able to identify the minimum 44 in., maximum 65 in., range 65 – 44, or 21 in., and mode 50 in.

**Adjusting the Activity** Some students may have difficulty finding the median. 56 in. Draw a number line on the board and ask students to convert the stem-and-leaf plot to a line plot (see below). Have them find the median using the line plot. Then return to the stem-and-leaf plot and find the same median there.

Unit: inches

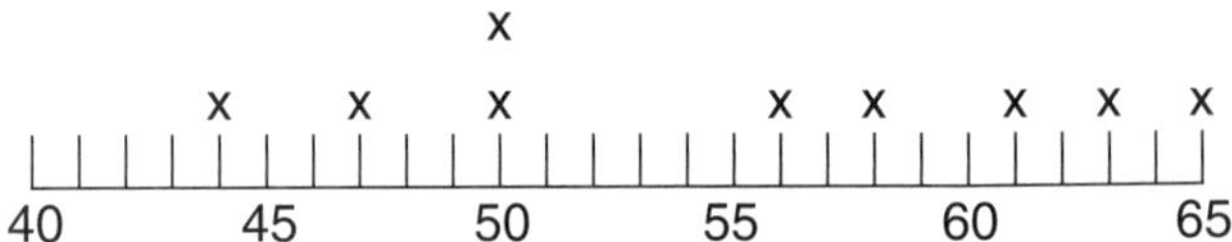


Line plot for the same data

## Identifying Mystery Line Plots
(*Math Journal 1*, pp. 182 and 183)

PARTNER ACTIVITY

Four sets of data are described on journal page 182. Students work with their partners and match each set with a line plot on journal page 183. Emphasize to students that they are looking for the matches that make the most sense.

Tell students that no plot is used more than once; and that one of the plots is not used at all.

After 10 to 15 minutes, gather the class and discuss the answers.

▷ Data Set 1, hours of TV watched, is represented by Plot #2.

▷ Data Set 2, ages of younger siblings, is represented by Plot #5.

None of the other plots could describe Data Sets 1 or 2, because the numbers in those other plots are too large.

If Plot #5 represented TV hours, then more than half of the students would have watched TV for 5 or more hours the previous night. That's possible, but unlikely. However, Plot #5 could represent hours on a nonschool day or when there is a significant national or international event, such as the Olympics, a disaster, or an emergency.

If Plot #2 represented sibling ages, then no fifth grader would have a sibling aged 7 through 10. That's possible, but unlikely.

▷ Data Set 3, heights, is represented by Plot #1.

▷ Data Set 4, ages of grandmothers, is represented by Plot #3.

Plot #3 cannot represent heights, because the largest numbers are too large (some students would be nearly 7 feet tall!). It does, however, show a reasonable range for grandmothers' ages.

Plot #4 does not represent any of the data described on page 182. Ask students if they can describe any data that could be represented by Plot #4. Sample answers: Ages of the students' mothers; time in minutes it takes to get home from school.

## ✦ Identifying Mystery Stem-and-Leaf Plots (*Math Journal 1,* p. 184; *Math Masters,* p. 479)

PARTNER ACTIVITY

In this activity, similar to the previous one, students match data with stem-and-leaf plots instead of with line plots.

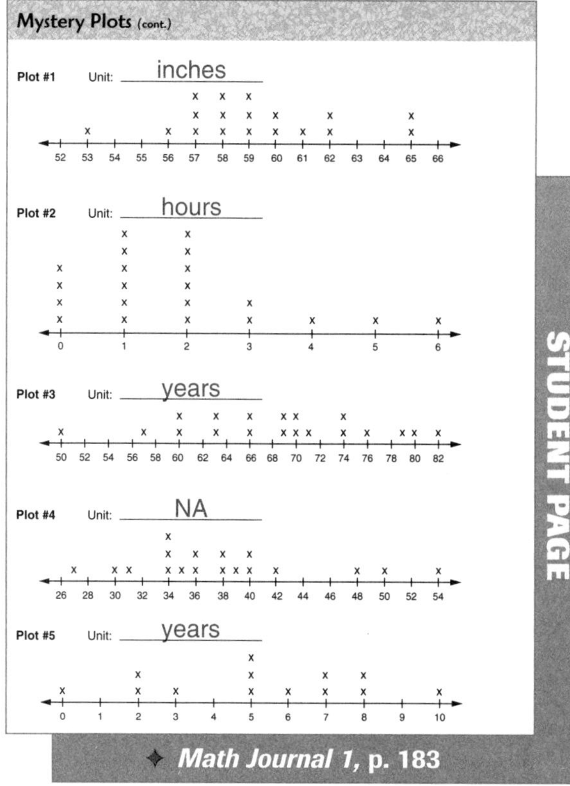


✦ *Math Journal 1,* p. 183

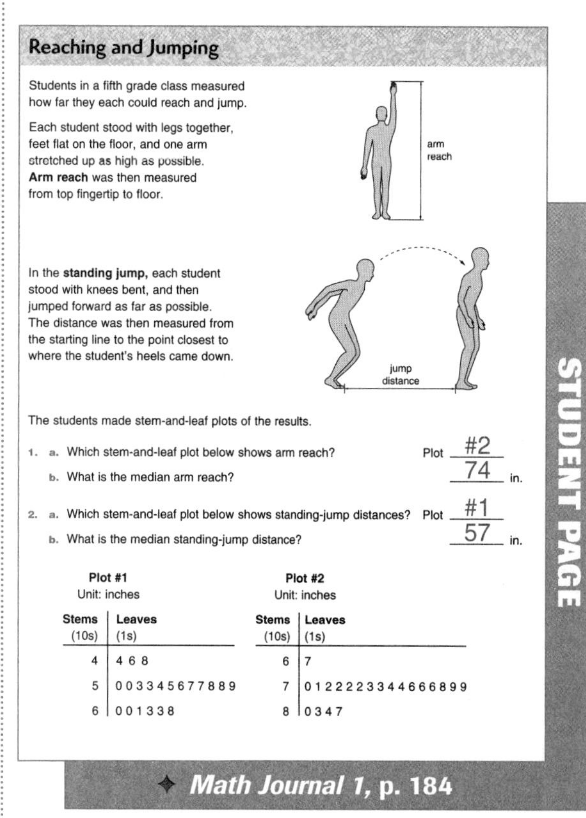

**Reaching and Jumping**

Students in a fifth grade class measured how far they each could reach and jump.

Each student stood with legs together, feet flat on the floor, and one arm stretched up as high as possible. **Arm reach** was then measured from top fingertip to floor.

In the **standing jump,** each student stood with knees bent, and then jumped forward as far as possible. The distance was then measured from the starting line to the point closest to where the student's heels came down.



The students made stem-and-leaf plots of the results.

1. a. Which stem-and-leaf plot below shows arm reach? Plot #2
   b. What is the median arm reach? 74 in.
2. a. Which stem-and-leaf plot below shows standing-jump distances? Plot #1
   b. What is the median standing-jump distance? 57 in.

Plot #1
Unit: inches

| Stems (10s) | Leaves (1s) |
|---|---|
| 4 | 4 6 8 |
| 5 | 0 0 3 3 4 5 6 7 7 8 8 9 |
| 6 | 0 0 1 3 3 8 |

Plot #2
Unit: inches

| Stems (10s) | Leaves (1s) |
|---|---|
| 6 | 7 |
| 7 | 0 1 2 2 2 2 3 3 4 4 6 6 6 8 9 9 |
| 8 | 0 3 4 7 |

✦ *Math Journal 1,* p. 184

## Comparing Left and Right Hands

Which is more flexible—the hand you write with or your other hand? This activity will help you find out.

Read the instructions below.

**Trace Your Hands**

**Step 1** In the air, stretch to make the largest possible angle between the thumb and little finger on one of your hands.

**Step 2** Now, lay that hand down on the back of this paper and use your other hand to trace around that hand with a pen or pencil. Label the tracing "right" or "left."

**Step 3** Repeat Steps 1 and 2 for your other hand.

**Mark and Measure**

1. On each tracing, draw straight lines through the middle of the little finger and thumb outlines. Be sure the lines intersect, forming an angle. (See the picture below.)

2. Use a protractor on your Geometry Template to measure the angle formed by each hand. Record your answers below.

   Measure of angle formed by right thumb and little finger: Answers vary.

   Measure of angle formed by left thumb and little finger: Answers vary.

   I write with my Answers vary. hand. (right or left)

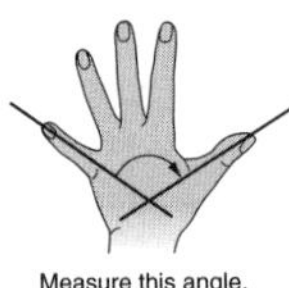

Measure this angle.

TEACHING MASTER

*Math Masters,* p. 83

## Math Boxes 6.4

1. Write a 10-digit numeral that has 7 in the billions place, 5 in the hundred-thousands place, 3 in the ten-millions place, 4 in the tens place, 8 in the hundreds place, and 2 in all other places.

   7 , 2 3 2 , 5 2 2 , 8 4 2

   Write the numeral in words.
   Seven billion, two hundred thirty-two million, five hundred twenty-two thousand, eight hundred forty-two

2. Round each number to the nearest whole number.
   a. 36.084 36
   b. 25.9 26
   c. 63.52 64
   d. 70.364 70
   e. 89.7 90

3. Write a fraction or a mixed number for each of the following.
   a. 5 minutes = $\frac{1}{12}$ hour
   b. 20 minutes = $\frac{1}{3}$ hour
   c. 35 minutes = $\frac{7}{12}$ hour
   d. 55 minutes = $\frac{11}{12}$ hour
   e. 10 minutes = $\frac{1}{6}$ hour

4. Rename each mixed number as a fraction.
   a. $3\frac{7}{8} = \frac{31}{8}$
   b. $4\frac{6}{9} = \frac{42}{9}$
   c. $10\frac{7}{12} = \frac{127}{12}$
   d. $8\frac{2}{3} = \frac{26}{3}$
   e. $6\frac{5}{14} = \frac{89}{14}$

5. Complete.
   a. 300 * 20 = 6,000
   b. 32,000 = 800 * 40
   c. 50 * 600 = 30,000
   d. 500 * 50 = 25,000
   e. 54,000 = 60 * 900

STUDENT PAGE

*Math Journal 1,* p. 181

**Adjusting the Activity** Students who have difficulty reading stem-and-leaf plots correctly should convert the two plots on the journal page to equivalent line plots before they begin working on the journal page.

Most students will correctly identify Plot #1 as standing-jump distance and Plot #2 as arm reach. Expect a variety of explanations. *For example:*

- The smallest number in Plot #2 is in the 60s. That's more than 5 feet, and lots of kids can't jump that far. So Plot #2 must be arm reach.
- The smallest numbers in Plot #1 are in the 40s. Four feet is 48 inches, so the smallest numbers are about 4 feet. Those numbers are too small to be arm reaches.
- I just held my arm up, and I found that I can reach about 15 inches above the top of my head. If you take 15 away from each number in Plot #2, you get numbers that are possible fifth graders' heights in inches. So Plot #2 is arm reach.

**ONGOING ASSESSMENT**

**Have students explain on an Exit Slip how they matched each stem-and-leaf plot to its data set on journal page 184.**

# 2 Ongoing Learning & Practice

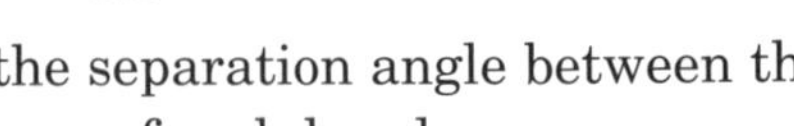

### Exploring If the Hand One Writes With Is More Flexible Than the Other Hand
(*Math Masters,* p. 83)

PARTNER ACTIVITY

Students measure the separation angle between the thumb and little finger of each hand.

Allow time for students to share their results. Discuss whether the class data clearly demonstrates that a person's writing hand is more, or less, flexible than the nonwriting hand.

## ◆ Playing *First to 21* (*Math Journal 1,* pp. 176 and 177)

PARTNER ACTIVITY

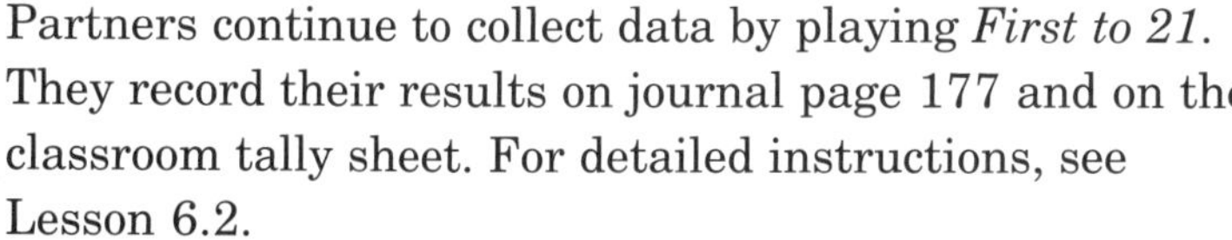

Partners continue to collect data by playing *First to 21*. They record their results on journal page 177 and on the classroom tally sheet. For detailed instructions, see Lesson 6.2.

NOTE: Remind students that the game data will be used in Lesson 6.6, so they must play at least 50 games by that time.

## ◆ Math Boxes 6.4 (*Math Journal 1,* p. 181)

INDEPENDENT ACTIVITY 

**Mixed Review** Math Boxes in this lesson are paired with Math Boxes in Lesson 6.1. The skill in Problem 1 is a prerequisite for Unit 7.

## ◆ Study Link 6.4 (*Math Masters,* p. 285)

**Home Connection** Students match descriptions of data sets with line plots.

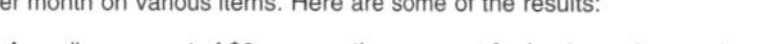

### How Much Do Students Spend?

Study Link 6.4

A fifth grade class collected data about how much students in the class spent per month on various items. Here are some of the results:

- A median amount of $6 per month was spent for books and magazines.
- A median amount of $10 per month was spent for tapes and CDs.
- A median amount of $8 per month was spent for movie tickets.

The number-line plots below display the data they collected. One plot shows monthly spending for books and magazines. One plot shows monthly spending for tapes and CDs. One plot shows monthly spending for movie tickets.

Match the plots with the items. Which plot is for books and magazines? Which is for tapes and CDs? Which is for movie tickets?

Fill in the correct title for each number-line plot.

1. Spending for: tapes and CDs in 1 month

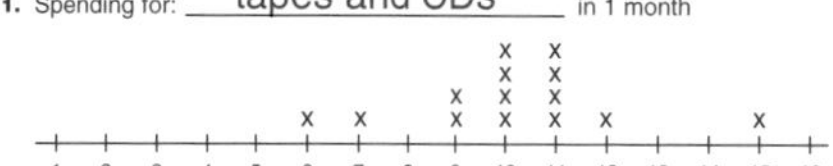

2. Spending for: books and magazines in 1 month

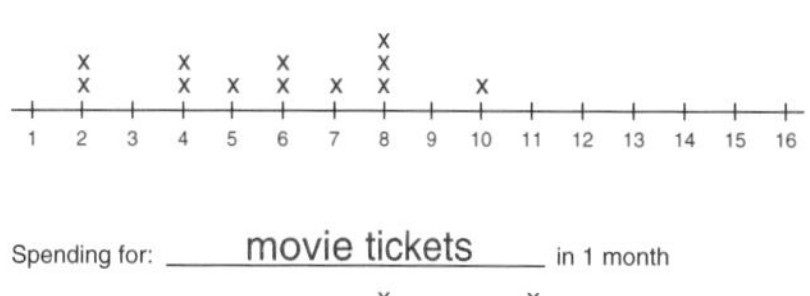

3. Spending for: movie tickets in 1 month

STUDY LINK MASTER

◆ Math Masters, p. 285

# 3 Options for Individualizing

## ◆ EXTRA PRACTICE Organizing the Data about States Visited into a Stem-and-Leaf Plot (*Math Journal 1,* pp. 170 and 171)

PARTNER ACTIVITY  **5–15 min**

Students organize data about the number of states visited from Lesson 6.1 into a stem-and-leaf plot.

## ◆ EXTRA PRACTICE Organizing Spelling-Test Scores (*Math Masters,* p. 82)

INDEPENDENT ACTIVITY  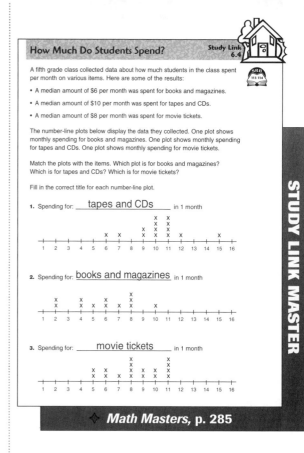 **15–30 min** 

Students make a stem-and-leaf plot of spelling test data; then they answer questions based on the plot.

### Organizing Spelling-Test Scores

Ms. Hallaran wanted to collect information on how her class was doing in spelling. After a test, she had students record their score on a sheet of paper. She listed all the scores on the board:

75 85 80 80 85 80 95 100 100 90 80 85

70 85 100 95 70 95 95 100 90 80 75 80

1. Would it have been better if Ms. Hallaran had displayed the data in a stem-and-leaf plot? Explain your answer.
Yes. A stem-and-leaf plot is clearer and makes it easier to find landmarks.

2. Make a stem-and-leaf plot for the spelling-test data.

| Stems (10s) | Leaves (1s) |
|---|---|
| 7 | 0 0 5 5 |
| 8 | 0 0 0 0 0 0 5 5 5 5 |
| 9 | 0 0 5 5 5 5 |
| 10 | 0 0 0 0 |

Use your stem-and-leaf plot to answer Problems 3 and 4.

3. a. What is the median score for the class? 85

b. What was the mode for the class? 80

**Challenge**

4. How many questions do you think there were on the test? 20, or a multiple of 20

5. On the back of this page, explain how you figured out your answer to Problem 4.
Answers vary.

TEACHING MASTER

◆ Math Masters, p. 82

# 6.5 Sample Size and Good Conclusions

**OBJECTIVE** **To investigate the relationship between sample size and reliability of predictions.**

| summaries | materials |
| --- | --- |
| **1 Teaching the Lesson** | |
| Students take small samples from a population and then combine these to form one large sample. They create circle graphs for these samples and conclude that a large sample provides a more trustworthy estimate than a small sample. [Data and Chance] | ☐ *Math Journal 1,* p. 185<br>☐ Study Link 6.4<br>☐ Teaching Master (*Math Masters,* p. 84; optional)<br>☐ Assessment Master (*Math Masters,* p. 479; optional)<br>☐ Geometry Template<br>☐ small pieces of colored candy<br>☐ crayons or markers (optional)<br>☐ calculator<br>***See* Advance Preparation** |
| **2 Ongoing Learning & Practice** | |
| Students continue to collect data by playing *First to 21.* [Data and Chance]<br>Students find fractions of whole sets and find whole sets, given fractions of sets. [Operations and Computation]<br>Students practice and maintain skills through Math Boxes and Study Link activities. | ☐ *Math Journal 1,* pp. 176, 177, 186, and 187<br>☐ Study Link Master (*Math Masters,* p. 286) |
| **3 Options for Individualizing** | |
| **Enrichment** Students predict the results of repeated chance experiments. They check their predictions by carrying out the experiments. [Data and Chance] | ☐ coins or dice |

## Additional Information

**Advance Preparation** For Part 1, you will need enough small, multicolored pieces of candy so that there are at least 5 candies per student. Place them in a bowl near the Math Message. Draw a large circle on a sheet of paper and mark the center. Optional: Make 2 or 3 copies of *Math Masters,* page 84 so that each pair of students has 1 blank circle.

**Vocabulary** • **sample**

# Getting Started

### Mental Math and Reflexes

Write all the factors for given numbers. *Suggestions:*

- What are all the factors of 8? 1, 2, 4, 8
- of 17? 1, 17
- of 24? 1, 2, 3, 4, 6, 8, 12, 24
- of 50? 1, 2, 5, 10, 25, 50

### Math Message

*The bowl contains pieces of candy of several colors. How would you find what percent of each color is in the bowl?*

### Study Link 6.4 Follow-Up

Briefly go over the answers and have students share strategies for matching the plots and the data sets.

# 1 Teaching the Lesson

## Math Message Follow-Up

WHOLE-CLASS DISCUSSION 

Students share how they would find the percent of each color in the bowl. Most will probably suggest that they count the total number of candies in the bowl and the number of each color.

If no one mentions looking at a **sample,** ask:

- Would it help to look at a sample of candies from the bowl and count the number of each color in the sample?
- How many candies should we include in the sample?

Tell students that they are going to do a candy-color counting experiment. The results will give them information they can use to predict the percent of each color in the bowl.

NOTE: Counting a whole population is rarely possible, which is why one is concerned with practical sampling and sampling sizes. Even if it were possible to count a whole population, this is often tedious and time-consuming.

## Taking a Small Sample of Candy Colors
(*Math Journal 1,* p. 185; *Math Masters,* p. 84)

PARTNER ACTIVITY 

Cover the bowl with a cloth. Have each student take 5 pieces of candy from the bowl, without looking (10 candies per partnership). Partnerships count and record the number and percent of each color of candy in their sample on journal page 185.

With samples of 10, percents are easy to calculate because the fractions are easily converted to percents. For example, 4 yellows out of 10 candies are $\frac{4}{10} = \frac{40}{100} =$ 40% of the sample. Point out that sample sizes are often chosen to make calculations easy.

**Sampling Candy Colors**

1. You and your partner each take 5 pieces of candy from the bowl. Combine your candies and record your results in the table under Our Sample of 10 Candies.

| Candy Color | Our Sample of 10 Candies | | Combined Class Sample | |
|---|---|---|---|---|
| | Count | Percent | Count | Percent |
| | | | | |
| | | | | |
| | | | | |
| | | | | |
| | | | | |
| | | | | |

2. Your class will work together to make a sample of 100 candies. Record the counts and percents of the class sample under Combined Class Sample in the table.

3. Finally, your class will count the total number of candies in the bowl and the number of each color.

   a. How well did your sample of 10 candies predict the number of each color in the bowl? Answers vary.

   b. How well did the combined class sample predict the number of each color in the bowl? Answers vary.

   c. Do you think that a larger sample is more trustworthy than a smaller sample? yes

   Explain your answer. Sample answer: Small samples jump all over. A larger sample can be trusted to give a better picture of the real situation than a smaller one.

STUDENT PAGE

Math Journal 1, p. 185

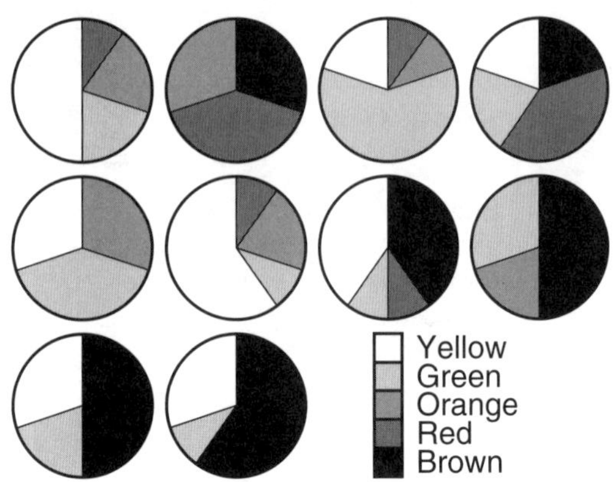


Each circle graph shows the result for one sample of 10 candies

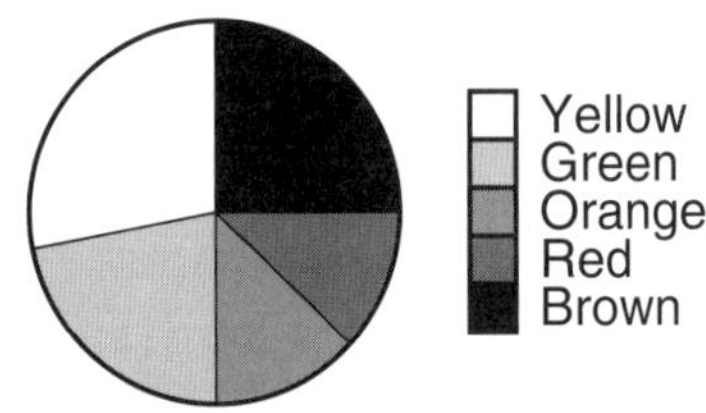


Circle graph of the combined samples of 100 candies

NOTE: If available, have students explore using data analysis software to organize, record, and display their data, as well as to construct various kinds of graphs.

When everyone has recorded the results, students put the candy back in the bowl.

**Adjusting the Activity** Have each partnership make a circle graph to show their sample result for 10 candies. They can color the sections of the graph with the candy colors *(see the margin)*. Students may use the Percent Circle on their Geometry Templates and circles you provide from copies of *Math Masters,* page 84. Make a class display of all the circle graphs.

## ✦ Graphing and Predicting on the Basis of a Sample (*Math Journal 1,* p. 185; *Math Masters,* p. 479)

WHOLE-CLASS ACTIVITY

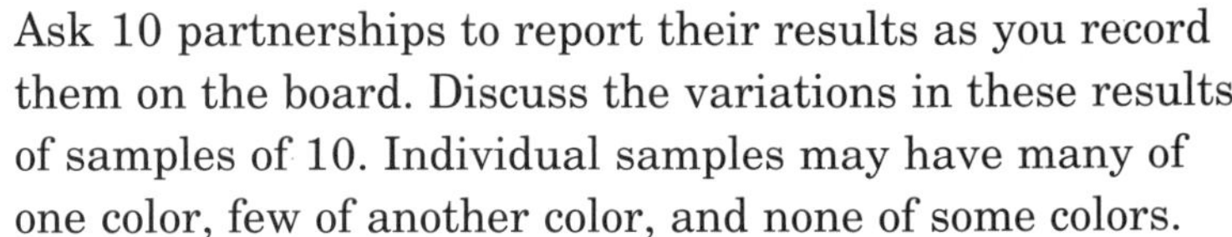

Ask 10 partnerships to report their results as you record them on the board. Discuss the variations in these results of samples of 10. Individual samples may have many of one color, few of another color, and none of some colors.

Combine the data from the partner samples. The combined sample data should represent the percent of each color in the bowl better than most of the individual samples of 10. By using results from 10 pairs of students, the combined sample total is 100—thereby making percent calculations simple. Tally the results by color on the board. Students record the tallies on journal page 185.

Make a circle graph of the combined sample. Use the large circle that you drew previously (see Advance Preparation). Ask volunteers to use a Percent Circle to mark the sections showing percents of colors in the combined sample. (*See the margin.*)

Discuss which is more trustworthy—a sample of 10 candies or the combined sample of 100. If necessary, prompt students with questions like the following:

- How do the small-sample results compare with one another? Sample answer: The results for our small samples jump all over. One of them shows 50% yellow, and one shows 10% yellow.
- How do the results of the combined-sample compare with the small ones? Are they better? Sample answer: The combined sample of 100 is better. You can trust 100 to give a better picture than just 10 does.

Ask students to predict what percent of each color is in the bowl. After the class agrees on predictions, have them count the total number of pieces of candy in the bowl and the number of each color. Use a calculator to find the percent of each color (divide the number of each color by the total number of candies in the bowl). Expect that the percent for each color in the bowl will be reasonably close to the percent on the circle graph for the large sample of 100.

### ONGOING ASSESSMENT

Have students complete an Exit Slip for one or both of the following questions:

- Why do you think our individual circle graphs look so different?
- Why do you think that the percent of each color in the bowl is almost the same as the percents our circle graph shows for the large sample of 100?

## 2 Ongoing Learning & Practice

### ✦ Playing *First to 21* (*Math Journal 1,* pp. 176 and 177)

PARTNER ACTIVITY 

Partners continue to collect data by playing *First to 21*. They record their results on journal page 177 and on the classroom tally sheet. For detailed instructions, see Lesson 6.2.

*Reminder:* The game data will be used in Lesson 6.6.

### ✦ Solving Part-Whole Fraction Problems (*Math Journal 1,* p. 186)

INDEPENDENT ACTIVITY 

Students solve fraction-of-a-set problems and fraction number stories.

**Solving Part-Whole Fraction Problems**

1. How much is $\frac{3}{5}$ of \$1? \$0.60
2. How much is $\frac{3}{5}$ of \$10? \$6
3. How much is $\frac{3}{5}$ of \$1,000? \$600
4. Eight counters is $\frac{1}{2}$ of the set. How many counters are in the set? 16 counters
5. Twenty counters is $\frac{2}{10}$ of the set. How many counters are in the set? 100 counters
6. A set has 40 counters. How many counters are in $\frac{3}{8}$ of the set? 15 counters
7. A set has 36 counters. How many counters are in $\frac{5}{6}$ of the set? 30 counters
8. Mariah shared her sandwich equally with her 3 friends. What fraction of a sandwich did Mariah get? $\frac{1}{4}$ of a sandwich
9. Bernice gave $\frac{2}{3}$ of her 18 fancy pencils to her best friend. How many pencils did Bernice have left? 6 pencils

**Challenge**

10. Jamie and his two friends shared $\frac{1}{2}$ of his 12 candies. How many candies did each friend get? 2 candies
11. Explain how you solved Problem 10. $\frac{1}{2}$ of 12 is 6. Since six candies were shared by 3 people, Jamie and each friend got $\frac{1}{3}$ of 6 candies, or 2 candies.

✦ *Math Journal 1,* p. 186

STUDENT PAGE

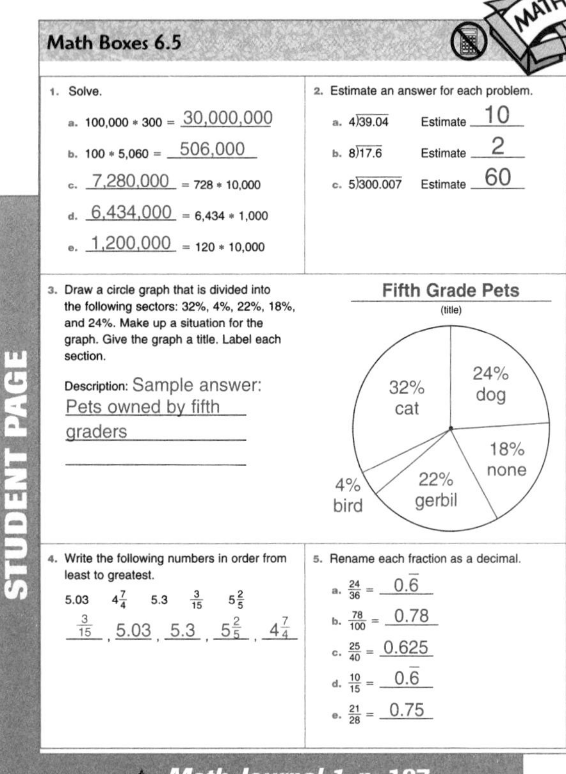

STUDENT PAGE

**Math Boxes 6.5**

1. Solve.
   a. 100,000 * 300 = 30,000,000
   b. 100 * 5,060 = 506,000
   c. 7,280,000 = 728 * 10,000
   d. 6,434,000 = 6,434 * 1,000
   e. 1,200,000 = 120 * 10,000

2. Estimate an answer for each problem.
   a. 4)39.04 Estimate 10
   b. 8)17.6 Estimate 2
   c. 5)300.007 Estimate 60

3. Draw a circle graph that is divided into the following sectors: 32%, 4%, 22%, 18%, and 24%. Make up a situation for the graph. Give the graph a title. Label each section.

   Description: Sample answer: Pets owned by fifth graders

   Fifth Grade Pets (title)



4. Write the following numbers in order from least to greatest.

   5.03 $4\frac{7}{4}$ 5.3 $\frac{3}{15}$ $5\frac{2}{5}$

   $\frac{3}{15}$, 5.03, 5.3, $5\frac{2}{5}$, $4\frac{7}{4}$

5. Rename each fraction as a decimal.
   a. $\frac{24}{36}$ = $0.\overline{6}$
   b. $\frac{78}{100}$ = 0.78
   c. $\frac{25}{40}$ = 0.625
   d. $\frac{10}{15}$ = $0.\overline{6}$
   e. $\frac{21}{28}$ = 0.75

◆ *Math Journal 1*, p. 187

## ◆ Math Boxes 6.5 (*Math Journal 1,* p. 187)

INDEPENDENT ACTIVITY 

**Mixed Review** Math Boxes in this lesson are paired with Math Boxes in Lesson 6.2. The skill in Problem 1 is a prerequisite for Unit 7.

## ◆ Study Link 6.5 (*Math Masters,* p. 286)

**Home Connection** Students make up a list of data to fit a given set of landmarks and then construct a bar graph.

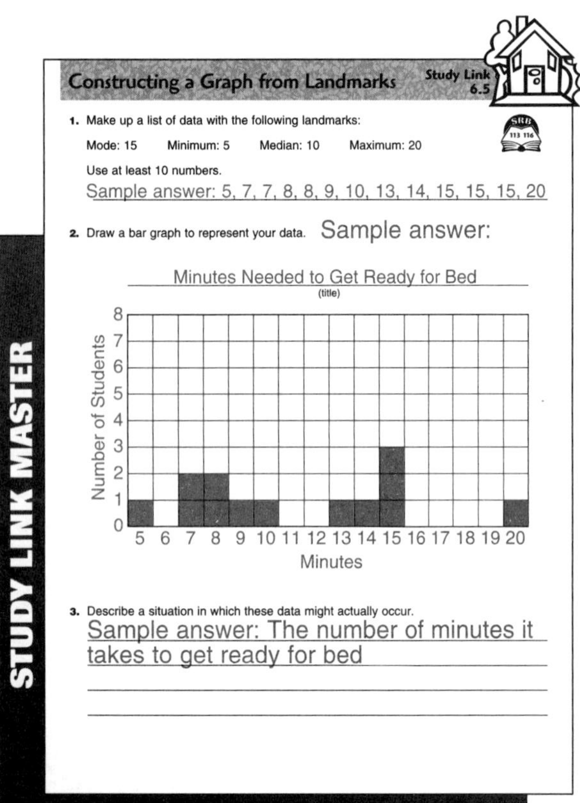

STUDY LINK MASTER

**Constructing a Graph from Landmarks** Study Link 6.5

1. Make up a list of data with the following landmarks:

   Mode: 15 Minimum: 5 Median: 10 Maximum: 20

   Use at least 10 numbers.

   Sample answer: 5, 7, 7, 8, 8, 9, 10, 13, 14, 15, 15, 15, 20

2. Draw a bar graph to represent your data. Sample answer:

   Minutes Needed to Get Ready for Bed (title)



3. Describe a situation in which these data might actually occur.

   Sample answer: The number of minutes it takes to get ready for bed

◆ *Math Masters*, p. 286

# 3 Options for Individualizing

## ◆ ENRICHMENT Investigating How Sample Size Affects the Results of Chance Events

PARTNER ACTIVITY  **15–30 min**

Choose an event with random outcomes—for example, flipping a coin or rolling a die. Ask students to predict the results of 10 trials, 100 trials, and 1,000 trials. Discuss their predictions and how they arrived at their predictions. For example, if the event you choose is flipping a coin, students might predict that the coin will land heads up about $\frac{1}{2}$ of the time; therefore, for 10 tosses, they might predict that the coin might land heads up 5 times.

Have each partnership perform 10 trials. They record their results with tally marks and check their predictions. Combine the totals for 10 partnerships to get results for 100 trials. If time permits, continue until 1,000 trials are completed. Compare the results for 1,000 with those for 100 and for 10.

Discuss differences in the results.

# 6.6 Analysis of Sample Data

**OBJECTIVE** **To display and analyze data from a repeated experiment and from a survey of students.**

| summaries | materials |
| --- | --- |
| **1 Teaching the Lesson** | |
| Students examine the class results of playing *First to 21* and draw conclusions about whether or not the game is fair. They display and analyze survey data collected by interviewing samples of students. [Data and Chance] | □ *Math Journal 1,* pp. 188 and 190–192<br>□ *Student Reference Book,* p. 110<br>□ Study Link 6.5<br>□ calculator<br>***See* Advance Preparation** |
| **2 Ongoing Learning & Practice** | |
| Students solve place-value problems. [Numeration]<br>Students practice and maintain skills through Math Boxes and Study Link activities. | □ *Math Journal 1,* pp. 189 and 193<br>□ Study Link Master (*Math Masters,* p. 287) |
| **3 Options for Individualizing** | |
| **Enrichment** Students look for data from samples and discuss how it might have been obtained. [Data and Chance] | □ newspapers and magazines |

**Additional Information**

**Advance Preparation** For Part 1, be sure that the daily tally sheet and graph of *First to 21* results are up to date.

Many teachers allow students to carry out their own survey project. Students then analyze the survey data they collect, rather than the data sets suggested for this lesson and listed in the *Student Reference Book.* If you select this option, allow at least one additional day for this lesson.

**Vocabulary** • **survey** • **decennial** • **population** • **sample** • **frequency table**

## Getting Started

### Mental Math and Reflexes

Rename fractions as mixed numbers.
*Suggestions:*

- $\frac{8}{2}$ 4
- $\frac{14}{5}$ $2\frac{4}{5}$
- $\frac{27}{4}$ $6\frac{3}{4}$

Rename mixed numbers as fractions. *Suggestions:*

- $7\frac{2}{3}$ $\frac{23}{3}$
- $3\frac{8}{10}$ $\frac{38}{10}$
- $5\frac{7}{4}$ $\frac{27}{4}$

### Math Message

*Complete journal page 188. Be prepared to discuss your answers.*

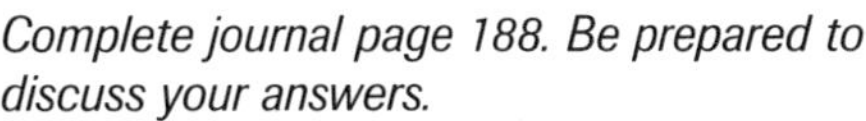

### Study Link 6.5 Follow-Up

Allow time for students to share their graphs and to explain how they decided on their answers for Problem 3.

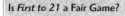

STUDENT PAGE

## Is *First to 21* a Fair Game?

1. What is the total number of *First to 21* games your class has played? ______ games   Answers vary for Problems 1–6.
2. How many games did the player going first win? ______ games
3. How many games did the player going second win? ______ games
4. What is your best estimate for the chance that the player going first will win? ______
5. What is your best estimate for the chance that the player going second will win? ______
6. Did your estimates change as more and more games were played? ______
7. Is *First to 21* a fair game? no   Sample answers:
   Why or why not? It is not a fair game because the player going second has a better chance of winning than the player going first.

   If *First to 21* isn't a fair game, how could you make it more fair? You could change the target number from 21 to a different number or could use a different set of number cards. Then play the game many times to check that it is more fair.

◆ *Math Journal 1,* p. 188

STUDENT PAGE

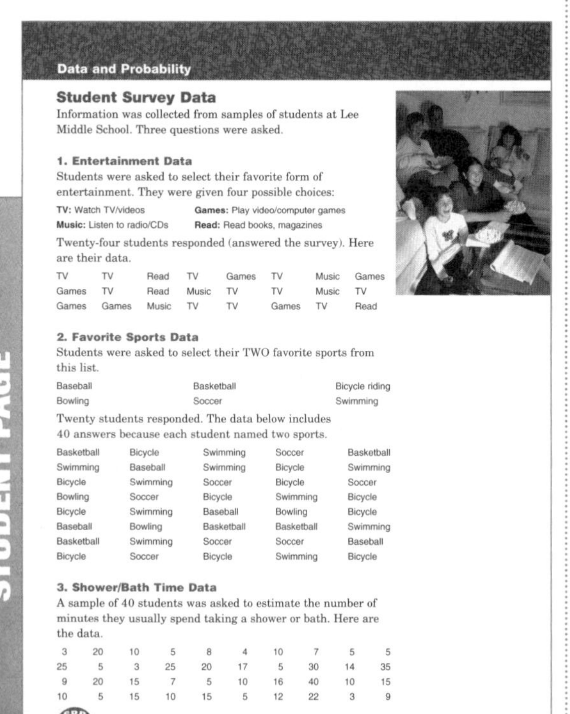

Data and Probability

**Student Survey Data**

Information was collected from samples of students at Lee Middle School. Three questions were asked.

**1. Entertainment Data**

Students were asked to select their favorite form of entertainment. They were given four possible choices:

**TV:** Watch TV/videos   **Games:** Play video/computer games
**Music:** Listen to radio/CDs   **Read:** Read books, magazines

Twenty-four students responded (answered the survey). Here are their data.

| TV | TV | Read | TV | Games | TV | Music | Games |
|---|---|---|---|---|---|---|---|
| Games | TV | Read | Music | TV | TV | Music | TV |
| Games | Games | Music | TV | TV | Games | TV | Read |

**2. Favorite Sports Data**

Students were asked to select their TWO favorite sports from this list.

Baseball   Basketball   Bicycle riding
Bowling   Soccer   Swimming

Twenty students responded. The data below includes 40 answers because each student named two sports.

| Basketball | Bicycle | Swimming | Soccer | Basketball |
|---|---|---|---|---|
| Swimming | Baseball | Swimming | Bicycle | Swimming |
| Bicycle | Swimming | Soccer | Bicycle | Soccer |
| Bowling | Soccer | Bicycle | Swimming | Bicycle |
| Bicycle | Swimming | Baseball | Bowling | Bicycle |
| Baseball | Bowling | Basketball | Basketball | Swimming |
| Basketball | Swimming | Soccer | Soccer | Baseball |
| Bicycle | Soccer | Bicycle | Swimming | Bicycle |

**3. Shower/Bath Time Data**

A sample of 40 students was asked to estimate the number of minutes they usually spend taking a shower or bath. Here are the data.

| 3 | 20 | 10 | 5 | 8 | 4 | 10 | 7 | 5 | 5 |
|---|---|---|---|---|---|---|---|---|---|
| 25 | 5 | 3 | 25 | 20 | 17 | 5 | 30 | 14 | 35 |
| 9 | 20 | 15 | 7 | 5 | 10 | 16 | 40 | 10 | 15 |
| 10 | 5 | 15 | 10 | 15 | 5 | 12 | 22 | 3 | 9 |

SRB 110 one hundred ten

◆ *Student Reference Book,* p. 110

# 1 Teaching the Lesson

## ◆ Math Message Follow-Up
(*Math Journal 1,* p. 188)

WHOLE-CLASS DISCUSSION 

For Questions 4 and 5, ask volunteers to share estimates and how they made them. Sample answers: *I calculated the fraction of all games that the first player won, and the fraction that the second player won.*

*I looked at the last bar on the graph to find the percent of games the first player won. I subtracted this percent from 100% to find the percent of games the second player won.*

The issue raised in Question 6 was taken up in the candy-sampling activity in the previous lesson. The larger a sample is, the more confident we can be of conclusions drawn from the results.

For Question 7, have students share whether or not they think the game is fair, and why. By now it should be clear to them that the player going second has an advantage. You may want to share the following explanation: The median number for any one draw is 6. So when the third card is drawn—by the first player—the total is most likely to be about 18. Therefore, when the fourth card is drawn—by the second player—the total is likely to be around 24.

Discuss how the rules could be changed to make it a fairer game. Changing the goal from 21 to a different number, or using a different set of number cards, might even the chances. If students are interested, have them suggest alternatives and try them. For example, different partners could play *First to 22, First to 23, First to 24,* and so on, and make graphs to display their results.

## ◆ Discussing the Definition and Purpose of a Survey (*Student Reference Book,* p. 110)

WHOLE-CLASS DISCUSSION 

**Social Studies Link** Explain to students the definition and the purpose of a **survey:** A survey is a study based on data collected from human respondents. Surveys are used to find out about people's characteristics, behaviors, opinions, interests, and so on.

Remind students that the **decennial** census is an example of a survey that includes all the people in the United States. (See Lesson 3.1.)

Most surveys, however, study smaller populations that are of special interest. A **population** is the set of people, things, or data that are being studied.

NOTE: A survey of physicians gathers information about a very special population—people who have medical degrees. A survey of teenagers collects information on the population of people aged 13 to 19.

In many surveys, the population is so large that it is not practical to interview everybody. For this reason, a representative part of the population is interviewed and used to represent the whole population. This part is called a **sample.**

Have students turn to the data sets listed on page 110 of the *Student Reference Book*. Ask volunteers to read the brief descriptions. Each set of data was obtained by conducting an interview with a sample of children from the Lee Middle School. The population of interest for this survey was all students who attend Lee school.

## ◆ Displaying and Analyzing the Survey Data
(*Math Journal 1,* pp. 190–192; *Student Reference Book,* p. 110)

PARTNER ACTIVITY

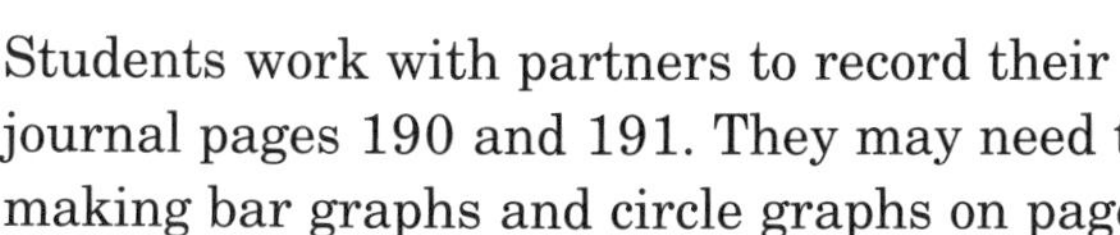

Students work with partners to record their work on journal pages 190 and 191. They may need to review making bar graphs and circle graphs on pages 116 and 120 in their *Student Reference Books.*

A **frequency table** is a chart on which data is tallied to find the frequency of given events or values. Students should use the frequency tables on journal page 190 to tally answers for the Entertainment and the Favorite-Sports survey data. To simplify tallying, have one partner read the data items and the other partner tally these. Students then count the tallies to find a total for each category, and calculate the fraction and percent for each category. They should use calculators to find the percents, rounding each to the nearest percent.

After completing the tables on journal page 190, partners should graph the Entertainment and Favorite-Sports data on journal page 191. One graph must be a bar graph and the other a circle graph, but students may graph the data sets in either order. For example, one partner may draw a bar graph for the sports data and a circle graph for the entertainment data, while the other partner draws a bar graph for the entertainment data and a circle graph for the sports data.

**Frequency Tables**

A **frequency table** is a chart on which data is tallied to find the frequency of given events or values.

Use the frequency tables below to tally the Entertainment data and Favorite-Sports data on page 110 in your *Student Reference Book.* Then complete the tables. If you conducted your own survey, use the frequency tables to tally the data you collected. Then complete the tables.

1. What is the survey question? What is your favorite form of entertainment?

| Category | Tallies | Number | Fraction | Percent |
|---|---|---|---|---|
| TV | 卌 卌 / | 11 | $\frac{11}{24}$ | 46% |
| Read | /// | 3 | $\frac{3}{24}$, or $\frac{1}{8}$ | $12\frac{1}{2}$% |
| Games | 卌 / | 6 | $\frac{6}{24}$, or $\frac{1}{4}$ | 25% |
| Music | //// | 4 | $\frac{4}{24}$, or $\frac{1}{6}$ | $16\frac{2}{3}$% |
| | | | | |
| | | | | |

Total number of tallies 24

2. What is the survey question? What are your two favorite sports?

| Category | Tallies | Number | Fraction | Percent |
|---|---|---|---|---|
| Baseball | //// | 4 | $\frac{4}{40}$, or $\frac{1}{10}$ | 10% |
| Basketball | 卌 | 5 | $\frac{5}{40}$, or $\frac{1}{8}$ | $12\frac{1}{2}$% |
| Bicycle Riding | 卌 卌 / | 11 | $\frac{11}{40}$ | $27\frac{1}{2}$% |
| Bowling | /// | 3 | $\frac{3}{40}$ | $7\frac{1}{2}$% |
| Soccer | 卌 // | 7 | $\frac{7}{40}$ | $17\frac{1}{2}$% |
| Swimming | 卌 卌 | 10 | $\frac{10}{40}$, or $\frac{1}{4}$ | 25% |

Total number of tallies 40

STUDENT PAGE

◆ *Math Journal 1,* p. 190

NOTE: If available, have students explore using data analysis software to organize, record, and display their data, as well as to construct various kinds of graphs.

**Data Graphs and Plots**

1. Draw a bar graph for one of the survey questions on journal page 190. Label the parts of the graph. Give the graph a title. Graphs vary for Problems 1–2.

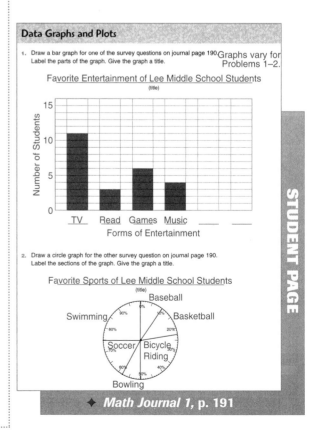

Favorite Entertainment of Lee Middle School Students
(title)

Number of Students
15
10
5
0
TV Read Games Music
Forms of Entertainment

2. Draw a circle graph for the other survey question on journal page 190. Label the sections of the graph. Give the graph a title.

Favorite Sports of Lee Middle School Students
(title)

Baseball
Basketball
Bicycle Riding
Bowling
Soccer
Swimming

STUDENT PAGE

◆ *Math Journal 1,* p. 191

## Data Graphs and Plots (cont.)

3. Make a stem-and-leaf plot for the Shower/Bath Time data on page 110 in your *Student Reference Book*. If you conducted your own survey, make a stem-and-leaf plot for the data you collected.

| Stems (10s) | Leaves (1s) |
|---|---|
| | 3 3 3 4 5 5 5 5 5 5 5 5 7 7 8 9 9 |
| 1 | 0 0 0 0 0 0 2 4 5 5 5 5 6 7 |
| 2 | 0 0 0 2 5 5 |
| 3 | 0 5 |
| 4 | 0 |

Find the landmarks for this set of data.

Minimum: 3

Maximum: 40

Range: 37

Median: 10

Mode: 5

**Challenge**

4. Calculate the mean (average).

Mean: 12.7

STUDENT PAGE

✦ *Math Journal 1*, p. 192

## Place-Value Puzzles

1. For each problem, tell what you would enter in your calculator to change the numbers.

| Starting Number | Ending Number | Calculator Key Strokes |
|---|---|---|
| 34,728 | 34,758 | (+) 30 (Enter) |
| 1,176 | 276 | (−) 900 (Enter) |
| 62,885 | 71,885 | (+) 9000 (Enter) |
| 109,784 | 110,084 | (+) 300 (Enter) |
| 9,002 | 8,996 | (−) 6 (Enter) |

2. Use the clues to write the 7-digit number.
The digit in the tens place is 7.
The digit in the hundred-thousands place is 6 less than double 7.
The digit in the ones place is $\frac{1}{4}$ of three times the digit in the hundred-thousands place.
The digit in the other places is the smallest even digit.

2 , 8 2 2 , 2 7 6

**Challenge**

3. Use the clues to write the 4-digit number.
The digit in the tens place is double the digit in the tenths place.
The digit in the hundredths place is $\frac{1}{2}$ the digit in the tenths place.
The digit in the ones place is the only 8 in the number.

4 8 . 2 1

4. I am a two-digit composite number. One of my digits is worth three times as much as the other digit. Double me is less than 100. I am not divisible by 3. What am I?

26

STUDENT PAGE

✦ *Math Journal 1*, p. 193

Journal page 192 provides a space for students to make a stem-and-leaf plot of the Shower/Bath survey data, and to record landmarks for the data set.

**Adjusting the Activity** You may need to remind students how a stem-and-leaf plot is used to record data. Remind them also that it is easier to identify landmarks when each row of leaves is written in numerical order. If one partner reads the data items in order—as the other partner records these in the stem-and-leaf plot—each row of leaves will be written in numerical order.

NOTE: If students carry out their own survey project, journal pages 190–192 may still be used to record and graph their survey data. Have them use pages 190 and 191 for questions that are answered by naming a category; have them use page 192 for questions that are answered by giving a measure.

Reserve some time for a follow-up discussion of students' findings. Some suggested topics:

- Which category is the mode for the Favorite-Sports data? Bicycle riding Do you think the survey results would have been very different if students had been asked to name only one favorite sport instead of two? Quite possibly. Suppose that bicycle riding was everyone's second choice, but no one's first choice. If students named only their one favorite sport, bicycle riding would never have been mentioned.
- What are the landmarks for the Favorite-Sports and the Entertainment data? Each set of data has a mode. But neither of these sets of data has a minimum, maximum, range, median, or mean (average). The sports and entertainment questions are answered by naming a category. The categories are not numbers; they cannot be arranged in order from smallest to largest, and there is no middle value; they cannot be added to find a mean.
- What is the median shower/bath time? 10 minutes What is the mode? 5 minutes Why do you think there are so many times that are multiples of 5 minutes—5, 10, 15, 20, and 25 minutes? It is hard to remember exact times. Many people likely estimate to the nearest 5 minutes.

# 2 Ongoing Learning & Practice

## ✦ Solving Place-Value Problems (*Math Journal 1,* p. 193)

INDEPENDENT ACTIVITY 

Students complete a page of place-value puzzles.

## ✦ Math Boxes 6.6 (*Math Journal 1,* p. 189)

INDEPENDENT ACTIVITY 

**Mixed Review** Math Boxes in this lesson are paired with Math Boxes in Lesson 6.3. The skill in Problem 1 is a prerequisite for Unit 7.

## ✦ Study Link 6.6 (*Math Masters,* p. 287)

**Home Connection** Students analyze a line plot and a stem-and-leaf plot in order to describe a situation that would go along with each. Students also identify the landmarks for each plot.

**Math Boxes 6.6**

1. The temperature in Chicago at 6 P.M. was 35°F. By midnight, the temperature had dropped 48 degrees. What was the temperature at midnight? −13°F

2. Write each numeral in number-and-word notation.
   a. 56,000,000 56 million
   b. 423,000 423 thousand
   c. 18,000,000,000 18 billion
   d. 9,500,000 9.5 million; or 9 million, 500 thousand

3. What kind of regular polygon could be partially hidden behind the wall? square

   Complete the shape.

4. Write the prime factorization of 132. $2 * 2 * 3 * 11$

5. Write a number story for $81 * 17$. Then solve it. Answers vary.

   Answer: 1,377

STUDENT PAGE

✦ *Math Journal 1,* p. 189

# 3 Options for Individualizing

## ✦ ENRICHMENT Interpreting Data in the News

INDEPENDENT ACTIVITY  **5–15 min**

Students find examples of data in newspapers and magazines that they think represent data from a number of sample trials or a sample population.

Have students write an explanation of how they think the data was collected, and whether they think the conjectures and statements made on the basis of the data are reasonable.

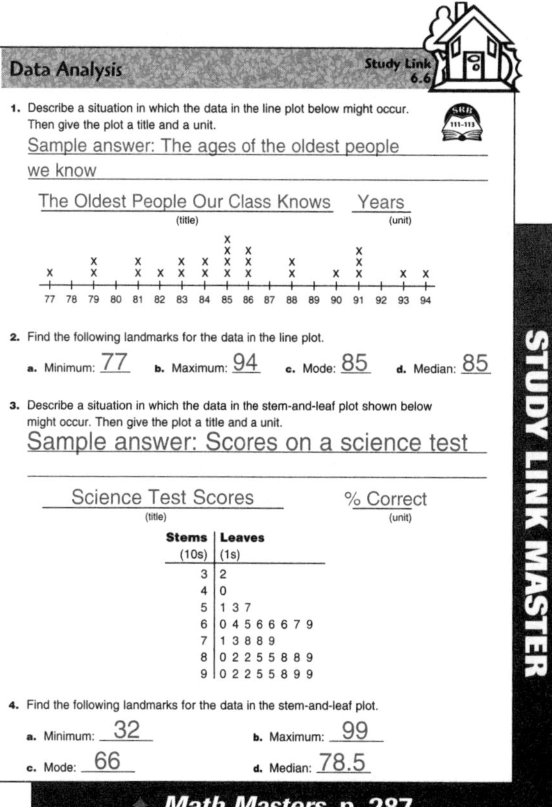

**Data Analysis** Study Link 6.6

1. Describe a situation in which the data in the line plot below might occur. Then give the plot a title and a unit.
   Sample answer: The ages of the oldest people we know

   The Oldest People Our Class Knows (title) Years (unit)

| 77 | 78 | 79 | 80 | 81 | 82 | 83 | 84 | 85 | 86 | 87 | 88 | 89 | 90 | 91 | 92 | 93 | 94 |
|---|---|---|---|---|---|---|---|---|---|---|---|---|---|---|---|---|---|
| X | | XX | | XX | X | XX | XX | XXXX | XXX | | XX | | X | XXX | | X | X |

2. Find the following landmarks for the data in the line plot.
   a. Minimum: 77 b. Maximum: 94 c. Mode: 85 d. Median: 85

3. Describe a situation in which the data in the stem-and-leaf plot shown below might occur. Then give the plot a title and a unit.
   Sample answer: Scores on a science test

   Science Test Scores (title) % Correct (unit)

| Stems (10s) | Leaves (1s) |
|---|---|
| 3 | 2 |
| 4 | 0 |
| 5 | 1 3 7 |
| 6 | 0 4 5 6 6 6 7 9 |
| 7 | 1 3 8 8 9 |
| 8 | 0 2 2 5 5 8 8 9 |
| 9 | 0 2 2 5 5 8 9 9 |

4. Find the following landmarks for the data in the stem-and-leaf plot.
   a. Minimum: 32 b. Maximum: 99
   c. Mode: 66 d. Median: 78.5

STUDY LINK MASTER

✦ *Math Masters,* p. 287

# 6.7 American Tour: Climate

**OBJECTIVE** To read and use contour maps.

| summaries | materials |
|---|---|
| **1 Teaching the Lesson** | |
| Students are introduced to maps with contour lines as a means for displaying data. They use contour maps for precipitation and growing seasons to compare the climate for various locations in the United States. [Data and Chance; Measurement and Reference Frames] | ☐ *Math Journal 1,* pp. 194 and 195<br>☐ *Student Reference Book,* p. 338; and pp. 339 and 334–335 (optional)<br>☐ Study Link 6.6<br>☐ physical and political map(s) of the United States for the classroom (optional) |
| **2 Ongoing Learning & Practice** | |
| Students solve number stories. [Operations and Computation]<br>Students practice and maintain skills through Math Boxes and Study Link activities. | ☐ *Math Journal 1,* pp. 196 and 197<br>☐ Assessment Master (*Math Masters,* p. 476; optional)<br>☐ Study Link Master (*Math Masters,* p. 288) |
| **3 Options for Individualizing** | |
| **Enrichment** Students find contour maps and list some of their features. [Data and Chance; Measurement and Reference Frames] | ☐ contour maps |

**Additional Information**

**Vocabulary** • **contour map** • **climate** • **precipitation** • **map legend (map key)** • **contour line**

## Getting Started

### Mental Math and Reflexes

Rename fractions as decimals and percents.
*Suggestions:*

- $\frac{3}{4}$ 0.75; 75%
- $\frac{8}{10}$ 0.8; 80%
- $\frac{9}{100}$ 0.09; 9%
- $\frac{6}{25}$ 0.24; 24%
- $\frac{2}{3}$ $0.\overline{6}$; $66.\overline{6}$%
- $\frac{6}{12}$ 0.5; 50%
- $\frac{8}{20}$ 0.40; 40%

Have students explain how they found decimals and percents for $\frac{8}{20}$ and $\frac{6}{25}$.

### Math Message

*Study the map "Average Yearly Precipitation in the U.S." on page 338 of the American Tour.*

- About how much precipitation (moisture such as rain and snow) does Chicago, Illinois, receive per year?
- About how much precipitation does Dallas, Texas, receive per year?

### Study Link 6.6 Follow-Up

Have volunteers share the situations they created for the data. Briefly review the landmarks.

# Teaching the Lesson

## ✦ Math Message Follow-Up
(*Student Reference Book,* p. 338)

WHOLE-CLASS DISCUSSION

**Science Link** Ask students to turn to the precipitation map on page 338 of the American Tour. This is an example of a **contour map.** Contour maps use curved lines to show the boundaries of areas that share the same feature, such as temperature, rainfall, elevation, and so on. *(See the margin.)*

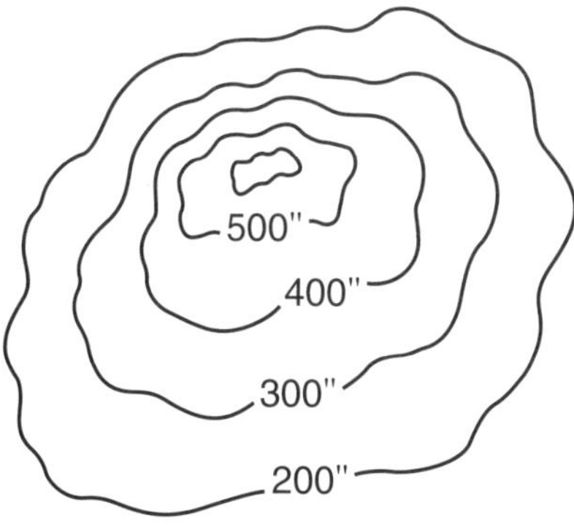


This contour map uses contour lines to show elevation.

The word **climate** refers to the usual weather conditions for a place. Temperature, precipitation, and wind are all features of climate. Maps in the American Tour give information about temperature, precipitation, and growing seasons for the United States.

NOTE: The contour maps used in this lesson are based on vast amounts of data collected over many years. The maps are data displays that include much more information than could conveniently be shown in a set of data tables.

Discuss **precipitation.** Students should understand that precipitation includes all moisture that falls as rain or as snow.

Draw students' attention to the **map legend,** also called the **map key.** The legend indicates that the map shows "Precipitation (in inches)." This is the total number of inches of moisture that falls in one year, on average. The average annual precipitation is simply an average, over many years, of the yearly totals.

NOTE: When snow falls, meteorologists melt a sample to determine the equivalent amount of rain. A light, fluffy snow 20 inches deep might contain the same amount of moisture as 1 inch of rain. A heavy, wet snow 6 inches deep might also be equivalent to 1 inch of rain.

The National Weather Service collects data on climate. It maintains about 12,000 weather stations in all parts of the United States. Some stations record weather data once a day, and others take hourly readings. New York City has kept weather records since 1868. New Haven, Connecticut, has kept weather records since 1781.

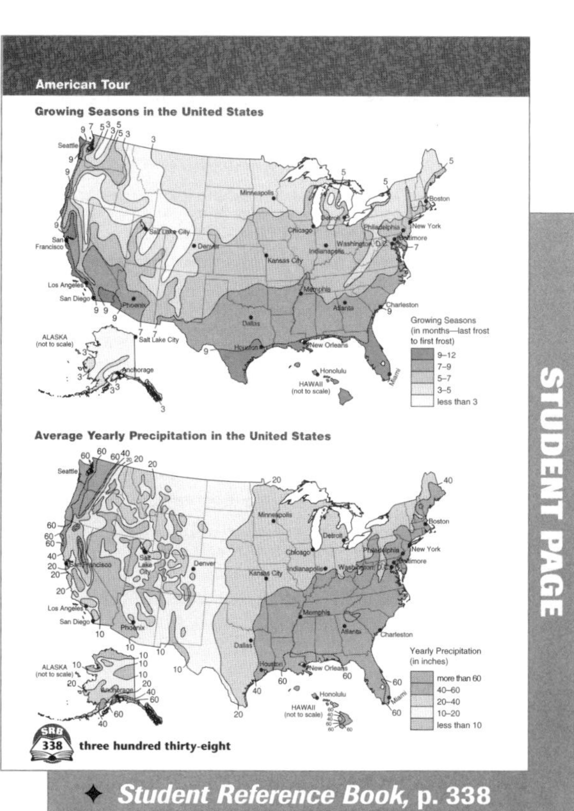


✦ *Student Reference Book,* p. 338

Ask students to share their answers to the Math Message questions. The average yearly precipitation in Chicago is about 20 to 40 inches. In Dallas, it is nearly 40 inches. Dallas is in the light green region but close to the dark green region. The color key shows that the separation between the light green and dark green regions occurs at 40 inches.

Follow up with similar questions about other cities in the United States. Include the following questions:

- Which parts of the United States receive the most moisture? Parts of the Northwest, the Gulf coast near New Orleans, the Miami area, an area north of Atlanta, part of Hawaii, part of New Hampshire, and the south coast of Alaska all receive more than 60 inches per year.
- Which parts of the United States receive the least moisture? Parts of northern Alaska and several desert regions in the West receive less than 10 inches per year.

The curved lines on the map that separate colors are called **contour lines.** Numbers are printed at the ends of some contour lines, and directly on other contour lines. The numbers indicate inches of precipitation. When a contour line passes through or near a city—such as Dallas or Phoenix—the precipitation can be estimated fairly precisely by reading the number for the contour line.

Ask questions similar to these:

- Is Phoenix, Arizona, near a contour line? Which one? What does that mean? Phoenix is on a 10-inch contour line; it receives about 10 inches of precipitation per year.
- Which contour line runs through Illinois? What does that mean? The 40-inch contour line cuts through Illinois. Most of the state is light green (20 to 40 inches per year). The southern part of Illinois is dark green (40 to 60 inches per year). Regions along the contour line get about 40 inches of precipitation per year.

STUDENT PAGE

**Climate Maps**

To answer the questions below, use the "Average Yearly Precipitation in the U.S." and "Growing Seasons in the U.S." maps on page 338 of your American Tour.

The precipitation map shows the average amount of moisture that falls as rain and snow in one year. Snow is translated into an equivalent amount of rain.

The growing seasons map shows the average number of months between the last frost in spring and the first frost in fall. During this time, the temperature remains above freezing (32°F or 0°C), and crops may be grown.

1. Denver, Colorado, receives about 10–20 inches of precipitation as rain and snow per year.
   Denver's growing season is about 3–5 months long.
2. Los Angeles, California, receives about 20 inches of precipitation per year.
   The growing season in Los Angeles is 9–12 months long.
3. a. According to these maps, how are Los Angeles and New Orleans similar?
   Sample answer: They both have long growing seasons of 9 to 12 months.

   b. Who is more likely to be worried about a lack of rain: a farmer near Los Angeles or a farmer near New Orleans? Why?
   Sample answer: A farmer near Los Angeles. New Orleans receives more than 60 inches of rain each year. Los Angeles receives only about 20 inches per year.

✦ *Math Journal 1,* p. 194

## ✦ Introducing the Growing Seasons Map (*Student Reference Book,* p. 338)

WHOLE-CLASS DISCUSSION

Ask students to look at the "Growing Seasons in the U.S." map on page 338 of the American Tour.

This map shows the average number of months between the last frost in spring and the first frost in fall. During this time, the temperature remains above freezing (32°F or 0°C), and crops can be grown.

Have students discuss and use the map legend. Ask questions such as these:

- What is the average length of the growing season near Houston, Texas? About 9 months. Houston is near the contour line marked 9.
- What is the average length of the growing season around Chicago, Illinois? Chicago is between the contour lines marked 5 and 7, but is closer to the line marked 5. So the growing season is probably 5 to 6 months.
- What is the average length of the growing season near Dallas, Texas? Dallas is about halfway between the 7-month and 9-month contour lines, so it probably has about an 8-month growing season.

## ✦ Using Climate Maps to Answer Questions
(*Math Journal 1,* pp. 194 and 195; *Student Reference Book,* pp. 338, 339, and 334–335)

INDEPENDENT ACTIVITY 

Problems 6–8 on journal page 195 refer to specific states and mountain ranges. Students can locate these states and landforms by using the maps on pages 338, 339, and 334–335 of the American Tour. Consider using stick-on notes to mark the locations on a classroom map.

Reserve time to discuss students' answers.

**Adjusting the Activity** If you have access to the Internet, you may want to explore the following sites:

▷ University of Michigan Weather:
http://cirrus.sprl.umich.edu/wxnet/

▷ National Weather Service Home Page:
http://www.nws.noaa.gov

# Ongoing Learning & Practice

## ✦ Solving Number Stories
(*Math Journal 1,* p. 196; *Math Masters,* p. 476)

INDEPENDENT ACTIVITY 

Students solve a set of number stories involving multiplication and division. Some of the problems have extraneous information or involve more than one step.

**Climate Maps** (cont.)

4. In general, does it rain more in the eastern states or in the western states? eastern

5. In general, is the growing season longer in the northern states or in the southern states? southern

6. Cotton needs a growing season of at least 6 months. In the list below, circle the states most likely to grow cotton.

(Texas) Nebraska (Mississippi) Ohio

7. North Dakota and Kansas are the largest wheat-producing states.

What is the length of the growing season in North Dakota? 3–5 months

What is the length of the growing season in Kansas? 5–7 months

About how much precipitation does North Dakota receive per year? 10–20 inches

About how much precipitation does eastern Kansas receive per year? 20–40 inches

8. a. Locate the Rocky Mountains on your landform map (American Tour, page 339).
What is the growing season for this mountain area?
Sample answer: In general, less than 3 months

b. What is the growing season for the Appalachian Mountains area?
Sample answer: In general, 3–5 months

STUDENT PAGE

✦ *Math Journal 1,* p. 195

**Number Stories** 

1. Brenda bought 4 cheeseburgers for her family for lunch. The total cost was $5.56. How much did 2 cheeseburgers cost? $2.78

2. Thomas's family went on a long trip over summer vacation. They drove for 5 days. The distances for the 5 days were as follows: 347 miles, 504 miles, 393 miles, 422 miles, and 418 miles.

a. To the nearest mile, what was the average distance traveled per day? 417 miles/day

b. Tell what you did with the remainder. Explain why. Sample answer: I wrote the remainder as a fraction, so the answer was $416\frac{4}{5}$. Then I rounded to the nearest mile, getting 417.

3. Justin's school has 15 classrooms. On an average, there are 28 students per room. One fifth of the classrooms are for fifth graders. About how many students are in the school? Exact answer: 15 ∗ 28 = 420 students; Estimate: 15 ∗ 30 = 450 students

4. Carolyn reads 45 pages of a book every night. How many pages did she read in the month of March (31 days)? 31 ∗ 45 = 1,395 pages

5. Lucienne and her class made 684 notecards for a school benefit.

a. How many boxes of eight can they fill? 85 boxes

b. Explain what the remainder represents and what you did with it. Sample answer: 684 ÷ 8 → 85 R4. The remainder was dropped because it represents 4 notecards and 4 notecards do not fill a box.

STUDENT PAGE

✦ *Math Journal 1,* p. 196

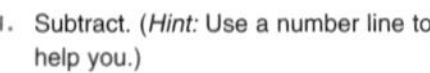

Math Boxes 6.7

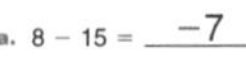

1. Subtract. (*Hint:* Use a number line to help you.)
   a. 8 − 15 = −7
   b. 16 − 18 = −2
   c. −4 = 47 − 51
   d. 6 = 30 − 24
   e. 3 = 32 − 29

2. Rewrite each number in expanded notation.
   a. $3^4$ = 3 ∗ 3 ∗ 3 ∗ 3
   b. $5^3$ = 5 ∗ 5 ∗ 5
   c. $7^4$ = 7 ∗ 7 ∗ 7 ∗ 7
   d. $2^5$ = 2 ∗ 2 ∗ 2 ∗ 2 ∗ 2
   e. $10^3$ = 10 ∗ 10 ∗ 10

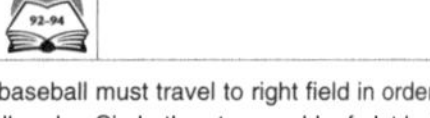

3. Below are the distances (in feet) a baseball must travel to right field in order to be a home run in various major-league baseball parks. Circle the stem-and-leaf plot below that represents this data.

330, 353, 330, 345, 325, 330, 325, 338, 318,
302, 333, 347, 325, 315, 330, 327, 314, 348

| Stems (100s and 10s) | Leaves (1s) |
|---|---|
| 30 | 0 2 5 |
| 31 | 0 0 8 |
| 32 | 5 5 5 5 5 |
| 33 | 0 0 8 8 8 |
| 34 | 5 7 |
| 35 | 3 |
| 36 | 1 |

| Stems (100s and 10s) | Leaves (1s) |
|---|---|
| 30 | 2 |
| 31 | 4 5 8 |
| 32 | 5 7 |
| 33 | 0 3 8 |
| 34 | 5 7 8 |
| 35 | 3 |
| 36 | |

| Stems (100s and 10s) | Leaves (1s) |
|---|---|
| 30 | 2 |
| 31 | 4 5 8 |
| 32 | 5 5 5 7 |
| 33 | 0 0 0 0 3 8 |
| 34 | 5 7 8 |
| 35 | 3 |
| 36 | |

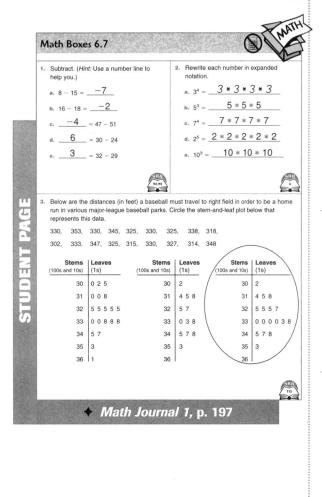

STUDENT PAGE

✦ *Math Journal 1*, p. 197

## ONGOING ASSESSMENT

Have students write their own number story. You may want to use the Number Story Math Log page (*Math Masters*, page 476). Use the number stories rubric in *Toward a Balanced Assessment* to assess students' approximate level of understanding.

## ✦ Math Boxes 6.7 (*Math Journal 1*, p. 197)

INDEPENDENT ACTIVITY

**Mixed Review** Math Boxes in this lesson are paired with Math Boxes in Lesson 6.9. The skill in Problem 1 is a prerequisite for Unit 7.

## ✦ Study Link 6.7 (*Math Masters*, p. 288)

**Home Connection** Students use a contour map for climate in the United States to answer questions.

Contour Map — Study Link 6.7

The contour map below shows the approximate percentage of sunny or partly sunny days for the months of December through February.

Percent of Sunny or Partly Sunny Days December – February

20–29%
30–49%
50–59%
60–90%

1. States where at least part of the state has sunny days more than 60% of the time between December and February.
   0 Washington ● Florida ● Arizona 0 New York
2. States that border the Pacific Ocean where, in some part of the state, more than 70% of the days are NOT sunny between December and February.
   0 California ● Oregon 0 Montana ● Washington
3. On the back of this page, make up your own question about the map. Answer your question. Answers vary.

Challenge

4. States with several regions where the amount of sunshine varies. Part of the state is sunny most of the time, but another part of the state is NOT sunny most of the time.
   ● Utah 0 Ohio ● Wyoming 0 Wisconsin

STUDY LINK MASTER

*Math Masters*, p. 288

# 3 Options for Individualizing

## ✦ ENRICHMENT Finding Contour Maps

INDEPENDENT ACTIVITY  **5–15 min**

Students bring in maps with contour lines for temperature, moisture, elevation, or other features. They list three things that can be learned from the map. The maps and students' lists can be posted on a bulletin board.

# 6.8 Using a Slide Rule to Add and Subtract Fractions

**OBJECTIVES To add and subtract fractions using a slide rule; and to review equivalent fractions.**

| summaries | materials |
|---|---|
| **1 Teaching the Lesson** | |
| Students make a slide rule and use it to solve fraction addition and subtraction problems. [Operations and Computation]<br>Students use fraction sticks to solve addition and subtraction problems. [Operations and Computation] | □ *Math Journal 1,* pp. 198 and 199<br>□ *Math Journal 2,* Activity Sheet 6<br>□ Study Link 6.7<br>□ Transparencies (*Math Masters,* pp. 25 and 85; optional)<br>***See* Advance Preparation** |
| **2 Ongoing Learning & Practice** | |
| Students play *Frac-Tac-Toe* to practice fraction-decimal-percent equivalencies. [Numeration; Operations and Computation]<br>Students practice and maintain skills through Math Boxes and Study Link activities. | □ *Math Journal 1,* p. 200<br>□ *Student Reference Book,* pp. 274–276<br>□ Study Link Master (*Math Masters,* p. 289)<br>□ *Frac-Tac-Toe* Number-Card Board (*Math Masters,* p. 62) and a Gameboard (*Math Masters,* pp. 63–74) |
| **3 Options for Individualizing** | |
| **Language Diversity** Students write number sentences to represent pattern-block designs. [Patterns, Functions, and Algebra]<br>**Reteaching** Students represent number patterns with variables. [Patterns, Functions, and Algebra] | □ Teaching Master (*Math Masters,* p. 86)<br>□ pattern blocks<br>□ slate |

### Additional Information

**Advance Preparation** Cut out and assemble the slide rule before the start of the lesson (*Math Journal 2,* Activity Sheet 6). Read how to use it on page 389, and then use it to solve the addition and subtraction problems on journal page 198. The slide rules will be used again in Unit 7, so be sure students treat them carefully.

**Vocabulary • slide rule • slider • holder**

## Getting Started

### Mental Math and Reflexes

Solve extended facts. *Suggestions:*

- $\frac{56}{8} = ?$ 7 $\quad \frac{560}{8} = ?$ 70 $\quad \frac{5{,}600}{80} = ?$ 70
- $\frac{32}{4} = ?$ 8 $\quad \frac{3{,}200}{4} = ?$ 800 $\quad \frac{3{,}200}{40} = ?$ 80
- $\frac{49}{7} = ?$ 7 $\quad \frac{490}{70} = ?$ 7 $\quad \frac{4{,}900}{70} = ?$ 70

### Math Message

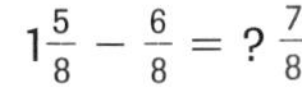

$\frac{3}{4} + \frac{3}{4} = ?$ $\frac{6}{4}$, or $1\frac{1}{2}$ $\qquad 1\frac{5}{8} - \frac{6}{8} = ?$ $\frac{7}{8}$

### Study Link 6.7 Follow-Up

Briefly review answers.

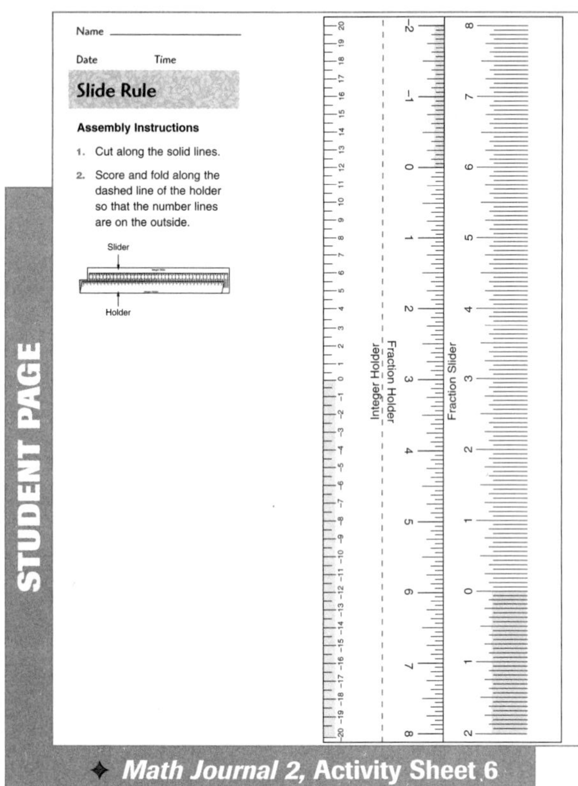
STUDENT PAGE

Name

Date Time

**Slide Rule**

**Assembly Instructions**

1. Cut along the solid lines.
2. Score and fold along the dashed line of the holder so that the number lines are on the outside.

Slider

Holder

Integer Holder

Fraction Holder

Fraction Slider

✦ *Math Journal 2*, Activity Sheet 6

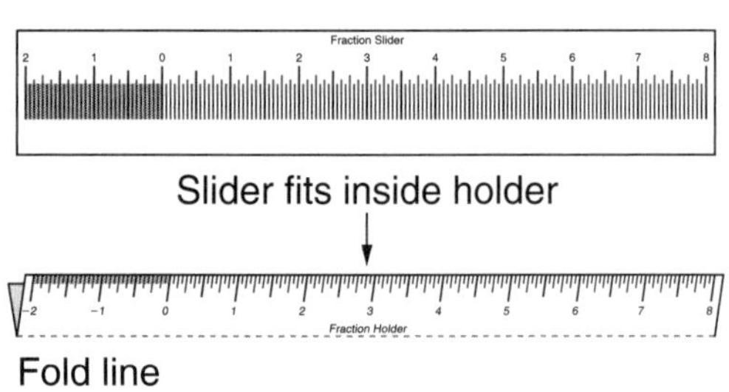


NOTE: Many calculators, such as the TI-15, have special keys for handling fractions, but students should not use them in this or the following two lessons. (See pages 235–236, 238–239, and 242 in the *Student Reference Book* for details about how the TI-15 handles fractions).

# 1 Teaching the Lesson

## ✦ Math Message Follow-Up

WHOLE-CLASS DISCUSSION 

Discuss how students solved the problems. Compare the various methods, pointing out the advantages and disadvantages of each.

Explain that in today's lesson students will make a tool that can be used to solve fraction addition and subtraction problems.

## ✦ Making a Fraction Slide Rule (*Math Journal 2*, Activity Sheet 6; *Math Masters*, pp. 25 and 85)

INDEPENDENT ACTIVITY

The **slide rule** consists of two pieces: a **slider** and a **holder.** Have students cut out the two pieces from Activity Sheet 6. Then tell them to fold the holder along the dashed center line, with the number lines on the outside. *(See the margin.)*

The slide rule is used as a manipulative for several reasons. First, it provides students with additional practice in locating and reading the fine markings on a ruler. Second, it demonstrates adding measures by actually measuring back from or onto the end of one measure, as carpenters often do. Third, it is helpful for students to visualize addition and subtraction as shifts or slides along a number line before learning procedures involving common denominators.

Discuss the following features of the slide rule:

- ▷ Number lines include positive and negative numbers.
- ▷ The slider and the holder each have two sides, one for integers and the other for fractions. When the slider is placed in the holder, the sides should match. Only the fraction side will be used in this unit. The integer side will be used later.
- ▷ The parts of the number lines for negative numbers are shaded.
- ▷ The number lines on the fraction holder and fraction sliders are marked like a ruler. The marks at the integers (−2, −1, 0, 1, 2, ...) are 1 inch apart.
- ▷ The smallest scale divisions on the fraction number lines are sixteenths of an inch. Halves, quarters, and eighths are also marked.

You may want to use an overhead transparency of *Math Masters,* page 85 to verify that students can locate fractions on the number lines on the slider and holder. Write fractions on the board ($\frac{1}{2}$, $\frac{5}{8}$, $\frac{7}{16}$, and so on) and have students locate them on the overhead number lines. Also point to marks on the overhead number lines and ask students to give fractions for those points. For example, point to the mark for $\frac{3}{4}$ and ask what equivalent fractions correspond to it ($\frac{3}{4}$, $\frac{6}{8}$, $\frac{12}{16}$).

## ✦ Adding and Subtracting with a Fraction Slide Rule (*Math Journal 2,* Activity Sheet 6)

PARTNER ACTIVITY

Give students a few minutes to experiment with their slide rules. Write problems similar to the following on the overhead or board, and have students work in partnerships to figure out how to use the slide rule to solve them.

- ▷ $1\frac{1}{2} + 2\frac{1}{4} = 3\frac{3}{4}$
- ▷ $\frac{3}{8} + \frac{1}{2} = \frac{7}{8}$
- ▷ $\frac{1}{4} + \frac{7}{8} = 1\frac{1}{8}$
- ▷ $1\frac{1}{4} - \frac{1}{2} = \frac{3}{4}$
- ▷ $2\frac{1}{4} - \frac{7}{8} = 1\frac{3}{8}$
- ▷ $2\frac{1}{16} - \frac{3}{4} = 1\frac{5}{16}$

Have students share their methods with the class. If they cannot devise their own procedures, use the overhead slide rule to demonstrate examples like the following:

*Example 1:* $\frac{3}{4} + \frac{1}{2} = ?$

1. Place the fraction side of the slider inside the fraction side of the holder.
2. Align the 0-mark on the slider with the mark for the first addend, $\frac{3}{4}$, on the holder.
3. Find the mark for the second addend, $\frac{1}{2}$, on the slider. It is aligned with the mark for $1\frac{1}{4}$ on the holder. This is the answer to the problem: $\frac{3}{4} + \frac{1}{2} = 1\frac{1}{4}$. *(See the margin.)*

*Example 2:* $2\frac{1}{4} - \frac{1}{2}$

1. Align the 0-mark on the slider with the mark for the first number (the minuend), $2\frac{1}{4}$, on the holder.
2. Find the mark for the second number (the subtrahend), $\frac{1}{2}$, on the negative part of the slider. It is aligned with the mark for $1\frac{3}{4}$ on the holder. This is the answer to the problem: $2\frac{1}{4} - \frac{1}{2} = 1\frac{3}{4}$. *(See the margin.)*

**Adjusting the Activity** For students who are struggling to see the fractions associated with marks on the slide rule transparency, you may choose to use an overhead transparency of the Geometry Template (*Math Masters,* page 25) for the exercise. Since this is a more familiar tool, it should help them make the connections and identify the fractions.

NOTE: The following activities emphasize equivalent fractions but do not require a common denominator in order to add or subtract fractions with unlike denominators.

NOTE: The examples also appear on page 69 in the *Student Reference Book.*

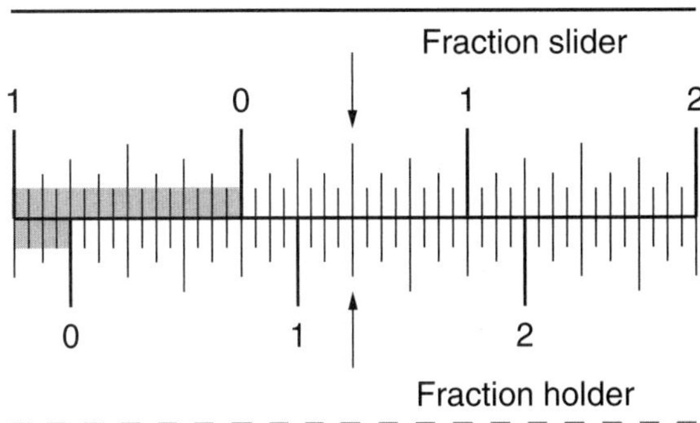


Example 1

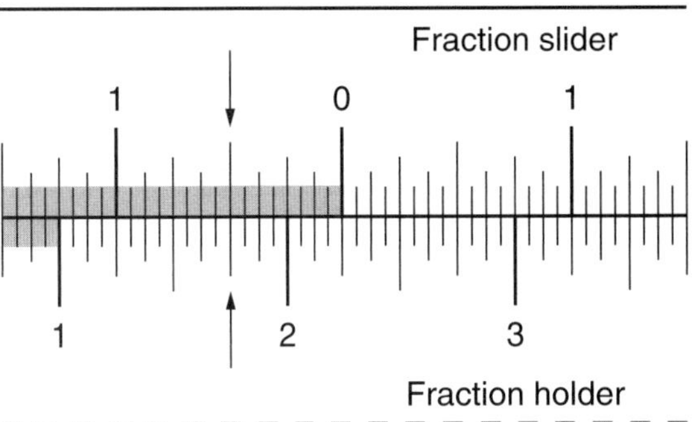


Example 2

Students may point out that some fraction problems can be solved using the integer side of the slide rule. The smallest divisions on the integer scale are halves. This means that problems involving halves, such as $10 - 7\frac{1}{2}$, can be solved directly; problems involving fourths, such as $1\frac{1}{4} + 5\frac{1}{2}$, can be solved by positioning the slider and reading the answer on the holder at points halfway between marks.

NOTE: Because the fraction holder is marked in inches like a conventional ruler, it may also be used to practice reading a ruler.

## ✦ Adding and Subtracting Fractions and Mixed Numbers on the Slide Rule

(*Math Journal 1,* p. 198)

WHOLE-CLASS DISCUSSION

Assign the journal page. Circulate and assist. Verify that students are correctly positioning the slider and reading the answer on the holder. When most students have finished the page, bring the class together.

Encourage students to tell which problems they were able to answer almost immediately, without using the slide rule. Expect them to identify such problems as $\frac{5}{8} + \frac{2}{8}$ and $\frac{7}{8} - \frac{3}{8}$.

Use students' ideas to lead into a discussion of responses to Problem 12. It's easy to add and subtract fractions with the same denominator, because the answer can be given using that same denominator. All that's necessary is to add or subtract the numerators. Many students will see this immediately. Others may need additional explanation and practice.

On the board, you may want to write number sentences in which the common denominator is thought of as a common unit. *For example:*

▷ 2 inches + 4 inches = 6 inches

▷ $\frac{5}{8} + \frac{2}{8} = ?$

To solve $\frac{5}{8} + \frac{2}{8}$, think:
5 eighths + 2 eighths = 7 eighths.

Compare number sentences with common denominators to those that have different denominators.

▷ 2 inches + 4 feet = ?

▷ $\frac{1}{2} + \frac{1}{4} = ?$

To add 2 inches + 4 feet, find a common unit (for example, 2 inches + 48 inches). To solve $\frac{1}{2} + \frac{1}{4}$, find a common denominator (for example $\frac{2}{4} + \frac{1}{4}$).

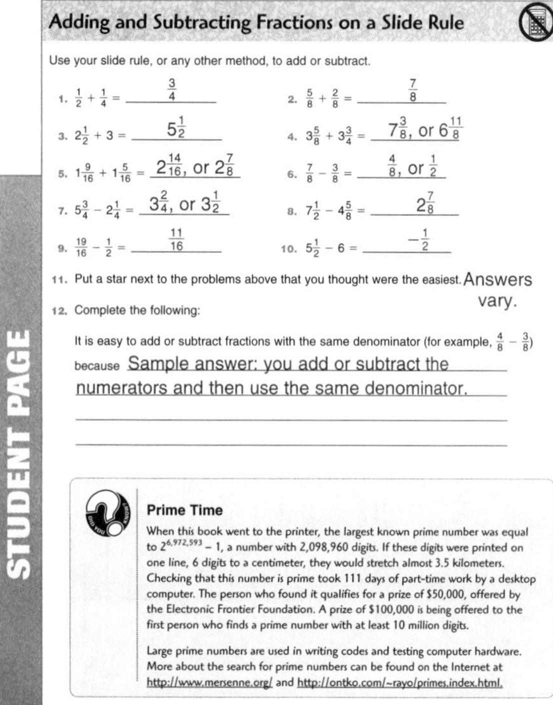
STUDENT PAGE

**Adding and Subtracting Fractions on a Slide Rule**

Use your slide rule, or any other method, to add or subtract.

1. $\frac{1}{2} + \frac{1}{4} = \frac{3}{4}$
2. $\frac{5}{8} + \frac{2}{8} = \frac{7}{8}$
3. $2\frac{1}{2} + 3 = 5\frac{1}{2}$
4. $3\frac{5}{8} + 3\frac{3}{4} = 7\frac{3}{8}$, or $6\frac{11}{8}$
5. $1\frac{9}{16} + 1\frac{5}{16} = 2\frac{14}{16}$, or $2\frac{7}{8}$
6. $\frac{7}{8} - \frac{3}{8} = \frac{4}{8}$, or $\frac{1}{2}$
7. $5\frac{3}{4} - 2\frac{1}{4} = 3\frac{2}{4}$, or $3\frac{1}{2}$
8. $7\frac{1}{2} - 4\frac{5}{8} = 2\frac{7}{8}$
9. $\frac{19}{16} - \frac{1}{2} = \frac{11}{16}$
10. $5\frac{1}{2} - 6 = -\frac{1}{2}$
11. Put a star next to the problems above that you thought were the easiest. Answers vary.
12. Complete the following:

It is easy to add or subtract fractions with the same denominator (for example, $\frac{4}{8} - \frac{3}{8}$) because Sample answer: you add or subtract the numerators and then use the same denominator.

**Prime Time**

When this book went to the printer, the largest known prime number was equal to $2^{6,972,593} - 1$, a number with 2,098,960 digits. If these digits were printed on one line, 6 digits to a centimeter, they would stretch almost 3.5 kilometers. Checking that this number is prime took 111 days of part-time work by a desktop computer. The person who found it qualifies for a prize of $50,000, offered by the Electronic Frontier Foundation. A prize of $100,000 is being offered to the first person who finds a prime number with at least 10 million digits.

Large prime numbers are used in writing codes and testing computer hardware. More about the search for prime numbers can be found on the Internet at http://www.mersenne.org/ and http://ontko.com/~rayo/primes.index.html.

✦ *Math Journal 1,* p. 198

**ONGOING ASSESSMENT**

Expect that most students can recognize how to add and subtract fractions and mixed numbers with common denominators, as long as regrouping is not necessary. Expect that many students will still write mixed-number answers with fraction portions greater than 1, if that is the answer they get from their computations.

After a discussion of responses to Problem 12, summarize addition and subtraction of fractions with the same denominator by writing on the board a statement using variables:

$\frac{a}{c} + \frac{b}{c} = \frac{a+b}{c}$ $\qquad$ $\frac{a}{c} - \frac{b}{c} = \frac{a-b}{c}$

This use of variables will be unfamiliar to students, so give several examples of these identities with numbers substituted for *a, b,* and *c:*

$a = 3, b = 4, c = 5$ $\qquad$ $a = 7, b = 1, c = 12$

$\frac{3}{5} + \frac{4}{5} = \frac{3+4}{5}$ $\qquad$ $\frac{7}{12} - \frac{1}{12} = \frac{7-1}{12}$

## ✦ Using Fraction Sticks (*Math Journal 1,* p. 199)

INDEPENDENT ACTIVITY 

Assign the journal page. Circulate and assist as necessary. The fraction-stick problems are visual exercises with like denominators that complement Problem 12 on journal page 198.

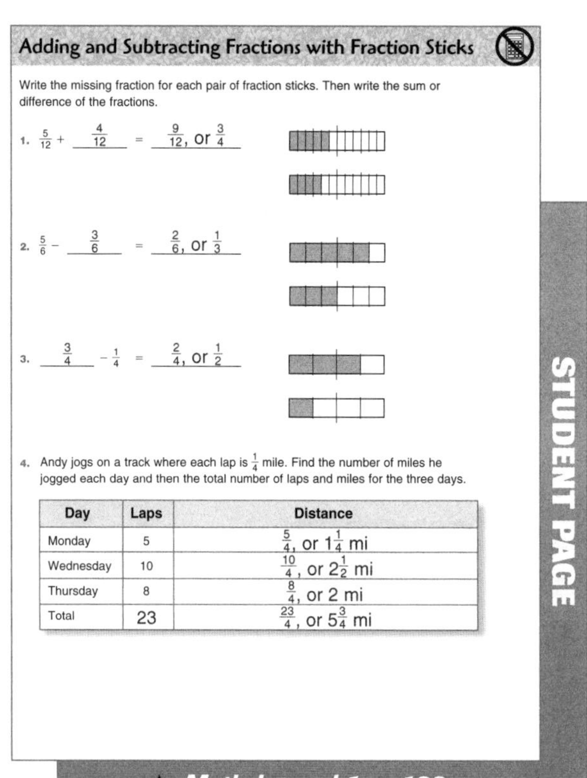

**Adding and Subtracting Fractions with Fraction Sticks**

Write the missing fraction for each pair of fraction sticks. Then write the sum or difference of the fractions.

1. $\frac{5}{12} + \frac{4}{12} = \frac{9}{12}$, or $\frac{3}{4}$
2. $\frac{5}{6} - \frac{3}{6} = \frac{2}{6}$, or $\frac{1}{3}$
3. $\frac{3}{4} - \frac{1}{4} = \frac{2}{4}$, or $\frac{1}{2}$
4. Andy jogs on a track where each lap is $\frac{1}{4}$ mile. Find the number of miles he jogged each day and then the total number of laps and miles for the three days.

| Day | Laps | Distance |
|---|---|---|
| Monday | 5 | $\frac{5}{4}$, or $1\frac{1}{4}$ mi |
| Wednesday | 10 | $\frac{10}{4}$, or $2\frac{2}{4}$ mi |
| Thursday | 8 | $\frac{8}{4}$, or 2 mi |
| Total | 23 | $\frac{23}{4}$, or $5\frac{3}{4}$ mi |

STUDENT PAGE

✦ *Math Journal 1,* p. 199

**Adjusting the Activity** If students continue to be puzzled by the use of variables to represent addition and subtraction of fractions with like denominators, do the Reteaching activity in Part 3 of this lesson.

# 2 Ongoing Learning & Practice

## ✦ Playing *Frac-Tac-Toe* (*Student Reference Book,* pp. 274–276; *Math Masters,* pp. 62–74)

PARTNER ACTIVITY 

Have students select one of the Gameboards (*Math Masters,* pages 63–74) and play a version of *Frac-Tac-Toe.* For detailed instructions, see Lesson 5.7.

## ✦ Math Boxes 6.8 (*Math Journal 1,* p. 200)

INDEPENDENT ACTIVITY 

**Mixed Review** Math Boxes in this lesson are paired with Math Boxes in Lesson 6.10. The skill in Problem 1 is a prerequisite for Unit 7.

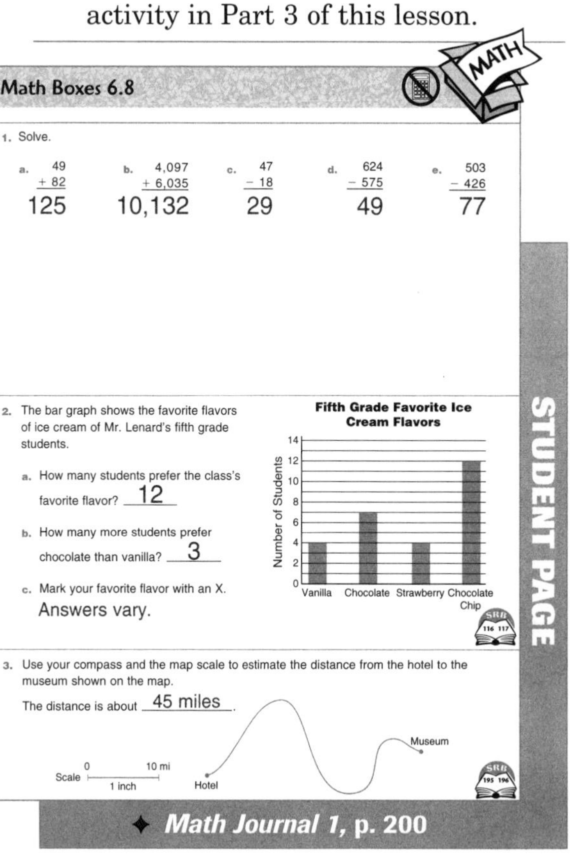

**Math Boxes 6.8**

1. Solve.
   a. 49 + 82 = 125
   b. 4,097 + 6,035 = 10,132
   c. 47 − 18 = 29
   d. 624 − 575 = 49
   e. 503 − 426 = 77
2. The bar graph shows the favorite flavors of ice cream of Mr. Lenard's fifth grade students.
   a. How many students prefer the class's favorite flavor? 12
   b. How many more students prefer chocolate than vanilla? 3
   c. Mark your favorite flavor with an X. Answers vary.



3. Use your compass and the map scale to estimate the distance from the hotel to the museum shown on the map.
   The distance is about 45 miles.



STUDENT PAGE

✦ *Math Journal 1,* p. 200

## Fraction Problems

Study Link 6.8

1. To maintain their energy during the racing season, professional bicycle racers eat between 6,000 and 8,000 calories per day.

   About $\frac{3}{20}$ of these calories come from fat, and about $\frac{5}{20}$ come from protein. The remaining calories come from carbohydrates.

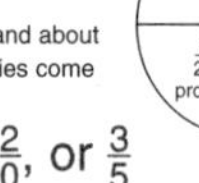

   What fraction of a bicycle racer's calories comes from carbohydrates? $\frac{12}{20}$, or $\frac{3}{5}$

2. Study the plan at the right for a small bookcase.

   All boards are $\frac{3}{4}$-inch thick.

   What is the width of each shelf? $18\frac{1}{2}$ inches

   If the shelves are evenly spaced, what is the height of the opening for each of the 3 spaces? 9 inches

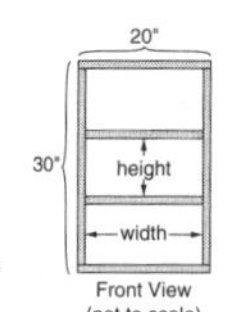



Each square in the grid at the right represents a city block. Each side of a block is $\frac{1}{8}$ mile long (that is, in this city, there are 8 blocks to each mile).

The distances below are measured along the sides of blocks.

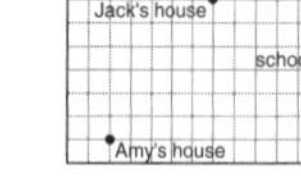



3. The distance from Amy's house to school is 14 blocks, or $1\frac{6}{8}$, or $1\frac{3}{4}$ mile(s).
4. The distance from Jack's house to school is 7 blocks, or $\frac{7}{8}$ mile(s).
5. How much farther from school is Amy's house than Jack's house? $\frac{7}{8}$ mile(s)
6. Amy walks from school to Jack's house and then home. How far is that? $2\frac{2}{8}$, or $2\frac{1}{4}$ mile(s).

STUDY LINK MASTER

**Math Masters, p. 289**

## Fraction Operations with Pattern Blocks

Whole: *hexagon*

Use your triangle, rhombus, trapezoid, and hexagon pattern blocks to solve the problems.

1. A trapezoid is worth $\frac{1}{2}$.
2. A rhombus is worth $\frac{1}{3}$.
3. A triangle is worth $\frac{1}{6}$.
4. Use your blocks to cover the shape at the right. Trace the outline of each block. Label each part with a fraction.
5. Write a number sentence to describe how you covered the shape in Problem 4.
   $\frac{1}{2} + \frac{1}{2} + \frac{1}{3} + \frac{1}{3} + \frac{1}{6} + \frac{1}{6} + \frac{1}{2} = 2\frac{1}{2}$
6. Arrange your blocks to make a shape that is worth $3\frac{1}{6}$. Trace your block design on the back of this page. Label each part with a fraction. Answers vary.
7. Write a number sentence to describe how you covered the shape you made in Problem 6. Answers vary.

**Challenge**

8. Build your shape from Problem 6 again. Use different blocks to build the shape. Trace your new block design on the back of this page. Label each part with a fraction. Write the number sentence for your shape. Answers vary.
9. Explain why the number sentence you wrote in Problem 7 is equivalent to the number sentence you wrote in Problem 8. The block designs and fractions are different, but the sums of the fractions are equal.

TEACHING MASTER

**Math Masters, p. 86**

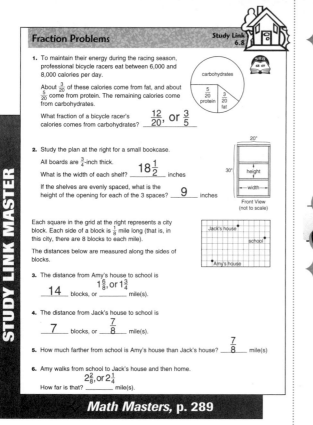

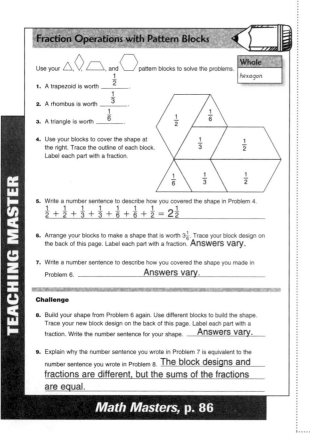

### ✦ Study Link 6.8 (*Math Masters,* p. 289)

**Home Connection** Students solve number stories by adding and subtracting fractions.

# 3 Options for Individualizing

### ✦ LANGUAGE DIVERSITY Adding and Subtracting Fractions with Pattern-Block Models (*Math Masters,* p. 86)

PARTNER ACTIVITY **5–15 min**

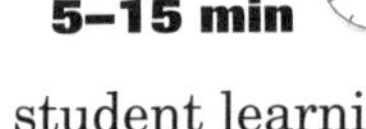

Pair a proficient English speaker with a student learning English. On *Math Masters,* page 86, students model addition and subtraction of fractions with pattern blocks. They write number sentences to represent the shapes they build.

When most of the students have completed the page, briefly review answers.

### ✦ RETEACHING Representing Patterns with Variables

WHOLE-CLASS ACTIVITY **5–15 min**

Write a series of number sentences on the board that follow a pattern.

| | |
|---|---|
| $3 * 1 = 3$ | $56 * 1 = 56$ |
| $704 * 1 = 704$ | $10{,}289 * 1 = 10{,}289$ |

Ask students to describe the general pattern in words. Expect answers such as: *The product of any number times 1 equals the number.*

Explain that "any number" can be represented by a variable. Ask students to write on their slates an open number sentence that they think describes the pattern—for example, $a * 1 = a$.

Repeat this process for several other general patterns. Give students a series of number sentences. Have them describe the pattern in words and finally write an open sentence to represent the pattern. *Suggestions:*

- ▷ $b * 0 = 0$
- ▷ $d + e = e + d$
- ▷ $c + 0 = c$
- ▷ $f * g = g * f$

# 6.9 Clock Fractions and Common Denominators

**OBJECTIVES** **To use a clock face to add and subtract fractions; and to investigate adding and subtracting fractions with unlike denominators.**

| summaries | materials |
|---|---|
| **1 Teaching the Lesson** | |
| Students use a clock face to find equivalent fractions and to model addition and subtraction of fractions. They also find common denominators by listing equivalent fractions for given fractions. [Operations and Computation] | □ *Math Journal 1,* pp. 201–203<br>□ *Student Reference Book,* p. 359<br>□ Study Link 6.8<br>□ slide rule (*Math Journal 2,* Activity Sheet 6) □ slate |
| **2 Ongoing Learning & Practice** | |
| Students play *Angle Tangle* to practice estimating and measuring the size of angles. [Geometry; Measurement and Reference Frames]<br>Students practice and maintain skills through Math Boxes and Study Link activities. | □ *Math Journal 1,* p. 204<br>□ *Student Reference Book,* p. 258<br>□ Study Link Master (*Math Masters,* p. 290) |
| **3 Options for Individualizing** | |
| **Extra Practice** Students play *Fraction Capture.* [Operations and Computation]<br>**Enrichment** Students write elapsed time number stories using fractions. [Operations and Computation] | □ Teaching Master (*Math Masters,* pp. 87 and 88)<br>□ 2 six-sided dice per partnership |

**Additional Information**

**Vocabulary • common denominator • unlike denominators**

## Getting Started

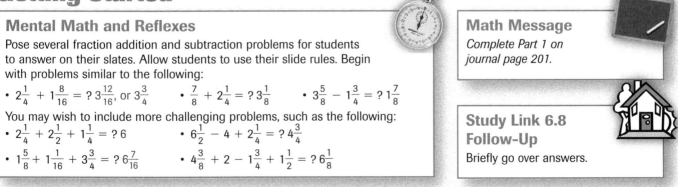

### Mental Math and Reflexes

Pose several fraction addition and subtraction problems for students to answer on their slates. Allow students to use their slide rules. Begin with problems similar to the following:

- $2\frac{1}{4} + 1\frac{8}{16} = ?\ 3\frac{12}{16}$, or $3\frac{3}{4}$
- $\frac{7}{8} + 2\frac{1}{4} = ?\ 3\frac{1}{8}$
- $3\frac{5}{8} - 1\frac{3}{4} = ?\ 1\frac{7}{8}$

You may wish to include more challenging problems, such as the following:

- $2\frac{1}{4} + 2\frac{1}{2} + 1\frac{1}{4} = ?\ 6$
- $6\frac{1}{2} - 4 + 2\frac{1}{4} = ?\ 4\frac{3}{4}$
- $1\frac{5}{8} + 1\frac{1}{16} + 3\frac{3}{4} = ?\ 6\frac{7}{16}$
- $4\frac{3}{8} + 2 - 1\frac{3}{4} + 1\frac{1}{2} = ?\ 6\frac{1}{8}$

### Math Message

*Complete Part 1 on journal page 201.*

### Study Link 6.8 Follow-Up

Briefly go over answers.

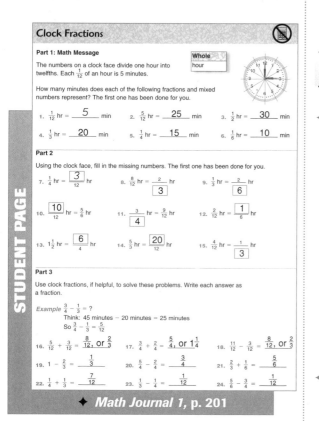

**Clock Fractions** 

**Part 1: Math Message**

| Whole |
|---|
| hour |

The numbers on a clock face divide one hour into twelfths. Each $\frac{1}{12}$ of an hour is 5 minutes.

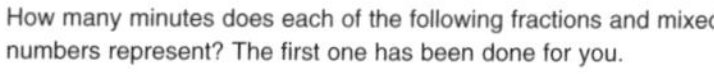

How many minutes does each of the following fractions and mixed numbers represent? The first one has been done for you.

1. $\frac{1}{12}$ hr = 5 min
2. $\frac{5}{12}$ hr = 25 min
3. $\frac{1}{2}$ hr = 30 min
4. $\frac{1}{3}$ hr = 20 min
5. $\frac{1}{4}$ hr = 15 min
6. $\frac{1}{6}$ hr = 10 min

**Part 2**

Using the clock face, fill in the missing numbers. The first one has been done for you.

7. $\frac{1}{4}$ hr = $\frac{3}{12}$ hr
8. $\frac{8}{12}$ hr = $\frac{2}{3}$ hr
9. $\frac{1}{3}$ hr = $\frac{2}{6}$ hr
10. $\frac{10}{12}$ hr = $\frac{5}{6}$ hr
11. $\frac{3}{4}$ hr = $\frac{9}{12}$ hr
12. $\frac{2}{12}$ hr = $\frac{1}{6}$ hr
13. $1\frac{1}{2}$ hr = $\frac{6}{4}$ hr
14. $\frac{5}{3}$ hr = $\frac{20}{12}$ hr
15. $\frac{4}{12}$ hr = $\frac{1}{3}$ hr

**Part 3**

Use clock fractions, if helpful, to solve these problems. Write each answer as a fraction.

*Example* $\frac{3}{4} - \frac{1}{3} = ?$
Think: 45 minutes − 20 minutes = 25 minutes
So $\frac{3}{4} - \frac{1}{3} = \frac{5}{12}$

16. $\frac{5}{12} + \frac{3}{12} = \frac{8}{12}$, or $\frac{2}{3}$
17. $\frac{3}{4} + \frac{2}{4} = \frac{5}{4}$, or $1\frac{1}{4}$
18. $\frac{11}{12} - \frac{3}{12} = \frac{8}{12}$, or $\frac{2}{3}$
19. $1 - \frac{2}{3} = \frac{1}{3}$
20. $\frac{5}{4} - \frac{2}{4} = \frac{3}{4}$
21. $\frac{2}{3} + \frac{1}{6} = \frac{5}{6}$
22. $\frac{1}{4} + \frac{1}{3} = \frac{7}{12}$
23. $\frac{1}{3} - \frac{1}{4} = \frac{1}{12}$
24. $\frac{5}{6} - \frac{3}{4} = \frac{1}{12}$

STUDENT PAGE

✦ *Math Journal 1*, p. 201

# 1 Teaching the Lesson

## ✦ Math Message Follow-Up
(*Math Journal 1,* p. 201)

WHOLE-CLASS DISCUSSION 

Review the answers to Part 1 with the class. You may wish to pose a few additional "easy" problems that have mixed numbers or fractions greater than 1. *Suggestions:*

- How many minutes are in $2\frac{1}{2}$ hours? 150 min
- How many minutes in $\frac{3}{2}$ hours? 90 min
- In $\frac{5}{2}$ hours? 150 min
- In $\frac{5}{4}$ hours? 75 min

## ✦ Using a Clock to Add and Subtract Fractions
(*Math Journal 1,* p. 201)

PARTNER ACTIVITY 

Make sure students understand that they may use the clock model to help them answer the problems on the journal page. At times, students may want to "think minutes," as in the example for Part 3. At other times, students may want to look at the clock face divided into twelfths.

You may want to work several of the problems in Part 2, or similar problems, with the class before students begin working in partnerships. Assign the remainder of the journal page.

## ✦ Discussing Strategies for Adding and Subtracting Fractions (*Math Journal 1,* p. 201)

WHOLE-CLASS DISCUSSION 

Discuss students' solutions to Part 3. Expect that some students will say they converted most fractions to minutes, did the operation, and then converted the answer in minutes back to a fraction. Others may say that they converted all fractions to twelfths and found the answer without any reference to the clock or time.

Ask students which problems of Part 3 were easily done without thinking about a clock face or time. Students will probably say Problems 16 through 18, and Problem 20. These fractions have the same denominator, so they can be added or subtracted mentally.

**Adjusting the Activity** To extend the activity, pose fraction problems with denominators of 30 and 60. *Suggestions:*

- $\frac{3}{4} + \frac{5}{60}$ $\frac{50}{60}$, or $\frac{5}{6}$
- $\frac{18}{30} + \frac{1}{3}$ $\frac{28}{30}$, or $\frac{14}{15}$
- $\frac{5}{12} + \frac{25}{60}$ $\frac{50}{60}$, or $\frac{5}{6}$

Remind students of the multiplication rule for finding equivalent fractions from Lesson 5.4. Expressed with variables, the rule is:

$$\frac{a}{b} = \frac{a * n}{b * n}$$

Verify that students can apply the rule by having them find a few equivalent fractions—for example, for $\frac{2}{3}$, $\frac{3}{8}$, and $\frac{25}{50}$. This rule is the basis for the next activity—finding a common denominator.

NOTE: A clock face is a convenient model for fraction operations involving halves, thirds, fourths, fifths, sixths, twelfths, and even thirtieths and sixtieths. The link between fractions and their equivalents in minutes allows students to add and subtract fractions with unlike denominators without rewriting the fractions with a common denominator. This is the same advantage as for the slide rule in Lesson 6.8.

## Using a Common Denominator

(*Math Journal 1,* pp. 202 and 203; *Student Reference Book,* p. 359)

PARTNER ACTIVITY 

Prepare the class for the next activity by discussing the following points:

▷ It is easy to add or subtract fractions if they have the same denominator—usually called a **common denominator.**

▷ One way to add or subtract fractions with different denominators—usually called **unlike denominators**—is to rewrite the fractions with a common denominator. Remind students that they often search for common units (denominators).

*Examples*

6 inches + 1 foot = 18 inches, if inch is the common unit.

6 inches + 1 foot = $1\frac{1}{2}$ feet, if foot is the common unit.

6 inches + 1 foot = $\frac{1}{2}$ yard, if yard is the common unit.

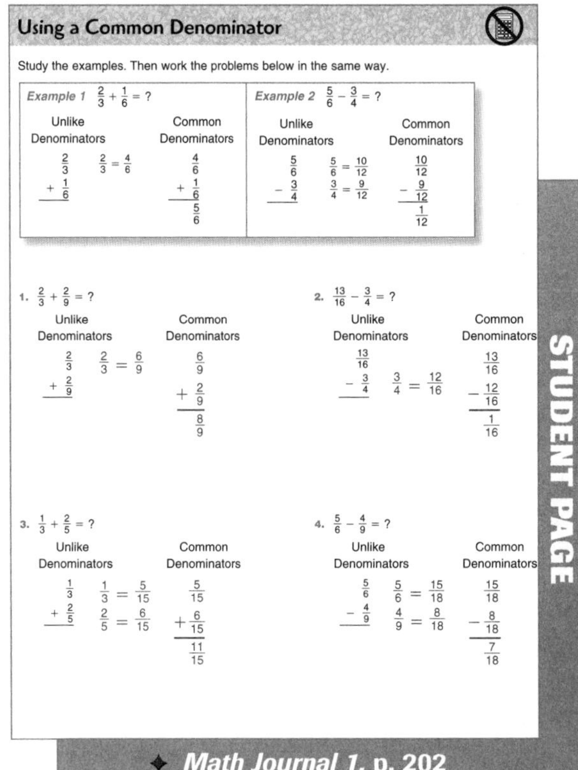

**Using a Common Denominator**

Study the examples. Then work the problems below in the same way.

*Example 1* $\frac{2}{3} + \frac{1}{6} = ?$

Unlike Denominators: $\frac{2}{3} + \frac{1}{6}$; $\frac{2}{3} = \frac{4}{6}$

Common Denominators: $\frac{4}{6} + \frac{1}{6} = \frac{5}{6}$

*Example 2* $\frac{5}{6} - \frac{3}{4} = ?$

Unlike Denominators: $\frac{5}{6} - \frac{3}{4}$; $\frac{5}{6} = \frac{10}{12}$; $\frac{3}{4} = \frac{9}{12}$

Common Denominators: $\frac{10}{12} - \frac{9}{12} = \frac{1}{12}$

1. $\frac{2}{3} + \frac{2}{9} = ?$
Unlike Denominators: $\frac{2}{3} + \frac{2}{9}$; $\frac{2}{3} = \frac{6}{9}$
Common Denominators: $\frac{6}{9} + \frac{2}{9} = \frac{8}{9}$

2. $\frac{13}{16} - \frac{3}{4} = ?$
Unlike Denominators: $\frac{13}{16} - \frac{3}{4}$; $\frac{3}{4} = \frac{12}{16}$
Common Denominators: $\frac{13}{16} - \frac{12}{16} = \frac{1}{16}$

3. $\frac{1}{3} + \frac{2}{5} = ?$
Unlike Denominators: $\frac{1}{3} + \frac{2}{5}$; $\frac{1}{3} = \frac{5}{15}$; $\frac{2}{5} = \frac{6}{15}$
Common Denominators: $\frac{5}{15} + \frac{6}{15} = \frac{11}{15}$

4. $\frac{5}{6} - \frac{4}{9} = ?$
Unlike Denominators: $\frac{5}{6} - \frac{4}{9}$; $\frac{5}{6} = \frac{15}{18}$; $\frac{4}{9} = \frac{8}{18}$
Common Denominators: $\frac{15}{18} - \frac{8}{18} = \frac{7}{18}$

STUDENT PAGE

◆ *Math Journal 1,* p. 202

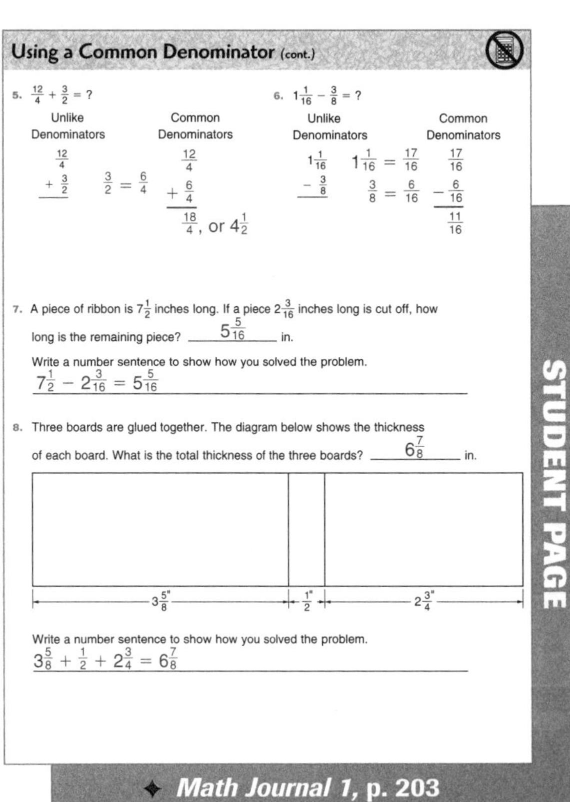

**Using a Common Denominator** (cont.)

5. $\frac{12}{4} + \frac{3}{2} = ?$
Unlike Denominators: $\frac{12}{4} + \frac{3}{2}$; $\frac{3}{2} = \frac{6}{4}$
Common Denominators: $\frac{12}{4} + \frac{6}{4} = \frac{18}{4}$, or $4\frac{1}{2}$

6. $1\frac{1}{16} - \frac{3}{8} = ?$
Unlike Denominators: $1\frac{1}{16} - \frac{3}{8}$; $1\frac{1}{16} = \frac{17}{16}$; $\frac{3}{8} = \frac{6}{16}$
Common Denominators: $\frac{17}{16} - \frac{6}{16} = \frac{11}{16}$

7. A piece of ribbon is $7\frac{1}{2}$ inches long. If a piece $2\frac{3}{16}$ inches long is cut off, how long is the remaining piece? $5\frac{5}{16}$ in.
Write a number sentence to show how you solved the problem.
$7\frac{1}{2} - 2\frac{3}{16} = 5\frac{5}{16}$

8. Three boards are glued together. The diagram below shows the thickness of each board. What is the total thickness of the three boards? $6\frac{7}{8}$ in.

Write a number sentence to show how you solved the problem.
$3\frac{5}{8} + \frac{1}{2} + 2\frac{3}{4} = 6\frac{7}{8}$

STUDENT PAGE

◆ *Math Journal 1,* p. 203

Tables and Charts

**Equivalent Fractions, Decimals, and Percents**

| | | | | | | | | | | | | | | | | |
|---|---|---|---|---|---|---|---|---|---|---|---|---|---|---|---|---|
| $\frac{1}{2}$ | $\frac{2}{4}$ | $\frac{3}{6}$ | $\frac{4}{8}$ | $\frac{5}{10}$ | $\frac{6}{12}$ | $\frac{7}{14}$ | $\frac{8}{16}$ | $\frac{9}{18}$ | $\frac{10}{20}$ | $\frac{11}{22}$ | $\frac{12}{24}$ | $\frac{13}{26}$ | $\frac{14}{28}$ | $\frac{15}{30}$ | 0.5 | 50% |
| $\frac{1}{3}$ | $\frac{2}{6}$ | $\frac{3}{9}$ | $\frac{4}{12}$ | $\frac{5}{15}$ | $\frac{6}{18}$ | $\frac{7}{21}$ | $\frac{8}{24}$ | $\frac{9}{27}$ | $\frac{10}{30}$ | $\frac{11}{33}$ | $\frac{12}{36}$ | $\frac{13}{39}$ | $\frac{14}{42}$ | $\frac{15}{45}$ | $0.\overline{3}$ | $33\frac{1}{3}$% |
| $\frac{2}{3}$ | $\frac{4}{6}$ | $\frac{6}{9}$ | $\frac{8}{12}$ | $\frac{10}{15}$ | $\frac{12}{18}$ | $\frac{14}{21}$ | $\frac{16}{24}$ | $\frac{18}{27}$ | $\frac{20}{30}$ | $\frac{22}{33}$ | $\frac{24}{36}$ | $\frac{26}{39}$ | $\frac{28}{42}$ | $\frac{30}{45}$ | $0.\overline{6}$ | $66\frac{2}{3}$% |
| $\frac{1}{4}$ | $\frac{2}{8}$ | $\frac{3}{12}$ | $\frac{4}{16}$ | $\frac{5}{20}$ | $\frac{6}{24}$ | $\frac{7}{28}$ | $\frac{8}{32}$ | $\frac{9}{36}$ | $\frac{10}{40}$ | $\frac{11}{44}$ | $\frac{12}{48}$ | $\frac{13}{52}$ | $\frac{14}{56}$ | $\frac{15}{60}$ | 0.25 | 25% |
| $\frac{3}{4}$ | $\frac{6}{8}$ | $\frac{9}{12}$ | $\frac{12}{16}$ | $\frac{15}{20}$ | $\frac{18}{24}$ | $\frac{21}{28}$ | $\frac{24}{32}$ | $\frac{27}{36}$ | $\frac{30}{40}$ | $\frac{33}{44}$ | $\frac{36}{48}$ | $\frac{39}{52}$ | $\frac{42}{56}$ | $\frac{45}{60}$ | 0.75 | 75% |
| $\frac{1}{5}$ | $\frac{2}{10}$ | $\frac{3}{15}$ | $\frac{4}{20}$ | $\frac{5}{25}$ | $\frac{6}{30}$ | $\frac{7}{35}$ | $\frac{8}{40}$ | $\frac{9}{45}$ | $\frac{10}{50}$ | $\frac{11}{55}$ | $\frac{12}{60}$ | $\frac{13}{65}$ | $\frac{14}{70}$ | $\frac{15}{75}$ | 0.2 | 20% |
| $\frac{2}{5}$ | $\frac{4}{10}$ | $\frac{6}{15}$ | $\frac{8}{20}$ | $\frac{10}{25}$ | $\frac{12}{30}$ | $\frac{14}{35}$ | $\frac{16}{40}$ | $\frac{18}{45}$ | $\frac{20}{50}$ | $\frac{22}{55}$ | $\frac{24}{60}$ | $\frac{26}{65}$ | $\frac{28}{70}$ | $\frac{30}{75}$ | 0.4 | 40% |
| $\frac{3}{5}$ | $\frac{6}{10}$ | $\frac{9}{15}$ | $\frac{12}{20}$ | $\frac{15}{25}$ | $\frac{18}{30}$ | $\frac{21}{35}$ | $\frac{24}{40}$ | $\frac{27}{45}$ | $\frac{30}{50}$ | $\frac{33}{55}$ | $\frac{36}{60}$ | $\frac{39}{65}$ | $\frac{42}{70}$ | $\frac{45}{75}$ | 0.6 | 60% |
| $\frac{4}{5}$ | $\frac{8}{10}$ | $\frac{12}{15}$ | $\frac{16}{20}$ | $\frac{20}{25}$ | $\frac{24}{30}$ | $\frac{28}{35}$ | $\frac{32}{40}$ | $\frac{36}{45}$ | $\frac{40}{50}$ | $\frac{44}{55}$ | $\frac{48}{60}$ | $\frac{52}{65}$ | $\frac{56}{70}$ | $\frac{60}{75}$ | 0.8 | 80% |
| $\frac{1}{6}$ | $\frac{2}{12}$ | $\frac{3}{18}$ | $\frac{4}{24}$ | $\frac{5}{30}$ | $\frac{6}{36}$ | $\frac{7}{42}$ | $\frac{8}{48}$ | $\frac{9}{54}$ | $\frac{10}{60}$ | $\frac{11}{66}$ | $\frac{12}{72}$ | $\frac{13}{78}$ | $\frac{14}{84}$ | $\frac{15}{90}$ | $0.1\overline{6}$ | $16\frac{2}{3}$% |
| $\frac{5}{6}$ | $\frac{10}{12}$ | $\frac{15}{18}$ | $\frac{20}{24}$ | $\frac{25}{30}$ | $\frac{30}{36}$ | $\frac{35}{42}$ | $\frac{40}{48}$ | $\frac{45}{54}$ | $\frac{50}{60}$ | $\frac{55}{66}$ | $\frac{60}{72}$ | $\frac{65}{78}$ | $\frac{70}{84}$ | $\frac{75}{90}$ | $0.8\overline{3}$ | $83\frac{1}{3}$% |
| $\frac{1}{7}$ | $\frac{2}{14}$ | $\frac{3}{21}$ | $\frac{4}{28}$ | $\frac{5}{35}$ | $\frac{6}{42}$ | $\frac{7}{49}$ | $\frac{8}{56}$ | $\frac{9}{63}$ | $\frac{10}{70}$ | $\frac{11}{77}$ | $\frac{12}{84}$ | $\frac{13}{91}$ | $\frac{14}{98}$ | $\frac{15}{105}$ | 0.143 | 14.3% |
| $\frac{2}{7}$ | $\frac{4}{14}$ | $\frac{6}{21}$ | $\frac{8}{28}$ | $\frac{10}{35}$ | $\frac{12}{42}$ | $\frac{14}{49}$ | $\frac{16}{56}$ | $\frac{18}{63}$ | $\frac{20}{70}$ | $\frac{22}{77}$ | $\frac{24}{84}$ | $\frac{26}{91}$ | $\frac{28}{98}$ | $\frac{30}{105}$ | 0.286 | 28.6% |
| $\frac{3}{7}$ | $\frac{6}{14}$ | $\frac{9}{21}$ | $\frac{12}{28}$ | $\frac{15}{35}$ | $\frac{18}{42}$ | $\frac{21}{49}$ | $\frac{24}{56}$ | $\frac{27}{63}$ | $\frac{30}{70}$ | $\frac{33}{77}$ | $\frac{36}{84}$ | $\frac{39}{91}$ | $\frac{42}{98}$ | $\frac{45}{105}$ | 0.429 | 42.9% |
| $\frac{4}{7}$ | $\frac{8}{14}$ | $\frac{12}{21}$ | $\frac{16}{28}$ | $\frac{20}{35}$ | $\frac{24}{42}$ | $\frac{28}{49}$ | $\frac{32}{56}$ | $\frac{36}{63}$ | $\frac{40}{70}$ | $\frac{44}{77}$ | $\frac{48}{84}$ | $\frac{52}{91}$ | $\frac{56}{98}$ | $\frac{60}{105}$ | 0.571 | 57.1% |
| $\frac{5}{7}$ | $\frac{10}{14}$ | $\frac{15}{21}$ | $\frac{20}{28}$ | $\frac{25}{35}$ | $\frac{30}{42}$ | $\frac{35}{49}$ | $\frac{40}{56}$ | $\frac{45}{63}$ | $\frac{50}{70}$ | $\frac{55}{77}$ | $\frac{60}{84}$ | $\frac{65}{91}$ | $\frac{70}{98}$ | $\frac{75}{105}$ | 0.714 | 71.4% |
| $\frac{6}{7}$ | $\frac{12}{14}$ | $\frac{18}{21}$ | $\frac{24}{28}$ | $\frac{30}{35}$ | $\frac{36}{42}$ | $\frac{42}{49}$ | $\frac{48}{56}$ | $\frac{54}{63}$ | $\frac{60}{70}$ | $\frac{66}{77}$ | $\frac{72}{84}$ | $\frac{78}{91}$ | $\frac{84}{98}$ | $\frac{90}{105}$ | 0.857 | 85.7% |
| $\frac{1}{8}$ | $\frac{2}{16}$ | $\frac{3}{24}$ | $\frac{4}{32}$ | $\frac{5}{40}$ | $\frac{6}{48}$ | $\frac{7}{56}$ | $\frac{8}{64}$ | $\frac{9}{72}$ | $\frac{10}{80}$ | $\frac{11}{88}$ | $\frac{12}{96}$ | $\frac{13}{104}$ | $\frac{14}{112}$ | $\frac{15}{120}$ | 0.125 | $12\frac{1}{2}$% |
| $\frac{3}{8}$ | $\frac{6}{16}$ | $\frac{9}{24}$ | $\frac{12}{32}$ | $\frac{15}{40}$ | $\frac{18}{48}$ | $\frac{21}{56}$ | $\frac{24}{64}$ | $\frac{27}{72}$ | $\frac{30}{80}$ | $\frac{33}{88}$ | $\frac{36}{96}$ | $\frac{39}{104}$ | $\frac{42}{112}$ | $\frac{45}{120}$ | 0.375 | $37\frac{1}{2}$% |
| $\frac{5}{8}$ | $\frac{10}{16}$ | $\frac{15}{24}$ | $\frac{20}{32}$ | $\frac{25}{40}$ | $\frac{30}{48}$ | $\frac{35}{56}$ | $\frac{40}{64}$ | $\frac{45}{72}$ | $\frac{50}{80}$ | $\frac{55}{88}$ | $\frac{60}{96}$ | $\frac{65}{104}$ | $\frac{70}{112}$ | $\frac{75}{120}$ | 0.625 | $62\frac{1}{2}$% |
| $\frac{7}{8}$ | $\frac{14}{16}$ | $\frac{21}{24}$ | $\frac{28}{32}$ | $\frac{35}{40}$ | $\frac{42}{48}$ | $\frac{49}{56}$ | $\frac{56}{64}$ | $\frac{63}{72}$ | $\frac{70}{80}$ | $\frac{77}{88}$ | $\frac{84}{96}$ | $\frac{91}{104}$ | $\frac{98}{112}$ | $\frac{105}{120}$ | 0.875 | $87\frac{1}{2}$% |
| $\frac{1}{9}$ | $\frac{2}{18}$ | $\frac{3}{27}$ | $\frac{4}{36}$ | $\frac{5}{45}$ | $\frac{6}{54}$ | $\frac{7}{63}$ | $\frac{8}{72}$ | $\frac{9}{81}$ | $\frac{10}{90}$ | $\frac{11}{99}$ | $\frac{12}{108}$ | $\frac{13}{117}$ | $\frac{14}{126}$ | $\frac{15}{135}$ | $0.\overline{1}$ | $11\frac{1}{9}$% |
| $\frac{2}{9}$ | $\frac{4}{18}$ | $\frac{6}{27}$ | $\frac{8}{36}$ | $\frac{10}{45}$ | $\frac{12}{54}$ | $\frac{14}{63}$ | $\frac{16}{72}$ | $\frac{18}{81}$ | $\frac{20}{90}$ | $\frac{22}{99}$ | $\frac{24}{108}$ | $\frac{26}{117}$ | $\frac{28}{126}$ | $\frac{30}{135}$ | $0.\overline{2}$ | $22\frac{2}{9}$% |
| $\frac{4}{9}$ | $\frac{8}{18}$ | $\frac{12}{27}$ | $\frac{16}{36}$ | $\frac{20}{45}$ | $\frac{24}{54}$ | $\frac{28}{63}$ | $\frac{32}{72}$ | $\frac{36}{81}$ | $\frac{40}{90}$ | $\frac{44}{99}$ | $\frac{48}{108}$ | $\frac{52}{117}$ | $\frac{56}{126}$ | $\frac{60}{135}$ | $0.\overline{4}$ | $44\frac{4}{9}$% |
| $\frac{5}{9}$ | $\frac{10}{18}$ | $\frac{15}{27}$ | $\frac{20}{36}$ | $\frac{25}{45}$ | $\frac{30}{54}$ | $\frac{35}{63}$ | $\frac{40}{72}$ | $\frac{45}{81}$ | $\frac{50}{90}$ | $\frac{55}{99}$ | $\frac{60}{108}$ | $\frac{65}{117}$ | $\frac{70}{126}$ | $\frac{75}{135}$ | $0.\overline{5}$ | $55\frac{5}{9}$% |
| $\frac{7}{9}$ | $\frac{14}{18}$ | $\frac{21}{27}$ | $\frac{28}{36}$ | $\frac{35}{45}$ | $\frac{42}{54}$ | $\frac{49}{63}$ | $\frac{56}{72}$ | $\frac{63}{81}$ | $\frac{70}{90}$ | $\frac{77}{99}$ | $\frac{84}{108}$ | $\frac{91}{117}$ | $\frac{98}{126}$ | $\frac{105}{135}$ | $0.\overline{7}$ | $77\frac{7}{9}$% |
| $\frac{8}{9}$ | $\frac{16}{18}$ | $\frac{24}{27}$ | $\frac{32}{36}$ | $\frac{40}{45}$ | $\frac{48}{54}$ | $\frac{56}{63}$ | $\frac{64}{72}$ | $\frac{72}{81}$ | $\frac{80}{90}$ | $\frac{88}{99}$ | $\frac{96}{108}$ | $\frac{104}{117}$ | $\frac{112}{126}$ | $\frac{120}{135}$ | $0.\overline{8}$ | $88\frac{8}{9}$% |

*Note:* The decimals for sevenths have been rounded to the nearest thousandth.

three hundred fifty-nine SRB 359

STUDENT PAGE

◆ *Student Reference Book,* p. 359

▷ One way to find common denominators is to use the multiplication rule (or the division rule) for finding equivalent fractions. Use the examples at the top of journal page 202 to illustrate this. Work through the examples as a class. Pose one or two similar problems, if necessary.

In addition to using the multiplication rule to find equivalent fractions, students can also refer to the Table of Equivalent Fractions, Decimals, and Percents on page 359 of the *Student Reference Book*.

Assign journal pages 202 and 203. Students may choose to solve Problems 7 and 8 either by finding a common denominator or by using their slide rules. In a follow-up discussion, ask students who did not use the slide rule to quickly check their answers using the slide rule.

**Adjusting the Activity** If students have trouble applying the multiplication rule or division rule, have them write out the rule as they make the conversions. For example: To find a common denominator for Example 1 on journal page 202, use the fact that $6 = 3 * 2$. Multiply numerator and denominator of $\frac{2}{3}$ by 2. Students write $\frac{2 * 2}{3 * 2} = \frac{4}{6}$.

**ONGOING ASSESSMENT**

**Expect that most students will have no problem doing fraction addition and subtraction with common denominators. Some may still struggle with finding common denominators.**

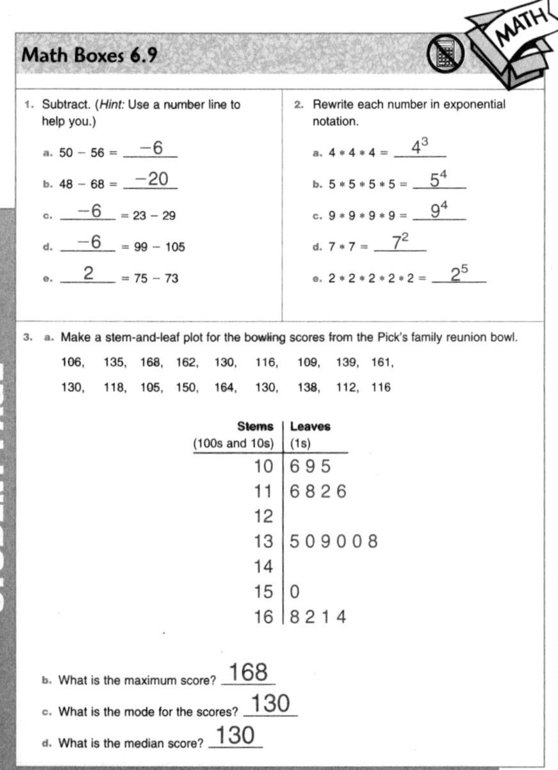

**Math Boxes 6.9**



1. Subtract. (*Hint:* Use a number line to help you.)
   a. 50 − 56 = −6
   b. 48 − 68 = −20
   c. −6 = 23 − 29
   d. −6 = 99 − 105
   e. 2 = 75 − 73

2. Rewrite each number in exponential notation.
   a. 4 ∗ 4 ∗ 4 = $4^3$
   b. 5 ∗ 5 ∗ 5 ∗ 5 = $5^4$
   c. 9 ∗ 9 ∗ 9 ∗ 9 = $9^4$
   d. 7 ∗ 7 = $7^2$
   e. 2 ∗ 2 ∗ 2 ∗ 2 ∗ 2 = $2^5$

3. a. Make a stem-and-leaf plot for the bowling scores from the Pick's family reunion bowl.

106, 135, 168, 162, 130, 116, 109, 139, 161,
130, 118, 105, 150, 164, 130, 138, 112, 116

| Stems (100s and 10s) | Leaves (1s) |
|---|---|
| 10 | 6 9 5 |
| 11 | 6 8 2 6 |
| 12 | |
| 13 | 5 0 9 0 0 8 |
| 14 | |
| 15 | 0 |
| 16 | 8 2 1 4 |

b. What is the maximum score? 168

c. What is the mode for the scores? 130

d. What is the median score? 130

STUDENT PAGE

◆ *Math Journal 1,* p. 204

In Problems 1, 2, 5, 6, 7, and 8, the common denominator is the same as one of the original denominators. In Problems 3 and 4, the common denominator is different from both of the original denominators.

## 2 Ongoing Learning & Practice

### ◆ Playing *Angle Tangle*
(*Student Reference Book,* p. 258)

PARTNER ACTIVITY 

Play this game to practice estimating and measuring angles. This game was introduced in lesson 3.6.

## ✦ Math Boxes 6.9 (*Math Journal 1,* p. 204)

INDEPENDENT ACTIVITY 

**Mixed Review** Math Boxes in this lesson are paired with Math Boxes in Lesson 6.7. The skill in Problem 1 is a prerequisite for Unit 7.

## ✦ Study Link 6.9 (*Math Masters,* p. 290)

**Home Connection** Students solve problems similar to those on journal pages 202 and 203. This will reinforce the idea that a common denominator can be found by finding fractions equivalent to the given fractions.

### Adding and Subtracting Fractions

Study Link 6.9

**Multiplication Rule**

To find a fraction equivalent to a given fraction, multiply both the numerator and the denominator of the fraction by the same number. $\frac{a}{b} = \frac{a * n}{b * n}$

SRB 65 68–71

***Example 1*** $\frac{4}{9} - \frac{1}{3} = ?$

$\frac{1}{3} = \frac{2}{6} = \frac{3}{9} = \frac{4}{12} = \frac{5}{15} = \frac{6}{18} = \ldots$

9 is a common denominator.

$\frac{4}{9} - \frac{1}{3} = \frac{4}{9} - \frac{3}{9} = \frac{1}{9}$

***Example 2*** $\frac{5}{8} + \frac{2}{5} = ?$

$\frac{5}{8} = \frac{10}{16} = \frac{15}{24} = \frac{20}{32} = \frac{25}{40} = \frac{30}{48} = \ldots$

$\frac{2}{5} = \frac{4}{10} = \frac{6}{15} = \frac{8}{20} = \frac{10}{25} = \frac{12}{30} = \frac{14}{35} = \frac{16}{40} = \frac{18}{45} = \ldots$

Both fractions can be rewritten with the common denominator 40.

$\frac{5}{8} + \frac{2}{5} = \frac{25}{40} + \frac{16}{40} = \frac{41}{40}$ (or $1\frac{1}{40}$)

Find a common denominator. Then add or subtract.

**1.** $\frac{2}{3} + \frac{4}{5} =$ $1\frac{7}{15}$

$\frac{2}{3} = \frac{10}{15}$

$\frac{4}{5} = \frac{12}{15}$

$\frac{10}{15} + \frac{12}{15} = \frac{22}{15}$, or $1\frac{7}{15}$

**2.** $\frac{8}{9} - \frac{5}{6} =$ $\frac{1}{18}$

$\frac{8}{9} = \frac{16}{18}$

$\frac{5}{6} = \frac{15}{18}$

$\frac{16}{18} - \frac{15}{18} = \frac{1}{18}$

**3.** $\frac{3}{4} + 1\frac{1}{2} =$ $2\frac{1}{4}$

$1\frac{1}{2} = \frac{3}{2} = \frac{6}{4}$

$\frac{3}{4} + \frac{6}{4} = \frac{9}{4}$, or $2\frac{1}{4}$

**4.** Lisa was 4 feet $10\frac{1}{2}$ inches tall at the end of fifth grade. During the year, she had grown $2\frac{3}{4}$ inches. How tall was Lisa at the start of fifth grade?

4 feet $7\frac{3}{4}$ inches

**5.** Bill was baking two different kinds of bread. One recipe called for $3\frac{1}{2}$ cups of flour. The other called for $2\frac{1}{3}$ cups of flour. How much flour did Bill need in all?

$5\frac{5}{6}$ cups

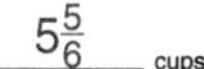

STUDY LINK MASTER

✦ *Math Masters,* p. 290

**ONGOING ASSESSMENT**

To assess students' understanding of writing a number story, you may want to use the rubric on page 53 in the *Assessment Handbook.*

# 3 Options for Individualizing

## ✦ EXTRA PRACTICE Playing *Fraction Capture* (*Math Masters,* pp. 87 and 88)

PARTNER ACTIVITY  **15–30 min** 

Players roll dice, form fractions, and claim corresponding sections of squares. The game rules are on *Math Masters,* page 87; the Gameboard, on page 88.

### *Fraction Capture*

**Materials** *Fraction Capture* Gameboard
2 six-sided dice

**Players** 2

**Object** To capture the most squares on the *Fraction Capture* Gameboard. A player captures a square if he or she shades **more than** $\frac{1}{2}$ of it.

**Directions**

**1.** Player 1 rolls two dice and makes a fraction with the numbers that come up. The number on either die can be the denominator. The number on the other die becomes the numerator.

A fraction equal to a whole number is NOT allowed. For example, if a player rolls 3 and 6, the fraction can't be $\frac{6}{3}$, because $\frac{6}{3}$ equals 2.

**2.** Player 1 initials sections of one or more gameboard squares to show the fraction formed. This **claims** the sections for the player.

***Example*** The player rolls a 4 and 5 and makes $\frac{5}{4}$. The player claims five $\frac{1}{4}$ sections by initialing them.

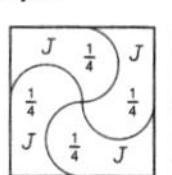


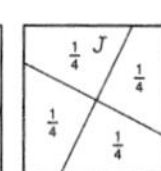


- Equivalent fractions can be claimed. For example, if a player rolls 1 and 2 and makes $\frac{1}{2}$, the player can initial one $\frac{1}{2}$ section of a square, or two $\frac{1}{4}$ sections, or three $\frac{1}{6}$ sections.
- The fraction may be split between squares. For example, a player can show $\frac{4}{3}$ by claiming $\frac{2}{3}$ on one square and $\frac{2}{3}$ on another square. However, **all** of the fractions must be shown.

**3.** Players take turns. If a player can't form a fraction and claim enough sections to show that fraction, the player's turn is over.

**4.** A player **captures** a square when that player has claimed sections making up **more than** $\frac{1}{2}$ of the square. If each player has initialed $\frac{1}{2}$ of a square, no one has captured that square.

- Blocking is allowed. For example, if Player 1 initials $\frac{1}{2}$ of a square, Player 2 may initial the other half, so that no one can capture the square.

**5.** Play ends when all of the squares have either been captured or blocked. The winner is the player who has captured the most squares.

TEACHING MASTER

✦ *Math Masters,* p. 87

## ✦ ENRICHMENT Writing Elapsed Time Number Stories

INDEPENDENT ACTIVITY  **15–30 min**

Students write number stories using fractions to represent amounts of elapsed time. Pose the following example problem for students:

> Maria started her piano practice at 3:15. She practiced for $\frac{8}{12}$ of an hour. At what time did she finish practicing? Tell students to think of $\frac{1}{12}$ hour as 5 minutes; $\frac{8}{12}$ hour is $8 * 5$ or 40 minutes; 40 minutes more than 3:15 is 3:55.

Ask students to solve each other's problems. You may want to have them explain their solution strategies in writing.

# 6.10 Quick Common Denominators

**OBJECTIVES** **To find common denominators quickly; and to use common denominators to compare, add, and subtract fractions.**

| summaries | materials |
|---|---|
| **1 Teaching the Lesson** | |
| Students use the fraction sticks, from Lesson 5.4, to develop a quick way to find common denominators. Students use common denominators to add, subtract, and compare fractions. [Operations and Computation] | ☐ *Math Journal 1,* pp. 205 and 206<br>☐ Study Link 6.9<br>☐ slide rule (*Math Journal 2,* Activity Sheet 6)<br>☐ slate |
| **2 Ongoing Learning & Practice** | |
| Students complete a data review page. [Data and Chance]<br>Students practice and maintain skills through Math Boxes and Study Link activities. | ☐ *Math Journal 1,* pp. 207 and 208<br>☐ Study Link Master (*Math Masters,* p. 291) |
| **3 Options for Individualizing** | |
| **Extra Practice** Students practice finding common denominators. [Operations and Computation] | ☐ Teaching Master (*Math Masters,* p. 89) |

### Additional Information

**Vocabulary • quick common denominator • simplest form**

## Getting Started

### Mental Math and Reflexes

Pose addition and subtraction problems with fractions and mixed numbers. Students may use their slide rules. Begin with problems similar to the following:

- $5\frac{1}{4} + 2\frac{1}{8} = ?$ $7\frac{3}{8}$
- $2\frac{3}{4} + \frac{7}{8} = ?$ $3\frac{5}{8}$
- $1\frac{5}{8} - \frac{7}{8} = ?$ $\frac{6}{8}$, or $\frac{3}{4}$
- $2\frac{3}{8} - 1\frac{3}{4} = ?$ $\frac{5}{8}$

You might try more challenging problems, such as the following:

- $5 - 4\frac{3}{4} + \frac{1}{8} = ?$ $\frac{3}{8}$
- $1\frac{7}{16} + 2\frac{1}{2} - \frac{1}{8} = ?$ $3\frac{13}{16}$
- $2\frac{5}{8} + \frac{3}{16} - \frac{1}{4} = ?$ $2\frac{9}{16}$

### Math Message

*Do Problems 1 and 2 on journal page 205. Then complete the statement in Problem 3.*

### Study Link 6.9 Follow-Up

Briefly go over the answers. Have volunteers explain their strategies for solving the problems that other students may have found difficult.

# 1 Teaching the Lesson

## ✦ Math Message Follow-Up (*Math Journal 1,* p. 205)

WHOLE-CLASS DISCUSSION 

Begin by reminding students that in Lesson 6.9 they used lists of equivalent fractions to find common denominators. The lists of equivalent fractions were either generated by writing consecutive multiples of the numerators and denominators or by consulting the Table of Equivalent Fractions, Decimals, and Percents on page 359 in the *Student Reference Book.* Point out that today's lesson is about a quicker way to find a common denominator.

Briefly discuss answers for Problems 1 and 2. Then point out that these problems suggest a way to find a common denominator for pairs of fractions with unlike denominators.

Ask volunteers to use their answers to Problem 3 to suggest ways to find a common denominator for $\frac{2}{3}$ and $\frac{3}{4}$. Accept all proposals. If no one suggests it, ask someone to explain how to generate a common denominator using the way suggested by the fraction sticks on journal page 205.

Demonstrate on the board or overhead projector by drawing two fraction sticks—a "thirds" stick with $\frac{2}{3}$ shaded and a "fourths" stick with $\frac{3}{4}$ shaded. Split each part of the thirds stick into 4 equal parts and each part of the fourths stick into 3 equal parts. Ask students how many parts are in each whole stick. 12 The fraction sticks show that $\frac{8}{12}$ is another name for $\frac{2}{3}$, and that $\frac{9}{12}$ is another name for $\frac{3}{4}$. *(See the margin.)*

Point out that splitting the parts of fraction sticks in this way shows that a common denominator for two fractions can be found by multiplying the two denominators. Have students include this with their Problem 3 answer.

In *Everyday Mathematics,* the product of the denominators is known as the **quick common denominator.**

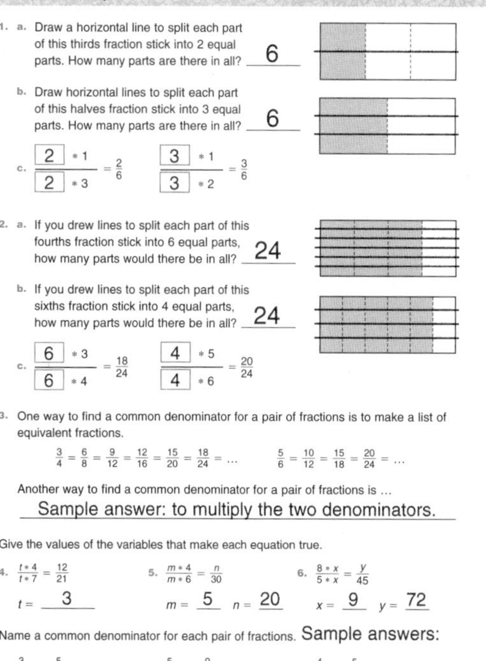

**Another Way to Find a Common Denominator**

1. a. Draw a horizontal line to split each part of this thirds fraction stick into 2 equal parts. How many parts are there in all? 6
   b. Draw horizontal lines to split each part of this halves fraction stick into 3 equal parts. How many parts are there in all? 6
   c. $\frac{2 * 1}{2 * 3} = \frac{2}{6}$ $\quad \frac{3 * 1}{3 * 2} = \frac{3}{6}$
2. a. If you drew lines to split each part of this fourths fraction stick into 6 equal parts, how many parts would there be in all? 24
   b. If you drew lines to split each part of this sixths fraction stick into 4 equal parts, how many parts would there be in all? 24
   c. $\frac{6 * 3}{6 * 4} = \frac{18}{24}$ $\quad \frac{4 * 5}{4 * 6} = \frac{20}{24}$
3. One way to find a common denominator for a pair of fractions is to make a list of equivalent fractions.
   $\frac{3}{4} = \frac{6}{8} = \frac{9}{12} = \frac{12}{16} = \frac{15}{20} = \frac{18}{24} = \dots$ $\quad \frac{5}{6} = \frac{10}{12} = \frac{15}{18} = \frac{20}{24} = \dots$
   Another way to find a common denominator for a pair of fractions is … Sample answer: to multiply the two denominators.

Give the values of the variables that make each equation true.

4. $\frac{t * 4}{t * 7} = \frac{12}{21}$ $\quad t =$ 3
5. $\frac{m * 4}{m * 6} = \frac{n}{30}$ $\quad m =$ 5 $\quad n =$ 20
6. $\frac{8 * x}{5 * x} = \frac{y}{45}$ $\quad x =$ 9 $\quad y =$ 72

Name a common denominator for each pair of fractions. Sample answers:

7. $\frac{3}{4}$ and $\frac{5}{16}$ = 16, or 64
8. $\frac{5}{8}$ and $\frac{9}{10}$ = 40, or 80
9. $\frac{4}{5}$ and $\frac{5}{6}$ = 30, or 60

STUDENT PAGE

✦ *Math Journal 1,* p. 205

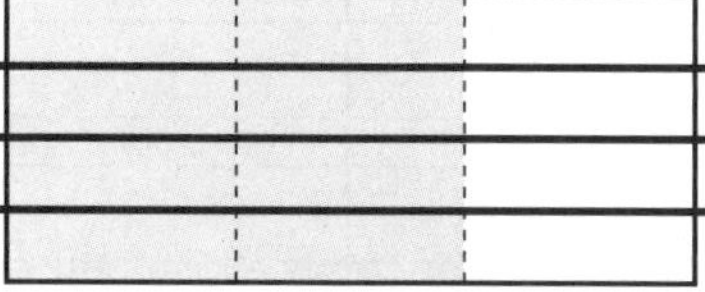

A thirds stick showing twelfths

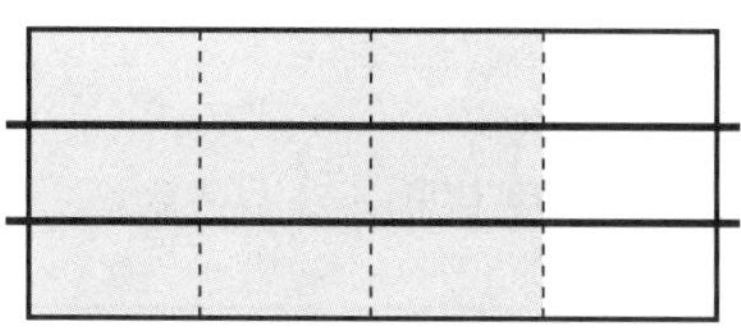

A fourths stick showing twelfths

## Using Common Denominators

Common denominators are useful not only for adding and subtracting fractions, but also for comparing fractions.

A quick way to find a common denominator for a pair of fractions is to find the product of the denominators.

*Example* Compare $\frac{2}{3}$ and $\frac{5}{8}$. Use 3 * 8 as a common denominator.

$\frac{2}{3} = \frac{(8 * 2)}{(8 * 3)} = \frac{16}{24}$  $\frac{5}{8} = \frac{(3 * 5)}{(3 * 8)} = \frac{15}{24}$

$\frac{16}{24} > \frac{15}{24}$, so $\frac{2}{3} > \frac{5}{8}$.

1. Rewrite each pair of fractions below as equivalent fractions with a common denominator. Then write < (less than) or > (greater than) to compare the fractions.

| | Original Fraction | Equivalent Fraction | > or < |
|---|---|---|---|
| a. | $\frac{4}{7}$ | $\frac{20}{35}$ | $\frac{4}{7} < \frac{3}{5}$ |
| | $\frac{3}{5}$ | $\frac{21}{35}$ | |
| b. | $\frac{9}{4}$ | $\frac{27}{12}$ | $\frac{9}{4} < \frac{7}{3}$ |
| | $\frac{7}{3}$ | $\frac{28}{12}$ | |

Find a common denominator. Then add or subtract.

2. $\frac{1}{2} - \frac{1}{3} =$ $\frac{3}{6} - \frac{2}{6} = \frac{1}{6}$
3. $\frac{7}{8} + \frac{2}{5} =$ $\frac{35}{40} + \frac{16}{40} = \frac{51}{40}$, or $1\frac{11}{40}$
4. $\frac{3}{4} - \frac{1}{2} =$ $\frac{6}{8} - \frac{4}{8} = \frac{2}{8}$, or $\frac{1}{4}$
5. $\frac{4}{5} + \frac{2}{3} =$ $\frac{12}{15} + \frac{10}{15} = \frac{22}{15}$, or $1\frac{7}{15}$
6. $\frac{9}{10} - \frac{5}{6}$  $\frac{9}{10} = \frac{54}{60}$  $\frac{5}{6} = \frac{50}{60}$  $\frac{54}{60} - \frac{50}{60} = \frac{4}{60}$, or $\frac{1}{15}$
7. $\frac{1}{10} + \frac{3}{4}$  $\frac{1}{10} = \frac{4}{40}$  $\frac{3}{4} = \frac{30}{40}$  $\frac{4}{40} + \frac{30}{40} = \frac{34}{40}$, or $\frac{17}{20}$

STUDENT PAGE

✦ *Math Journal 1,* p. 206

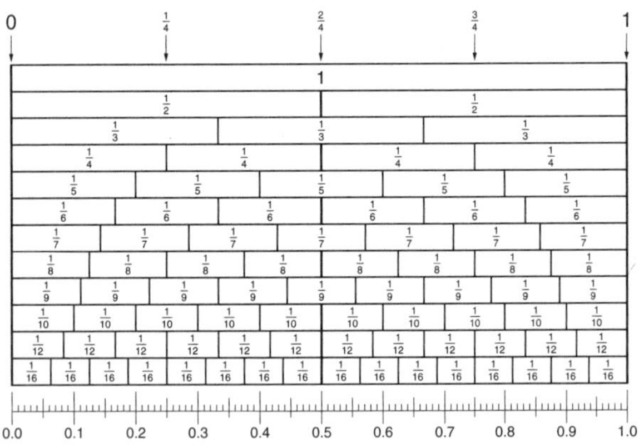


Fraction-Stick Chart

| | | | | | | | | | | | |
|---|---|---|---|---|---|---|---|---|---|---|---|
| $\frac{1}{2}$ | $\frac{2}{4}$ | $\frac{3}{6}$ | $\frac{4}{8}$ | $\frac{5}{10}$ | $\frac{6}{12}$ | $\frac{7}{14}$ | $\frac{8}{16}$ | $\frac{9}{18}$ | $\frac{10}{20}$ | 0.5 | 50% |
| $\frac{1}{3}$ | $\frac{2}{6}$ | $\frac{3}{9}$ | $\frac{4}{12}$ | $\frac{5}{15}$ | $\frac{6}{18}$ | $\frac{7}{21}$ | $\frac{8}{24}$ | $\frac{9}{27}$ | $\frac{10}{30}$ | $0.\overline{3}$ | $33\frac{1}{3}$% |
| $\frac{2}{3}$ | $\frac{4}{6}$ | $\frac{6}{9}$ | $\frac{8}{12}$ | $\frac{10}{15}$ | $\frac{12}{18}$ | $\frac{14}{21}$ | $\frac{16}{24}$ | $\frac{18}{27}$ | $\frac{20}{30}$ | $0.\overline{6}$ | $66\frac{2}{3}$% |
| $\frac{1}{4}$ | $\frac{2}{8}$ | $\frac{3}{12}$ | $\frac{4}{16}$ | $\frac{5}{20}$ | $\frac{6}{24}$ | $\frac{7}{28}$ | $\frac{8}{32}$ | $\frac{9}{36}$ | $\frac{10}{40}$ | 0.25 | 25% |
| $\frac{3}{4}$ | $\frac{6}{8}$ | $\frac{9}{12}$ | $\frac{12}{16}$ | $\frac{15}{20}$ | $\frac{18}{24}$ | $\frac{21}{28}$ | $\frac{24}{32}$ | $\frac{27}{36}$ | $\frac{30}{40}$ | 0.75 | 75% |

Table of Equivalent Fractions, Decimals, and Percents

## ✦ Using Fraction Sticks to Demonstrate Another Way to Find Common Denominators (*Math Journal 1,* p. 205)

WHOLE-CLASS ACTIVITY 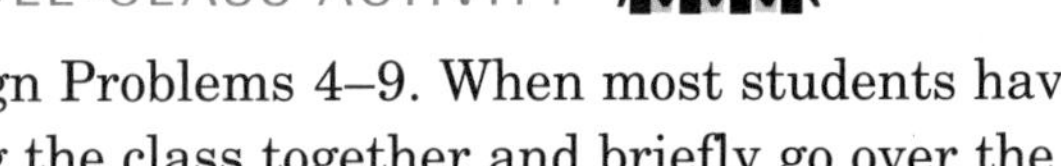

Assign Problems 4–9. When most students have finished, bring the class together and briefly go over the answers. Encourage students to share their methods for finding a common denominator.

The quick common denominators for Problems 7–9 are 64, 80, and 30. The pairs of denominators in Problems 7 and 8 share factors, however, so smaller common denominators are possible. In Problem 7, 16 is a common denominator; in Problem 8, 40 is a common denominator.

NOTE: Fraction sticks were used in Lesson 5.4 to find equivalent fractions. Most students will remember this approach. When dividing a fraction stick into smaller parts, it is helpful to use horizontal lines so that the original fraction divisions can still be seen.

Do not require answers to have the "lowest common denominator." Any common denominator can be used to add, subtract, or compare fractions. Requiring students to use lowest common denominators does not enhance their conceptual understanding of the operations.

## ✦ Using Common Denominators When Comparing, Adding, and Subtracting Fractions (*Math Journal 1,* p. 206)

PARTNER ACTIVITY

Have students complete journal page 206. The example reminds students that they can use the product of denominators to find a common denominator. They can also use the Table of Equivalent Fractions, Decimals, and Percents on page 359 in the *Student Reference Book,* and can check their answers using the Fraction-Stick Chart on page 357 of the *Student Reference Book.* (*See the margin.*) Circulate and assist as needed.

For the follow-up discussion, consider asking students to explain their solutions for Problems 6 and 7. Students who list or think equivalent fractions for each given fraction are likely to use 30 as a common denominator for Problem 6 and 20 for Problem 7. Students who use the "multiply the denominators" approach suggested in this lesson are likely to use 60 as a common denominator for Problem 6 and 40 for Problem 7.

Encourage but do not require students to write their answers in **simplest form.** A fraction is in simplest form if the numerator and denominator do not have any common factors except 1. In Problem 7, if 40 is used as the common denominator, the sum is $\frac{34}{40}$. The division rule for finding equivalent fractions can be applied to $\frac{34}{40}$, using 2, a common factor of 34 and 40:

$$\frac{34 \div 2}{40 \div 2} = \frac{17}{20}$$

Since 17 and 20 have no common factors except 1, the division rule can't be applied to $\frac{17}{20}$. Therefore, the simplest form of $\frac{34}{40}$ is the equivalent fraction $\frac{17}{20}$.

# 2 Ongoing Learning & Practice

## ✦ Reviewing Data (*Math Journal 1,* p. 207)

INDEPENDENT ACTIVITY 

Students complete a journal page that reviews some data concepts.

**ONGOING ASSESSMENT**

**Use this page to assess students' understanding of the organization of stem-and-leaf plots as well as their knowledge of data landmarks and their ability to interpret data.**

You may want to ask a volunteer who finishes early to record his or her data on an overhead transparency. As most of the students finish, have the volunteer share the data and describe the situation in which the data might occur—for example, weights of a group of dogs or heights of sunflower plants at different stages of growth.

## ✦ Math Boxes 6.10 (*Math Journal 1,* p. 208)

INDEPENDENT ACTIVITY 

**Mixed Review** Math Boxes in this lesson are paired with Math Boxes in Lesson 6.8. The skill in Problem 1 is a prerequisite for Unit 7.

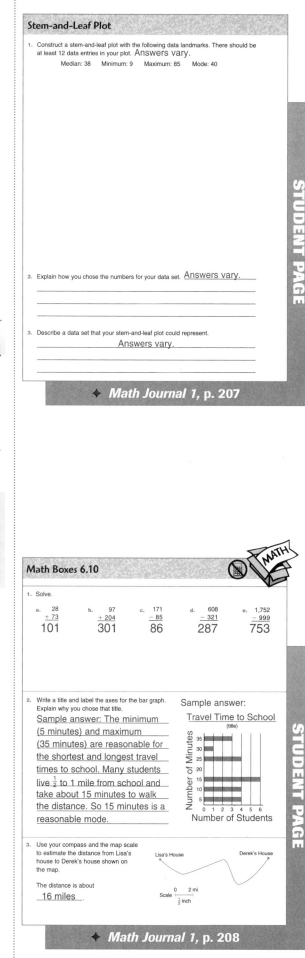

**Stem-and-Leaf Plot**

1. Construct a stem-and-leaf plot with the following data landmarks. There should be at least 12 data entries in your plot. Answers vary.

Median: 38 Minimum: 9 Maximum: 85 Mode: 40

2. Explain how you chose the numbers for your data set. Answers vary.

3. Describe a data set that your stem-and-leaf plot could represent.

Answers vary.

STUDENT PAGE

✦ *Math Journal 1,* p. 207

**Math Boxes 6.10**

1. Solve.

a. 28 + 73 = 101

b. 97 + 204 = 301

c. 171 − 85 = 86

d. 608 − 321 = 287

e. 1,752 − 999 = 753

2. Write a title and label the axes for the bar graph. Explain why you chose that title.

Sample answer: The minimum (5 minutes) and maximum (35 minutes) are reasonable for the shortest and longest travel times to school. Many students live $\frac{1}{2}$ to 1 mile from school and take about 15 minutes to walk the distance. So 15 minutes is a reasonable mode.

Sample answer:

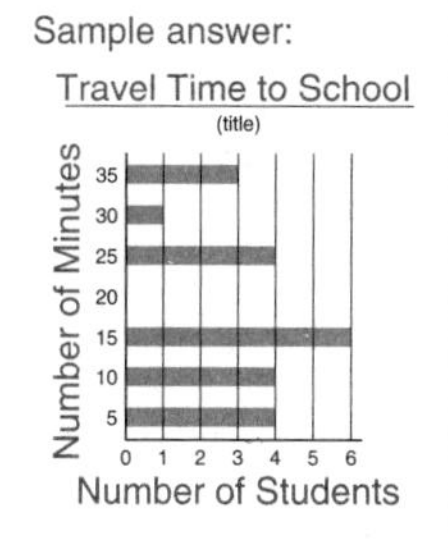


3. Use your compass and the map scale to estimate the distance from Lisa's house to Derek's house shown on the map.

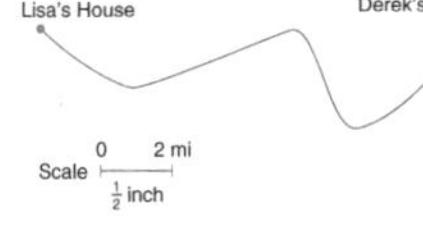


The distance is about 16 miles.

STUDENT PAGE

✦ *Math Journal 1,* p. 208

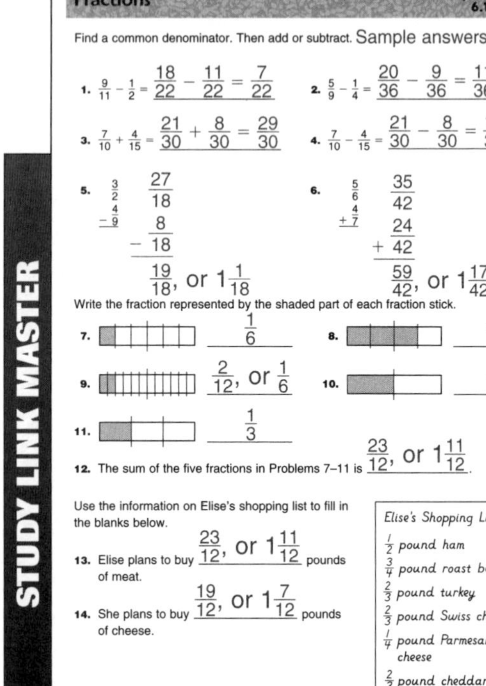

STUDY LINK MASTER

**Fractions** — Study Link 6.10

Find a common denominator. Then add or subtract. Sample answers:

1. $\frac{9}{11} - \frac{1}{2} = \frac{18}{22} - \frac{11}{22} = \frac{7}{22}$
2. $\frac{5}{9} - \frac{1}{4} = \frac{20}{36} - \frac{9}{36} = \frac{11}{36}$
3. $\frac{7}{10} + \frac{4}{15} = \frac{21}{30} + \frac{8}{30} = \frac{29}{30}$
4. $\frac{7}{10} - \frac{4}{15} = \frac{21}{30} - \frac{8}{30} = \frac{13}{30}$
5. $\frac{3}{2} - \frac{4}{9}$: $\frac{27}{18} - \frac{8}{18} = \frac{19}{18}$, or $1\frac{1}{18}$
6. $\frac{5}{6} + \frac{4}{7}$: $\frac{35}{42} + \frac{24}{42} = \frac{59}{42}$, or $1\frac{17}{42}$

Write the fraction represented by the shaded part of each fraction stick.

7. $\frac{1}{6}$
8. $\frac{3}{4}$
9. $\frac{2}{12}$, or $\frac{1}{6}$
10. $\frac{1}{2}$
11. $\frac{1}{3}$
12. The sum of the five fractions in Problems 7–11 is $\frac{23}{12}$, or $1\frac{11}{12}$.

Use the information on Elise's shopping list to fill in the blanks below.

13. Elise plans to buy $\frac{23}{12}$, or $1\frac{11}{12}$ pounds of meat.
14. She plans to buy $\frac{19}{12}$, or $1\frac{7}{12}$ pounds of cheese.

Elise's Shopping List
- $\frac{1}{2}$ pound ham
- $\frac{3}{4}$ pound roast beef
- $\frac{2}{3}$ pound turkey
- $\frac{2}{3}$ pound Swiss cheese
- $\frac{1}{4}$ pound Parmesan cheese
- $\frac{2}{3}$ pound cheddar cheese

**Math Masters, p. 291**

TEACHING MASTER

**Common Denominators** 

1. For each pair of fractions below:
   - Find a common denominator.
   - Rewrite the fractions with this common denominator.
   - Add the fractions.

| Original Fractions | Fractions with a Common Denominator | Sum |
|---|---|---|
| $\frac{1}{2}$ and $\frac{3}{4}$ | $\frac{2}{4}$ and $\frac{3}{4}$ | $\frac{2}{4} + \frac{3}{4} = \frac{5}{4}$, or $1\frac{1}{4}$ |
| $\frac{2}{9}$ and $\frac{7}{3}$ | $\frac{2}{9}$ and $\frac{21}{9}$ | $\frac{2}{9} + \frac{21}{9} = \frac{23}{9}$, or $2\frac{5}{9}$ |
| $\frac{3}{8}$ and $\frac{5}{16}$ | $\frac{6}{16}$ and $\frac{5}{16}$ | $\frac{6}{16} + \frac{5}{16} = \frac{11}{16}$ |
| $\frac{3}{5}$ and $\frac{9}{20}$ | $\frac{12}{20}$ and $\frac{9}{20}$ | $\frac{12}{20} + \frac{9}{20} = \frac{21}{20}$, or $1\frac{1}{20}$ |
| $\frac{7}{14}$ and $\frac{6}{8}$ | $\frac{2}{4}$ and $\frac{3}{4}$ | $\frac{2}{4} + \frac{3}{4} = \frac{5}{4}$, or $1\frac{1}{4}$ |
| $\frac{8}{10}$ and $\frac{15}{25}$ | $\frac{4}{5}$ and $\frac{3}{5}$ | $\frac{4}{5} + \frac{3}{5} = \frac{7}{5}$, or $1\frac{2}{5}$ |
| $\frac{6}{9}$ and $\frac{8}{12}$ | $\frac{2}{3}$ and $\frac{2}{3}$ | $\frac{2}{3} + \frac{2}{3} = \frac{4}{3}$, or $1\frac{1}{3}$ |
| $\frac{2}{3}$ and $\frac{3}{4}$ | $\frac{8}{12}$ and $\frac{9}{12}$ | $\frac{8}{12} + \frac{9}{12} = \frac{17}{12}$, or $1\frac{5}{12}$ |
| $\frac{1}{5}$ and $\frac{3}{8}$ | $\frac{8}{40}$ and $\frac{15}{40}$ | $\frac{8}{40} + \frac{15}{40} = \frac{23}{40}$ |
| $\frac{3}{10}$ and $\frac{6}{7}$ | $\frac{21}{70}$ and $\frac{60}{70}$ | $\frac{21}{70} + \frac{60}{70} = \frac{81}{70}$, or $1\frac{11}{70}$ |

2. Explain how you found a common denominator for one of the fraction pairs above.
   Sample answer: For $\frac{7}{14}$ and $\frac{6}{8}$, $\frac{7}{14} = \frac{1}{2}$ and $\frac{6}{8} = \frac{3}{4}$. Since $\frac{1}{2} = \frac{2}{4}$, $\frac{7}{14} = \frac{2}{4}$. 4 is a common denominator.

**Math Masters, p. 89**

## ✦ Study Link 6.10 (*Math Masters,* p. 291)

**Home Connection** Students practice adding and subtracting fractions with unlike denominators.

# 3 Options for Individualizing

## ✦ EXTRA PRACTICE Finding Common Denominators (*Math Masters,* p. 89)

INDEPENDENT ACTIVITY  **15–30 min** 

Students find common denominators for pairs of fractions and then add the fractions.

In the first four fraction pairs, the common denominator is the denominator of one of the pair, as in $\frac{3}{8}$ and $\frac{5}{16}$. One equivalent fraction for $\frac{3}{8}$ is $\frac{6}{16}$.

For the next three fraction pairs, one strategy is to reduce the fractions before finding a common denominator. For example, $\frac{7}{14} = \frac{1}{2}$ and $\frac{6}{8} = \frac{3}{4}$; rename $\frac{1}{2}$ as $\frac{2}{4}$.

In the last three fraction pairs, an easy way to find a common denominator is to multiply the numerator and denominator of each fraction by the denominator of the other fraction. For example, multiply $\frac{2 * 4}{3 * 4}$ and $\frac{3 * 3}{4 * 3}$ to get equivalent fractions with a common denominator of 12.

To extend the activity, have students change their sums to simplest form and mixed numbers.

# 6.11 Unit 6 Review and Assessment

**OBJECTIVE** **To review and assess students' progress on the material covered in Unit 6.**

## 1 Assess Progress

| learning goals | activities |
|---|---|
| 6a **Beginning/Developing Goal** Construct stem-and-leaf plots. **(Lesson 6.3)** | ❑ Written Assessment, Problem 22 |
| 6b **Beginning/Developing Goal** Read and interpret stem-and-leaf plots. **(Lesson 6.4)** | ❑ Written Assessment, Problems 7 and 22 |
| 6c **Developing Goal** Add and subtract fractions with like denominators. **(Lessons 6.8–6.10)** | ❑ Written Assessment, Problems 9, 11, and 17c |
| 6d **Developing Goal** Add and subtract fractions with unlike denominators. **(Lessons 6.8–6.10)** | ❑ Written Assessment, Problems 10, 12–16, and 17b |
| 6e **Developing Goal** Understand how sample size affects results. **(Lesson 6.5)** | ❑ Written Assessment, Problems 5b, 5c, and 8e |
| 6f **Developing Goal** Find common denominators. **(Lessons 6.9 and 6.10)** | ❑ Written Assessment, Problems 12–16, 17b, and 18–20 |
| 6g **Developing/Secure Goal** Convert between fractions, decimals, and percents. **(Lessons 6.5, 6.8, and 6.10)** | ❑ Slate Assessment, Problems 2, 4, and 5<br>❑ Written Assessment, Problems 6 and 8b–8d |
| 6h **Secure Goal** Identify and use data landmarks. **(Lessons 6.1, 6.5, and 6.6)** | ❑ Written Assessment, Problems 1–5, 7, and 21 |

**materials**

- ☐ *Math Journal 1,* p. 209
- ☐ Study Link 6.10
- ☐ Teaching Master (*Math Masters,* p. 86)
- ☐ Assessment Masters (*Math Masters,* pp. 392–394; and pp. 414–418, optional)
- ☐ slate
- ☐ pattern blocks

## 2 Build Background for Unit 7

| summaries | materials |
|---|---|
| Students practice and maintain skills through Math Boxes. | ☐ *Math Journal 1,* p. 210<br>☐ Study Link Masters (*Math Masters,* pp. 292–295) |

Each **learning goal** listed above indicates a level of performance that might be expected at this point in the *Everyday Mathematics* K–6 curriculum. For a variety of reasons, the levels indicated may not accurately portray your class's performance.

### Additional Information

**Advance Preparation** For additional information on assessment for Unit 6, see the *Assessment Handbook,* pages 52–54. For assessment checklists, see *Math Masters,* pages 438, 439, and 469–471.

## Getting Started

**Math Message**

*Complete the Time to Reflect questions on journal page 209.*

**Study Link 6.10 Follow-Up**

Briefly review answers.

NOTE: Some of these assessment suggestions relate to learning goals that have been addressed in previous units. Now is a good time to evaluate students' progress toward these goals.

STUDENT PAGE

**Time to Reflect**

1. If you wanted to find out what the top 3 favorite TV shows of fifth graders are, about how many students would you ask? ______ students

   Explain your answer.

   Answers vary.

2. Explain one advantage of organizing data into stem-and-leaf plots.

   *Example* Heights in inches of Mr. Bernard's fifth grade boys

   57, 62, 64, 60, 59, 60, 57, 61, 63, 67, 59, 60

| Stems (10s) | Leaves (1s) |
|---|---|
| 5 | 7 7 9 9 |
| 6 | 0 0 0 1 2 3 4 7 |

   Sample answer: The stems are arranged in increasing order. If the leaves on each stem are rewritten in increasing order, then the entire data set is listed in order. This makes it easy to identify the minimum, maximum, mode(s), and median.

✦ *Math Journal 1*, p. 209

# 1 Assess Progress

## ✦ Math Message Follow-Up

WHOLE-CLASS DISCUSSION

Students share their responses to questions about the unit.

## ✦ Slate Assessment

*Slate Assessment Suggestions*

WHOLE-CLASS ACTIVITY

If the suggested problems below are not appropriate for your class's level of performance, adjust the numbers or the problems themselves to better assess your students' abilities.

1. Round:
   - 489 to the nearest ten. 490
   - 608 to the nearest ten. 610
   - 23,605 to the nearest hundred. 23,600
   - 18.27 to the nearest tenth. 18.3
   - 12.17 to the nearest whole number. 12
   - 15.98 to the nearest tenth. 16.0
   - 200.73 to the nearest whole number. 201
2. Write the decimal and percent for each fraction.
   - $\frac{2}{3}$ $0.\overline{6}$; $66\frac{2}{3}\%$
   - $\frac{4}{8}$ 0.5; 50%
   - $\frac{4}{5}$ 0.8; 80%
   - $\frac{3}{10}$ 0.3; 30%
   - $\frac{7}{25}$ 0.28; 28%
   - $\frac{15}{50}$ 0.3; 30% **Goal 6g**

3. Show "thumbs up" if a number is divisible by a given number and "thumbs down" if it is not divisible.
   - Is 729 divisible by 2? down By 3? up By 4? down By 5? down By 6? down By 9? up
   - Is 1,256 divisible by 2? up By 3? down By 4? up By 5? down By 6? down By 9? down
4. Rename as mixed or whole numbers:
   - $\frac{15}{4}$ $3\frac{3}{4}$
   - $\frac{21}{5}$ $4\frac{1}{5}$
   - $\frac{11}{3}$ $3\frac{2}{3}$
   - $\frac{64}{8}$ 8
   - $\frac{52}{25}$ $2\frac{2}{25}$ **Goal 6g**
5. Rename as improper fractions:
   - $2\frac{3}{7}$ $\frac{17}{7}$
   - $4\frac{1}{2}$ $\frac{9}{2}$
   - $3\frac{8}{6}$ $\frac{26}{6}$
   - $7\frac{3}{8}$ $\frac{59}{8}$
   - $10\frac{4}{5}$ $\frac{54}{5}$ **Goal 6g**

## ✦ Written Assessment
(*Math Masters*, pp. 392–394)

INDEPENDENT ACTIVITY 

Depending on the needs of students, you may want to work through an example together, reading a problem aloud, discussing it, and providing additional examples as necessary before students work the problem independently.

- Define data landmarks (median, maximum, mode, minimum). (Problems 1–4) **Goal 6h**
- Find the median of a set of data and understand how sample size affects results. (Problems 5a–5c) **Goals 6e and 6h**
- Convert between fractions and percents. (Problem 6) **Goal 6g**
- Find the median and mode of the data in a stem-and-leaf plot. (Problem 7) **Goals 6b and 6h**
- Match survey data to a bar graph and interpret the bar graph. (Problem 8) **Goals 6e and 6g**

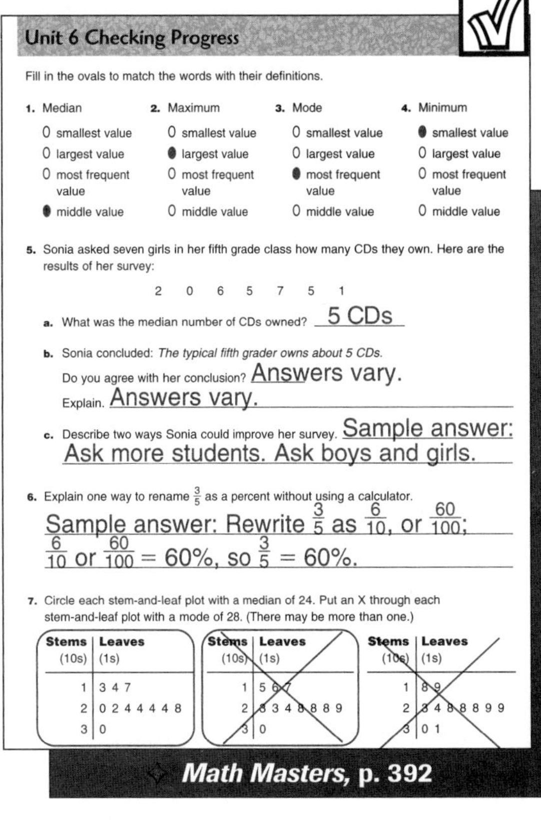

**Unit 6 Checking Progress**

Fill in the ovals to match the words with their definitions.

1. Median: smallest value / largest value / most frequent value / ● middle value
2. Maximum: smallest value / ● largest value / most frequent value / middle value
3. Mode: smallest value / largest value / ● most frequent value / middle value
4. Minimum: ● smallest value / largest value / most frequent value / middle value

5. Sonia asked seven girls in her fifth grade class how many CDs they own. Here are the results of her survey:

2 0 6 5 7 5 1

a. What was the median number of CDs owned? 5 CDs

b. Sonia concluded: *The typical fifth grader owns about 5 CDs.*
Do you agree with her conclusion? Answers vary.
Explain. Answers vary.

c. Describe two ways Sonia could improve her survey. Sample answer: Ask more students. Ask boys and girls.

6. Explain one way to rename $\frac{3}{5}$ as a percent without using a calculator.
Sample answer: Rewrite $\frac{3}{5}$ as $\frac{6}{10}$, or $\frac{60}{100}$; $\frac{6}{10}$ or $\frac{60}{100} = 60\%$, so $\frac{3}{5} = 60\%$.

7. Circle each stem-and-leaf plot with a median of 24. Put an X through each stem-and-leaf plot with a mode of 28. (There may be more than one.)

| Stems (10s) | Leaves (1s) |
|---|---|
| 1 | 3 4 7 |
| 2 | 0 2 4 4 4 4 8 |
| 3 | 0 |

| Stems (10s) | Leaves (1s) |
|---|---|
| 1 | 5 6 7 |
| 2 | 3 3 4 8 8 8 9 |
| 3 | 0 |

| Stems (10s) | Leaves (1s) |
|---|---|
| 1 | 8 9 |
| 2 | 3 4 8 8 8 9 9 |
| 3 | 0 1 |

ASSESSMENT MASTER

✦ Math Masters, p. 392

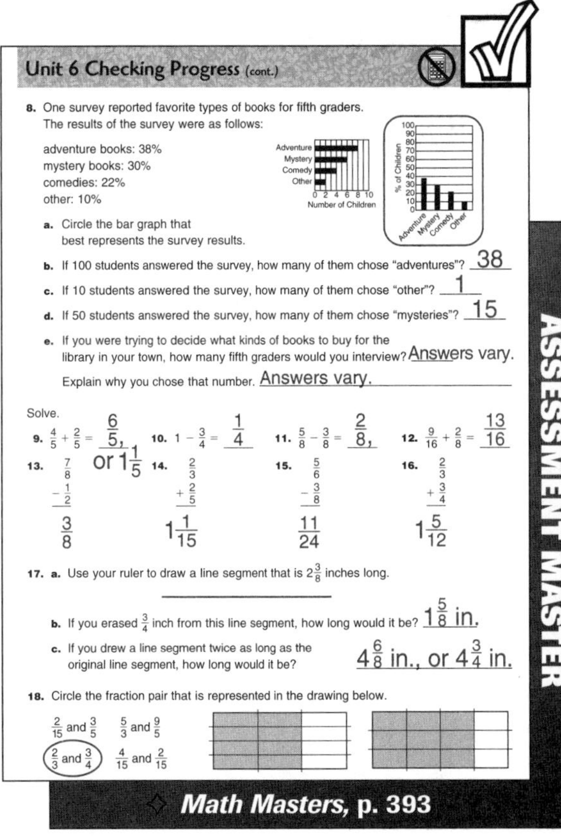

**Unit 6 Checking Progress (cont.)**

8. One survey reported favorite types of books for fifth graders. The results of the survey were as follows:

adventure books: 38%
mystery books: 30%
comedies: 22%
other: 10%



a. Circle the bar graph that best represents the survey results.

b. If 100 students answered the survey, how many of them chose "adventures"? 38

c. If 10 students answered the survey, how many of them chose "other"? 1

d. If 50 students answered the survey, how many of them chose "mysteries"? 15

e. If you were trying to decide what kinds of books to buy for the library in your town, how many fifth graders would you interview? Answers vary.
Explain why you chose that number. Answers vary.

Solve.

9. $\frac{4}{5} + \frac{2}{5} =$ $\frac{6}{5}$, or $1\frac{1}{5}$

10. $1 - \frac{3}{4} =$ $\frac{1}{4}$

11. $\frac{5}{8} - \frac{3}{8} =$ $\frac{2}{8}$,

12. $\frac{9}{16} + \frac{2}{8} =$ $\frac{13}{16}$

13. $\frac{7}{8} - \frac{1}{2}$ = $\frac{3}{8}$

14. $\frac{2}{3} + \frac{2}{5}$ = $1\frac{1}{15}$

15. $\frac{5}{6} - \frac{3}{8}$ = $\frac{11}{24}$

16. $\frac{2}{3} + \frac{3}{4}$ = $1\frac{5}{12}$

17. a. Use your ruler to draw a line segment that is $2\frac{3}{8}$ inches long.

b. If you erased $\frac{3}{4}$ inch from this line segment, how long would it be? $1\frac{5}{8}$ in.

c. If you drew a line segment twice as long as the original line segment, how long would it be? $4\frac{6}{8}$ in., or $4\frac{3}{4}$ in.

18. Circle the fraction pair that is represented in the drawing below.

$\frac{2}{15}$ and $\frac{3}{5}$ $\frac{5}{3}$ and $\frac{9}{5}$ ($\frac{2}{3}$ and $\frac{3}{4}$) $\frac{4}{15}$ and $\frac{2}{15}$

ASSESSMENT MASTER

✦ Math Masters, p. 393

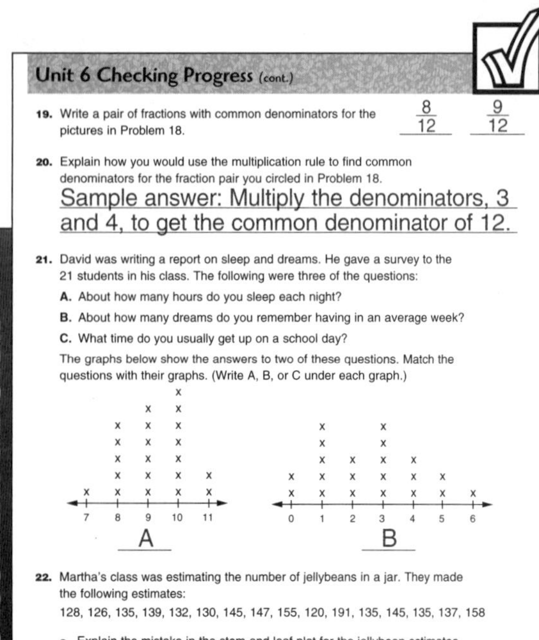

Unit 6 Checking Progress (cont.)

19. Write a pair of fractions with common denominators for the pictures in Problem 18. $\frac{8}{12}$ $\frac{9}{12}$

20. Explain how you would use the multiplication rule to find common denominators for the fraction pair you circled in Problem 18.
Sample answer: Multiply the denominators, 3 and 4, to get the common denominator of 12.

21. David was writing a report on sleep and dreams. He gave a survey to the 21 students in his class. The following were three of the questions:
A. About how many hours do you sleep each night?
B. About how many dreams do you remember having in an average week?
C. What time do you usually get up on a school day?
The graphs below show the answers to two of these questions. Match the questions with their graphs. (Write A, B, or C under each graph.)



22. Martha's class was estimating the number of jellybeans in a jar. They made the following estimates:
128, 126, 135, 139, 132, 130, 145, 147, 155, 120, 191, 135, 145, 135, 137, 158

a. Explain the mistake in the stem-and leaf plot for the jellybean estimates.
Sample answer: 135 appears only once, and it should appear 3 times. 145 appears once; it should appear 2 times.

| Stems (10s) | Leaves (1s) |
|---|---|
| 12 | 8 6 0 |
| 13 | 5 9 2 0 7 5 5 |
| 14 | 5 7 5 |
| 15 | 5 8 |
| 19 | 1 |

b. Correct the stem-and-leaf plot at the right.

***Math Masters*, p. 394**

- Add and subtract fractions. (Problems 9–17) **Goals 6c, 6d, and 6f**
- Find a common denominator for a pair of fractions. (Problems 18–20) **Goal 6f**
- Match survey questions with graphs of possible answers. (Problem 21) **Goal 6h**
- Find the mistake in a stem-and-leaf plot and then make a correct stem-and-leaf plot. (Problem 22) **Goals 6a and 6b**

## ✦ ALTERNATIVE ASSESSMENT OPTION
## Create a Set of Data for Given Data Landmarks

INDEPENDENT ACTIVITY 

To assess students' understanding of data landmarks, have them create a data set for the following landmarks. There should be at least seven numbers in their final set.

The median is 12.

The maximum is 15.

The minimum is 1.

The mode is 10.

## ✦ ALTERNATIVE ASSESSMENT OPTION
## Add and Subtract Fractions with Pattern-Block Models (*Math Masters,* p. 86)

INDEPENDENT ACTIVITY 

Use the activity from Part 3 of Lesson 6.8 to assess students' ability to recognize the value of fractional parts, find equivalent fractions, represent concrete models with number sentences, and find sums for fraction problems.

## ✦ Midyear Assessment
(*Math Masters,* pp. 414–418)

The Midyear and End-of-Year Assessment Masters (*Math Masters,* pages 414–426) provide additional assessment opportunities that you may want to use as part of your balanced assessment plan. These tests cover some of the important concepts and skills presented in *Fifth Grade Everyday Mathematics.* They should be used to complement the ongoing, product, and periodic assessments that appear within lessons and at the end of the units. Please see the *Assessment Handbook* for further information.

# Build Background for Unit 7

## ✦ Math Boxes 6.11 (*Math Journal 1,* p. 210)

INDEPENDENT ACTIVITY 

**Mixed Review** The skills in Problems 1–4 are prerequisites for Unit 7.

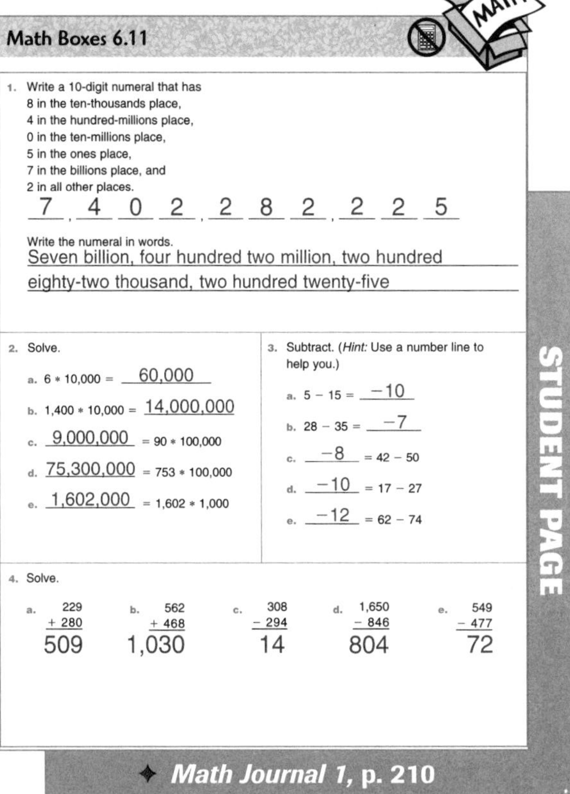

**Math Boxes 6.11**

1. Write a 10-digit numeral that has
8 in the ten-thousands place,
4 in the hundred-millions place,
0 in the ten-millions place,
5 in the ones place,
7 in the billions place, and
2 in all other places.
7, 4 0 2, 2 8 2, 2 2 5

Write the numeral in words.
Seven billion, four hundred two million, two hundred eighty-two thousand, two hundred twenty-five

2. Solve.
a. 6 ∗ 10,000 = 60,000
b. 1,400 ∗ 10,000 = 14,000,000
c. 9,000,000 = 90 ∗ 100,000
d. 75,300,000 = 753 ∗ 100,000
e. 1,602,000 = 1,602 ∗ 1,000

3. Subtract. (*Hint:* Use a number line to help you.)
a. 5 − 15 = −10
b. 28 − 35 = −7
c. −8 = 42 − 50
d. −10 = 17 − 27
e. −12 = 62 − 74

4. Solve.
a. 229 + 280 = 509
b. 562 + 468 = 1,030
c. 308 − 294 = 14
d. 1,650 − 846 = 804
e. 549 − 477 = 72

STUDENT PAGE

✦ *Math Journal 1,* p. 210

## ✦ Study Link 6.11: Unit 7 Family Letter
(*Math Masters,* pp. 292–295)

**Home Connection** This Study Link is a four-page newsletter that introduces parents and guardians to Unit 7's topic and terms. The letter also offers ideas for mathematics activities that are supportive of classroom work and can be done at home.

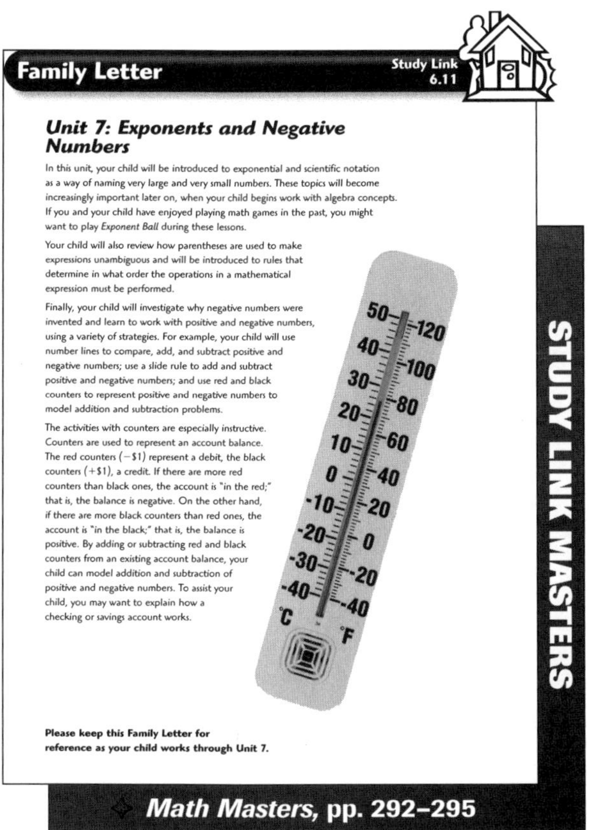

**Family Letter** Study Link 6.11

***Unit 7: Exponents and Negative Numbers***

In this unit, your child will be introduced to exponential and scientific notation as a way of naming very large and very small numbers. These topics will become increasingly important later on, when your child begins work with algebra concepts. If you and your child have enjoyed playing math games in the past, you might want to play *Exponent Ball* during these lessons.

Your child will also review how parentheses are used to make expressions unambiguous and will be introduced to rules that determine in what order the operations in a mathematical expression must be performed.

Finally, your child will investigate why negative numbers were invented and learn to work with positive and negative numbers, using a variety of strategies. For example, your child will use number lines to compare, add, and subtract positive and negative numbers; use a slide rule to add and subtract positive and negative numbers; and use red and black counters to represent positive and negative numbers to model addition and subtraction problems.

The activities with counters are especially instructive. Counters are used to represent an account balance. The red counters (−$1) represent a debit, the black counters (+$1), a credit. If there are more red counters than black ones, the account is "in the red;" that is, the balance is negative. On the other hand, if there are more black counters than red ones, the account is "in the black;" that is, the balance is positive. By adding or subtracting red and black counters from an existing account balance, your child can model addition and subtraction of positive and negative numbers. To assist your child, you may want to explain how a checking or savings account works.



**Please keep this Family Letter for reference as your child works through Unit 7.**

STUDY LINK MASTERS

✦ *Math Masters,* pp. 292–295

# Appendices

contents

PROJECT

1

# The Sieve of Eratosthenes

**OBJECTIVES** **To use the Sieve of Eratosthenes to identify the prime numbers from 1 to 100; and to look for patterns in the prime numbers.**

## background information

**Recommended Use:** During or after Unit 1

See the discussion of Projects in the Management Guide section of the *Teacher's Reference Manual.*

## materials

- ☐ *Math Masters,* pp. 175–179
- ☐ crayons, markers, or coloring pencils

***See*** **Advance Preparation**

### Project Information

The Sieve of Eratosthenes is an ancient, simple graphic device for identifying prime numbers by crossing out composite numbers.

**Advance Preparation** Make an overhead transparency of *Math Masters,* page 177 to demonstrate the Sieve of Eratosthenes. You will also need markers of various colors.

**Vocabulary** • **composite number** • **factor** • **multiple** • **prime number** • **sieve of Eratosthenes** • **twin primes**

PROJECT MASTER

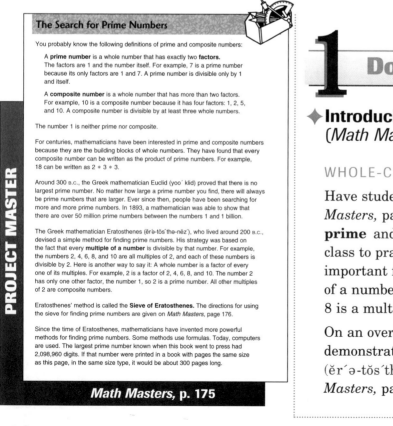

**The Search for Prime Numbers**

You probably know the following definitions of prime and composite numbers:

A **prime number** is a whole number that has exactly two **factors.** The factors are 1 and the number itself. For example, 7 is a prime number because its only factors are 1 and 7. A prime number is divisible only by 1 and itself.

A **composite number** is a whole number that has more than two factors. For example, 10 is a composite number because it has four factors: 1, 2, 5, and 10. A composite number is divisible by at least three whole numbers.

The number 1 is neither prime nor composite.

For centuries, mathematicians have been interested in prime and composite numbers because they are the building blocks of whole numbers. They have found that every composite number can be written as the product of prime numbers. For example, 18 can be written as 2 * 3 * 3.

Around 300 B.C., the Greek mathematician Euclid (yoo´ klid) proved that there is no largest prime number. No matter how large a prime number you find, there will always be prime numbers that are larger. Ever since then, people have been searching for more and more prime numbers. In 1893, a mathematician was able to show that there are over 50 million prime numbers between the numbers 1 and 1 billion.

The Greek mathematician Eratosthenes (ĕrə-tŏs´thə-nēz´), who lived around 200 B.C., devised a simple method for finding prime numbers. His strategy was based on the fact that every **multiple of a number** is divisible by that number. For example, the numbers 2, 4, 6, 8, and 10 are all multiples of 2, and each of these numbers is divisible by 2. Here is another way to say it: A whole number is a factor of every one of its multiples. For example, 2 is a factor of 2, 4, 6, 8, and 10. The number 2 has only one other factor, the number 1, so 2 is a prime number. All other multiples of 2 are composite numbers.

Eratosthenes' method is called the **Sieve of Eratosthenes.** The directions for using the sieve for finding prime numbers are given on *Math Masters,* page 176.

Since the time of Eratosthenes, mathematicians have invented more powerful methods for finding prime numbers. Some methods use formulas. Today, computers are used. The largest prime number known when this book went to press had 2,098,960 digits. If that number were printed in a book with pages the same size as this page, in the same size type, it would be about 300 pages long.

***Math Masters,* p. 175**

## 1 Doing the Project

### ✦ Introducing the Sieve of Eratosthenes (*Math Masters,* pp. 175–177)

WHOLE-CLASS DISCUSSION 

Have students read and discuss the essay on *Math Masters,* page 175. Be sure to review the definitions of **prime** and **composite** numbers. You may also want the class to practice finding **multiples** of numbers. It is important for students to understand that every multiple of a number $n$ has $n$ as one of its **factors.** For example, 8 is a multiple of 2; therefore, 2 is a factor of 8.

On an overhead transparency of *Math Masters,* page 177 demonstrate how to use the sieve of Eratosthenes (ĕr´ə-tŏs´thə-nēz´) by doing the first three steps on *Math Masters,* page 176 with the class.

## ✦ Using the Sieve of Eratosthenes to Identify the Prime Numbers from 1 to 100
(*Math Masters,* pp. 177 and 178)

PARTNER ACTIVITY 

Students continue to circle numbers that have not already been crossed out and then cross out their multiples until all the numbers from 1 to 100 have either been circled or crossed out. Then they list all prime numbers from 1 to 100 and answer the questions on *Math Masters,* page 178.

Bring students together to go over their answers on *Math Masters,* page 178. Encourage students to search for patterns on their own, even if these are not obvious at first.

### The Sieve of Eratosthenes

Follow the directions below for *Math Masters,* page 177. When you have finished, you will have crossed out in the grid every number from 1 to 100 that is not a prime number.

1. Since 1 is not a prime number, cross it out.
2. Circle 2 with a colored marker or crayon. Then count by 2, crossing out all multiples of 2, that is, 4, 6, 8, 10, and so on.
3. Circle 3 with a different colored marker or crayon. Cross out every third number after 3 (6, 9, 12, and so on). If a number is already crossed out, make a mark in a corner of the box. The numbers you have crossed out or marked are multiples of 3.
4. Skip 4, since it is already crossed out, and go on to 5. Use a new color to circle 5 and cross out multiples of 5.
5. Continue. Start each time by circling the next number that is not crossed out. Cross out all multiples of that number. If a number is already crossed out, make a mark in a corner of the box. Use a different color for each new set of multiples.
6. Stop when there are no more numbers to be circled or crossed out. The circled numbers are the prime numbers from 1 to 100.

**Squaring Magic**

The square of 13 is 169. Reverse 169 and you get 961. The square root of 961 is 31, which, when reversed, gets you back to 13.

Can you find any other number that will do this?

PROJECT MASTER

✦ *Math Masters,* p. 176

### The Sieve of Eratosthenes (cont.)

| 1 | 2 | 3 | 4 | 5 | 6 | 7 | 8 | 9 | 10 |
|---|---|---|---|---|---|---|---|---|---|
| 11 | 12 | 13 | 14 | 15 | 16 | 17 | 18 | 19 | 20 |
| 21 | 22 | 23 | 24 | 25 | 26 | 27 | 28 | 29 | 30 |
| 31 | 32 | 33 | 34 | 35 | 36 | 37 | 38 | 39 | 40 |
| 41 | 42 | 43 | 44 | 45 | 46 | 47 | 48 | 49 | 50 |
| 51 | 52 | 53 | 54 | 55 | 56 | 57 | 58 | 59 | 60 |
| 61 | 62 | 63 | 64 | 65 | 66 | 67 | 68 | 69 | 70 |
| 71 | 72 | 73 | 74 | 75 | 76 | 77 | 78 | 79 | 80 |
| 81 | 82 | 83 | 84 | 85 | 86 | 87 | 88 | 89 | 90 |
| 91 | 92 | 93 | 94 | 95 | 96 | 97 | 98 | 99 | 100 |

PROJECT MASTER

✦ *Math Masters,* p. 177

### The Sieve of Eratosthenes (cont.)

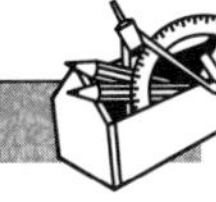

1. List all the prime numbers from 1 to 100.
   2, 3, 5, 7, 11, 13, 17, 19, 23, 29, 31, 37, 41, 43, 47, 53, 59, 61, 67, 71, 73, 79, 83, 89, 97
2. What are the crossed-out numbers greater than 1 called?
   Composite numbers
3. Notice that 6 is a multiple of both 2 and 3. Find two other numbers that are multiples of both 2 and 3.
   Sample answers: 42, 96, or any multiple of 6
4. Find a number that is a multiple of 2, 3, and 5. (*Hint:* Look at the colors.)
   Sample answers: 30, 60, 90
5. Find a number that is a multiple of 2, 3, 4, and 5. 60
6. Choose any crossed-out number between 50 and 60. List all of its factors.
   Sample answer: factors of 54 are 1, 2, 3, 6, 9, 18, 27, 54
7. List the crossed-out numbers that have no marks in the corners of their boxes.
   1, 4, 8, 9, 16, 25, 27, 32, 49, 64, 81
8. Find a pair of consecutive prime numbers. 2, 3
   Are there any others? no If yes, list them.
9. The numbers 3 and 5 are called **twin primes** because they are separated by just one composite number. List all the other twin primes from 1 to 100.
   5 and 7, 11 and 13, 17 and 19, 29 and 31, 41 and 43, 59 and 61, 71 and 73
10. Why do you think this grid is called a sieve? Sample answer: The grid is used like a sieve or a strainer to separate prime and non-prime numbers.

PROJECT MASTER

✦ *Math Masters,* p. 178

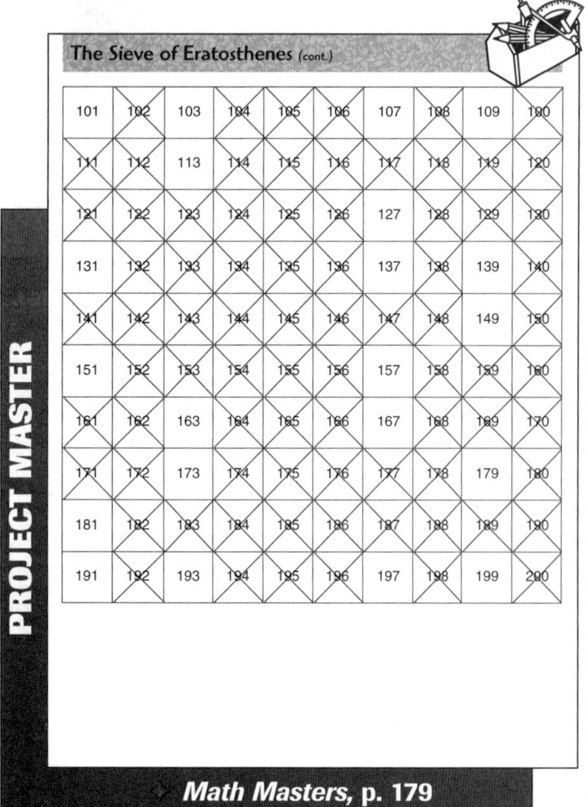

The Sieve of Eratosthenes (cont.)

| | | | | | | | | | |
|---|---|---|---|---|---|---|---|---|---|
| 101 | 102 | 103 | 104 | 105 | 106 | 107 | 108 | 109 | 110 |
| 111 | 112 | 113 | 114 | 115 | 116 | 117 | 118 | 119 | 120 |
| 121 | 122 | 123 | 124 | 125 | 126 | 127 | 128 | 129 | 130 |
| 131 | 132 | 133 | 134 | 135 | 136 | 137 | 138 | 139 | 140 |
| 141 | 142 | 143 | 144 | 145 | 146 | 147 | 148 | 149 | 150 |
| 151 | 152 | 153 | 154 | 155 | 156 | 157 | 158 | 159 | 160 |
| 161 | 162 | 163 | 164 | 165 | 166 | 167 | 168 | 169 | 170 |
| 171 | 172 | 173 | 174 | 175 | 176 | 177 | 178 | 179 | 180 |
| 181 | 182 | 183 | 184 | 185 | 186 | 187 | 188 | 189 | 190 |
| 191 | 192 | 193 | 194 | 195 | 196 | 197 | 198 | 199 | 200 |

PROJECT MASTER

*Math Masters*, p. 179

## Using the Sieve of Eratosthenes to Identify the Prime Numbers from 101 to 200
(*Math Masters*, p. 179)

INDEPENDENT ACTIVITY 

Encourage students to identify prime numbers greater than 100 by crossing out multiples of the prime numbers from 1 to 100 on the extended sieve of Eratosthenes on *Math Masters*, page 179.

## Learning about Prime Numbers

INDEPENDENT ACTIVITY 

Invite students to find out more about prime numbers in encyclopedias and math books and to visit Internet sites dealing with prime numbers. For example, http://www.utm.edu/research/primes has information on the search for larger prime numbers and links to other prime-number sites. A prize of $100,000 has been offered for finding the first prime number with more than 10 million digits.

PROJECT

2

# Deficient, Abundant, and Perfect Numbers

**OBJECTIVE** **To classify the whole numbers through 50 according to the sums of their proper factors.**

**background information**

**Recommended Use:** After Unit 1

See the discussion of Projects in the Management Guide section of the *Teacher's Reference Manual.*

**materials**

- □ *Math Masters,* pp. 180–183
- □ calculator

**Project Information**

Vocabulary • **abundant number** • **deficient number** • **factor** • **perfect number** • **proper factor**

PROJECT MASTER

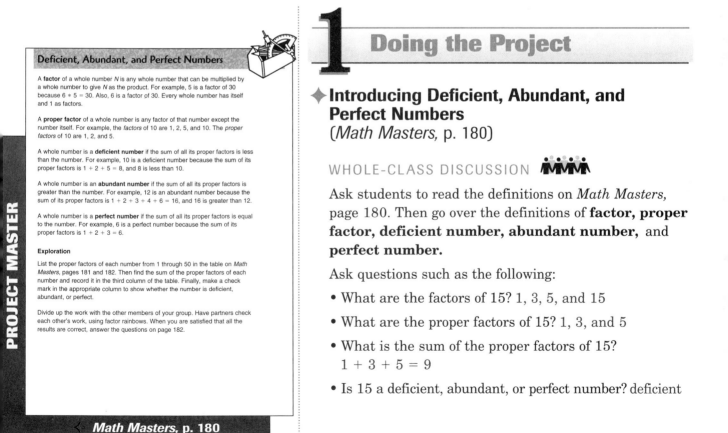

**Deficient, Abundant, and Perfect Numbers**

A **factor** of a whole number *N* is any whole number that can be multiplied by a whole number to give *N* as the product. For example, 5 is a factor of 30 because 6 ∗ 5 = 30. Also, 6 is a factor of 30. Every whole number has itself and 1 as factors.

A **proper factor** of a whole number is any factor of that number except the number itself. For example, the *factors* of 10 are 1, 2, 5, and 10. The *proper factors* of 10 are 1, 2, and 5.

A whole number is a **deficient number** if the sum of all its proper factors is less than the number. For example, 10 is a deficient number because the sum of its proper factors is 1 + 2 + 5 = 8, and 8 is less than 10.

A whole number is an **abundant number** if the sum of all its proper factors is greater than the number. For example, 12 is an abundant number because the sum of its proper factors is 1 + 2 + 3 + 4 + 6 = 16, and 16 is greater than 12.

A whole number is a **perfect number** if the sum of all its proper factors is equal to the number. For example, 6 is a perfect number because the sum of its proper factors is 1 + 2 + 3 = 6.

**Exploration**

List the proper factors of each number from 1 through 50 in the table on *Math Masters,* pages 181 and 182. Then find the sum of the proper factors of each number and record it in the third column of the table. Finally, make a check mark in the appropriate column to show whether the number is deficient, abundant, or perfect.

Divide up the work with the other members of your group. Have partners check each other's work, using factor rainbows. When you are satisfied that all the results are correct, answer the questions on page 182.

***Math Masters,* p. 180**

## 1 Doing the Project

### ✦ Introducing Deficient, Abundant, and Perfect Numbers
(*Math Masters,* p. 180)

WHOLE-CLASS DISCUSSION 

Ask students to read the definitions on *Math Masters,* page 180. Then go over the definitions of **factor, proper factor, deficient number, abundant number,** and **perfect number.**

Ask questions such as the following:

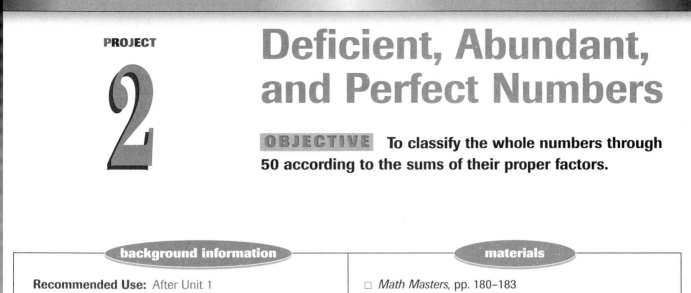

- What are the factors of 15? 1, 3, 5, and 15
- What are the proper factors of 15? 1, 3, and 5
- What is the sum of the proper factors of 15? 1 + 3 + 5 = 9
- Is 15 a deficient, abundant, or perfect number? deficient

PROJECT MASTER

**Deficient, Abundant, and Perfect Numbers** (cont.)

| Number | Proper Factors | Sum of Proper Factors | Deficient | Abundant | Perfect |
|---|---|---|---|---|---|
| 1 | | 0 | ✓ | | |
| 2 | 1 | 1 | ✓ | | |
| 3 | 1 | 1 | ✓ | | |
| 4 | 1, 2 | 3 | ✓ | | |
| 5 | 1 | 1 | ✓ | | |
| 6 | 1, 2, 3 | 6 | | | ✓ |
| 7 | 1 | 1 | ✓ | | |
| 8 | 1, 2, 4 | 7 | ✓ | | |
| 9 | 1, 3 | 4 | ✓ | | |
| 10 | 1, 2, 5 | 8 | ✓ | | |
| 11 | 1 | 1 | ✓ | | |
| 12 | 1, 2, 3, 4, 6 | 16 | | ✓ | |
| 13 | 1 | 1 | ✓ | | |
| 14 | 1, 2, 7 | 10 | ✓ | | |
| 15 | 1, 3, 5 | 9 | ✓ | | |
| 16 | 1, 2, 4, 8 | 15 | ✓ | | |
| 17 | 1 | 1 | ✓ | | |
| 18 | 1, 2, 3, 6, 9 | 21 | | ✓ | |
| 19 | 1 | 1 | ✓ | | |
| 20 | 1, 2, 4, 5, 10 | 22 | | ✓ | |
| 21 | 1, 3, 7 | 11 | ✓ | | |
| 22 | 1, 2, 11 | 14 | ✓ | | |
| 23 | 1 | 1 | ✓ | | |
| 24 | 1, 2, 3, 4, 6, 8, 12 | 36 | | ✓ | |
| 25 | 1, 5 | 6 | ✓ | | |
| 26 | 1, 2, 13 | 16 | ✓ | | |
| 27 | 1, 3, 9 | 13 | ✓ | | |
| 28 | 1, 2, 4, 7, 14 | 28 | | | ✓ |
| 29 | 1 | 1 | ✓ | | |
| 30 | 1, 2, 3, 5, 6, 10, 15 | 42 | | ✓ | |
| 31 | 1 | 1 | ✓ | | |
| 32 | 1, 2, 4, 8, 16 | 31 | ✓ | | |
| 33 | 1, 3, 11 | 15 | ✓ | | |
| 34 | 1, 2, 17 | 20 | ✓ | | |

**Math Masters, p. 181**

PROJECT MASTER

**Deficient, Abundant, and Perfect Numbers** (cont.)

| Number | Proper Factors | Sum of Proper Factors | Deficient | Abundant | Perfect |
|---|---|---|---|---|---|
| 35 | 1, 5, 7 | 13 | ✓ | | |
| 36 | 1, 2, 3, 4, 6, 9, 12, 18 | 55 | | ✓ | |
| 37 | 1 | 1 | ✓ | | |
| 38 | 1, 2, 19 | 22 | ✓ | | |
| 39 | 1, 3, 13 | 17 | ✓ | | |
| 40 | 1, 2, 4, 5, 8, 10, 20 | 50 | | ✓ | |
| 41 | 1 | 1 | ✓ | | |
| 42 | 1, 2, 3, 6, 7, 14, 21 | 54 | | ✓ | |
| 43 | 1 | 1 | ✓ | | |
| 44 | 1, 2, 4, 11, 22 | 40 | ✓ | | |
| 45 | 1, 3, 5, 9, 15 | 33 | ✓ | | |
| 46 | 1, 2, 23 | 26 | ✓ | | |
| 47 | 1 | 1 | ✓ | | |
| 48 | 1, 2, 3, 4, 6, 8, 12, 16, 24 | 76 | | ✓ | |
| 49 | 1, 7 | 8 | ✓ | | |
| 50 | 1, 2, 5, 10, 25 | 43 | ✓ | | |

Source: *The Math Teacher's Book of Lists.* Englewood Cliffs: Prentice Hall, 1995.

Refer to the results in your table.

1. What are the perfect numbers up to 50? 6 and 28
2. Is there an abundant number that is not an even number? no
3. Are all deficient numbers odd numbers? no
4. What is the next number greater than 50 for which the sum of its proper factors is 1? 53
5. The sum of the proper factors of 4 is 1 less than 4. List all the other numbers up through 50 for which the sum of the proper factors is 1 less than the number itself. 2, 4, 8, 16, 32
6. What do you think is the next number greater than 50 for which the sum of its proper factors is 1 less than the number itself? Sample answer: 64

**Math Masters, p. 182**

If students have no trouble answering these questions, repeat the sequence with a more challenging number, such as 60. Point out that the terms *deficient, abundant,* and *perfect* have historical origins but are merely labels. They don't reflect on the "worthiness" or "importance" of the numbers.

## ✦ Classifying the Whole Numbers from 1 through 50 According to the Sums of Their Proper Factors

(*Math Masters,* pp. 180–182)

SMALL-GROUP ACTIVITY 

Have students read the instructions at the bottom of *Math Masters,* page 180. Suggest that each group divide the work among partnerships. Partners should check each other's work. When members of each group have reached agreement on the answers for each number, they record the results in the table on *Math Masters,* pages 181 and 182. Then they answer the questions at the bottom of *Math Masters,* page 182.

Bring the groups together to report their findings. Problems 5 and 6 reveal an interesting pattern:

- ▷ The sum of the *proper factors* of a power of 2 ($2^1$, $2^2$, $2^3$, and so on) is 1 less than the power of 2. For example, $2^4 = 16$, and the sum of the proper factors of $2^4$, or 16, is $16 - 1 = 15$.
- ▷ The sum of *all the factors* of a power of 2 is equal to the sum of the proper factor plus the power itself. This can be found by doubling the number and subtracting 1. For example, the sum of all the factors of $2^4$, or 16, is $(2 * 16) - 1 = 31$.

The classification of whole numbers according to the sums of their proper factors should help students choose the best possible numbers when playing *Factor Captor.* Encourage students to play the game (*Student Reference Book,* page 271).

## Looking for Additional Perfect Numbers (*Math Masters,* p. 183)

INDEPENDENT ACTIVITY 

Students work independently or in small groups to try to find the third and fourth perfect numbers, using the method described on *Math Masters,* page 183.

**Adjusting the Activity** A very ambitious student might want to try to find the fifth perfect number. The next starting number whose factors add up to a prime number is 4,096. The sum of its factors is $(2 * 4{,}096) - 1 = 8{,}191$. The product of 4,096 and 8,191 is 33,550,336, which is the fifth perfect number.

# Extending the Project

## Learning More about Perfect Numbers

INDEPENDENT ACTIVITY 

The search for perfect numbers is based on the ideas presented on *Math Masters,* page 181. As noted earlier, the sum of the proper factors of $2^n$ is equal to $2^n - 1$. Numbers of this form are called *Mersenne numbers.* If a Mersenne number is a prime number, it is called a *Mersenne prime.* Mersenne primes are used to generate perfect numbers.

Some students might want to look in encyclopedias and other reference books for more information on perfect numbers and Mersenne numbers. A number of Internet sites are devoted to prime numbers, perfect numbers, and Mersenne primes. Most will probably be difficult for students to understand, but they show the continued interest in these subjects, and they may report new discoveries.

The following site offers lessons on perfect numbers: http://home.pacific.net.sg/~novelway/MEW2.lesson1.html.

The GIMPS (Great Internet Mersenne Primes Search) site has information on Mersenne primes and invites people to use their own computers to join the search for Mersenne primes: http://www.mersenne.org/prime.htm.

### A Perfect-Number Challenge

Perfect numbers become big very quickly. The third perfect number has 3 digits, the fourth has 4 digits, the fifth has 8 digits, the sixth has 10 digits, and the thirty-second has 455,663 digits! In other words, perfect numbers are hard to find.

You can find perfect numbers without having to find the sum of the proper factors of every number. Here is what you do:

1. Complete the pattern of starting numbers in the first column in the table.
2. List the factors of each starting number in the second column.
3. Write the sum of the factors of each starting number in the third column.
4. If the sum of the factors of the starting number is prime, multiply this sum by the starting number. The product is a perfect number. Record it in the last column.

The first perfect number is 6. Try to find the next three perfect numbers.

| Starting Number | Factors | Sum of Factors | Perfect Number |
|---|---|---|---|
| 2 | 1, 2 | 3 | 6 |
| 4 | 1, 2, 4 | 7 | 28 |
| 8 | 1, 2, 4, 8 | 15 | |
| 16 | 1, 2, 4, 8, 16 | 31 | 496 |
| 32 | 1, 2, 4, 8, 16, 32 | 63 | |
| 64 | 1, 2, 4, 8, 16, 32, 64 | 127 | 8,128 |
| 128 | 1, 2, 4, 8, 16, 32, 64, 128 | 255 | |

People have been fascinated by perfect numbers for centuries. The ancient Greeks knew the first four. The fifth perfect number was not found until the year 1456. The search for perfect numbers is now carried out on computers. When this book went to press, 38 perfect numbers had been identified. All the perfect numbers found so far are even numbers.

PROJECT MASTER

*Math Masters,* p. 183

**PROJECT**

# An Ancient Multiplication Algorithm

**OBJECTIVES** **To examine a multiplication algorithm that was invented in Egypt more than 4,000 years ago; and to compare multiplication algorithms and list their advantages and disadvantages.**

| background information | materials |
|---|---|
| **Recommended Use:** During or after Unit 2<br>See the discussion of Projects in the Management Guide section of the *Teacher's Reference Manual.* | ☐ *Math Masters,* pp. 184–187 |

**An Ancient Multiplication Method**

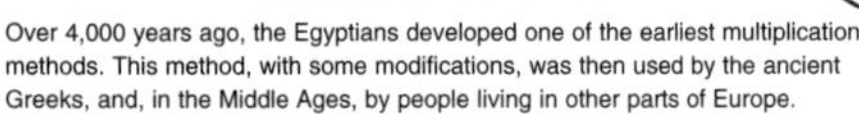

Over 4,000 years ago, the Egyptians developed one of the earliest multiplication methods. This method, with some modifications, was then used by the ancient Greeks, and, in the Middle Ages, by people living in other parts of Europe.

Study the examples of the Egyptian method below. Each problem has been solved by this method of multiplication. Try to figure out how the method works.

| 13 * 25 = 325 | 18 * 17 = 306 | 26 * 31 = 806 |
|---|---|---|
| ✓1 25 (1 * 25) | ~~1 17~~ | ~~1 31~~ |
| ~~2 50 (2 * 25)~~ | ✓2 34 | ✓2 62 |
| ✓4 100 (4 * 25) | ~~4 68~~ | ~~4 124~~ |
| ✓8 200 (8 * 25) | ~~8 136~~ | ✓8 248 |
| 325 (13 * 25) | ✓16 272 | ✓16 496 |
| | 306 | 806 |

Make up a multiplication problem. Then solve it by using the Egyptian method.

22 * 37 =

~~1 37~~
2 74
4 148
~~8 296~~
16 592
814

Sample answer:

**PROJECT MASTER**

*Math Masters,* p. 184

# 1 Doing the Project

## ✦ Exploring an Ancient Method of Multiplication (*Math Masters,* pp. 184 and 185)

SMALL-GROUP ACTIVITY 

Each problem on *Math Masters,* page 184 has been solved using an ancient Egyptian multiplication algorithm. Have students analyze these problems and try to figure out how the algorithm works. If they are able to do so, they should make up a problem of their own to solve using the Egyptian algorithm. Circulate and observe, but do not offer any help.

After about 10 minutes, ask students to share what they have discovered. Explain the algorithm if no one can produce an explanation.

Students then try to solve the three multiplication problems at the top of *Math Masters,* page 185, using the Egyptian algorithm.

Finally, have students look at the first two problems at the bottom of *Math Masters,* page 185, which have been solved using a variation of the Egyptian algorithm. Have them try to solve the third problem by the same method. Recreational Mathematics books call this method the "Russian Peasant Algorithm." It is performed by repeatedly halving the number in the left column, ignoring any nonzero remainders, and doubling the number in the right column. All rows that have an even number in the left column are crossed out, and the remaining numbers in the right column are added. The sum of these numbers is the answer to the multiplication problem.

## ✦ Comparing Multiplication Algorithms
(*Math Masters,* p. 186)

INDEPENDENT ACTIVITY 

Students consider the multiplication algorithms they know and record the advantages and disadvantages of each. This should help students decide which algorithm works best for them. However, this need not be the only algorithm they use. It is also important to stress that a paper-and-pencil algorithm may not be the most efficient way to solve a problem. Mental computation, a calculator, or an estimate may be a better choice.

When students have completed their comparison chart, bring them together to share preferences. Have students support their choices with examples.

NOTE: This exercise on comparing multiplication algorithms provides a good assessment tool for measuring how well students are grasping concepts of multiplication.

### An Ancient Multiplication Method (cont.)

1. Try to solve these problems using the Egyptian method.

| 85 ∗ 14 = 1190 | 38 ∗ 43 = 1634 | 45 ∗ 29 = 1305 |
|---|---|---|
| 1 14 | ~~1 43~~ | 1 29 |
| ~~2 28~~ | 2 86 | ~~2 58~~ |
| 4 56 | 4 172 | 4 116 |
| ~~8 112~~ | ~~8 344~~ | 8 232 |
| 16 224 | ~~16 688~~ | ~~16 464~~ |
| ~~32 448~~ | 32 1376 | 32 928 |
| 64 896 | 1634 | 1305 |
| 1190 | | |

**Challenge**

2. Here is another ancient multiplication method, based on the Egyptian method. People living in rural areas of Russia, Ethiopia, and the Near East still use this method. See if you can figure out how it works. Then try to complete the problem in the third box, using this method.

| 13 ∗ 25 = 325 | 38 ∗ 43 = 1634 | 45 ∗ 29 = 1305 |
|---|---|---|
| 13 25 | ~~38 43~~ | 45 29 |
| ~~6 50~~ | 19 86 | ~~22 58~~ |
| 3 100 | 9 172 | 11 116 |
| 1 200 | ~~4 344~~ | 5 232 |
| 325 | ~~2 688~~ | ~~2 464~~ |
| | 1 1376 | 1 928 |
| | 1634 | 1305 |

PROJECT MASTER

✧ *Math Masters,* p. 185

### Comparing Multiplication Algorithms

Think about the advantages and disadvantages of each multiplication method that you know. Record your thoughts in the chart below. Sample answers:

| Algorithm | Advantages | Disadvantages |
|---|---|---|
| **Partial Products**<br>43<br>∗ 62<br>60 [40s] = 2400<br>60 [3s] = 180<br>2 [40s] = 80<br>2 [3s] = 6<br>2666 | I can do it in easy steps. | I must be sure not to confuse 60s and 40s with 6s and 4s. |
| **Lattice**<br>4 3<br>2 \| 2/4 \| 1/8 \| 6<br>6 \| 0/8 \| 0/6 \| 2<br>6 6 | I work only with small numbers. | I have to line up the numbers very carefully. |
| **Egyptian**<br>43 ∗ 62<br>✓ 1 62<br>✓ 2 124<br>~~4 248~~<br>✓ 8 496<br>~~16 992~~<br>✓ 32 1984<br>2666 | It's easy to work with doubles of numbers. | It takes too long to double numbers. |

PROJECT MASTER

✧ *Math Masters,* p. 186

**PROJECT MASTER**

## Old Math

1. The ancient Egyptians used picture symbols, called hieroglyphs, to write numbers. Here is how they might have multiplied 11 * 13 using the algorithm you learned in this project.

| = 1
∩ = 10
= 100
= 1,000
= 10,000
= 100,000
= 1,000,000

| | | |
|---|---|---|
| ✓ \| | ∩\|\|\| | (1 * 13) |
| ✓ \|\| | ∩∩\|\|\|\|\|\| | (2 * 13) |
| \|\|\|\| | ∩∩∩∩∩\|\| | (4 * 13) |
| ✓ \|\|\|\| \|\|\|\| | ?\|\|\|\| | (8 * 13) |
| | ?∩∩∩∩\|\|\| | (11 * 13) |

On the back of this sheet, try to multiply 21 * 16 using the Egyptian algorithm and Egyptian numerals.

2. Do you know Roman numerals? They were used in Europe for centuries, until they were replaced by Hindu-Arabic numerals. Today they appear mainly in dates on cornerstones and in copyright notices.

   It is sometimes said that "multiplication with Roman numerals was impossible." Is that true? See whether you can multiply 12 * 15 using Roman numerals and the Egyptian algorithm. Use the back of this sheet.

   Some Roman Numerals

   I = 1 II = 2 III = 3 IV = 4 V = 5 VI = 6 IX = 9 X = 10 XX = 20

   XL = 40 L = 50 LX = 60 C = 100 D = 500 M = 1000

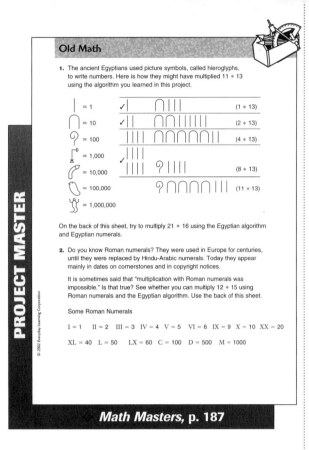



***Math Masters, p. 187***

NOTE: Encourage students to use the Internet to research and compare different numeral systems, such as the Egyptian, Roman, and Babylonian numeral systems. (The Babylonian numeral system uses a base of 60.)

| Hindu-Arabic | 0 | 1 | 2 | 3 | 4 | 5 | 6 | 7 | 8 | 9 | 10 |
|---|---|---|---|---|---|---|---|---|---|---|---|
| Babylonian | | ▾ | ▾▾ | ▾▾▾ | ▾▾▾▾ | ▾▾▾ ▾▾ | ▾▾▾ ▾▾▾ | ▾▾▾▾ ▾▾▾ | ▾▾▾▾ ▾▾▾▾ | ▾▾▾▾▾ ▾▾▾▾ | < |
| Egyptian | | \| | \|\| | \|\|\| | \|\|\|\| | \|\|\| \|\| | \|\|\| \|\|\| | \|\|\|\| \|\|\| | \|\|\|\| \|\|\|\| | \|\|\| \|\|\| \|\|\| | ∩ |
| Mayan | ⊖ | • | •• | ••• | •••• | — | •— | ••— | •••— | ••••— | = |
| Greek | | α | β | Υ | δ | ϵ | ϕ | ζ | η | θ | ι |
| Roman | | I | II | III | IV | V | VI | VII | VIII | IX | X |

# 2 Extending the Project

## ◆ Using Ancient Numerals in Multiplication Algorithms (*Math Masters,* p. 187)

PARTNER ACTIVITY 

Problem 1 on *Math Masters,* page 187 shows how the ancient Egyptians might have used their numerals and algorithm to multiply two numbers. Students work another problem with Egyptian numerals.

Problem 2 asks students to use the Egyptian algorithm to multiply with Roman numerals. It is sometimes said that "multiplication with Roman numerals was impossible," but—at least for smaller numbers—it seems possible with this algorithm.

Much information about Egyptian mathematics is found on a scroll called the Rhind papyrus. This scroll, copied about 1650 B.C., is named after the man who purchased it in Egypt in A.D. 1858. It is now in the British Museum in London.

PROJECT

4

# Magic Computation Tricks

**OBJECTIVE** **To figure out, perform, and explain computation tricks.**

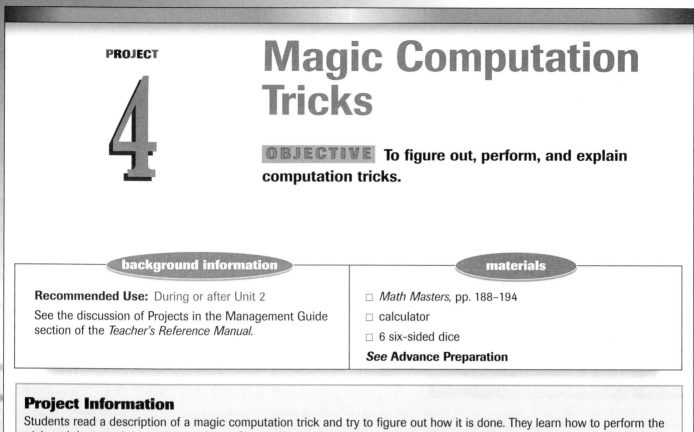

**background information**

**Recommended Use:** During or after Unit 2

See the discussion of Projects in the Management Guide section of the *Teacher's Reference Manual.*

**materials**

- ☐ *Math Masters,* pp. 188–194
- ☐ calculator
- ☐ 6 six-sided dice

***See* Advance Preparation**

## Project Information

Students read a description of a magic computation trick and try to figure out how it is done. They learn how to perform the trick and then teach it to other students. On completing this project, students should be able to perform and explain three computation tricks.

**Advance Preparation** You will need at least 6 six-sided dice for the dice trick. You may want to practice the trick before you try it with the class.

Students will be divided into 3 groups. One group will need *Math Masters,* pages 188 and 192. A second group will need *Math Masters,* pages 189 and 193. The third group will need *Math Masters,* pages 190, 191, and 194, as described below.

## 1 Doing the Project

### ✦ Demonstrating a Magic Number Trick with Dice

WHOLE-CLASS ACTIVITY

Say that you are going to perform a magic number trick. Tell students to watch you carefully and try to figure out how you did it.

1. Ask a student to roll 5 dice and find the sum of all the numbers on the top and bottom of the dice. Before the student has had much time to think, play "magician" and announce that the sum of all the numbers on the top and on the bottom of the dice is 35.
2. Perform the trick again, this time with 6 dice. Again, give the answer quickly—42.

PROJECT MASTER

## Computation Trick #1—Super Speedy Addition

***Set the Stage:*** Tell a friend that you have become a whiz at addition. To prove it, you are going to add five 3-digit numbers in your head within seconds.

***Props Needed:*** calculator

| ***Performing the Trick:*** | ***Examples*** Trial 1 | Trial 2 | Trial 3 |
|---|---|---|---|
| **1.** Ask your friend to jot down a 3-digit number on a piece of paper. Each digit must be different. | 493 | 261 | 682 |
| **2.** Ask your friend to write another 3-digit number below the first number. Each digit must be different. | 764 | 503 | 149 |
| **3.** One more time. (This is the **"notice me number."**) | 175 | 935 | 306 |
| **4.** Now it is your turn. Write a number so that the sum of your number and the first number is 999. (For example, in Trial 1, 493 + 506 = 999.) | 506 | 738 | 317 |
| **5.** Write another number so that the sum of this number and the second number is 999. (For example, in Trial 1, 764 + 235 = 999.) | + 235 | + 496 | + 850 |
| **6.** Pause a few seconds and give the sum of the five numbers. Have your friend check your super speedy addition on a calculator. | 2173 | 2933 | 2304 |

Figure out how to do this trick. How does it work?

Sample answer: You know that your partner's first two numbers and your last two numbers total two less than two thousand. Subtract two from the third number. Add the results to two thousand.

✦ ***Math Masters, p. 188***

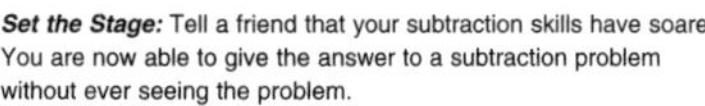

PROJECT MASTER

## Computation Trick #2—Subtraction Surprise

***Set the Stage:*** Tell a friend that your subtraction skills have soared. You are now able to give the answer to a subtraction problem without ever seeing the problem.

***Props Needed:*** calculator

| ***Performing the Trick:*** | ***Examples*** Trial 1 | Trial 2 |
|---|---|---|
| **1.** Ask your friend to **secretly** write a 3-digit number on a piece of paper. Each digit must be different. | 135 | 562 |
| **2.** Tell your friend to reverse the digits and write the new number below the first number. | 531 | 265 |
| **3.** Now have your friend use a calculator to subtract the smaller number from the larger number. | 531<br>− 135<br>396 | 562<br>− 265<br>297 |
| **4.** Say: "Tell me either the digit in the hundreds place or the digit in the ones place." | "3 in the hundreds place" | "7 in the ones place" |
| **5.** Pause a few seconds and give the answer. | 396 | 297 |

Figure out how to do this trick. How does it work?

Sample answer: The sum of the digits in the ones place and hundreds place is always nine. The tens place is always nine.

✦ ***Math Masters, p. 189***

**3.** Repeat with other numbers of dice. Ask each time whether anyone has figured out how to do the trick. The sum is equal to 7 times the number of dice rolled. For example, with 4 dice, the sum is 28; with 8 dice, the sum is 56; and so on.

At some point, someone is likely to notice the pattern. If no one figures it out, share it with the class:

- On a six-sided die, the sum of the numbers on each pair of opposite faces is 7. Therefore, with 5 dice, the sum of the numbers on the top and bottom is $7 * 5 = 35$, no matter what numbers come up on top when the dice are rolled. With 6 dice, the sum is $7 * 6$, and so on.

## ✦ Learning a Magic Computation Trick (*Math Masters,* pp. 188–194)

SMALL-GROUP ACTIVITY

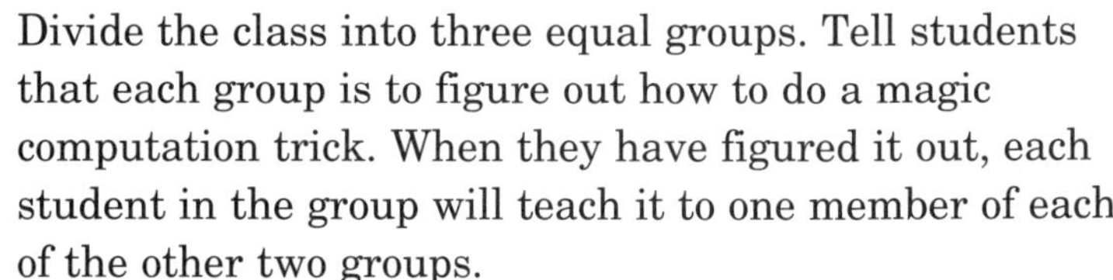

Divide the class into three equal groups. Tell students that each group is to figure out how to do a magic computation trick. When they have figured it out, each student in the group will teach it to one member of each of the other two groups.

Give each student in one group a copy of *Math Masters,* page 188. Give each student in a second group one copy of *Math Masters,* page 189, and each student in the third group a copy of *Math Masters,* pages 190 and 191. Give the groups 10 to 15 minutes to figure out how the trick works and to write a brief explanation.

Then give one or more copies of *Math Masters,* page 192 to the first group; *Math Masters,* page 193 to the second group; and *Math Masters,* page 194 to the third group. Each page explains the group's trick.

Each group works together until all members are certain they can perform and explain the trick.

## ✦ Teaching Computation Tricks to Other Students

SMALL-GROUP ACTIVITY

Mix up the groups and form groups of three students, consisting of one student from each of the original three groups. Each student in a group performs a trick and teaches it to the other two students in the group.

You can form groups of three by having students in each of the original groups count off "1, 2, 3, ...." Then all the 1s form a group, all the 2s another group, and so on. If the original groups do not have the same number of members, you can team up a pair of students to present the same trick in one of the other groups.

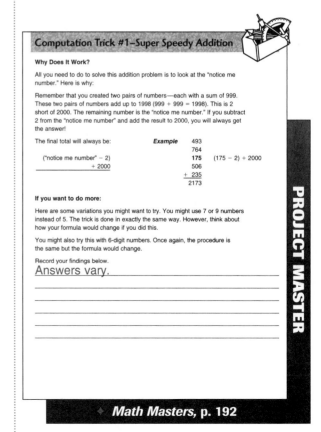

### Computation Trick #3—Crazy Calendar Addition

***Set the Stage:*** Tell a friend that you have become so good at addition that you now can tell what an addition problem is by merely looking at the answer.

***Props Needed:*** calculator and a calendar

***Performing the Trick:***

Give your friend a calendar.

1. Ask your friend to choose a month and to **secretly** circle any three dates that are next to each other, either in a row or in a column.
2. Now ask your friend to add the three dates on a calculator and to give you the calculator showing the sum in the display.
3. Ask: "Are the three dates you circled in a row or in a column?"
4. Pause a few seconds and give the answer.

***Examples***

| Sun. | Mon. | Tue. | Wed. | Thu. | Fri. | Sat. |
|---|---|---|---|---|---|---|
| | | 1 | 2 | 3 | 4 | 5 |
| 6 | 7 | 8 | 9 | 10 | 11 | 12 |
| 13 | 14 | 15 | 16 | 17 | 18 | 19 |
| 20 | 21 | 22 | 23 | 24 | 25 | 26 |
| 27 | 28 | 29 | 30 | 31 | | |

| | Trial 1 | Trial 2 | Trial 3 |
|---|---|---|---|
| 2. | 30 | 27 | 39 |
| 3. | "column" | "row" | "column" |
| 4. | 3, 10, 17 | 8, 9, 10 | 6, 13, 20 |

Figure out how to do this trick. How does it work?

Sample answer: Divide the total by 3. That is the middle number. If the three numbers are in a column, subtract and add 7 to get the other two numbers. If the numbers are in a row, subtract and add 1.

PROJECT MASTER

✦ Math Masters, p. 190

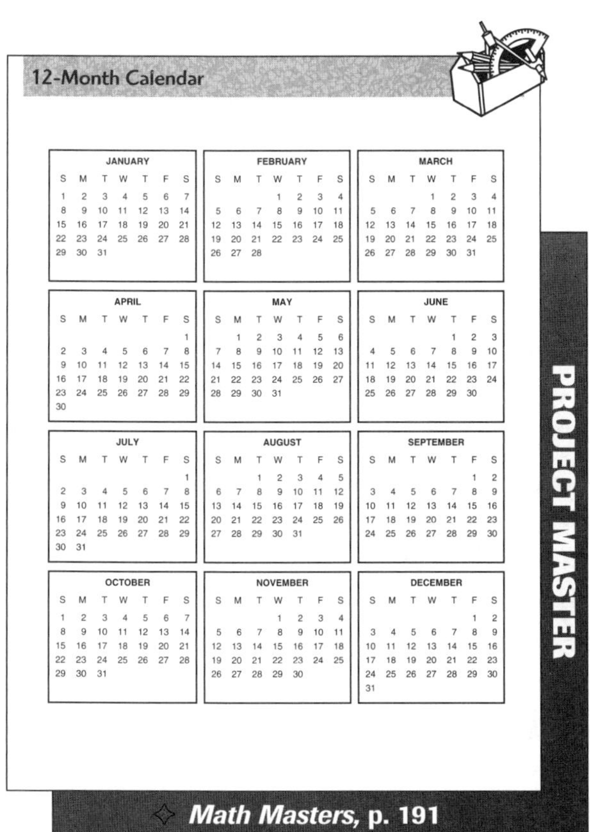

12-Month Calendar

JANUARY

| S | M | T | W | T | F | S |
|---|---|---|---|---|---|---|
| 1 | 2 | 3 | 4 | 5 | 6 | 7 |
| 8 | 9 | 10 | 11 | 12 | 13 | 14 |
| 15 | 16 | 17 | 18 | 19 | 20 | 21 |
| 22 | 23 | 24 | 25 | 26 | 27 | 28 |
| 29 | 30 | 31 | | | | |

FEBRUARY

| S | M | T | W | T | F | S |
|---|---|---|---|---|---|---|
| | | | 1 | 2 | 3 | 4 |
| 5 | 6 | 7 | 8 | 9 | 10 | 11 |
| 12 | 13 | 14 | 15 | 16 | 17 | 18 |
| 19 | 20 | 21 | 22 | 23 | 24 | 25 |
| 26 | 27 | 28 | | | | |

MARCH

| S | M | T | W | T | F | S |
|---|---|---|---|---|---|---|
| | | | 1 | 2 | 3 | 4 |
| 5 | 6 | 7 | 8 | 9 | 10 | 11 |
| 12 | 13 | 14 | 15 | 16 | 17 | 18 |
| 19 | 20 | 21 | 22 | 23 | 24 | 25 |
| 26 | 27 | 28 | 29 | 30 | 31 | |

APRIL

| S | M | T | W | T | F | S |
|---|---|---|---|---|---|---|
| | | | | | | 1 |
| 2 | 3 | 4 | 5 | 6 | 7 | 8 |
| 9 | 10 | 11 | 12 | 13 | 14 | 15 |
| 16 | 17 | 18 | 19 | 20 | 21 | 22 |
| 23 | 24 | 25 | 26 | 27 | 28 | 29 |
| 30 | | | | | | |

MAY

| S | M | T | W | T | F | S |
|---|---|---|---|---|---|---|
| | 1 | 2 | 3 | 4 | 5 | 6 |
| 7 | 8 | 9 | 10 | 11 | 12 | 13 |
| 14 | 15 | 16 | 17 | 18 | 19 | 20 |
| 21 | 22 | 23 | 24 | 25 | 26 | 27 |
| 28 | 29 | 30 | 31 | | | |

JUNE

| S | M | T | W | T | F | S |
|---|---|---|---|---|---|---|
| | | | | 1 | 2 | 3 |
| 4 | 5 | 6 | 7 | 8 | 9 | 10 |
| 11 | 12 | 13 | 14 | 15 | 16 | 17 |
| 18 | 19 | 20 | 21 | 22 | 23 | 24 |
| 25 | 26 | 27 | 28 | 29 | 30 | |

JULY

| S | M | T | W | T | F | S |
|---|---|---|---|---|---|---|
| | | | | | | 1 |
| 2 | 3 | 4 | 5 | 6 | 7 | 8 |
| 9 | 10 | 11 | 12 | 13 | 14 | 15 |
| 16 | 17 | 18 | 19 | 20 | 21 | 22 |
| 23 | 24 | 25 | 26 | 27 | 28 | 29 |
| 30 | 31 | | | | | |

AUGUST

| S | M | T | W | T | F | S |
|---|---|---|---|---|---|---|
| | | 1 | 2 | 3 | 4 | 5 |
| 6 | 7 | 8 | 9 | 10 | 11 | 12 |
| 13 | 14 | 15 | 16 | 17 | 18 | 19 |
| 20 | 21 | 22 | 23 | 24 | 25 | 26 |
| 27 | 28 | 29 | 30 | 31 | | |

SEPTEMBER

| S | M | T | W | T | F | S |
|---|---|---|---|---|---|---|
| | | | | | 1 | 2 |
| 3 | 4 | 5 | 6 | 7 | 8 | 9 |
| 10 | 11 | 12 | 13 | 14 | 15 | 16 |
| 17 | 18 | 19 | 20 | 21 | 22 | 23 |
| 24 | 25 | 26 | 27 | 28 | 29 | 30 |

OCTOBER

| S | M | T | W | T | F | S |
|---|---|---|---|---|---|---|
| 1 | 2 | 3 | 4 | 5 | 6 | 7 |
| 8 | 9 | 10 | 11 | 12 | 13 | 14 |
| 15 | 16 | 17 | 18 | 19 | 20 | 21 |
| 22 | 23 | 24 | 25 | 26 | 27 | 28 |
| 29 | 30 | 31 | | | | |

NOVEMBER

| S | M | T | W | T | F | S |
|---|---|---|---|---|---|---|
| | | | 1 | 2 | 3 | 4 |
| 5 | 6 | 7 | 8 | 9 | 10 | 11 |
| 12 | 13 | 14 | 15 | 16 | 17 | 18 |
| 19 | 20 | 21 | 22 | 23 | 24 | 25 |
| 26 | 27 | 28 | 29 | 30 | | |

DECEMBER

| S | M | T | W | T | F | S |
|---|---|---|---|---|---|---|
| | | | | | 1 | 2 |
| 3 | 4 | 5 | 6 | 7 | 8 | 9 |
| 10 | 11 | 12 | 13 | 14 | 15 | 16 |
| 17 | 18 | 19 | 20 | 21 | 22 | 23 |
| 24 | 25 | 26 | 27 | 28 | 29 | 30 |
| 31 | | | | | | |

PROJECT MASTER

✧ Math Masters, p. 191

### Computation Trick #1—Super Speedy Addition

**Why Does It Work?**

All you need to do to solve this addition problem is to look at the "notice me number." Here is why:

Remember that you created two pairs of numbers—each with a sum of 999. These two pairs of numbers add up to 1998 (999 + 999 = 1998). This is 2 short of 2000. The remaining number is the "notice me number." If you subtract 2 from the "notice me number" and add the result to 2000, you will always get the answer!

The final total will always be:

("notice me number" − 2)
+ 2000

***Example***

493
764
**175** (175 − 2) + 2000
506
+ 235
2173

**If you want to do more:**

Here are some variations you might want to try. You might use 7 or 9 numbers instead of 5. The trick is done in exactly the same way. However, think about how your formula would change if you did this.

You might also try this with 6-digit numbers. Once again, the procedure is the same but the formula would change.

Record your findings below.

Answers vary.

PROJECT MASTER

✦ Math Masters, p. 192

### Computation Trick #2—Subtraction Surprise

**Why Does It Work?**

The trick is in the way in which you had your classmate create the subtraction problem. There are only 9 possible solutions to a subtraction problem created in that way:

99 198 297 396 495 594 693 792 891

You may have noticed that the digit in the tens place is always 9. And the digits in the hundreds place and the ones place always add up to 9.

For example, if your classmate tells you that the digit in the hundreds place is 4, then you know that the digit in the ones place must be 5, since 4 + 5 = 9. You know that the digit in the tens place is always 9. Therefore the answer is 495.

What is the answer if your classmate tells you that the digit in the ones place is 9? 99

**If you want to do more:**

Will this trick work with a 4-digit number? With a 5-digit number? Describe your findings.

Sample answer: There are patterns that you can find in the answers, but they are not as easy to use as with 3-digit numbers.

PROJECT MASTER

◆ *Math Masters,* **p. 193**

### Computation Trick #3—Crazy Calendar Addition

**Why Does It Work?**

If three numbers are evenly spaced, you can find the middle number by dividing the sum of the numbers by 3.

***Example***

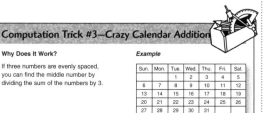

| Sun. | Mon. | Tue. | Wed. | Thu. | Fri. | Sat. |
|---|---|---|---|---|---|---|
| | | 1 | 2 | 3 | 4 | 5 |
| 6 | 7 | 8 | 9 | 10 | 11 | 12 |
| 13 | 14 | 15 | 16 | 17 | 18 | 19 |
| 20 | 21 | 22 | 23 | 24 | 25 | 26 |
| 27 | 28 | 29 | 30 | 31 | | |

The numbers in a row and the numbers in a column of a calendar are evenly spaced.

- The numbers in a row are consecutive whole numbers. They are 1 apart.
- The numbers in a column are 7 apart. This is because there are 7 days in a week.

Once you find the middle number by dividing the sum of the numbers by 3, it is easy to find the other two numbers.

- If the three numbers are in a row, then subtract 1 from the middle number to get the first number. Add 1 to the middle number to get the third number.
- If the three numbers are in a column, subtract 7 from the middle number to get the first number. Add 7 to the middle number to get the third number.

**If you want to do more:**

What would happen if the three dates chosen were on a diagonal? Would the trick still work? Why or why not?

Sample answer: You could still find the number in the middle, but you would have to know which way the diagonal goes to figure out whether to add and subtract 8 or 6.

PROJECT MASTER

◆ *Math Masters,* **p. 194**

## ◆ Discussing the Computation Tricks

WHOLE-CLASS DISCUSSION 

Bring students together to discuss the computation tricks. Possible questions:

- Which trick did you find easiest to learn? The hardest to learn?
- Was it easy or hard to teach your trick to others? Why?
- Which trick would you most like to share with someone at home? Why?

# 2 Extending the Project

## ◆ Learning More Tricks (*Math Masters,* pp. 192–194)

INDEPENDENT ACTIVITY 

*Math Masters,* pages 192 through 194 contain variations of the computation tricks at the bottom of each page under the heading If You Want to Do More. Invite students to try these.

There are many books of math and science tricks and puzzles that student can explore. *For example:*

George Barr, *Science Tricks and Magic for Young People.* New York: Dover, 1987.

Raymond Blum, *Mathemagic.* New York: Sterling, 1992.

Vicki Cobb and Kathy Darling, *Bet You Can't!: Science Impossibilities to Fool You.* New York: Avon, 1983.

——— *Bet You Can!: Science Possibilities to Fool You.* New York: Avon, 1989.

——— *Wanna Bet?: Science Challenges to Fool You.* New York: Lothrop Lee & Shepard, 1993.

Martin Gardner, *Mental Magic: Surefire Tricks to Amaze Your Friends.* New York: Sterling, 1999.

Terry Stickels, *Are You As Smart As You Think?: 150 Original Mathematical, Logical, and Spatial-Visual Puzzles for All Levels of Puzzle Solvers.* New York: St. Martin's, 2000.

——— *Mind-Bending Puzzles: A Bundle of Bogglers to Baffle Your Brain.* Rohnert Park, CA: Pomegranate, 1998.

——— *Mind-Bending Puzzles: More Bushels of Brilliance to Boggle Your Brain.* Rohnert Park, CA: Pomegranate, 1998.

PROJECT

# How Would You Spend $1,000,000?

**OBJECTIVES** **To research and plan how to spend a million dollars; to compute with large numbers; and to report on the plan and analyze and display data.**

## background information

**Recommended Use:** During or after Unit 5

The project used as a model was done by Emily Maneck, a student in Glenview, Illinois. The project design was created by Catherine Tucci and Gayle Zis, teachers in Glenview, Illinois.

See the discussion of Projects in the Management Guide section of the *Teacher's Reference Manual.*

## materials

- ☐ *Math Masters,* pp. 195–201
- ☐ calculator

***See* Advance Preparation**

## Project Information

In this long-term project, students work independently to research and plan how they would spend $1,000,000 while guided by a consistent, original theme. They present their results to the class, using any appropriate format, such as a written report or a display board. As part of their presentations, students describe how they spent their money by grouping their purchases into categories and recording the items purchased in each category. Then they use their project data to practice percent skills and make circle graphs. Allow about two weeks, outside of class time, for the project.

If you want to grade students on this project, tell them that they will be graded on choice of theme, thoroughness of research, accuracy of accounting, and clarity of display. A suggested rubric is provided below.

| Level | Theme | Research | Accounting | Display |
|---|---|---|---|---|
| 1 | No theme evident: random and unrelated purchases | Very little evidence of research | Very little evidence of organization<br><br>Considerably less or more than $1,000,000 spent | Minimal effort in presenting project |
| 2 | Majority of purchases relate to a theme | Evidence of some research | Good organization indicating how money was spent<br><br>$1,000,000 (or very close to it) spent | Interesting and complete presentation of project |
| 3 | All purchases relate to an original theme | Evidence of very detailed research | Excellent organization indicating how money was spent<br><br>Exactly $1,000,000 spent | Outstanding presentation of project |

**Advance Preparation** Each student will need several copies of *Math Masters,* page 199 (itemized accounting sheet for a major category).

**Vocabulary** • **unit price**

PROJECT MASTER

## How Would You Spend $1,000,000?—Emily's Idea

Emily decided that if she had $1,000,000 she would spend it on a fabulous ten-day trip to Florida for her, 19 of her friends, and 4 chaperons—24 people altogether. She thought that this should be a trip that no one would ever forget, and with $1,000,000, she knew that she could make that happen!

Emily began by thinking about all of the things she and her friends might need for their trip. She visited a local department store to find out how much different items cost. She decided to purchase a **vacation wardrobe** for everyone, including the chaperons, at a cost of $50,750. Her next stop was a **sporting goods** store for items such as snorkel gear, swimsuits, and sunglasses. The store clerk calculated that all of her purchases there would cost $24,100.

Emily knew that **transportation** to Florida and for getting around while in Florida would be needed. She made a few telephone calls to find out the prices for the transportation. Emily found that when she politely explained her project to people, most of them were willing to help her. After a bit of research, she chartered an airplane for the flight from Chicago to Orlando and back ($54,780). She purchased two stretch limos for use in Florida ($165,160 + $10,000 for gas and two around-the-clock chauffeurs). She also purchased a minivan to take the chaperons and the luggage ($20,700) while in Florida.

**Lodging** was another consideration. Emily decided that her group would stay at one of the resorts inside the theme park ($33,550). She went to a travel agency to get some information about many of the **activities** that she and her friends might try while they were there. For $177,200, Emily made reservations for several special breakfasts as well as dinner shows, rented a water park for 12 hours, and purchased 10-day passes to the theme park.

Math Masters, p. 195

PROJECT MASTER

## How Would You Spend $1,000,000?

**Emily's Idea (cont.)**

Emily decided to keep a record of the money she was spending by listing her purchases in major categories. At the right is part of the chart that she began to make.

| Major Category | Cost |
|---|---|
| Vacation Wardrobe | $ 50,750 |
| Sports Equipment | $ 24,100 |
| Transportation | $250,640 |
| Lodging | $ 33,550 |
| Activities | $177,200 |

Emily also decided that for each category she would keep a detailed record so that she would know exactly how she was spending the $1,000,000.

Here is an example of her record for one category:

| Major Category – Vacation Wardrobe | | | |
|---|---|---|---|
| Item | Quantity | Unit Price | Total Price |
| Boxer shorts | 100 | $ 12.50 | $ 1,250.00 |
| Socks | 200 | $ 5.50 | $ 1,100.00 |
| Shorts | 240 | $ 38.00 | $ 9,120.00 |
| T-shirts | 200 | $ 32.00 | $ 6,400.00 |
| Long-sleeve shirts | 100 | $ 36.00 | $ 3,600.00 |
| Jeans | 100 | $ 34.00 | $ 3,400.00 |
| Sweatshirts | 60 | $ 36.00 | $ 2,160.00 |
| Flannel shirts | 60 | $ 38.00 | $ 2,280.00 |
| Vests | 20 | $ 47.50 | $ 950.00 |
| Sweaters | 40 | $ 48.00 | $ 1,920.00 |
| Tax | | | $ 2,570.00 |
| Chaperons' Wardrobe Allotment | | $4,000.00 per person | $ 16,000.00 |
| | | Total | $50,750.00 |

These are examples of just a few of the expenses for Emily's amazing trip.

About how much money has Emily spent so far? $536,240

About how much money does Emily have left to spend? $463,760

Math Masters, p. 196

# 1 Doing the Project

## Introducing the Project
(*Math Masters,* pp. 195 and 196)

WHOLE-CLASS DISCUSSION 

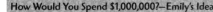

Ask students to imagine that they have $1,000,000 and to think about ways they would spend it. Then have them share a few of their ideas.

Ask students to read *Math Masters,* pages 195 and 196. The essay describes how Emily decided on a theme and began her investigation of how she would spend $1,000,000. The essay serves as a model for the project. The discussion of the essay should include these points:

- ▷ Emily's theme for spending her $1,000,000 was a Florida vacation.
- ▷ Emily researched her project by going to stores and making phone calls. She found that when she politely explained her project to people, they were happy to help her. (You may want to make students aware, however, that not everyone they speak to will be enthusiastic about answering hypothetical purchasing questions. Realistically, many people do not have the time. Encourage students to politely thank those who are too busy to help and to try again somewhere else.)
- ▷ Emily organized her purchases into major categories. She also listed the items that made up each category.
- ▷ Point out that the term **unit price** refers to the cost for one item. Unit costs should be rounded to the nearest dollar or half-dollar. Encourage students to round larger prices to larger values—for example, to the nearest $10 or nearest $100 for major category costs.
- ▷ Emily has spent about $536,240 for the items listed. She has about $463,760 left over for more purchases.

## Assigning the Project
(*Math Masters,* pp. 197–199)

WHOLE-CLASS DISCUSSION 

The guidelines for completing the project are given on *Math Masters,* page 197. Review them with the class. The guidelines provide students with a common framework within which to begin. However, try to keep the spirit of the project as open ended as possible.

Encourage students to pursue their own creative ideas. Projects have included starting a sports grill and ice-cream shop, opening an animal shelter, investing in the stock market, sponsoring a dog show, and opening a gas station and car service center. Encourage students not only to imagine projects that entertain or make a profit, but also to explore projects that benefit society.

One benefit of this project is that it provides students with the opportunity to investigate subjects of their own choosing. In gathering information, students will need to use a variety of resources and possibly speak with many different people. Because some students will have greater access to resources than will others, expect some projects to be more detailed than others. Students who are not usually highly motivated have successfully completed this project, while at the same time sharing with the class a topic about which they are knowledgeable.

*Math Masters,* pages 198 and 199 are provided as possible resources for students to use in organizing and recording their purchases.

The goal of the project is to spend as close to $1,000,000 as possible, without going over. As this may be difficult to do, you might allow students to contribute a specified amount (for example, not less than $10,000 and not more than $50,000) to a charity to bring the total to $1,000,000. This contribution could be used to account for small unspent amounts of money.

## Presenting the Project

WHOLE-CLASS DISCUSSION 

Schedule time for students to present their completed projects to the class. Students will enjoy sharing their plans for spending $1,000,000, as well as hearing how other students choose to spend it. The presentations can be brief—students can give quick summaries of their themes and highlight any special parts of their projects.

Collect the accounting sheets (*Math Masters,* pages 198 and 199) from students after their presentations. Verify that the totals in all of the categories do indeed total $1,000,000. If not, return the sheets to the students for correction before proceeding to the next activity.

**How Would You Spend $1,000,000?**

**Project Guidelines**

Imagine that you have just inherited $1,000,000. One of the conditions for you to receive the money is that you must first investigate, research, and present exactly how you will spend it. The following guidelines must be followed:

**Theme** The $1,000,000 must be spent carrying out one particular plan.

*For example:* A plan that would help save the rain forest; a plan to build new parks and playgrounds in your city; a plan for a trip around the world; or a plan to open a ballet studio.

**Goal** Spend as close to $1,000,000 as possible, but not more than $1,000,000.

**Research** All of the expenses involved in carrying out the details of your plan must be included.

*For example:* If you are opening a ballet studio, you must consider how many teachers you will need and how much you will pay them. If you are buying a car, you will need to consider the cost of gas, maintenance, and insurance for the length of time you will own the car.

**Accounting** Record, in an organized way, exactly how the $1,000,000 will be spent. The purchases needed to carry out your plan should be organized in several major categories. The purchases in each major category must total at least $10,000.

*For example:* Think about the way in which Emily organized the purchases for her Florida vacation, as described on *Math Masters,* pages 195 and 196.

**Display** Present the research and accounting for your plan in a report, on a display board, on a posterboard, or in a portfolio. You might even do a video production.

*For example:* Emily presented her project as a report. In addition to her calculations, she included pictures and sample receipts whenever possible.

PROJECT MASTER

***Math Masters,* p. 197**

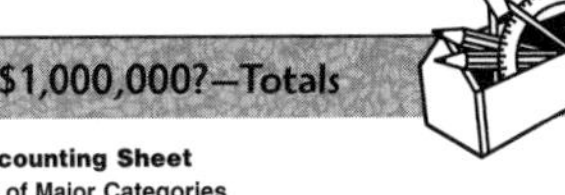

**How Would You Spend $1,000,000?—Totals**

**Accounting Sheet**
**Totals of Major Categories**

| Major Category | Cost |
|---|---|
| | |
| | |
| | |
| | |
| | |
| | |
| | |
| | |
| | |
| | |
| | |
| **Total** | **$1,000,000** |

PROJECT MASTER

***Math Masters,* p. 198**

PROJECT MASTER

## How Would You Spend $1,000,000?—Itemized

**Accounting Sheet**
A Major Category—Itemized

Category: ______________________________

| Item | Quantity | Unit Price | Total Price |
|---|---|---|---|
| | | | |
| | | | |
| | | | |
| | | | |
| | | | |
| | | | |
| | | | |
| | | | |
| | | | |
| | | | |
| | | | |

Total $ ____________

***Math Masters*, p. 199**

# 2 Extending the Project

## Displaying Project Data
(*Math Masters,* pp. 200 and 201)

INDEPENDENT ACTIVITY 

Distribute the accounting sheets that you collected after the students' presentations. Students use their data to complete *Math Masters,* pages 200 and 201.

You may need to clarify the directions on *Math Masters,* page 201. Because each percent has been rounded to the nearest whole percent, the percents may not total 100%. To compensate for this, the smaller categories should be graphed first and the largest one graphed last. If a category is only 2% of the total, and it is off by 1%, that is a relatively large error. However, if a category is 34% of the total, and it is off by 1%, the error is much less significant. By starting with the smallest category, the relative errors can be minimized.

Consider making a display of students' graphs.

PROJECT MASTER

## How Would You Spend $1,000,000?—Categories

In the table below, list all of your major expense categories and the total amount for each. (Refer to your accounting sheets—*Math Masters,* pages 198 and 199.) Write each amount as a fraction, decimal, and percent of $1,000,000. Round each decimal to the nearest hundredth. Round each percent to the nearest whole percent.

| Category | Total $ Spent | Fraction | Decimal | Percent |
|---|---|---|---|---|
| | | 1,000,000 | | |
| | | 1,000,000 | | |
| | | 1,000,000 | | |
| | | 1,000,000 | | |
| | | 1,000,000 | | |
| | | 1,000,000 | | |
| | | 1,000,000 | | |
| | | 1,000,000 | | |
| | | 1,000,000 | | |
| | | 1,000,000 | | |
| | | 1,000,000 | | |
| | | 1,000,000 | | |
| | | 1,000,000 | | |

***Math Masters*, p. 200**

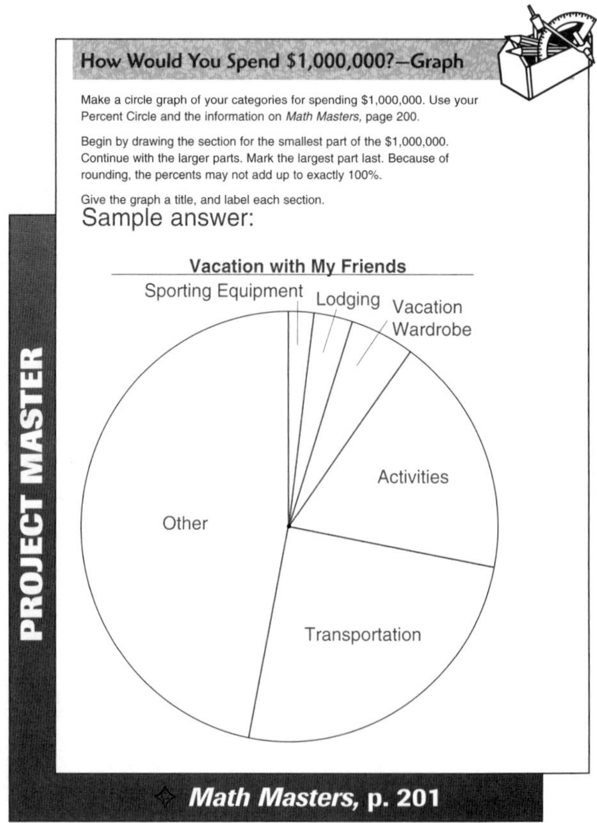
PROJECT MASTER

How Would You Spend $1,000,000?—Graph

Make a circle graph of your categories for spending $1,000,000. Use your Percent Circle and the information on *Math Masters,* page 200.

Begin by drawing the section for the smallest part of the $1,000,000. Continue with the larger parts. Mark the largest part last. Because of rounding, the percents may not add up to exactly 100%.

Give the graph a title, and label each section.

Sample answer:



***Math Masters*, p. 201**

PROJECT

# Sports Areas

**OBJECTIVE** **To calculate the area of the playing field or surface for a variety of sports.**

**background information**

**Recommended Use:** During or after Unit 9

See the discussion of Projects in the Management Guide section of the *Teacher's Reference Manual.*

**materials**

- □ *Math Masters,* pp. 202–204
- □ calculator □ ruler

***See* Advance Preparation**

## Project Information

Students are given the dimensions of the playing field or surface for a variety of sports. They calculate the area of each and identify areas greater than 1 acre.

This project provides practice calculating the areas of rectangles, converting between units, and converting mixed units to decimals (for example, 39 feet 3 inches to 39.25 feet).

**Vocabulary** • **perspective drawing** • **scale drawing**

## 1 Doing the Project

### ✦ Discussing Scale Drawings and Dimensions of Sports Surfaces
(*Math Masters,* pp. 202 and 203)

WHOLE-CLASS DISCUSSION 

The dimensions of the playing surface for each sport are given in the rules for that sport. Playing areas vary greatly from sport to sport.

Discuss the two scale drawings on *Math Masters,* pages 202 and 203. Be sure to cover the following points:

▷ The drawings are **scale drawings.** The relationships between lengths in a scale drawing are the same as the relationships between lengths in the actual object. For example, the playing surface for field hockey is 300 feet

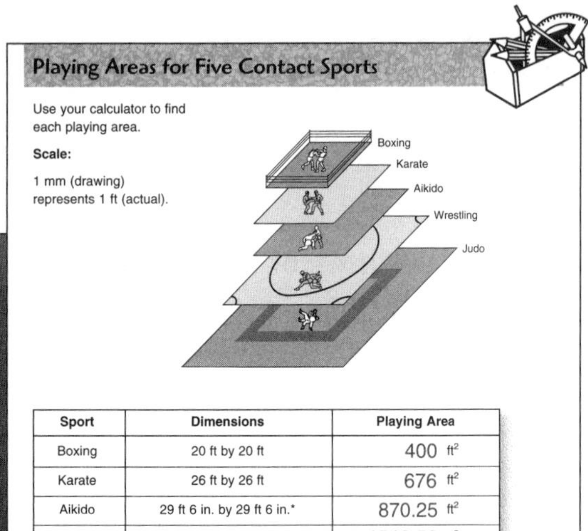



PROJECT MASTER

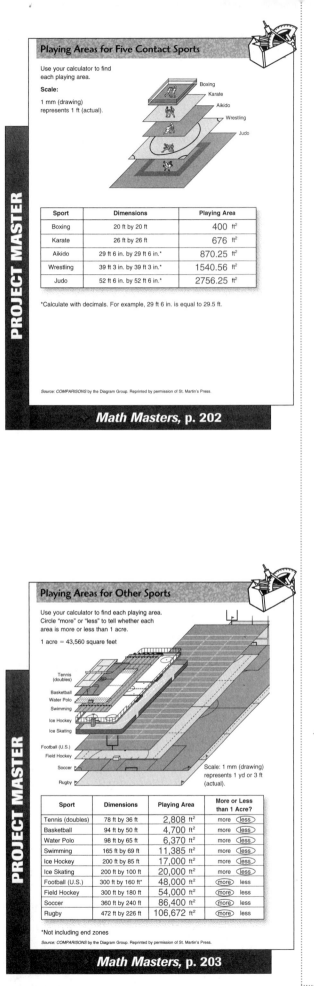

**Playing Areas for Five Contact Sports**

Use your calculator to find each playing area.

**Scale:**

1 mm (drawing) represents 1 ft (actual).

| Sport | Dimensions | Playing Area |
|---|---|---|
| Boxing | 20 ft by 20 ft | 400 ft² |
| Karate | 26 ft by 26 ft | 676 ft² |
| Aikido | 29 ft 6 in. by 29 ft 6 in.* | 870.25 ft² |
| Wrestling | 39 ft 3 in. by 39 ft 3 in.* | 1540.56 ft² |
| Judo | 52 ft 6 in. by 52 ft 6 in.* | 2756.25 ft² |

*Calculate with decimals. For example, 29 ft 6 in. is equal to 29.5 ft.

*Source: COMPARISONS* by the Diagram Group. Reprinted by permission of St. Martin's Press.

**Math Masters, p. 202**

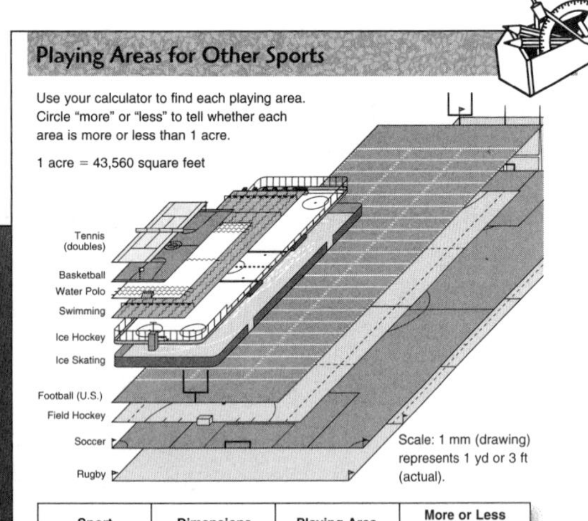



PROJECT MASTER

**Playing Areas for Other Sports**

Use your calculator to find each playing area. Circle "more" or "less" to tell whether each area is more or less than 1 acre.

1 acre = 43,560 square feet

| Sport | Dimensions | Playing Area | More or Less than 1 Acre? |
|---|---|---|---|
| Tennis (doubles) | 78 ft by 36 ft | 2,808 ft² | more (less) |
| Basketball | 94 ft by 50 ft | 4,700 ft² | more (less) |
| Water Polo | 98 ft by 65 ft | 6,370 ft² | more (less) |
| Swimming | 165 ft by 69 ft | 11,385 ft² | more (less) |
| Ice Hockey | 200 ft by 85 ft | 17,000 ft² | more (less) |
| Ice Skating | 200 ft by 100 ft | 20,000 ft² | more (less) |
| Football (U.S.) | 300 ft by 160 ft* | 48,000 ft² | (more) less |
| Field Hockey | 300 ft by 180 ft | 54,000 ft² | (more) less |
| Soccer | 360 ft by 240 ft | 86,400 ft² | (more) less |
| Rugby | 472 ft by 226 ft | 106,672 ft² | (more) less |

*Not including end zones

*Source: COMPARISONS* by the Diagram Group. Reprinted by permission of St. Martin's Press.

**Math Masters, p. 203**

by 180 feet, or 100 yards by 60 yards. The scale drawing on *Math Masters,* page 203 is 100 millimeters by 60 millimeters.

- ▷ The drawings are not **perspective drawings.** In perspective drawings, parallel lines that move away from the viewer are drawn so that they come together at a vanishing point. The proportions in a perspective drawing are not the same as the proportions of the actual object.
- ▷ The surfaces for contact sports shown on *Math Masters,* page 202 are drawn to the scale of 1 millimeter to 1 foot. Have students measure the boxing ring or one of the other surfaces with a ruler and use the scale to convert their measurements to feet. They can check their measurements against the dimensions listed below the drawing.
- ▷ The surfaces for other popular sports shown on *Math Masters,* page 203 were too large to draw with the same scale used on *Math Masters,* page 202. The scale is 1 millimeter to 1 yard (3 feet). If each length and width on page 203 were enlarged to three times its current size, then the playing surfaces shown on both pages would all be drawn to the same scale.

Remind students of the work they did in Lesson 4.3, when they learned how to use a map scale to measure distances on a map. For example, 1 inch on a map might represent 10 miles. On another map, 1 inch might represent 100 miles.

Work through at least one problem from each page with the class. Multiply length times width to find the playing area in square feet. Point out that some dimensions are given in feet and inches. Such measures must be converted to decimals in order to enter them into a calculator.

## ✦ Calculating Sports Areas
(*Math Masters,* pp. 202 and 203)

PARTNER ACTIVITY

Have students complete *Math Masters,* pages 202 and 203. Remind them that they can compare an area to an acre if they know the area in square feet. A sports area of more than 43,560 square feet will be more than 1 acre.

Students may recall that a football field (minus the end zones) is about 1 acre. They will have little difficulty in identifying football, field hockey, soccer, and rugby as sports whose playing areas exceed 1 acre.

# 2 Extending the Project

## ✦ Finding the "Footprints" of Famous Buildings
*(Math Masters, p. 204)*

PARTNER ACTIVITY

Students are given the ground areas in square feet, or "footprints," of seven famous large buildings. Using an equivalence of 1 acre to about 50,000 square feet, they convert these areas to acres.

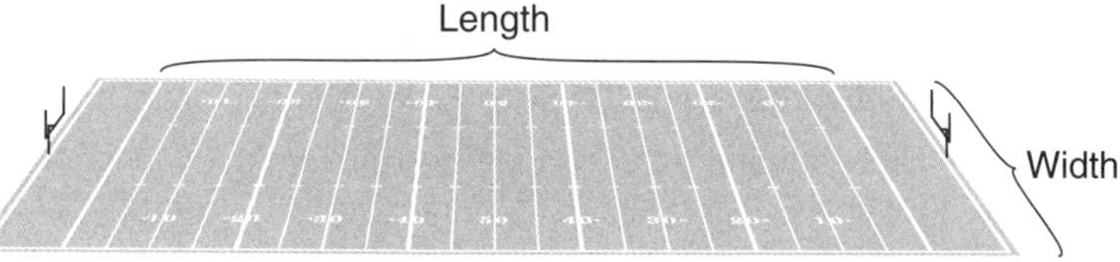


The area of a football field without the end zones is approximately 1 acre.

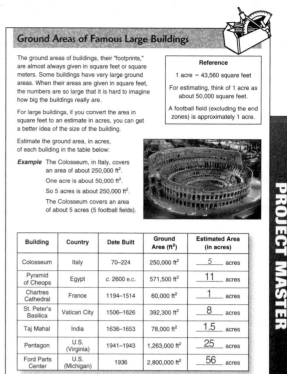

### Ground Areas of Famous Large Buildings

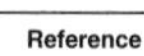

The ground areas of buildings, their "footprints," are almost always given in square feet or square meters. Some buildings have very large ground areas. When their areas are given in square feet, the numbers are so large that it is hard to imagine how big the buildings really are.

For large buildings, if you convert the area in square feet to an estimate in acres, you can get a better idea of the size of the building.

**Reference**

1 acre = 43,560 square feet

For estimating, think of 1 acre as about 50,000 square feet.

A football field (excluding the end zones) is approximately 1 acre.

Estimate the ground area, in acres, of each building in the table below:

***Example*** The Colosseum, in Italy, covers an area of about 250,000 ft$^2$.
One acre is about 50,000 ft$^2$.
So 5 acres is about 250,000 ft$^2$.
The Colosseum covers an area of about 5 acres (5 football fields).

| Building | Country | Date Built | Ground Area (ft$^2$) | Estimated Area (in acres) |
|---|---|---|---|---|
| Colosseum | Italy | 70–224 | 250,000 ft$^2$ | 5 acres |
| Pyramid of Cheops | Egypt | *c.* 2600 B.C. | 571,500 ft$^2$ | 11 acres |
| Chartres Cathedral | France | 1194–1514 | 60,000 ft$^2$ | 1 acres |
| St. Peter's Basilica | Vatican City | 1506–1626 | 392,300 ft$^2$ | 8 acres |
| Taj Mahal | India | 1636–1653 | 78,000 ft$^2$ | 1.5 acres |
| Pentagon | U.S. (Virginia) | 1941–1943 | 1,263,000 ft$^2$ | 25 acres |
| Ford Parts Center | U.S. (Michigan) | 1936 | 2,800,000 ft$^2$ | 56 acres |

PROJECT MASTER

✦ *Math Masters,* p. 204

PROJECT

# Polygon Areas and Pick's Formula

**OBJECTIVE** **To find the areas of polygons and apply Pick's Formula for area.**

**background information**

**Recommended Use:** During or after Unit 9

See the discussion of Projects in the Management Guide section of the *Teacher's Reference Manual.*

**materials**

- □ *Math Masters,* pp. 205–207
- □ geoboard and rubber bands, or geoboard dot paper (optional)

***See* Advance Preparation**

## Project Information

Students extend the rectangle method or choose other methods to find areas of polygons. Pick's Formula is introduced as an alternative way to find the area of a figure drawn on a square grid or formed on a geoboard.

**Advance Preparation** Geoboards will be helpful in this lesson. You may want to borrow enough to supply one geoboard per partnership. You may also want to use an overhead geoboard and elastic bands, or make an overhead transparency of geoboard dot paper.

**Vocabulary • grid points • interior • vertices**

## 1 Doing the Project

### ✦ Finding Areas of Polygons
(*Math Masters,* p. 205)

PARTNER ACTIVITY 

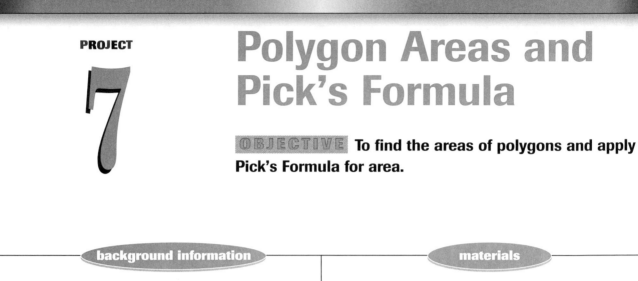

Students find the areas of the polygons on *Math Masters,* page 205 and record them in the table. Encourage students to use any of the strategies they know for finding areas.

When most students have completed the page, discuss the methods they used to find the areas. Keep a list of the strategies. The rectangle method can be used with all the figures. Examples of other strategies:

- ▷ Figure A: Measure a base and height and use the *formula for the area of a triangle.* Remind students that the height of the triangle must be measured perpendicular to the base of the triangle.

NOTE: For figures that are "tilted" on the grid, it may not be possible to read lengths of bases or heights directly from the grid. Students who use area formulas may need to be advised to measure "slant" lengths very carefully (to millimeters) and to use their calculators to multiply the resulting decimals to get close approximations of the areas.

- ▷ Figure B: Carefully measure the sides (about 3.6 cm each) and use the *formula for the area of a rectangle.*
- ▷ Figure C: *Count squares and half-squares* to find the area of the figure.
- ▷ Figure D: *Partition* the trapezoid into a square and a triangle. Measure bases and heights carefully and then calculate the areas and add them together.
- ▷ Figure E: This figure is challenging to most students. The *rectangle method* works very nicely here. Partitioning the polygon into many triangles is possible but tedious.
- ▷ Figure F: Measure carefully and use the *formula for the area of a triangle.* Once again, caution students that the height of the triangle is measured perpendicular to the base of the triangle.

## ✦ Introducing Pick's Formula
(*Math Masters,* p. 206)

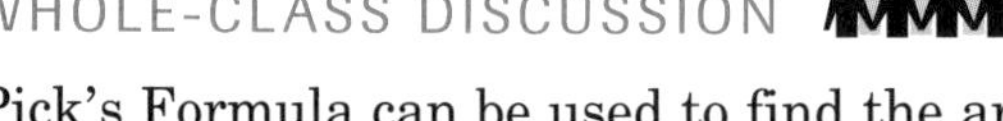


Pick's Formula can be used to find the area of any polygon that has its vertices at grid points on a square grid or geoboard.

Have students read the description of Pick's Formula and the example on *Math Masters,* page 206. Discuss the formula. Be sure students understand how $P$ (the number of **grid points** on the polygon, including **vertices**) and $I$ (the number of grid points in the **interior** of the polygon) are counted and how they are used in the calculation of area.

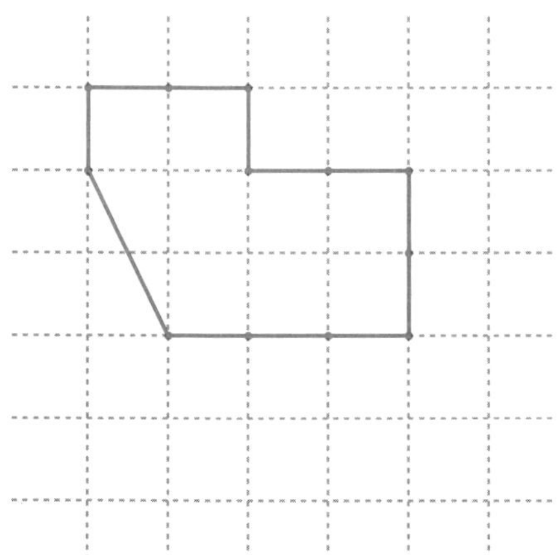

You may want to draw several figures on an overhead transparency of geoboard dot paper and work through Pick's Formula with the class to find the areas of the figures. Alternatively, form the figures on a geoboard for the overhead projector.

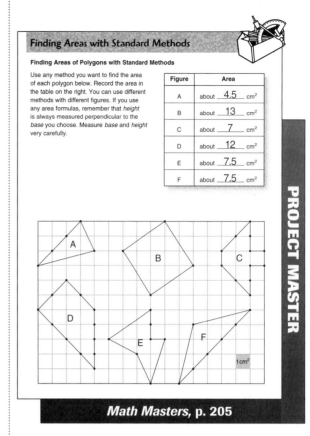

**Finding Areas with Standard Methods**

**Finding Areas of Polygons with Standard Methods**

Use any method you want to find the area of each polygon below. Record the area in the table on the right. You can use different methods with different figures. If you use any area formulas, remember that *height* is always measured perpendicular to the *base* you choose. Measure *base* and *height* very carefully.

| Figure | Area |
| --- | --- |
| A | about 4.5 cm² |
| B | about 13 cm² |
| C | about 7 cm² |
| D | about 12 cm² |
| E | about 7.5 cm² |
| F | about 7.5 cm² |

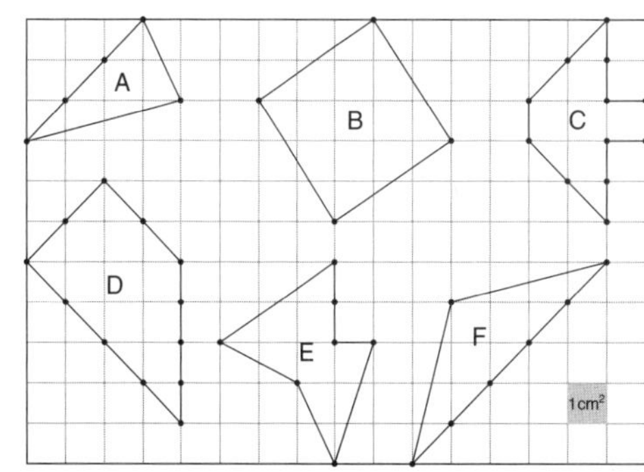


PROJECT MASTER

*Math Masters,* p. 205

NOTE: Pick's Formula, also called Pick's Theorem, was first published in 1899 by Austrian mathematician Georg Alexander Pick (1859–1943?). The proof of this odd but elegant formula is beyond the scope of this book, as is the proof that it is equivalent to the formula linking the number of edges ($e$), faces ($f$), and vertices ($v$) of any polyhedron: $e = f + v - 2$.

## Finding Areas with Pick's Formula

Read the paragraphs below and then use Pick's Formula to find the areas of the polygons on the previous page. Record them in the table below. Compare them to your results recorded in the table on the previous page. You should expect some differences—measures are always estimates.

**Pick's Formula for Finding Polygon Areas by Counting**

In 1899 Georg Pick, an Austrian mathematician, discovered a formula for finding the area of a polygon on a square grid (such as graph paper). If a polygon has its vertices at grid points, its area can be found by counting the number of grid points on the polygon *(P)* and the number of grid points in the interior of the polygon *(I)* and then using the formula $A = (\frac{1}{2} * P) + I - 1$. The unit of area is one square on the grid.

For figure B on the previous page, the unit of area is $cm^2$.

$P = 4$ (grid points on polygon)

$I = 12$ (grid points in interior)

$A = (\frac{1}{2} * P) + I - 1$

$= (\frac{1}{2} * 4) + 12 - 1$

$= 13\ cm^2$

| Figure | P | I | Area = $(\frac{1}{2} * P) + I - 1$ |
|---|---|---|---|
| A | 5 | 3 | 4.5 $cm^2$ |
| B | 4 | 12 | 13 $cm^2$ |
| C | 12 | 2 | 7 $cm^2$ |
| D | 12 | 7 | 12 $cm^2$ |
| E | 7 | 5 | 7.5 $cm^2$ |
| F | 7 | 5 | 7.5 $cm^2$ |

Draw two polygons. Be sure that the vertices are at grid points.
Use Pick's Formula to find the areas of the polygons.

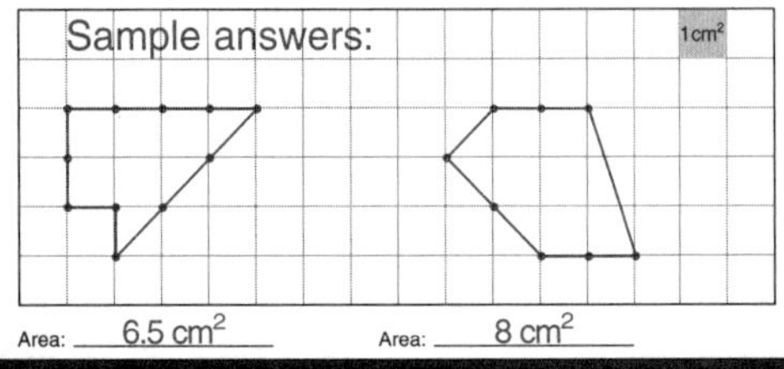


Area: 6.5 $cm^2$ Area: 8 $cm^2$

PROJECT MASTER

Math Masters, p. 206

## Finding Areas with Pick's Formula (cont.)

You may have found the area of this shaded path in Lesson 9.6.

Now use Pick's Formula to find the area.

1 cm²

The area of the path is 33 $cm^2$.

Do you think Pick's Formula is a good way to find this area?

Explain. Answers vary.

PROJECT MASTER

Math Masters, p. 207

## Using Pick's Formula

(*Math Masters,* pp. 205 and 206)

PARTNER ACTIVITY 

Geoboards provide a fine way to practice using Pick's Formula quickly with many polygons.

Have students use Pick's Formula to find the areas of the polygons on *Math Masters,* page 205. They record the areas on *Math Masters,* page 206.

If students have geoboards, they may want to form the figures before using Pick's Formula. Encourage partners who finish early to create new problems for each other on a geoboard or geoboard dot paper.

# 2 Extending the Project

## Using Pick's Formula to Find the Area of an Irregular Path

(*Math Masters,* p. 207)

INDEPENDENT ACTIVITY  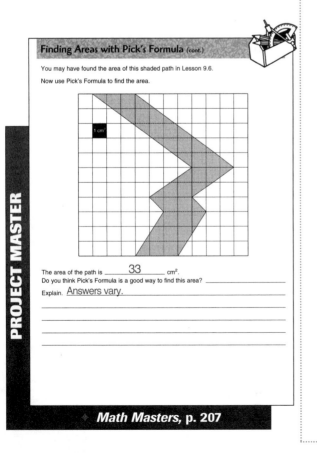

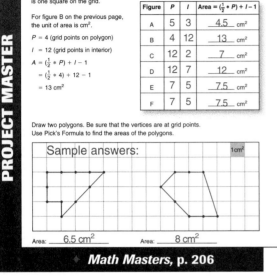

Students use Pick's Formula to find the area of the path on *Math Masters,* page 207. This path appeared in Lesson 9.6 (*Math Masters,* page 130).

Students discuss whether they think Pick's Formula is an efficient method for calculating this area.

PROJECT

# Pendulums

**OBJECTIVE To investigate whether the length of a pendulum affects the duration of one complete swing of the pendulum; whether the length of the arc of a pendulum affects the duration of the swing; and whether the amount of weight at the end of a pendulum affects the duration of the swing.**

## background information

**Recommended Use:** During or after Unit 10

See the discussion of Projects in the Management Guide section of the *Teacher's Reference Manual.*

## materials

- ☐ *Math Masters,* pp. 208–210
- ☐ per small group:
  - string pendulum
  - ruler or meter stick
  - watch or clock to time seconds (preferable to tenths of a second)
  - at least 10 metal washers or similar weights

***See* Advance Preparation**

## Project Information

According to legend, Galileo discovered the principle of the pendulum in 1583 while watching a hanging lamp swing back and forth in a cathedral in Pisa. Both Galileo and Christiaan Huygens (1656) are credited with designing a clock controlled by the motion of a pendulum.

After a whole-class introduction to pendulums, students work in small groups to investigate how the length of a pendulum affects the time it takes the pendulum to make one complete swing. They also investigate whether the length of the swing's arc, or the amount of weight at the end of a pendulum, affects the duration of the swing. These activities provide a review of measuring, gathering and recording data; finding averages; graphing; and drawing conclusions.

**Advance Preparation** Prepare one string pendulum for each small group. Cut as many strings, about $1\frac{1}{2}$ meters long, as there are groups. Tie a paper clip to one end of each string. Then, as a helper stretches all the strings tight, use a felt-tip marker to make marks on each string 5 cm, 10 cm, 20 cm, 30 cm, 50 cm, 75 cm, and 1 meter from the end of the paper clip. Open up the clip so that large metal washers or similar weights can be hung on it. (You may want to have students assist in making the pendulums.)

Provide at least 10 metal washers or other weights, a meterstick or ruler, and a seconds timer for each small group.

Prepare one additional pendulum for demonstration purposes with a string at least 2 meters long and a paper clip at one end. Make marks on the string 50 cm, 75 cm, and 2 m from the paper clip.

**Vocabulary • complete swing • pendulum**

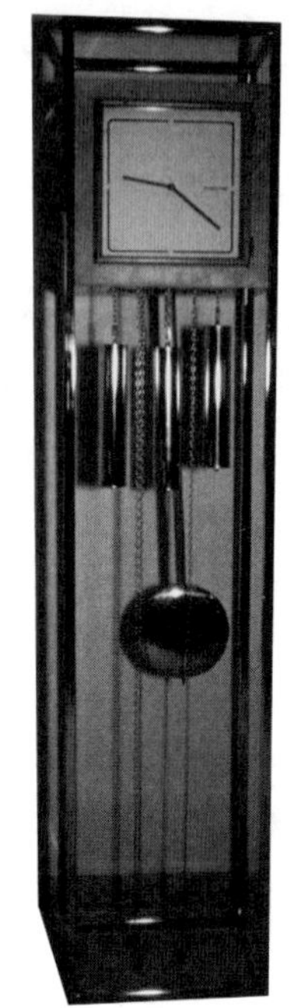

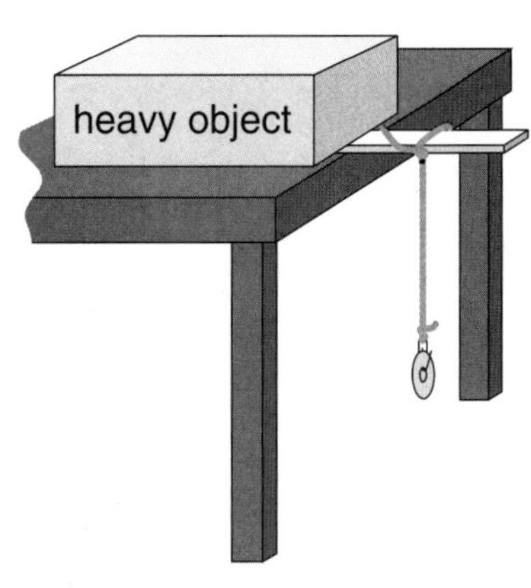


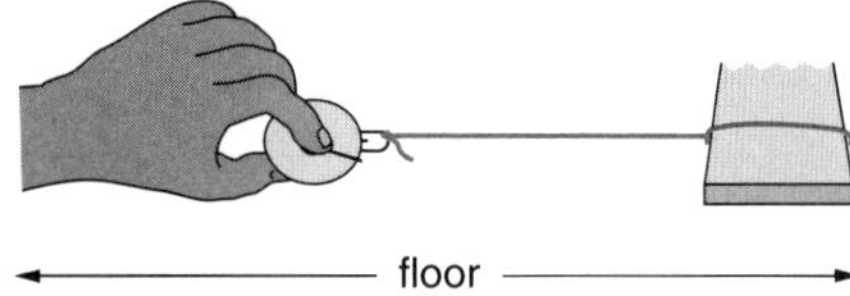


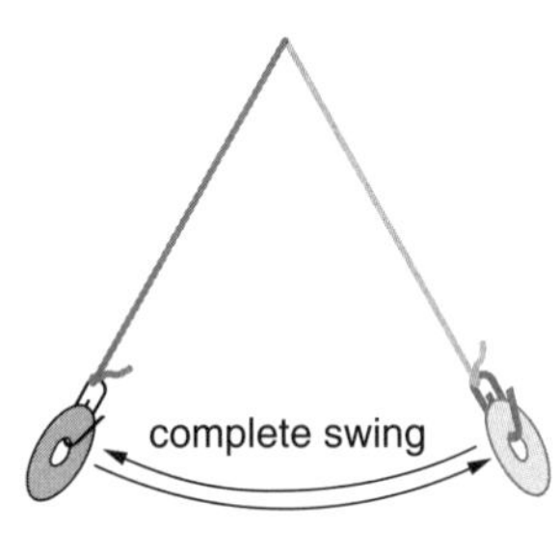


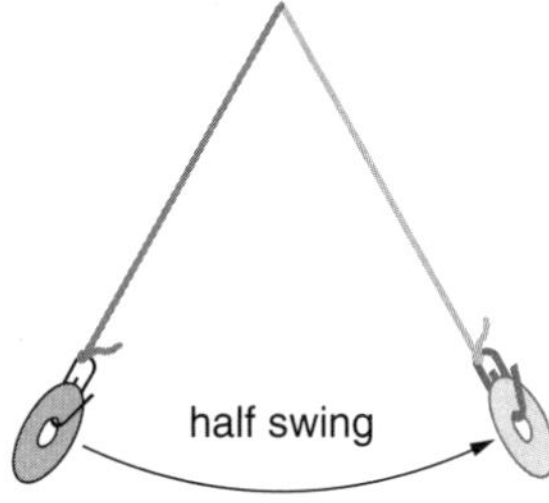


# 1 Doing the Project

## ✦ Discussing Pendulums

WHOLE-CLASS DISCUSSION

A **pendulum** consists of an object (called the *bob*) suspended from a fixed support in such a way that the object can swing freely back and forth under the influence of gravity.

Ask students to share their ideas of what pendulums are. One example would be the pendulum in a clock, but some students may not be familiar with this type of clock. Some students may have been to a science museum and seen a very long pendulum (a Foucault pendulum) that demonstrates the rotation of the Earth.

## ✦ Demonstrating and Timing a Pendulum (*Math Masters,* p. 208)

WHOLE-CLASS DISCUSSION

Demonstrate how to set up a string pendulum on a desk or table, as follows:

1. Form a pendulum 50 cm long.
2. Hold the pendulum fairly high (approximately parallel to the floor) and release it. In a **complete swing,** the pendulum swings forward, stops for an instant, swings back (almost) to its starting position, and stops for an instant. Swinging in just one direction is a half-swing.
3. Tell students that they will perform experiments to try to answer the question, "Does the time it takes a pendulum to make a complete swing depend on the length of the string?" Ask students to predict what the answer will be.

Now use the pendulum to demonstrate how to time 10 complete swings of the pendulum.

1. Ask a student to keep time with a seconds timer.
2. Pull the pendulum to one side. As you release it, say "Go." The student starts timing.
3. With the class, count out 10 complete swings (not half-swings).
4. When the pendulum finishes its tenth complete swing, say "Stop." The student stops timing.
5. The student gives the elapsed time (to the nearest tenth of a second, if possible).

6. Ask students to use the time for 10 swings to calculate the approximate time for one complete swing, to the nearest tenth or hundredth of a second. Divide by 10. Have students record the times for 10 swings and for 1 swing in Problem 1 on *Math Masters,* page 208, and in the table at the bottom of the page.

Some students may wonder why it is necessary to time 10 complete swings in order to obtain an accurate time measurement for a single swing. Why not simply time a single swing? Point out that timing a single complete swing can be tricky, and the chance of error is great. But timing 10 swings is easy—even the shortest pendulum will take about 5 seconds for 10 swings.

NOTE: The time for one complete swing is called the *period* of the pendulum. A later activity in the project shows that even though the pendulum doesn't swing quite as far on each subsequent swing, this does not affect the period.

## ✦ Investigating the Swing Times for Pendulums of Various Lengths
(*Math Masters,* pp. 208 and 209)

SMALL-GROUP ACTIVITY 

### 1. Practicing Timing Swings of a 75-cm Pendulum

Have each group form a 75-cm pendulum and time 10 swings. Ask groups to do several additional practice trials. Circulate, observe, and assist.

When students have demonstrated that they have acquired the knack for timing the pendulum, have them do a trial that "counts." They should then record the time for 10 complete swings and 1 complete swing in Problem 2 and in the table at the bottom of *Math Masters,* page 208.

### 2. Collecting Data for Pendulums of Various Lengths

Ask for three volunteers. Two stand on chairs about 2 meters apart. One of them holds the demonstration pendulum by the weighted end. The other holds the string at the 2-meter mark. The third student prepares to keep time. The volunteers then time 10 complete swings of this pendulum. Students calculate the duration of one swing and record the results in the table.

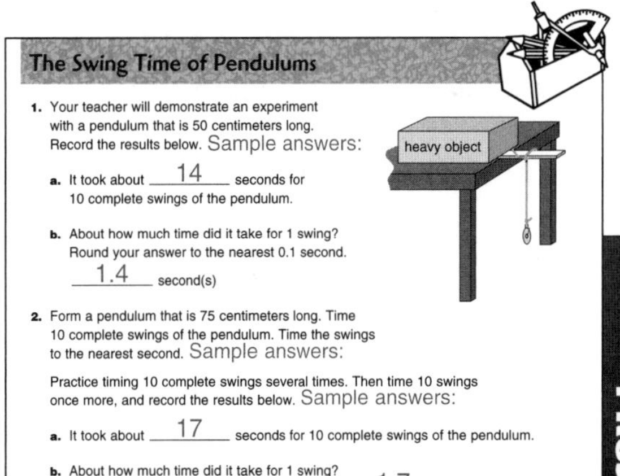

**The Swing Time of Pendulums**



1. Your teacher will demonstrate an experiment with a pendulum that is 50 centimeters long. Record the results below. Sample answers:
   a. It took about 14 seconds for 10 complete swings of the pendulum.
   b. About how much time did it take for 1 swing? Round your answer to the nearest 0.1 second. 1.4 second(s)
2. Form a pendulum that is 75 centimeters long. Time 10 complete swings of the pendulum. Time the swings to the nearest second. Sample answers:
   Practice timing 10 complete swings several times. Then time 10 swings once more, and record the results below. Sample answers:
   a. It took about 17 seconds for 10 complete swings of the pendulum.
   b. About how much time did it take for 1 swing? Round your answer to the nearest 0.1 second. 1.7 second(s)
3. Record the results for a 50-cm and a 75-cm pendulum in the table at the right. Sample answers:
4. Experiment with different lengths of pendulum string.

   Find the time for 10 complete swings for each of the other pendulum lengths. Time the 10 swings to the nearest 0.1 second. Record your results in the table.

   After collecting your data, divide each of the times by 10 to estimate the time for 1 complete swing. Record your answers in the table, rounded to the nearest 0.1 second.

| Length of pendulum | Time for: 10 complete swings (to nearest 0.1 sec) | 1 complete swing (to nearest 0.1 sec) |
|---|---|---|
| 5 cm | 4.5 sec | 0.5 sec |
| 10 cm | 6.3 sec | 0.6 sec |
| 20 cm | 9.0 sec | 0.9 sec |
| 30 cm | 11.0 sec | 1.1 sec |
| 50 cm | 14.0 sec | 1.4 sec |
| 75 cm | 17.4 sec | 1.7 sec |
| 100 cm | 20.0 sec | 2.0 sec |
| 200 cm | 28.4 sec | 2.8 sec |

PROJECT MASTER

✦ *Math Masters,* p. 208

Students work in groups to continue the investigation by timing 10 swings for pendulums with string lengths 5 cm, 10 cm, 20 cm, 30 cm, and 1 m. Circulate and help as needed. Each student records the time for 10 swings and divides by 10 to find the average time for a single swing, to the nearest tenth of a second.

Check the reasonableness of data entries of groups that finish early. They may go on to Problem 6 while waiting for the others to catch up. They should not begin the graphing exercise in Problem 5 on *Math Masters,* page 209 until you say so.

### 3. Graphing the Results

After all groups have completed their trials and found the average time for 10 swings to the nearest tenth of a second, help students plot one or two data points on the grid in Problem 5 on *Math Masters,* page 209. Students then plot the rest of the results recorded in the table on *Math Masters,* page 208.

Ask students to connect the dots to form a broken-line graph. In discussing the graph, ask questions such as the following:

- Does the length of the string affect the duration of the swing? The time for one complete swing increases as the length of the pendulum string increases. Some students may notice that quadrupling the length of the pendulum string doubles the swing time.
- About how many seconds (to the nearest tenth of a second) would it take for a complete swing of a 150-cm pendulum? About 2.4 seconds
- About how long is a pendulum that takes 2 seconds to complete a swing? 100 cm
- Based on the results, what might be the swing time for a much longer pendulum—say 10, 20, or even 30 meters long? Possible responses: 10 m: about 6 seconds; 20 m: about 9 seconds; 30 m: about 11 seconds

NOTE: If a group's results are markedly different from the others, discuss how this might have happened (for example, counting half-swings instead of complete swings; starting or stopping timing too early or too late; making the pendulum the wrong length). In such cases, suggest that the group use data from another group for the graphing exercise.

**Adjusting the Activity** Suggest that students make long pendulums that they can safely swing from high places, time the swings, and report the results to the class. If several students do this activity, you or the students might prepare a larger graph incorporating the results.

NOTE: For your information, the formula for calculating the time needed for a complete swing of a pendulum based on its length is:
Time in seconds $= 2 * \pi * \sqrt{\frac{\text{length in meters}}{9.8}}$

## ✦ Investigating the Effect of the Arc on Swing Time (*Math Masters,* p. 209)

SMALL-GROUP ACTIVITY

Have students start the swing of a pendulum at various positions. They try to answer the question, "Does the size of the arc make much of a difference in the amount of time it takes for 10 complete swings?" They record their answer in Problem 6 on *Math Masters,* page 209. For a given pendulum length, the position of the starting point should not significantly affect the time for a complete swing.

## ✦ Investigating the Effect of Weight on Swing Time (*Math Masters,* p. 210)

SMALL-GROUP ACTIVITY

Students try to answer the question, "Does the amount of weight at the end of a pendulum affect the time for 10 complete swings?" Using the 50-cm pendulum, they vary the weight by adding or removing washers. For a given pendulum length, different weights should make little difference in the time for a complete swing. However, the heavier the weight, the longer the pendulum is likely to keep swinging.

**The Swing Time of Pendulums** (cont.)

Wait for instructions from your teacher before drawing the graph in Problem 5.

**5.** Construct a graph to show the amount of time it took for each length of the pendulum to complete 1 swing.

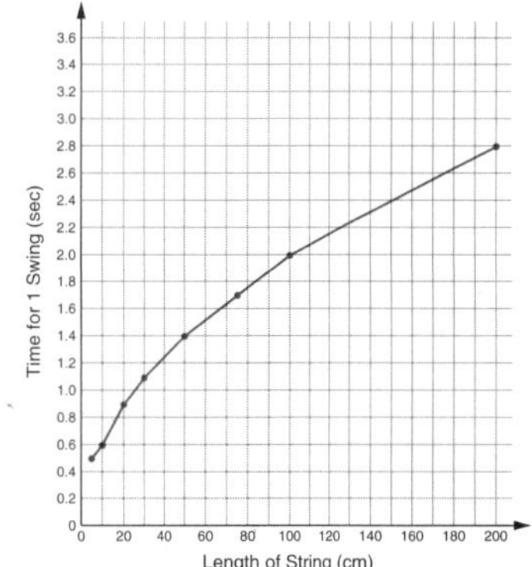


**6.** Experiment with different arc sizes. The largest arc is formed when the string of the pendulum is in a horizontal position. Does the size of the arc make much of a difference in the amount of time it takes for 10 complete swings?

no

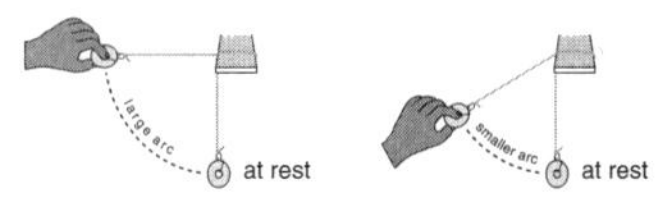


PROJECT MASTER

◇ *Math Masters,* p. 209

# 2 Extending the Project

## ✦ Learning More about Pendulums

INDEPENDENT ACTIVITY 

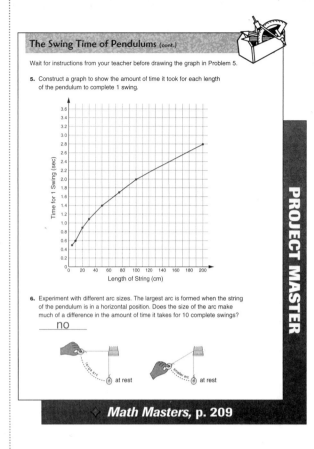

Invite students to find out more about the history, types, and uses of pendulums by looking in encyclopedias and science books. The book *Longitude* by Dava Sobel (New York: Walker, 1995; illustrated edition 1998) tells the fascinating story of the search for a way to determine longitude aboard ships at sea. The solution came in the eighteenth century in the form of precise clocks designed so that a ship's motion and variations in temperature and humidity did not affect the clocks' pendulums.

**The Swing Time of Pendulums** (cont.)

**7.** Does the weight of the object at the end of a pendulum affect the time for a complete swing? Using a pendulum with a string 50 cm long, try different numbers of objects to find out if weight makes a difference in the time of the swing.

| Length of pendulum | Number of weights (washers or other objects) | Time for 10 swings (to nearest 0.1 sec) | Time for 1 swing (to nearest 0.1 or 0.01 sec) |
|---|---|---|---|
| 50 cm | 1 | 14 sec | 1.4 sec |
| 50 cm | 3 | 14 sec | 1.4 sec |
| 50 cm | 5 | 14 sec | 1.4 sec |
| 50 cm | 10 | 14 sec | 1.4 sec |

My conclusion: It seems that Sample answer: the weight of the attached object does not seem to have an effect on the duration of a complete swing.

**A Long Time?**

The Convention Center in Portland, Oregon, has one of the longest pendulums in the world. The "string" is 90 feet long, and the weight at the end is 900 pounds. Visitors may walk beneath the pendulum with the weight swinging 23 feet above their heads.

Source: *The Guinness Book of Records 1993.*

PROJECT MASTER

◇ *Math Masters,* p. 210

# Fifth Grade Key Vocabulary

**account balance** An amount of money that you have or that you owe. See "*in the black*" and "*in the red.*"

**acute angle** An angle with a measure greater than 0° and less than 90°.

acute angles

**adjacent angles** Two angles with a common side and vertex that do not otherwise overlap.

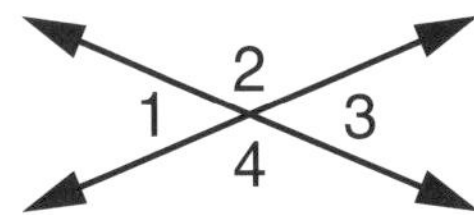


Angles 1 and 2, 2 and 3, 3 and 4, and 4 and 1 are pairs of adjacent angles.

**apex** In a pyramid or cone, the vertex opposite the base. In a pyramid, all the non-base faces meet at the apex.

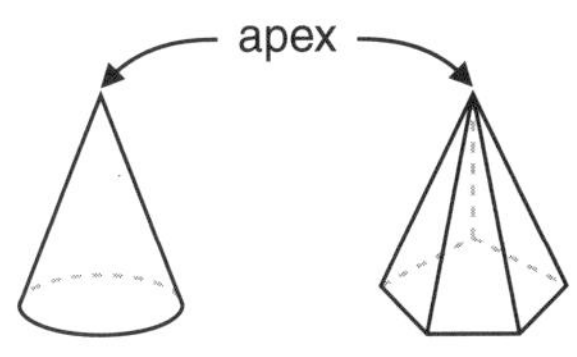


**area** A measure of a bounded surface. The boundary might be a triangle or rectangle in a plane or the boundaries of a state or country on Earth's surface. Area is expressed in square units such as square miles, square inches, or square centimeters, and can be thought of as the approximate number of non-overlapping squares that will "tile" or "cover" the surface within the boundary.

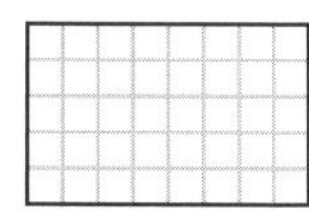

40 square units 21 square units

**area model** (1) A model for multiplication in which the length and width of a rectangle represent the factors and the area of the rectangle represents the product.

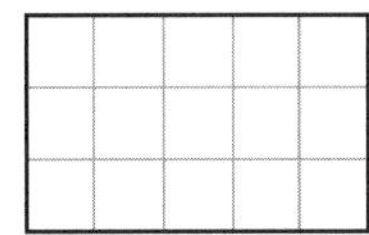

area model for $3 * 5 = 15$

(2) A model for fractions that represents parts of a whole. The whole is a region, such as a circle or a rectangle, representing the number ONE.

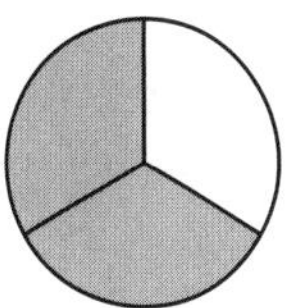

area model for $\frac{2}{3}$

**axis** (1) Either of the two number lines used to form a coordinate grid. Plural *axes.*

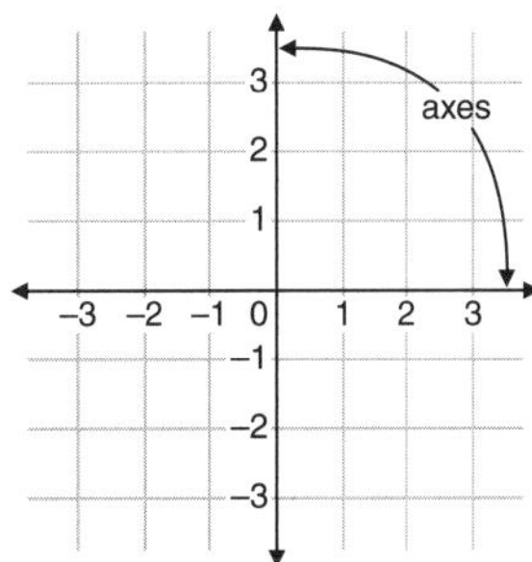


(2) A line about which a solid figure rotates.

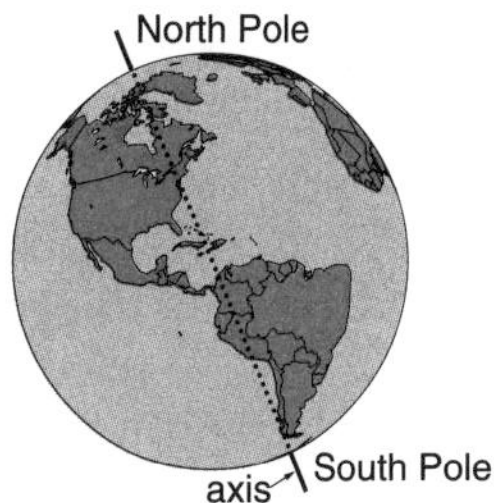


**bar graph** A graph that shows relationships in data by the use of bars to represent quantities. See examples on page 440.

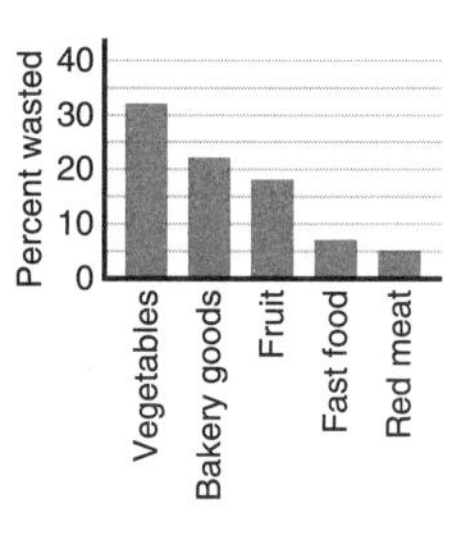

Source: The Garbage Product

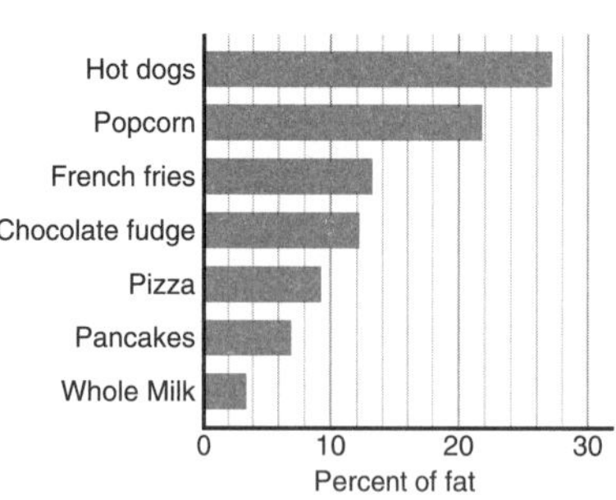

Source: The New York Public Library Desk Reference

**base** (1) Geometry: A side of a polygon, usually used for area computations along with the "altitude," or height, perpendicular to it. See *base of a parallelogram* and *base of a triangle.*

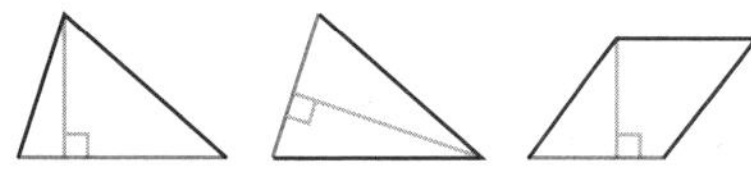

Bases are shown in blue, altitudes in grey.

(2) Geometry: Either of two parallel and congruent faces that define the shape of a prism or cylinder, or the face that defines the shape of a cone or pyramid. See *base of a prism or cylinder* and *base of a pyramid or cone.*

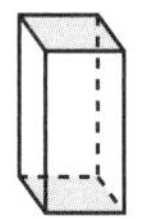 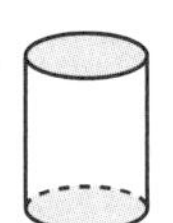  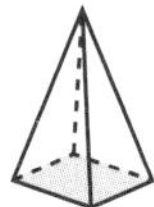

Bases are shown in blue.

(3) Arithmetic: See *exponential notation.*
(4) Arithmetic: The foundation number for a numeration system. For example, our ordinary system for writing numbers is a base-ten place-value system, with 1, 10, 100, 1,000 and other powers of 10 as the values of the places in whole numbers. In computers, bases of two, eight, or sixteen are usual, instead of base ten.

$$356 = 300 + 50 + 6$$

expanded notation for a base-ten number

**base of a parallelogram** One of the sides of a parallelogram; also, the length of this side. In calculating area, the base is used along with the height, or altitude, which is measured on a perpendicular to the side opposite this base. See *height of a parallelogram.*

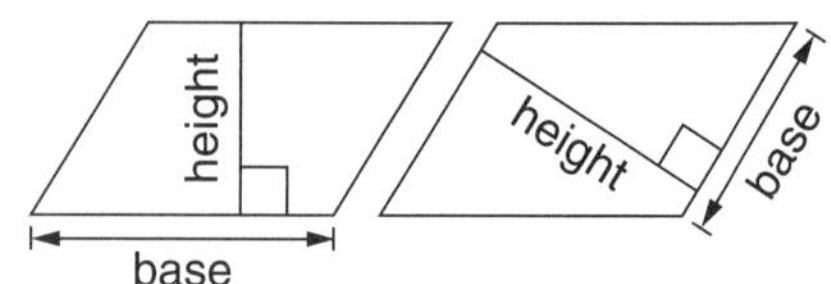


**base of a prism or cylinder** Either of the two parallel, congruent faces of a prism or cylinder that define its shape and are used to determine its name and classification. In a cylinder, the base is a circle or ellipse. See *height of a prism or cylinder.*

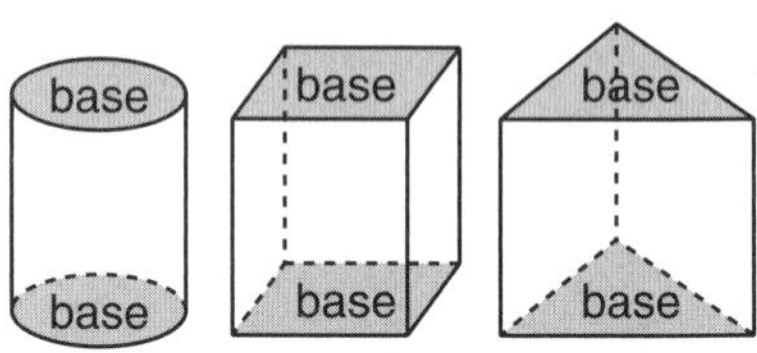


cylinder and two prisms

**base of a pyramid or cone** The face of a pyramid that defines its shape and is used to name and classify the pyramid. The base of a pyramid is the face opposite the apex, which is the vertex where all the other faces meet. The base of a cone is a circle. See *height of a pyramid or cone.*

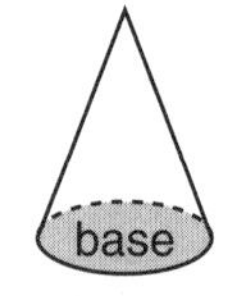 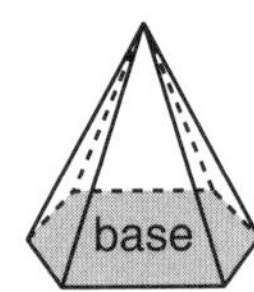


cone and a hexagonal pyramid

**base of a triangle** The side of a triangle to which an altitude is drawn; also, the length of this side. The height, or altitude, is the length of the shortest line segment between the line containing the base and the vertex opposite the base; the height is perpendicular to the base. See *height of a triangle.*

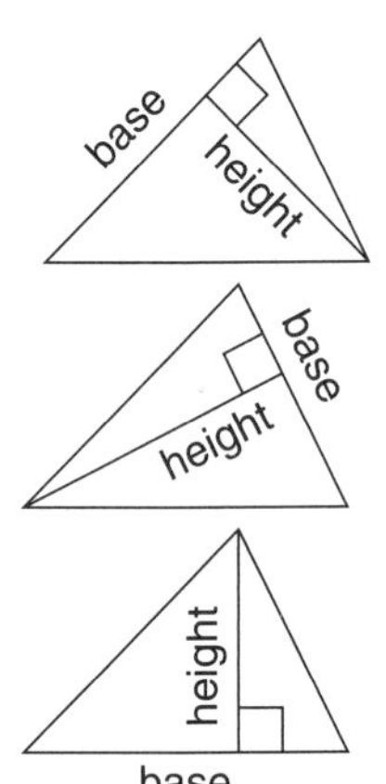


**calibrate** To divide or mark something, such as a thermometer, with gradations.

**capacity** (1) A measure of how much a container can hold, usually in such units as *quart, gallon, cup,* or *liter.* See *volume.*
(2) The maximum weight a scale can measure.

**census** An official count of population and the recording of such data as age, sex, income, education, and so on.

**center** Of a circle: The point in the plane of a circle equally distant from all points on the circle.
Of a sphere: The point equally distant from all points on the sphere.

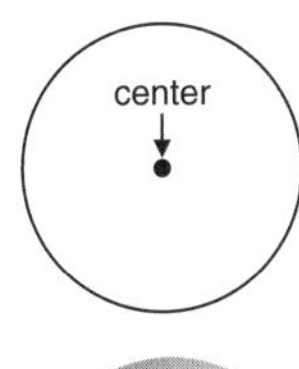

**change diagram** In *Everyday Mathematics*, a diagram used to represent situations in which quantities are either increased or decreased. The diagram includes the starting quantity, the ending quantity, and the amount of change. Change diagrams can be helpful in solving many one-step addition and subtraction problems. See *situation diagram*.

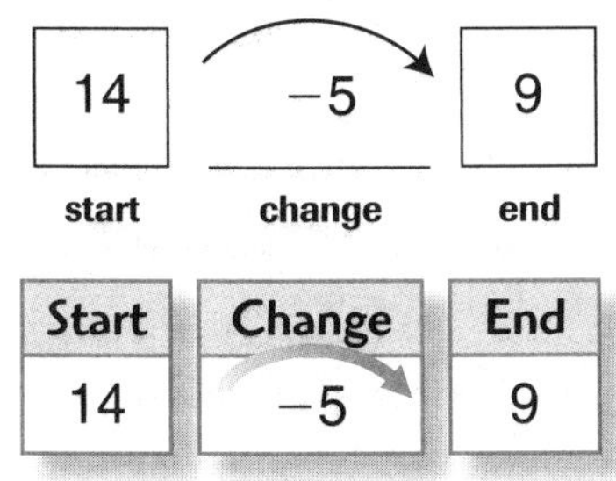


change diagrams for 14 − 5 = 9

**change-to-less story** A number story that describes a change situation in which the ending quantity is less than the starting quantity. A number story about spending money is an example of a change-to-less story. Compare to *change-to-more story*.

**change-to-more-story** A number story that describes a change situation in which the ending quantity is more than the starting quantity. A number story about earning money is an example of a change-to-more story. Compare to *change-to-less story*.

**circle graph** A graph in which a circle and its interior are divided into parts to represent the parts of a set of data. The whole circle represents the whole set of data. Same as *pie graph*.

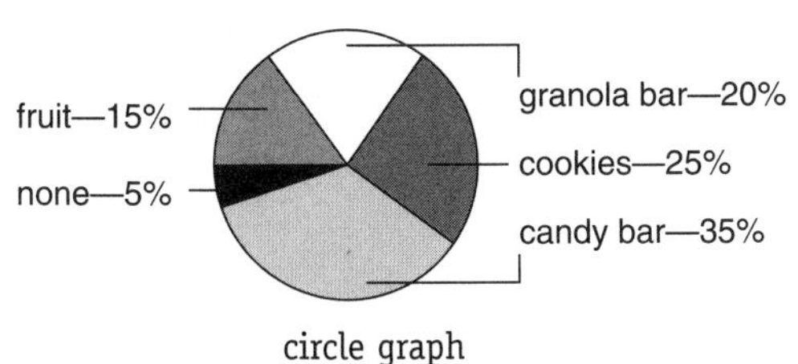


circle graph

**circumference** The distance around a circle or maximum distance around a sphere.

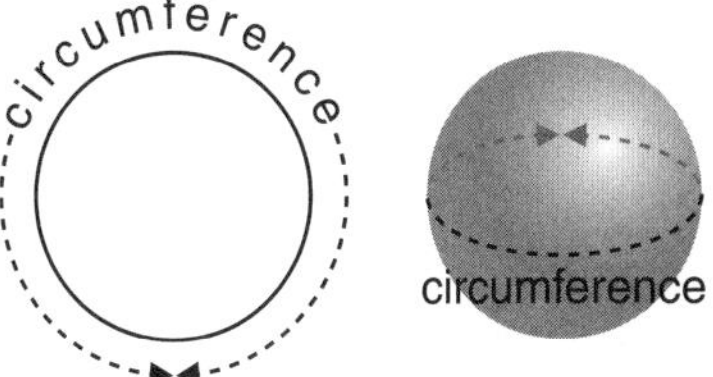


**column-addition method** An addition procedure in which the addends' digits are first added in each place-value column separately, and then 10-for-1 trades are made until each column has only one digit. Lines may be drawn to separate the place-value columns.

**common denominator** Any nonzero number that is a multiple of the denominators of two or more fractions. For example, the fractions $\frac{1}{2}$ and $\frac{2}{3}$ have common denominators 6, 12, 18, and so on. See *denominator*.

**common factor** Any number that is a factor of two or more numbers. The common factors of 18 and 24 are 1, 2, 3, and 6. See *factor*.

**commutative property** A property of addition and multiplication (but not division or subtraction) that says that changing the order of the elements being added or multiplied will not change the sum or product.

For addition: $a + b = b + a$, so $5 + 10 = 10 + 5$
For multiplication: $a \times b = b \times a$,
so $5 \times 10 = 10 \times 5$.

**composite number** A whole number that has more than two factors. For example, 10 is a composite number because it has more than two factors: 1, 2, 5, and 10. A composite number is divisible by at least three whole numbers. Compare to *prime number*.

**cone** A 3-dimensional shape having a circular base, a curved lateral surface, and one vertex, called the *apex*.

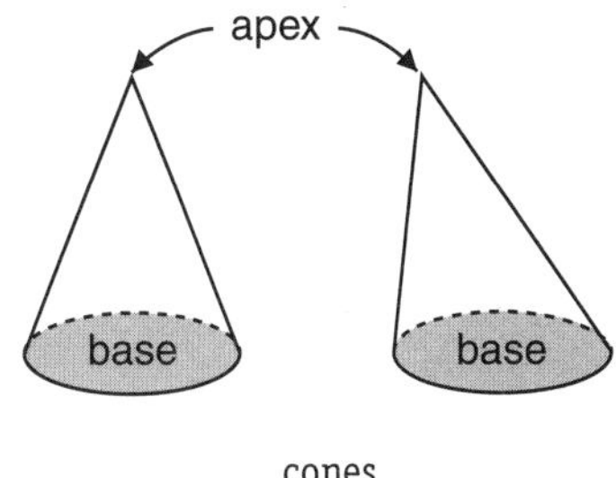


cones

**congruent** Having the same size and shape. Two figures are congruent if a combination of slides, flips, and turns can be used to move one of the figures so that it exactly fits "on top of" the other figure. In diagrams of congruent figures, the congruent sides may be marked with the same number of tick marks. The symbol $\cong$ means "is congruent to."

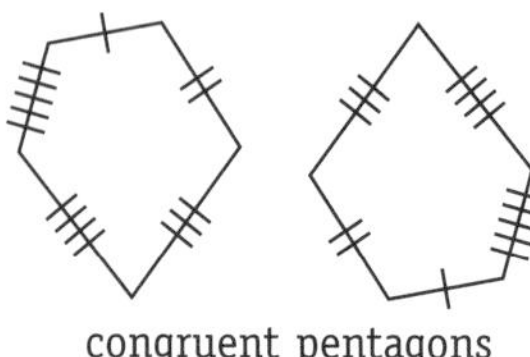

congruent pentagons

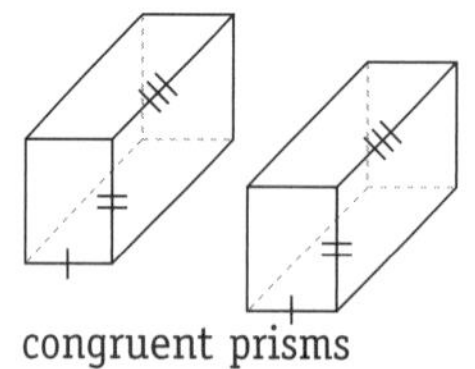

congruent prisms

**contour line** A curve on a map through places where a measurement (such as temperature, elevation, air pressure, or growing season) is constant.

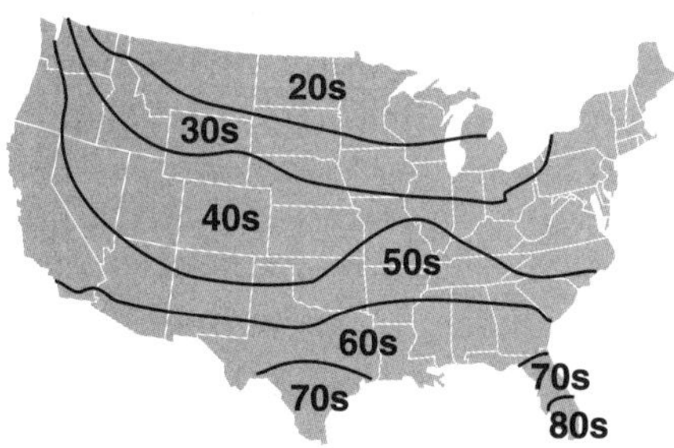


**contour map** A map that uses contour lines to delineate areas according to a particular feature, such as elevation or climate. See *contour line*.

**coordinate** A number used to locate a point on a number line, or one of two numbers used to locate a point on a coordinate grid.

**coordinate grid** A device for locating points in a plane by means of ordered pairs of numbers. A rectangular coordinate grid is formed by two number lines that intersect at right angles at their zero points.

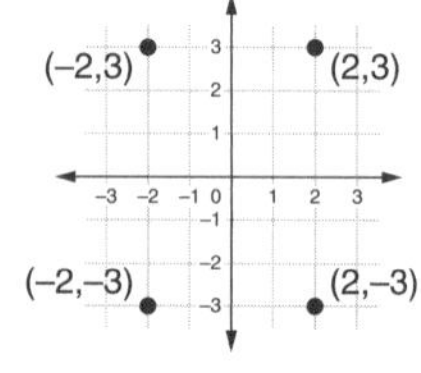


coordinate grid

**cube** A polyhedron with six square faces. One of the 5 regular polyhedra. See *regular polyhedron*.

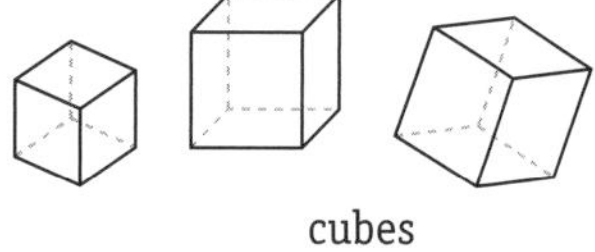

cubes

**cubic centimeter (cc or cm$^3$)** A metric unit of volume; the volume of a cube that is 1 centimeter on a side. 1 cubic centimeter is equal to 1 milliliter.

**cubic unit** A unit used in measuring volume. Common cubic units include cubic centimeters, cubic inches, cubic feet, and cubic meters.

**cubit** An ancient unit of length, measured from the point of the elbow to the end of the middle finger. The cubit has been standardized at various times to be between 18 and 22 inches. The Latin word cubitum means "elbow."

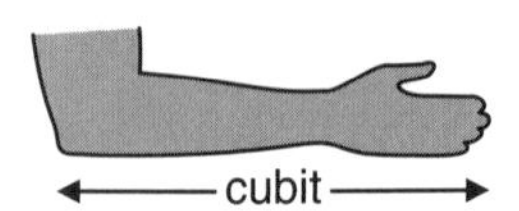


**cup** In the U.S. customary system, a unit of capacity equal to 8 fluid ounces; $\frac{1}{2}$ pint.

**curved surface** (1) A surface which does not lie in a plane; for example, a sphere or the lateral surface of a cylinder.
(2) A non-base surface of a cone or cylinder.

**cylinder** A 3-dimensional shape having a curved surface and parallel, congruent, circular or elliptical bases. A can is a common object shaped like a cylinder.

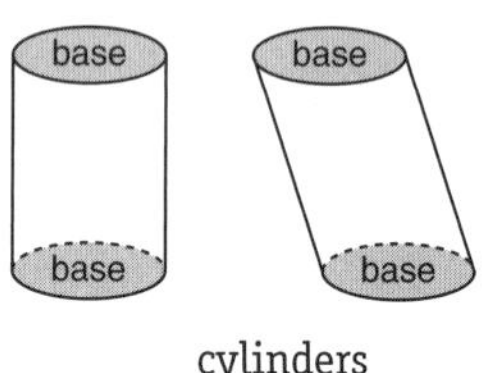


cylinders

**denominator** In a fraction, the number written below the line or to the right of the slash. In the fraction $\frac{a}{b}$ or *a*/*b*, *b* is the denominator. In a part-whole fraction, the denominator is the number of equal parts into which the whole (or ONE) has been divided. Compare to *numerator*.

**diameter** A line segment that passes through the center of a circle or sphere and has endpoints on the circle or sphere; also, the length of such a line segment. The diameter of a circle or sphere is twice the length of the radius. See *sphere*.

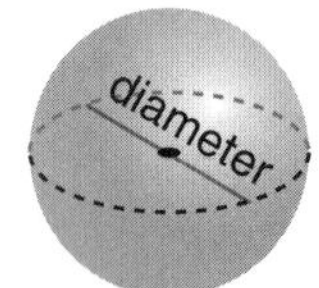

**direction symbol** Same as *map direction symbol.*

**discount** The amount by which the regular price of an item is reduced, expressed as a fraction or percent of the original price. For example, a \$4.00 item that is on sale for \$2.00 is discounted by 50 percent or by $\frac{1}{2}$. Or, when a \$10.00 item has a discount percent of 10% (or the equivalent discount fraction of $\frac{1}{10}$) its sale price is \$9.00.

**displace** To move something from one position to another.

**dividend** In division, the number that is being divided. For example, in 35 ÷ 5 = 7, the dividend is 35.

divisor<br>
dividend → 35 / 5 = 7 ← quotient

quotient → 3<br>
divisor → 12)36 ← dividend

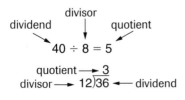

**divisible** One whole number is divisible by another whole number if the result of the division is a whole number with remainder 0. For example, 28 is divisible by 7, because 28 divided by 7 is 4 with remainder 0. If a number $n$ is divisible by a number $d$, then $d$ is a factor of $n$. See *factor*.

**divisibility test** A procedure to determine whether a whole number can be divided evenly by another whole number, without actually doing the division. To check whether a number is divisible by 3, for example, check whether the sum of its digits is divisible by 3. Since the sum of the digits of 51 is divisible by 3 (5 + 1 = 6, which is divisible by 3), 51 passes the divisibility test for 3, so we know that 51 is divisible by 3. To check that a number is divisible by 5, see if the ones digit is either 0 or 5. Since 51 does not end in 0 or 5, it does not pass the divisibility test for 5, so we know that 51 is not divisible by 5.

**divisor** In division, the number that divides another number (the dividend). For example, in 40 ÷ 8 = 5, the divisor is 8.

divisor<br>
dividend → 40 ÷ 8 = 5 ← quotient

quotient → 3<br>
divisor → 12)36 ← dividend

**edge** A line segment where two faces of a polyhedron meet.

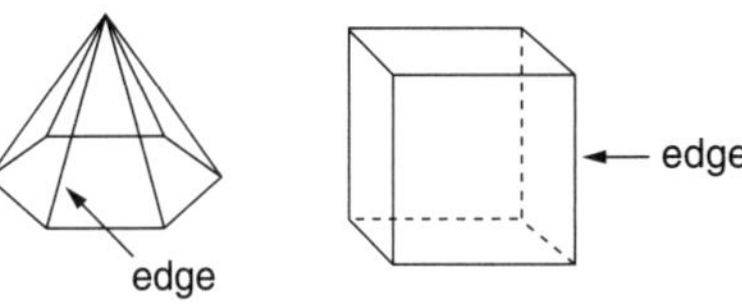


**equal chance** When none of the possible outcomes of an event is more likely to occur than any other, it is an equal chance situation.

**equation** A mathematical sentence that asserts the equality of two quantities.

**equilateral polygon** A polygon in which all sides are the same length.

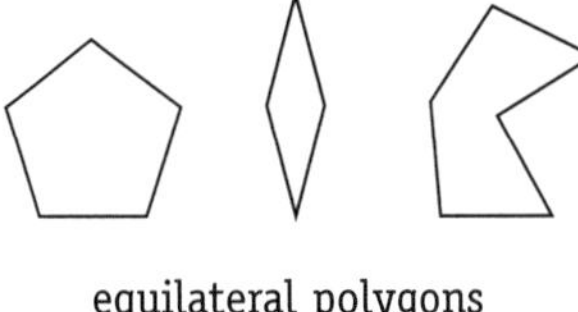

equilateral polygons

**equilateral triangle** A triangle in which all three sides are the same length and all three angles are the same measure.

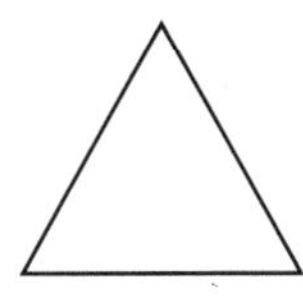

equilateral triangle

**equivalent fractions** Fractions that have different denominators but represent the same number.

**even number** A whole number that can be evenly divided by 2. Compare to *odd number.*

**exponent** See *exponential notation.*

**exponential notation** A way of representing repeated multiplication by the same factor. For example, $2^3$ is exponential notation for 2 * 2 * 2. The small, raised 3, called the *exponent*, indicates how many times the number 2, called the *base*, is used as a *factor.*

$$2^3 = 2 * 2 * 2 = 8$$
$$4^5 = 4 * 4 * 4 * 4 * 4 = 1{,}024$$

**expression** A group of mathematical symbols (numbers, operation signs, variables, grouping symbols) that represent or can represent a number if values are assigned to any variables that the expression contains.

**face** (1) Any of the polygonal regions that form 3-dimensional prisms, pyramids, or polyhedra. Some special faces are called bases. See *base*. (2) Any flat surface of a cylinder, cone, or other geometric solid.

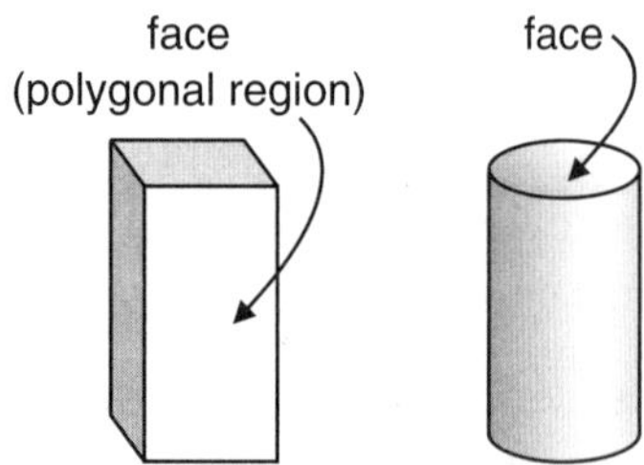


**factor** (1) A number being multiplied in a multiplication number model. In the number model $6 * 0.5 = 3$, 6 and 0.5 are factors and 3 is the product. See *multiplication*. (2) A whole number that can divide another whole number without a remainder. For example, 4 and 7 are both factors of 28 because 28 is divisible by both 4 and by 7. (3) To represent a number as a product of factors. To factor 21, for example, is to write it as $7 * 3$.

**factor pair** Two whole-number factors of a number whose product is the number. A number may have more than one factor pair. For example, the factor pairs for 24 are 1 and 24, 2 and 12, 3 and 8, and 4 and 6.

**factor rainbow** A way to show factor pairs in a list of all the factors of a number. A factor rainbow can be used to check whether a list of factors is correct.

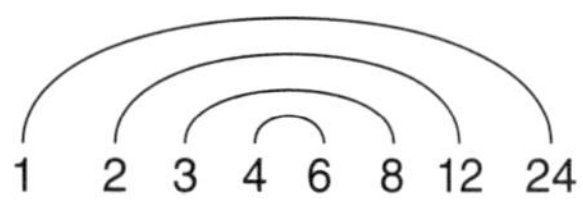


factor rainbow for 24

**factor string** A name for a number written as a product of at least two whole-number factors other than 1. For example, a factor string for the number 24 is $2 \times 3 \times 4$. This factor string has three factors, so its length is 3. By convention, the number 1 is not allowed in factor strings. For example, $1 \times 2 \times 3 \times 4$ is not a factor string for 24 because it contains the number 1.

**factor tree** A method used to obtain the prime factorization of a number. The original number is represented as a product of factors, and each of those factors is represented as a product of factors, and so on, until the factors are all prime numbers. Factor trees are drawn upside down, with the root at the top and the leaves at the bottom. See *prime factorization*.

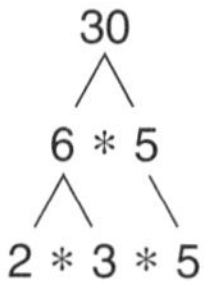


factor tree for 30

**fair game** A game in which every player has the same chance of winning. If any player has an advantage or disadvantage at the beginning (for example, by playing first), then the game is not fair.

**false number sentence** A number sentence in which the relation symbol does not accurately relate the two sides. For example, $8 = 5 + 5$ is a false number sentence. Compare to *true number sentence*.

**fathom** A unit used mainly by people who work with boats and ships to measure depth of water and lengths of cables. A fathom is 6 feet, or 2 yards. Same as *arm span*.

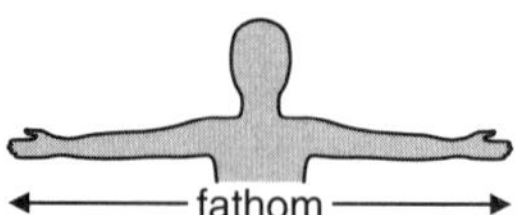


**formula** A general rule for finding the value of something. A formula is often written symbolically using letters, called variables, to stand for the quantities involved. For example, a formula for distance traveled can be written as $d = s \times t$, where $d$ stands for distance, $s$ for speed, and $t$ for time.

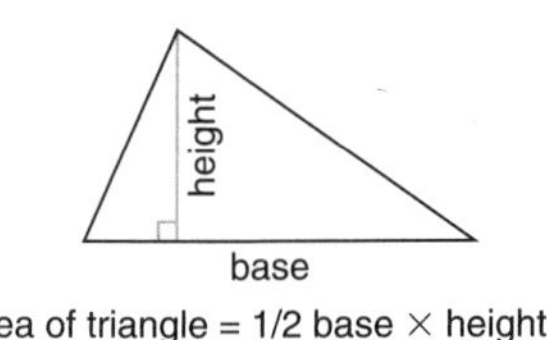


**fraction stick** A diagram used in *Everyday Mathematics* to represent simple fractions.

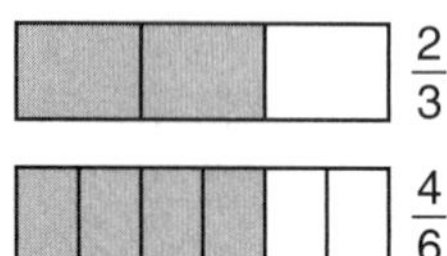


**frequency** (1) The number of times a value occurs in a set of data. (2) The number of vibrations per second of a sound wave; more generally, the number of repetitions per unit of time.

**frequency graph** A graph showing how often each value in a data set occurs.

**Colors in a Bag of Gumdrops**

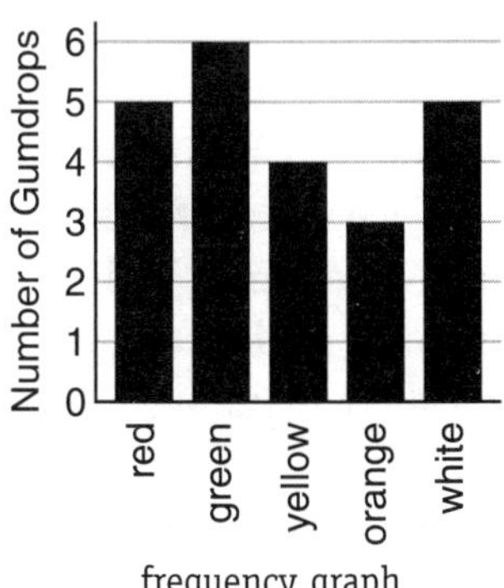


frequency graph

**frequency table** A chart on which data is tallied to find the frequency of given events or values.

| Color | Number of Gumdrops |
|---|---|
| red | 𝍸 5 |
| green | 𝍸 \| 6 |
| yellow | \|\|\|\| 4 |
| orange | \|\|\| 3 |
| white | 𝍸 5 |

frequency table

**geometric solid** A 3-dimensional shape bounded by surfaces. Common geometric solids include the *rectangular prism, square-based pyramid, cylinder, cone,* and *sphere.* Despite its name, a geometric solid in *Everyday Mathematics* is defined as the surface only (it is "hollow") and does not include the points in its interior. Sometimes, however, in informal discussion and in certain dictionaries, a solid is defined as both the surface and its interior.

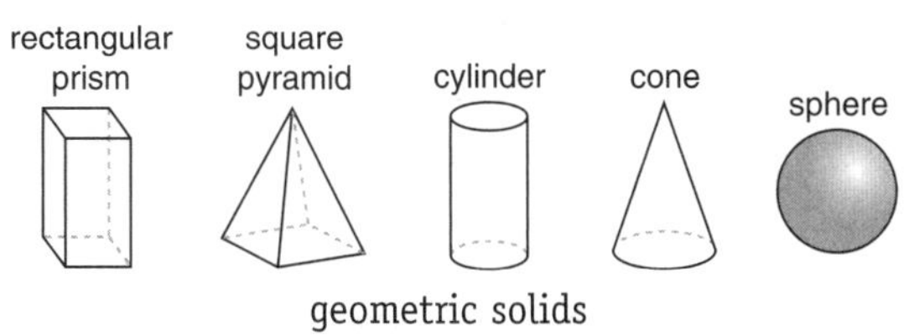


geometric solids

**Geometry Template** An *Everyday Mathematics* tool that includes a millimeter ruler, a ruler with sixteenth-inch intervals, a half-circle and a full-circle protractor, a percent circle, pattern-block shapes, and other geometric figures. Tiny holes at selected inch and centimeter marks allow the template to serve as a compass.

**great span** The distance from the tip of the thumb to the tip of the little finger (pinkie), when the hand is stretched as far as possible. The great span averages about 9 inches for adults. Compare to *normal span.*

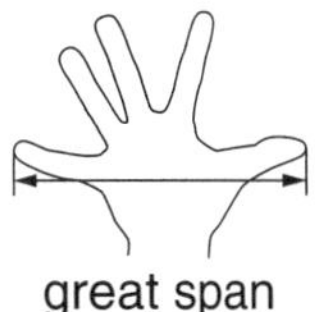

great span

**height** A measure of how tall something is.

**height of a parallelogram** The length of the shortest line segment between a base and the line containing the opposite side of a parallelogram. The height is perpendicular to the base. Also, the line segment itself. See *base of a parallelogram.*

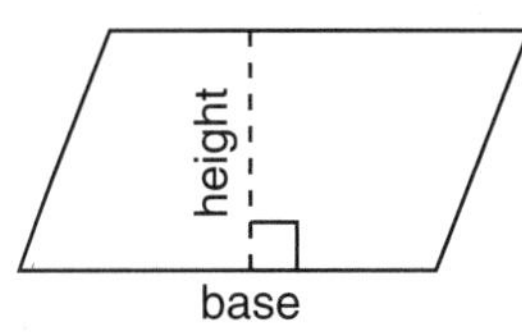

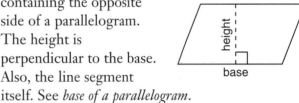

**height of a prism or cylinder** The length of the shortest line segment from a base of a prism or cylinder to the plane containing the opposite side.

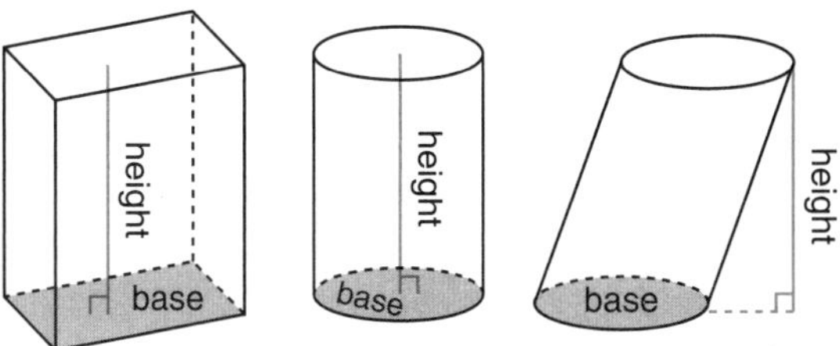


**height of a pyramid or cone** The length of the shortest line segment from the vertex of a pyramid or cone to the plane containing the opposite side, or base. See *base of a pyramid* or *cone.*

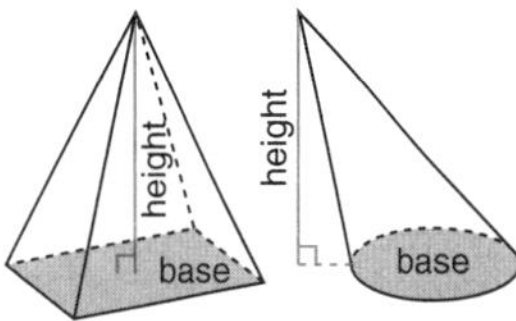


**height of a triangle** The shortest length between the line containing a base of a triangle and the vertex opposite that base. See *base of a triangle.*

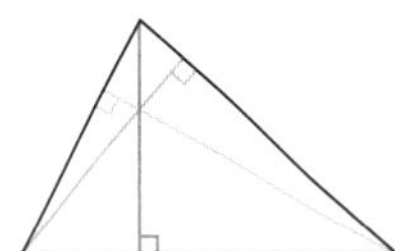

The heights of the triangle are indicated in blue.

**horizontal** Positioned in a left-to-right orientation. Parallel to the line of the horizon.

**improper fraction** A term for a fraction whose numerator is greater than or equal to its denominator. An improper fraction names a number greater than or equal to 1. For example, $\frac{4}{3}$, $\frac{5}{2}$, $\frac{4}{4}$, and $\frac{24}{12}$ are all improper fractions. In *Everyday Mathematics*, improper fractions are sometimes called top-heavy fractions.

**inequality** A number sentence stating that two quantities are not equal, or might not be equal. Relation symbols for inequalities include $\neq$, $<$, $>$, $\geq$, and $\leq$.

**"in the black"** Having a positive balance; having more money than is owed.

**"in the red"** Having a negative balance; owing more money than is available.

**irrational number** A number that cannot be written as a fraction where both the numerator and denominator are integers and the denominator is not zero. For example, $\sqrt{2}$ and $\pi$ are irrational numbers. An irrational number can be represented by a nonterminating, nonrepeating decimal. For example, the decimal for $\pi$, 3.141592653..., continues without a repeating pattern. The number 1.10100100010000... is also irrational; although there is a pattern in the decimal, it does not repeat.

**irregular polygon** A polygon with sides of different lengths or angles of different measures.

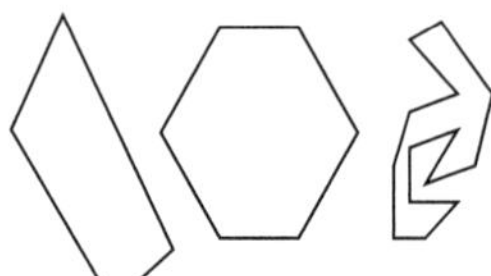

three irregular polygons

**isosceles triangle** A triangle with at least two sides that are the same length and at least two angles that are the same measure.

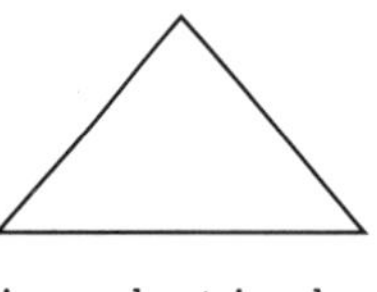

isocsceles triangle

**kite** A quadrilateral with exactly two pairs of adjacent sides that are the same length. (A rhombus is not a kite.)

**landmark** A notable feature of a data set. Landmarks include *median*, *mode*, *maximum*, *minimum*, and *range*.

**latitude** The angular distance of a point on Earth's surface, north or south from the equator measured on the meridian of the point. See *latitude lines.* Compare to *longitude*.

**latitude lines** Lines of constant latitude drawn on a map or globe. Lines of latitude are used to indicate the location of a place with reference to the equator. Latitude is measured in degrees, from 0° to 90°, north or south of the equator. Lines of latitude are also called "parallels," because they are parallel to the equator and to each other. See *latitude*. Compare to *longitude lines*.

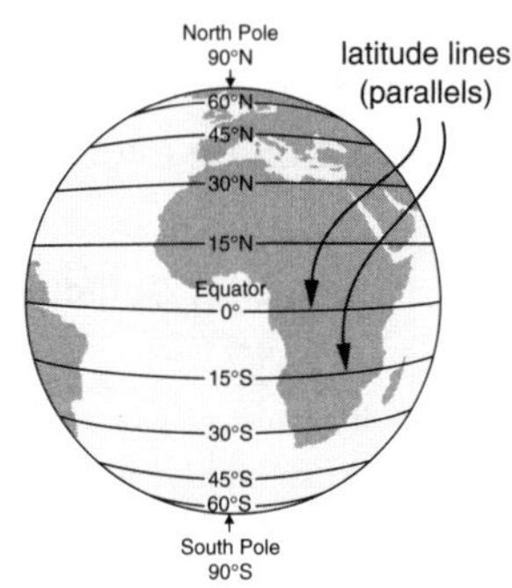


**lattice method** An algorithm for multiplying multidigit numbers. Lattice multiplication is a very old method, requiring little more than a knowledge of basic multiplication facts and the ability to add strings of 1-digit numbers. Once the lattice is drawn, the method is highly efficient and can be used to multiply very large numbers, including numbers too large to enter into most calculators.

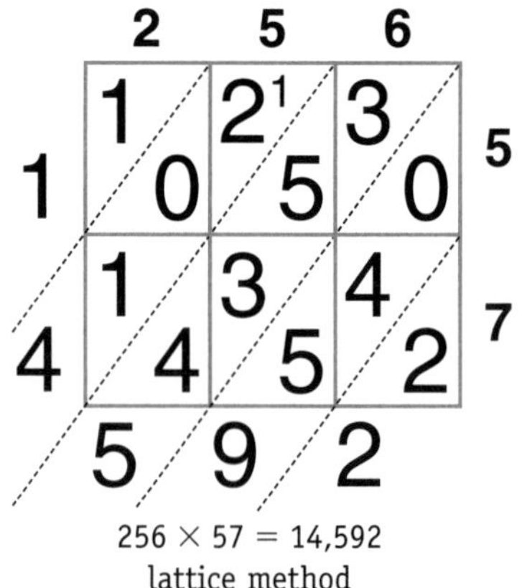


$256 \times 57 = 14{,}592$

lattice method

**least common multiple (LCM)** The smallest number that is a multiple of two or more given numbers. For example, while some common multiples of 6 and 8 are 24, 48, and 72, the least common multiple of 6 and 8 is 24.

**length of a factor string** The number of factors in a factor string. See *factor string.*

**line graph** A graph in which data points are connected by a line or line segments.

**line plot** A sketch of data in which check marks, X's, or other symbols above a labeled line show the frequency of each value.

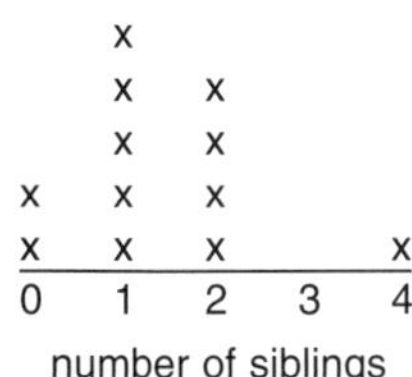


**liter (L)** In the metric system, a unit of capacity equal to the volume of a cube that measures 10 centimeters on a side. 1 L = 1,000 mL = 1,000 $cm^3$. A liter is a little larger than a quart.

**longitude** A measure of how far east or west of the prime meridian a location on Earth is. Longitude is the measure, usually in degrees, of the angle formed by the plane containing the meridian of a particular place and the plane containing the *Prime Meridian*. Compare to *latitude*. See *longitude lines*.

**longitude lines** Lines of constant longitude; semicircles connecting the North and South Poles. Longitude lines are used to locate places with reference to the *Prime Meridian*. Lines of longitude are also called meridians. See *longitude*. Compare to *latitude lines*.

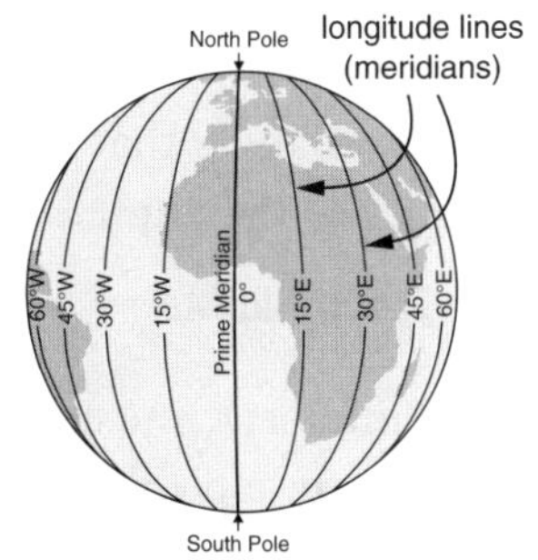


**magnitude estimate** A rough estimate of the size of a numerical result—whether it is in the 1s, 10s, 100s, 1,000s, and so on. In *Everyday Mathematics*, students are often asked to give magnitude estimates for problems like "How many dimes in $200?" or "How many halves are in 30?"

**majority** More than half of a total amount.

**map direction symbol** A symbol on a map that identifies north, south, east, and west. Sometimes only north is indicated.

map direction symbol

**map legend** A diagram that explains the symbols, markings, and colors on a map. Also called a *map key*.

**map scale** A device for relating distances on a map to corresponding distances in the real world. One inch on a map, for example, might correspond to 1 mile in the real world. A map scale is often represented by a labeled line segment, similar to a ruler; by a ratio of distances (for example $\frac{1}{63,360}$ when an inch represents a mile); or by an incorrect use of the = symbol (as in "1 inch = 1 mile").

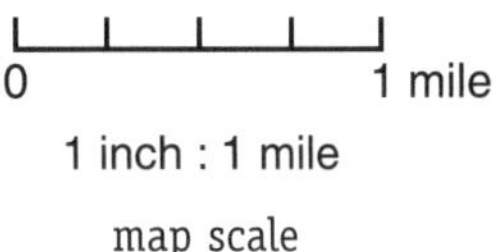

map scale

**maximum** The largest amount; the greatest number in a set of data. Compare to *minimum*.

**mean** A measure of central tendency. It is found by adding the numbers in the set and dividing the sum by the number of numbers. It is often referred to as the average.

**median** The middle value in a set of data when the data are listed in order from least to greatest (or greatest to least). If there is an even number of data points, the median is the mean of the two middle values. The median is also known as the *middle value*. Compare to *mean* and *mode*.

**milliliter (mL)** In the metric system, a unit of capacity equal to $\frac{1}{1,000}$ of a liter; 1 cubic centimeter.

**minimum** The smallest amount; the smallest number in a set of data. Compare to *maximum*.

**minuend** The number that is reduced in subtraction. For example, in 19 – 5 = 14, the minuend is 19.

**mixed number** A number that is written using both a whole number and a fraction. For example, $2\frac{1}{4}$ is a mixed number equal to $2 + \frac{1}{4}$.

**mode** The value or values that occur most often in a set of data. Compare to *median* and *mean*. In the data set 3, 4, 4, 4, 5, 5, 6, the mode is 4.

**name-collection box** In *Everyday Mathematics*, a box-like diagram tagged with a given number and used for collecting equivalent names for that number.

| 16 |
|---|
| $4^2$ |
| $\sqrt{256}$ |
| $(4 + 6) * 6 - 4 * 11$ |
| XVI |

A typical name-collection box for 16—there are infinitely many possibilities

**negative number** A number less than 0; a number to the left of 0 on a horizontal number line or below 0 on a thermometer or other vertical number line.

**normal span** The distance from the end of the thumb to the end of the index (first) finger of an outstretched hand. For estimating lengths, many people can adjust this distance to approximately 6 inches or 20 centimeters. Same as *span*. Compare to *great span*.

**number model** A number sentence that models or fits a situation. For example, the situations "Sally had \$5 and then she earned \$8," "A young plant 5 cm high grew 8 cm," and "Harry is 8 years older than his 5-year-old sister Sally" can all be modeled by the number sentence $5 + 8 = 13$.

**number sentence** A sentence made up of at least two numbers or expressions and a single relation symbol ($=$, $<$, $>$, $\neq$, $\leq$, or $\geq$). Number sentences usually contain at least one operation symbol. They may also have grouping symbols, such as parentheses. If a number sentence contains one or more variables, it is called an open sentence. See *open number sentence*.

$$5 + 5 = 10$$
$$a \times b \geq 16$$
$$(x + y) / 2 - 4 < 20$$

number sentences

**numerator** In a fraction, the number written above the line or to the left of the slash. In a part-whole fraction, where the whole is divided into a number of equal parts, the numerator names the number of equal parts being considered. In the fraction $\frac{a}{b}$ or $a/b$, $a$ is the numerator. Compare to *denominator*.

**obtuse angle** An angle measuring more than 90° and less than 180°.

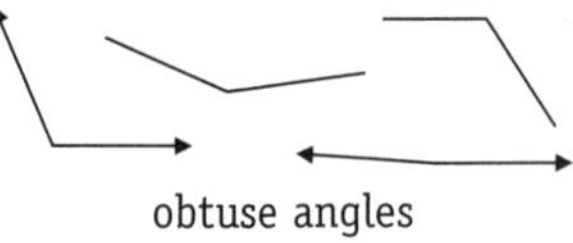

obtuse angles

**odd number** A whole number that cannot be evenly divided by 2. Compare to *even number*.

**open number sentence** A number sentence which is neither true nor false because one or more variables hold the place of missing numbers. For example, the number sentences $9 + \_\_ = 15$ and $\_\_ - 24 < 10$ are open. As an introduction to algebra, *Everyday Mathematics* regards a ?, blank, or frame as a variable.

$9 + ? = 15$ $\quad$ $5 - \_\_ \geq 3$

$9 + \square = 15$ $\quad$ $5 - x \geq 3$

open sentences

**operation symbol** A symbol used in number sentences to stand for a particular mathematical operation. The operation symbols most often used in school mathematics are:

$+$ for addition
$-$ for subtraction
$\times$, $*$, and $\bullet$ for multiplication
$\div$ and / for division

**opposite angles**

(1) Of a quadrilateral: angles that do not share a common side.

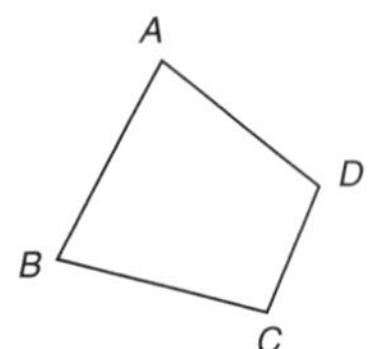


Angles $A$ and $C$ and Angles $B$ and $D$ are pairs of opposite angles.

(2) Of a triangle: an angle is opposite the side of a triangle that is not one of the sides of the angle.

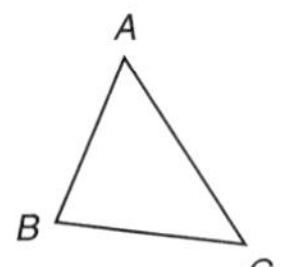


Angle $C$ is opposite Side $AB$.

(3) When two lines intersect, the angles that do not share a common side are opposite angles. Opposite angles have equal measures. Also called *vertical angles*.

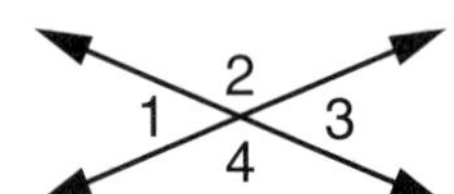

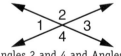

Angles 2 and 4 and Angles 1 and 3 are pairs of opposite, or vertical, angles.

**opposite of a number** A number that is the same distance from zero on the number line as the given number, but on the opposite side of zero. The opposite of any number $n$ is written as (op)$n$ or $-n$. If $n$ is a negative number, (op)$n$ or $-n$ will be a positive number. For example, if $n = -5$, then $-n$, or (op)$n$, is (op)$-5 = 5$. The sum of a number and its opposite is zero.

**ordered pair** (1) A pair of numbers used to locate a point on a coordinate grid. The first number corresponds to position along the horizontal axis, and the second number corresponds to position along the vertical axis. 2) Any pair of objects or numbers in a particular order.

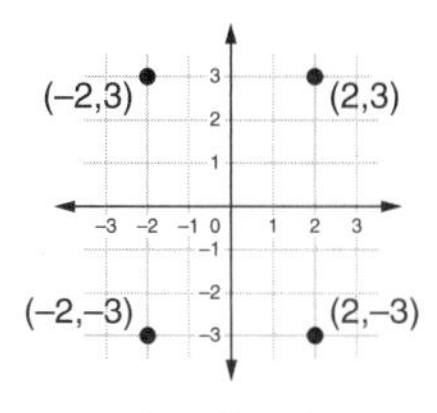


ordered pairs

**pan balance** A device used to weigh objects or compare their weights.

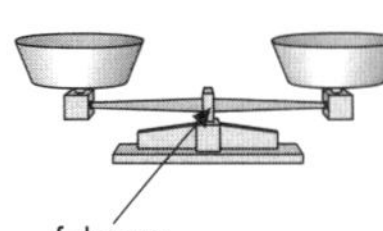


**parallel** Lines, rays, line segments, and planes that are equidistant at all points, no matter how far extended.

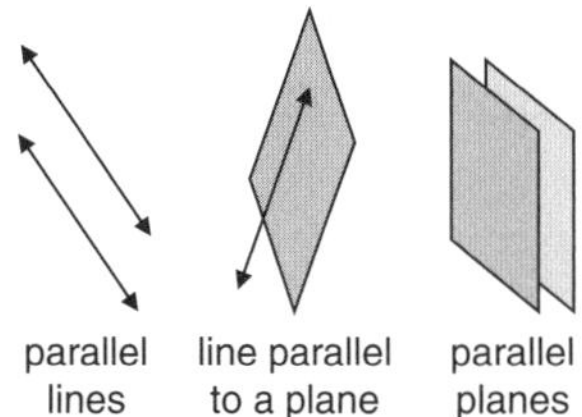


**parallelogram** A quadrilateral that has two pairs of parallel sides. All rectangles are parallelograms, but not all parallelograms are rectangles because parallelograms do not need to have right angles.

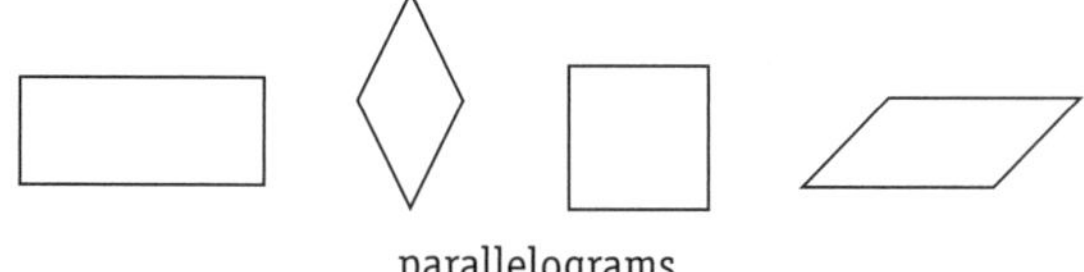

parallelograms

**partial-differences method** A subtraction procedure in which differences are computed for each place separately and then added to yield the final answer.

| | | |
|---|---|---|
| | | 932 |
| | | − 356 |
| Subtract 100s: 900 − 300 | → | 600 |
| Subtract 10s: 30 − 50 | → | − 20 |
| Subtract 1s: 2 − 6 | → | − 4 |
| Add the partial differences (600 − 20 − 4, done mentally) | → | 576 |

**partial-products method** A way to multiply in which the value of each digit in one factor is multiplied by the value of each digit in the other factor. The final product is the sum of these partial products.

| | | |
|---|---|---|
| | | 67 |
| | | × 53 |
| $50 \times 60$ | → | 3000 |
| $50 \times 7$ | → | 350 |
| $3 \times 60$ | → | 180 |
| $3 \times 7$ | → | + 21 |
| | | 3551 |

**partial-quotients method** A division procedure in which the quotient is found in several steps. In each step, a partial quotient is found. The partial quotients are then added to find the final quotient.

| | | |
|---|---|---|
| 22)400 | | |
| − 220 | 10 | (10 [22s] in 400) |
| 180 | | |
| − 110 | 5 | (5 [22s] in 180) |
| 70 | | |
| − 44 | 2 | (2 [22s] in 70) |
| 26 | | |
| − 22 | 1 | (1 [22] in 26) |
| 4 | 18 | |

400 / 22 → 18R4

**partial-sums method** An addition procedure in which sums are computed for each place separately and then added to yield a final sum.

| | | |
|---|---|---|
| | | 268 |
| | | + 483 |
| Add 100s: 200 + 400 | → | 600 |
| Adds 10s: 60 + 80 | → | 140 |
| Add 1s: 8 + 3 | → | + 11 |
| Add partial sums | → | 751 |

**parts-and-total diagram** In *Everyday Mathematics*, a diagram used to represent problems in which two or more quantities are combined to form a total quantity. It is often used when the parts are known and the total is unknown. It can also be used when the total and one or more parts are known, but one part is unknown. See *situation diagram*.

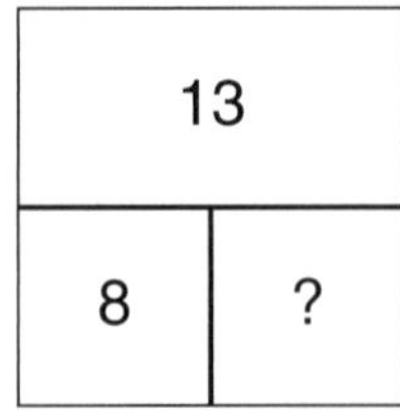


| Total | |
|---|---|
| 13 | |
| Part | Part |
| 8 | ? |

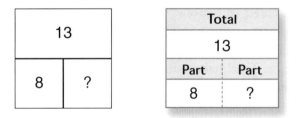

parts-and-total diagrams for $13 = 8 + N$

**parts-and-total story** A number story about a situation in which there is some whole that is made up of distinct parts. An example of a parts-and-total story is, "There are 15 girls and 12 boys in Mrs. Dorn's class. How many students are there in all?"

**pentagon** A 5-sided polygon.

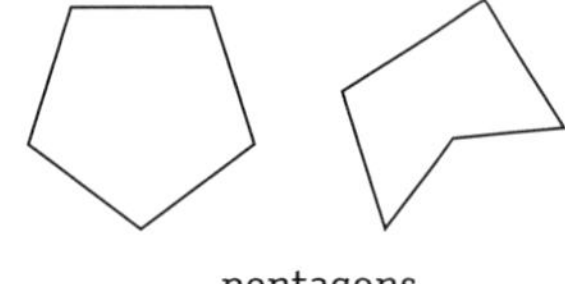

pentagons

**percent (%)** Per hundred, or out of a hundred. 1% means $\frac{1}{100}$ or 0.01. For example, "48% of the students in the school are boys" means that out of every 100 students in the school, 48 are boys.

**Percent Circle** A device on the Geometry Template used to measure or draw figures (such as circle graphs) involving percents. See *Geometry Template*.

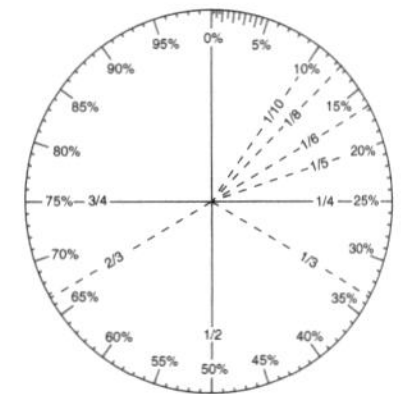

**perimeter** The distance around a closed plane figure or region. *Peri-* comes from the Greek word for "around," and *meter* comes from the Greek word for "measure"; perimeter means "around measure."

**perpendicular** Rays, lines, line segments, or planes that form right angles are perpendicular to each other.

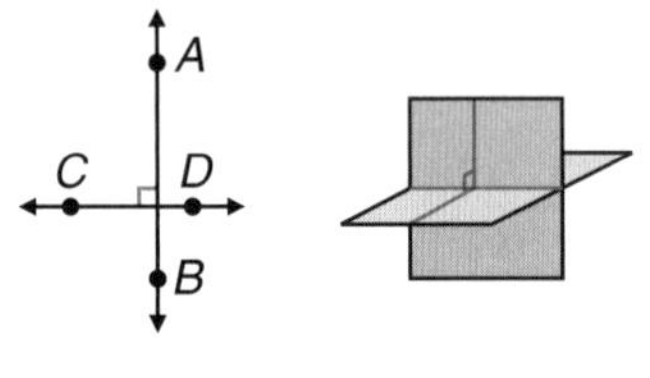


perpendicular lines

perpendicular planes

**perpetual calendar** A table that can be used to determine the correct day of the week for any date in a wide range of years.

**personal measurement reference** A convenient approximation for a standard unit of measurement. For example, many people have thumbs that are approximately one inch wide.

**pi ($\pi$)** The ratio of the circumference of a circle to its diameter. Pi, which is approximately 3.14, is the same for every circle. Pi is also the ratio of a circle's area to the square of its radius. Also written as the Greek letter $\pi$. The first twenty digits of $\pi$ are:

3.1415926535897932384.

**pie graph** Same as *circle graph*.

**place value** The relative worth of each digit in a number, which is determined by its position. Each place has a value ten times that of the place to its right and one-tenth of the value of the place to its left.

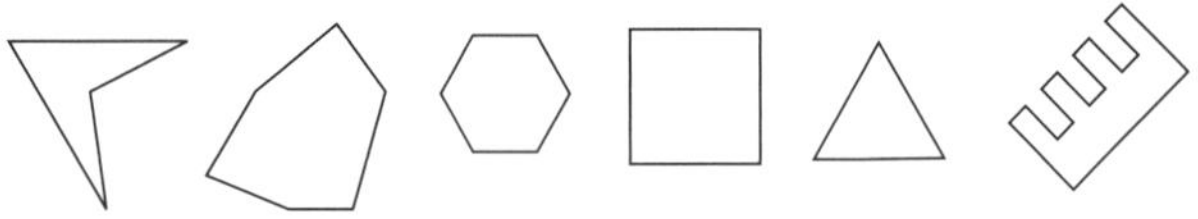

| thousands | hundreds | tens | ones | tenths | hundredths |
|---|---|---|---|---|---|
| | | | | | |

a place-value chart

**polygon** A closed plane figure formed by three or more line segments that meet only at their endpoints. Exactly two sides come together at each corner of a polygon.

 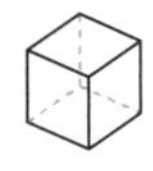 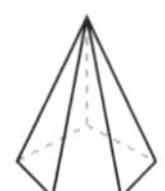 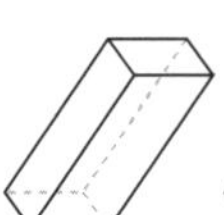 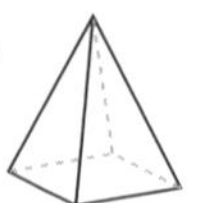

polygons

**polyhedron** A closed 3-dimensional shape, all of whose surfaces (faces) are flat. Each face consists of a polygon and its interior.

polyhedrons

**population** (1) The total number of people living within a certain geographical area. (2) In data collection, the collection of people or objects that is the focus of study. The population is often larger than the target audience for a given survey, in which case a smaller, representative sample is considered. See *sample*.

**power** (1) The exponent to which a "base" number is raised in exponential notation; the number $a$ in $n^a$, where $n$ is the base. If $n$ is any number and $a$ is a positive whole number, $a$ tells how many times to use $n$ as a factor in a product. For example, $5^3 = 5 * 5 * 5 = 125$, and is read "5 to the third power." See *power of 10* for more examples, including examples in which $a$ is a negative integer. (2) The result of a "powering" or "exponential" operation $x^y$.

**power of 10** (1) A whole number that can be written as a product using only 10 as a factor; also called a positive power of 10. For example, 100 is equal to $10 * 10$, or $10^2$. 100 can also be called ten squared, the second power of 10, or 10 to the second power. (2) More generally, any number that can be written as a product using only 10s or $\frac{1}{10}$s as factors. For example, 0.01 is equal to $0.1 * 0.1$, or $10^{-2}$. Other powers of 10 include $10^1 = 10$ and $10^0 = 1$. See *power.*

**powers key** The [^] or [$y^x$] key on a calculator, used to calculate powers. Keying in 4 [^] 5 gives 4 raised to the fifth power, or $4^5$, which equals $4 * 4 * 4 * 4 * 4$, or 1,024. See *power.*

**predict** To tell what will happen ahead of time; to make an educated guess about what might happen.

**prime factorization** A whole number expressed as a product of prime factors. For example, the prime factorization of 24 is $2 \times 2 \times 2 \times 3$. See *prime number*.

**prime number** A whole number greater than 1 that has exactly two whole-number factors, 1 and itself. For example, 7 is a prime number because its only factors are 1 and 7. The first five prime numbers are 2, 3, 5, 7, and 11. Compare to *composite number*.

**prism** A polyhedron with two parallel faces (bases) that are the same size and shape and other faces that are bounded by parallelograms. In a right prism, the non-base faces are rectangles. Prisms are classified according to the shape of the two parallel bases.

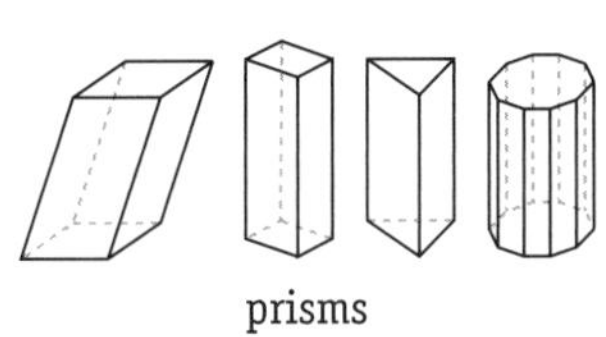
prisms

**probability** A number from 0 to 1 that indicates the likelihood that an event will happen. The closer a probability is to 1, the more likely that the event will happen. The closer a probability is to 0, the less likely that the event will happen. For example, the probability that a fair coin will show heads is 1/2.

**Probability Meter** In *Everyday Mathematics*, a tool used to show probabilities expressed as fractions, decimals, and percents.

**product** The result of a multiplication. In the number model $4 \times 3 = 12$, the product is 12.

**pyramid** A polyhedron in which one face (the base) is a polygon and all other faces are triangles with a common vertex called the *apex*. Pyramids are classified according to the shapes of their bases.

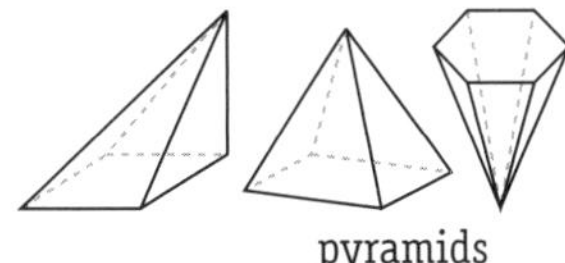
pyramids

**quart** In the U.S. customary system, a unit of capacity equal to 32 fluid ounces, 2 pints, or 4 cups.

**quick common denominator** The product of the denominators of two or more fractions. The quick common denominator of $\frac{a}{b}$ and $\frac{c}{d}$ is $b \times d$. For example, the quick common denominator of $\frac{3}{4}$ and $\frac{5}{6}$ is $4 \times 6$ or 24.

**quotient** The result of dividing one number by another number. In the division model in $10 \div 5 = 2$, the quotient is 2.

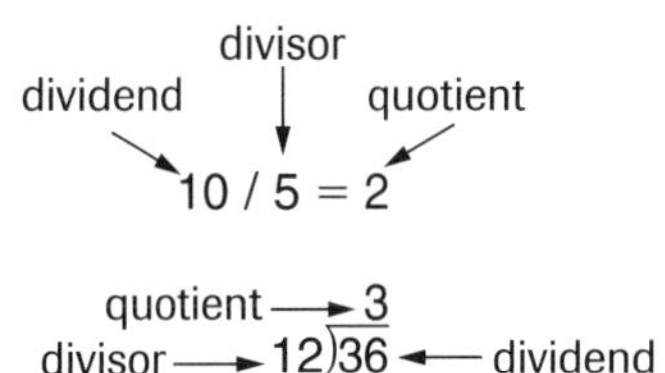


**radius** A line segment from the center of a circle (or sphere) to any point on the circle (or sphere); also, the length of such a line segment.

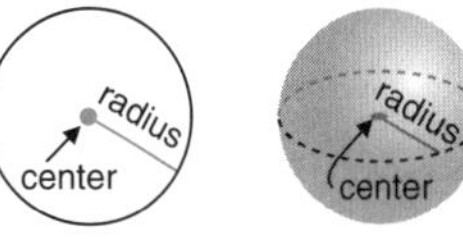


**range** The difference between the greatest and least values in a set of data.

**rate** A comparison by division of two quantities with different units. For example, traveling 100 miles in 2 hours can be expressed as 100 mi/2 hr or 50 miles per hour. In this case, the rate compares distance (miles) to time (hours). Compare to *ratio.*

**ratio** A comparison by division of two quantities with the same units. Ratios can be expressed as fractions, decimals, or percents, as well as in words. Ratios can also be written with a colon between the two numbers being compared. For example, if a team wins 3 games out of 5 games played, the ratio of wins to total games is $\frac{3}{5}$, 3/5, 0.6, 60%, 3 to 5, or 3:5 (read "three to five"). Compare to *rate.*

**rectangle method** A method for finding area in which one or more rectangles are drawn around a figure or parts of a figure. The sides of the rectangle(s), together with the sides of the original figure, define regions that are either rectangles or triangular halves of rectangles. The area of the original figure can be found by adding and subtracting the areas of these rectangular and triangular regions.

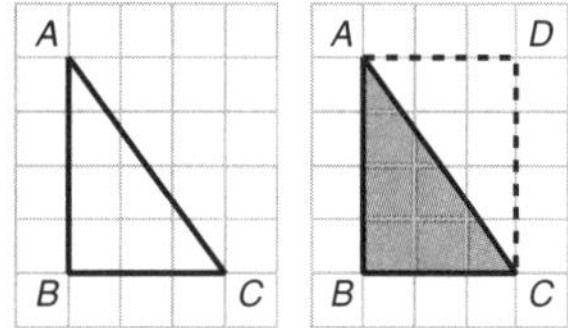


rectangle method diagram

**rectangular array** A rectangular arrangement of objects in rows and columns such that each row has the same number of objects and each column has the same number of objects.

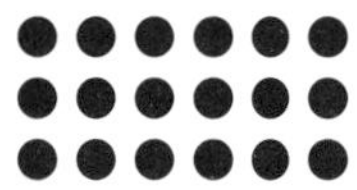

rectangular array

**rectangular prism** (1) In common usage, a prism whose faces (including the bases) are all rectangles. Many packing boxes have the shape of rectangular prisms. (2) More generally, any prism with rectangular bases, some of the faces of which might be non-rectangle parallelograms.

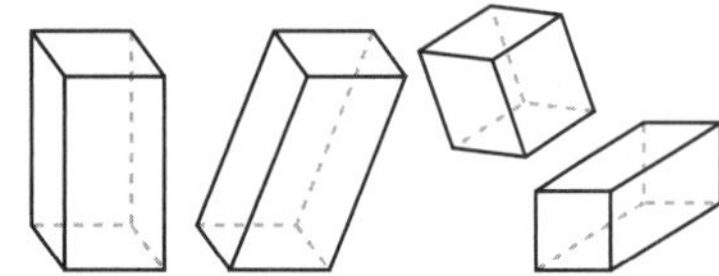

rectangular prisms

**reflex angle** An angle with a measure between 180° and 360°.

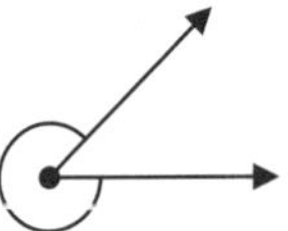

**regular polygon** A polygon whose sides are the same length and whose angles are all equal.

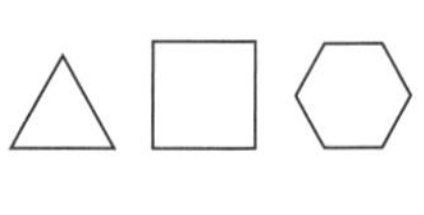

**regular polyhedron** A polyhedron whose faces are all congruent regular polygons and with the same number of faces meeting at every vertex, all at the same angle. There are five regular polyhedra, known as the Platonic solids:

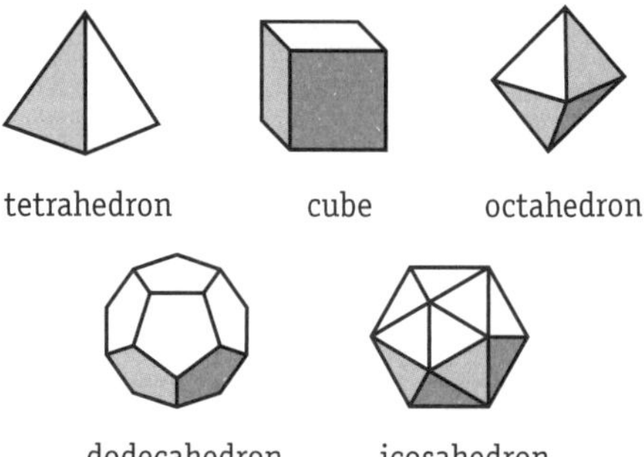


| | |
|---|---|
| tetrahedron: | 4 faces, each an equilateral triangle |
| cube: | 6 faces, each a square |
| octahedron: | 8 faces, each an equilateral triangle |
| dodecahedron: | 12 faces, each a regular pentagon |
| icosahedron: | 20 faces, each an equilateral triangle |

**regular tessellation** A tessellation made up of only one kind of regular polygon. There are only three regular tessellations. See *tessellation.*

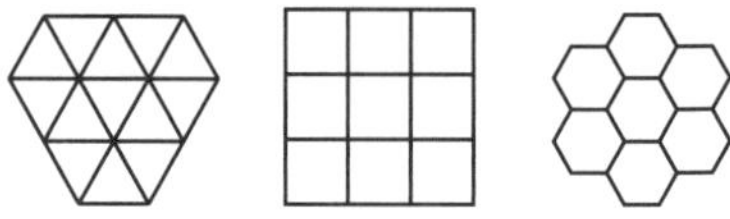

the three regular tessellations

**relation symbol** A symbol used to express a relationship between two quantities. Some relation symbols used in number sentences include: = for "is equal to," ≠ for "is not equal to," < for "is less than," > for "is greater than," ≤ for "is less than or equal to," and ≥ for "is greater than or equal to."

**remainder** An amount left over when one number is divided by another. In the division number model 16 ÷ 3 → 5 R1, the remainder is 1.

**repeating decimal** A decimal in which one digit, or a group of digits, is repeated without end. For example, 0.3333. . . and $0.\overline{147}$ are repeating decimals.

**right** (1) Of an angle: An angle whose measure is 90°.

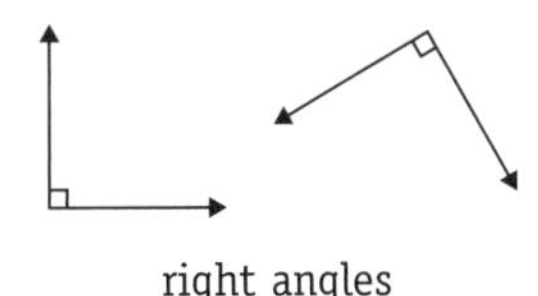

right angles

(2) Of a prism or cylinder: Having lateral faces or surfaces that are all perpendicular to their bases.

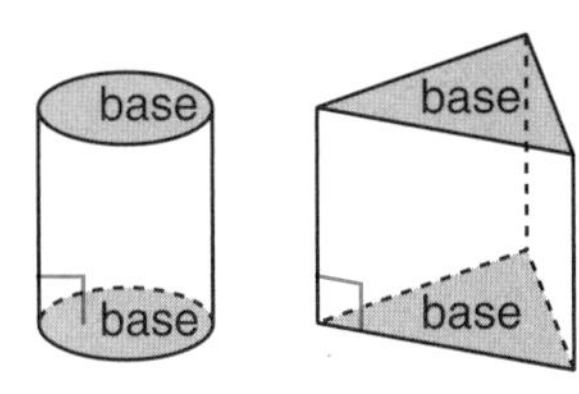


a right circular cylinder and a right triangular prism

(3) Of a pyramid or cone: Having an apex directly above the center of its base.

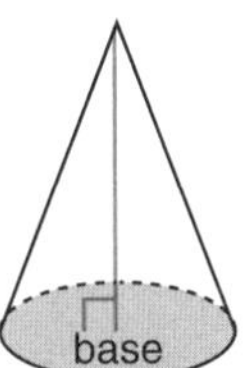


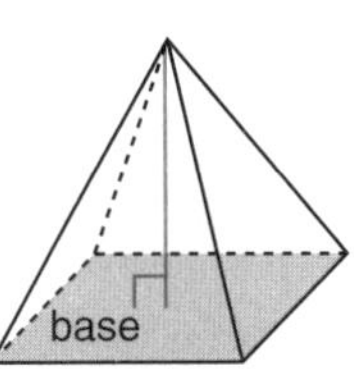


a right circular cone and a right square pyramid

(4) Of a triangle: Having a right angle.

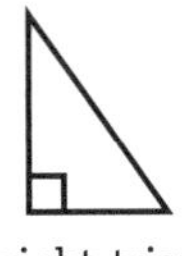

right triangle

**round** (1) Arithmetic: To express a number in a simplified way. Examples of rounding include expressing a measure of weight to the nearest pound and expressing an amount of money to the nearest dollar. (2) Geometry: Circular in shape.

**sample** A part of a population intended to represent the whole.

**scalene triangle** A triangle with sides of three different lengths and angles of three different sizes.

**scientific notation** A system for representing numbers in which a number is written as the product of a power of 10 and a number that is at least 1 and less than 10. Scientific notation allows writing big and small numbers with only a few symbols. For example, 4,300,000 in scientific notation is $4.3 \times 10^6$, and 0.00001 in scientific notation is $1 \times 10^{-5}$. Compare to *standard notation.*

**simplest form** (1) Of proper fractions: Having numerator and denominator with no common factors (other than 1). For example, $\frac{10}{15}$ and $\frac{2}{3}$ are equivalent fractions. However, $\frac{10}{15}$ is not in simplest form because the numerator and denominator can each be divided by 5; $\frac{2}{3}$ is in simplest form because 2 and 3 have no common factors (other than 1). (2) Of mixed numbers and improper fractions: Being in mixed number form in which the fraction part is proper and in simplest form. For example, $1\frac{7}{3}$ is not in simplest form because the fraction part is not proper.
*Note:* Simplest form is not emphasized in *Everyday Mathematics* because other equivalent forms are often equally or more useful. For example, when comparing or adding fractions, fractions written with a common denominator are easier to work with than those in simplest form.

**situation diagram** Any of various diagrams used to organize information in simple problem situations. Same as operation diagram. See *change diagram*, and *parts-and-total diagram.*

**slide rule** (1) A mechanical tool composed of a ruler and a sliding insert. Slide rules can be used to do many types of calculations, but have been rendered obsolete by electronic calculators.
(2) An *Everyday Mathematics* tool made of paper or cardstock that can be used for adding and subtracting integers and fractions.

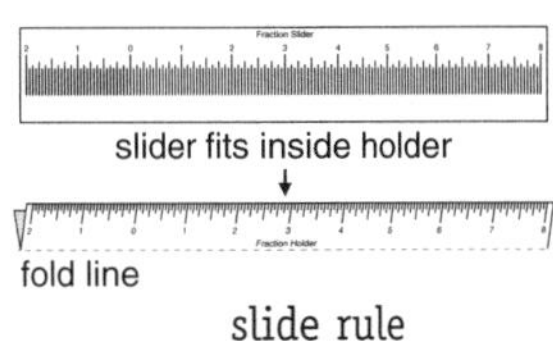


slide rule

**solution** (1) Of an open sentence: A value or values for the variable(s) which make the sentence true. For example, the open sentence 4 + __ = 10 has the solution 6. See *open number sentence.*
(2) Of a problem: The answer or the method by which the answer was obtained.

**span** Same as *normal span.*

**sphere** A 3-dimensional shape whose curved surface is, at all points, a given distance from its center point. A ball is shaped like a sphere. A sphere is hollow; it does not include the points in its interior.

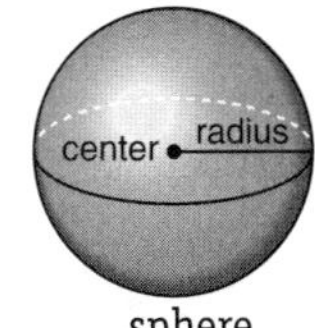


sphere

**square number** A number that is the product of a whole number and itself; a whole number to the second power. For example, 25 is a square number, because 25 = 5 * 5. A square number can be represented by a square array. See *rectangular array*.

**square of a number** The product of a number and itself. The square of a number is symbolized by a raised 2. For example, $3.5^2 = 3.5 * 3.5 = 12.25$.

**square root key** The [√] key on certain calculators. The [√] key undoes the result of squaring a non-negative number.

**square root of a number** The square root of a number *n* is a number which, when multiplied by itself, results in the number *n*. For example, 4 is a square root of 16, because 4 * 4 = 16. Normally, square root refers to the positive square root, but the opposite of a positive square root is also a square root. For example, −4 is also a square root of 16 because (−4) * (−4) = 16.

**square unit** A unit used to measure area. A square unit represents a square with the measure of each side being a related unit of length. For example, a square inch is the area of a square that measures one inch on each side.

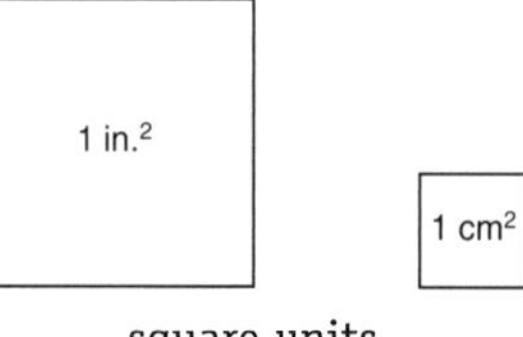

square units

**standard notation** The most familiar way of representing whole numbers, integers, and decimals. Standard notation is base-ten place-value numeration. For example, standard notation for three hundred fifty-six is 356. Compare to *scientific notation*.

**stem-and-leaf plot** A display of data in which digits with larger place values are "stems" and digits with smaller place values are "leaves."

| Stems 10's | Leaves 1's |
|---|---|
| 2 | 4 4 5 6 7 7 |
| 3 | 1 1 2 2 6 6 |
| 4 | 1 1 3 5 8 |
| 5 | 0 2 |

stem-and-leaf plot

**step graph** A graph that looks like steps because the values are the same for an interval and then change (or "step") for another interval. The horizontal axis of a step graph often represents time.

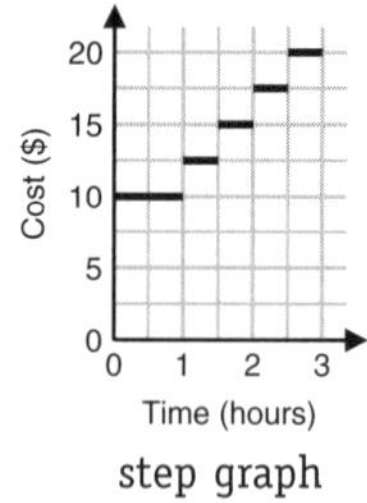

step graph

**straight angle** An angle measuring 180°.

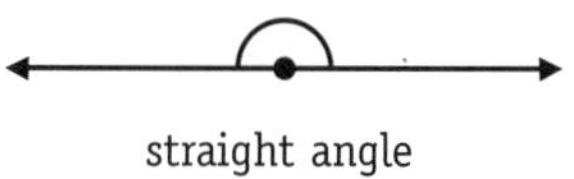
straight angle

**surface area** A measure of the surface of a 3-dimensional figure. The surface area of a polyhedron is the sum of the areas of its faces. See *area*.

**survey** A study that collects data. Surveys are used to find out about people's characteristics, behaviors, interests, opinions, and so on. In *Everyday Mathematics*, surveys are used to generate data for graphing and analysis.

**tessellate** (1) To make a tessellation or tiling. See *tessellation*. (2) To fit into a tessellation. Any quadrilateral will tessellate.

**tessellation** An arrangement of closed shapes that covers a surface completely without overlaps or gaps.

tessellation

**trade-first method** A subtraction procedure in which all necessary trades are done before any subtractions are carried out. Doing so simplifies the algorithm since the user can concentrate on one thing at a time.

| 100s | 10s | 1s |
|---|---|---|
| | 13 | |
| 7 | ~~3~~ | 16 |
| ~~8~~ | ~~4~~ | ~~6~~ |
| − 2 | 8 | 7 |
| | | |

| 100s | 10s | 1s |
|---|---|---|
| | 13 | |
| 7 | ~~3~~ | 16 |
| ~~8~~ | ~~4~~ | ~~6~~ |
| − 2 | 8 | 7 |
| 5 | 5 | 9 |

trade-first subtraction

**transformation** An operation on a geometric figure that produces a new figure, called the image, from the original figure, called the preimage. Transformations are sometimes thought of as moving a figure from one place to another and sometimes changing its size or shape. The study of transformations is called *transformation geometry*.

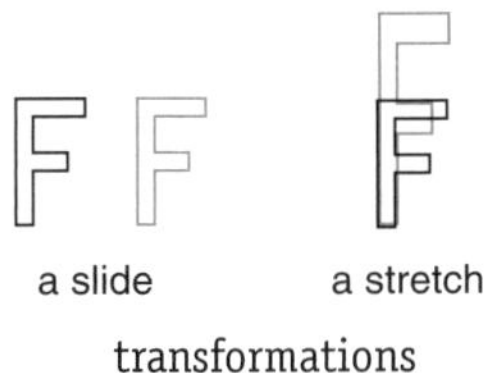


transformations

**tree diagram** A network of points connected by line segments and containing no closed loops. One special point is the root of the tree. Tree diagrams can be used to factor numbers and to represent probability situations in which there is a series of events. The first tree diagram below shows the prime factorization of 30. The second tree diagram represents flipping one coin two times. See *factor tree*.

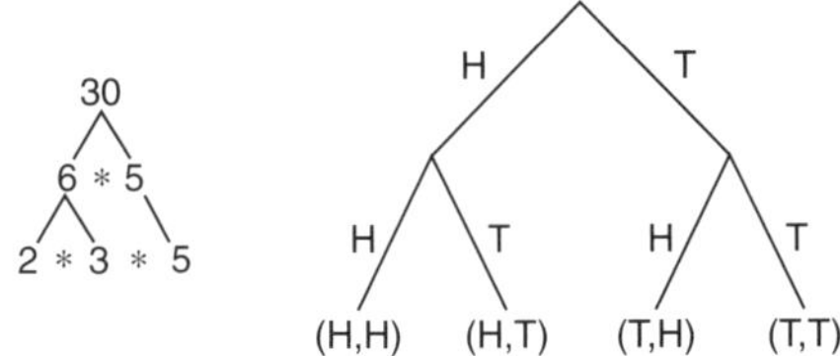


**true number sentence** A number sentence in which the relation symbol accurately reflects the relation between the two sides of the sentence. $75 = 25 + 50$ is a true number sentence. Compare to *false number sentence*.

**turn-around rule** A principle, based on the *commutative property*, for solving math fact problems. If you know, for example, that $6 \times 8 = 48$, then by the turn-around rule you also know that $8 \times 6 = 48$.

**unit** A label, descriptive word, or unit of measure used to put a number in context. Using units with numbers reinforces the idea that numbers refer to something. Fingers, snowballs, miles, and cents are examples of units.

**unit fraction** A fraction whose numerator is 1. For example, $\frac{1}{2}$, $\frac{1}{3}$, $\frac{1}{5}$, and $\frac{1}{100}$ are all unit fractions.

**unlike** (1) Of denominators: Being unequal. The fractions $\frac{1}{2}$ and $\frac{2}{3}$ have unlike denominators. (2) Of fractions: Having different denominators. Compare to *like fractions*.

**value** A specific number or quantity represented by a variable. In the equation $y = 4x + 3$, if the value of $x$ is 7, then the value of $y$ is 31.

**variable** A letter or other symbol that represents a number. A variable need not represent one specific number; it can stand for many different values. For example, in the expression $2x + 3y$, $x$ and $y$ are variables, and in the equation $a + 12 = 2b + 6$, $a$ and $b$ are variables.

**vertex** The point at which the rays or line segments of an angle, the sides of a polygon, or the edges of a polyhedron meet.

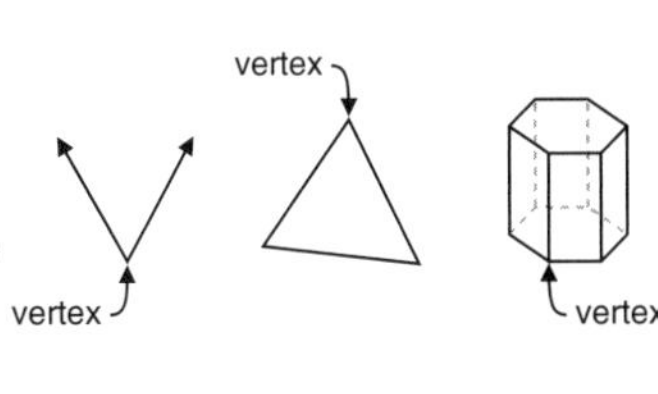


**vertical** Upright; perpendicular to the horizon.

**vertical angles** When two lines intersect, the angles that do not share a common side; the angles opposite each other. Vertical angles have equal measures. Same as *opposite angles (3)*.

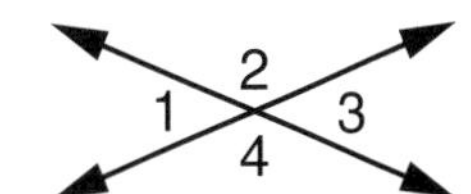


Angles 1 and 3 and Angles 2 and 4 are pairs of vertical angles.

**volume** A measure of the amount of space occupied by a 3-dimensional shape, generally expressed in "cubic" units, such as $cm^3$, cubic inches, or cubic feet.

**whole** The entire object, collection of objects, or quantity being considered; the unit, 100%.

# Scope and Sequence Chart

Throughout *Everyday Mathematics,* students repeatedly experience concepts and skills in each of the mathematical strands. Each exposure builds on and extends students' understanding. They study important concepts over consecutive years through a variety of formats. The Scope and Sequence Chart shows the units in which exposures occur and the developmental level of the skill or concept. The three levels of skill and concept development used in the chart are Beginning, Developing, and Secure. These levels refer here to unit content within the *K–6 Everyday Mathematics* curriculum rather than performance expectations for students.

The skills and concepts are divided according to the mathematical strands below.

## Mathematical Strands



## How to Read the Scope and Sequence Chart

Each section of the chart includes a mathematical strand title, three grade level columns divided by units, and a list of specific skills and concepts grouped by major concepts.

### Numeration

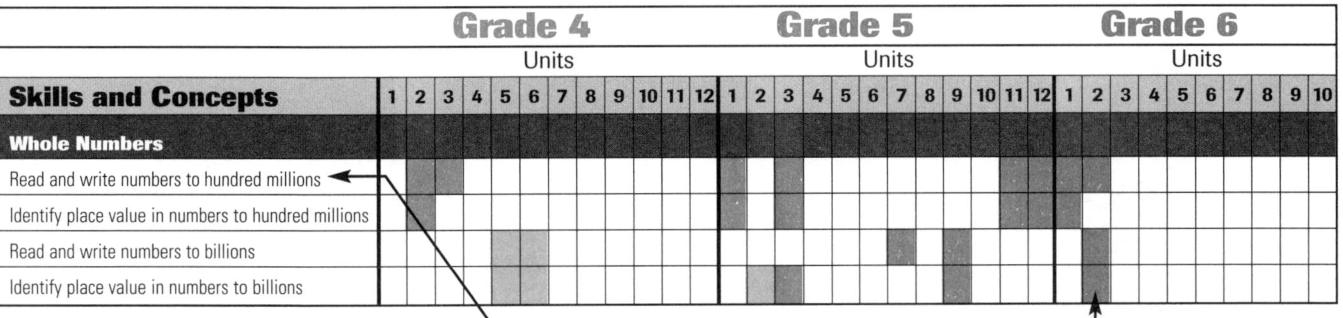


Major mathematical concepts within each strand. A list of related skills and concepts appear below this head.

Find specific skills and concepts in this list and then follow across the row for units in which they appear at each grade level.

The shading in the cells indicates the skill and concept development level for a particular exposure. The lightest shading shows beginning or beginning/developing exposures, the medium shading designates developing or developing/secure exposures, and the darkest shading indicates secure exposures.

# Numeration

| | **Grade 4** | | | | | | | | | | | | **Grade 5** | | | | | | | | | | | | **Grade 6** | | | | | | | | | |
|---|---|---|---|---|---|---|---|---|---|---|---|---|---|---|---|---|---|---|---|---|---|---|---|---|---|---|---|---|---|---|---|---|---|---|
| | Units | | | | | | | | | | | | Units | | | | | | | | | | | | Units | | | | | | | | | |
| **Skills and Concepts** | 1 | 2 | 3 | 4 | 5 | 6 | 7 | 8 | 9 | 10 | 11 | 12 | 1 | 2 | 3 | 4 | 5 | 6 | 7 | 8 | 9 | 10 | 11 | 12 | 1 | 2 | 3 | 4 | 5 | 6 | 7 | 8 | 9 | 10 |
| **Whole Numbers** | | | | | | | | | | | | | | | | | | | | | | | | | | | | | | | | | | |
| Read and write numbers to hundred millions | | | | | | | | | | | | | | | | | | | | | | | | | | | | | | | | | | |
| Read and write numbers to billions | | | | | | | | | | | | | | | | | | | | | | | | | | | | | | | | | | |
| Explore numbers to trillions | | | | | | | | | | | | | | | | | | | | | | | | | | | | | | | | | | |
| Read and write numbers to trillions | | | | | | | | | | | | | | | | | | | | | | | | | | | | | | | | | | |
| Identify place value in numbers to hundred millions | | | | | | | | | | | | | | | | | | | | | | | | | | | | | | | | | | |
| Identify place value in numbers to billions | | | | | | | | | | | | | | | | | | | | | | | | | | | | | | | | | | |
| Name the values of digits in numbers to billions | | | | | | | | | | | | | | | | | | | | | | | | | | | | | | | | | | |
| Compare larger numbers | | | | | | | | | | | | | | | | | | | | | | | | | | | | | | | | | | |
| Find equivalent names for numbers | | | | | | | | | | | | | | | | | | | | | | | | | | | | | | | | | | |
| Identify even and odd numbers | | | | | | | | | | | | | | | | | | | | | | | | | | | | | | | | | | |
| Find the factors of numbers | | | | | | | | | | | | | | | | | | | | | | | | | | | | | | | | | | |
| Identify prime and composite numbers | | | | | | | | | | | | | | | | | | | | | | | | | | | | | | | | | | |
| Find the prime factorization of numbers | | | | | | | | | | | | | | | | | | | | | | | | | | | | | | | | | | |
| Find the least common multiple of two numbers | | | | | | | | | | | | | | | | | | | | | | | | | | | | | | | | | | |
| Find the greatest common factor of two numbers | | | | | | | | | | | | | | | | | | | | | | | | | | | | | | | | | | |
| Understand and apply powers of 10 | | | | | | | | | | | | | | | | | | | | | | | | | | | | | | | | | | |
| Use exponential notation | | | | | | | | | | | | | | | | | | | | | | | | | | | | | | | | | | |
| Rename numbers written in exponential notation | | | | | | | | | | | | | | | | | | | | | | | | | | | | | | | | | | |
| Understand and apply exponential notation | | | | | | | | | | | | | | | | | | | | | | | | | | | | | | | | | | |
| Understand and apply scientific notation | | | | | | | | | | | | | | | | | | | | | | | | | | | | | | | | | | |
| Understand square numbers and their square roots | | | | | | | | | | | | | | | | | | | | | | | | | | | | | | | | | | |
| Understand properties of rational numbers | | | | | | | | | | | | | | | | | | | | | | | | | | | | | | | | | | |
| Round whole numbers to a given place | | | | | | | | | | | | | | | | | | | | | | | | | | | | | | | | | | |

| Money and Decimals |
| --- |
| Read and write decimals to thousandths |
| Identify place value in decimals to hundredths and thousandths |
| Round decimals to a given place |
| **Fractions** |
| Find equivalent fractions |
| Compare and order fractions |
| Convert between fractions and mixed numbers |
| Find common denominators |
| Rename fractions and mixed numbers in simplest forms |
| Identify the whole for fractions |
| Find a fraction of a number |
| Identity fractional parts of regions |
| Relate fractions and decimals |
| Convert between fractions, decimals, and percents |
| Use a calculator to rename any fraction as a decimal or percent |
| Find opposites and reciprocals of numbers |
| **Positive/Negative Numbers (Integers)** |
| Explore uses for positive and negative numbers |
| Compare and order integers |
| **Ratio, Proportion, and Percent** |
| Find a percent of a number |
| Estimate and calculate percent |
| Find the whole, given a percent of the whole |
| Convert between fractions, decimals, mixed numbers, and percents |
| Estimate equivalent percents for fractions |

**Beginning** **Developing** **Secure**

# Operations and Computation

| | Grade 4 Units | | | | | | | | | | | | Grade 5 Units | | | | | | | | | | | | Grade 6 Units | | | | | | | | | |
|---|---|---|---|---|---|---|---|---|---|---|---|---|---|---|---|---|---|---|---|---|---|---|---|---|---|---|---|---|---|---|---|---|---|---|
| **Skills and Concepts** | 1 | 2 | 3 | 4 | 5 | 6 | 7 | 8 | 9 | 10 | 11 | 12 | 1 | 2 | 3 | 4 | 5 | 6 | 7 | 8 | 9 | 10 | 11 | 12 | 1 | 2 | 3 | 4 | 5 | 6 | 7 | 8 | 9 | 10 |
| **Addition and Subtraction** | | | | | | | | | | | | | | | | | | | | | | | | | | | | | | | | | | |
| Solve addition/subtraction number stories | | | | | | | | | | | | | | | | | | | | | | | | | | | | | | | | | | |
| Practice basic facts and extended facts | | | | | | | | | | | | | | | | | | | | | | | | | | | | | | | | | | |
| Use mental arithmetic to add/subtract | | | | | | | | | | | | | | | | | | | | | | | | | | | | | | | | | | |
| Add/subtract multidigit numbers | | | | | | | | | | | | | | | | | | | | | | | | | | | | | | | | | | |
| Use column addition | | | | | | | | | | | | | | | | | | | | | | | | | | | | | | | | | | |
| Use estimation to add/subtract | | | | | | | | | | | | | | | | | | | | | | | | | | | | | | | | | | |
| Use addition/subtraction algorithms | | | | | | | | | | | | | | | | | | | | | | | | | | | | | | | | | | |
| Add/subtract positive and negative numbers | | | | | | | | | | | | | | | | | | | | | | | | | | | | | | | | | | |
| **Addition and Subtraction with Decimals** | | | | | | | | | | | | | | | | | | | | | | | | | | | | | | | | | | |
| Use dollar-and-cents notation | | | | | | | | | | | | | | | | | | | | | | | | | | | | | | | | | | |
| Add/subtract money amounts/decimals | | | | | | | | | | | | | | | | | | | | | | | | | | | | | | | | | | |
| Add/subtract 1- or 2-digit decimals | | | | | | | | | | | | | | | | | | | | | | | | | | | | | | | | | | |
| Solve decimal addition/subtraction number stories | | | | | | | | | | | | | | | | | | | | | | | | | | | | | | | | | | |
| Add/subtract multidigit whole numbers and decimals | | | | | | | | | | | | | | | | | | | | | | | | | | | | | | | | | | |
| **Addition and Subtraction with Fractions** | | | | | | | | | | | | | | | | | | | | | | | | | | | | | | | | | | |
| Add/subtract fractions with like denominators | | | | | | | | | | | | | | | | | | | | | | | | | | | | | | | | | | |
| Find common denominators | | | | | | | | | | | | | | | | | | | | | | | | | | | | | | | | | | |
| Add/subtract fractions with unlike denominators | | | | | | | | | | | | | | | | | | | | | | | | | | | | | | | | | | |
| Solve fraction addition/subtraction number stories | | | | | | | | | | | | | | | | | | | | | | | | | | | | | | | | | | |
| Use an algorithm to add/subtract mixed numbers with like denominators | | | | | | | | | | | | | | | | | | | | | | | | | | | | | | | | | | |

| **Addition and Subtraction with Fractions (cont.)** |
|---|
| Estimate sums/differences of fractions |
| Use an algorithm to add/subtract mixed numbers with unlike denominators |
| **Multiplication and Division** |
| Solve multiplication/division number stories |
| Interpret a remainder in division problems |
| Investigate properties of multiplication/division |
| Practice multiplication/division facts |
| Practice extended multiplication/division facts |
| Model multiplication with arrays |
| Use estimation to multiply/divide |
| Make magnitude estimates for products |
| Find the product of multidigit whole numbers |
| Solve multiplication/division problems involving multiples of 10, 100, and 1,000 |
| Solve multidigit multiplication/division problems |
| Use the lattice method for multiplication |
| Use a calculator to multiply/divide |
| Use mental arithmetic to multiply/divide |
| Multiply/divide multiples of 10, 100, and 1,000 by 1-digit numbers |
| Multiply/divide money amounts |
| Use multiplication/division algorithms |
| Use divisibility tests to determine if a number is divisible by another number |
| Express remainders as fractions or decimals |
| Express quotients as mixed numbers or decimals |
| Rename fractions as decimals |

Beginning Developing Secure

# Operations and Computation (cont.)

| | Grade 4 | | | | | | | | | | | | Grade 5 | | | | | | | | | | | | Grade 6 | | | | | | | | | |
|---|---|---|---|---|---|---|---|---|---|---|---|---|---|---|---|---|---|---|---|---|---|---|---|---|---|---|---|---|---|---|---|---|---|---|
| | Units | | | | | | | | | | | | Units | | | | | | | | | | | | Units | | | | | | | | | |
| **Skills and Concepts** | 1 | 2 | 3 | 4 | 5 | 6 | 7 | 8 | 9 | 10 | 11 | 12 | 1 | 2 | 3 | 4 | 5 | 6 | 7 | 8 | 9 | 10 | 11 | 12 | 1 | 2 | 3 | 4 | 5 | 6 | 7 | 8 | 9 | 10 |
| **Multiplication and Division (cont.)** | | | | | | | | | | | | | | | | | | | | | | | | | | | | | | | | | | |
| Divide by 1-digit numbers | | | | | | | | | | | | | | | | | | | | | | | | | | | | | | | | | | |
| Divide by 2-digit numbers | | | | | | | | | | | | | | | | | | | | | | | | | | | | | | | | | | |
| Solve open number sentences | | | | | | | | | | | | | | | | | | | | | | | | | | | | | | | | | | |
| Use parentheses in number sentences | | | | | | | | | | | | | | | | | | | | | | | | | | | | | | | | | | |
| Understand and apply the order of operations to evaluate expressions and solve number sentences | | | | | | | | | | | | | | | | | | | | | | | | | | | | | | | | | | |
| Multiply/divide positive and negative numbers | | | | | | | | | | | | | | | | | | | | | | | | | | | | | | | | | | |
| Multiply by positive and negative powers of 10 | | | | | | | | | | | | | | | | | | | | | | | | | | | | | | | | | | |
| **Multiplication and Division with Decimals** | | | | | | | | | | | | | | | | | | | | | | | | | | | | | | | | | | |
| Use an estimation strategy to multiply/divide decimals by whole numbers | | | | | | | | | | | | | | | | | | | | | | | | | | | | | | | | | | |
| Multiply decimals by whole numbers | | | | | | | | | | | | | | | | | | | | | | | | | | | | | | | | | | |
| Multiply decimals by decimals | | | | | | | | | | | | | | | | | | | | | | | | | | | | | | | | | | |
| Divide decimals by whole numbers | | | | | | | | | | | | | | | | | | | | | | | | | | | | | | | | | | |
| Estimate products and multiply decimals | | | | | | | | | | | | | | | | | | | | | | | | | | | | | | | | | | |
| Estimate the quotient and divide a decimal by a whole number | | | | | | | | | | | | | | | | | | | | | | | | | | | | | | | | | | |
| Round a decimal quotient to a specified place | | | | | | | | | | | | | | | | | | | | | | | | | | | | | | | | | | |
| Locate the decimal point in a product | | | | | | | | | | | | | | | | | | | | | | | | | | | | | | | | | | |
| Multiply/divide decimals by powers of 10 | | | | | | | | | | | | | | | | | | | | | | | | | | | | | | | | | | |
| Solve multiplication/division decimal number stories | | | | | | | | | | | | | | | | | | | | | | | | | | | | | | | | | | |

| Multiplication and Division with Fractions |
| --- |
| Relate fractions and division |
| Use an algorithm to multiply fractions |
| Use an algorithm to multiply mixed numbers |
| Solve "fraction-of-a-fraction" problems |
| Use a common denominator to divide fractions |
| Use an algorithm to multiply/divide fractions and mixed numbers |
| Solve multiplication/division fraction number stories |
| **Ratio, Proportion, and Percent** |
| Find unit rates |
| Calculate unit prices |
| Collect and compare rate data |
| Evaluate reasonableness of rate data |
| Use rate tables to solve problems |
| Represent rates with formulas, tables, and graphs |
| Solve rate and ratio number stories |
| Explore uses of ratios and ways of expressing ratios |
| Write open proportions to solve model problems |
| Solve problems involving a size-change factor |
| Use cross-multiplication to solve open proportions |
| Solve percent problems |

**Beginning** **Developing** **Secure**

**Notes on Scope and Sequence**

# Patterns, Functions, and Algebra

| | Grade 4 | | | | | | | | | | | | Grade 5 | | | | | | | | | | | | Grade 6 | | | | | | | | | |
|---|---|---|---|---|---|---|---|---|---|---|---|---|---|---|---|---|---|---|---|---|---|---|---|---|---|---|---|---|---|---|---|---|---|---|
| | Units | | | | | | | | | | | | Units | | | | | | | | | | | | Units | | | | | | | | | |
| **Skills and Concepts** | 1 | 2 | 3 | 4 | 5 | 6 | 7 | 8 | 9 | 10 | 11 | 12 | 1 | 2 | 3 | 4 | 5 | 6 | 7 | 8 | 9 | 10 | 11 | 12 | 1 | 2 | 3 | 4 | 5 | 6 | 7 | 8 | 9 | 10 |
| **Visual Patterns** | | | | | | | | | | | | | | | | | | | | | | | | | | | | | | | | | | |
| Create patterns with 2-dimensional shapes | | | | | | | | | | | | | | | | | | | | | | | | | | | | | | | | | | |
| Explore and extend visual patterns | | | | | | | | | | | | | | | | | | | | | | | | | | | | | | | | | | |
| Define and create tessellations/frieze patterns | | | | | | | | | | | | | | | | | | | | | | | | | | | | | | | | | | |
| Identify and use notation for semiregular tessellations | | | | | | | | | | | | | | | | | | | | | | | | | | | | | | | | | | |
| Identify regular tessellations | | | | | | | | | | | | | | | | | | | | | | | | | | | | | | | | | | |
| **Number Patterns** | | | | | | | | | | | | | | | | | | | | | | | | | | | | | | | | | | |
| Find patterns in addition, subtraction, multiplication, and division facts | | | | | | | | | | | | | | | | | | | | | | | | | | | | | | | | | | |
| Identify or investigate square numbers | | | | | | | | | | | | | | | | | | | | | | | | | | | | | | | | | | |
| Plot points on a coordinate grid | | | | | | | | | | | | | | | | | | | | | | | | | | | | | | | | | | |
| Find locations on a map or globe | | | | | | | | | | | | | | | | | | | | | | | | | | | | | | | | | | |
| Find number patterns in data | | | | | | | | | | | | | | | | | | | | | | | | | | | | | | | | | | |
| Find and extend numerical patterns | | | | | | | | | | | | | | | | | | | | | | | | | | | | | | | | | | |
| **Functions** | | | | | | | | | | | | | | | | | | | | | | | | | | | | | | | | | | |
| Complete a table of values | | | | | | | | | | | | | | | | | | | | | | | | | | | | | | | | | | |
| Collect and compare rate data | | | | | | | | | | | | | | | | | | | | | | | | | | | | | | | | | | |
| Solve rate number stories | | | | | | | | | | | | | | | | | | | | | | | | | | | | | | | | | | |
| Represent rates with formulas, tables, and graphs | | | | | | | | | | | | | | | | | | | | | | | | | | | | | | | | | | |

| Number Sentences and Equations |
| --- |
| Write/solve addition and subtraction number sentences |
| Write/solve multiplication number sentences |
| Write/solve division number sentences |
| Apply the use of parentheses in number sentences |
| Write and solve open sentences for number stories |
| Determine if number sentences are true or false |
| Understand and apply the order of operations to evaluate expressions and solve number sentences |
| Translate number stories into expressions |
| Determine the value of a variable |
| Solve equations with a variable |
| Use variables to describe general patterns |
| Use a spreadsheet |
| Use variables and formulas in spreadsheets |
| Interpret mystery graphs |
| Evaluate formulas |
| Use formulas to solve problems |
| Apply the distributive property |
| Understand and apply the identity property for multiplication |
| Understand and apply the commutative property for addition and multiplication |
| Understand and apply the associative property for addition and multiplication |

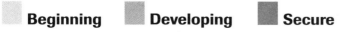

**Beginning** **Developing** **Secure**

# Patterns, Functions, and Algebra (cont.)

| | Grade 4 | | | | | | | | | | | | Grade 5 | | | | | | | | | | | | Grade 6 | | | | | | | | | |
|---|---|---|---|---|---|---|---|---|---|---|---|---|---|---|---|---|---|---|---|---|---|---|---|---|---|---|---|---|---|---|---|---|---|---|
| | Units | | | | | | | | | | | | Units | | | | | | | | | | | | Units | | | | | | | | | |
| **Skills and Concepts** | 1 | 2 | 3 | 4 | 5 | 6 | 7 | 8 | 9 | 10 | 11 | 12 | 1 | 2 | 3 | 4 | 5 | 6 | 7 | 8 | 9 | 10 | 11 | 12 | 1 | 2 | 3 | 4 | 5 | 6 | 7 | 8 | 9 | 10 |
| **Inequalities and Expressions** | | | | | | | | | | | | | | | | | | | | | | | | | | | | | | | | | | |
| Compare numbers using < and > symbols | | | | | | | | | | | | | | | | | | | | | | | | | | | | | | | | | | |
| Evaluate expressions using <, >, and = symbols | | | | | | | | | | | | | | | | | | | | | | | | | | | | | | | | | | |
| Write algebraic expressions to describe situations | | | | | | | | | | | | | | | | | | | | | | | | | | | | | | | | | | |
| Evaluate algebraic expressions and formulas | | | | | | | | | | | | | | | | | | | | | | | | | | | | | | | | | | |
| Describe a pattern with a number sentence that has one or two variables | | | | | | | | | | | | | | | | | | | | | | | | | | | | | | | | | | |
| Solve and graph solutions for inequalities | | | | | | | | | | | | | | | | | | | | | | | | | | | | | | | | | | |
| Simplify expressions and equations that have parentheses | | | | | | | | | | | | | | | | | | | | | | | | | | | | | | | | | | |
| Combine like terms to simplify expressions and equations | | | | | | | | | | | | | | | | | | | | | | | | | | | | | | | | | | |
| Write and identify equivalent expressions and equivalent equations | | | | | | | | | | | | | | | | | | | | | | | | | | | | | | | | | | |
| Write and solve equations that represent problem situations | | | | | | | | | | | | | | | | | | | | | | | | | | | | | | | | | | |
| **Positive/Negative Numbers (Integers)** | | | | | | | | | | | | | | | | | | | | | | | | | | | | | | | | | | |
| Compare and order integers | | | | | | | | | | | | | | | | | | | | | | | | | | | | | | | | | | |
| Use properties of positive and negative numbers | | | | | | | | | | | | | | | | | | | | | | | | | | | | | | | | | | |
| Compute with positive and negative integers | | | | | | | | | | | | | | | | | | | | | | | | | | | | | | | | | | |

**Notes on Scope and Sequence**

# Geometry

| | Grade 4 | | | | | | | | | | | | Grade 5 | | | | | | | | | | | | Grade 6 | | | | | | | | | |
|---|---|---|---|---|---|---|---|---|---|---|---|---|---|---|---|---|---|---|---|---|---|---|---|---|---|---|---|---|---|---|---|---|---|---|
| | Units | | | | | | | | | | | | Units | | | | | | | | | | | | Units | | | | | | | | | |
| **Skills and Concepts** | 1 | 2 | 3 | 4 | 5 | 6 | 7 | 8 | 9 | 10 | 11 | 12 | 1 | 2 | 3 | 4 | 5 | 6 | 7 | 8 | 9 | 10 | 11 | 12 | 1 | 2 | 3 | 4 | 5 | 6 | 7 | 8 | 9 | 10 |
| **2-Dimensional Shapes (Polygons)** | | | | | | | | | | | | | | | | | | | | | | | | | | | | | | | | | | |
| Identify 2-dimensional shapes | | | | | | | | | | | | | | | | | | | | | | | | | | | | | | | | | | |
| Explore shape relationships | | | | | | | | | | | | | | | | | | | | | | | | | | | | | | | | | | |
| Identify characteristics of 2-dimensional shapes | | | | | | | | | | | | | | | | | | | | | | | | | | | | | | | | | | |
| Construct/draw 2-dimensional shapes | | | | | | | | | | | | | | | | | | | | | | | | | | | | | | | | | | |
| Solve problems involving 2-dimensional shapes | | | | | | | | | | | | | | | | | | | | | | | | | | | | | | | | | | |
| Classify and name polygons | | | | | | | | | | | | | | | | | | | | | | | | | | | | | | | | | | |
| Identify properties of polygons | | | | | | | | | | | | | | | | | | | | | | | | | | | | | | | | | | |
| Use a compass and a straightedge to construct geometric figures | | | | | | | | | | | | | | | | | | | | | | | | | | | | | | | | | | |
| Classify quadrilaterals according to side and angle properties | | | | | | | | | | | | | | | | | | | | | | | | | | | | | | | | | | |
| Name, draw, and label angles, triangles, and quadrilaterals | | | | | | | | | | | | | | | | | | | | | | | | | | | | | | | | | | |
| Identify types of triangles | | | | | | | | | | | | | | | | | | | | | | | | | | | | | | | | | | |
| Verify and apply the Pythagorean Theorem | | | | | | | | | | | | | | | | | | | | | | | | | | | | | | | | | | |
| Define and create tessellations/frieze patterns | | | | | | | | | | | | | | | | | | | | | | | | | | | | | | | | | | |
| **3-Dimensional Shapes** | | | | | | | | | | | | | | | | | | | | | | | | | | | | | | | | | | |
| Identify 3-dimensional shapes | | | | | | | | | | | | | | | | | | | | | | | | | | | | | | | | | | |
| Identify characteristics of 3-dimensional shapes | | | | | | | | | | | | | | | | | | | | | | | | | | | | | | | | | | |
| Construct 3-dimensional shapes | | | | | | | | | | | | | | | | | | | | | | | | | | | | | | | | | | |
| Identify faces, edges, vertices, and bases of prisms and pyramids | | | | | | | | | | | | | | | | | | | | | | | | | | | | | | | | | | |

**Beginning** **Developing** **Secure**

# Geometry (cont.)

| Skills and Concepts | Grade 4 Units | Grade 5 Units | Grade 6 Units |
|---|---|---|---|
| **3-Dimensional Shapes (cont.)** | | | |
| Describe properties of geometric solids | | | |
| Perform topological transformations | | | |
| **Symmetry** | | | |
| Identify symmetrical figures | | | |
| Identify lines of symmetry | | | |
| Rotate figures | | | |
| Translate figures on a coordinate grid | | | |
| Identify lines of reflection, reflected figures, and figures with line symmetry | | | |
| Explore rotation and point symmetry | | | |
| Explore transformations of geometric figures in a plane | | | |
| **Congruence and Similarity** | | | |
| Identify congruent figures | | | |
| Identify similar figures | | | |
| Draw or form a figure congruent to a given figure | | | |
| **Points, Lines, and Angles** | | | |
| Draw line segments to a specified length | | | |
| Identify parallel and nonparallel line segments | | | |
| Identify and name points | | | |
| Identify and name line segments | | | |
| Identify and name lines | | | |
| Identify and name intersecting lines | | | |

| Points, Lines, and Angles (cont.) |
|---|
| Identify and name rays |
| Draw lines and rays |
| Name, draw, and label line segments, lines, and rays |
| Identify and describe right angles, parallel lines, and line segments |
| Explore the relationship between endpoints and midpoints |
| Solve construction problems |
| Identify and name angles |
| Model clockwise/counterclockwise turns/rotations |
| Measure angles with degree units to within 2° |
| Solve degree problems |
| Identify acute, obtuse, straight, and reflex angles |
| Make turns and fractions of turns; relate turns to angles |
| Use full-circle and half-circle protractors to measure and draw angles |
| Determine angle measures based on relationships among angles |
| Estimate the measure of an angle |
| Find angle sums for geometric shapes |
| Use a compass to draw a circle and angles formed by intersecting lines |
| Measure angles formed by intersecting lines |
| Apply properties of supplementary angles and vertical angles |
| Apply properties of angles formed by two parallel lines and a transversal |
| Apply properties of angles of parallelograms |

**Beginning** **Developing** **Secure**

# Geometry (cont.)

| | Grade 4 | | | | | | | | | | | | Grade 5 | | | | | | | | | | | | Grade 6 | | | | | | | | | |
|---|---|---|---|---|---|---|---|---|---|---|---|---|---|---|---|---|---|---|---|---|---|---|---|---|---|---|---|---|---|---|---|---|---|---|
| | Units | | | | | | | | | | | | Units | | | | | | | | | | | | Units | | | | | | | | | |
| **Skills and Concepts** | 1 | 2 | 3 | 4 | 5 | 6 | 7 | 8 | 9 | 10 | 11 | 12 | 1 | 2 | 3 | 4 | 5 | 6 | 7 | 8 | 9 | 10 | 11 | 12 | 1 | 2 | 3 | 4 | 5 | 6 | 7 | 8 | 9 | 10 |
| **Points, Lines, and Angles (cont.)** | | | | | | | | | | | | | | | | | | | | | | | | | | | | | | | | | | |
| Calculate the degree measure of each sector in a circle graph; use a protractor to construct the graph | | | | | | | | | | | | | | | | | | | | | | | | | | | | | | | | | | |
| Apply properties of sums of angle measures of triangles and quadrilaterals | | | | | | | | | | | | | | | | | | | | | | | | | | | | | | | | | | |
| Use a transparent mirror to draw the reflection of a figure | | | | | | | | | | | | | | | | | | | | | | | | | | | | | | | | | | |
| Plot ordered number pairs on a four-quadrant coordinate grid | | | | | | | | | | | | | | | | | | | | | | | | | | | | | | | | | | |
| Plot ordered pairs on a one-quadrant coordinate grid | | | | | | | | | | | | | | | | | | | | | | | | | | | | | | | | | | |
| Use ordered number pairs to name points in four quadrants | | | | | | | | | | | | | | | | | | | | | | | | | | | | | | | | | | |

**Notes on Scope and Sequence**

# Measurement and Reference Frames: Measurement

| Skills and Concepts | Grade 4 Units | | | | | | | | | | | | Grade 5 Units | | | | | | | | | | | | Grade 6 Units | | | | | | | | | |
|---|---|---|---|---|---|---|---|---|---|---|---|---|---|---|---|---|---|---|---|---|---|---|---|---|---|---|---|---|---|---|---|---|---|---|
| | 1 | 2 | 3 | 4 | 5 | 6 | 7 | 8 | 9 | 10 | 11 | 12 | 1 | 2 | 3 | 4 | 5 | 6 | 7 | 8 | 9 | 10 | 11 | 12 | 1 | 2 | 3 | 4 | 5 | 6 | 7 | 8 | 9 | 10 |
| **Length** | | | | | | | | | | | | | | | | | | | | | | | | | | | | | | | | | | |
| Estimate and compare distances | | | D | D | D | D | | D | | | | | | | | | | | | | D | | | | | | | | | | | | | |
| Estimate and compare lengths/heights of objects | | | D | D | D | | | D | | | | | | | | | | | | | D | | | | | | | | | | S | | S | |
| Measure to the nearest foot | | | | | | | | S | | | | | | | | | | S | | | | | | | | | | | | | S | | | |
| Measure to the nearest inch | | | | | | | | S | | | | | | | | | | S | | | | | | | | | | | | | S | | | |
| Draw and measure line segments to the nearest centimeter | | D | | D | | | | D | | | | | | | | | | D | | | | | | | | | | | | | | | | |
| Investigate the meter | | | | D | | | | | | | | | | | | | | D | | | | | | | | | | | | | | | | |
| Measure to the nearest $\frac{1}{2}$ inch | | | S | | | | | S | | | | | | | | | S | | | | | | | | | | | | | | | | | |
| Measure to the nearest $\frac{1}{2}$ centimeter | | D | | | | | | | | | | | | | | | | | | | | | | | | | | | | | | | | |
| Identify equivalent customary units of length | | | | | | | | D | | | | | | | | | D | | | | | | | | S | | | | | | | S | | |
| Identify equivalent metric units of length | | | | D | | | | | | | | | | | | | | D | | | | | | | S | | | | | S | | | | |
| Investigate the mile | | | S | | S | | | | | | | | | | | | | | | | | | | | | | | | | | | | | |
| Solve length/height/distance number stories | | | D | D | D | | | D | | | | | | | | | | D | | | D | | | | | | | | | | | D | | |
| Use a map scale | | | D | | D | D | | D | | | | | | | | D | | | | | | | | | | | | | | | | D | | |
| Use a mileage map | | | D | | D | | | | | | | | | | | | | | | | | | | | | | | | | | | D | | |
| Make and interpret scale drawings | | | | | | | | B | | | | | | | | B | | | | | | | | | | | | | | | | D | | |
| Identify locations for given latitudes and longitudes | | | | | | B | | | | | | | | | | | | | | | D | | | | | | | | | | | | | |
| Find latitude and longitude for given locations | | | | | | B | | D | | | | | | | | | | | | | D | | | | | | | | | | | | | |
| Measure to the nearest $\frac{1}{4}$ inch | | | | | | | | S | | | | | | | | | S | | | | | | | | | | | | | | | S | | |
| Measure to the nearest $\frac{1}{8}$ inch | | | | | | | | | | | | | | | | | S | | | | | | | | | | | | | | | S | | |
| Draw and measure line segments to the nearest millimeter | | | | D | | | | | | | | | | | | | | D | | | | | | | | | | | | | | S | | |
| Measure diameter and circumference | | | | | | | | | | | | | | | | | | | | | | | D | | | | | | | | | | | |

B = Beginning  D = Developing  S = Secure

# Measurement and Reference Frames: Measurement (cont.)

| | Grade 4 Units | | | | | | | | | | | | Grade 5 Units | | | | | | | | | | | | Grade 6 Units | | | | | | | | | |
|---|---|---|---|---|---|---|---|---|---|---|---|---|---|---|---|---|---|---|---|---|---|---|---|---|---|---|---|---|---|---|---|---|---|---|
| **Skills and Concepts** | 1 | 2 | 3 | 4 | 5 | 6 | 7 | 8 | 9 | 10 | 11 | 12 | 1 | 2 | 3 | 4 | 5 | 6 | 7 | 8 | 9 | 10 | 11 | 12 | 1 | 2 | 3 | 4 | 5 | 6 | 7 | 8 | 9 | 10 |
| **Length (cont.)** | | | | | | | | | | | | | | | | | | | | | | | | | | | | | | | | | | |
| Express metric measures with decimals | | | | | | | | | | | | | | | | | | | | | | | | | | | | | | | | | | |
| Convert between metric measures | | | | | | | | | | | | | | | | | | | | | | | | | | | | | | | | | | |
| Use personal references to estimate lengths in metric units | | | | | | | | | | | | | | | | | | | | | | | | | | | | | | | | | | |
| Establish personal references for customary units of length | | | | | | | | | | | | | | | | | | | | | | | | | | | | | | | | | | |
| **Capacity and Volume** | | | | | | | | | | | | | | | | | | | | | | | | | | | | | | | | | | |
| Understand the concept of capacity | | | | | | | | | | | | | | | | | | | | | | | | | | | | | | | | | | |
| Identify customary units of capacity | | | | | | | | | | | | | | | | | | | | | | | | | | | | | | | | | | |
| Identify equivalent customary units of capacity | | | | | | | | | | | | | | | | | | | | | | | | | | | | | | | | | | |
| Identify metric units of capacity | | | | | | | | | | | | | | | | | | | | | | | | | | | | | | | | | | |
| Identify equivalent metric units of capacity | | | | | | | | | | | | | | | | | | | | | | | | | | | | | | | | | | |
| Calculate capacity | | | | | | | | | | | | | | | | | | | | | | | | | | | | | | | | | | |
| Solve capacity number stories | | | | | | | | | | | | | | | | | | | | | | | | | | | | | | | | | | |
| Understand the concept of volume of a figure | | | | | | | | | | | | | | | | | | | | | | | | | | | | | | | | | | |
| Understand the relationships between the volumes of pyramids and prisms, and the volumes of cones and cylinders | | | | | | | | | | | | | | | | | | | | | | | | | | | | | | | | | | |
| Use a formula to calculate volumes of rectangular prisms | | | | | | | | | | | | | | | | | | | | | | | | | | | | | | | | | | |
| Estimate volume | | | | | | | | | | | | | | | | | | | | | | | | | | | | | | | | | | |
| Solve cube-stacking volume problems | | | | | | | | | | | | | | | | | | | | | | | | | | | | | | | | | | |
| Use formulas to calculate volumes of 3-dimensional shapes | | | | | | | | | | | | | | | | | | | | | | | | | | | | | | | | | | |
| Examine the relationships among the liter, milliliter, and cubic centimeter | | | | | | | | | | | | | | | | | | | | | | | | | | | | | | | | | | |

| Weight |
| --- |
| Use a pan balance/spring scale |
| Solve pan-balance problems |
| Solve weight number stories |
| Identify customary units of weight |
| Identify metric units of weight |
| Estimate and compare weights |
| Identify equivalent customary units of weight |
| Identify equivalent metric units of weight |
| Estimate/weigh objects in ounces or grams |
| **Perimeter and Area** |
| Investigate area |
| Estimate area |
| Find the perimeters of irregular shapes |
| Find the perimeters of regular shapes |
| Find the areas of regular shapes |
| Compare perimeter and area |
| Find the areas of irregular shapes |
| Find the area of a figure by counting unit squares and fractions of unit squares inside the figure |
| Use formulas to find areas of rectangles, parallelograms, and triangles |
| Estimate surface area |
| Identify the bases and heights of triangles and parallelograms |
| Use a formula to find the circumference of a circle |
| Use a formula to find the area of a circle |

**Beginning** **Developing** **Secure**

# Measurement and Reference Frames: Measurement (cont.)

| | Grade 4 | | | | | | | | | | | | Grade 5 | | | | | | | | | | | | Grade 6 | | | | | | | | | |
|---|---|---|---|---|---|---|---|---|---|---|---|---|---|---|---|---|---|---|---|---|---|---|---|---|---|---|---|---|---|---|---|---|---|---|
| | Units | | | | | | | | | | | | Units | | | | | | | | | | | | Units | | | | | | | | | |
| **Skills and Concepts** | 1 | 2 | 3 | 4 | 5 | 6 | 7 | 8 | 9 | 10 | 11 | 12 | 1 | 2 | 3 | 4 | 5 | 6 | 7 | 8 | 9 | 10 | 11 | 12 | 1 | 2 | 3 | 4 | 5 | 6 | 7 | 8 | 9 | 10 |
| **Perimeter and Area (cont.)** | | | | | | | | | | | | | | | | | | | | | | | | | | | | | | | | | | |
| Distinguish between circumference and area of a circle | | | | | | | | | | | | | | | | | | | | | | | | | | | | | | | | | | |
| Find the surface areas of prisms, cylinders, and pyramids | | | | | | | | | | | | | | | | | | | | | | | | | | | | | | | | | | |
| Find an approximate value for $\pi$ (pi) | | | | | | | | | | | | | | | | | | | | | | | | | | | | | | | | | | |
| Use personal references for common units of area | | | | | | | | | | | | | | | | | | | | | | | | | | | | | | | | | | |
| **Money** | | | | | | | | | | | | | | | | | | | | | | | | | | | | | | | | | | |
| Solve money number stories | | | | | | | | | | | | | | | | | | | | | | | | | | | | | | | | | | |
| Add/subtract money amounts | | | | | | | | | | | | | | | | | | | | | | | | | | | | | | | | | | |
| Estimate costs | | | | | | | | | | | | | | | | | | | | | | | | | | | | | | | | | | |
| Divide money amounts | | | | | | | | | | | | | | | | | | | | | | | | | | | | | | | | | | |
| Calculate unit price | | | | | | | | | | | | | | | | | | | | | | | | | | | | | | | | | | |
| Determine the better buy | | | | | | | | | | | | | | | | | | | | | | | | | | | | | | | | | | |
| Multiply money amounts | | | | | | | | | | | | | | | | | | | | | | | | | | | | | | | | | | |
| Identify/find fractional parts of units of money | | | | | | | | | | | | | | | | | | | | | | | | | | | | | | | | | | |

# Measurement and Reference Frames: Reference Frames

| | Grade 4 | | | | | | | | | | | | Grade 5 | | | | | | | | | | | | Grade 6 | | | | | | | | | |
|---|---|---|---|---|---|---|---|---|---|---|---|---|---|---|---|---|---|---|---|---|---|---|---|---|---|---|---|---|---|---|---|---|---|---|
| | Units | | | | | | | | | | | | Units | | | | | | | | | | | | Units | | | | | | | | | |
| **Skills and Concepts** | 1 | 2 | 3 | 4 | 5 | 6 | 7 | 8 | 9 | 10 | 11 | 12 | 1 | 2 | 3 | 4 | 5 | 6 | 7 | 8 | 9 | 10 | 11 | 12 | 1 | 2 | 3 | 4 | 5 | 6 | 7 | 8 | 9 | 10 |
| **Time** | | | | | | | | | | | | | | | | | | | | | | | | | | | | | | | | | | |
| Calculate elapsed time | | | | | | | | | | | | | | | | | | | | | | | | | | | | | | | | | | |
| Tell time to the nearest minute | | | | | | | | | | | | | | | | | | | | | | | | | | | | | | | | | | |
| Convert units of time | | | | | | | | | | | | | | | | | | | | | | | | | | | | | | | | | | |
| **Temperature** | | | | | | | | | | | | | | | | | | | | | | | | | | | | | | | | | | |
| Convert units of temperature | | | | | | | | | | | | | | | | | | | | | | | | | | | | | | | | | | |

**Beginning** **Developing** **Secure**

**Notes on Scope and Sequence**

# Data and Chance

| | Grade 4 | | | | | | | | | | | | Grade 5 | | | | | | | | | | | | Grade 6 | | | | | | | | | |
|---|---|---|---|---|---|---|---|---|---|---|---|---|---|---|---|---|---|---|---|---|---|---|---|---|---|---|---|---|---|---|---|---|---|---|
| | Units | | | | | | | | | | | | Units | | | | | | | | | | | | Units | | | | | | | | | |
| **Skills and Concepts** | 1 | 2 | 3 | 4 | 5 | 6 | 7 | 8 | 9 | 10 | 11 | 12 | 1 | 2 | 3 | 4 | 5 | 6 | 7 | 8 | 9 | 10 | 11 | 12 | 1 | 2 | 3 | 4 | 5 | 6 | 7 | 8 | 9 | 10 |
| **Collecting Data** | | | | | | | | | | | | | | | | | | | | | | | | | | | | | | | | | | |
| Collect data by counting/interviewing | | | | | | | | | | | | | | | | | | | | | | | | | | | | | | | | | | |
| Collect data from print sources | | | | | | | | | | | | | | | | | | | | | | | | | | | | | | | | | | |
| Collect data from a map | | | | | | | | | | | | | | | | | | | | | | | | | | | | | | | | | | |
| Make predictions about data | | | | | | | | | | | | | | | | | | | | | | | | | | | | | | | | | | |
| Explore random sampling | | | | | | | | | | | | | | | | | | | | | | | | | | | | | | | | | | |
| Conduct a survey | | | | | | | | | | | | | | | | | | | | | | | | | | | | | | | | | | |
| Record/compare numerical data | | | | | | | | | | | | | | | | | | | | | | | | | | | | | | | | | | |
| Organize and tabulate survey data | | | | | | | | | | | | | | | | | | | | | | | | | | | | | | | | | | |
| Collect and compare rate data | | | | | | | | | | | | | | | | | | | | | | | | | | | | | | | | | | |
| **Recording/Displaying Data** | | | | | | | | | | | | | | | | | | | | | | | | | | | | | | | | | | |
| Make a tally chart | | | | | | | | | | | | | | | | | | | | | | | | | | | | | | | | | | |
| Interpret and construct bar graphs | | | | | | | | | | | | | | | | | | | | | | | | | | | | | | | | | | |
| Record data in a table/chart | | | | | | | | | | | | | | | | | | | | | | | | | | | | | | | | | | |
| Record data on a map | | | | | | | | | | | | | | | | | | | | | | | | | | | | | | | | | | |
| Interpret and construct broken-line graphs | | | | | | | | | | | | | | | | | | | | | | | | | | | | | | | | | | |
| Interpret and construct circle graphs | | | | | | | | | | | | | | | | | | | | | | | | | | | | | | | | | | |
| Construct stem-and-leaf plots | | | | | | | | | | | | | | | | | | | | | | | | | | | | | | | | | | |
| Interpret and construct step graphs | | | | | | | | | | | | | | | | | | | | | | | | | | | | | | | | | | |
| Construct and interpret Venn diagrams | | | | | | | | | | | | | | | | | | | | | | | | | | | | | | | | | | |

| Evaluating Data |
|---|
| Find/use the range |
| Find/use the mode |
| Find/use the median |
| Find/use the mean |
| Compare two sets of data |
| Find/use the minimum/maximum |
| Interpret tables, graphs, and maps |
| Use data in problem solving |
| Summarize and interpret data |
| Understand how sample size affects results |
| Read and interpret stem-and-leaf plots |
| Explore misleading ways of presenting data |
| **Probability and Chance** |
| Explore equal-chance events |
| Predict outcomes |
| Record outcomes |
| Conduct experiments |
| Explore *fair* and *unfair* games |
| Solve problems involving chance outcomes |
| Understand and use tree diagrams to solve problems |
| Compute the probability of equally-likely outcomes |
| Calculate the probability of simple events |
| Understand and apply the concept of random numbers to probability situations |
| Understand how increasing the number of trials affects experimental results |

**Beginning** **Developing** **Secure**

# Index

## E



## F

## M



## N

## O



## P

## Q



## R

## S



## T



## U

## V



## W



## Z

ISBN 0-07-600038-9



The McGraw·Hill Companies

ISBN 0-07-600038-9

90000

9 780076 000388

McGraw Hill Wright Group